TARTAGLIA (1499 -1557)
Nicolo Tartaglia, an Italian mathematician, discovered a method
for solving any cubic equation.

A sketch of a proposed flying mechanis...
by Leonardo da Vinci (1452-1519),
Italian painter, sculptor, architect, an...
engineer

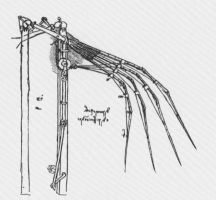

CARDANO (1501-1576)
The Italian Girolamo
Cardano was the first
person to use imaginary
numbers. He made
contributions to algebra,
astronomy, physics, and
medicine.

NAPIER (1550 -1617)
John Napier, a Scottish nobleman,
spent twenty years developing
logarithms, a major contribution to
mathematics. He also developed a
device called "Napier's bones," used
for multiplying, dividing, and finding
the square roots of numbers.

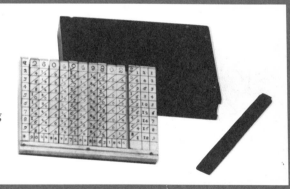

GALILEO (1564 -1642)
Galileo Galilei, a brilliant Italian astronomer and
physicist, invented the microscope, built the most
powerful telescope of the time, and discovered the
equation that describes the motion of a falling object.
We attribute to Galileo the modern spirit of science
based on theory, experiment, and mathematics.

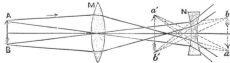

By 1550 Mexicans were
factoring quadratic
equations to solve
word problems.

1400

1600

Intermediate Algebra

THE PRINDLE, WEBER & SCHMIDT SERIES IN MATHEMATICS

Althoen and Bumcrot, Introduction to Discrete Mathematics
Bean, Sharp, and Sharp, Precalculus
Boye, Kavanaugh, and Williams, Elementary Algebra
Boye, Kavanaugh, and Williams, Intermediate Algebra
Burden and Faires, Numerical Analysis, Fifth Edition
Cass and O'Connor, Fundamentals with Elements of Algebra
Cullen, Linear Algebra and Differential Equations, Second Edition
Dick and Patton, Calculus, Volume I & Volume II
Dick and Patton, Technology in Calculus: A Sourcebook of Activities
Eves, In Mathematical Circles
Eves, Mathematical Circles Squared
Eves, Return to Mathematical Circles
Faires and Burden, Numerical Methods
Fletcher, Hoyle, and Patty, Foundations of Discrete Mathematics
Fletcher and Patty, Foundations of Higher Mathematics, Second Edition
Fraser, Intermediate Algebra: An Early Functions Approach
Gantner and Gantner, Trigonometry
Geltner and Peterson, Geometry for College Students, Second Edition
Gilbert and Gilbert, Elements of Modern Algebra, Third Edition
Gobran, Beginning Algebra, Fifth Edition
Gobran, Intermediate Algebra, Fourth Edition
Gordon, Calculus and the Computer
Hall, Beginning Algebra
Hall, Intermediate Algebra
Hall, Algebra for College Students, Second Edition
Hall, College Algebra with Applications, Third Edition
Hartfiel and Hobbs, Elementary Linear Algebra
Huff and Peterson, College Algebra Activities for the TI-81 Graphics Calculator
Humi and Miller, Boundary-Value Problems and Partial Differential Equations
Kaufmann, Elementary Algebra for College Students, Fourth Edition
Kaufmann, Intermediate Algebra for College Students, Fourth Edition
Kaufmann, Elementary and Intermediate Algebra: A Combined Approach
Kaufmann, Algebra for College Students, Fourth Edition
Kaufmann, Algebra with Trigonometry for College Students, Third Edition
Kaufmann, College Algebra, Second Edition
Kaufmann, Trigonometry
Kaufmann, College Algebra and Trigonometry, Second Edition
Kaufmann, Precalculus, Second Edition
Kennedy and Green, Prealgebra for College Students
Laufer, Discrete Mathematics and Applied Modern Algebra
Lavoie, Discovering Mathematics
Nicholson, Elementary Linear Algebra with Applications, Second Edition
Nicholson, Introduction to Abstract Algebra
Pence, Calculus Activities for Graphic Calculators
Pence, Calculus Activities for the TI-81 Graphic Calculator
Pence, Calculus Activities for the HP-48X and the TI-85 Calculators, Second Edition

Plybon, An Introduction to Applied Numerical Analysis
Powers, Elementary Differential Equations
Powers, Elementary Differential Equations with Boundary-Value Problems
Proga, Arithmetic and Algebra, Third Edition
Proga, Basic Mathematics, Third Edition
Rice and Strange, Plane Trigonometry, Sixth Edition
Rogers, Haney, and Laird, Fundamentals of Business Mathematics
Schelin and Bange, Mathematical Analysis for Business and Economics, Second Edition
Sgroi and Sgroi, Mathematics for Elementary School Teachers
Swokowski and Cole, Fundamentals of College Algebra, Eighth Edition
Swokowski and Cole, Fundamentals of Algebra and Trigonometry, Eighth Edition
Swokowski and Cole, Fundamentals of Trigonometry, Eighth Edition
Swokowski and Cole, Algebra and Trigonometry with Analytic Geometry, Eighth Edition
Swokowski, Precalculus: Functions and Graphs, Sixth Edition
Swokowski, Calculus, Fifth Edition
Swokowski, Calculus, Fifth Edition, Late Trigonometry Version
Swokowski, Calculus of a Single Variable
Tan, Applied Finite Mathematics, Third Edition
Tan, Calculus for the Managerial, Life, and Social Sciences, Second Edition
Tan, Applied Calculus, Second Edition
Tan, College Mathematics, Second Edition
Trim, Applied Partial Differential Equations
Venit and Bishop, Elementary Linear Algebra, Alternate Second Edition
Venit and Bishop, Elementary Linear Algebra, Third Edition
Wiggins, Problem Solver for Finite Mathematics and Calculus
Willard, Calculus and Its Applications, Second Edition
Wood and Capell, Arithmetic
Wood and Capell, Intermediate Algebra
Wood, Capell, and Hall, Developmental Mathematics, Fourth Edition
Zill, Calculus, Third Edition
Zill, A First Course in Differential Equations, Fifth Edition
Zill and Cullen, Elementary Differential Equations with Boundary-Value Problems, Third Edition
Zill and Cullen, Advanced Engineering Mathematics

THE PRINDLE, WEBER & SCHMIDT SERIES IN ADVANCED MATHEMATICS

Brabenec, Introduction to Real Analysis
Ehrlich, Fundamental Concepts of Abstract Algebra
Eves, Foundations and Fundamental Concepts of Mathematics, Third Edition
Keisler, Elementary Calculus: An Infinitesimal Approach, Second Edition
Kirkwood, An Introduction to Real Analysis
Patty, Foundations of Topology
Ruckle, Modern Analysis: Measure Theory and Functional Analysis with Applications
Sieradski, An Introduction to Topology and Homotopy

Intermediate Algebra

AN EARLY FUNCTIONS APPROACH

W. Roy Fraser

Skyline College

PWS PUBLISHING COMPANY

BOSTON

PWS
Publishing Company

20 Park Plaza
Boston, Massachusetts 02116

PWS Publishing Company is a division of Wadsworth, Inc.

Library of Congress Cataloging-in-Publication Data

Fraser, W. Roy.
   Intermediate algebra: an early functions approach / W. Roy Fraser.
     p.   cm.
   Includes index.
   ISBN 0-534-93240-1
   1. Algebra.   I. Title.
QA154.2.F73 1993
512.9 — dc20
                                   92-23613
                                      CIP

The Math in Time border designs were created by Gillian M. Fraser.

Illustration credits for the Time Line (appearing on the endsheets):
North Wind Picture Archives for Babylonian cuneiform (p. 1), Giotto's Plato and Aristotle relief (p. 1), Pythagoras (p. 1), shekel from Israel (p. 1), Hipparchus (p. 1), Leonardo da Vinci's flying mechanism (p. 2), Cardano (p. 2), Napier (p. 2), Galileo (p. 2), Galileo's telescope (p. 2), Descartes (p. 4), Fermat (p. 4), Euler (p. 4), metric system (p. 4). **The Granger Collection, New York** for Fibonacci (p. 1). **Historical Pictures/Stock Montage** for Einstein (p. 3). **The Bettmann Archive** for Tartaglia (p. 2), Kovalevsky (p. 3), Pascal (p. 4). **CIBA-GEIGY Corporation** for Blackwell (p. 3). **Courtesy of International Business Machines Corporation** for Napier's bones (p. 2), Babbage's analytic engine (p. 3)

Sponsoring Editor: Timothy L. Anderson
Production Coordinator and Cover Designer: Robine Andrau
Manufacturing Coordinator: Lisa Flanagan
Interior Designer: Julia Gecha
Editorial Assistant: Anita Amelia
Interior Illustrations: Network Graphics
Cover Photo: © 1992 Orion/Westlight
Typesetter: Better Graphics, Inc.
Cover Printer: Henry N. Sawyer Company
Printer and Binder: R.R. Donnelley & Sons/Willard

Printed in the United States of America
93 94 95 96 97 — 10 9 8 7 6 5 4 3 2

This book is dedicated to my sons,
Bruce and Christopher Fraser.

Contents

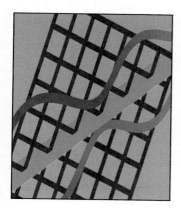

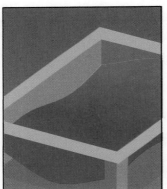
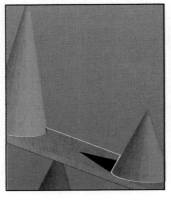

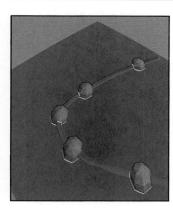

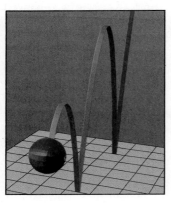

used consistently and pedagogically throughout the text; for example, relations and functions are always graphed in blue, and their inverses, in red.

 ## Calculators

Instruction on the use of a calculator is given in several places in the book, such as with fractional exponents (Section 7.2), scientific notation (Section 7.7), and logarithms (Section 10.4). Students are encouraged to use a calculator whenever such use is helpful.

Geometry

Geometry is strongly emphasized throughout the text. In addition to graphing, the following topics are covered: complementary and supplementary angles, the sum of the angles of a triangle, types of triangles, area and volume formulas and their applications, combined geometric figures, and a variety of word problems and applications that involve geometric concepts.

Examples

Each section includes a large number of worked-out, step-by-step examples. To encourage students to study the examples, checks are often left as exercises, and alternative methods of solving the problems in the examples are indicated in the exercises. Often a standard type of word problem is used to solve a real-world application. Students should be encouraged to read Section 2.4, which discusses how to solve word problems.

Exercises

All exercise sets are graded by type and level of difficulty. Exercises under the "A" label are the easiest and are grouped by numbered subtopics. "B" exercises are more challenging and extend the concepts in the examples. "C" exercises contain writing and enrichment problems. Most exercise sets end with Review Exercises, which review previous concepts and skills that will be used in the next section.

The chapter ends with a Chapter Summary, which contains key words, definitions, properties, and procedures; each topic is keyed to the section in the text where it is discussed. The Chapter Review Exercises follow the Chapter Summary; these exercises are also keyed to the corresponding sections in the text. After the Review Exercises comes the Chapter Test. In Chapters 3, 6, 9, and 11, the Cumulative Review exercises follow the Chapter Test.

The answers to the odd-numbered exercises, review exercises, chapter review exercise, chapter tests, and cumulative review exercises are all provided in the answer section at the back of the book.

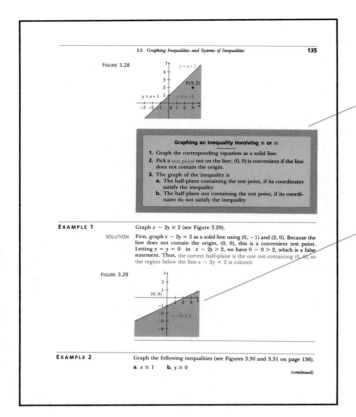

Boxes highlight important concepts and steps for students to follow and review.

Full color enhances graphs and other illustrations.

Calculator icons identify exercises that encourage the use of a calculator.

Pencil icons identify questions that require a written answer.

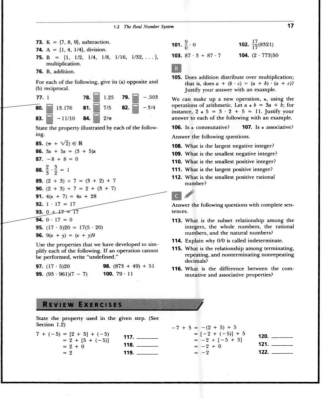

Math in Time sections examine the multicultural aspects and the historical development of mathematics.

Math in Time

ZERO AND MAYAN MATHEMATICS

The invention of zero occurred independently in two different parts of the world. The earliest known use of zero is in a Hindu inscription of A.D. 876. Through Arab scholars, knowledge of zero was transmitted to Europe.

Between 300 B.C. and A.D. 300, the Mayan Indians of Central America had performed many amazing astronomical calculations, such as determining the orbit of Venus with an error of 1 day in 6012 years. These results have led many archaeologists to believe that the Mayans were the first people to invent zero. The evidence for this is strong, but circumstantial, as the sixteenth-century Spanish conquerors destroyed nearly all of the Mayan written records, believing them to be "the work of the devil." The symbol the Mayans used for zero was a shell.

Mayan merchants used a base-20 number system. They wrote their numbers vertically, so that as one moved up the column, the numbers increased by a factor of 20. Bar-and-dot numerals were used; the dot ($\bullet$) represented 1, and the bar ($\underline{\quad}$) represented 5. In our base-10 system we write the numbers 1 to 9 and then use our

zero symbol to write 10. In the base-20 system the Mayans wrote the numbers 1 to 19 and then used their zero symbol to write 20:

The last number written above is expressed in our Hindu-Arabic system as $10 \cdot 20^2 + 4 \cdot 20 + 8 \cdot 1 = 4088$. The simplicity of Mayan addition is illustrated with these numbers. The sum of 6 and 13 is found by combining all the dots and bars of 6 and 13, giving the numeral for 19. The accompanying figure from a Mayan manuscript illustrates the mixture of religious text and arithmetic.

In arithmetic we learn that subtraction is the inverse of addition: $8 - 2 = 6$ and $6 + 2 = 8$. In a similar way, finding a square root is the inverse of squaring a number—that is, if $b^2 = a$, then b is a square root of a. For example, $6^2 = (-6)^2 = 36$, so 6 and -6 are the square roots of 36. These are written $\sqrt{36} = 6$ and $-\sqrt{36} = -6$ (note that $\sqrt{36} \neq 6$ and -6; $\sqrt{36}$ has only one answer, 6). Every positive number a has two square roots, $\sqrt{a}$ and $-\sqrt{a}$. Also, $\sqrt{0} = 0$. A negative number does not have a real square root because $b^2 \geq 0$, if b is real. For instance, $\sqrt{-25}$ is not a real number.

Radicals have many important properties. We will now introduce the two needed for the Pythagorean theorem in the next chapter and

29

$$1.5(r + 30) = 2(r - 30) + 45$$
$$1.5r + 45 = 2r - 60 + 45$$
$$-.5r + 45 = -15$$
$$-.5r = -60$$
$$r = 120$$

Thus, the speed of the plane in still air is 120 mph.

Calvin and Hobbes   by Bill Watterson

© 1987 Universal Press Syndicate. Reproduced by permission.

Math-related cartoons and anecdotes appear throughout the text to motivate students.

EXERCISE SET 2.4

A

Letters in exercise sets indicate the level of difficulty.

1

1. Solve the word problem in Example 1 (page 66) by letting W = the number of votes cast for the winner.

2. Check the solution to Example 2 (page 66).

Solve the following problems.

3. Yoko scored 71 and 85 on her first two algebra tests. What score does she need on the third test to have an average of 80?

4. Dan's first three geometry tests had scores of 61, 71, and 74. What score does he need on the fourth test to have an average of 68?

5. A carpenter must cut a 20-foot board into two pieces so that the shorter piece is 1 foot less than one-half the longer piece. How long is each piece?

6. Carlos earns time and a half for every hour worked over 40 in a week. Last week he worked 46 hours and earned $612.50. What is his normal hourly rate?

7. Chuck gets double time for every hour worked over 40 in a week. Last week he worked 47 hours and earned $459. What is his normal hourly rate?

8. Diane has five times as much money as Paula. If they each had two more dollars, then Diane would have four times as much money as Paula. How much money do they each have?

9. An electrician's bill was $84.08. This included $18 for parts and $1.08 for tax; the balance was for 2.5 hours of labor. Find the hourly labor rate.

10. On a physics test the sum of the highest and

SUPPLEMENTS

For the Instructor

- An *Instructor's Edition* of the textbook contains answers to all the exercises.
- A *Complete Solutions Manual* by Stephen Taylor of Bucks County College and Mark Serebransky of Camden County College provides complete solutions.
- A *Printed Test Bank* of chapter tests includes two forms of tests for each chapter.
- *EXPTest*, a computerized test bank for IBM-PCs and compatibles, allows users to view, edit, add to, and delete all tests. Instructors can modify hundreds of existing questions and print any number of student tests. A graphics importation feature permits the display and printing of graphs. Demonstration disks are available.
- *ExamBuilder*, a computerized test bank for the Macintosh, is a simple testing program that allows instructors to create, view, and edit existing test items. Questions can be stored by objective so that tests can be created using multiple-choice, true/false, fill-in-the-blank, essay, and matching formats. Questions can be scrambled to avoid duplicate testing, and graphs can be generated and printed. Demonstration disks are available.
- A *TrueBasic* algebra software package, which is available for IBM-PCs, compatibles, and Macintosh computers, contains a disk and user manual for self-study, free exploration of topics, and solution of problems. The program includes a record and playback feature that makes it ideal for classroom demonstrations.

For the Student

- *Student's Partial Solutions Manual* by Mark Serebransky of Camden County College and Stephen Taylor of Bucks County College contains the solutions to every other odd-numbered problem in the text.
- *Expert Algebra Tutor* (Version 3.0) by Sergei Ovchinnikov of San Francisco State University is an intelligent tutoring system for IBM-PCs and compatibles. This text-specific expert system has been completely updated, expanded, and enhanced for 1993. The program defines the exact level of tutoring needed, determines the sources of misconceptions, and establishes individually tailored tutoring strategies. The student is continually evaluated on his or her need for further study or advancement. Students in need of more study are referred to specific sections in the text where further development is provided. Demonstration disks are available.

■ *Algebra Lecture Videotape Series* by John Jobe of Oklahoma State University is a set of 19 VHS videotapes that can be used by the student to review the intermediate algebra topics presented in the textbook. A demonstration video tape is available.

ACKNOWLEDGMENTS

I would like to thank Terry Popp of Cape Cod Community College for doing a thorough error check of the manuscript and the following Skyline College instructors for their help in the indicated areas.

Elizabeth Armstrong: *Chemistry*   Leonard Herzstein: *Business*
Christine Case: *Biology*   Richard Lambert: *Geology*
Patricia Deamer: *African Mathematics*   Melvin Zucker: *Geology*
Paul Goodman: *Physics*

I wish to express my appreciation to the following reviewers who have made many excellent suggestions that have added considerably to the book:

Susan L. Addington
California State University—San Bernardino

Robert D. Baer
Miami University—Hamilton

Carol DeVille
Louisiana Tech University

Margaret D. Dolgas
University of Delaware

Michael D. Eurgubian
Santa Rosa Junior College

Elaine Hubbard
Kennesaw State College

Alice Kaseberg
Lane Community College

Laura Coffin Koch
University of Minnesota

Larry R. Lance
Columbus State Community College

Ira Lansing
College of Marin

Jann W. MacInnes
Florida Community College— Jacksonville

Carol D. Misner
Hartnell College

Murray B. Peterson
College of Marin

Terry Popp
Cape Cod Community College

Richard Semmler
Northern Virginia Community College

Mark Serebransky
Camden County College

Roger Waggoner
University of Southwestern Louisiana

Finally, I want to thank the staff of PWS-KENT for bringing this project to fruition. In particular, Tim Anderson's enthusiasm and encouragement, Anita Amelia's research and assistance, and Robine Andrau's guidance and thoroughness have made the publication of this book an enjoyable and rewarding experience for me.

To the Student

"*M*athematics cannot be made easy but it can be made easier" (Albert Einstein, 1879–1955). This quotation sums up the main objective of this book. Every effort has been made to provide you with a text that will make your study of intermediate algebra as successful as possible. However, learning algebra is not a passive activity. Mathematics is *not* a spectator sport; you have to be actively involved in the process.

The first step to success is getting in the right frame of mind. Algebra is not an easy subject for most people, and many topics cannot be completely understood the first time around. The student is not at fault; it is the nature of the subject. As a result, algebra takes more time than many people expect.

If you received a grade of C or better in elementary algebra in the past year, then two hours of study outside of class for every hour spent in class is a good rule of thumb. If you took elementary algebra more than a year ago, then you will probably have to spend an extra hour or two each week for review.

A good schedule is an hour or so of study in the morning and another hour later in the day, five or six days a week. Don't try to learn algebra when you are tired or to cover a week's work in one day.

Perseverance is another factor in succeeding in algebra. Students who say, "I'll never understand this stuff," give up too easily. Try to develop the attitude, "I can learn algebra if I try hard enough and I'll get some help from the professor or my friends when I have problems."

Forming a study group with other students in your class is a good idea. By discussing the material in small groups, all the participating students develop a better understanding of algebra. If your college has a math lab or tutorial center, get extra help from this service. The following are some other guidelines that many students find helpful:

1. Go to all classes on time and participate in the discussions. Most students who do poorly in algebra also have a poor attendance record. Looking over new material before class will help you understand the lecture. Taking notes in class will keep your mind from wandering, and notes are helpful when you are doing homework or studying for a test. The preface has a description of the various types of exercises in each section in the text and at the end of the chapter. Looking over this material before you start the course would be a good idea. You might also consider buying the *Student Solutions Manual*, which contains the complete solutions to every other odd-numbered exercise.

2. Many students find word problems difficult. Before you start the word problems, carefully read Section 2.4, which discusses how to solve word problems.

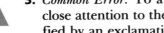

3. *Common Error*. To avoid the commonly made mistakes in algebra, pay close attention to the common error sections. These sections are identified by an exclamation point icon.

O N E

The Real Numbers

*Although Venn diagrams are usually drawn in two dimensions, they
can describe situations in three or more dimensions.*

In many ways elementary algebra is an extension of arithmetic. For instance, the arithmetic fact $3 + 4 = 4 + 3$ is generalized to $a + b = b + a$. In a similar way many topics in intermediate algebra are extensions of concepts developed in elementary algebra. For example, the material dealing with integer exponents in elementary algebra is generalized to rational exponents in this text. Just as a reasonable command of arithmetic is needed to be successful in elementary algebra, a basic knowledge of elementary algebra is needed to succeed in intermediate algebra.

The first chapter reviews sets and the real number system. We will discuss different types of real numbers, some of their properties, and their basic operations, such as addition. Because most of this material will be familiar, you might be tempted to save some time by giving it the "once over lightly" treatment. Doing so, however, could cause you to miss details that might come back to haunt you later in the course, such as the difference between a rational and an irrational number. Therefore, paying close attention to the material in Chapter 1 and other chapters that reviews topics in elementary algebra is suggested.

1.1 SETS

1	**Basic Definitions**
2	**Sets**
3	**Subsets; Union and Intersection of Sets**

1   Basic Definitions

Our study of intermediate algebra begins with definitions of variables and constants. A **variable** is a symbol, usually a lowercase letter, that represents one or more numbers. Thus, $a + b$ represents the sum of *any* two numbers. A **constant** is a symbol that has a fixed value. For example, the symbol "3" always represents the number three.

The operation and comparison symbols are summarized in the following charts.

Operation Symbols		
Addition:	$a + b$	The sum of a and b; a and b are terms.
Subtraction:	$a - b$	The difference of a and b.
Multiplication:	$ab,\ a \cdot b,\ a(b),$ $(a)b,\ (a)(b)$	The product of a and b; a and b are factors.
Division:	$a \div b,\ a/b,\ \dfrac{a}{b}$	The quotient of a and b, $b \neq 0$.

Comparison Symbols

$a = b$	a is equal to b
$a \neq b$	a is not equal to b
$a < b$	a is less than b
$a \leq b$	a is less than or equal to b
$a > b$	a is greater than b
$a \geq b$	a is greater than or equal to b

EXAMPLE 1

Place $<$, $\leq$, $>$, or $\geq$ in each blank to make a true statement; each problem has two correct answers.

a. 5 ____ 7   **b.** 6 ____ 6   **c.** 10 ____ 8

SOLUTION   **a.** $5 < 7$ or $5 \leq 7$ **b.** $6 \leq 6$ or $6 \geq 6$
c. $10 > 8$ or $10 \geq 8$

2   Sets

The topic sets is used throughout mathematics. For instance, in geometry we deal with sets of circles and triangles, whereas in algebra we study sets of numbers and equations. A **set** is a collection of objects, called **elements** or **members**. Capital letters — A, B, C, and so on — are commonly used to name sets. Braces, { }, are used to enclose the elements of a set, and the symbol $\in$ is used to indicate that an object is contained in a set. For example, if A = $\{a, b, k, t\}$, then $b \in$ A means that "b is a member of A" or "b is an element of A." To indicate that r is *not* a member of A, we use the symbol $\notin$ and write $r \notin$ A. Two sets are **equal** if they contain exactly the same elements, regardless of order. Thus, $\{1, 2, 3\} = \{1, 3, 2\}$, but $\{7, 8\} \neq \{8, 9\}$.

A set with no elements is called the **empty set** (or null set). The symbol $\varnothing$ is used to represent the empty set. For example,

$$\{\text{All months with 50 days}\} = \varnothing$$

$$\{\text{All people living on Jupiter}\} = \varnothing$$

A list of all the students in a class is called a "class roster." Similarly, when we describe a set by listing all of its members, it is called the **roster method**. For example, if A is the set of the first three letters of the alphabet, then A = $\{a, b, c\}$. Let B be the set of all the letters of the alphabet. It would be tedious to write each letter. Therefore, we use three dots, . . . , and write

$$B = \{a, b, c, \ldots, z\}$$

Enough of the elements of the set are listed to indicate the pattern, the three dots indicate that the pattern continues, and the last element is listed. The three dots, or ellipsis, are read "and so forth."

Many sets do not have last elements. Two important ones are $\mathbb{N}$, the set of **natural numbers** (or counting numbers), and $\mathbb{W}$, the set of **whole numbers**. To list all the elements in these sets would be impossible because they go on forever. We use three dots and write

$$\mathbb{N} = \{1, 2, 3, 4, \ldots\} \quad \text{and} \quad \mathbb{W} = \{0, 1, 2, 3, \ldots\}$$

Because there are a fixed number of elements in the sets $\{a, b, c\}$ and $\{a, b, c, \ldots, z\}$, the sets are called **finite** sets. Because $\mathbb{N}$ and $\mathbb{W}$ have an unlimited number of elements, they are called **infinite** sets.*

Sometimes, representing a set with the roster method (as in defining the rational numbers) is inconvenient. A second method, which uses a rule that describes each element in the set, is called **set-builder notation**. A variable is frequently used in this case. For example, if V is the set of all vowels, then

$$\begin{array}{lll} V = \{a, e, i, o, u\} & & \text{roster method} \\ V = \{x \mid x \text{ is a vowel}\} & & \text{set-builder notation} \end{array}$$

The vertical bar, $\mid$, is read "such that," so V is read "the set of all letters x such that x is a vowel."

EXAMPLE 2

Express the following with set-builder notation.

a. $\{0, 1, 2, 3, 4\}$ **b.** $\{2, 4, 6, 8, \ldots\}$

SOLUTION   **a.** $\{x \mid x \text{ is a whole number less than 5}\}$, or $\{x \in \mathbb{W} \mid x < 5\}$
b. $\{$even natural numbers$\}$, or $\{n \in \mathbb{N} \mid n \text{ is divisible by 2}\}$

EXAMPLE 3

Express each of the following with the roster method.

a. $\{$odd natural numbers$\}$ **b.** $\{t \in \mathbb{W} \mid t \leq 100\}$

SOLUTION   **a.** $\{1, 3, 5, \ldots\}$ **b.** $\{0, 1, 2, \ldots, 100\}$

---

3   Subsets; Union and Intersection of Sets

We now consider the concept of a **subset**. This relationship occurs when all elements of one set are elements of a second set. For example, let A = $\{3, 4\}$ and B = $\{3, 4, 5\}$. Each member of A is a member of B, so A is a subset of B, which is written A $\subseteq$ B. Because every natural number is a whole number, $\mathbb{N} \subseteq \mathbb{W}$. Also, every set is a subset of itself, and the empty set is a subset of every set.

---

* "The infinite! No other question has ever moved so profoundly the spirit of man."— *David Hilbert* (1862–1943).

    "It was Georg Cantor (1845–1918) who, in the years 1871–1884, created a completely new and very special mathematical discipline, the theory of sets, in which was founded, for the first time in a thousand years of argument back and forth, a theory of infinity with all the incisiveness of modern mathematics."—*Hans Hahn.*

> ### Subset
>
> Let A and B be sets. If every element of A is an element of B, then A is a subset of B, written $A \subseteq B$. For all sets A, $A \subseteq A$ and $\varnothing \subseteq A$.

EXAMPLE 4

List all the subsets of $\{4, 5, 6\}$.

SOLUTION

$\varnothing$, $\{4\}$, $\{5\}$, $\{6\}$, $\{4, 5\}$, $\{4, 6\}$, $\{5, 6\}$, and $\{4, 5, 6\}$. In general, to list all the subsets of a set, start with the empty set, list all subsets with one element, list all subsets with two elements, and so on; the last subset listed is the set itself.

Let A and B be sets. We can form a new set from A and B by combining all the elements of A with all the elements of B. This new set is called the **union** of A and B, which is written $A \cup B$ and read "A union B." For example, if $A = \{0, 2, 6\}$ and $B = \{2, 6, 8\}$, then $A \cup B = \{0, 2, 6, 8\}$. Thus, $A \cup B$ consists of all elements in A, or in B, or in both A and B.

We can form a second set from A and B called their **intersection**, which is written $A \cap B$ and read "A intersection B." This set consists of all elements in A *and* B. For instance, if $A = \{0, 2, 6\}$ and $B = \{2, 6, 8\}$, then $A \cap B = \{2, 6\}$. In many instances no elements are common to two given sets. In this case the intersection is the empty set, and the two sets are said to be **disjoint**. For example, if $X = \{7, 8, 9\}$ and $Y = \{2, 3\}$, then $X \cap Y = \varnothing$.

> ### Union and Intersection
>
> Let A and B be sets. The union of A and B is $A \cup B = \{x \mid x \in A$ or $x \in B\}$. Their intersection is $A \cap B = \{x \mid x \in A$ and $x \in B\}$. If $A \cap B = \varnothing$, then A and B are said to be disjoint.

Note that "or" is used to indicate that x may be an element of A, of B, or of both A and B.

EXAMPLE 5

Find the union and intersection of the given sets.

a. $A = \{a, b, c\}$ and $B = \{c, d\}$.
b. $E = \{2, 4, 6, \ldots\}$ and $F = \{1, 3, 5, \ldots\}$.

SOLUTION

a. $A \cup B = \{a, b, c, d\}$ and $A \cap B = \{c\}$.
b. $E \cup F = \{1, 2, 3, 4, \ldots\} = \mathbb{N}$ and $E \cap F = \varnothing$.

A convenient way to illustrate set relationships is with **Venn diagrams**, which are named for the English logician John Venn (1837–1923). These diagrams are useful not only in algebra but also in other areas of mathematics, such as probability theory. The Venn diagram in Figure 1.1 shows that A is a subset of B because all the points in A are in B. In Figures 1.2 and 1.3 the light purple areas represent the union and intersection of two sets that are not disjoint. Disjoint sets are represented by circles that do not intersect.

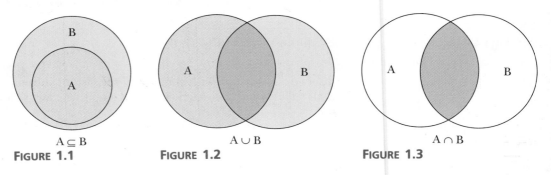

$A \subseteq B$
FIGURE 1.1

$A \cup B$
FIGURE 1.2

$A \cap B$
FIGURE 1.3

EXAMPLE 6   Let A = {1, 2, 3}   and   B = {3, 4, 5}. Illustrate **a.** A ∪ B and **b.** A ∩ B with Venn diagrams.

SOLUTION   **a.** A ∪ B = {1, 2, 3, 4, 5} (see Figure 1.4)
b. A ∩ B = {3} (see Figure 1.5)

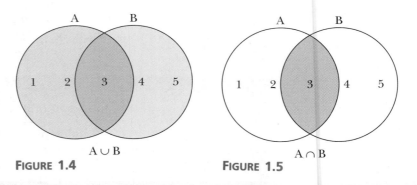

$A \cup B$
FIGURE 1.4

$A \cap B$
FIGURE 1.5

PEANUTS reprinted by permission of UFS, Inc.

EXERCISE SET 1.1

A

1 Determine which of the following are true and which are false.

1. $3 \cdot 6 \neq 9$ **2.** $7 \geq 7$ **3.** $19 < 17$
4. $21 \geq 30$ **5.** $8 > 8$ **6.** $9 \leq 9$

In each of the following, write a statement with the same meaning by reversing the inequality sign.

7. $6 > 4$ **8.** $30 \geq 25$ **9.** $5 \leq 5$
10. $5 \leq 6$ **11.** $0 < 14$ **12.** $17 \geq 17$

Place $<$, $\leq$, $>$, or $\geq$ in each blank to make a true statement; each exercise has two correct answers.

13. $9 \underline{\hspace{1em}} 5$ **14.** $12 \underline{\hspace{1em}} 12$
15. $0 \underline{\hspace{1em}} 0$ **16.** $1 \underline{\hspace{1em}} 6$

Use $<$, $\leq$, $>$, or $\geq$ to write the following inequalities.

17. 10 is less than or equal to 12.
18. 12 is greater than 6.
19. 30 is less than 40.
20. 13 is greater than or equal to 9.

2 Determine which of the following sets are finite and which are infinite.

21. All whole numbers less than 1000
22. All whole numbers greater than 1000
23. All natural numbers divisible by 7
24. All the hydrogen atoms in all the stars in our galaxy

Express the following with set-builder notation.

25. $\{1, 2, 3, 4, 5, 6\}$ **26.** $\{0, 1, 2, \ldots, 25\}$
27. $\{7, 8, 9, 10\}$ **28.** $\{0, 5, 10, 15, 20\}$

Express the following with the roster method. If the set is empty, write $\emptyset$.

29. $\{n \in \mathbb{W} \mid n \leq 4\}$
30. $\{m \in \mathbb{N} \mid m < 50\}$

31. $\{x \in \mathbb{N} \mid 5 < x < 6\}$
32. $\{n \in \mathbb{W} \mid 8 < n \leq 100\}$
33. $\{x \in \mathbb{W} \mid x \text{ is divisible by 7}\}$
34. $\{k \mid k \text{ is a letter in the word } calculus\}$

3 List all the subsets of each given set.

35. $\{x\}$ **36.** $\{a, b\}$ **37.** $\{7, 8\}$
38. $\emptyset$ **39.** $\{0, 1, 2\}$ **40.** $\{1, 2, 3, 4\}$

Let $A = \{2, 3, 5, 7\}$, $B = \{3, 5, 8, 9\}$, $C = \{2, 7\}$, $D = \{1\}$, and $E = \{3, 8\}$. Find the following unions and intersections and illustrate them with Venn diagrams. Illustrate the subset relationships with Venn diagrams.

41. $A \cup B$ **42.** $A \cup C$ **43.** $B \cup C$
44. $C \cup E$ **45.** $A \cap C$ **46.** $B \cap E$
47. $C \cap E$ **48.** $B \cap D$ **49.** $A \cup E$
50. $A \cap E$ **51.** $C \subseteq A$ **52.** $E \subseteq B$

Place $\in$, $\notin$, $\subseteq$, $\not\subseteq$ in each blank to make a true statement (more than one correct answer is possible). $E = \{2, 4, 6, \ldots\}$ and $F = \{1, 3, 5, \ldots\}$.

53. $a \underline{\hspace{1em}} \{a, b\}$ **54.** $\{a\} \underline{\hspace{1em}} \{a, b\}$
55. $\{c\} \underline{\hspace{1em}} \{a, b\}$ **56.** $c \underline{\hspace{1em}} \{a, b\}$
57. $\mathbb{N} \underline{\hspace{1em}} \mathbb{W}$ **58.** $\{1, 2, 3\} \underline{\hspace{1em}} \{1, 2, 3\}$
59. $12 \underline{\hspace{1em}} F$ **60.** $\emptyset \underline{\hspace{1em}} \mathbb{W}$
61. $E \underline{\hspace{1em}} F$ **62.** $E \underline{\hspace{1em}} \mathbb{N}$

Determine which of the following are true and which are false.

63. $\{a, b\} \neq \{b, a\}$ **64.** $\{3\} \subseteq \{3, 4\}$
65. $\{1, 2\} \subseteq \{2, 1\}$ **66.** $\{9\} \in \{8, 9, 10\}$
67. $\emptyset \subseteq \emptyset$ **68.** $\{1, 2, 5\} \not\subseteq \{2, 5, 1\}$
69. $7 \notin \{1, 3, 6\}$ **70.** $\emptyset \in \mathbb{N}$
71. $6 \in \{2, 4, 6\}$ **72.** $\{1, 5\} \neq \{5, 2\}$
73. $6 \leq 1$ **74.** $97 > 100$

B

75. $A \cup B = B \cup A$
76. $A \cap B = B \cap A$
77. $A \cup \varnothing = A$
78. $\varnothing \cap A = A$
79. If $A \subseteq B$ and $B \subseteq C$, then $A \subseteq C$.
80. If $A \cap B = A \cap C$, then $B = C$.
81. If $A \subseteq B$ and $B \subseteq A$, then $A = B$.
82. If $A \subseteq B$ and $B \subseteq C$, then $A \cup B \subseteq C$.
83. Every whole number is a natural number.
84. $\varnothing = \{\varnothing\}$

C 🖊

Answer the following questions with complete sentences.

85. Describe the difference between a variable and a constant.
86. Translate $3 \leq 3$ into English.
87. What is the difference between a finite set and an infinite set?
88. Describe the difference between representing a set by the roster method and by the set-builder notation. Give an example of each.

1.2 THE REAL NUMBER SYSTEM

1   **The Number Line**

2   **The Set of Real Numbers**

3   **Properties of the Real Numbers**

1   **The Number Line**

In the last section two basic subsets of the set of real numbers were given: $\mathbb{N} = \{1, 2, 3, \ldots\}$, the set of natural numbers, and $\mathbb{W} = \{0, 1, 2, \ldots\}$, the set of whole numbers. This section discusses other important subsets of the real numbers and reviews some of their properties. We begin with the number line, which allows us to visualize numbers as points on a line.

To construct a **number line** draw a line and label a convenient point with the number 0 (Figure 1.6). This point is called the **origin**. Next pick a point to the right of the origin to correspond to 1. The distance between these points is called the **unit distance**. We use the unit distance to represent the rest of the whole numbers as equally spaced points. The arrow on the number line indicates that the numbers increase in value as we move from left to right.

FIGURE 1.6

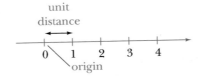

Each point on the number line has a unique real number called its **coordinate**, and each real number has a unique point on the number line called its **graph**. For convenience we will use the words *point* and *number* interchangeably, and we will make statements such as "3 is to the left of 4 on the number line." This is simpler than saying "the graph of the number 3 is to the left of the graph of the number 4 on the number line." We use the symbol $\mathbb{R}$ to stand for the set of real numbers.

The inequality $a < b$ means that a is to the left of b on the number line. In a similar way $b > a$ means that b is to the right of a on the number line. For example, in Figure 1.6, 3 is to the right of 2, so $3 > 2$.

EXAMPLE 1

Graph the set {0, 1/3, 1.75, 2, 3, 3.5} (see Figure 1.7). Label each point with its coordinate.

SOLUTION

FIGURE 1.7

2   The Set of Real Numbers

One motivation for developing new number systems is to solve new types of equations. Because $7 - 5 = 2$, the solution of the equation $x + 5 = 7$ is the whole number 2. As $7 - 9 \notin \mathbb{W}$, we have to extend the whole numbers to the **integers** to be able to solve equations such as $x + 9 = 7$. We denote the set of integers with the symbol $\mathbb{Z}$, from the German word *Zählen*, meaning "number." "The positive integers" is another description of "the natural numbers," and we will use these expressions interchangeably. $\mathbb{Z}$ consists of the positive integers, the corresponding negative integers, and 0, which is neither positive nor negative. Thus,

$$\mathbb{Z} = \{\ldots, -4, -3, -2, -1, 0, 1, 2, 3, 4, \ldots\}$$

EXAMPLE 2

Determine which of the following are true and which are false. Use Figure 1.8 to justify your answer.

a. $-4 \leq 3$ **b.** $-2 > -1$ **c.** $3 \geq 3$ **d.** $0 > -3$

FIGURE 1.8

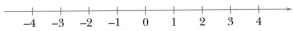

SOLUTION

a. True; -4 is to the left of 3 on the number line.
b. False; -2 is smaller than -1 because -2 is to the left of -1 on the number line.
c. True; $3 = 3$.
d. True; 0 is to the right of -3 on the number line.

The equation $9x = 7$ has no solution in the set of integers because $7 \div 9 \notin \mathbb{Z}$. Therefore, to solve such equations we must extend the integers to the rational numbers. The quotient of two numbers is often called a **ratio**. Any number that can be written as the ratio of two integers, a/b, with $b \neq 0$, is called a **rational number** (a is called the **numerator**, and b is the **denominator**). Examples are

$$\frac{2}{3}, \quad \frac{-5}{12}, \quad -4\frac{1}{2} = -\frac{9}{2}, \quad \text{and} \quad 7 = \frac{7}{1}$$

Because every integer a can be written as $a/1$, the integers are a subset of the rational numbers. We denote the set of rational numbers by the symbol $\mathbb{Q}$, from the word **Q**uotient. Symbolically,

$$\mathbb{Q} = \left\{ \frac{a}{b} \,\middle|\, a, \ b \in \mathbb{Z}, \ b \neq 0 \right\} \quad \text{and} \quad \mathbb{N} \subseteq \mathbb{W} \subseteq \mathbb{Z} \subseteq \mathbb{Q}$$

We can justify the statement that $a/0$ is undefined by using the **multiplication property of 0, $0 \cdot c = 0$** for all numbers c, and the relationship between division and multiplication. For example, $8/2 = 4$ because $8 = 2 \cdot 4$, and, in general,

$$\frac{a}{b} = c \quad \text{if} \quad a = bc$$

From this definition, $8/0 = c$ if $8 = 0 \cdot c$. But $8 = 0 \cdot c$ is not true for any value of c because $0 \cdot c = 0$. Therefore, $8/0$ cannot be a real number, so it is *undefined*. Now, $0/0 = c$ if $0 = 0 \cdot c$. But $0 = 0 \cdot c$ is true for all values of c. Thus, $0/0 = 1$ and $0/0 = 9$ would both be correct, because $0 = 0 \cdot 1$ and $0 = 0 \cdot 9$ are both true statements. We require a unique answer for every arithmetic operation, so we say that $0/0$ is **undefined** ($0/0$ is also called **indeterminate**, because it could have any value). No problem is seen with $0/b$, if $b \neq 0$. For example, consider $0/3$. Let $0/3 = c$. Then $0 = 3 \cdot c$, so $c = 0$. Thus, $0/3 = 0$. In general, $0/b = 0$ if $b \neq 0$ because $0 = b \cdot 0$. On a calculator, $0 \div 3 = 0$, but $8 \div 0$ results in the statement *Error*. To summarize:

$$0 \cdot a = 0, \quad \frac{a}{0} \text{ is undefined}, \quad \text{and} \quad \frac{0}{b} = 0 \text{ if } b \neq 0.$$

We often express rational numbers in decimal form. For example, $7/4 = 1.75$ and $-3/5 = -0.6$; these are called **terminating decimals** because the long division terminates with a remainder of 0. In converting $2/3$ and $7/11$ to decimal form, the division process does not terminate; these are called **repeating decimals**, and are written

$$\frac{2}{3} = 0.66\overline{6} \text{ or } 0.\overline{6} \qquad \frac{7}{11} = 0.63\overline{63} \text{ or } 0.\overline{63}$$

With repeating decimals, the division is carried out far enough to determine the pattern, and the bar indicates that the pattern repeats forever. On a calculator $2 \div 3 = 0.66 \ldots 67$ and $7 \div 11 = 0.63 \ldots 6364$. Remember that these decimals are rounded off and are not the exact values.

Every rational number has either a terminating or a repeating decimal expansion. Thus, $\mathbb{Q}$ is the set of all real numbers whose decimal expansion terminates or repeats:

$$\mathbb{Q} = \{\text{terminating or repeating decimals}\}$$

We now consider a third type of decimal that does not terminate or repeat, as indicated by three dots. Two examples are

$$0.1234567891011 \ldots \quad \text{and} \quad -1.01001000100001 \ldots$$

These are **nonterminating nonrepeating decimals** and cannot be expressed as the ratio of two integers. They are examples of **irrational numbers**. The set of irrational numbers is denoted by the symbol $\mathbb{H}$:

$$\mathbb{H} = \{\text{nonterminating nonrepeating decimals}\}$$

Two other examples of irrational numbers are π (pi), the ratio of the circumference to the diameter of a circle (Figure 1.9), and $\sqrt{2}$ (the square root of 2), the length of the diagonal of a unit square (Figure 1.10). Calculate π and $\sqrt{2}$ on your calculator.

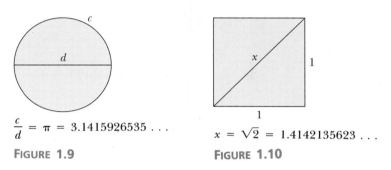

$\dfrac{c}{d} = \pi = 3.1415926535 \ldots$

FIGURE 1.9

$x = \sqrt{2} = 1.4142135623 \ldots$

FIGURE 1.10

We have discussed the set of rational numbers, $\mathbb{Q}$, and the set of irrational numbers, $\mathbb{H}$. The union of these two sets is the set of **real numbers**, $\mathbb{R}$. That is, $\mathbb{R} = \mathbb{Q} \cup \mathbb{H}$. Every real number x either can be expressed as the ratio of two integers, a/b, and is rational, or cannot be expressed as the ratio of two integers and is irrational. Thus, $\mathbb{Q} \cap \mathbb{H} = \varnothing$. See Figure 1.11 and the boxed summary of the real number system.

The Real Number System

$\mathbb{N}$ = natural numbers = $\{1, 2, 3, \ldots\}$

$\mathbb{W}$ = whole numbers = $\{0, 1, 2, 3, \ldots\}$

$\mathbb{Z}$ = integers = $\{\ldots, -3, -2, -1, 0, 1, 2, 3, \ldots\}$

$\mathbb{Q}$ = rational numbers
  = $\{x \in \mathbb{R} \mid x = a/b; \quad a, b \in \mathbb{Z}, \quad b \neq 0\}$
  = $\{\text{terminating or repeating decimals}\}$

$\mathbb{H}$ = irrational numbers
  = $\{x \in \mathbb{R} \mid x \neq a/b; \quad a, b \in \mathbb{Z}, \quad b \neq 0\}$
  = $\{\text{nonterminating nonrepeating decimals}\}$

$\mathbb{R}$ = real numbers = $\mathbb{Q} \cup \mathbb{H}$, $\mathbb{N} \subseteq \mathbb{W} \subseteq \mathbb{Z} \subseteq \mathbb{Q} \subseteq \mathbb{R}$, and $\mathbb{H} \subseteq \mathbb{R}$

FIGURE **1.11**

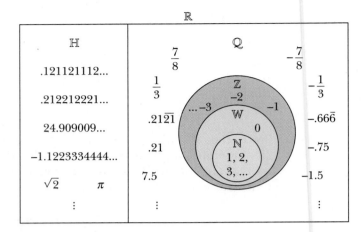

EXAMPLE 3   Put an **x** in each box that describes the given expression.

	ℕ	𝕎	ℤ	ℚ	ℍ	ℝ	**Undefined**
13	x	x	x	x		x	
0		x	x	x		x	
1.83				x		x	
1.83$\overline{83}$				x		x	
1.838338333 . . .					x	x	
−20			x	x		x	
7/8				x		x	
7/0							x
0/8		x	x	x		x	
0/0							x

<blockquote>**3**</blockquote> **Properties of the Real Numbers**

This section reviews some of the basic properties of the real numbers. Other properties will be discussed later as needed.

We mentioned earlier that $7 - 9 \notin \mathbb{W}$. However, $7 + 9 \in \mathbb{W}$, and, in general, if a and b are any whole numbers, then $a + b$ is a whole number. This illustrates the concept of **closure**. We say that "𝕎 is closed under addition," but "𝕎 is not closed under subtraction." The concept of closure applies to other operations as well. Also, the set of real numbers is closed under addition, subtraction, multiplication, and division (except by 0).

Closure under Addition

Let A be a set with a and b any elements of A. A is closed under addition if $a + b$ is an element of A.

EXAMPLE 4

Let A = $\{0, 1\}$. Determine if A is closed under:

a. addition   **b.** multiplication

SOLUTION

a. $0 + 0 = 0 \in$ A   and $0 + 1 = 1 \in$ A, but $1 + 1 = 2 \notin$ A. Therefore, A is not closed under addition.

b. $0 \cdot 0 = 0 \in$ A, $0 \cdot 1 = 0 \in$ A,   and $1 \cdot 1 = 1 \in$ A. Thus, A is closed under multiplication.

For the rest of the properties in this section, a, b, and c represent real numbers.

The **commutative property** says that the **order** in which we add or multiply two numbers does not change the answer. For example, $3 + 5 = 5 + 3 = 8$.

Commutative Properties

$$a + b = b + a$$
$$ab = ba$$

The **associative property** says that when three numbers are added or multiplied the **grouping** does not change the answer. For example, $(2 \cdot 3)4 = 6 \cdot 4 = 24$ and $2(3 \cdot 4) = 2 \cdot 12 = 24$, so $(2 \cdot 3)4 = 2(3 \cdot 4)$.

Associative Properties

$$(a + b) + c = a + (b + c)$$
$$(ab)c = a(bc)$$

The **distributive property** links multiplication and addition, and we say that *multiplication distributes over addition*. For instance, $4(3 + 7) = 4(10) = 40$ and $4 \cdot 3 + 4 \cdot 7 = 12 + 28 = 40$, so $4(3 + 7) = 4 \cdot 3 + 4 \cdot 7$.

Distributive Property

$$a(b + c) = ab + ac$$
$$(b + c)a = ba + ca$$

The distributive property can be extended to the sum of three or more numbers, as illustrated in our next example. Notice how the use of these properties simplifies the computations.

EXAMPLE 5

Simplify each of the following.

a. $8 \cdot 3 + 8 \cdot 6 + 8 \cdot 11$ **b.** $97 \cdot 101$
c. $(132 + 4) + 296$ **d.** $(4 \cdot 57)25$

SOLUTION

a. $8 \cdot 3 + 8 \cdot 6 + 8 \cdot 11 = 8(3 + 6 + 11)$ Distributive property
$= 8(20)$
$= 160$

b. $97 \cdot 101 = 97(100 + 1)$ Distributive property
$= 97 \cdot 100 + 97 \cdot 1$
$= 9700 + 97$
$= 9797$

c. $(132 + 4) + 296 = 132 + (4 + 296)$ Associative property
$= 132 + 300$
$= 432$

d. $(4 \cdot 57)25 = (57 \cdot 4)25$ Commutative property
$= 57(4 \cdot 25)$ Associative property
$= 57(100)$
$= 5700$

The numbers 0* and 1 have important properties. In the statement $1 \cdot 5 = 5$, the identity, or value, of 5 is unchanged when it is multiplied by 1. In a similar way, $0 + 5 = 5$, and the value of 5 is unchanged when 0 is added. Zero is called the **identity element** for addition, or the **additive identity**; and 1 is called the **identity element** for multiplication, or the **multiplicative identity**.

Identity Properties

0 and 1 are the unique real numbers such that

$$0 + a = a + 0 = a$$
$$1 \cdot a = a \cdot 1 = a$$

---

* Superstitious people in the Middle Ages believed that zero was invented by the devil because it is a symbol that either means nothing or changes the number that it follows.

A pair of numbers such as 6 and -6 are called opposites or additive inverses, because their sum is 0, the identity element for addition. Similarly, 6 and 1/6 are called reciprocals or multiplicative inverses, because their product is 1, the identity element for multiplication—that is,

$$6 + (-6) = 0 \quad \text{and} \quad 6 \cdot \frac{1}{6} = 1$$

Opposite or Additive Inverse

The opposite of the number a is $-a$, the opposite of $-a$ is $-(-a) = a$, and

$$a + (-a) = -a + a = 0$$

Reciprocal or Multiplicative Inverse

For $a \neq 0$, the reciprocal of a is $1/a$, and

$$\frac{1}{a} \cdot a = a \cdot \frac{1}{a} = 1$$

EXAMPLE 6

For the given number a, find its opposite, $-a$, and its reciprocal, $1/a$.

a. -7 **b.** 0 **c.** $\frac{5}{4}$ **d.** $-\frac{2}{9}$ **e.** .478

SOLUTION

a. $-a = 7; \dfrac{1}{a} = -\dfrac{1}{7}$ **b.** $-a = 0; \dfrac{1}{a}$ is undefined.

c. $-a = -\dfrac{5}{4}; \dfrac{1}{a} = \dfrac{4}{5}$ **d.** $-a = \dfrac{2}{9}; \dfrac{1}{a} = -\dfrac{9}{2}$

e. $-a = -.478$; to find $1/a$, use the $1/x$ key on your calculator (enter .478 and press the $1/x$ key). Thus, $1/a = 2.092$, to three decimal places.

EXERCISE SET 1.2

A

1 Graph each set of points on a number line. Label each point with its coordinate.

1. $\{0, 2, 4, 6, 8\}$

2. $\{0, -2, -4, -6, -8\}$

3. $\{-5, -1, 1, 3, 4\}$

4. $\left\{\dfrac{1}{4}, \dfrac{1}{3}, -\dfrac{1}{2}, -\dfrac{3}{4}\right\}$

5. $\left\{\dfrac{1}{5}, \dfrac{4}{5}, -\dfrac{1}{5}, -\dfrac{7}{6}\right\}$

6. $\left\{-1\dfrac{1}{2}, 3\dfrac{1}{4}, -2\dfrac{1}{2}, -\dfrac{2}{3}\right\}$

2 Use either < or > to make the following statements true.

7. 5 _____ 7

8. −5 _____ −7

9. 10 _____ −8

10. −10 _____ 8

11. −20 _____ −15

12. −12 _____ −30

Determine which of the following are true and which are false. Justify your answer as in Example 2.

13. $-6 \leq 4$

14. $6 \leq -4$

15. $-3 > -7$

16. $3 < 7$

17. $-100 \geq -75$

18. $18 > -30$

Express each of the following as decimals and classify them as repeating or terminating decimals. Give the exact value.

19. $\dfrac{7}{20}$

20. $-3\dfrac{1}{6}$

21. $\dfrac{17}{99}$

22. $\dfrac{17}{100}$

23. $-\dfrac{2}{111}$

24. $\dfrac{1}{125}$

Approximate the following numbers to four decimal places.

25. $\dfrac{\pi}{4}$

26. $\dfrac{\sqrt{2}}{2}$

27. $\sqrt{5}$

28. $\sqrt{17}$

Let $A = \{8, -5, 0, \sqrt{2}, 0.77, 0.7\overline{7}, 0.717273 \ldots, -4/11, 9/2\}$. List all the elements of A that are

29. Positive integers

30. Negative integers

31. Rational

32. Irrational

Find the following unions and intersections.

33. $\mathbb{H} \cap \mathbb{Q}$

34. $\mathbb{H} \cup \mathbb{Q}$

35. $\mathbb{W} \cap \mathbb{Z}$

36. $\mathbb{R} \cap \mathbb{H}$

37. $\mathbb{R} \cup \mathbb{N}$

38. $\mathbb{Z} \cap \mathbb{Q}$

39. $\mathbb{Z} \cap \mathbb{H}$

40. $\mathbb{N} \cup \mathbb{W}$

Determine whether the given statement is true or false. Justify your answer.

41. 1 is both rational and irrational.

42. 1/0 is a whole number.

43. Every natural number is a real number.

44. Some rational numbers are integers.

45. The real numbers that are not rational are irrational.

46. 1.22333444455555 . . . is a rational number.

47. −8 is not a rational number.

48. Every natural number is a rational number.

49. Every point on the number line has a rational coordinate.

50. Every real number has a unique graph on the number line.

Put an **x** in each box that describes the given expression.

	N	W	Z	Q	H	R	Undefined
51. −35				X			
52. 8/3							
53. 8/2		X					
54. −3/4							
55. π						X	
56. 0/9							
57. 9/0							
58. 0.02002000200002 . . .							
59. $0.0\overline{202}$							
60. 0.02							

3 Determine whether the given statement is true or false.

61. The integers are closed under subtraction.

62. The integers are closed under division.

63. The rational numbers are closed under addition.

64. $4(3 + 7) = 4 \cdot 3 + 7$

65. $2(a + 8) = 2a + 16$

66. $5(2 \cdot 9) = (5 \cdot 2)9$

67. $4(3 \cdot 7) = (4 \cdot 3)(4 \cdot 7)$

68. Every real number has a reciprocal.

69. Every real number has an additive inverse.

70. The commutative property is a grouping property.

Determine whether the given set is closed under the operation. If not, justify your answer with an example.

71. $F = \{1, 3, 5, 7, \ldots \}$, addition.

72. F, multiplication.

73. K = {7, 8, 9}, subtraction.

74. A = {1, 4, 1/4}, division.

75. B = {1, 1/2, 1/4, 1/8, 1/16, 1/32, ... }, multiplication.

76. B, addition.

For each of the following, give its (a) opposite and (b) reciprocal.

77. 1   **78.** 1.25   **79.** −.503

80. 13.176   **81.** 7/5   **82.** −3/4

83. −11/10   **84.** 2/π

State the property illustrated by each of the following.

85. $(\pi + \sqrt{2}) \in \mathbb{R}$

86. $3x + 5x = (3 + 5)x$

87. $-8 + 8 = 0$

88. $\frac{2}{3} \cdot \frac{3}{2} = 1$

89. $(2 + 3) + 7 = (3 + 2) + 7$

90. $(2 + 3) + 7 = 2 + (3 + 7)$

91. $4(x + 7) = 4x + 28$

92. $1 \cdot 17 = 17$

93. $0 + 17 = 17$

94. $0 \cdot 17 = 0$

95. $(17 \cdot 5)20 = 17(5 \cdot 20)$

96. $9(x + y) = (x + y)9$

Use the properties that we have developed to simplify each of the following. If an operation cannot be performed, write "undefined."

97. $(17 \cdot 5)20$ **98.** $(873 + 49) + 51$

99. $(93 \cdot 961)(7 - 7)$ **100.** $79 \cdot 11$

101. $\frac{9}{0} \cdot 0$ **102.** $\frac{17}{17}(8321)$

103. $87 \cdot 3 + 87 \cdot 7$ **104.** $(2 \cdot 773)50$

B

105. Does addition distribute over multiplication; that is, does $a + (b \cdot c) = (a + b) \cdot (a + c)$? Justify your answer with an example.

We can make up a new operation, ∗, using the operations of arithmetic. Let $a * b = 3a + b$; for instance, $2 * 5 = 3 \cdot 2 + 5 = 11$. Justify your answer to each of the following with an example.

106. Is ∗ commutative?   **107.** Is ∗ associative?

Answer the following questions.

108. What is the largest negative integer?

109. What is the smallest negative integer?

110. What is the smallest positive integer?

111. What is the largest positive integer?

112. What is the smallest positive rational number?

C ✏

Answer the following questions with complete sentences.

113. What is the subset relationship among the integers, the whole numbers, the rational numbers, and the natural numbers?

114. Explain why 0/0 is called indeterminate.

115. What is the relationship among terminating, repeating, and nonterminating nonrepeating decimals?

116. What is the difference between the commutative and associative properties?

REVIEW EXERCISES

State the property used in the given step. (See Section 1.2)

$7 + (-5) = [2 + 5] + (-5)$
$\qquad = 2 + [5 + (-5)]$
$\qquad = 2 + 0$
$\qquad = 2$

117. _____

118. _____

119. _____

$-7 + 5 = -(2 + 5) + 5$
$\qquad = [-2 + (-5)] + 5$
$\qquad = -2 + [-5 + 5]$
$\qquad = -2 + 0$
$\qquad = -2$

120. _____

121. _____

122. _____

1.3 ADDITION AND SUBTRACTION OF REAL NUMBERS

1	Absolute Value
2	Addition
3	Subtraction
4	Word Problems

1   Absolute Value

The last section covered several properties of the real numbers. This section uses some of these properties to review addition of real numbers. Before doing this we will discuss opposites in more detail and introduce the concept of absolute value.

The opposite of 6 is -6, because $6 + (-6) = 0$. In a similar way the opposite of -7 is $-(-7) = 7$, because $-7 + 7 = 0$. In general, the opposite of a is $-a$, and $-(-a) = a$, which is called the **double negative property**. The statement $-(-7) = 7$ illustrates two uses of the minus sign:

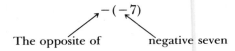

The opposite of   negative seven

We have three uses for the minus sign. It is used to indicate the following.

1. The operation of subtraction: $8 - 5 = 3$

2. The opposite of: $-(6)$

3. A negative number: -7

We write the opposite of the number x as $-x$. Is $-x$ a negative number? Not necessarily! If $x = 4$, then $-x = -4$; if $x = -7$, then $-x = 7$; if $x = 0$, then $-x = 0$.

COMMON ERROR   A common mistake is to think that $-x$ is a negative number. In fact, $-x$ can be negative, positive, or zero.

Because 3 and -3 are opposites of each other, the graph of -3 is the same distance to the left of 0 as 3 is to the right of 0 (Figure 1.12). The distance from number a to 0 is called the **absolute value of a** and is denoted $|a|$. Absolute value represents distance, so it is never negative. That is, $|a| \geq 0$. Thus, $|3| = 3$, $|-3| = 3$, and $|0| = 0$. Also, because a and $-a$ are equal distances from 0, $|-a| = |a|$.

FIGURE 1.12

We often must deal with the absolute value of an algebraic expression. To do so we need a more formal definition of $|a|$ than the geometric one just given. If $a \geq 0$, then $|a| = a$, such as $|3| = 3$. Thus, the absolute value of a positive number, or 0, is that number. If $a < 0$, then $|a| = -a$, such as $|-3| = -(-3) = 3$. That is, the absolute value of a negative number is the opposite of that number, which is positive. Note the boxed summary of the properties of absolute value.

> ### Absolute Value
>
> $|a| =$ the distance from a to 0
>
> $$|a| = \begin{cases} a, & \text{if } a \geq 0 \\ -a, & \text{if } a < 0 \end{cases}$$
>
> $$|a| \geq 0 \qquad |-a| = |a|$$

EXAMPLE 1

Simplify each of the following.

a. $|-8|$ **b.** $-|-1|$ **c.** $6|7-3|$ **d.** $-(|-6| + |-5|)$

SOLUTION

a. $|-8| = -(-8) = 8$
b. $-|-1| = -[-(-1)] = -[1] = -1$
c. $6|7-3| = 6|4| = 6(4) = 24$
d. $-(|-6| + |-5|) = -(6 + 5) = -11$

$-(6 + 5)$
$-(11) \quad -11$

2 Addition

The addition of real numbers can be broken into several cases. We learn in arithmetic how to find the sum of positive rational numbers; and we have just discussed the case of opposites. We are now ready to review the remaining three cases: the sum of two negative numbers, the sum of a positive and a negative number where the answer is positive, and the sum of a positive and a negative number where the answer is negative.

We begin by evaluating $-4 + (-5)$ in terms of money. Suppose Steve has $0 in his checking account and he writes two checks, one for $4 and the other for $5. He is now $9 overdrawn. If we represent the checks by -4 and -5 and the final balance by -9, then

$$-4 + (-5) = -(4 + 5) = -9$$

> Let a and b be positive numbers. Then,
>
> $$-a + (-b) = -(a + b)$$

As an example of the second case, we will find the sum $9 + (-6)$ by using three properties of the real numbers:

$$9 + (-6) = [3 + 6] + (-6) \quad \text{Express 9 as } 3 + 6.$$
$$= 3 + [6 + (-6)] \quad \text{Associative property}$$
$$= 3 + 0 \quad \text{Opposites: } a + (-a) = 0$$
$$= 3 \quad \text{Identity: } a + 0 = a$$

The short way to find $9 + (-6)$ is to use subtraction: $9 + (-6) = 9 - 6 = 3$. In general:

> Let a and b be positive numbers with $a > b$. Then,
> $$a + (-b) = a - b$$

An example of our final case is $-9 + 6$. Again, let us evaluate this with properties of the real numbers:

$$-9 + 6 = -(3 + 6) + 6 \quad \text{Express 9 as } 3 + 6.$$
$$= [-3 + (-6)] + 6 \quad -(a + b) = -a + (-b)$$
$$= -3 + [-6 + 6] \quad \text{Associative property}$$
$$= -3 + 0 \quad -a + a = 0$$
$$= -3 \quad a + 0 = a$$

The short way to find $-9 + 6$ is to use subtraction and opposites: $-9 + 6 = -(9 - 6) = -3$. In general:

> Let a and b be positive numbers with $a > b$. Then,
> $$-a + b = -(a - b)$$

EXAMPLE 2

Find the following sums.

a. $-12 + (-8)$ **b.** $-40 + 50$ **c.** $-1572 + 519$
d. $-6 + (-4) + (-17)$

SOLUTION

a. $-12 + (-8) = -(12 + 8) = -20$
b. $-40 + 50 = 50 + (-40) = 50 - 40 = 10$

c. ▢ $-1572 + 519 = -(1572 - 519) = -1053$

d. $-6 + (-4) + (-17) = -(6 + 4 + 17) = -27$

We have given intuitive definitions for the sum of two real numbers. A more formal approach involves absolute value. Use whichever method you find easier. Example 3 contains an example of each of the following rules.

> ### Addition of Two Real Numbers
> ——
> 1. **Same sign**   Add their absolute values. The sum has the same sign as the numbers.
> 2. **Different signs**   Subtract the smaller absolute value from the larger. The sum has the sign of the number with the larger absolute value. If they are opposites, then the sum is 0.

EXAMPLE 3

Use absolute value to find the following sums.

a. $4 + 5$ **b.** $-4 + (-5)$ **c.** $9 + (-6)$
d. $-9 + 6$ **e.** $6 + (-6)$

SOLUTION   **a.** $4 + 5 = |4| + |5| = 4 + 5 = 9$
b. $-4 + (-5) = -(|-4| + |-5|) = -(4 + 5) = -9$
c. $9 + (-6) = |9| - |-6| = 9 - 6 = 3$
d. $-9 + 6 = -(|-9| - |6|) = -(9 - 6) = -3$
e. $6 + (-6) = 0$

3   Subtraction

We have just seen that subtracting 6 from 9 is the same as adding the opposite of 6 to 9: $9 - 6 = 9 + (-6) = 3$. In general:

> ### Subtraction of Real Numbers
> ——
> Let $a, b \in \mathbb{R}$. Then,
> $$a - b = a + (-b)$$

EXAMPLE 4

Convert the following differences to sums, then simplify the sums.

a. $12 - 16$ **b.** $-9 - 11$ **c.** $-9 - (-11)$

SOLUTION   **a.** $12 - 16 = 12 + (-16) = -4$
b. $-9 - 11 = -9 + (-11) = -20$
c. $-9 - (-11) = -9 + [-(-11)] = -9 + 11 = 2$

In the last section we saw that multiplication distributes over addition: $a(b + c) = ab + ac$. Because subtraction can be converted to addition, multiplication distributes over subtraction:

$$a(b - c) = a[b + (-c)] = ab + a(-c) = ab - ac$$

Distributive Property
Let $a, b, c \in \mathbb{R}$. Then,

$$a(b - c) = ab - ac$$
$$(b - c)a = ba - ca$$

EXAMPLE 5

Use the distributive property to rewrite the following. Simplify when possible.

    a. $4(2x - 5)$ **b.** $(3 - 7y)6z$ **c.** $9x - 7x$

SOLUTION   **a.** $4(2x - 5) = 4 \cdot 2x - 4 \cdot 5 = 8x - 20$
    b. $(3 - 7y)6z = 3 \cdot 6z - 7y \cdot 6z = 18z - 42yz$
    c. $9x - 7x = (9 - 7)x = 2x$

---

4   Word Problems

Positive numbers are used to indicate a gain or increase, and negative numbers are used to represent a loss or decrease. For example, 12 represents a gain of 12 yards in a football game, whereas -25 indicates a loss of $25 if one has bet on the losing team. Our concluding examples illustrate the concepts of gain and loss expressed with addition and subtraction of signed numbers.

EXAMPLE 6

Dina was scuba diving at a depth of 20 feet. She descended another 35 feet. Find her new depth.

SOLUTION   Let -20 represent her original depth and -35 the additional 35 feet she descended. Then,
$-20 + (-35) = -55$;
her new depth is 55 feet below sea level.

EXAMPLE 7

Pythagoras was born approximately 580 B.C., and Galileo was born in A.D. 1564. Find the difference in time between Galileo's birth and Pythagoras's birth.

SOLUTION   Let $-580 = $ Pythagoras's birth and $1564 = $ Galileo's birth. Then,
$1564 - (-580) = 1564 + 580 = 2144$;
the difference between their births is 2144 years.

EXERCISE SET 1.3

A

1 Identify the use of the minus sign in each of the following.

1. $5 - 4$ **2.** $5 + [-(4)]$

3. $5 + [-4]$ **4.** -12

Graph the given number and find its absolute value.

5. 4 **6.** -4 **7.** -5 **8.** 5

Simplify each of the following.

9. $3 \mid 10 \mid$ **10.** $- \mid -12 \mid$

11. $-6 \mid -(-8) \mid$ **12.** $4 \mid 0 \mid$

Use $<$ or $>$ to make the following statements true.

13. $\mid -5 \mid \underline{\hspace{1em}} \mid 9 \mid$ **14.** $\mid -9 \mid \underline{\hspace{1em}} \mid -21 \mid$

15. $\mid -11 \mid \underline{\hspace{1em}} \mid 0 \mid$ **16.** $- \mid -6 \mid \underline{\hspace{1em}} \mid 4 \mid$

Use *always, sometimes,* or *never* to make the following statements true.

17. $-x$ is $\underline{\hspace{4em}}$ a negative number.

18. $\mid -x \mid$ is $\underline{\hspace{4em}}$ a negative number.

19. $\mid x \mid$ is $\underline{\hspace{4em}}$ a positive number.

20. $\mid b - a \mid$ is $\underline{\hspace{4em}}$ a nonnegative number.

2 Simplify the following.

21. $-8 + (-7)$

22. $-8 + 7$

23. ▦ $80{,}491 + (-71{,}956)$

24. $-2290 + 4760$

25. $-60 + (-40)$

26. $5 + (-30)$

27. $-7 + 6 + (-9)$

28. ▦ $-10.63 + 2.47$

29. ▦ $-1.514 + (-0.355)$

30. $-\dfrac{7}{4} + \dfrac{1}{2}$

31. $-\dfrac{5}{12} + (-1)$

32. $-\dfrac{1}{6} + \dfrac{7}{9}$

3

33. $6 - 20$

34. $-5 - 4$

35. $-5 - (-4)$

36. $12 - (-6)$

37. $-\dfrac{3}{8} - \dfrac{7}{10}$

38. $-\dfrac{1}{3} - \left(-\dfrac{1}{27}\right)$

39. ▦ $-.75 - .31$

40. ▦ $-1.2 - (-3.61)$

41. ▦ $8 - 4 + (-1)$

42. ▦ $70{,}165 - 94{,}172$

43. ▦ $-213 - (-9751)$

44. $\mid 8 \mid - \mid -10 \mid$

45. $\mid 8 - (-10) \mid$

46. $3 \mid -7 \mid + 4 \mid -2 \mid$

47. $- \mid -(-9) \mid$

48. $-(\mid -1 \mid - \mid -3 \mid)$

49. $6 \mid 3 - 3 \mid$

50. $8 - 2 \mid 1 - 4 \mid$

Use the distributive property to rewrite the following. Simplify when possible.

51. $3(2x - 7)$ **52.** $(6x - 1)4y$

53. $3ab(8x - 5y)$ **54.** $5(10 - 3k)$

55. $2(3x - 7)$ **56.** $6a + 7a$

57. $5a - 5b$ **58.** $5a - 5$

59. $8x + x$ **60.** $3xy + 2xz$

4 Solve the following using positive numbers, or negative numbers, or both. Remember, the difference between a and b is $a - b$.

61. Jan is \$20 in debt and Ken is \$95 in debt. Find the difference between Jan's debt and Ken's debt.

62. A football team lost 25 yards on a play. On the next play it gained 40 yards. What was the net result of the two plays?

63. The temperature at 6 A.M. was −28° F; it rose 13° F by noon. What was the new temperature?

64. The temperature at noon was −8° C, and it fell 18° C by sunset. What was the new temperature?

65. The elevation at the top of Heavenly Valley ski resort is 10,040 feet. Death Valley is 280 feet below sea level. Find the difference in altitude between the top of Heavenly Valley and Death Valley.

66. The Trojan War described in Homer's *Iliad* took place in approximately 1300 B.C. in Turkey. The Battle of Hastings took place in A.D. 1066 in England. Find the difference in time between the Battle of Hastings and the Trojan War.

67. In a given week a small company spends $6200 and takes in $5650. Find the loss for that week.

68. Dinosaurs first appeared during the early Triassic Period some 225 million years ago. The oldest known fossil of a hominid (humanlike creature) is from the Pliocene Epoch, approximately 5 million years ago. Find the time span between the first hominids and the first dinosaurs.

69. Dinosaurs became extinct at the end of the Cretaceous Period, 65 million years ago. This is one of several mass extinctions that seem to have occurred approximately every 27 million years. Some scientists believe that these extinctions are caused by a companion star to our sun that passes close to our solar system every 27 million years, resulting in comets hitting the earth. If this hypothesis is correct, the next mass extinction should occur some 16 million years from now. Find the difference in time between the next possible mass extinction and the extinction of the dinosaurs.

70. Use exercises 68 and 69 to determine how long the dinosaurs survived.

B

Find real numbers a, b, and c such that:

71. $a - b \neq b - a$

72. $a - b = b - a$

73. $(a - b) - c = a - (b - c)$

74. $(a - b) - c \neq a - (b - c)$

75. Why do we say that subtraction is not commutative when $a - b = b - a$ is true for some real numbers and false for other real numbers?

76. Why do we say that subtraction is not associative when $(a - b) - c = a - (b - c)$ is true for some real numbers and false for other real numbers?

Determine which of the following sets are closed under (a) addition and (b) subtraction.

77. $\mathbb{N}$, the natural numbers

78. $\mathbb{Q}$, the rational numbers

79. {even integers}

80. $\{-1, 0, 1\}$

C

Answer the following questions with complete sentences.

81. Is $-x$ a negative number? Discuss the possible values of $-x$.

82. Why is $|a|$ never negative?

REVIEW EXERCISES

State the property used in the given step. (See Section 1.2.)

$0 = 4 \cdot 0$
  $= 4[6 + (-6)]$
  $= 4 \cdot 6 + 4(-6)$

83. _____

84. _____

85. _____

$0 = (-6) \cdot 0$
  $= (-6)[4 + (-4)]$
  $= (-6)4 + (-6)(-4)$

86. _____

87. _____

88. _____

1.4 MULTIPLICATION AND DIVISION OF REAL NUMBERS

1	**Multiplication and Division**
2	**Exponents and Square Roots**
3	**Order of Operations**
4	**Algebraic Expressions**

1 Multiplication and Division

This section continues to review the basic operations of real numbers and covers multiplication, division, and the order of operations. Also introduced are exponents, square roots, and algebraic expressions, topics that will be developed in later chapters.

In the last section we used certain properties to show that $9 + (-6) = 3$. With the multiplication property of 0, we can justify that $3(-5) = -15$:

$$
\begin{aligned}
0 &= 3 \cdot 0 & &\quad 0 = a \cdot 0 \\
&= 3[5 + (-5)] & &\quad 0 = a + (-a) \\
&= 3 \cdot 5 + 3(-5) & &\quad \text{Distributive property} \\
&= 15 + 3(-5)
\end{aligned}
$$

We know that -15 is the only real number that we can add to 15 to get a sum of 0. Therefore, if

$$15 + 3(-5) = 0 \quad \textit{and} \quad 15 + (-15) = 0, \quad \text{then } 3(-5) = -15$$

This example illustrates that the product of a positive and a negative number is *always* negative:

> Let a and b be positive numbers. Then,
> $$a(-b) = (-a)b = -(ab)$$

An important special case of this result is $(-1)a = -(1 \cdot a) = -a$—that is, the opposite of a is the product of -1 and a. For instance, $(-1)6 = -(1 \cdot 6) = -6$.

> $$-a = (-1)a$$

We have just seen that $(-5)3 = -15$. The same approach can be used to show that $(-5)(-3) = 15$:

$$
\begin{aligned}
0 &= (-5) \cdot 0 & 0 &= a \cdot 0 \\
&= (-5)[3 + (-3)] & 0 &= a + (-a) \\
&= (-5)3 + (-5)(-3) & &\text{Distributive property} \\
&= -15 + (-5)(-3)
\end{aligned}
$$

Now, 15 is the only real number that we can add to -15 to get a sum of 0. Therefore, if

$$-15 + (-5)(-3) = 0 \quad and \quad -15 + 15 = 0, \quad \text{then } (-5)(-3) = 15.$$

This illustrates that the product of two negative numbers is always positive:

Let a and b be positive numbers. Then,

$$(-a)(-b) = ab$$

EXAMPLE 1

Simplify each of the following.

a. $2(-8)$ **b.** $-2(-8)$ **c.** $(-1)9$ **d.** $-4(-5)(-6)$

SOLUTION

a. $2(-8) = -(2 \cdot 8) = -16$
b. $-2(-8) = 2 \cdot 8 = 16$
c. $(-1)9 = -9$
d. $-4(-5)(-6) = [-4(-5)](-6) = 20(-6) = -120$

In Section 1.2 we used the following definition of division to show that division by 0 is undefined:

Division of Real Numbers

Let $a, b, c \in \mathbb{R}$, $b \neq 0$. Then,

$$\frac{a}{b} = c \quad \text{if} \quad a = bc$$

The rules for division of signed numbers follow from this definition. For example,

$$\frac{-8}{2} = -4 \quad \text{because} \quad -8 = 2(-4), \qquad \frac{8}{-2} = -4 \quad \text{because}$$

$$8 = -2(-4), \quad \text{and} \quad \frac{-8}{-2} = 4 \quad \text{because} \quad -8 = -2 \cdot 4$$

From examples we see that the rules for division are the same as the rules for multiplication — that is, a quotient involving a positive and a negative number is negative, and a quotient involving two negative numbers is positive:

> Let a and b be positive numbers. Then,
>
> $$\frac{-a}{b} = \frac{a}{-b} = -\frac{a}{b} \quad \text{and} \quad \frac{-a}{-b} = \frac{a}{b}$$

EXAMPLE 2

Simplify the following expressions.

a. $\dfrac{30}{-5}$ **b.** $\dfrac{-42}{-77}$ **c.** $\dfrac{0}{-16}$ **d.** $\dfrac{-16}{0}$

SOLUTION

a. $\dfrac{30}{-5} = \dfrac{-30}{5} = -6$

b. $\dfrac{-42}{-77} = \dfrac{42}{77} = \dfrac{6 \cdot \cancel{7}}{11 \cdot \cancel{7}} = \dfrac{6}{11}$

c. $\dfrac{0}{-16} = 0, \quad$ as $0 = -16 \cdot 0$

d. $\dfrac{-16}{0}$ is undefined

We know from arithmetic that 12 divided by 3 is the same as 12 multiplied by $\frac{1}{3}$ — that is,

$$\frac{12}{3} = \frac{1}{3} \cdot 12 = 4$$

Thus, division by 3 is the same as multiplication by the reciprocal of 3. This illustrates another useful definition of division:

> Let $a, b \in \mathbb{R}$, $b \neq 0$. Then,
>
> $$\frac{a}{b} = a \div b = a \cdot \frac{1}{b} = \frac{1}{b} \cdot a$$

EXAMPLE 3

Use reciprocals to simplify the following.

a. $\dfrac{-30}{6}$ **b.** $2\dfrac{1}{6} \div 3\dfrac{1}{4}$

(continued)

SOLUTION   **a.** $\dfrac{-30}{6} = \dfrac{1}{6}(-30) = -5$

b. $2\dfrac{1}{6} \div 3\dfrac{1}{4} = \dfrac{13}{6} \div \dfrac{13}{4} = \dfrac{13}{6} \cdot \dfrac{4}{13} = \dfrac{2}{3}$

2   Exponents and Square Roots

For a number used as a factor several times the product is often conveniently expressed in **exponential notation**. For instance, $3 \cdot 3 \cdot 3 \cdot 3 = 3^4$, which is read "3 to the 4th power." The superscript 4 is called the **exponent**, and 3 is called the **base**. Other examples are

$$6^2 = 6 \cdot 6 = 36, \quad \text{read "6 squared" or "6 to the 2nd power"}$$
$$2^3 = 2 \cdot 2 \cdot 2 = 8, \quad \text{read "2 cubed" or "2 to the 3rd power"}$$
$$7^1 = 7, \quad \text{read "7 to the 1st power"}$$

> Let n be a natural number and a be a real number:
> $a^n = a \cdot a \cdot \ldots \cdot a$, n factors of a, and $a^1 = a$.

EXAMPLE 4   Simplify the following.

a. 2^6 **b.** $\left(-\dfrac{2}{5}\right)^3$ **c.** $(-3)^2$ **d.** -3^2

SOLUTION   **a.** $2^6 = (2 \cdot 2 \cdot 2)(2 \cdot 2 \cdot 2) = (8)(8) = 64$

b. $\left(-\dfrac{2}{5}\right)^3 = \left(-\dfrac{2}{5}\right)\left(-\dfrac{2}{5}\right)\left(-\dfrac{2}{5}\right) = \dfrac{4}{25}\left(-\dfrac{2}{5}\right) = -\dfrac{8}{125}$

c. $(-3)^2 = (-3)(-3) = 9$

d. $-3^2 = -(3 \cdot 3) = -9$

In example 4, $(-3)^2$ means the square of negative 3, which is 9. However, -3^2 means the opposite of 3^2, which is -9. Thus, $-a^2 \neq (-a)^2 = a^2$.

 COMMON ERROR   A common mistake is to confuse $-a^n$ with $(-a)^n$:

$$-2^4 = -(2 \cdot 2 \cdot 2 \cdot 2) = -16 \quad \text{but} \quad (-2)^4 = (-2)(-2)(-2)(-2) = 16$$

We have seen that the product of two negative numbers is positive and the product of three negative numbers is negative. In general, the product of an even number of negative numbers is positive, and the product of an odd number of negative numbers is negative. These facts can be used to simplify $(-1)^n$, where n is a natural number:

$$(-1)^n = \begin{cases} 1, & \text{if } n \text{ is even} \\ -1, & \text{if } n \text{ is odd} \end{cases} \qquad \begin{array}{l} (-1)^{80} = 1 \\ (-1)^{93} = -1 \end{array}$$

Math in Time

ZERO AND MAYAN MATHEMATICS

The invention of zero occurred independently in two different parts of the world. The earliest known use of zero in India is in a Hindu inscription of A.D. 876. Through Arab scholars, knoweldge of zero was transmitted to Europe.

Between 300 B.C. and A.D. 300, the Mayan Indians of Central America had performed many amazing astronomical calculations, such as determining the orbit of Venus with an error of 1 day in 6012 years. These results have led many archaeologists to believe that the Mayans were the first people to invent zero. The evidence for this is strong, but circumstantial, as the sixteenth-century Spanish conquerors destroyed nearly all of the Mayan written records, believing them to be "the work of the devil." The symbol the Mayans used for zero was a shell, ⬭.

Mayan merchants used a base-20 number system. They wrote their numbers vertically, so that as one moved up the column, the numbers increased by a factor of 20. Bar-and-dot numerals were used; the dot (●) represented 1, and the bar (_____) represented 5. In our base-10 system we write the numbers 1 to 9 and then use our zero symbol to write 10. In the base-20 system the Mayans wrote the numbers 1 to 19 and then used their zero symbol to write 20:

$$6: \quad \bullet \qquad 13: \overset{\bullet\bullet\bullet}{=} \qquad 19: \overset{\bullet\bullet\bullet\bullet}{\equiv} \qquad 20: \underset{\bullet}{\textstyle\bigcirc} \qquad 4{,}088: \overset{\bullet\bullet\bullet}{\underset{\bullet\bullet\bullet\bullet}{\equiv}}$$

- 20^2's
- 20's
- 1's

The last number written above is expressed in our Hindu–Arabic system as $10 \cdot 20^2 + 4 \cdot 20 + 8 \cdot 1 = 4088$. The simplicity of Mayan addition is illustrated with these numbers. The sum of 6 and 13 is found by combining all the dots and bars of 6 and 13, giving the numeral for 19. The accompanying figure from a Mayan manuscript illustrates the mixture of religious text and arithmetic.

In arithmetic we learn that subtraction is the inverse of addition: $8 - 2 = 6$ and $6 + 2 = 8$. In a similar way, finding a square root is the inverse of squaring a number—that is, if $b^2 = a$, then b is a **square root** of a. For example, $6^2 = (-6)^2 = 36$, so 6 and -6 are the square roots of 36. These are written $\sqrt{36} = 6$ and $-\sqrt{36} = -6$ (note that $\sqrt{36} \neq 6$ and -6; $\sqrt{36}$ has only one answer, 6). Every positive number a has two square roots, $\sqrt{a}$ and $-\sqrt{a}$. Also, $\sqrt{0} = 0$. A negative number does not have a real square root because $b^2 \geq 0$, if b is real. For instance, $\sqrt{-25}$ is not a real number.

Radicals have many important properties. We will now introduce the two needed for the Pythagorean theorem in the next chapter and develop the subject in detail in Chapter 6. Because $\sqrt{a} = b$, $b \geq 0$, if $b^2 = a$, $(\sqrt{a})^2 = (b)^2 = a$. For example, $(\sqrt{9})^2 = (3)^2 = 9$. The second property is called the **product rule**: $\sqrt{ab} = \sqrt{a}\sqrt{b}$, if a and b are nonnegative. For example, $\sqrt{4 \cdot 25} = \sqrt{100} = 10$ and $\sqrt{4}\sqrt{25} = 2 \cdot 5 = 10$, so $\sqrt{4 \cdot 25} = \sqrt{4}\sqrt{25}$. The following is a summary of this discussion:

Properties of Square Roots

If a and b represent nonnegative real numbers, then

$$\sqrt{a} = b \quad \text{if} \quad b^2 = a \qquad (\sqrt{a})^2 = a \qquad \sqrt{ab} = \sqrt{a}\sqrt{b}$$

EXAMPLE 5

Simplify the following.

a. $\sqrt{49}$ **b.** $-\sqrt{64}$ **c.** $(\sqrt{21})^2$ **d.** $\sqrt{12}$ **e.** $3\sqrt{125}$

SOLUTION

a. $\sqrt{49} = 7$ **b.** $-\sqrt{64} = -8$ **c.** $(\sqrt{21})^2 = 21$
d. $\sqrt{12} = \sqrt{4 \cdot 3} = \sqrt{4}\sqrt{3} = 2\sqrt{3}$
e. $3\sqrt{125} = 3\sqrt{25 \cdot 5} = 3\sqrt{25}\sqrt{5} = 3 \cdot 5\sqrt{5} = 15\sqrt{5}$

---

3   Order of Operations

Many expressions involve two or more operations. We often use grouping symbols to tell us the order in which to perform the operations. The most common are parentheses, ( ); brackets, [ ], the fraction bar, —, the radical sign, $\sqrt{}$; and absolute value, | |. For example,

$$2(8 - \sqrt{9 + 16}) = 2(8 - \sqrt{25}) = 2(8 - 5) = 2(3) = 6$$

Note that $5 = \sqrt{25} = \sqrt{9 + 16} \neq \sqrt{9} + \sqrt{16} = 3 + 4 = 7$. In general, $\sqrt{a + b} \neq \sqrt{a} + \sqrt{b}$.

In many cases we write expressions involving more than one operation without using grouping symbols. To do this we must be in common agreement on the order in which operations will be done. For example, $2 + 3 \cdot 4$ could mean either $5 \cdot 4 = 20$ or $2 + 12 = 14$. Common agreement requires multiplication to be done before addition. Thus,

$$2 + 3 \cdot 4 = 2 + 12 = 14$$

If we want to do the addition before the multiplication, then we have to use grouping symbols and write $(2 + 3)4$. To ensure that each expression has only one answer, we make the following assumptions about the use of grouping symbols and the **order of operations**.

> **Order of Operations**
>
> **A.** If no grouping symbols are present, simplify an expression in the following order:
>
>   **1.** Evaluate all numbers with exponents.
>
>   **2.** Multiplication and division are done in order from left to right.
>
>   **3.** Addition and subtraction are done in order from left to right.
>
> **B.** If grouping symbols are present:
>
>   **1.** First perform any operations in parentheses, ( ); brackets, [ ]; the radical sign, $\sqrt{}$; or the absolute value signs, $|\ \ |$; start with the innermost one and work outward.
>
>   **2.** Perform any operation above or below a fraction bar as in part A; division is done last.
>
>   **3.** Then follow the steps in part A.

EXAMPLE 6   Simplify the following.

a. $1 - 4 \cdot 3^2$ **b.** $2 - \sqrt{81} \div 3 + 4$

c. $8 + 2[4 - (5 - 9)]$ **d.** $\dfrac{16 + 2^3}{2(1 + 3)}$

SOLUTION

a. $1 - 4 \cdot 3^2 = 1 - 4 \cdot 9 = 1 - 36 = -35$

b. $2 - \sqrt{81} \div 3 + 4 = 2 - 9 \div 3 + 4 = 2 - 3 + 4 = -1 + 4 = 3$

c. $8 + 2[4 - (5 - 9)] = 8 + 2[4 - (-4)] = 8 + 2[4 + 4] = 8 + 2[8] = 8 + 16 = 24$

d. $\dfrac{16 + 2^3}{2(1 + 3)} = \dfrac{16 + 8}{2(4)} = \dfrac{24}{8} = 3$

4   Algebraic Expressions

Variables allow us to generalize numerical expressions to **algebraic expressions**. An algebraic expression is any combination of constants, variables, exponents, grouping symbols, and algebraic operations. Examples are

$$3x - 7, \qquad x^3 - 9y^2, \qquad 5t^2 - 6t + 4, \qquad \text{and} \qquad \frac{y^3 - \sqrt{y}}{x - 5}$$

An algebraic expression such as $3x - 7$ takes on a numerical value whenever x is replaced by a number. For example, if $x = -4$, then $3x - 7 = 3(-4) - 7 = -19$. The process of finding the value of an algebraic expression is called **evaluating algebraic expressions**. Note that the order of operations applies to algebraic expressions as well as numerical expressions.

EXAMPLE 7

Evaluate the following for $x = 5$ and $y = -2$.

a. $3(x + 4y)$ **b.** $2x^2 - 4xy + y^2$ **c.** $\dfrac{y^3 - 1}{x - 5}$

SOLUTION

a. $3(x + 4y) = 3[5 + 4(-2)] = 3[5 - 8] = 3[-3] = -9$

b. $2x^2 - 4xy + y^2 = 2 \cdot 5^2 - 4 \cdot 5(-2) + (-2)^2 =$
$2 \cdot 25 + 40 + 4 = 50 + 44 = 94$

c. $\dfrac{y^3 - 1}{x - 5} = \dfrac{(-2)^3 - 1}{5 - 5} = \dfrac{-9}{0}$, which is undefined.

To use algebraic tools to solve problems, we must be able to translate English statements into algebraic expressions. For example, "the sum of a number and 5" can be expressed as $n + 5$ or $5 + n$, where n represents any number. Note that we have to be careful with subtraction and division. The difference of a and b, $a - b$, is not the same as the difference of b and a, $b - a$. Similarly, the quotient of a and b, $a \div b$, is not the same as the quotient of b and a, $b \div a$. For example, $5 - 2 \neq 2 - 5$ and $5 \div 2 \neq 2 \div 5$.

EXAMPLE 8

Express the following as an algebraic expression. Let n denote the unknown number.

a. The difference of 10 and twice a number
b. The quotient of a number and 30
c. 20 more than -5 times a number
d. 5 less than three times a number
e. 6 times the sum of 3 and 4 times a number
f. The cube of a number is less than the number.

SOLUTION

a. $10 - 2n$ (*Note:* $2n - 10$ is incorrect.)
b. $n \div 30$ (*Note:* $30 \div n$ is incorrect.)
c. $-5n + 20$ **d.** $3n - 5$
e. $6(3 + 4n)$ **f.** $n^3 < n$

EXERCISE SET 1.4

A

1 Simplify the following.

1. $3(-4)$

2. $-3(-4)$

3. $(-1)7$

4. $-12 \div (-3)$

5. $0(-8)$

6. $-1(-6)(-2)$

7. ▦ $-823 \cdot 972$

8. ▦ $171(-18)(19)$

9. $\dfrac{-15}{3}$

10. $\dfrac{15}{-3}$

11. $\dfrac{-15}{-3}$

12. ▦ $\dfrac{5508}{-324}$

13. $0 \div (-7)$

14. $-7 \div 0$

15. $\dfrac{1}{4}(-8)$

16. $-\dfrac{9}{7} \div \dfrac{15}{14}$

2

17. 5^2

18. 2^4

19. 13^1

20. -7^2

21. $(-7)^2$

22. -2^5

23. $(-2)^5$

24. 0^{87}

25. $(-1)^{23}$

26. $(-1)^{90}$

27. $\sqrt{0}$

28. $(\sqrt{64})^2$

29. $2(\sqrt{11})^2$

30. $\sqrt{50}$

31. $\sqrt{27}$

32. $2\sqrt{72}$

33. $-3\sqrt{20}$

34. $\sqrt{4 + 36}$

35. $\sqrt{4} + \sqrt{36}$

36. $\sqrt{81} + 9$

3

37. $4 + 3 \cdot 5$

38. $1 - 3 - 11$

39. $5^2 - |-12|$

40. $16 - 3^2 - \sqrt{100}$

41. $2 + 8 \div 4 - 6^2$

42. $6 + 4\,|\,6 - 2(8)\,|$

43. $2 - 3[1 - (-5)]$

44. $6(-1)^{19} - 10 \div 2$

45. $10^2 + 20\sqrt{100} - 19$

46. $|\,12 \div 6 - 10\,|$

47. $8 - 6\,|\,3 - 9\,|$

48. $2 \cdot 5^2 - 40\,|\,6 - (\sqrt{7})^2\,|$

49. $\dfrac{100 + 25}{10 + 5}$

50. $\dfrac{16 - 3 \cdot 2}{4^2 + \sqrt{25 - 9}}$

51. $\dfrac{8 - 3^2}{2(5 - 5)}$

52. $\dfrac{11 - 3^4}{2 - 3\,|\,1 - 5\,|}$

53. $2^3 (-1)^{30} + |-4\,|^2$

54. $[4(-3) + \sqrt{10^2}]^3$

55. $4 - [-3(-2)^3 \div (-8)]^2$

56. $8 + 2[3(-3)^2 - \sqrt{64}]$

4 Evaluate the following for $x = 2, y = -3$, and $z = -5$.

57. $(x + y)^3$

58. $x^3 + y^3$

59. $xy - 2z$

60. $(y + z)(y - z)$

61. $y^2 - z^2$

62. $\sqrt{y^2 + 8x}$

63. $\dfrac{3x - 2z}{|\,xyz\,|}$

64. $\dfrac{10x - y}{5xy - 6z}$

65. $\dfrac{18 - xy^2}{(xyz)^{100}}$

Evaluate the following for $a = -4, b = 6$, and $c = 3$.

66. $a^2 - ab - 2b^2$

67. $(a - 2b)(a + b)$

68. $(a + b)^2$

69. $a^2 + 2ab + b^2$

70. $3ab - 2bc$

71. $4a - 2b + 7c$

72. $b^2 - 4ac$

73. $a + b \div c$

74. $\sqrt{bc} - |\,a\,|$

Express the following as algebraic expressions. Let x denote the unknown number.

75. The sum of a number and 5

76. The difference of a number and -8

77. The product of 30 and a number

78. The quotient of -20 and a number

79. A number is greater than -6.

80. A number is less than or equal to 5.

81. 12 less than a number

82. 7 more than a number

83. 7 less than 5 times a number squared

84. 7 less than the square of 5 times a number

85. 3 more than twice a number

86. 4 times the sum of a number and 8

87. The sum of 4 times a number and 8

88. Three-fourths the difference of -6 and a number

89. Subtract 3 from the product of 5 and x.

B

90. A number is at least 30.

91. A number is no more than -20.

92. Two consecutive integers

93. Two consecutive even integers

Justify your answer to the following with an example.

94. Let $a * b = 3a + 3b$. Is $*$ commutative? Is $*$ associative?

95. Let $a \wedge b = a^b$. Is $\wedge$ commutative? Is $\wedge$ associative?

C

Answer the following questions with complete sentences.

96. Discuss the two origins of zero.

97. Why is the square root of a negative number not a real number?

98. Why is -3^2 not the same as $(-3)^2$?

99. Why are the rules for division of signed numbers the same as the rules for multiplication of signed numbers?

Chapter Summary

DEFINITIONS AND PROPERTIES

Definitions

Sets (See Sections 1.1 and 1.2.)

$a \in A$	a is an element of A	$2 \in \{1, 2\}$
$\emptyset$	empty set	{men 20 feet tall} $= \emptyset$
$A \subseteq B$	subset	$\{1\} \subseteq \{1, 2\}$
$A \cup B$	union	$\{1, 2\} \cup \{3\} = \{1, 2, 3\}$
$A \cap B$	intersection	$\{1, 2\} \cap \{2, 3\} = \{2\}$

Subsets of $\mathbb{R}$, the Set of Reals (See Sections 1.1 and 1.2.)

$\mathbb{N}$ = natural numbers = $\{1, 2, 3, \ldots\}$

$\mathbb{W}$ = whole numbers = $\{0, 1, 2, \ldots\}$

$\mathbb{Z}$ = integers = $\{\ldots, -2, -1, 0, 1, 2, \ldots\}$

$\mathbb{Q}$ = rational numbers = $\{x \in \mathbb{R} | x = a/b;$ $a, b \in \mathbb{Z}, \; b \neq 0\}$

$\mathbb{H}$ = irrational numbers = $\{x \in \mathbb{R} | x \neq a/b;$ $a, b \in \mathbb{Z}, \; b \neq 0\}$

$\mathbb{R} = \mathbb{Q} \cup \mathbb{H}, \quad \mathbb{N} \subseteq \mathbb{W} \subseteq \mathbb{Z} \subseteq \mathbb{Q} \subseteq \mathbb{R},$ $\mathbb{H} \subseteq \mathbb{R}$

Properties of the Real Numbers (See Section 1.2.)

Let $a, b, c \in \mathbb{R}$.

	Addition	Multiplication
Closure	$a + b \in \mathbb{R}$	$ab \in \mathbb{R}$
Commutative	$a + b = b + a$	$ab = ba$
Associative	$(a + b) + c =$ $a + (b + c)$	$(ab)c = a(bc)$
Identity	$a + 0 = 0 +$ $a = a$	$a \cdot 1 = 1 \cdot$ $a = a$
Inverse	$a + (-a) =$ $-a + a = 0$	$a \cdot \dfrac{1}{a} = \dfrac{1}{a} \cdot$ $a = 1,$ $a \neq 0$
Distributive	$a(b + c) = ab + ac$ $(b + c)a = ba + ca$	

Other Properties of the Real Numbers (See Sections 1.2, 1.3, and 1.4.)

Distributive (subtraction: $a(b - c) = ab - ac$ $(b - c)a = ba - ca$

Opposite (additive inverse) of a: $-a$

Reciprocal (multiplicative inverse) of a: $1/a$, $a \neq 0$

Absolute value: $|a|$ = the distance from a to 0.

$$|a| = \begin{cases} a, & \text{if } a \geq 0 \\ -a, & \text{if } a < 0 \end{cases}$$

$$|a| \geq 0 \qquad |-a| = |a|$$

Exponents: $a^1 = a; \quad a^n = a \cdot a \cdot \ldots \cdot a,$ n factors of $a, \quad n \in \mathbb{N}$.

Square roots: $\sqrt{a} = b$ if $b^2 = a$; $b \geq 0$
$$\sqrt{ab} = \sqrt{a}\sqrt{b}; \quad a, b \geq 0$$
$$(\sqrt{a})^2 = a; \quad a \geq 0$$

$-a = (-1)a \qquad -(-a) = a \qquad 0 \cdot a = 0$

$\dfrac{a}{1} = a \qquad\qquad \dfrac{a}{a} = 1, \ a \neq 0 \qquad \dfrac{0}{a} = 0, a \neq 0$

$\dfrac{a}{0}$ is undefined.

Order of Operations (See Section 1.4.)

1. Perform any operations indicated by grouping symbols: ( ), [ ], ——, $\sqrt{\ }$, and $|\ \ |$, starting with the innermost one and working outward.
2. Next evaluate all numbers with exponents.
3. Then perform multiplication and division in order from left to right.
4. Finally, perform addition and subtraction in order from left to right.

Operations with Positive and Negative Numbers (See Sections 1.3 and 1.4.)

Let a and b be positive real numbers.

$(-a) + (-b) =$ $-(a + b)$	$(-6) + (-2) =$ $-(6 + 2) = -8$
$a > b: \ a + (-b) =$ $a - b$	$6 + (-2) =$ $6 - 2 = 4$
$a > b: \ -a + b =$ $-(a - b)$	$-6 + 2 =$ $-(6 - 2) = -4$
$(-a)(-b) = ab$	$(-6)(-2) =$ $6 \cdot 2 = 12$
$(-a)b = a(-b) =$ $-(ab)$	$(-6)2 = 6(-2) =$ $-(6 \cdot 2) = -12$
$\dfrac{-a}{-b} = \dfrac{a}{b}$	$\dfrac{-6}{-2} = \dfrac{6}{2} = 3$
$\dfrac{-a}{b} = \dfrac{a}{-b} = \dfrac{-a}{b}$	$\dfrac{-6}{2} = \dfrac{6}{-2} = \dfrac{-6}{2} = -3$

CHAPTER REVIEW EXERCISES

The answers to the following problems are given in the answer section. If you have any trouble with them, review the material and homework problems in the sections listed.

Let A = {1, 2, 3}, B = {3, 5}, and C = {4, 6}. Find the following and illustrate them with Venn diagrams. (See Section 1.1.)

1. A ∪ B   **2.** B ∪ C

3. A ∩ B   **4.** B ∩ C

Find all the subsets of the following set.

5. {w, x, y}

Place ∈, ∉, ⊆, or ⊄ in each blank to make a true statement. (More than one right answer is possible.) (See Sections 1.1 and 1.2.)

6. {r} —— {r, s}   **7.** r —— {r, s}

8. −8 —— ℕ   **9.** ℤ —— 𝕎

Use <, =, or > to make the following statements true. (See Sections 1.2 and 1.3.)

10. −9 —— 6

11. $|-9|$ —— $|6|$

12. $|8 - 4|$ —— $|4 - 8|$

Express each of the following as decimals and classify them as repeating or terminating decimals. (See Section 1.2.)

13. $\dfrac{8}{33}$ **14.** $\dfrac{7}{8}$

Let A = {−8, 0, 7, 3/4, $\sqrt{7}$, $\sqrt{-9}$, 0.1, $0.1\overline{1}$, 0.1010010001 . . . }. List all the elements of A that are the following. (See Section 1.2.)

15. Whole numbers

16. Rational

17. Irrational

Find the following unions and intersections. (See Section 1.2.)

18. $\mathbb{Q} \cup \mathbb{H}$ **19.** $\mathbb{N} \cap \mathbb{H}$ **20.** $\mathbb{Z} \cap \mathbb{R}$

Solve the following using positive numbers, negative numbers, or both. (See Section 1.3.)

21. Joe had $60 in his checking account. He wrote a check for $75. What was his new balance?

22. The temperature at noon was $-6°$ C; that evening it was $-19°$ C. Find the difference between the noon and the evening temperatures.

Express the following as algebraic expressions. Let y denote the unknown number. (See Section 1.4.)

23. A number is greater than its square.

24. 8 less than 4 times a number

25. The quotient of twice a number and -9

26. 6 times the difference of twice a number and 5

Evaluate the following for $x = -4, y = 2,$ and $z = -1$. (See Section 1.4.)

27. $x^2 + 3xy - y^3$ **28.** $(x - y)(x^2 + xy + y^2)$

29. $x^3 - y^3$ **30.** $\dfrac{xz - 5y}{x^2 - z^4}$

Simplify each of the following. (See Sections 1.3 and 1.4.)

31. $-8 + 3(-2)$

32. $-5^2 + (-1)^{55}$

33. $1 + 9[6 - (8 - 2)]$

34. $-3 + 24 \div (-9 + \sqrt{36})$

35. $\dfrac{25 + 9}{5 + 3}$

36. $\dfrac{\sqrt{12 + 14}}{|8 - 10|}$

37. $3\sqrt{75}$

38. $-8[1 - (-7)] - 4^2$

39. $5 + \dfrac{3}{4} - \dfrac{7}{6}$

40. $1865 - \dfrac{8602}{-374}$

CHAPTER TEST

Treat this test as a class test and allow 50 minutes for completion. When done, use the answer section to grade it. For any incorrect answers refer to the corresponding problems in the review section.

Let $A = \{0, 3, 5\}$ and $B = \{0, 4, 5\}$. Find the following and illustrate with Venn diagrams.

1. $A \cup B$ **2.** $A \cap B$

Place $\in, \notin, \subseteq,$ or $\not\subseteq$ in each blank to make a true statement (more than one right answer is possible).

3. $\mathbb{W}$ ____ $\mathbb{Z}$ **4.** -6 ____ $\mathbb{Q}$ **5.** $1/2$ ____ $\mathbb{Z}$

Use $<, =,$ or $>$ to make the following statements true.

6. $|6 - (-9)|$ ____ $|-9 - 6|$

7. $-|-15|$ ____ $|-12|$

Let $B = \{6, \pi, 0, 2/3, \sqrt{5}, 1/0, -9, 0.\overline{37}, 0.37, 0.3738393103 \ldots \}$. List all the elements of B that are

8. Integers   **9.** Irrational   **10.** Rational

Solve the following using positive numbers, negative numbers, or both.

11. Monica owed $7600 on her car, and Sue had $2400 invested in an IRA. Find the difference between Sue's investment and Monica's debt.

Express the following as algebraic expressions. Let n denote the unknown number.

12. The square of the sum of a number and 8

13. 6 more than twice a number

14. 4 less than the square of a number

Evaluate the following for $a = 3$, $b = -2$, and $c = -5$.

15. $2a^2 - 3ab + b^2$ **16.** $a(2b - 1) - 3c$

Simplify each of the following.

17. $6 + (-2)(-7)$

18. $-12 + [6 - (8 - 2)]$

19. $-3^2 + 12 \div (-4)(-1)^{50}$

20. $18 + 2[8\sqrt{100} - 9^2]$

21. $\dfrac{\sqrt{18} + 6^2}{-|-3|}$

22. $\dfrac{3 + 2 \cdot 7}{49 - 7^2}$

23. $3\sqrt{9} + 16 - |6 - (-8)|$

24. $-8752 + (-274)(84)$

25. $\dfrac{1}{2} + \dfrac{2}{3} - \dfrac{5}{9}$

Linear Equations and Inequalities in One Variable

The surface area of a sphere of radius r is $S(r) = 4\pi r^2$, which is equivalent to the area of a disk with a radius twice as large.

An equation or inequality containing one variable with an exponent of 1 is called **linear** or **first degree**. For instance, $6x + 5 = 4x - 7$ is a linear equation, and $2 - 3y \geq y$ is a first-degree inequality.

In this chapter we will discuss methods for solving these equations and inequalities. With these skills we will be able to deal with a variety of applied problems. Many of these, such as uniform motion and mixture problems, will be familiar. Certain topics, such as linear equations and inequalities involving absolute value, may be new material; two examples are $|4x| = 5$ and $|6 - t| < 8$. The methods of solving these equations and inequalities are a result of the concepts concerning absolute value as discussed in Chapter 1.

2.1 LINEAR EQUATIONS

1	**Simplifying Expressions**
2	**Properties and Types of Equations**
3	**Solving $ax + b = cx + d$**
4	**Solving Number Problems**

1 Simplifying Expressions

The first step in solving an equation such as $4x - 6 + 3x = 8$ is to simplify the expression $4x - 6 + 3x$. To do so, we reduce it to an expression containing as few terms and factors as possible. We begin by reviewing some terminology.

Recall that in the expression $a + b$, a and b are called *terms;* in the expression ab, however, a and b are called *factors.* In general, **terms** are the parts of an algebraic expression that are added or subtracted; a term includes the sign that precedes it. Thus, the terms of $7xz - xy + 15$ are $7xz$, $-xy$, and 15. A **factor** is each of the constants, variables, or both multiplied together to obtain a given product. Thus, 3 and 5 are the factors of $3 \cdot 5$, whereas 7, x, and z are the factors of $7xz$. A **numerical coefficient** is the numerical factor of a product. Therefore, 7 is the numerical coefficient of $7xz$, and -1 is the numerical coefficient of $-xy$, because $-xy = -1 \cdot xy$.

Terms with the same variables and the same exponents are called **like terms**. For instance, $4x$ and $3x$ are like terms, as are $5a^2b^4$ and $-3a^2b^4$. However, $4x$ and $3y$ are **unlike terms** because they have different variables.

Like terms are significant because they can be expressed as a single term when added or subtracted; for example, $4x + 3x = (4 + 3)x = 7x$. Unlike terms cannot be expressed as one term because they are not in the form $ba + ca = (b + c)a$, as in $4x + 3y$. We simplify like terms with the distributive property. Sometimes the commutative and associative properties must be used first to group like terms, as illustrated in Example 1.

EXAMPLE 1

Simplify the following expressions.

a. $4a - 8a - a$ **b.** $5a^2b^4 + 9ab^2 - 3a^2b^4$

SOLUTION

a. $4a - 8a - a = 4a - 8a - 1a = (4 - 8 - 1)a = -5a$

b. $5a^2b^4 + 9ab^2 - 3a^2b^4 = (5a^2b^4 - 3a^2b^4) + 9ab^2 =$
$$(5 - 3)a^2b^4 + 9ab^2 = 2a^2b^4 + 9ab^2$$

COMMON ERROR

A common mistake is to think that unlike terms can be written as one term. Only like terms can be combined.

$$4x + 3y \neq 7xy \qquad \text{and} \qquad 8 - 5x^2 \neq 3x^2$$

Many equations contain expressions such as $3(2x + 9) - 5$. To simplify this expression we first use the distributive property and then combine like terms:

$$3(2x + 9) - 5 = 3(2x) + 3 \cdot 9 - 5 = 6x + 27 - 5 = 6x + 22$$

EXAMPLE 2

Simplify the following expressions.

a. $4x - (3 - 8x)$ **b.** $8 + 2[x - 3(x - 5)]$

SOLUTION

a. $4x - (3 - 8x) = 4x + (-1)(3 - 8x) = 4x + (-3) + 8x =$
$$4x + 8x - 3 = 12x - 3$$

b. $8 + 2[x - 3(x - 5)] = 8 + 2[x - 3x + 15] =$
$$8 + 2[-2x + 15] = 8 - 4x + 30 = 38 - 4x$$

2   Properties and Types of Equations

This section discusses types of equations and the properties needed to solve them. A number is called a **solution**, or **root**, of an equation if it makes the equation a true statement. For instance, $x = 5$ is a root of $x^2 = 25$. We will use the capital letter **S** to denote the **solution set**, which is the set of all real numbers that satisfy the equation. For example, the solution set of $y + 5 = 9$ is S $= \{4\}$. We deal with three types of equations, which are classified according to their solutions:

1. *Identities* (or true equations) are true statements for all numbers for which the equation is defined:

$$x + 3 = 3 + x, \quad S = \mathbb{R}$$

2. *False equations* are false statements for all real numbers:

$$0x = 8, \quad S = \emptyset, \text{ the empty set}$$

3. *Conditional equations* are true for at least one real number and false for at least one real number:

$$x^2 = 9, \quad S = \{3, -3\}$$

To solve an equation such as $4x + 1 = 9$, we can transform it into a simpler equation with the same root. Two equations are called **equivalent** if they have the same solution set. For instance, $4x + 1 = 9$, $4x = 8$, and $x = 2$ are all equivalent equations because the solution to each one is $S = \{2\}$. The properties needed to solve linear equations are now considered.

A convenient property of equations is the **symmetric property of equality**, which allows us to interchange the two sides of an equation. Symbolically, if $a = b$, then $b = a$. For example, if $12 = x$, then $x = 12$.

Recall that adding the same number to both sides of an equation produces an equivalent equation, which is known as the **addition property of equality**. The **subtraction property of equality** allows us to subtract the same number from both sides of an equation. The following examples illustrate the properties just discussed:

1.
$$x - 6 = -20$$
$$x - 6 + 6 = -20 + 6$$
$$x + 0 = -14$$
$$x = -14$$

2.
$$26 = x + 5$$
$$26 - 5 = x + 5 - 5$$
$$21 = x + 0$$
$$21 = x$$
$$x = 21$$

The **multiplication** and **division properties of equality** allow us to multiply or divide both sides of an equation by the same nonzero number to produce an equivalent equation. For example,

$$5x = 20$$
$$\frac{1}{5} \cdot 5x = \frac{1}{5} \cdot 20$$
$$1 \cdot x = 4$$
$$x = 4$$

or

$$5x = 20$$
$$\frac{5x}{5} = \frac{20}{5}$$
$$1 \cdot x = 4$$
$$x = 4$$

Properties of Equality

Let $a, b, c \in \mathbb{R}$.

If $a = b$, then $b = a$.

If $a = b$, then $a + c = b + c$ and $a - c = b - c$.

If $a = b$ and $c \neq 0$, then $ac = bc$ and $\dfrac{a}{c} = \dfrac{b}{c}$.

---

3 Solving $ax + b = cx + d$

We have just seen that the properties of equality allow us to solve equations of the form $x + b = c$ and $ax = c$. By combining these properties, we can solve equations of the type $ax + b = c$ and $ax + b = cx + d$. We begin with $ax + b = c$.

To solve $ax + b = c$ we usually begin by eliminating b from the left side of the equation with the addition or subtraction property. Then we can eliminate a with the multiplication or division property. This procedure isolates the variable on one side of the equation. To check for arithmetic mistakes we substitute our answer in the original equation (see Example 3a).

EXAMPLE 3

Solve the following equations. Check the answer to **a.**

a. $4x + 1 = 8$ **b.** $\frac{1}{3}x - 5 = -12$

SOLUTION   **a.**
$$4x + 1 = 8$$
$$4x + 1 - 1 = 8 - 1$$
$$4x = 7$$
$$\frac{4x}{4} = \frac{7}{4}$$
$$x = \frac{7}{4}$$

b.
$$\frac{1}{3}x - 5 = -12$$
$$\frac{1}{3}x - 5 + 5 = -12 + 5$$
$$\frac{1}{3}x = -7$$
$$3 \cdot \frac{1}{3}x = 3(-7)$$
$$x = -21$$

 CHECK   **a.** $4x + 1 = 4 \cdot \frac{7}{4} + 1 = 7 + 1 = 8$

We now turn to equations of the form $ax + b = cx + d$. Usually, eliminating the variable from one side of the equation is the first step in solving this equation. Which side we eliminate the variable from does not matter. However, because we want x = "a number," eliminating the variable on the right is usually easier. As illustrated in our next example, we often must simplify one or both sides of an equation to put it in the form $ax + b = cx + d$.

EXAMPLE 4

Solve the following equations.

a. $6x + 5 = 4x - 7$ **b.** $4(2 + y) + 6 = 7 - y$
c. $2(3x + 1) = 2 + 6x$ **d.** $3(4x - 2) = -2(7 - 6x)$

SOLUTION   **a.**

$6x + 5 = 4x - 7$	Eliminate $4x$.
$-4x + 6x + 5 = -4x + 4x - 7$	Add $-4x$.
$2x + 5 = -7$	Eliminate 5.
$2x + 5 - 5 = -7 - 5$	Subtract 5.
$2x = -12$	Eliminate 2.
$\frac{2x}{2} = \frac{-12}{2}$	Divide by 2.
$x = -6$ and $S = \{-6\}$	

b.

$4(2 + y) + 6 = 7 - y$	
$8 + 4y + 6 = 7 - y$	Distributive property
$4y + 8 + 6 = 7 - y$	
$4y + 14 = 7 - y$	Add y.
$5y + 14 = 7$	Subtract 14.
$5y = -7$	Divide by 5.
$y = -\frac{7}{5}$ and $S = \{-7/5\}$	

(continued)

c. $2(3x + 1) = 2 + 6x$
$2(3x) + 2 \cdot 1 = 2 + 6x$
$6x + 2 = 2 + 6x$

Because this equation is in the form $a + b = b + a$, it is an identity, and $S = \mathbb{R}$.

d. $3(4x - 2) = -2(7 - 6x)$
$12x - 6 = -14 + 12x$
$-12x + 12x - 6 = -14 + 12x - 12x$
$-6 = -14$

This is a false equation, so $S = \emptyset$.

4   Solving Number Problems

In Section 1.4 we had practice in translating English phrases into algebraic expressions, such as "5 less than twice a number." With this skill we can translate English sentences into algebraic equations, and we can solve certain number problems by using our knowledge of solving linear equations.

EXAMPLE 5

The difference of twice a number and 7 is 35. Find the number.

SOLUTION   Let n = the number. Then,
$2n$ = twice the number n, and
$2n - 7$ = the difference of twice n and 7.
This result is equal to 35, so our equation is
$2n - 7 = 35$ Add 7.
$2n = 42$ Divide by 2.
$n = 21$ (*Check it!*)

EXAMPLE 6

Three times the sum of a number and 4 is equal to 8 less than the number. Find the number and check the answer.

SOLUTION   Let x = the number. Then,
$x + 4$ = the sum of x and 4,
$3(x + 4)$ = 3 times the sum of x and 4, and
$x - 8$ = 8 less than x
Our equation is
$3(x + 4) = x - 8$
$3x + 12 = x - 8$ Subtract x.
$2x + 12 = -8$ Subtract 12.
$2x = -20$ Divide by 2.
$x = -10$

✔ CHECK   If $x = -10$, then
$3(x + 4) = 3(-10 + 4) = 3(-6) = -18$, and
$x - 8 = -10 - 8 = -18$.

EXERCISE SET 2.1

A

1 Simplify the following expressions.

1. $4x + 6x$

2. $-7a^2 + 2a^2$

3. $2t - 7t - t$

4. $r + 6r - 11r$

5. $7y + 3y^2 - 6y$

6. $6a^2b - ab^2 + 5a^2b$

7. $3 + 2(x + 8)$

8. $5x - 3(6 - 2x)$

9. $3z - (z - 12)$

10. $8 - (16 - 8z)$

11. $3x^2 + 2x(x + 4)$

12. $2(y - 1) - 3(2y + 5)$

13. $5(2x - y) + 2(x + 4y)$

14. $7a(2a - b) - 3b(b - 6a)$

15. $6(3x - 4) - (-4 - 2x)$

16. $5s^3 - s(s^2 - 4) + s$

2 Solve the following equations.

17. $x + 7 = -4.$ **18.** $y - 8 = 30$

19. $a + 4 = 4 + a$ **20.** $a + 4 = 5 + a$

21. $0x = 4$ **22.** $4x = 30$

23. $\dfrac{0}{x} = 0$ **24.** $\dfrac{x}{12} = -3$

25. $\dfrac{2}{5}x = \dfrac{1}{3}$ **26.** $\dfrac{1}{7}y = \dfrac{3}{8}$

27. $\dfrac{2a}{3} = \dfrac{-8}{27}$ **28.** $\dfrac{-7}{5} = -\dfrac{14x}{15}$

3 Solve the following equations. Check each answer.

29. $5x + 10 = 5$

30. $-28 = 2 - 3y$

31. $3z - 2 = 0$

32. $6x - 1 = 5x + 4$

33. $3(3a + 1) - a = 2a - 11$

34. $6 - 5x + 5 = 2x$

Find the solution set for the following.

35. $17x - 2 = 8x - 10$

36. $3(2x + 1) = 6x + 1$

37. $x - 8 = 8 - x$

38. $2(3x - 1) = 10x$

39. $(6 + x) + 3 = 6 + (x + 3)$

40. $6(2x - 1) = 3(5x - 2)$

41. $\dfrac{3}{4}y - 1 = 11$

42. $6 = 1 - \dfrac{10}{9}x$

43. $3(2a + 5) = 6a + 15$

44. $7 - (4 - x) = (7 - 4) - x$

45. $|x| = 0$

46. $t - (5 - 2t) = 3(t + 1)$

47. $3(x - 5) + x = 2(1 + 2x)$

48. $0.1y - 4 = 0.6$

49. $0.5x - 3 = 1 - 0.4x$

50. $1 - (5 - 8x) = 4(2x - 1)$

51. $1 - [3 - (2 - x)] = 6x$

52. $7 + 3[y - (1 - 4y)] = 9$

4 Find the number described in each problem. Follow these steps (see Example 6): a. state what your variable represents; b. write an equation to represent the problem; c. solve the equation; d. check your answer.

53. The difference of a number and 5 is -17.

54. The difference of 5 and a number is -17.

55. The quotient of twice a number and 9 is 3.

56. 7 plus a number is equal to 19 decreased by the number.

57. The sum of 5 times a number and 1 is 33 more than the number.

58. One more than a number is the same as one less than four times the number.

59. 30 less than 3 times a number is 10 more than the number.

60. If a number, four times the number, and nine times the number are added to 30, then the result is zero.

61. When one-half of a number is subtracted from 1, the result is 6.

62. Six times the sum of one and twice a number is equal to three times the sum of two and five times the number.

63. A number is 30 more than its opposite.

64. A number is 12 less than twice its opposite.

B

Solve the following equations.

65. $3(2z - 1) - 2(9 - z) = 4z - (-z + 7) + 5$

66. $x + 4[3 - (1 - 2x)] = 5 + 5[x + 3(2x - 1)]$

67. $x - [x - (x - 3)] = 2x - [3x - (4x - 5)]$

68. $x^2 + 6x - 1 = x^2 + 4x + 5$

C

Answer the following questions with complete sentences.

69. What is the difference between like and unlike terms?

70. What are the three basic types of equations? Illustrate each type with your own example.

71. What is meant by "equivalent equations"?

72. Explain how you would solve $3x - 5 = 28$.

REVIEW EXERCISES

Simplify the following. (See Section 1.3.)

73. $|-3|$ **74.** $|-8 + 2|$ **75.** $3 - 2\left| 1 - 4 \cdot \dfrac{13}{4} \right|$

2.2 SOLVING EQUATIONS INVOLVING FRACTIONS AND ABSOLUTE VALUE

1	Solving Equations Involving Fractions and Decimals
2	Solving $\|ax + b\| = k$ and $\|ax + b\| = \|cx + d\|$
3	Converting Repeating Decimals to Fractions
4	Solving Number Problems

1 Solving Equations Involving Fractions and Decimals

Many equations contain fractions, decimals, or absolute values. This section will consider certain types of these equations. We will also study other number problems and a method for converting repeating decimals to fractions. We begin with fractional equations whose denominators are integers.

Solving an equation containing fractions is often easiest to begin by converting it to an equation containing only integers. We do this by multiplying both sides of the equation by the **least common denominator (LCD)** of all the denominators. (The LCD is reviewed in Appendix D [4]).

> The least common denominator for a set of rational numbers is the smallest natural number that is divisible by each denominator.

For example, in the following equation the LCD of 6, 2, and 9 is 18, so we multiply both sides of the equation by 18:

$$\frac{1}{6}x + \frac{1}{2} = \frac{5}{9} \qquad \text{LCD} = 18$$

$$18\left(\frac{1}{6}x + \frac{1}{2}\right) = 18 \cdot \frac{5}{9} \qquad \text{Multiply by 18.}$$

$$18 \cdot \frac{1}{6}x + 18 \cdot \frac{1}{2} = 2 \cdot 5 \qquad \text{Distributive property}$$

$$3x + 9 = 10$$

$$3x = 1$$

$$x = \frac{1}{3}, \quad \text{so the solution is S} = \{1/3\}.$$

✔ **CHECK** $\dfrac{1}{6}x + \dfrac{1}{2} = \dfrac{1}{6} \cdot \dfrac{1}{3} + \dfrac{1}{2} = \dfrac{1}{18} + \dfrac{9}{18} = \dfrac{10}{18} = \dfrac{5}{9}$

EXAMPLE 1

Solve $\dfrac{y + 6}{8} - \dfrac{y - 2}{12} = \dfrac{5}{6}$

SOLUTION

$$\frac{y + 6}{8} - \frac{y - 2}{12} = \frac{5}{6} \qquad \text{LCD} = 24$$

$$24\left(\frac{y + 6}{8} - \frac{y - 2}{12}\right) = 24 \cdot \frac{5}{6}$$

$$24\left(\frac{y + 6}{8}\right) - 24\left(\frac{y - 2}{12}\right) = 4 \cdot 5 \qquad \text{Distributive property}$$

$$3(y + 6) - 2(y - 2) = 20 \qquad \text{\textit{Note:} } -2(y - 2) \neq -2y - 2$$

$$3y + 18 - 2y + 4 = 20$$

$$y + 22 = 20$$

$$y = -2, \quad \text{so the solution is S} = \{-2\}.$$

We can solve the equation $x - 1.2 = 7.4$ by adding 1.2 to both sides. However, with a more complicated equation involving decimals, converting it to an equation containing only integers can be simpler. (When using a calculator, staying with the original equation is often just as easy; see Solution 2 to the next example.) A terminating decimal is a fraction whose denominator is a power of 10, so an equation containing these decimals is a fractional equation. Therefore, we multiply both sides by the LCD, which is a power of 10. For example:

$$0.3x - 1.02 = 1.38$$

(continued)

Solution 1

$$0.3x - 1.02 = 1.38$$
$$\frac{3x}{10} - \frac{102}{100} = \frac{138}{100} \quad \text{LCD} = 100.$$
$$100\left(\frac{3x}{10} - \frac{102}{100}\right) = 100 \cdot \frac{138}{100}$$
$$30x - 102 = 138$$
$$30x = 240$$
$$x = 8$$

Solution 2

$$0.3x - 1.02 = 1.38$$
$$0.3x = 1.38 + 1.02$$
$$0.3x = 2.4$$
$$x = \frac{2.4}{0.3}$$
$$x = 8$$

Normally, we don't convert the decimals to fractions, we just determine the power of 10 needed to change all the decimals to integers, as illustrated in our next example.

EXAMPLE 2

Solve $.125s + .08(s + 3000) = 650$

SOLUTION

$$.125s + .08(s + 3000) = 650 \qquad \text{LCD} = 1000$$
$$1000[.125s + .08(s + 3000)] = 1000 \cdot 650$$
$$1000(.125s) + 1000[.080(s + 3000)] = 650{,}000$$
$$125s + 80(s + 3000) = 650{,}000$$
$$125s + 80s + 240{,}000 = 650{,}000$$
$$205s = 410{,}000$$
$$s = 2000, \quad \text{so the solution is}$$
$$\text{S} = \{2000\}.$$

2   Solving $|ax + b| = k$ and $|ax + b| = |cx + d|$

Section 1.3 introduced the concept of absolute value. Recall that the absolute value of a, $|a|$, is the distance from a to 0 on the number line. Because 3 and -3 are the same distance from 0, $|3| = |-3| = 3$. Therefore, the equation $|x| = 3$ means "find all numbers x whose distance from 0 is 3 units," so $x = 3$ or $x = -3$. In general, $|x| = k$ if $x = k$ or $x = -k$, for $k \geq 0$.

EXAMPLE 3

Solve $|x + 2| = 6$ and check the answer.

SOLUTION   We are asked to find all numbers x such that the graph of $x + 2$ (Figure 2.1) is 6 units from 0; that is,

$$x + 2 = 6 \quad \text{or} \quad x + 2 = -6$$
$$x = 4 \quad \text{or} \quad x = -8$$

FIGURE 2.1

CHECK   If $x = 4$, then $|x + 2| = |4 + 2| = |6| = 6$.
If $x = -8$, then $|x + 2| = |-8 + 2| = |-6| = -(-6) = 6$.
Thus, the solution is $\text{S} = \{4, -8\}$.

$$| ax + b | = k \quad \text{if } ax + b = k \quad \text{or} \quad ax + b = -k, \quad k \geq 0.$$

EXAMPLE 4

Solve the following equations.

a. $| 3x | = 12$ **b.** $| m + 7 | = -2$
c. $3 - 2 | 1 - 4x | = -21$

SOLUTION

a. $| 3x | = 12$ if $3x = 12$ or $3x = -12$
$\qquad\qquad\qquad\qquad\qquad x = 4$ or $x = -4,$ so S $= \{4, -4\}.$

b. Because $| a | \geq 0$ for all values of a, no value of m exists such that $| m + 7 | = -2$. Therefore,

c. First, isolate $| 1 - 4x |$:
$$3 - 2 | 1 - 4x | = -21$$
$$-2 | 1 - 4x | = -24$$
$$| 1 - 4x | = 12$$
$$1 - 4x = 12 \quad \text{or} \quad 1 - 4x = -12$$
$$-4x = 11 \qquad\qquad -4x = -13$$
$$x = -\frac{11}{4} \quad \text{or} \quad x = \frac{13}{4}, \quad \text{so S} = \{-\frac{11}{4}, \frac{13}{4}\}$$

We now consider equations such as $| 2x - 3 | = | x |$. Because $2x - 3$ and x have equal absolute values, they are the same distance from zero on the number line. Therefore, $2x - 3$ must be equal to x or $-x$. Thus,

$$| 2x - 3 | = | x | \quad \text{if} \quad 2x - 3 = x \quad \text{or} \quad 2x - 3 = -x$$
$$x - 3 = 0 \qquad\qquad 3x - 3 = 0$$
$$x = 3 \qquad\qquad x = 1$$

$$| ax + b | = | cx + d | \text{ if}$$
$$ax + b = cx + d \quad \text{or} \quad ax + b = -(cx + d)$$

EXAMPLE 5

Solve the following equations.

a. $| y - 1 | = | y + 7 |$ **b.** $| n - 4 | = | 4 - n |$

SOLUTION

a. $| y - 1 | = | y + 7 |$ if
$$y - 1 = y + 7 \quad \text{or} \quad y - 1 = -(y + 7)$$
$$-1 = 7 \qquad\qquad\qquad y - 1 = -y - 7$$
$$\text{S} = \varnothing \qquad\qquad\qquad 2y = -6$$
$$\text{S} = \varnothing \qquad\qquad\qquad y = -3$$

The first equation results in a false statement, so it does not give us a solution. Thus, S $= \{-3\}.$

(continued)

b. $|n - 4| = |4 - n|$ if

$$
\begin{array}{lll}
n - 4 = 4 - n & \text{or} & n - 4 = -(4 - n) \\
2n = 8 & & n - 4 = -4 + n \\
n = 4 & & -4 = -4 \\
\quad\quad n = 4 & \text{or} & S = \mathbb{R}
\end{array}
$$

The second equation is an identity, so $|n - 4| = |4 - n|$ is a true statement for all real numbers. Thus, $S = \mathbb{R}$.

3   Converting Repeating Decimals to Fractions

We saw in Section 1.2 that a rational number can be expressed as either a terminating decimal, such as $7/4 = 1.75$, or as a repeating decimal, such as $2/3 = .6\overline{6}$. We can convert a terminating decimal such as $.77$ to a fraction by multiplying it by $100/100$:

$$
.77 = \frac{.77}{1} \cdot \frac{100}{100} = \frac{77}{100}
$$

This technique does not apply to a repeating decimal such as $.7\overline{7}$ because, as the bar indicates, the 7s repeat forever.

To convert repeating decimals to fractions we must use this fact: If $a = b$ and $c = d$, then $a - c = b - d$. To express $.7\overline{7}$ as a fraction let $x = .7\overline{7}$ and multiply this equation by 10. This process moves the decimal point one place to the right and produces the equation $10x = 7.7\overline{7}$. Now subtract the first equation, $x = .7\overline{7}$, from the second equation, $10x = 7.7\overline{7}$:

$$
\begin{array}{r}
10x = 7.7\overline{7} \\
-x = -.7\overline{7} \\
\hline
9x = 7.0\overline{0}
\end{array}
$$

$$
9x = 7 \quad \text{and} \quad x = \frac{7}{9}. \text{ Thus, } .7\overline{7} = \frac{7}{9}
$$

To convert a repeating decimal to the ratio of two integers:

1. Let $x =$ the number.

2. If one digit repeats, multiply both sides of the equation by 10; if two digits repeat, multiply by 100; if three digits repeat, multiply by 1000, and so on.

3. Subtract the first equation from the second one and solve for x.

EXAMPLE 6

Express $4.21\overline{313}$ as the ratio of two integers.

SOLUTION   First we eliminate the repeating part of the decimal. Then we multiply 417.1 by 10 to produce an integer.

Let $x = 4.21\overline{313}$ and $100x = 421.31\overline{313}$. Then,

$$
\begin{array}{r}
100x = 421.31\overline{313} \\
-x = -4.21\overline{313} \\
\hline
99x = 417.10\overline{000}
\end{array}
$$

$$
x = \frac{417.1}{99} = \frac{417.1}{99} \cdot \frac{10}{10} = \frac{4171}{990}
$$

4 Solving Number Problems

Many problems involve the sum or difference of two numbers. For example, suppose the difference of two numbers is 10. If the smaller number is 5, then the larger one is $10 + 5 = 15$; or if the smaller number is -5, then the larger one is $10 + (-5) = 5$. In general, if the smaller number is s, then the larger number is $10 + s$, because $(10 + s) - s = 10$. In our next example the sum of two numbers is 30. If one of them is s, then the other one is $30 - s$, because $s + (30 - s) = 30$.

EXAMPLE 7

The sum of two numbers is 30. One-half the smaller number is 13 less than two-thirds the larger number. Find the numbers and check the answer.

SOLUTION Let $s =$ the smaller number. Then,

$$30 - s = \text{the larger number;}$$

$$\frac{1}{2}s = \frac{1}{2} \quad \text{the smaller number,}$$

$$\frac{2}{3}(30 - s) = \frac{2}{3} \quad \text{the larger number, and}$$

$$\frac{2}{3}(30 - s) - 13 = 13 \text{ less than } \frac{2}{3} \text{ the larger number.}$$

$$\frac{1}{2}s = \frac{2}{3}(30 - s) - 13 \qquad\qquad \text{LCD} = 6$$

$$6 \cdot \frac{1}{2}s = 6\left[\frac{2}{3}(30 - s) - 13\right]$$

$$3s = 4(30 - s) - 78$$

$$3s = 120 - 4s - 78$$

$$7s = 42$$

$$s = 6, \quad \text{so } 30 - s = 24$$

 CHECK $\frac{1}{2}s = \frac{1}{2} \cdot 6 = 3$, and $\frac{2}{3}(24) - 13 = 16 - 13 = 3$, so the two numbers are 6 and 24.

Word problems that require us to find more than one unknown quantity may offer an alternate method of solution. For instance, in Example 7 we could let $L =$ the larger number and $30 - L =$ the smaller number (see Exercise 69 on page 53). Throughout the text certain exercises suggest alternate methods of solutions to particular word problems.

This section concludes with an example of **consecutive integer problems**. Three consecutive integers — such as 7, 8, and 9 — can be represented as $x, x + 1$, and $x + 2$. Three consecutive even or odd integers can be represented by $x, x + 2$, and $x + 4$. For example, $x = 12$, $x + 2 = 14$, and $x + 4 = 16$ are three consecutive even integers.

EXAMPLE 8

Find three consecutive odd integers such that 3 times the first minus the second is 4 more than 4 times the third.

(continued)

SOLUTION   Let x, $x + 2$, and $x + 4$ represent the integers. Then, $3x - (x + 2) = 3$ times the first minus the second, $4(x + 4) + 4 = 4$ more than 4 times the third one, so

$$3x - (x + 2) = 4(x + 4) + 4$$
$$3x - x - 2 = 4x + 16 + 4$$
$$2x - 2 = 4x + 20$$
$$-2x = 22$$
$$x = -11, \quad \text{so } x + 2 = -9 \quad \text{and} \quad x + 4 = -7$$

Thus, the integers are $\{-11, -9, -7\}$. (*Check it!*)

EXERCISE SET 2.2

A

1 Solve the following equations and check your answers.

1. $\dfrac{-5x}{14} = \dfrac{5}{7}$

2. $\dfrac{3x}{8} = \dfrac{x}{4} + 2$

3. $\dfrac{k}{6} = \dfrac{k - 3}{9} - \dfrac{1}{2}$

4. $\dfrac{2 - y}{3} + \dfrac{5}{6} = \dfrac{y + 1}{8}$

5. $.7x - .3 = 3.1$

6. $.14y + .48 = .02y$

7. $.05n + .1(21 - n) = 1.65$

8. $1.3t + 2.2 = 4.01t + 3.555$

Solve the following equations.

9. $\dfrac{3x}{5} = \dfrac{7}{4}$

10. $\dfrac{x - 1}{2} = \dfrac{11x}{8}$

11. $\dfrac{k}{6} + \dfrac{k}{4} = 1$

12. $\dfrac{3m}{2} - \dfrac{4m}{7} = -1$

13. $\dfrac{3x}{2} - \dfrac{5x}{6} = \dfrac{3}{8}$

14. $\dfrac{x - 1}{12} - \dfrac{x}{9} = \dfrac{1}{18}$

15. $\dfrac{x}{5} - \dfrac{2x - 1}{4} = \dfrac{x}{10}$

16. $z = \dfrac{2 - z}{9} + 1 = \dfrac{3z + 1}{3}$

17. $\dfrac{r + 1}{8} - \dfrac{r - 1}{5} = \dfrac{2r + 1}{20}$

18. $\dfrac{1}{6}(x + 1) - \dfrac{2}{15}(1 - 3x) = \dfrac{1}{10}$

19. $\quad .1x = .08(x + 1000)$

20. $\quad .2(x + 60) = .35(60)$

21. $\quad 6c + 4.5(20 - c) = 5(20)$

22. $\quad .06x + .15(2) = .12(x + 2)$

23. $\quad 1.02x - 2.3 = 1.25x$

24. $\quad .1x + .01x - .001x = -9.4$

25. $\quad .1x + .08(x + 3000) = 600$

26. $\quad .03x + .06 \cdot 13 = .05(x + 13)$

2 Solve the following equations and check your answers.

27. $|x| = 9$

28. $|4y| = 20$

29. $|x - 7| = 8$

30. $1 + |2x - 1| = 11$

31. $|3z + 1| = |z|$

32. $|x + 5| = |2x|$

33. $|a + 1| = |2a - 3|$

34. $|x + 2| = |x - 16|$

Solve the following equations.

35. $|2t - 3| = 7$ **36.** $|4x + 1| = 3$

37. $|x + 9| = 0$ **38.** $|x - 5| = -6$

39. $|4y| = -20$

40. $|9 - 2x| = 0$

41. $\left|\dfrac{k + 4}{2}\right| = 10$

42. $\left|\dfrac{2}{3}x - \dfrac{1}{6}\right| = \dfrac{1}{4}$

43. $6 = |x| - 8$

44. $3|x - 1| = 24$

45. $2 + 2|6x| = 11$

46. $6 - |1 - 2x| = -5$

47. $|2x - 7| = |x|$

48. $|y| = |1 - 4y|$

49. $|c - 1| = |2c|$

50. $|6k + 1| = |5k - 4|$

51. $|x + 4| = |x - 3|$

52. $|x - 3| = |3 - x|$

53. $|3x| = |7x|$

54. $|2a - 3| = |a + 4|$

55. $|2y - 1| = |1 - 2y|$

56. $|x + 1| = |x - 1|$

---

3 Express each of the following as the ratio of two integers.

57. $.44$ **58.** $.4\overline{4}$ **59.** $.21\overline{21}$

60. $.2121$ **61.** $-1.34\overline{34}$ **62.** $.123\overline{123}$

63. $3.\overline{205}$ **64.** $.16\overline{6}$ **65.** $-1.258\overline{8}$

66. $0.345\overline{21}$ **67.** $0.2\overline{678}$ **68.** $1.2\overline{157}$

---

4 Express the following as algebraic equations. State what each variable represents, solve each equation to find the number(s), and check your answer.

69. Solve the word problem in Example 7 (page 51) by letting L = the larger number and $30 - L$ = the smaller number.

70. One-fourth a number subtracted from two-thirds the number is 3 more than one-sixth the number.

71. One-third the sum of a number plus 4 is 5 more than one-fifth the difference of the number and 7.

72. The sum of two numbers is 25. If the larger number is subtracted from twice the smaller number, the difference is -4.

73. The sum of two numbers is -20. The larger number is 28 more than 3 times the smaller number.

74. The difference of two numbers is 10. The sum of the smaller number and 4 times the larger number is 65.

75. The difference of two numbers is 24. The smaller number is equal to 5 times the larger number.

76. The distance between a number and zero is 9.

77. The distance between a number and 4 is 6.

78. Find all numbers x such that $6x - 1$ and $4x + 7$ are the same distance from zero.

79. Find three consecutive integers such that the sum of the first two is 18 less than 3 times the third.

80. The sum of four consecutive integers is -42.

81. Find three consecutive odd integers such that the difference of twice the first and the third is 4 more than three times the second.

82. Find three consecutive odd integers such that the sum of 3 times the first and twice the second is equal to the sum of 3 times the third plus 1 more than the first.

B

83. Show that for any three consecutive integers the sum of the first two is 3 less than twice the third.

84. Show that for any three consecutive even or odd integers the middle integer is the average of the other two.

85. Show that three consecutive integers do not exist such that the sum of the first two is twice the third. (*Hint:* Assume they do exist and find a contradiction.)

86. Show that four consecutive odd integers do not exist whose sum is 5 times the smallest integer.

Solve the following equations.

87. $x - .\overline{5} = 1$ **88.** $.2x + .\overline{2} = -3$

89. $1.4x + .\overline{32} = 2.7$ **90.** $.\overline{87}x - .2 = 1.07$

C Express the following as fractions in reduced form. Some answers have both a terminating and a repeating decimal expansion.

91. $.249\overline{9}$ **92.** $.49\overline{9}$

93. $.749\overline{9}$ **94.** $.9\overline{9}$

95. The decimal expansion of 10/81 starts repeating after 9 decimal places. Find 10/81 correct to 12 decimal places.

Answer the following questions with complete sentences.

96. Why does the equation $|x + 2| = -6$ have no solution?

97. Describe how you would convert a repeating decimal, with one digit repeating, to the ratio of two integers.

REVIEW EXERCISES

Solve the following equations. (See Sections 2.1 and 2.2.)

98. $2W + 10 = 42$

99. $2x - 7 = 5(3 - x)$

100. $\frac{9}{5}(C + 32) = -4$

101. $\frac{y}{3} - \frac{5}{2} = 1$

Simplify the following (See Section 1.4.)

102. $-\sqrt{36}$ **103.** $-\sqrt{12}$

104. $2\sqrt{18}$ **105.** $(\sqrt{21})^2$

2.3 FORMULAS

1	Evaluating Formulas and Literal Equations
2	Solving Formulas and Literal Equations; Solving $x^2 = d$
3	The Pythagorean Theorem

1 Evaluating Formulas and Literal Equations

Equations that contain more than one variable are called literal equations. Formulas are literal equations that describe relationships in the physical world. Examples are

$$I = Prt \qquad \text{(Business: simple interest formula)}$$

$$IQ = \frac{100MA}{CA} \qquad \text{(Psychology: intelligence quotient)}$$

$$\frac{V_1}{P_2} = \frac{V_2}{P_1} \qquad \text{(Chemistry: Boyle's Law)}$$

$$S = 4\pi r^2 \qquad \text{(Geometry: surface area of a sphere)}$$

Formulas are essential in nearly every subject that uses algebra. In this section we will learn how to evaluate a literal equation, given all but one of its variables, and how to solve it for a given variable. We begin with motion and geometric formulas, which will be used in the next section to solve word problems.

The formula **$d = rt$** gives the relationship between the distance d that an object travels at a uniform rate of speed r for t units of time. For example, if Don jogs at 8 kilometers per hour (km/h) for 2 hours, then he travels $d = 8 \cdot 2 = 16$ kilometers.

EXAMPLE 1

An oil rig in west Texas can drill at an average rate of 4 feet per hour. How many days, to the nearest day, will it take to drill an oil well that is to be 7800 feet deep?

SOLUTION $d = 7800$ and $r = 4$; $d = rt$, so $d/r = t$. Thus,

$$t = \frac{d}{r} = \frac{7800}{4} = 1950 \text{ hours} = \frac{1950}{24} \text{ days} = 81.25 \text{ days}$$

Approximately 81 days will be needed to drill the well.

EXAMPLE 2

Maria leaves Denver, Colorado, heading north at 42 miles per hour (mph). At the same time Analisa leaves Denver heading south at 51 mph. How far apart will they be after 3 hours?

SOLUTION $d = rt$. For Maria, $r = 42$ and $t = 3$, so $d = 42 \cdot 3 = 126$ miles is her distance.

For Analisa, $r = 51$ and $t = 3$, so $d = 51 \cdot 3 = 153$ miles is her distance. Because they are traveling in opposite directions, the sum of their distances gives the answer — that is, they will be $126 + 153 = 279$ miles apart after 3 hours.

Many problems in mathematics and science involve geometric formulas. The table in Appendix E gives the formulas needed for the problems in this text.

EXAMPLE 3

The perimeter of a rectangle is 24 centimeters and its width is 3 centimeters (see Figure 2.2). Find its length and area.

FIGURE 2.2

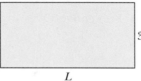

L

SOLUTION Let $L = $ its length. $W = 3$ and $P = 24$. Thus,

$$2L + 2W = P$$
$$2L + 2 \cdot 3 = 24$$
$$2L + 6 = 24$$
$$2L = 18$$
$$L = 9$$

The length is 9 centimeters and the area is $A = LW = 9 \cdot 3 = 27$ cm^2 (centimeters squared).

EXAMPLE 4

Norman windows have rectangular bases and semicircular tops. They were used in the construction of cathedrals in England and France in the Middle Ages. Such a window's base dimensions are 8 feet by 12 feet (see Figure 2.3). Find the window's perimeter and area.

FIGURE 2.3

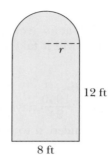

12 ft

8 ft

SOLUTION

The radius, r, of the semicircle is one-half the width of the rectangle. Thus, $r = 4$. The window's perimeter is

$$P = 8 + 2 \cdot 12 + \frac{1}{2} \cdot 2\pi r$$
$$= 8 + 24 + \pi \cdot 4$$
$$= 32 + 4\pi \text{ feet}$$

The window's area is

$$A = 8 \cdot 12 + \frac{1}{2}\pi r^2 = 96 + \frac{1}{2}\pi \cdot 16 = 96 + 8\pi \text{ feet}^2$$

The Fahrenheit and Celsius scales are commonly used to measure temperature. The former is named for German physicist Gabriel Fahrenheit (1686–1736); the latter for Swedish astronomer Anders Celsius (1701–1744). Converting a temperature from one scale to the other is a common problem in such fields as nursing.

EXAMPLE 5

The normal human body temperature is approximately 98.6° F. Use the formula $\frac{9}{5}C + 32 = F$ to convert this to a Celsius temperature.

$$\frac{9}{5}C + 32 = F \qquad F = 98.6$$

$$\frac{9}{5}C + 32 = 98.6 \qquad \text{Subtract 32.}$$

$$\frac{9}{5}C = 66.6 \qquad \text{Multiply by } \frac{5}{9}.$$

$$\frac{5}{9} \cdot \frac{9}{5}C = \frac{5}{9}(66.6) \qquad \frac{5}{9}(66.6) = \frac{333}{9} = 37$$

$C = 37$, so 98.6° F = 37° C.

2 **Solving Formulas and Literal Equations; Solving $x^2 = d$**

You need no new algebraic skills to solve the literal equations in this section; the techniques used for solving linear equations are sufficient. To illustrate this, the following two equations are solved for *x*:

$$2x - 7 = 5(3 - x)$$
$$2x - 7 = 15 - 5x$$
$$5x + 2x - 7 = 15$$
$$5x + 2x = 15 + 7$$
$$(5 + 2)x = 22$$
$$x = \frac{22}{7}$$

$$2x - b = a(3 - x)$$
$$2x - b = 3a - ax$$
$$ax + 2x - b = 3a$$
$$ax + 2x = 3a + b$$
$$(a + 2)x = 3a + b$$
$$x = \frac{3a + b}{a + 2}$$

In Example 5 the formula $9/5C + 32 = F$ was solved for C, given F = 98.6. In Example 6a, this formula is solved in general for C. Compare the two examples to see whether the methods of solution are the same.

EXAMPLE 6

Solve the following equations for the indicated variable.

a. $\frac{9}{5}C + 32 = F$; C   **b.** $\frac{y}{3} - \frac{x}{2} = 1$; *y*

c. $\frac{a - b + c}{w} = cV$; *c*

SOLUTION **a.** $\frac{9}{5}C + 32 = F$ Subtract 32.

$$\frac{9}{5}C = F - 32$$ Multiply by $\frac{5}{9}$.

$$\frac{5}{9} \cdot \frac{9}{5}C = \frac{5}{9}(F - 32)$$

$$C = \frac{5}{9}(F - 32)$$

b. $\frac{y}{3} - \frac{x}{2} = 1$ LCD = 6
                                                      Multiply by 6.

$$6\left(\frac{y}{3} - \frac{x}{2}\right) = 6 \cdot 1$$

$$6\left(\frac{y}{3}\right) - 6\left(\frac{x}{2}\right) = 6$$ Distributive property

$$2y - 3x = 6$$ Add 3*x*.

$$2y = 3x + 6$$ Divide by 2.

$$y = \frac{3x + 6}{2}$$

(continued)

c. $\dfrac{a - b + c}{w} = cV$ Multiply by w.

$$a - b + c = wcV \qquad \text{Subtract } c.$$
$$a - b = cwV - c \qquad c = c \cdot 1$$
$$a - b = cwV - c \cdot 1 \qquad \text{Distributive property}$$
$$a - b = c(wV - 1) \qquad \text{Divide by } wV - 1.$$
$$\frac{a - b}{wV - 1} = c$$
$$c = \frac{a - b}{wV - 1}$$

COMMON
ERROR

A common mistake is made in problems such as Example 6c. If we take $a - b + c = wcV$ and write it as $c = wcV - a + b$, we have not solved the equation for c. To solve for c means that c occurs only once — on one side of the equation and with a coefficient of 1.

We saw in Section 1.4 that 6 and -6 are the square roots of 36; that is, if $x^2 = 36$, then $x = \sqrt{36} = 6$ and $x = -\sqrt{36} = -6$. We commonly write these solutions as $x = \pm 6$. An equation such as $x^2 = 36$ is called a **quadratic equation**. In general:

> If $d > 0$ and $x^2 = d$,   then $x = \sqrt{d}$ or $x = -\sqrt{d}$.
> This result is usually written as $x = \pm\sqrt{d}$.

EXAMPLE 7

Solve the following equations.

a. $k^2 - 1 = 6$ **b.** $2x^2 + 1 = 25$

SOLUTION

a. Write the equation in the form $x^2 = d$:

$$k^2 - 1 = 6 \qquad\qquad\qquad \text{Add 1.}$$
$$k^2 = 7$$
$$k = \pm\sqrt{7}$$

b. $2x^2 + 1 = 25$ Subtract 1.

$$2x^2 = 24 \qquad\qquad\qquad \text{Divide by 2.}$$
$$x^2 = 12$$
$$x = \pm\sqrt{12} \qquad\qquad\quad \sqrt{ab} = \sqrt{a}\sqrt{b}$$
$$x = \pm\sqrt{4 \cdot 3} = \pm\sqrt{4}\sqrt{3} = \pm 2\sqrt{3}$$

---

3   The Pythagorean Theorem

In the next chapter we will find the distance between two points on a plane. To find such a distance we will need one of the oldest and most important formulas in the history of mathematics, the Pythagorean theorem (see p. 60).

Math in Time

BECAUSE RIGHT ANGLES are so common in nature, the formula we know now as the Pythagorean theorem was discovered by several cultures. Four thousand years ago the Babylonians had found at least 38 natural number solutions to the theorem. Some were simple [such as (3, 4, 5)], but others [such as (3367, 3456, 4825)] indicate considerable skill with arithmetic. The Chinese had some knowledge of the formula by 1200 B.C. and the Hindus knew it by the 6th century B.C. History, however, has given Pythagoras (ca. 580–500 B.C.) the credit for first proving that for every right triangle the square of the hypotenuse is equal to the sum of the squares of the two legs.

Pythagoras was born on the Greek island of Samos off the west coast of what is now Turkey. He spent some 30 years traveling in Egypt, India, and Babylonia, where he studied mathematics, mysticism, and astronomy. In approximately 530 B.C. he settled in Crotona, a Greek colony in southern Italy. There he founded a semireligious and semimathematical secret society of several hundred disciples that was similar to some cults we see today. Believing in reincarnation, the Pythagoreans were forbidden to eat meat to avoid accidentally eating an ancestor. To escape the "wheel of birth" they sought purification of the body through abstinence and moderation and purification of the mind through the study of mathematics and science.

"Number rules the universe," taught Pythagoras, and the brotherhood's members

Pythagoras
North Wind Picture Archives

believed that all of nature could be explained in terms of natural numbers and fractions. They developed rules of musical harmony using strings of lengths 1, 1/2, 2/3, and 3/4. Pythagoras believed that the earth and planets were spheres traveling through space and that their different speeds produced different musical tones according to these rules. He and others called the combined harmony "the music of the spheres." In the course of his studies, Pythagoras proved that the diagonal of a unit square, $\sqrt{2}$, is irrational. This was a death blow to the theory that all of nature could be described with rational numbers, and the Pythagoreans swore an oath to suppress this discovery. However, according to legend, Hippasus revealed the secret and was drowned for his crime.

One objective of the Pythagoreans was the moral reformation of society. Their meddling in local politics incited the citizens of Crotona to revolt against the Pythagoreans. Many members of the brotherhood were murdered and their homes burned. Pythagoras fled Crotona and died in exile; but the society, although scattered, existed for another 200 years. Perhaps the best epitaph for Pythagoras is "three-fifths of him genius and two-fifths sheer fudge" (J. R. Lowell).

Pythagorean Theorem

In any right triangle, the square of the hypotenuse is equal to the sum of the squares of the two legs, as in Figure 2.3.

$$c^2 = a^2 + b^2$$

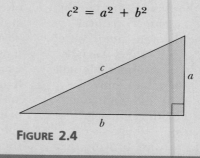

FIGURE 2.4

EXAMPLE 8

The hypotenuse of a right triangle is 13 centimeters, and one of its legs is 12 centimeters (see Figure 2.5). Find the other leg.

FIGURE 2.5

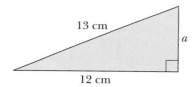

SOLUTION   Let $a = $ the length of the other leg. Then,

$$a^2 + 12^2 = 13^2$$
$$a^2 + 144 = 169$$
$$a^2 = 25$$
$$a = \sqrt{25} = 5 \text{ centimeters}$$

Note that the solutions to $a^2 = 25$ are $a = \pm 5$, but -5 is meaningless in a geometric problem, so we disregard it in this problem.

The converse of the Pythagorean theorem is also true: It can be used to determine whether a triangle with three known sides is a right triangle.

Converse of the Pythagorean Theorem

If the sum of the squares of the two shorter sides of a triangle is equal to the square of the longest side, then the triangle is a right triangle. The right angle is opposite the longest side.

EXAMPLE 9

Is a triangle with sides 11, 10, and $\sqrt{21}$ a right triangle? (See Figure 2.6.)

FIGURE 2.6

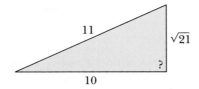

SOLUTION

$11^2 \overset{?}{=} 10^2 + (\sqrt{21})^2$
$121 \overset{?}{=} 100 + 21$
$121 = 121$
It is a right triangle.

An **isosceles triangle** has two equal sides and two equal angles. An **isosceles right triangle** has two equal legs and two equal angles of 45°. In this case $a = b$, so $c^2 = a^2 + a^2 = 2a^2$ (Figure 2.7). Another type of right triangle is one containing angles of 30° and 60° (Figure 2.8). In a 30°–60°–90° triangle, the length of the hypotenuse is twice the length of the leg opposite the 30° angle. Problems involving isosceles right triangles are left as exercises.

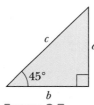

FIGURE 2.7

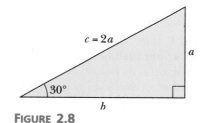

FIGURE 2.8

EXAMPLE 10

In a 30°–60°–90° triangle the side opposite the 30° angle is 6 units (Figure 2.9). Find the other two sides.

FIGURE 2.9

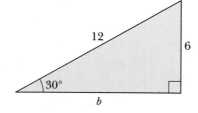

SOLUTION

Because $a = 6$, $c = 2a = 12$, so
$b^2 + 6^2 = 12^2$
$b^2 + 36 = 144$
$b^2 = 108$
$b = \sqrt{108} = \sqrt{36 \cdot 3} = \sqrt{36}\sqrt{3} = 6\sqrt{3}$ units.

EXERCISE SET 2.3

A

1   Solve the following motion problems.

1. How far does Rhea drive in 3 hours if her average speed is 48 mph?

2. How long does it take Lisa to drive 144 kilometers if she can average 64 km/h?

3. Kyung cycles 25 miles in 2 hours and 30 minutes. Find his average speed. (*Note:* Express 30 minutes as .5 hour.)

4. A truck leaves Albuquerque, New Mexico, heading east at 47 mph. At the same time a car leaves Albuquerque heading west at 53 mph. How far apart will they be after 2 hours and 15 minutes?

5. A car leaves Toledo, Ohio, at 8 A.M. and heads south at 50 mph. At 9 A.M. a truck leaves Toledo along the same road at 40 mph. How far ahead of the truck is the car at 11 A.M.?

6. Taeko drives the 24 miles from her home to her office in the morning rush hour at 30 mph. In the afternoon she returns home at 36 mph. Find the total number of minutes she spends driving to work and returning home.

Solve the following geometry problems.

7. A copper wire 84 centimeters long is bent into the shape of a rectangle. The length of the rectangle is 30 centimeters. Find its width.

8. The area of a trapezoid is 34 feet squared (ft²). Find its height if the bases are 12 and 5 ft.

9. The side of a square pool is 18 feet; the pool is surrounded by a gravel walk 3 feet wide. Find the area of the walk.

10. The diameter of a copper washer is 24 millimeters and the diameter of the hole is 18 millimeters. How many square millimeters of copper are in 100 washers? Use $\pi \approx 3.14$.

11. Find the surface area and volume of a sphere having a diameter of 14 inches. Use $\pi \approx 22/7$.

12. The volume of a right circular cone is 48π cubic centimeters, and its radius is 6 centimeters. Find its height.

Values for all but one of the variables are given for the following equations. Find the value of the remaining variable in each equation.

13. $y = 4x - 2$, $x = -3$

14. $3x - 2y = 6$, $y = -2$

15. $\dfrac{x}{4} - \dfrac{y}{3} = 1$, $x = -8$

16. $I = Prt$, $I = 54$, $P = 300$, $r = 9\%$

17. $A = P + Prt$, $A = 520$, $r = 10\%$, $t = 3$

18. $A = P + Prt$, $A = 2040$, $P = 600$, $r = 12\%$

19. $A = \dfrac{1}{2}bh$, $A = 30$, $b = 12$

20. $S = 2LH + 2WH + 2LW$, $S = 132$, $L = 8$, $W = 2$

21. $C = \dfrac{5}{9}(F - 32)$, $C = -10°$

22. $D = ad - bc$, $D = 22$, $a = 2$, $b = 3$, $d = 5$

2   Solve the following for the indicated variables.

23. $y = 3x - 7$; x

24. $y = -2x + 8$; x

25. $3x - 5y = 15$; x

26. $3x - 5y = 15$; y

27. $Ax + By = C$; y

28. $y = mx + b$; x

29. $at - br = bt$; t

30. $A = P + Prt$; P

31. $a(x - 3) = b(x + 4)$; x

32. $S = 2LH + 2WH + 2LW$; L

33. $C = \dfrac{5}{9}(F - 32)$; F

34. $\dfrac{PV}{T} = 30$; T

35. $\dfrac{x}{a} + \dfrac{y}{b} = 1$; y

36. $\dfrac{y-a}{b} = \dfrac{y-c}{d};\quad y$

37. $K = 7 + (a+1)b;\quad a$

38. $K = 7 + (a+1)b;\quad b$

39. $D = ad - bc;\quad a$

40. $m = mn + 3p;\quad m$

41. $p = \dfrac{S}{S+F};\quad F$

42. $p = \dfrac{S}{S+F};\quad S$

Solve the following equations.

43. $x^2 = 16$ **44.** $y^2 = 49$

45. $z^2 = 18$ **46.** $x^2 = 20$

47. $10a^2 = 100$ **48.** $c^2 - 2 = 23$

49. $3k^2 + 1 = 13$ **50.** $2x^2 - 1 = 63$

3 Find the missing side of each right triangle with legs a and b and hypotenuse c. Sketch each triangle.

51. $a = 6,\ b = 8$ **52.** $a = b = 1$

53. $c = 4, b = 2$ **54.** $a = .5,\ b = 1.2$

55. $c = \sqrt{29},\ a = 2$

56. $c = 4, b = \sqrt{7}$

57. $c = 17,\ a = 8$

58. $a = 1/3,\ b = 1/4$

Find the missing sides of each isosceles right triangle with hypotenuse c.

59. $a = 3$ **60.** $b = \sqrt{5}$

61. $c = 4$ **62.** $c = 2\sqrt{5}$

63. $c = 10$ **64.** $a = 4$

Find the missing sides of each 30°–60°–90° triangle with hypotenuse c; a is the side opposite the 30° angle.

65. $a = 4$ **66.** $c = 2$

67. $b = 6$ **68.** $b = \sqrt{15}$

69. $c = 8$ **70.** $a = \sqrt{2}$

Determine whether the three numbers are the lengths of the sides of a right triangle.

71. $(6, 9, 11)$ **72.** $(3, 5, \sqrt{34})$

73. $(1.5, 2, 2.5)$ **74.** $(4, 6, 7)$

75. $(2, \sqrt{3}, \sqrt{6})$ **76.** $(9, 40, 41)$

Solve the following.

77. A 15-foot ladder is leaning against a building, its bottom 9 feet from the building's base. How high is the top of the ladder?

78. A barn door is 7 feet high and 3 feet wide. Can a square sheet of tin, 7.5 feet on a side, be carried through the doorway? Justify your answer.

79. In Figure 2.10, find the area inside the square and outside the circle. Find the difference between the perimeter of the square and the circumference of the circle.

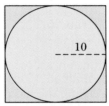

FIGURE 2.10

80. Find the area in Figure 2.11 enclosed by the rectangle and the semicircles. Find the perimeter determmned by the four semicircles.

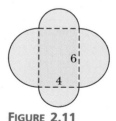

FIGURE 2.11

81. In Figure 2.12, find the area enclosed by the triangle and the semicircles. Find the perimeter determined by the three semicircles.

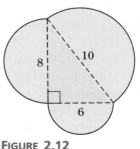

FIGURE 2.12

82. Find the area enclosed by the triangle and the squares in Figure 2.13. Find the perimeter determined by the triangle and the two squares.

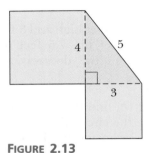

FIGURE 2.13

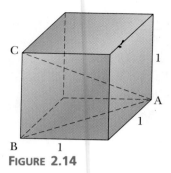

FIGURE 2.14

86. The dimensions of a rectangular solid are 4, 3, and 2 units (Figure 2.15).
   a. Find the distance from A to B.
   b. Find the length of the diagonal from A to C.
   c. Find the solid's volume and surface area.

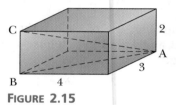

FIGURE 2.15

B

83. Jane is standing on a dock 11 feet above the water and pulling in her windsurfer with a 61-foot rope. When she has pulled in 46 feet of rope, how far, to the nearest foot, has she moved the windsurfer?

84. Larry drove due west at a rate of 45 mph for 20 minutes. He then hiked due south at a rate of 3 mph for 2 hours and 40 minutes. How far was he from his starting point at the end of the trip?

85. A unit cube has all of its edges 1 unit long (Figure 2.14).
   a. Find the distance from A to B.
   b. Find the length of the diagonal from A to C.

C

Answer the following questions with complete sentences.

87. What is the difference between a literal equation and a formula?

88. Discuss some of the beliefs of the Pythagoreans.

REVIEW EXERCISES

Solve the following number problems. (See Sections 2.1 and 2.2.)

89. The sum of two numbers is 50. The larger number is 2 more than twice the smaller number. Find the numbers.

90. The sum of two numbers is 90. The larger number is 8 less than 6 times the smaller number. What are the numbers?

91. Find three consecutive integers whose sum is 42.

92. Find three consecutive even integers such that 3 times the smallest integer is equal to the sum of the other two.

2.4 WORD PROBLEMS

> **1** Solving Word Problems
> **2** Applying Number Problems
> **3** Solving Geometry Problems
> **4** Solving Uniform Motion Problems

1 Solving Word Problems

In the last three sections we solved a variety of word problems. This section will consider some extensions of those problems. Because these new problems are more complex, this is a good place to discuss general suggestions for solving word problems.

Perseverance and a positive frame of mind are key factors in solving word problems. Work at developing the attitude, "I can solve most of these problems if I try hard enough, and I'll get some help on the ones that I can't solve." In addition to a positive approach, the following guidelines are helpful in dealing with word problems:

1. Read the problem very carefully, several times if necessary, to understand what is to be found and what is known.

2. Represent what is to be found by a variable, say x, or by a letter that helps to describe the unknown quantity. For example, "Let s = the smaller number," "Let k = Kathy's current age," and so on. Be careful to precisely define the variable; do not write, "Let k = Kathy."

3. Sometimes more than one unknown quantity is involved. In this chapter we will be able to express all unknowns in terms of one variable. For example, s and $30 - s$ describe two numbers whose sum is 30.

4. When possible, as in geometry problems, draw a sketch or diagram to help illustrate the problem. Clearly label the figure, indicating known and unknown parts.

5. Translate the English phrases into algebraic expressions. When possible, as in motion problems, use a chart to help organize the information. Combine the expressions into an equation; often a formula, such as $d = rt$, can be used.

6. Solve the equation and check the answer in the original problem. Remember that if more than one unknown quantity is involved, more than one answer is required. Think about the answer to see if it is reasonable. If Sue is jogging at a rate of 80 mph, then something went wrong somewhere.

7. Carefully read the examples in the text, because they are similar to the exercises.

8. If you are not making headway with a problem, leaving it for awhile and trying it again later is often better. Also, do not try to solve word problems when you are tired or short of time. If you cannot solve a

particular problem, do not become discouraged; proficiency with word problems takes a lot of time and practice.

2 Applying Number Problems

We have solved several types of number problems involving two or more numbers. These problems have many applications: determining the results of an election, solving problems involving money, and so on. The checks for some examples in this section are left as exercises.

EXAMPLE 1

In an election for mayor in a small town, 2800 votes were cast for the two candidates. The winner had 160 more votes than the loser. How many votes were cast for each candidate?

SOLUTION

Let L = the number of votes cast for the loser. Then $L + 160$ = the number of votes cast for the winner. Because a total of 2800 votes were cast,

$$L + (L + 160) = 2800$$
$$2L + 160 = 2800$$
$$2L = 2640$$
$$L = 1320$$

The number of votes cast for the winner was $L + 160 = 1320 + 160 = 1480$. Thus, the winner received 1480 votes and the loser 1320 votes.

  CHECK

$1480 + 1320 = 2800$, the total number of votes cast, and $1320 + 160 = 1480$.

EXAMPLE 2

The average salary of three teachers is $36,000. Flor teaches at a state college and earns $19,000 more than Ken, who teaches at a high school. Bianca teaches at a community college and earns $1,000 more than twice Ken's salary. Find each person's salary.

SOLUTION

Let k = Ken's salary. Then, $k + 19,000$ = Flor's salary, and $2k + 1,000$ = Bianca's salary. To find the average of three numbers, we divide their sum by 3. Thus,

$$\frac{k + (k + 19,000) + (2k + 1,000)}{3} = 36,000$$

$$\frac{4k + 20,000}{3} = 36,000 \qquad \text{Multiply both sides by 3.}$$

$$4k + 20,000 = 108,000$$
$$4k = 88,000$$
$$k = 22,000$$
$$k + 19,000 = 41,000$$
$$2k + 1,000 = 44,000 + 1,000 = 45,000$$

Thus, Ken's salary is $22,000, Flor's is $41,000, and Bianca's is $45,000.

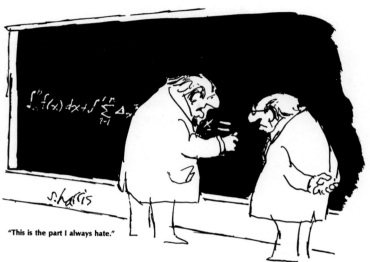

"This is the part I always hate."

© *1992 by Sidney Harris. Reprinted with permission.*

3   Solving Geometry Problems

Many problems involve the perimeter of a geometric figure. Our next example combines this concept with the idea of consecutive integers.

EXAMPLE 3

The sides of a triangle are three consecutive integers. The perimeter is 4 less than 4 times the shortest side (Figure 2.16). Find the sides of the triangle.

FIGURE 2.16

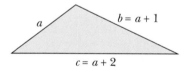

SOLUTION   The formula for the perimeter of a triangle is $P = a + b + c$. Let $a =$ the shortest side, $a + 1 =$ the longer side, and $a + 2 =$ the longest side:
$P = a + (a + 1) + (a + 2) = 3a + 3$ and
$P = 4a - 4$
Thus,
$4a - 4 = 3a + 3$
$a - 4 = 3$
$a = 7$, so $a + 1 = 8$, and $a + 2 = 9$

 CHECK $P = 7 + 8 + 9 = 24$, and $P = 4a - 4 = 4 \cdot 7 - 4 = 24$.

Several important relationships involve angles; three are stated here. The first is used in Example 4, and the second and third are considered in the exercises.

1. Two angles are **complementary** if the sum of their measures is 90°.

2. Two angles are **supplementary** if the sum of their measures is 180°.

3. The sum of the measures of the angles of a triangle is 180°.

EXAMPLE 4

The smaller of two complementary angles is 3° more than one-half the larger angle (Figure 2.17). Find the angles.

FIGURE 2.17

SOLUTION   Let L = the larger angle. Then, $\frac{1}{2}L + 3$ = the smaller angle. The sum of the two angles is 90°, so

$$L + \left(\frac{1}{2}L + 3\right) = 90 \qquad L + \frac{1}{2}L = \left(1 + \frac{1}{2}\right)L = \frac{3}{2}L$$

$$\frac{3}{2}L + 3 = 90$$

$$\frac{3}{2}L = 87$$

$$\frac{2}{3} \cdot \frac{3}{2}L = \frac{2}{3} \cdot 87$$

$$L = 58, \text{ and } \frac{1}{2}L + 3 = \frac{1}{2} \cdot 58 + 3 = 29 + 3 = 32.$$

Thus, the larger angle is 58° and the smaller one is 32°.

EXAMPLE 5

The satellite 1985U1 is one of those discovered in orbit around Uranus in 1985 by the Voyager 2 spacecraft. It is nearly spherical in shape and with an approximate diameter of 170 kilometers. Find its approximate surface area and volume to two decimal places. Use $\pi \approx 3.14$.

SOLUTION   We need the formulas $S = 4\pi r^2$ and $V = \frac{4}{3}\pi r^3$.

The radius of a sphere is half its diameter, so $r = \frac{1}{2} \cdot 170 = 85$ km. Using a calculator we have

$$S \approx 4(3.14)(85^2) = 12.56(7225) = 90{,}746 \text{ square kilometers (km}^2)$$

$$V \approx \frac{4}{3}(3.14)(85^3) = \frac{1}{3}(12.56)(614{,}125) = \frac{1}{3}(7{,}713{,}410)$$

$$\approx 2{,}571{,}137 \text{ km}^3.$$

4 Solving Uniform Motion Problems

Recall from the last section that if an object travels a distance d at a uniform rate r for t units of time, then $d = rt$. Motion problems can take many forms: motion in opposite directions, motion in the same direction, and so on. A chart and a diagram are often helpful in organizing the information.

EXAMPLE 6

Sheri drove from San Jose to Lake Tahoe, a distance of 221 miles, in 5 hours. During the first part of the trip, she averaged 26 mph in rush-hour traffic. Her average speed for the rest of the trip was 52 mph. Find the time and distance traveled at each rate.

SOLUTION

Let t = the time spent traveling at 26 mph. Then $5 - t$ = the time spent traveling at 52 mph. The information is organized in the following table and Figure 2.18.

	Rate	• Time	= Distance
1st part	26	t	$26t$
2nd part	52	$5 - t$	$52(5 - t)$

FIGURE 2.18

Because the sum of the two distances is 221 miles,
$$26t + 52(5 - t) = 221$$
$$26t + 260 - 52t = 221$$
$$-26t = -39$$
$$t = \frac{-39}{-26} = \frac{3}{2} = 1.5 \text{ hours, and } 5 - t = 3.5 \text{ hours}$$

$26t = 26(1.5) = 39$ miles at 26 mph, and $52(5 - t) = 52.(3.5) = 182$ miles at 52 mph

---

Two waves produced by earthquakes are P waves (primary) and S waves (secondary). Their speeds vary with the density of the earth, but a good approximation is 8 km/sec for P waves and 4.5 km/sec for S waves. By determining the time interval between the arrival of these waves, a seismologist can calculate the distance of the focus, or source, of the earthquake.

EXAMPLE 7

A seismograph in Santa Cruz, California, recorded the S waves from an earthquake 156 seconds after it received the P waves. Find the distance of the earthquake from Santa Cruz.

(continued)

SOLUTION   Let t = the time it took the P waves to arrive. Then $t + 156$ = the time it took the S waves to arrive.

	Rate • Time = Distance		
P waves	8	t	$8t$
S waves	4.5	$t + 156$	$4.5(t + 156)$

Because both waves traveled the same distance,

$$8t = 4.5(t + 156)$$
$$8t = 4.5t + 702$$
$$3.5t = 702$$
$$t = 201 \text{ to the nearest second}$$

Thus, the earthquake occurred $8(201) = 1608$ kilometers from Santa Cruz.

Rates of travel are affected by such forces as wind and current. For example, suppose a motor boat can travel at 10 mph in still water, and the current of a river is 4 mph. When the boat is traveling down river, the current pushes the boat so that its rate is $10 + 4 = 14$ mph. When the boat travels up river, the current holds the boat back, and its rate is $10 - 4 = 6$ mph. The same principle applies to planes and wind, as illustrated in our last example.

EXAMPLE 8

The jet stream travels from west to east across the Pacific Ocean, and on a certain day its speed is 30 mph. In the morning a small plane travels with the jet steam from Seattle to Spokane, Washington, in 1 hour and 30 minutes. On the return trip that afternoon, the plane is 45 miles from Seattle after 2 hours. What is the speed of the plane in still air (that is, without the jet stream)?

SOLUTION   Let r = the speed of the plane in still air. Then $r + 30$ = its rate from Seattle to Spokane, and $r - 30$ = its rate on the return trip; 1 hour and 30 minutes = 1.5 hours (let Se = Seattle, Sp = Spokane). (See table and Figure 2.19).

	Rate • Time = Distance		
Se to Sp	$r + 30$	1.5	$1.5(r + 30)$
Sp to Se	$r - 30$	2	$2(r - 30)$

FIGURE 2.19

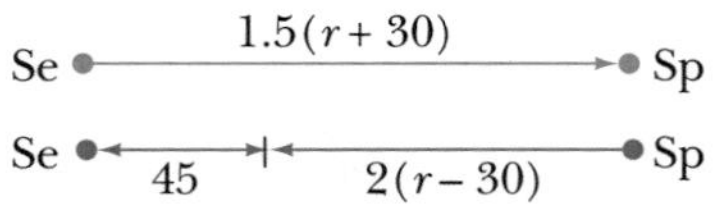

The distance traveled in 1.5 hours from Seattle to Spokane is equal to the distance traveled in 2 hours on the return trip plus 45 miles:

$$1.5(r + 30) = 2(r - 30) + 45$$
$$1.5r + 45 = 2r - 60 + 45$$
$$-.5r + 45 = -15$$
$$-.5r = -60$$
$$r = 120$$

Thus, the speed of the plane in still air is 120 mph.

Calvin and Hobbes   by Bill Watterson

© 1987 Universal Press Syndicate. Reproduced by permission.

EXERCISE SET 2.4

A

1

1. Solve the word problem in Example 1 (page 66) by letting W = the number of votes cast for the winner.

2. Check the solution to Example 2 (page 66).

Solve the following problems.

3. Yoko scored 71 and 85 on her first two algebra tests. What score does she need on the third test to have an average of 80?

4. Dan's first three geometry tests had scores of 61, 71, and 74. What score does he need on the fourth test to have an average of 68?

5. A carpenter must cut a 20-foot board into two pieces so that the shorter piece is 1 foot less than one-half the longer piece. How long is each piece?

6. Carlos earns time and a half for every hour worked over 40 in a week. Last week he worked 46 hours and earned $612.50. What is his normal hourly rate?

7. Chuck gets double time for every hour worked over 40 in a week. Last week he worked 47 hours and earned $459. What is his normal hourly rate?

8. Diane has five times as much money as Paula. If they each had two more dollars, then Diane would have four times as much money as Paula. How much money do they each have?

9. An electrician's bill was $84.08. This included $18 for parts and $1.08 for tax; the balance was for 2.5 hours of labor. Find the hourly labor rate.

10. On a physics test the sum of the highest and

lowest scores was 75 points. The highest grade was 3 more than 5 times the lowest grade. Find the two grades.

2

11. Check the solution to Example 4 (page 68).

Solve the following geometry problems.

12. A rectangle's length is 2 feet less than 3 times the width. The perimeter is 36 feet. Find the rectangle's widths, length, and area.

13. The longest side of a triangle is 3 more than the shortest side. The third side is 3 less than twice the shortest side. If the perimeter is 20 inches (in.), what are the lengths of the sides of the triangle?

14. The area of a circle is 16π centimeters squared (cm^2). Find the circle's radius, diameter, and circumference.

15. A square has an area of 12 meters squared (m^2). Find the side and perimeter of the square.

16. One base of a trapezoid is 4 times the length of the other base, the other two sides are 3 meters and 6 meters, and the perimeter is 19 meters. Find the two bases.

17. One side of a triangle is one-sixth the perimeter, the second side is two less than one-half the perimeter, and the third side is 14 feet. Find the triangle's perimeter and other two sides.

18. Two circles have radii that are consecutive even integers and combined circumferences of 36π meters. Find each circle's radius and area.

19. The side of an **equilateral triangle** (three equal sides and three equal angles) is 2 more than the side of a square. The perimeter of the square is 1 less than the perimeter of the triangle. Find the sides of both figures.

20. Find the angles of a triangle if they are consecutive integers.

21. The second angle of a triangle is twice the first, and the third angle is 5° more than the second. Find the three angles.

22. The two equal angles of an isosceles triangle are called the **base angles**. The third angle of an isosceles triangle is 20° more than three times the base angle. Find the three angles.

23. One angle of a triangle is 60°. Find the other two angles if their difference is 20°.

24. Two angles are complementary; their difference is 50°. Find the two angles.

25. One angle is 3/4 its complement. Find the two angles.

26. Two supplementary angles are consecutive odd integers. Find the angles.

27. Two angles are suplementary, and one is 5° more than twice the other. Find the angles.

28. The supplement of an angle is 25° more than twice its complement. Find the three angles.

29. The complement of an angle is 20° less than one-half its supplement. Find the three angles.

30. The volume of a rectangular solid is 150 m³, its length is 6 meters, and its width is equal to its height. Find the solid's width, height, and surface area.

31. A **cube** is a rectangular solid with $L = W = H$. Find the volume and surface area of a cube with an edge of 3 centimeters.

32. Find the radius of a sphere with a surface area of 72π inches squared ($in.^2$). Find its volume.

33. The **slant height**, s, of a right circular cone is 6 times its radius; the cone's surface area is 28π centimeters squared (cm^2). Find its radius, slant height, height, and volume.

3

34. Check the solution to Example 7 (page 69).

35. Check the solution to Example 8 (page 70).

36. Solve the word problem in Example 6 (page 69) by letting $T = $ the time spent traveling at 52 mph.

Solve the following motion problems.

37. Solve the word problem in the Calvin cartoon on page 71.

38. Ted drove 245 miles in 5.5 hours. The second part of his trip took 2 hours and 30 minutes, and he drove 10 mph faster than during the first part of the trip. What was his speed during the first part of the trip?

39. A truck leaves Portland, Maine, at a speed of 40 mph. One hour later a car leaves Portland and travels the same route as the truck at 45 mph. How long will it take for the car to overtake the truck?

40. Thirty minutes after a cruiser leaves Miami, Florida, a motorboat follows at 15 mph faster than the cruiser. If the motorboat takes one hour to overtake the cruiser, what is the cruiser's speed?

41. At 9 A.M. a plane flies east from London at 512 mph. At 10:30 A.M. a second plane leaves London and travels west at 480 mph. At what time are the two planes 1152 miles apart?

42. Towns A and B are 112 miles apart. A truck leaves A for B at the same time that a car leaves B for A, and they pass each other after two hours. If the car travels 8 mph faster than the truck, what is the truck's speed?

43. A car and a truck leave the same point at the same time and travel in the same direction. The car's speed is 56 km/h, and the speed of the truck is 42 km/h. How long does it take for the car to be 49 km ahead of the truck?

44. Juliet jogs to school and walks home in 5 hours. If she jogs at 6 mph and walks at 4 mph, how long does it take her to jog to school?

45. A chair lift at Heavenly Valley Resort travels at 10 mph. Sonya needed 16 minutes to ride the lift and then ski under the lift to its base. If she skied at 6 mph, how long did it take her to ride the chair lift? What is its length?

46. Towns A and B are 80 km apart. Ed drove from A to B at 80 km/h and returned to A at 40 km/h. Is 60 km/h his average speed for the entire trip? Justify your answer.

47. A seismograph measures a time interval of 2 minutes 55 seconds between the arrival of an earthquake's P and S waves. P waves travel at 8 km/sec and S waves at 4.5 km/sec. Determine the time it took each wave to reach the seismic station and the distance from the focus of the earthquake to the seismic station.

48. P waves travel 2.3 miles per second faster than S waves. The 1985 Mexico City earthquake produced P waves and S waves that took 9 minutes 20 seconds and 17 minutes 0 seconds respectively, to reach a seismograph in the United States. Find the speeds of the two waves in miles per second. How many miles are between Mexico City and the seismic station?

49. With a tail wind of 10 mph, a small jet requires 6 hours to fly from Vancouver to Winnipeg. The return trip against the wind takes 6.5 hours. Find the jet's speed in still air.

50. The speed of Mike's plane in still air is 180 mph. With a tail wind he flies from Las Vegas to Albuquerque in 2 hours and 30 minutes. On returning against the wind, he is 130 miles from Las Vegas after 3 hours. What is the wind's speed?

51. Anne's motor boat travels 9 mph in still water. She made a trip downstream in 40 minutes. On the return trip she was 2 miles from her starting point after one hour. Find the speed of the current.

B

52. A vertical pole is placed in the ground at Granite Pass, Wyoming, to measure snow accumulation. If 1/8 of the pole is in the ground, 3/4 is in snow, and 2 feet are above snow, how long is the pole? How deep is the snow?

53. Is it possible for the angles of a triangle to be three consecutive odd integers? Justify your answer.

54. A rectangular piece of cardboard is 20 centimeters long and 14 centimeters wide. A square 2 centimeters by 2 centimeters is cut from each corner and the resulting sides are turned up to form a box. What is the volume of the box?

55. The legs of an isosceles right triangle are 6 centimeters long. A right circular cone is produced by revolving the triangle around one of its legs. Find the cone's volume and surface area.

56. Felix can run a mile in 4 minutes, and Joe can run it in 5 minutes. They start a one-mile race at the same time. When is Joe 3 times farther from the finish line than Felix?

57. Karen lives 41 miles northwest of Mark. Twenty minutes after Karen starts cycling due south, Mark starts walking due west. Karen cycles 4 times as fast as Mark walks. They meet 3 hours after Mark starts walking. How fast does Mark walk? How far does each travel?

Answer the following questions with complete sentences.

58. What is the difference between complementary and supplementary angles?

59. Discuss how rates of travel are affected by such forces as wind and current.

REVIEW EXERCISES

Answer the following questions. (See Section 2.2.)

60. If the sum of two numbers is 8500 and one of them is x, what is the other number?

61. If the sum of two numbers is 30 and one of them is $2n + 2$, what is the other number?

Express each of the following as a decimal. (See Section 2.2.)

62. $4\frac{1}{6}$ **63.** $6\frac{1}{4}$ **64.** $2\frac{3}{5}$ **65.** $3\frac{1}{3}$

2.5 OTHER WORD PROBLEMS

1	Solving Coin Problems
2	Solving Age Problems
3	Solving Percent and Investment Problems
4	Solving Mixture Problems

1 Solving Coin Problems

This section continues our study of word problems. Most of this material reviews topics covered in elementary algebra. The checks for example solutions are left as exercises.

Problems involving money (coins or paper), stamps, or other objects of monetary value are called **coin problems**. Remember to distinguish between the objects themselves and their monetary value.

EXAMPLE 1

Paul has 30 pennies, nickels, and dimes worth $1.39. He has two more dimes than nickels. How many of each type of coin does he have?

SOLUTION   Let n = the number of nickels. Then, $n + 2$ = the number of dimes, and $2n + 2$ = the total number of nickels and dimes. Because there is a total of 30 coins,
$30 - (2n + 2) = 28 - 2n$ = the number of pennies.

$1(28 - 2n) =$ the value of the pennies in cents
$5n =$ the value of the nickels in cents and
$10(n + 2) =$ the value of the dimes in cents.
The total value of all the coins is 139 cents, so

$$1(28 - 2n) + 5n + 10(n + 2) = 139$$
$$28 - 2n + 5n + 10n + 20 = 139$$
$$13n + 48 = 139$$
$$13n = 91$$
$$n = 7 = \text{the number of nickels,}$$
$$n + 2 = 9 = \text{the number of dimes, and}$$
$$28 - 2n = 14 = \text{the number of pennies}$$

Paul has 14 pennies, 7 nickels, and 9 dimes.

 **COMMON ERROR**   A common mistake is to express one side of an equation in cents and the other side in dollars. In Example 1, $1(28 - 2n) + 5n + 10(n + 2) \neq 1.39$.

EXAMPLE 2

Is it possible to change a \$10 bill into an equal number of nickels, dimes, and quarters? If so, how many of each kind of coin would be needed?

SOLUTION   Let x represent the number of nickels, the number of dimes, and the number of quarters needed (assuming a solution exists). Then,
$5x =$ the value of the nickels in cents,
$10x =$ the value of the dimes in cents, and
$25x =$ the value of the quarters in cents.
The total value of the coins is $\$10 = 1000¢$, so

$$5x + 10x + 25x = 1000$$
$$40x = 1000$$
$$x = 25$$

Thus, a \$10 bill can be changed into 25 nickels, 25 dimes, and 25 quarters.

2 Solving Age Problems

Age problems usually refer to two or more individuals' ages at different times, and we are required to find their ages at a specific time, which is often the present. The general approach is to use a variable to represent current ages. If we need their ages a specific number of years in the future, we add that number to their current ages. For example, if $k =$ Kathy's age now, then $k + 4$ represents her age 4 years from now. A chart is often helpful in organizing the information.

EXAMPLE 3

Steve is 9 years older than Kathy. In 4 years he will be twice her age. Find their present ages.

(continued)

SOLUTION   Let k = Kathy's age now. Then $k + 9$ = Steve's age now.

	Now	4 Years from Now
Kathy	k	$k + 4$
Steve	$k + 9$	$(k + 9) + 4 = k + 13$

In 4 years Steve's age will be twice Kathy's age, so
$$k + 13 = 2(k + 4)$$
$$k + 13 = 2k + 8$$
$$k = 5$$
Kathy is 5 years old, and Steve is 14 years old.

EXAMPLE 4

Seven years from how Susan will be 3 times as old as Juan was five years ago. The sum of their current ages is 38. How old are they now?

SOLUTION   Let s = Susan's age now. Then $38 - s$ = Juan's age now.

	Now	7 Years from Now	5 Years Ago
Susan	s	$s + 7$	
Juan	$38 - s$		$(38 - s) - 5 = 33 - s$

Susan's age in 7 years, $s + 7$, will be 3 times Juan's age 5 years ago, $33 - s$. Thus,
$$s + 7 = 3(33 - s)$$
$$s + 7 = 99 - 3s$$
$$4s = 92$$
$$s = 23, \quad \text{so } 38 - s = 15.$$
Susan is 23 years old, and Juan is 15 years old.

3   Solving Percent and Investment Problems

In certain situations we need to express a fraction as a decimal. In other cases a percent is preferable. Because *percent* means "per hundred," we must write 3/4 as a fraction with a denominator of 100 to convert it to a percent:

$$\frac{3}{4} = .75 = \frac{75}{100} = 75\%$$

Many problems involving percent can be expressed in the form

$$x\% \text{ of } y \text{ is } z \qquad \text{or} \qquad \frac{x}{100} \cdot y = z$$

Given any two of these variables we can find the third.

Math in Time

BY 3000 B.C. the Hindus had developed basic mathematics and engineering skills. The main contributions of Indian mathematicians were made between A.D. 450 and 1150. They invented zero and negative numbers, solved word problems similar to the ones in modern texts, and made contributions to algebra, geometry, and trigonometry. The Hindus were fond of puzzle problems, which were written in verse. The following are three examples of the types of problems they used for entertainment.

1. Two ascetics lived at the top of a cliff of height 100, whose base was a distance of 200 from a village. One ascetic descended the cliff and walked to the village. The other, being a wizard, flew up a certain distance and then flew in a straight line to the village. If the distance traveled by each was the same, how high did the wizard fly? (Brahmagupa A.D. 630) Answer: 50.

2. A powerful, unvanquished, excellent black snake, which is 80 angulas in length, enters into a hole at the rate of 15/2 angulas in 5/14 of a day, and in the course of 1/4 of a day its tail grows 11/4 of an angula. O ornament of arithmeticians, tell me by what time this serpent enters fully into the hole? (Mahavira A.D. 850) Answer: 8 days.

3. The square root of half the number of bees in a swarm has flown out upon a jessamine bush, 8/9 of the swarm has remained behind; one female bee flies about a male that is buzzing within a lotus flower into which he was allured in the night by its sweet odor but now is imprisoned in. Tell me, most enchanting lady, the number of bees. (Bhaskara A.D. 1150) Answer: 72 bees.

EXAMPLE 5

Solve the following problems.

a. 32 is 40% of what number?
b. 30.6 is what percent of 360?

SOLUTION

a. 40% of y is 32, or

$.4y = 32$

$y = 80$, so 40% of 80 is 32.

$$40\% = \frac{40}{100} = .4$$

b. $x\%$ of 360 is 30.6, or

$.01x(360) = 30.6$

$3.6x = 30.6$

$x = 8.5$, so 8.5% of 360 is 30.6.

$$x\% = \frac{x}{100} = .01x$$

Many consumer problems involving percent can be solved by reducing them to algebraic equations. Two common types deal with *selling price* and *sale price*. The basic concepts are

$$\text{cost} + \text{profit} = \text{selling price}$$
$$\text{original price} - \text{discount} = \text{sale price}$$

EXAMPLE 6

A sofa was marked down 35% to $698.75. What was the sofa's original price?

SOLUTION

Let x = the original price of the sofa. Then, $.35x$ = 35% of x = the discount, and

$x - .35x = 698.75$	$x - .35x =$
$.65x = 698.75$	$1x - .35x =$
$x = 1075$	$(1 - .35)x = .65x$

The original price of the sofa was $1075.

COMMON ERROR

Mistakes are often made in solving discount problems. In Example 6,

$$x - .35 \neq 698.75 \quad \text{and} \quad x \neq 698.75 + .35(698.75)$$

Investment problems commonly involve two amounts of money invested at different rates of interest. We are given relationships between the amounts invested and the interest earned. Then we are asked to determine how much is invested at each rate. It is important to distinguish between the amounts invested and the interest earned.

EXAMPLE 7

Gail inherited $8500. She invested part of it in a mutual fund at 12% and the rest in bonds at 7.5%. The annual interest earned from the mutual funds was $45 more than the income earned from the bonds. How much did she invest at each rate?

SOLUTION

Let x = the amount invested at 12%. Then,
$8500 - x$ = the amount invested at 7.5%.
$.12x$ = the interest earned at 12%, and
$.075(8500 - x)$ = the interest earned at 7.5%.
The interest earned at 12% was $45 more than the interest earned at 7.5%, so

$$.12x = .075(8500 - x) + 45$$
$$1000(.12x) = 1000[.075(8500 - x) + 45]$$
$$120x = 75(8500 - x) + 45,000$$
$$120x = 637,500 - 75x + 45,000$$
$$195x = 682,500$$
$$x = 3500, \quad \text{and} \quad 8500 - x = 5000.$$

Thus, Gail invested $3500 at 12% and $5000 at 7.5%.

4 Solving Mixture Problems

Manufacturers often mix different goods to sell at a given price. Mixed nuts, processed cheese, and house paint are examples. The first type of mixture problem that we consider involves *prices*. In the usual problem two quantities and their prices per unit are specified. We are asked to mix them in such a way to produce a given amount at a given price. It is important to distinguish between the amount and the value of the quantities.

EXAMPLE 8

A merchant has peanuts worth \$2 a pound that she wishes to mix with 30 pounds of cashews worth \$6 a pound to get a mixture worth \$5 a pound. How many pounds of peanuts are needed?

SOLUTION

Let p = the number of pounds of peanuts needed. Then,
$p + 30$ = the number of pounds in the mixture.
$2p$ = the value of the peanuts,
$6(30)$ = the value of the cashews, and
$5(p + 30)$ = the value of the mixture.
The value of the peanuts plus the value of the cashews is equal to the value of the mixture:

$$2p + 6(30) = 5(p + 30)$$
$$2p + 180 = 5p + 150$$
$$-3p = -30$$
$$p = 10$$

Thus, 10 pounds of peanuts are needed.

We now consider mixture problems dealing with percent. In the following example two acid solutions of different concentrations are combined to produce a mixture with a third concentration. These problems involve two important concepts: the amounts in the different solutions and the amount of pure ingredient in each solution (pure acid, pure salt, and so on). A picture illustrating the situation before and after mixing can be helpful.

EXAMPLE 9

One solution is 30% acid, and a second solution is 20% acid (Figure 2.20). How many liters of each should be mixed to produce 25 liters of 28% acid?

FIGURE 2.20

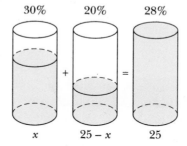

SOLUTION

Let x = the number of liters of the 30% solution;
$25 - x$ = the number of liters of the 20% solution;
$.30x$ = the amount of pure acid in the 30% solution;
$.20(25 - x)$ = the amount of pure acid in the 20% solution; and
$.28(25)$ = the amount of pure acid in the 28% mixture.
The amount of pure acid in the 30% solution plus the amount of pure acid in the 20% solution is equal to the amount of pure acid in the 28% mixture:

$$.30x + .20(25 - x) = .28(25) \quad \text{Multiply by 100.}$$
$$30x + 20(25 - x) = 28(25)$$
$$30x + 500 - 20x = 700$$
$$10x = 200$$
$$x = 20, \quad \text{and } 25 - x = 5. \text{ Thus, we need to mix 20 liters}$$

of the 30% solution and 5 liters of the 20% solution.

In some situations distilled water is added to dilute a solution. In such a case the amount of pure ingredient before and after mixing is the same. One could also add pure ingredient to strengthen a mixture. This second case is illustrated in our concluding example.

EXAMPLE 10

A 20-quart radiator full of water and antifreeze contains 25% antifreeze. How much of this mixture must be drained out and replaced with pure antifreeze to increase the concentration to 40% antifreeze?

SOLUTION   Let x = the amount of mixture that must be drained. Then $20 - x$ quarts are left in the radiator. Also, x = the amount of pure antifreeze that must be added. Figure 2.21 shows the problem at the point when $20 - x$ quarts of mixture are in the radiator.

FIGURE 2.21

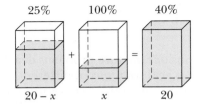

$.25(20 - x)$ = the amount of antifreeze in the 25% solution,
$1.00x = x$ = the amount of antifreeze added,
$.40(20) = 8$ = the amount of antifreeze in the 40% solution, so
$.25(20 - x) + x = 8$
$5 - .25x + x = 8$ $-.25x + x =$
$.75x = 3$ $(-.25 + 1)x$
$x = 4$

Thus, 4 quarts of the mixture must be drained and replaced by 4 quarts of pure antifreeze.

EXERCISE SET 2.5

A

1

1. Check the solution to Example 1 (page 74).

2. Check the solution to Example 2 (page 75).

Solve the following coin problems.

3. Brian has 20 dimes and quarters that total $3.95. How many of each type of coin does he have?

4. Rajesh has 4 times as many 29¢ stamps as 19¢ stamps, for a total of $16.20. How many of each type of stamp does he have?

5. Amy bought 5 more candy bars than packs of gum. The candy bars cost $.35 each and the gum $.20 each. If she spent $3.40, how many packs of gum and bars of candy did she buy?

6. Hamid spent $3.85 for 30 stamps. He bought twice as many 10¢ stamps as 18¢ stamps. The rest were 13¢ stamps. How many of each kind of stamp did he buy?

7. A pay phone's deposit box contains 61 nickels, dimes, and quarters worth $8.15. If 13 nickels are in the collection box, how many dimes and quarters does it contain?

8. Judith has 17 $5 and $10 bills. If the number of $10 bills is 1 less than twice the number of $5 bills, how many $5 and $10 bills does she have?

9. A music teacher's collection of classical music includes 109 CDs of Haydn, Beethoven, and Mozart works. The number of Beethoven CDs is 9 less than twice the number of Haydn CDs, and the number of Mozart CDs is 17 more than the number of Beethoven CDs. How many CDs does the teacher have of each composer?

10. Is it possible to change a $10 bill into an equal number of half-dollars, quarters, and dimes? If so, how many of each kind of coin would be needed?

11. Is it possible to change a $20 bill into an equal number of nickels, dimes, and quarters? If so, how many of each kind of coin would be needed?

12. At a school play the price of admission was $2 for a child and $5 for an adult. A total of 383 tickets were sold for $1252. How many child and adult tickets were sold?

13. A museum has three admission prices: $1.50 for children, $4 for adults, and $2 for seniors. On a Sunday 395 tickets were sold for a total of $1000. Thirty more children's tickets than adult tickets were sold. How many of each type of ticket was sold?

14. A performance of *King Lear* had three admission prices: $22 for adults, $16 for seniors, and $13 for students. The theater sold 5 times as many adult tickets as student tickets and 120 fewer senior tickets than adult tickets. The adult tickets brought in $3127 more than the combined value of the student and senior tickets. How many of each type of ticket was sold?

2

15. Check the solution to Example 3 (page 75).
16. Check the solution to Example 4 (page 76).

Solve the following age problems.

17. Bob is now twice as old as his son. Fifteen years ago he was three times as old. Find their current ages.

18. Guido is now 4 times as old as Teresa. In 22 years Guido will be twice as old as Teresa will be then. How old is each person now?

19. Al's age is now two-fifths of Betty's age. Eight years ago Al's age was two-ninths of Betty's age. Find their current ages.

20. Jim's father is 26 years older than Jim. In 10 years the sum of their ages will be 80. Find their current ages.

21. Sixteen years ago Joshua was one-fourth as old as he will be two years from now. How old is he now?

22. The difference between Ken's mother's age and his age is 23 years. In 12 years she will be 3 times as old as he was 5 years ago. Find their current ages.

23. Bob is 30 years old, which is 3 times Sharon's age. When will his age be twice her age?

24. Mark is 30 years old, which is 12 years older than Beth. How long ago was his age 3 years less than twice her age?

25. Thomas Jefferson was born 11 years after George Washington. In 1762 Washington's age was 3 years more than 3 times Jefferson's age in 1752. How old was each man in 1755?

26. Joseph Haydn was born 24 years before Wolfgang Mozart. In 1760 Haydn was 16 years older than one-half Mozart's age in 1780. How old was each man in 1776?

3

27. Check the solution to Example 6 (page 78).
28. Check the solution to Example 7 (page 78).

Express the following as percents:

29. 91   **30.** 2.03   **31.** $2\frac{3}{5}$ **32.** $3\frac{1}{3}$

Express the following as both decimals and fractions in reduced form.

33. 16%   **34.** 125%   **35.** 2.7%   **36.** $\frac{1}{5}$%

Solve the following problems.

37. What is 25% of 16?
38. 36 is what percent of 240?
39. 9 is what percent of 600?
40. 77 is 22% of what number?

Solve the following problems.

41. Dan's scores on three algebra tests are 66%, 74%, and 78%. What score must he get on the fourth test to have an average of 76%?

42. On a test of 80 questions a student got 52 correct. What percent were correct?

43. On a test of 125 questions Gary got 10 wrong. What percent were correct?

44. Diane spends $688 a month for rent. This is 32% of her monthly income. Find her monthly income.

45. A pair of skis was marked down 55% to $125.10. Find the skis' original price.

46. Solve the word problem in Example 7 (page 78) by letting *y* = the amount invested at 7.5%.

47. A ski shop marked up a pair of bindings 80% and sold them for $116.60. How much did the bindings cost the shop?

48. When water is frozen, its volume increases by 9%. How much water would produce 450 cubic centimeters (cc) of ice to the nearest cubic centimeter?

49. Shing invested part of $10,000 at 9% and the rest at 13%. The total annual interest earned from the two investments was $1152. How much did he invest at each rate?

50. Gary invested a certain amount of money at 11%. He invested $3000 more than this amount at 15%. How much would he have to invest at 11% to have an annual income of $2530?

51. Katerina invested a certain amount of money at 8% and 3 times that amount at 15%. The interest earned from the 15% investment was $20 more than 5 times the amount earned at 8%. How much did she invest at each rate?

52. Terry invested $10,000 at 8%. How much would he have to invest at 14% so that his total interest per year would equal 10% of the two investments?

53. Carol invested $15,000. She put part of the sum in a relative's business venture and lost 5%. She put the rest in stocks and made 12%. The net result was a profit of $270. How much was in each investment?

54. Steve invested $10,000. He put part of it in bonds and the rest in a gold mine stock. He made an 8% profit on the bonds but took a 10% loss on the stock. The net result was a loss of $280. How much was in each investment?

4

55. Check the solution to Example 8 (page 79).

56. Check the solution to Example 9 (page 79)?

57. Check the solution to Example 10 (page 80).

Solve the following mixture problems.

58. The owner of a market is going to mix pecans that are worth $2.40 per pound with peanuts that are worth $1.10 per pound to get 30 pounds of a mixture worth $1.75 per pound. How many pounds of each kind of nut must he use?

59. A 100-pound mixture of Delicious and Jonathan apples costs $22. If the Delicious apples costs 20¢ per pound and the Jonathan apples cost 25¢ per pound, how many pounds of each kind of apple are in the mixture?

60. A coffee merchant blended coffee worth 93¢ a pound with one-half that number of pounds of coffee worth $1.20 a pound to produce a mixture worth $30.60. How many pounds of the 93¢ coffee must she use?

61. Karl is going to mix 45 pounds of Valencia oranges worth 30¢ a pound with 5 pounds of Navel oranges to produce a mixute worth 29¢ a pound. What is the cost per pound of the Navel oranges?

62. Solve the word problem in Example 9 (page 79) by letting *y* = the number of liters of the 20% solution?

63. A nurse mixes 30 cubic centimeters of a 50% saline solution with a 10% saline solution to produce a 25% saline solution. How many cubic centimeters of the 10% solution are needed?

64. A chemist mixes 20 liters of a 4% acid solution with a 10% acid solution to produce 30 liters of a mixture. What is the percent of acid in the resulting mixture?

65. How much pure acid should be added to 5 gallons of a 20% acid solution to increase its strength to 25% acid?

66. Four liters of pure water are added to 1 liter of a 20% acid solution. What percent acid is the final solution?

67. How many liters of water must be evaporated from 60 liters of a 5% salt solution to obtain a 25% salt solution?

68. How many cubic centimeters of water must be evaporated from 9 cubic centimeters of a 3% boric acid solution to obtain a 4% boric acid solution?

69. A pharmacist has 20 liters of a 20% betadine solution. How many liters of this should be drained and replaced with 100% betadine to obtain a 40% betadine solution?

70. A 4-gallon radiator full of water and antifreeze contains 40% antifreeze. How much of this mixture must be drained out and replaced with pure antifreeze to increase the concentration to 50% antifreeze?

71. A 12-liter radiator full of water and antifreeze contains 80% antifreeze. How much of this mixture must be drained and replaced with water to decrease the mixture's concentration to 60% antifreeze?

72. A chemist has 30 liters of a 70% acid solution. How much of this mixture must be drained and replaced with distilled water to obtain 30 liters of a 56% acid solution?

B

73. A pharmacist must fill a prescription calling for 5 ounces of a 12% argyrol solution. She has 5 ounces of a 15% solution and 5 ounces of a 5% solution. If she starts with the 15% solution, how much must she drain and replace with the 5% solution in order to fill the prescription?

74. Jan has a collection of coins worth $9.13. She has twice as many dimes as quarters, four more nickels than dimes, and twice as many pennies as nickels. How many coins of each type does she have?

75. In a group of 180 men, one-half as many men are more than 40 years of age as there are men between 30 and 40, and one-third as many men between 30 and 40 as there are men under 30. How many men are in each age group?

76. Steve is six years older than Marilyn. He is also twice as old as Marilyn was when he was Marilyn's current age. How old is each person now?

77. Larry invested $27,000, part at 8%, twice that amount at 9.25%, and the rest at 16%. The total annual income was $2815. How much did he invest at each rate?

78. Solve problem 1 in the Math in Time section (page 77).

79. The third part of a necklace of pearls, broken in an amorous embrace, fell to the ground; its fifth part rested on the couch; the sixth part was saved by the woman; and the tenth part was taken by her lover; six pearls remained strung. Say, of how many pearls was the necklace composed? (Hindu problem; A.D. 750.)

C

Answer the following questions with complete sentences.

80. Discuss the Hindu contributions to mathematics.

81. What are the two main concepts involved in solving an investment problem?

82. What are the two main concepts involved in solving a mixture problem dealing with percent?

REVIEW EXERCISES

Use either < or > to make the following statements true. (See Section 1.2.)

83. 4 ____ 10

84. −8 ____ −20

85. −6 ____ 5

Classify each of the following equations as an *identity, false equation,* or *conditional equation.* (See Section 2.1.)

86. $3 - 4x = 27$ 87. $3(2x) = 6x$

88. $4(2x - 3) = 8x$

Let A = {1, 2, 3},   B = {3, 5, 7, 9},   and C = {5, 9}. Find the following unions and intersections. (See Section 1.1.)

89. A ∪ B   **90.** B ∪ C

91. A ∩ B   **92.** A ∩ C

2.6 LINEAR INEQUALITIES

1	**Interval Notation and Properties of Inequalities**
2	**Solving Linear Inequalities**
3	**Solving Compound and Continued Inequalities**
4	**Solving Word Problems**

1 Interval Notation and Properties of Inequalities

Many problems are solved with inequalities rather than with equations. In this section we will cover the methods of solving linear inequalities in one variable and use them to solve word problems. **Linear inequalities** are expressions such as

$$x + 6 < 2, \qquad 4 - 2y \geq 7, \qquad \text{and} \qquad 6t - 1 > 2t + 7$$

We begin by introducing interval notation. In our study of inequalities we deal with **intervals of real numbers**. A *bounded interval* is the set of all real numbers bounded by two real numbers, which are called *endpoints*. An example is $-2 < x < 1$; this is read "x is greater than -2 and less than 1." This inequality is called an **open interval** because it does not contain its endpoints of -2 and 1. In **interval notation** parentheses are used to indicate this, and $-2 < x < 1$ is written $(-2, 1)$. To graph $(-2, 1)$ we place open circles at -2 and 1 to indicate that they are not in the interval. Then we shade the number line between -2 and 1 to represent all real numbers bounded by these points (Figure 2.22).

FIGURE 2.22

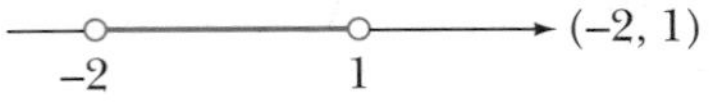

If an interval contains its endpoints, then it is called a **closed interval**. An example is $2 \leq x \leq 4$; this is read "x is greater than or equal to 2 and less than or equal to 4." In interval notation brackets are used to indicate that the endpoints are included in the set, and $2 \leq x \leq 4$ is written $[2, 4]$. In graphing $[2, 4]$, closed circles are placed at 2 and 4 to show that these points are in the interval. Then the number line between these points is shaded (Figure 2.23).

FIGURE 2.23

If an interval contains one endpoint but not the other, then it is called **half-open** (or half-closed). An example is $-1 < x \le 3$; this is written $(-1, 3]$ in interval notation and is graphed in Figure 2.24.

FIGURE 2.24

An interval such as $x > 2$ is called *unbounded* because it continues forever to the right of 2. The symbol for infinity, ∞,* is used to write $x > 2$ in interval notation; that is, $x > 2$ is written $(2, \infty)$. Note that ∞ is *not* a number; it is used to indicate that no largest number exists in the interval $x > 2$; therefore, a bracket is not placed around ∞. In a similar way, $x \le 1$ is written $(-\infty, 1]$. The symbols ∞ and $-\infty$ are read "positive infinity" and "negative infinity." Both $(2, \infty)$ and $(-\infty, 1]$ are graphed in Figure 2.25.

FIGURE 2.25

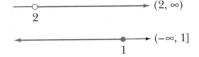

Sometimes set-builder notation is used to describe intervals, as illustrated in Example 1.

EXAMPLE 1

Write the following sets in interval notation and graph them on a number line (Figure 2.26).

a. $\{x \mid -3 \le x < 0\}$ **b.** $\{y \mid y \ge -1\}$

FIGURE 2.26

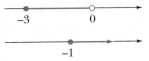

SOLUTION **a.** $[-3, 0)$
b. $[-1, \infty)$

Figure 2.27 on page 86 provides a summary of interval notation.

The methods for solving a linear inequality are very similar to those for solving a linear equation. For instance, to solve $x - 2 < 6$, we need to add 2 to both sides of the inequality. In general, we can add the same number) to both sides of an inequality (or subtract the same number) to produce an equivalent inequality. Throughout this section the properties are stated for

---

* English mathematician John Wallis (1616–1703) was the first person to use this symbol for infinity.

<; they are also valid if < is replaced by ≤, >, or ≥; for example

$$x - 2 < 6, \quad \text{so} \quad (x - 2) + 2 < 6 + 2, \quad \text{or} \quad x < 8$$

$$x + 3 < 8, \quad \text{so} \quad (x + 3) - 3 < 8 - 3, \quad \text{or} \quad x < 5$$

FIGURE 2.27

Interval Notation	Inequality Notation	Graph
(a, b)	$a < x < b$	
$[a, b]$	$a \le x \le b$	
$(a, b]$	$a < x \le b$	
$[a, b)$	$a \le x < b$	
(a, ∞)	$x > a$	
$[a, \infty)$	$x \ge a$	
$(-\infty, a)$	$x < a$	
$(-\infty, a]$	$x \le a$	
$(-\infty, \infty)$	$\{x \mid x \in \mathbb{R}\}$	

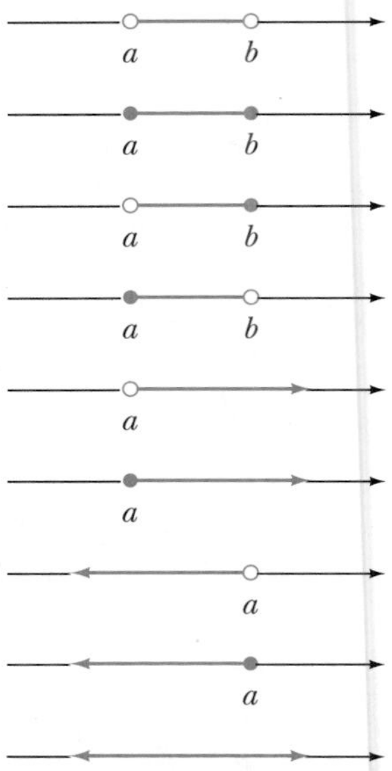

Addition–Subtraction Property of Inequality

Let $a, b, c \in \mathbb{R}$.
If $a < b$, then $a + c < b + c$ and $a - c < b - c$.

To solve inequalities such as $\frac{x}{3} < -12$ and $-2x \ge 8$ we need the multiplication–division property of inequality. This property says that if we multiply (or divide) both sides of an inequality by a positive number, c, then we do not change the inequality symbol. However, if c is negative, then we must reverse the inequality symbol. For example,

$c > 0$	$3 < 5$	$-8 \le -3$	$6 > -2$
	$2(3) < 2(5)$	$3(-8) \le 3(-3)$	$4(6) > 4(-2)$
	$6 < 10$	$-24 \le -9$	$24 > -8$
$c < 0$	$3 < 5$	$-8 \le -3$	$6 > -2$
	$-2(3) > -2(5)$	$-3(-8) \ge -3(-3)$	$-4(6) < -4(-2)$
	$-6 > -10$	$24 \ge 9$	$-24 < 8$

Multiplication–Division Property of Inequality

Let $a, b, c \in \mathbb{R}$.

If $a < b$ and $c > 0$, then $ac < bc$ and $\dfrac{a}{c} < \dfrac{b}{c}$.

If $a < b$ and $c < 0$, then $ac > bc$ and $\dfrac{a}{c} > \dfrac{b}{c}$.

EXAMPLE 2

Solve the following inequalities and write the answers in interval notation.

a. $\dfrac{x}{3} < -12$ **b.** $-2x \geq 8$

SOLUTION **a.** $\dfrac{x}{3} < -12$ **b.** $-2x \geq 8$

$3 \cdot \dfrac{x}{3} < 3(-12)$ $\dfrac{-2x}{-2} \leq \dfrac{8}{-2}$ Reverse $\geq$; $-2 < 0$.

$x < -36$ $x \leq -4$

$(-\infty, -36)$ $(-\infty, -4]$

---

2   Solving Linear Inequalities

In Section 2.1 [2] we discussed three types of linear equations: an *identity* (or *true equation*), a *false equation*, and a *conditional equation*. Inequalities have the same type of solution sets; for example,

---

Identity: $x + 1 > x$; true for all real numbers x.
False: $x^2 < 0$; false for all real numbers x.
Conditional: $x \geq 5$; true if $x = 6$, and false if $x = 4$.

The following example illustrates the methods of solving general linear inequalities. They are the same as for linear equations, except for multiplying or dividing by a negative number.

EXAMPLE 3

Solve the following inequalities; write your answers in interval notation and graph them (Figures 2.28, 2.29, 2.30).

a. $3 - 4x \leq 27$ **b.** $2(3y - 2) < 7 + 4y - 1$
c. $3(2x - 5) < 6x$

FIGURE 2.28

-6

(continued)

SOLUTION   **a.** $3 - 4x \leq 27$ Add -3.

$$-3 + 3 - 4x \leq -3 + 27$$
$$-4x \leq 24$$ Divide by -4;
$$x \geq -6$$ reverse $<$.
$$[-6, \infty)$$

FIGURE 2.29

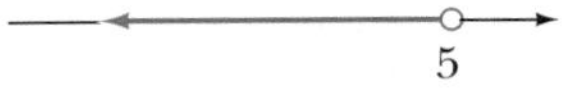

5

b. $2(3y - 2) < 7 + 4y - 1$ Simplify.
$$6y - 4 < 6 + 4y$$ Add $-4y$.
$$-4y + 6y - 4 < 6 + 4y - 4y$$
$$2y - 4 < 6$$ Add 4.
$$2y < 10$$ Divide by 2.
$$y < 5$$
$$(-\infty, 5)$$

FIGURE 2.30

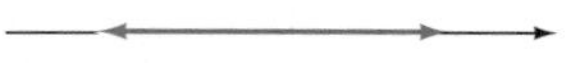

c. $3(2x - 5) < 6x$
$$6x - 15 < 6x$$ Add $-6x$.
$$-6x + 6x - 15 < -6x + 6x$$
$$-15 < 0, \text{ which is a true statement.}$$

Thus, $3(2x - 5) < 6x$ is an identity, so $S = \mathbb{R} = (-\infty, \infty)$ is the solution set.

---

3   Solving Compound and Continued Inequalities

The words *or* and *and* are used in mathematics to write **compound statements**. In Section 1.1 [3] we covered two types: the union and the intersection of sets.

Recall that the union of the sets A and B, A $\cup$ B, is the set of all elements that are in either A *or* B. For example, if A = {2, 3} and B = {3, 4}, then A $\cup$ B = {2, 3, 4}. As an English example of a compound statement, suppose Ted says, "Today I will go to the bookstore *or* I will go to the library." This is a true statement if Ted goes only to the bookstore *or* he goes only to the library. It is a false statement if he goes to neither the bookstore nor the library.

In a similar way, **compound inequality** using *or* is true if either statement is true. For example, let A = $\{x \mid x < -2\}$ and B = $\{x \mid x \geq 2\}$. Then, A $\cup$ B = $\{x \mid x < -2$ or $x \geq 2\}$ (Figure 2.31).

FIGURE 2.31

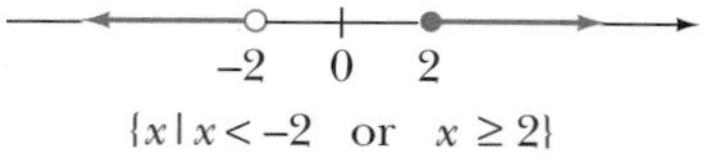

$$-2 \quad 0 \quad 2$$
$$\{x \mid x < -2 \quad \text{or} \quad x \geq 2\}$$

EXAMPLE 4   Let C = $\{x \mid 3 - x < 4\}$ and D = $\{x \mid 2x - 3 \geq -1\}$. Graph C, D, and C $\cup$ D (Figure 2.32).

SOLUTION $C \cup D$ is the compound inequality
$3 - x < 4$ or $2x - 3 \geq -1$. Solve each one for x:

$$-x < 1 \qquad \text{or} \qquad 2x \geq 2$$
$$x > -1 \qquad \text{or} \qquad x \geq 1, \text{ so}$$
$$C = \{x \mid x > -1\}, \quad D = \{x \mid x \geq 1\}, \quad \text{and}$$
$$C \cup D = \{x \mid x > -1 \quad \text{or} \quad x \geq 1\} = \{x \mid x > -1\}.$$

FIGURE 2.32

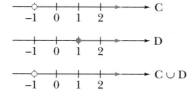

We now turn to compound statements involving *and*. Recall that the intersection of the sets A and B, $A \cap B$, is the set of all elements that are in both A and B. If $A = \{2, 3\}$ and $B = \{3, 4\}$,   then $A \cap B = \{3\}$. Returning to our English example, suppose Ted says, "Today I will go to the bookstore *and* I will go to the library." This is a true statement only if Ted goes to both places. In Example 4, $C = \{x \mid x > -1\}$ and $D = \{x \mid x \geq 1\}$. $C \cap D$ and its graph are shown in Figure 2.33.

$$C \cap D = \{x \mid x > -1 \quad \text{and} \quad x \geq 1\} = \{x \mid x \geq 1\}$$

FIGURE 2.33

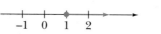

Thus, the graph of $C \cap D$ is the portion of the number line where the graphs of C and D intersect or overlap.

EXAMPLE 5 Solve the following inequalities. Graph **a**   (Figure 2.34).

a. $3y + 1 \geq -5$ and $2y - 4 \leq 2$
b. $1 - 2x > 5$ and $2 + 5x > 12$

SOLUTION **a.** $3y + 1 \geq -5$ and $2y - 4 \leq 2$
$$3y \geq -6 \quad \text{and} \qquad 2y \leq 6$$
$$y \geq -2 \quad \text{and} \qquad y \leq 3$$
which can be written $-2 \leq y \leq 3$

FIGURE 2.34

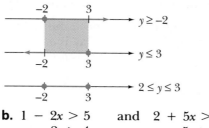

b. $1 - 2x > 5$ and $2 + 5x > 12$
$$-2x > 4 \qquad\qquad\quad 5x > 10$$
$$x < -2 \quad \text{and} \qquad x > 2$$
Now, no number is less than -2 *and* greater than 2. Thus, this is a false inequality and its solution is the empty set, $\varnothing$.

An inequality in the form $a < b < c$ is called a **continued inequality** (or double inequality). Such inequalities are solved as follows.

EXAMPLE 6

Solve each of the following and graph its solution (Figures 2.35 and 2.36).

a. $-1 \le 2x - 3 < 1$ **b.** $-\dfrac{1}{3} < \dfrac{4 - 3x}{2} < \dfrac{1}{6}$

SOLUTION   **a.**

$$-1 \le 2x - 3 < 1 \qquad \text{Add 3 to each term.}$$
$$-1 + 3 \le 2x - 3 + 3 < 1 + 3$$
$$2 \le 2x < 4 \qquad \text{Divide each term by 2.}$$
$$\frac{2}{2} \le \frac{2x}{2} < \frac{4}{2}$$
$$1 \le x < 2$$

FIGURE 2.35

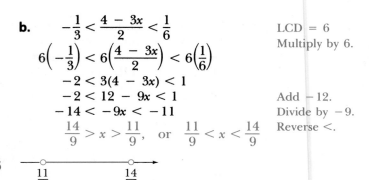

b.
$$-\frac{1}{3} < \frac{4 - 3x}{2} < \frac{1}{6} \qquad \text{LCD} = 6$$
$$\qquad\qquad\qquad\qquad\qquad \text{Multiply by 6.}$$
$$6\left(-\frac{1}{3}\right) < 6\left(\frac{4 - 3x}{2}\right) < 6\left(\frac{1}{6}\right)$$
$$-2 < 3(4 - 3x) < 1$$
$$-2 < 12 - 9x < 1 \qquad \text{Add} -12.$$
$$-14 < -9x < -11 \qquad \text{Divide by } -9.$$
$$\frac{14}{9} > x > \frac{11}{9}, \quad \text{or} \quad \frac{11}{9} < x < \frac{14}{9} \qquad \text{Reverse } <.$$

FIGURE 2.36

4   Solving Word Problems

Many word problems involving inequalities contain phrases such as "is at least," "is at most," and "is between." To solve these problems, we have to choose the inequality symbols that correspond to these phrases.

EXAMPLE 7

Use the variable provided to express the following as inequalities.

a. Susan's age (s) has to be *at least* 18 for her to vote.
b. The temperature (t) today is *at most* 85° F.
c. The cost (c) of the paint is *between* $10 and $15.

SOLUTION   **a.** $s \ge 18$ **b.** $t \le 85$ **c.** $10 < c < 15$

EXAMPLE 8

If the temperature is between $-35°$ C and $-30°$ C inclusive, and the speed of the wind is between 10 and 20 mph, then the windchill factor is between 1650 and 2150 (exposed flesh freezes in one minute). What is this temperature range in Fahrenheit degrees?

SOLUTION $C = \frac{5}{9}(F - 32)$ is the conversion formula we need.

$$-35 \le C \le -30$$

$$-35 \le \frac{5}{9}(F - 32) \le -30$$

$$\frac{9}{5}(-35) \le \frac{9}{5} \cdot \frac{5}{9}(F - 32) \le \frac{9}{5}(-30)$$

$$-63 \le F - 32 \le -54 \qquad \text{Add 32.}$$

$$-31° \le F \le -22°$$

EXAMPLE 9

The average of three consecutive integers is no more than 15. Find their largest possible values.

SOLUTION Let $x, x + 1$, and $x + 2$ represent the integers. Their average is less than or equal to 15. Thus,

$$\frac{x + (x + 1) + (x + 2)}{3} \le 15$$

$$\frac{3x + 3}{3} \le 15 \qquad \frac{3x + 3}{3} = \frac{3x}{3} + \frac{3}{3}$$

$$x + 1 \le 15$$

$$x \le 14$$

If $x = 14$, then $x + 1 = 15$ and $x + 2 = 16$, which are the largest possible values for the integers.

EXAMPLE 10

A dental insurance company offers two types of coverage. With plan A the patient pays $50, and the company pays 60% of the remaining bill. With plan B the patient pays $200, and the company pays 80% of the remaining bill. Find the amounts of dental bills for which plan B is better than plan A.

SOLUTION Let T = the total bill.
Plan A: If the patient pays $50, then the rest of the bill is $T - 50$. If the company pays 60% of $T - 50$, then the patient pays 40% of $T - 50$, or $.4(T - 50)$. Thus, the patient pays a total of:
$50 + .4 (T - 50)$
Plan B: If the patient pays $200, then the company pays 80% of $T - 200$ and the patient pays 20% of $T - 200$, or $.2(T - 200)$. Then the total bill is:
$200 + .2(T - 200)$
We are asked to find the values of T for which plan B cost less than plan A; that is,

$$200 + .2(T - 200) < 50 + .4(T - 50)$$

$$200 + .2T - 40 < 50 + .4T - 20$$

$$.2T + 160 < .4T + 30 \qquad \text{Subtract } .4T.$$

$$-.2T + 160 < 30 \qquad \text{Subtract 160.}$$

$$-.2T < -130 \qquad \text{Divide by } -.2;$$

$$T > 650 \qquad \text{reverse } <.$$

Thus, plan B is better than plan A when the total bill, T, is greater than $650.

EXERCISE SET 2.6

A

1 Write the following in interval notation and then graph each one.

1. $1 < x < 3$ **2.** $1 \leq x \leq 3$

3. $-4 < y \leq -1$ **4.** $-2 \leq t \leq 5$

5. $1 \geq x > -1$ **6.** $x > 3$

7. $x \geq -2$ **8.** $y \leq 1$

9. $y < -4$

Write the following in inequality notation and graph each one.

10. $[-6, -3]$ **11.** $(-1, 2)$

12. $[-2, 4)$ **13.** $(3, 7]$

14. $(0, \infty)$ **15.** $[-2, \infty)$

16. $(-\infty, 4]$ **17.** $(-\infty, -5)$

18. $[-1, \infty)$

Use the appropriate inequality symbol to make each of the following statements true.

19. $5 > -2$ and $5 + 3$ _____ $-2 + 3$

20. $-6 \leq -4$ and $-6 - 1$ _____ $-4 - 1$

21. $6 > -3$ and $4(6)$ _____ $4(-3)$

22. $6 > -3$ and $-4(6)$ _____ $-4(-3)$

23. $-8 < -2$ and $\dfrac{-8}{-2}$ _____ $\dfrac{-2}{-2}$

24. $9 \geq 6$ and $\dfrac{9}{3}$ _____ $\dfrac{6}{3}$

2 Solve the following inequalities and graph their solutions. Write the answers in interval notation.

25. $x - 3 > 1$ **26.** $y + 2 \leq 5$

27. $2x \geq 10$ **28.** $-2x \geq 10$

29. $\dfrac{x}{-3} < -1$ **30.** $\dfrac{3x}{4} > 12$

3

31. $x > 1$ or $x \geq -2$

32. $x > 1$ and $x \geq -2$

33. $t + 1 \leq 3$ and $3t < -3$

34. $t + 1 \leq 3$ or $3t < -3$

35. $x + 1 > 0$ and $2x < 4$

36. $x + 1 > 0$ or $2x < 4$

37. $-12 \leq 4x \leq 12$

38. $-2 < y - 1 < 3$

39. $\{x \mid 6 - x > 8\} \cup \{x \mid 5x - 2 > 13\}$

40. $\{k \mid 4k + 1 \leq k + 13\} \cap \{k \mid 2(3 - 2k) \leq 18\}$

Solve the following inequalities and write your answers in interval notation.

41. $5x - 2 < 3x + 12$

42. $1 - 4x \geq x - 19$

43. $6 - (7 - y) \leq 2(y - 3)$

44. $t - 8 > 3 - 2(4t + 1)$

45. $2x - 1 \leq 2(3 + x)$

46. $4(3 - x) - 2(2x + 1) > 0$

47. $-9 < 2x - 1 < 9$

48. $-3 < 1 - 4k < 3$

49. $2 < 6x - 4 < 14$

50. $-3m < 6$ or $m - 7 \leq -4$

51. $-5 < \dfrac{t}{4} + 2 < 6$ **52.** $-\dfrac{1}{2} < \dfrac{1 - x}{8} \leq \dfrac{3}{4}$

53. $y + 8 \geq 7$ or $4y - 1 > -5$

54. $2x > 6$ or $2(3x + 5) > x$

55. $\dfrac{3x - 2}{9} - \dfrac{1 - 4x}{3} > 1$

56. $\dfrac{x - 4}{2} - \dfrac{3x - 4}{5} \leq \dfrac{3}{10}$

4 Use the variable provided to express each of the following as inequalities.

57. The perimeter (p) of a triangle is no more than 8 feet.

58. Ted's height (h) is not less than 6 feet.

59. The rent (r) will be at least $650 per month.

60. The length (L) of a yard is at most 125 feet.

61. The diameter (d) of a circle is not greater than 20 centimeters.

62. The airfare (*a*) is between $80 and $125.

63. The speed of the truck (*r*) ranged from 45 mph to 50 mph inclusive.

64. The temperature (*t*) was between 60° F and 75° F and included 75° F.

Solve the following word problems.

65. Hypothermia occurs when a person's body temperature is between 25° C and 35° C. Find this temperature range in Fahrenheit degrees; $C = \frac{5}{9}(F - 32)$.

66. A person suffering from heat stroke has a body temperature of 106° F or higher. Find this temperature range in Celsius degrees; $F = \frac{9}{5}C + 32$.

67. A person's intelligence quotient (IQ) is determined by the formula $IQ = \frac{MA \cdot 100}{CA}$, where MA = mental age and CA = chronological age. A 10th-grade geometry class of 15-year-old students has an IQ range from 95 to 165 inclusive. Find the range of the students' mental ages.

68. A number is between -3 and 4. What is its opposite between?

69. The average of three consecutive even integers is not less than 18. Find the integers' smallest possible values.

70. The sum of three consecutive odd integers is less than four times the largest integer. Find the smallest possible values for the integers.

71. For three consecutive integers, the sum of the first two is less than twice the third one. Find all such integers.

72. Three less than 4 times a number is greater than 4 times the sum of the number and 1. Find all such numbers.

73. A car traveling at 53 mph passes a truck traveling at 41 mph. How long will it take for the car to be more than 18 miles ahead of the truck?

74. Two cars traveling in opposite directions pass each other and continue at their speeds of 63 and 55 mph. When will they be at least 90 miles apart?

75. To get a grade in the A range in an algebra class, a student must have an average of at least 87%. Gina's scores on the first three tests were 92%, 93%, and 88%. What is the lowest possible score she can get on the fourth test to remain in the A range?

76. To get a grade in the C range in a geometry class, a student must have an average of at least 68% but less than 77%. Mark's scores on the first four tests are 68%, 75%, 80%, and 78%. What range of scores on a fifth test would give him a C in the class?

77. The perimeter of a triangular garden is no more than 35 feet. The second side is twice the shortest side, and the third side is 1 less than 3 times the shortest side. What are the largest possible lengths of the sides of the garden?

78. The width of a rectangle is 5 meters. The area must be between 30 meters squared and 40 meters squared, inclusive. What are the possible lengths of the rectangle?

79. Penny inherited $27,500. She wants to invest part of it at 12% and the rest of it at 9% in such a way that her total yearly interest from the two investments will be at least $3000. What is the least amount of money that she can invest at the 12% interest rate?

80. Alan invests $6000 at $8\frac{1}{2}$% yearly interst. How much does he have to invest at 10% so that his yearly interest from the two investments is between $1750 and $1800 inclusive?

81. An aide in a mathematics department earns $4 per hour for grading papers and $9 per hour for tutoring. If she wants to work 25 hours per week and earn at least $190, what is the maximum number of hours that she can spend grading papers?

82. Jose has 20 dimes and quarters. What is the minimum number of dimes he must have in order to have a maximum total of $3.85? What is the value of the 20 coins?

83. Carl has 17 nickels and quarters. What is the minimum number of quarters he must have in order to have a minimum total of $1.25?

84. A medical insurance company offers two types of coverage. With plan A the patient pays $100, and the company pays 65% of the remaining bill. With plan B the patient pays

$300, and the company pays 85% of the remaining bill. Find the amounts of medical bills for which plan B is better than plan A.

85. Adrienne has been given a job selling electronic equipment. The store has two income options. Under option A she would receive a salary of $1000 per month plus a commission of 8% of sales above $7000. Under option B she would receive $800 per month plus a commission of 5% of all her sales. Assume that her monthly sales are always greater than $7000. Find her monthly sales for which option A is better than option B.

86. Flat Rate Rent-A-Car has two rental options. Under option A the customer pays $14.50 per day, has 50 free miles, and pays 10¢ per mile for each additional mile. Under option B the customer pays $18.50 per day, has 150 free miles, and pays 15¢ per mile for each additional mile. Find the daily mileages for which option B is cheaper than option A.

B

87. Vacation Rent-A-Car has two rental options. Under option A the customer pays $15 per day, has 100 free miles, and pays 10¢ per mile for each additional mile. Under option B the customer pays $20 per day, has 180 free miles, and pays 10¢ per mile for each additional mile. Find the daily mileages for which option B is cheaper than option A.

88. A college student plans to earn at least 26 units in English, mathematics, and geol-ogy. She intends to take twice as much geology as English and two-thirds as much mathematics as geology. What are the minimum number of units that she will have to earn in each subject?

89. Three-halves of Shana's age 3 years ago is at least three-fourths of her age 12 years from now. At least what age is she now?

90. Kevin is 3 times as old as Paul. Kevin's age in 6 years is at least 4 times Paul's age 2 years ago. At most, how old is Paul?

Graph the solution sets of the following.

91. $-2 < x < 2$ or $x > 3$
92. $-3 \le x \le -1$ or $1 \le x \le 3$
93. $x < -2$,   or $x > 2$,   or $x = 1$
94. $(x < 3$ and $x > -3)$ or $x \ge 5$

C

Answer the following questions with complete sentences.

95. How does the solution set of a conditional linear inequality differ from the solution set of a conditional linear equation? (See Sections 2.1 and 2.6.)

96. How does an open interval differ from a closed interval?

97. How does the graph of an open interval differ from the graph of a closed interval?

98. What is wrong with the "interval" $[3,\infty]$?

REVIEW EXERCISES

Simplify the following. (See Section 1.3.)

99. $|3|$ **100.** $|4|$ **101.** $|-4|$ **102.** $|-3|$

Solve the following equations. (See Section 2.2.)

103. $|x| = 3$
105. $|x| = -4$
107. $3 + |2x| = 8$

104. $2|y| = 12$
106. $|x + 2| = 6$
108. $5|2x - 1| = 10$

2.7 INEQUALITIES INVOLVING ABSOLUTE VALUE

1	Solving $|ax + b| < k$ and $|ax + b| \le k$
2	Solving $|ax + b| > k$ and $|ax + b| \ge k$

1 Solving $|ax + b| < k$ and $|ax + b| \leq k$

In Section 1.3 [1] we defined the absolute value of a number a, $|a|$, to be the distance from a to zero on the number line. This idea was used in Section 2.2 [2] to solve equations such as $|x| = 3$ and $|x + 2| = 6$. This section uses this concept of distance to solve linear inequalities such as $|x| < 3$ and $|x + 2| \geq 6$.

Recall that the equation $|x| = 3$ means "find all numbers x whose distance from 0 is 3 units." Because $|3| = |-3| = 3$, the solution to $|x| = 3$ is $\{3, -3\}$. In a similar way, $|x| < 3$ means "find all numbers x whose distance from 0 is less than 3 units." The solution is all values of x between -3 and 3 (see Figure 2.37); that is,

$$\text{if } |x| < 3, \quad \text{then} \quad -3 < x < 3$$

FIGURE 2.37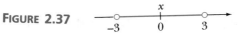

To solve $|x + 2| \leq 6$, we have to find all numbers x such that the distance between $x + 2$ and 0 is less than or equal to 6 (as in Figure 2.38).

$$|x + 2| \leq 6 \text{ if}$$
$$-6 \leq x + 2 \leq 6, \quad \text{or}$$
$$-8 \leq x \leq 4$$

FIGURE 2.38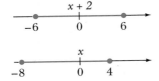

If $|ax + b| < k$, then $-k < ax + b < k$; $k > 0$.

EXAMPLE 1

Solve the following inequalities. For **a** and **d** write the answers in interval notation and graph them (Figures 2.39 and 2.40).

a. $|3x + 4| < 8$ **b.** $|2y| < -4$ **c.** $|3x - 12| \leq 0$
d. $7|1 - 2x| \leq 35$

SOLUTION   **a.** If $|3x + 4| < 8$, then

$$-8 < 3x + 4 < 8 \qquad \text{Add } -4.$$
$$-12 < 3x < 4 \qquad \text{Divide by 3.}$$
$$-4 < x < \frac{4}{3}, \quad \text{or} \quad \left(-4, \frac{4}{3}\right)$$

FIGURE 2.39

(continued)

b. Because absolute value represents distance, $|a| \geq 0$ for all values of a. Thus, $|2y| < -4$ is a false inequality, and its solution is $\varnothing$.

c. $|3x - 12|$ cannot be less than 0, but it can be equal to 0. Thus, $|3x - 12| \leq 0$ if $3x - 12 = 0$, so $x = 4$.

d.

$$7|1 - 2x| \leq 35 \qquad \text{Divide by 7.}$$
$$|1 - 2x| \leq 5$$
$$-5 \leq 1 - 2x \leq 5 \qquad \text{Add } -1.$$
$$-6 \leq -2x \leq 4 \qquad \text{Divide by } -2;$$
$$3 \geq x \geq -2, \quad \text{or} \qquad \text{reverse } <.$$
$$-2 \leq x \leq 3, \quad \text{or } [-2, 3]$$

FIGURE 2.40

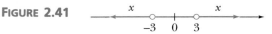

-2   3

---

2   Solving $|ax + b| > k$ and $|ax + b| \geq k$

We have just seen that $|x| < 3$ represents all numbers x whose distance from zero is less than 3 units. The concept of distance also applies to inequalities such as $|x| > 3$. Thus, $|x| > 3$ means "find all numbers x whose distance from 0 is greater than 3 units." One set of solutions consists of all numbers less than -3; an example is -4, because $|-4| = 4 > 3$. The second set of solutions consists of all numbers greater than 3 (see Figure 2.41; an example is 5, because $|5| = 5 > 3$. Thus,

$$\text{if } |x| > 3, \quad \text{then } x < -3 \quad or \quad x > 3$$

FIGURE 2.41

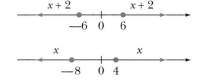

To solve $|x + 2| \geq 6$, we have to find all numbers x such that the distance from $x + 2$ to 0 is greater than or equal to 6; that is, $x + 2$ has to be less than or equal to -6 *or* greater than or equal to 6 (Figure 2.42):

$$|x + 2| \geq 6 \text{ if}$$
$$x + 2 \leq -6 \quad \text{or} \quad x + 2 \geq 6$$
$$x \leq -8 \quad \text{or} \quad x \geq 4$$

FIGURE 2.42

We may be tempted to write "$x \leq -8$ or $x \geq 4$" as "$4 \leq x \leq -8$." However, the statement $4 \leq x \leq -8$ says that $4 \leq x$ *and* $x \leq -8$, which implies that $4 \leq -8$, thereby violating the transitive property.

Transitive Property

Let a, b, and c be real numbers.
If $a \leq b$ and $b \leq c$, then $a \leq c$.

 COMMON ERROR A common mistake is to write a compound inequality involving *or* as a continued inequality. But $x < -2$ or $x > 3$ cannot be written as $3 < x < -2$, because this statement implies that $3 < -2$.

If $|ax + b| > k$, then $ax + b < -k$ or $ax + b > k$; $k > 0$.

EXAMPLE 2

Solve the following inequalities. Write your answers in interval notation and graph them (Figures 2.43, 2.44, 2.45, and 2.46).

a. $|2x - 3| > 5$ **b.** $|2y| > -4$ **c.** $|3x - 12| > 0$

d. $1 + \dfrac{|5 - 2t|}{3} \geq 4$

SOLUTION

a. If $|2x - 3| > 5$, then

$$2x - 3 < -5 \quad \text{or} \quad 2x - 3 > 5 \qquad \text{Add 3.}$$
$$2x < -2 \qquad\qquad 2x > 8 \qquad \text{Divide by 2.}$$
$$x < -1 \quad \text{or} \qquad x > 4$$
$$(-\infty, -1) \cup (4, \infty)$$

FIGURE 2.43

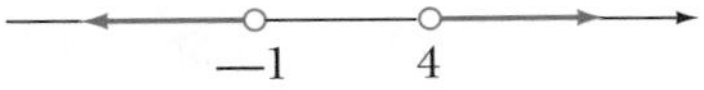

$$\xleftarrow{} \overset{\circ}{\underset{-1}{}} \quad \overset{\circ}{\underset{4}{}} \xrightarrow{}$$

b. By the transitive property and $|a| \geq 0$, $\quad -4 < 0$ and $0 \leq |2y|$, so $-4 < |2y|$ is true for all y. For instance, if $y = -3$, then $|2y| = |-6| = 6 > -4$. Thus, $|2y| > -4$ is an identity and its solution set is $S = \mathbb{R} = (-\infty, \infty)$.

FIGURE 2.44

$$\xleftarrow{}\xrightarrow{}$$

c. $|a| > 0$ for all values of $a \neq 0$. Thus, $|3x - 12| > 0$ for all x such that $3x - 12 \neq 0$; that is, $x \neq 4$. So the solution set is $S = \{x \mid x \neq 4\}$ or $(-\infty, 4) \cup (4, \infty)$.

FIGURE 2.45

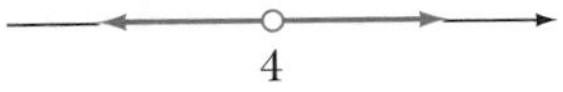

$$\xleftarrow{} \overset{\circ}{\underset{4}{}} \xrightarrow{}$$

(continued)

d. $1 + \dfrac{|\,5 - 2t\,|}{3} \geq 4$ Subtract 1.

$\dfrac{|\,5 - 2t\,|}{3} \geq 3$ Multiply by 3.

$|\,5 - 2t\,| \geq 9$

$5 - 2t \leq -9$ or $5 - 2t \geq 9$

$-2t \leq -14$ $-2t \geq 4$

$t \geq 7$ or $t \leq -2$

$(-\infty, -2] \cup [7, \infty)$

FIGURE 2.46

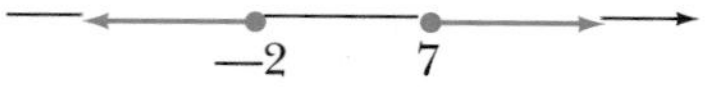

EXERCISE SET 2.7

A

1 Solve the following and graph their solutions.

1. $|\,x\,| < 2$

2. $|\,y\,| \leq 4$

3. $|\,3y\,| \leq 12$

4. $|\,k - 3\,| < 1$

5. $|\,z + 4\,| \leq 6$

6. $|\,3 - x\,| \leq 2$

2

7. $|\,x\,| > 2$

8. $|\,y\,| \geq 4$

9. $|\,2t\,| > 0$

10. $|\,r + 3\,| \geq 2$

11. $|\,1 - x\,| > 5$

12. $|\,z - 4\,| \geq 0$

Solve the following and write your answers in interval notation.

13. $|\,4x\,| < 12$

14. $|\,x - 2\,| \leq 2$

15. $|\,5x\,| \geq 10$

16. $|\,2 - x\,| > 3$

17. $|\,3y\,| \geq -6$

18. $|\,3 - 2t\,| \leq 7$

Solve the following inequalities and equations (for the equations, see Section 2.2). For the inequalities with nonempty solutions, write the answers in interval notation.

19. $|\,2x - 1\,| \leq 7$

20. $|\,3x - 4\,| \geq 6$

21. $|\,4k - 8\,| > 0$

22. $|\,3t - 4\,| \geq 0$

23. $|\,2x - 3\,| \leq -1$

24. $3 \geq |\,x - 2\,|$

25. $|\,2x\,| = 10$

26. $|\,2m - 6\,| > 7$

27. $|\,3x - 1\,| = 14$

28. $|\,1 - 4y\,| < 0$

29. $|\,4k - 3\,| \leq 0$

30. $|\,6 - 9t\,| > -5$

31. $|\,6t\,| < -9$

32. $|\,6t\,| > -9$

33. $-\,|\,3t + 1\,| > -6$

34. $5\,|\,3x\,| > 0$

35. $|\,3x - 2\,| = -4$

36. $|\,6x + 5\,| = 0$

37. $\left|\dfrac{x + 1}{3}\right| < 2$

38. $\left|\dfrac{2x + 1}{4}\right| > 2$

39. $\left|\dfrac{1 - 3x}{2}\right| \geq 1$

40. $3\,|\,1 - 2x\,| < 21$

41. $-2\,|\,x + 4\,| \leq -6$

42. $5 + |\,4x\,| > 6$

43. $1 + 3\,|\,2x - 1\,| < 13$

44. $5\,|\,1 - 4x\,| - 2 \geq 18$

45. $\dfrac{1}{2}\,|\,2 - 3z\,| - 1 \geq 8$

46. $\dfrac{|3 + 4t|}{3} - 1 < 5$

47. $|2t - 6| = |t|$

48. $|x + 4| = |x - 8|$

Write the following as inequalities involving absolute value and then solve them.

49. The distance between a number and zero is less than 5.

50. The distance between a number and zero is greater than 6.

51. The distance from $x - 3$ to zero is greater than 8.

52. The distance from $x + 4$ to zero is less than or equal to 7.

Write the following as inequalities involving absolute value.

53. $-9 \le x \le 9$

54. $-6 < y < 6$

55. $x < -7$ or $x > 7$

56. $k \le -1$ or $k \ge 1$

B

57. $-2 < x < 4$

58. $0 \le y \le 6$

59. $x \le -6$ or $x \ge 4$

60. $t < 3$ or $t > 5$

Solve the following inequalities.

61. $6|x| < 4|x| + 6$

62. $7|x - 1| \ge 3|x - 1| + 12$

C

Answer the following questions with complete sentences.

63. What is the geometric interpretation of $|x| < 4$?

64. What is the geometric interpretation of $|x| > 4$?

65. What is the difference between the solution set of $|x| < 3$ and the solution set of $|x| \le 3$?

66. What is the difference between the solution set of $|x| < -5$ and the solution set of $|x| > -5$?

Chapter Summary

KEY WORDS, DEFINITIONS, AND PROPERTIES

Key Words

Terms: the parts of an algebraic expression that are added or subtracted. (See Section 2.1)

Like terms: terms that have the same variables with the same exponents. (See Section 2.1.)

Equivalent: two equations or inequalities with the same solution. (See Section 2.1.)

LCD: the least common denominator for a set of rational numbers is the smallest natural number that is divisible by each denominator. (See Section 2.2.)

Literal equation: an equation that contains more than one variable.

Formula: a literal equation from the physical world. (See Section 2.3.)

Interval Notation (See Section 2.6.)

$(a, b) = \{x \mid a < x < b\}$ $[a, b] = \{x \mid a \le x \le b\}$

$(a, b] = \{x \mid a < x \le b\}$ $[a, b) = \{x \mid a \le x < b\}$

$(a, \infty) = \{x \mid x > a\}$ $[a, \infty) = \{x \mid x \ge a\}$

$(-\infty, a) = \{x \mid x < a\}$ $(-\infty, a] = \{x \mid x \le a\}$

$(-\infty, \infty) = \{x \mid x \in \mathbb{R}\}$

Types of Equations and Inequalities (See Sections 2.1 and 2.6.)

S, the solution set of an equation or inequality, is the set of all real numbers that make the equation or inequality a true statement.

1. **Identities** are true statements for all numbers for which the equation or inequality is defined: $0x = 0$, $x + 2 > x + 1$; $S = \mathbb{R}$.

2. **False equations** or inequalities are false statements for all real numbers: $0x = 7$, $x < x - 4$; $S = \emptyset$.

3. **Conditional equations** or inequalities are true for at least one real number and false for at least one real number: $2x = 8$, $S = \{4\}$; $2x < 8$, $S = (-\infty, 4)$.

Properties of Equations and Inequalities (See Sections 2.1, 2.6, and 2.7)

Let $a, b, c \in \mathbb{R}$.

Symmetric	If $a = b$, then $b = a$.
Transitive	If $a \leq b$ and $b \leq c$, then $a \leq c$.
Addition	If $a = b$, then $a + c = b + c$, $a - c = b - c$.
Subtraction and	If $a < b$, then $a + c < b + c$, $a - c < b - c$.
Multiplication and	If $a = b$, then $ac = bc$, $\dfrac{a}{c} = \dfrac{b}{c}$; $c \neq 0$.
Division, $c \neq 0$	If $a < b$ and $c > 0$, then $ac < bc$, $\dfrac{a}{c} < \dfrac{b}{c}$.
	If $a < b$ and $c < 0$, then $ac > bc$, $\dfrac{a}{c} > \dfrac{b}{c}$.

These properties hold if $<$ is replaced by $\leq$, $>$, or $\geq$.

Solutions of Equations and Inequalities (See Sections 2.2, 2.3, and 2.7.)

If $x^2 = d$, then $x = \pm\sqrt{d}$; $d > 0$.
$|ax + b| = k$ if $ax + b = k$ or $ax + b = -k$; $k \geq 0$.
$|ax + b| = |cx + d|$ if $ax + b = cx + d$ or $ax + b = -(cx + d)$.
If $|ax + b| < k$, then $-k < ax + b < k$; $k > 0$.
If $|ax + b| > k$, then $ax + b < -k$ or $ax + b > k$; $k > 0$.

Geometry (See Sections 2.3 and 2.4.)

Pythagorean theorem and its converse: In any right triangle, the square of the hypotenuse is equal to the sum of the squares of the two legs ($c^2 = a^2 + b^2$); if the sum of the squares of the two shorter sides of a triangle is equal to the square of the longest side, then the triangle is a right triangle, and the right angle is opposite the longest side. An **isosceles right triangle** has two equal legs ($a = b$, so $c^2 = 2a^2$). In a **30°–60°–90°** triangle the length of the hypotenuse is twice the length of the leg opposite the 30° angle ($c = 2a$).

Two angles are **complementary** if the sum of their measures is 90°. Two angles are **supplementary** if the sum of their measures is 180°. The sum of the measures of the angles of a triangle is 180°.

CHAPTER REVIEW EXERCISES

The answers to the following problems are given in the answer section. If you have any trouble, then review the material and homework problems in the sections indicated.

Simplify the following expressions. (See Section 2.1.)

1. $4 - (3 - 2x)$ **2.** $3(y - 4) + 2(8 - 9y)$

Express the following as ratios of two integers in reduced form. (See Section 2.2.)

3. $2.13\overline{3}$ **4.** $.14\overline{7147}$

5. Solve $D = ad - bc$ for d, given $D = 30$, $a = 2$, $b = -2$, and $c = 5$. (See Section 2.3.)

Solve the following for the indicated variables. (See Section 2.3.)

6. $2x - 3y = 18$; x **7.** $t = 6 + (a - 4)$; a

Solve the following equations. (See Sections 2.1, 2.2, and 2.3.)

8. $25 = 4 - 7x$

9. $8x - 3 = 2x + 15$

10. $\dfrac{2x - 1}{3} = \dfrac{x + 2}{2}$

11. $\dfrac{1}{3} - \dfrac{2 - k}{5} = \dfrac{2k}{15}$

12. $m - (1 - 4m) = m = 7$

13. $2x^2 = 38$

14. $.15y + 2.7 = 1 - .02y$

15. $1 + |\, 3x \,| = 13$

16. $|\, 2 - 5y \,| = 17$

17. $|\, x + 3 \,| = |\, 2x \,|$

Find the number(s) described in each problem. (See Sections 2.1 and 2.2.)

18. Three times a number is equal to the number increased by 20.

19. A number is 18 more than twice its opposite.

20. Two more than one-fourth a number is the same as one less than one-third the number.

21. Divide 37 into two numbers such that the larger one exceeds the smaller one by 5.

22. Find three consecutive integers such that the sum of the first two is 12 less than one-half the third.

Express the following in interval notation and graph each one. (See Section 2.6.)

23. $x \leq 4$ **24.** $-3 \leq x < 2$

Solve the following inequalities. For the inequalities with nonempty solutions, write the answers in interval notation. (See Sections 2.6 and 2.7.)

25. $1 - 3x \geq -20$

26. $-8 \leq 2y + 3(y - 4) < 9$

27. $3 \,|\, 3 - 2m \,| \leq 27$

28. $x - 8 < 11 - (3x - 1)$

29. $6 + |\, 7 + 8t \,| \geq 29$

30. $|\, 2k - 7 \,| < -3$

31. $3x - 6 \geq 9$ or $2(10 - x) > 6$

Solve the following word problems. (See Sections 2.3, 2.4, 2.5, and 2.6.)

32. The best treatment for deep frostbite is rapid rewarming in a bath at a temperature range of 102° F to 108° F inclusive. Find this temperature range in Celsius degrees; $F = \dfrac{9}{5}C + 32$.

33. The hypotenuse of a 30°–60°–90° triangle is 12 feet. Find the lengths of the legs.

34. Two angles are complementary, and the larger is 9 more than twice the smaller. Find the angles.

35. The radius and height of a can of tuna are equal. If the surface area is $169\pi/16$ inches squared, find the can's radius and volume.

36. The sum of the perimeters of a square and a rectangle is 32 meters. The length of the rectangle is 1 more than twice its width, and the width is equal to the side of the square. Find the dimensions of the two figures. What are their areas?

37. Heather began a 400-mile trip. After 2 hours she reduced her driving speed by 20 mph. She took a 1-hour lunch break and reached her destination 9 hours after she began her trip. What was her initial speed?

38. The speed of a river is 2 mph. Bob traveled downstream for 2 hours in his motorboat. On the return trip he went 4 miles past his starting point in 4 hours. What was the speed of his motorboat?

39. Kay had scores of 72 and 75 on two English tests. What score does she need on the third test to have an average of 78?

40. Carina has 22 nickels and dimes totaling $1.80. How many coins of each type does she have?

41. Steve is 2 years older than Michele. Twelve years from how Michele will be twice as old as Steve was 5 years ago. Find their current ages.

42. A sports coat was marked down 35% to $116.35. What was the coat's original price?

43. A coffee shop owner wants to mix coffee A, worth $5 per kilogram, with coffee B, worth $6.50 per kilogram, to produce a blend of 75 kilograms, worth $6 per kilogram. How much of each type of coffee must she use?

CHAPTER TEST

Treat this test as a class test and allow 50 minutes for completion. When finished, use the answer section for grading. If you have any wrong answers, refer to the corresponding problems in the review section.

Solve the following for the indicated variables.

1. $5x + 3y = 15$; y **2.** $V = \frac{1}{4}[L(3f - 4)]$; f

Solve the following equations and inequalities. For the inequalities, write your answers in interval notation and sketch their graphs.

3. $8 - 2x < 14$

4. $2x + 5 > 7$ and $5x \leq 20$

5. $11x - 2 = 7x + 18$

6. $|3x - 1| > -2$

7. $.08x + .12(3) = .09(x + 3)$

8. $2(3y - 4) + y = 1 - (1 - y)$

9. $\frac{x}{3} - \frac{x - 1}{4} = \frac{1}{6}$

10. $|3x - 1| = 8$

11. $|2x + 7| = |2x - 5|$

12. $|2 - 3x| \geq 7$

13. $2|5y + 1| \leq 10$

14. Express $.\overline{36}$ as the ratio of two integers in reduced form.

Solve the following word problems.

15. Dante has $7 in half-dollars and quarters. If he has a total of 24 coins, how many are half-dollars and how many are quarters?

16. Eight years ago Mike was one-fourth as old as he will be one year from now. How old is he now?

17. Chen leaves Dallas, Texas, and cycles north at a rate of 6 mph. Two hours later Jean leaves Dallas and cycles after Chen at a rate of 7.5 mph. How long will it take for Jean to overtake Chen?

18. Two trucks traveling in opposite directions pass each other and continue at their speeds of 48 and 42 mph. When will they be at least 135 miles apart?

19. Find all numbers x such that x and $3x - 2$ are the same distance from zero.

20. Frank received $2555 interest per year on his capital investments. One-third of his capital is invested at 9%, one-fifth at 12%, and the rest at 14.5%. How much capital does he have invested?

21. How many liters of a 3% salt solution must be mixed with 5 liters of a 2% salt solution to produce a 2.8% salt solution?

22. A 6-liter radiator full of water and antifreeze contains 36% antifreeze. How much of this mixture must be drained and replaced by pure antifreeze to increase the concentration to 60% antifreeze?

23. One angle of a triangle is 20° larger than the smallest angle. The third angle is 34° larger than the smallest angle. Find the three angles.

24. The hypotenuse of an isosceles right triangle is 6 centimeters. Find the lengths of the triangle's legs.

25. Two angles are supplementary, and the larger one is twice the smaller one. Find the two angles.

THREE

Linear Equations and Inequalities in Two Variables; Functions

Reflection around the line y = x transforms the graph of a function into the graph of its inverse.

In Chapter 2 we solved linear equations in *one* variable, such as $4x + 5 = 17$. The solution to this equation, $x = 3$, is interpreted geometrically as a point on the number line. In Chapter 3 we will extend these ideas to linear equations in *two* variables, such as $4x + 5y = 17$. One solution to this equation is $x = 3$ and $y = 1$. This solution is also represented as a point, but in a plane, not on a line. We studied inequalities such as $3x - 2 < 6$ in Chapter 2. In this chapter we will consider inequalities such as $3x - 2y < 6$.

Depicting numbers as points is the first step in the study of **analytic geometry**. This subject merges algebra and geometry into one discipline and allows us to represent algebraic equations as geometric shapes and to describe geometric concepts in algebraic terms. This chapter will interpret linear equations as lines in a plane, and later chapters will describe curves, such as circles, with other types of equations.

This chapter also begins the study of **functions**, an important topic in mathematics and the sciences. A function helps us describe how one quantity changes with another; for example, how temperature varies depending on the time of day.

3.1 CARTESIAN COORDINATE SYSTEM; GRAPHS OF LINEAR EQUATIONS

1	**Cartesian Coordinate System**
2	**Solving Equations in Two Variables**
3	**Graphing Linear Equations; *x*- and *y*-Intercepts**
4	**Graphing Equations Involving Absolute Value**

1　Cartesian Coordinate System

The number line is used to graph solutions to equations in one variable. We will now extend these concepts to the plane to be able to graph the solutions to equations in two variables. We begin with a brief review of the number line (Section 1.2).

An example of a **number line** is given in Figure 3.1. The point corresponding to zero is called the **origin**, and the other integers are represented by equally spaced points. The distance between 0 and 1 is called the **unit distance**. The arrow indicates the positive direction. Each number has a unique point on the number line, called its **graph**, and each point on the number line has a corresponding unique real number, called its **coordinate**. For convenience we use the words "point" and "number" interchangeably.

FIGURE 3.1

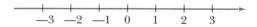

To construct a **Cartesian coordinate system**, we draw a horizontal number line, the **x-axis**, and a vertical number line, the **y-axis**. The axes (plural of axis), intersect at their origins. We use the same unit distance on both axes, with the arrows indicating the positive directions. The axes divide the plane into four regions, which are called **quadrants** and numbered I, II, III, and IV (Figure 3.2a). The points on the axes are not in any quadrant. Other names used for the Cartesian coordinate system are the "Cartesian plane," the "*xy*-plane," and the "rectangular coordinate system."

FIGURE 3.2

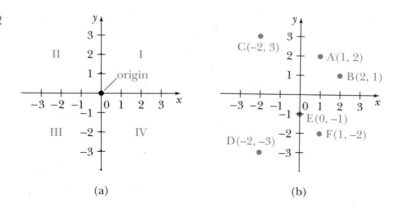

(a)   (b)

In Chapter 2 we used the symbol (1, 2) to stand for the open interval from 1 to 2. The symbol is also used to describe a point in the *xy*-plane and is called the **ordered pair** in this situation. The use of this notation is usually clear from the context of the discussion, but to prevent any confusion, we will use the phrases "the interval (a, b)" or "the ordered pair (a, b)."

Let A be the point in the first quadrant that is one unit from the *y*-axis and two units from the *x*-axis. Point A is denoted by the ordered pair (1, 2), and we write **A(1, 2)**. The number 1 is the *x*-**coordinate** (or **abscissa**), and the number 2 is the *y*-**coordinate** (or **ordinate**) of A. As with the number line, we will use "point" and "ordered pair" interchangeably. To graph B(2, 1), move two units in the positive *x*-direction from the origin because $2 > 0$; then move one unit in the positive *y*-direction, because $1 > 0$. We can see from the graphs of A and B in Figure 3.2b that $(1, 2) \neq (2, 1)$; hence, the reason for the word "ordered." To graph C(-2, 3), move two units in the negative *x*-direction from the origin, because $-2 < 0$, and three units in the positive *y*-direction. Three other points are graphed in Figure 3.2b.

In general, for each ordered pair of real numbers (a, b), a unique point P exists in the *xy*-plane, called its **graph**; and for each point P in the *xy*-plane there corresponds a unique ordered pair of real numbers (a, b), called its **coordinates**. Thus, a one-to-one correspondence exists between the set of ordered pairs of real numbers and the set of points in the Cartesian plane. We denote the point P and its coordinates (a, b) by **P(a, b)**; see Figure 3.3. Note that $(a, b) \neq (b, a)$ unless $a = b$.

FIGURE 3.3

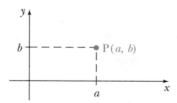

2   Solving Equations in Two Variables

Analytic geometry, which combines algebra and geometry into one discipline, deals with two basic types of problems:

1. Given an algebraic equation, finding its geometric graph
2. Given a geometric curve, finding its algebraic equation

In this and later chapters we discuss many examples of both problem types.

To graph an algebraic equation we must find points whose coordinates satisfy the equation; that is, we must find ordered pairs (a, b) that are solutions to the equation. For instance, we can find solutions to $y = 2x - 1$ by picking values of one variable, substituting them in the equation, and finding the corresponding values of the other variable:

$$y = 2x - 1$$

If $x = 3$, then $y = 2 \cdot 3 - 1 = 5$.
If $x = 0$, then $y = 2 \cdot 0 - 1 = -1$.
If $y = 0$, then $0 = 2x - 1$, $1 = 2x$, and $x = 1/2$.
Thus, $\{(3, 5), (0, -1), (1/2, 0)\}$ are three solutions to $y = 2x - 1$.

EXAMPLE 1

Complete the following solutions for $2x - 3y = 12$; $(0, \ )$, $(9, \ )$, $(\ , 0)$

SOLUTION

If $x = 0$, then $2 \cdot 0 - 3y = 12$, $-3y = 12$, and $y = -4$.
If $x = 9$, then $2 \cdot 9 - 3y = 12$, $-3y = -6$, and $y = 2$.
If $y = 0$, then $2x - 3 \cdot 0 = 12$, $2x = 12$, and $x = 6$.
$\{(0, -4), (9, 2) (6, 0)\}$ are the solutions.

3   Graphing Linear Equations; *x*- and *y*-Intercepts

We now consider the graphs of linear equations. Two common forms for a linear, or first-degree, equation in two variables are

$$y = mx + b \qquad \text{and} \qquad Ax + By = C$$

where m, b, A, B, and C are constants. These forms are equivalent, because $y = mx + b$ can be written as $-mx + y = b$ (A $= -m$, B $= 1$, C $= b$). The graph of a linear equation in two variables is a line (the word "line" in this text means a straight line). Because two points determine a line, we only need to find two ordered pairs that are solutions to the equation. However, if an arithmetic mistake is made in calculating one of the coordinates, then the graph will be incorrect. Therefore, graphing a third point as a check for arithmetic errors is a good idea.

EXAMPLE 2

Graph the equation $y = 2x + 4$ (see Figure 3.4 on page 108).

SOLUTION

We could select any three values for x, but -3, -2, and 0 are convenient ones.

(continued)

Math in Time

The development of analytic geometry is one of several cases of major discoveries that were made by two people working independently of each other. The Englishmen Charles Darwin (1809–1882) and Alfred Wallace (1823–1913) developed the theory of evolution in the early 19th century, and the Frenchmen Pierre de Fermat (1601–1665) and René Descartes (1596–1650) invented analytic geometry in the early 17th century.

The credit for creating analytic geometry should go to Fermat, but Descartes published his results in 1637 before Fermat's work became known. In 1629 Fermat made important discoveries using coordinates to describe curves. A basic difference existed in their approaches to this subject. Whereas Descartes began with a curve and looked for its equation, Fermat started with an equation and found its graph.

Descartes was the son of a French aristocrat from whom he inherited enough money to spend his life in study and travel. After receiving his early education in a Jesuit college, he moved to Paris at age 16 and soon developed a passion for gambling and women. He quickly tired of this, however, and spent several years traveling as a gentleman soldier and meeting the leading intellectuals of Europe. He settled in Holland at age 33 to study mathematics, science, and philosophy.

Descartes' scientific investigations were rather hit-or-miss. He correctly explained the rainbow in terms of refracted light but then went on to claim that thunder was produced when a higher cloud falls on a lower one. A born skeptic, Descartes felt that the philosophy he learned from the Jesuits was baseless superstition. He maintained that knowledge could only come from scientific experimentation and mathematical reasoning. His main contribution to Western thought is this spirit of skepticism and inquiry, a spirit that helped to bring about the scientific revolution.

René Descartes
North Wind Picture Archives

In contrast to the flamboyant Descartes, Fermat was a shy and retiring man. The son of a leather merchant, he studied law and spent most of his life as a provincial

Pierre de Fermat
North Wind Picture Archives

judge. This occupation allowed him plenty of free time to pursue mathematics. Besides being the coinventor of analytic geometry, he jointly developed the basic concepts of probability with Blaise Pascal. To Fermat these activities were minor compared with his consuming passion, the theory of numbers. In this field he made the greatest contributions since Diophantus (A.D. 250) and is the founder of the modern theory of numbers. As an example of Fermat's brilliance, he was once asked if 100,895,598,169 is prime. Without hesitation he replied that it is the product of 112,303 and 898,423.

If $x = -3$,   then $y = 2(-3) + 4 = -2$.
If $x = -2$,   then $y = 2(-2) + 4 = 0$.
If $x = 0$,   then $y = 2(0) + 4 = 4$.
The points $\{(-3, -2), (-2, 0), (0, 4)\}$ determine the line. **The arrows indicate that the line continues indefinitely in both directions.**

FIGURE 3.4

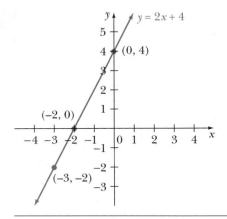

The graph of $y = 2x + 4$ (Example 2) goes through the y-axis at the point $(0, 4)$; the number 4 is called the **y-intercept**. The line crosses the x-axis at $(-2, 0)$, and the number -2 is called the **x-intercept** of $y = 2x + 4$. In general, to find the y-intercept of an equation, let $x = 0$ and solve for y. To find the x-intercept, let $y = 0$ and solve for x. These concepts are illustrated in our next example.

EXAMPLE 3

Graph the equation $2x + 3y = 6$ using the intercepts (see Figure 3.5).

SOLUTION

To find the y-intercept, let $x = 0$: $2 \cdot 0 + 3y = 6$, $3y = 6$,   and $y = 2$.
To find the x-intercept, let $y = 0$: $2x + 3 \cdot 0 = 6$, $2x = 6$,   and $x = 3$.
The points on the graph corresponding to the intercepts are $(0, 2)$ and $(3, 0)$. To find a checkpoint, pick a convenient value of x, say $x = -3$. Then, $2(-3) + 3y = 6$, $3y = 12$,   and $y = 4$. Thus, $(-3, 4)$ is a third point on the line.

FIGURE 3.5

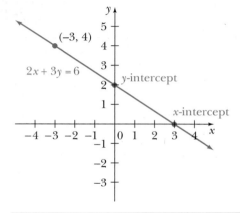

An equation such as $x = 3$ is in the form $Ax + By = C$ if we write it as $x + 0y = 3$. In this form $x = 3$ for any value of y, because $0y = 0$. Thus, $(3, 2)$, $(3, 0)$, and $(3 - 1)$ are three points on the line. The graph of $x = 3$ is a *vertical line* with an x-intercept of 3 and no y-intercept. Similarly, $y = -1$ is a *horizontal line* with a y-intercept of -1 and no x-intercept; three points on the line are $(-2, -1)$, $(0, -1)$, and $(3, -1)$ (see Figure 3.6). In general, $x = C$ is a **vertical line** with an x-intercept of C and no y-intercept. $y = C$ is a **horizontal line** with a y-intercept of C and no x-intercept.

FIGURE 3.6

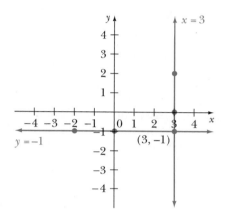

4   Graphing Equations Involving Absolute Value

In many applications of linear equations, we must place restrictions on the variables. For example, if x represents the number of miles flown per year by an executive, then $x \geq 0$. In graphing an equation where x is defined on an interval, we plot an endpoint as a solid circle if its x-coordinate is in the interval and as an open circle if it is not in the interval. This is illustrated in the following example.

E X A M P L E 4

Graph each of the following over the given interval (see Figure 3.7).

a. $y = 3x - 6$; $x \geq 1$ **b.** $y = 1$; $[-4, -1)$

FIGURE 3.7

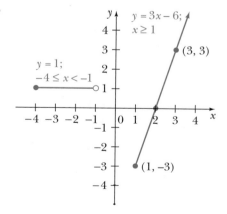

(continued)

SOLUTION   **a.** If $x = 1$,   then $y = 3 \cdot 1 - 6 = -3$.
If $x = 2$,   then $y = 3 \cdot 2 - 6 = 0$.
If $x = 3$,   then $y = 3 \cdot 3 - 6 = 3$.
The points $(1, -3)$, $(2, 0)$, and $(3, 3)$ determine the line $y = 3x - 6$. However, because $x \geq 1$, we only graph the equation over the interval $[1, \infty)$. (The graph of a linear equation over the interval $(-\infty, a]$ or $[a, \infty)$ is called a **ray**.)
b. The graph of $y = 1$, for $-4 \leq x < -1$, is the portion of the horizontal line $y = 1$ where the domain is the interval $[-4, -1)$. $(-4, 1)$ is graphed as a solid circle and $(-1, 1)$ as an open circle.

In many situations we may conveniently use **subscripts**. A subscript is a number or letter written below and to the right of a variable, such as y_1, v_2, and F_x. These are read, y sub one," "v sub two," and "F sub x." Subscripts are used in Example 5.

In graphing equations that involve an absolute value, rays arise in a natural way. We begin by using the definition of absolute value to reduce the given equation to the graphs of two rays. Recall that $|a| = a$, if $a \geq 0$, and $|a| = -a$, if $a < 0$. To graph equations such as $y = |x|$, we conveniently make a slight change in this definition and let $|a| = -a$, if $a \leq 0$.

EXAMPLE 5   Graph the equation $y = |x|$ (see Figure 3.8).

SOLUTION $$y = |x| = \begin{cases} x, & \text{if } x \geq 0 \\ -x, & \text{if } x \leq 0 \end{cases}$$
Let $y_1 = x$, for $x \geq 0$, and $y_2 = -x$, for $x \leq 0$. The points $\{(0, 0), (1, 1), (2, 2)\}$ determine the ray y_1, and the points $\{(0, 0), (-1, 1), (-2, 2)\}$ determine the ray y_2.

FIGURE 3.8

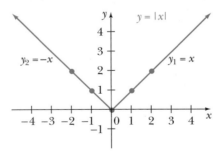

EXAMPLE 6   Graph the equation $y = |x + 2| - 1$ (see Figure 3.9).

SOLUTION $$y = |x + 2| - 1 = \begin{cases} (x + 2) - 1, & \text{if } x + 2 \geq 0 \\ -(x + 2) - 1, & \text{if } x + 2 \leq 0 \end{cases}$$
$$= \begin{cases} y_1 = x + 1, & \text{if } x \geq -2 \\ y_2 = -x - 3, & \text{if } x \leq -2 \end{cases}$$
$\{(-2, -1), (-1, 0), (0, 1)\}$ determines y_1, and $\{(-2, -1), (-3, 0), (-4, 1)\}$ determines y_2.

FIGURE 3.9

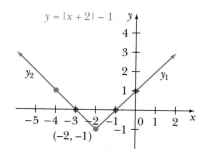

$$y = |x + 2| - 1$$

In many applications of linear equations we may conveniently use variables other than x and y. For example, in a problem involving time and velocity the variables, t and v are used instead of x and y.

EXAMPLE 7

Graph the equation $v = \frac{1}{2}t - 1$ for $t \geq 0$ (see Figure 3.10).

SOLUTION   Three points that determine the graph are $(0, -1)$, $(2, 0)$, and $(4, 1)$.

FIGURE 3.10

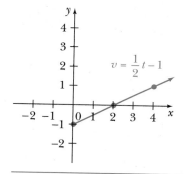

$$v = \frac{1}{2}t - 1$$

EXERCISE SET 3.1

A

1 Give the coordinates of each point in Figure 3.11. Express each answer as an ordered pair.

1. A   **2.** B   **3.** C   **4.** D
5. E   **6.** F   **7.** G   **8.** H
9. I   **10.** J   **11.** K   **12.** L

Graph each set of ordered pairs in an *xy*-plane.

13. $\{(0, 0), (1, 3), (-1, -3)\}$
14. $\{(0, 1), (1/2, 0) (1, -1)\}$

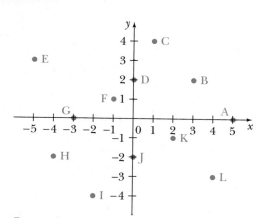

FIGURE 3.11

15. {(0, 3), (0, −3), (−3, 0), (3, 0), (−1, 2.5), (1, −2.5)}

16. {(0, −1), (−1, 0), (1, 0), (−2, 3) (2, 3)}

2 Determine if the ordered pair is a solution to the given equation.

17. $y = 3x - 1$; $(-2, -7)$

18. $y = -6x + 2$; $(5, -32)$

19. $3x - 4y = 12$, $(0, 3)$

20. $4x + 5y = 20$; $(5, 0)$

21. $x = 5$; $(5, -7)$

22. $y = -4$; $(-4, 3)$

Complete the following solutions for the given equation.

23. $y = -3x + 1$ (0,), (, 0), (−2,)

24. $y = \frac{3}{4}x$ (0,), (4,), (−4,)

25. $y = 3$ (−2,) (0,), (4,)

26. $x = -4$ (, −2), (, 0), (, 3)

27. $2x - 3y = 6$ (0,), (, 0), (5,)

28. $\frac{2x}{5} + \frac{y}{6} = 1$ (0,), (, 0), (, 12)

3 If they exist, determine the x- and y-intercepts for the following. Then graph each line.

29. $y = 3x - 3$ **30.** $2x - y = 4$

31. $4x + 5y = 20$ **32.** $y = 3x$

33. $x = -4$ **34.** $y = 2$

35. $y = \frac{3}{5}x + 1$ **36.** $\frac{x}{3} - \frac{y}{2} = 1$

Graph the following lines.

37. $y = -2x + 6$ **38.** $y = 4x - 3$

39. $2x - 4y = 4$ **40.** $3y - 5x = 6$

41. $3y + 1 = x$ **42.** $4y - x = 0$

43. $y = \frac{1}{3}x - 2$ **44.** $y = -\frac{2}{5}x + 1$

45. $\frac{x}{2} + \frac{y}{3} = 1$ **46.** $\frac{3x}{4} - \frac{y}{2} = 1$

47. $y + 3 = 0$ **48.** $x - 5 = 0$

49. $x = 0$ **50.** $y = 0$

4 Graph the following over the given interval.

51. $y = x$; $x \geq 0$

52. $y = -x$; $x < 0$

53. $y = 2x - 4$; $x > 1$

54. $y = -3x - 5$; $(-\infty, -1)$

55. $3x + 2y = 6$; $[2, \infty)$

56. $y = 2$; $[1, 5]$

57. $y = -2$; $(-3, 1)$

58. $y = x + 1$; $[0, 4)$

59. $v = -t + 5$; $[0, 5]$

60. $s = 3t + 2$; $[0, \infty)$

61. $a = 2t + 1$; $[1, \infty)$

62. $h = x - 5$; $[0, 6)$

Graph the following equations.

63. $C = 2x - 1$ **64.** $A = 3x + 2$

65. $y = |2x|$ **66.** $y = |x| + 2$

67. $y = |x + 2|$ **68.** $y = |x - 2|$

69. $y = -|x|$ **70.** $y = -|3x|$

71. $y = -3|x|$ **72.** $y = -|x - 3|$

73. $y = 2|x| - 1$ **74.** $y = -4|x| + 2$

B

75. $y = -\frac{1}{2}|x| + 2$

76. $y = \frac{2}{3}|x| - 4$

77. $y = -|x + 1| - 3$

78. $y = |x - 4| + 1$

79. $y = 3|x - 2| - 1$

80. $y = -2|x + 3| + 2$

C ✏️

Answer the following questions with complete sentences.

81. What is the difference between Descartes' and Fermat's approach to analytic geometry?

82. What are the geometric interpretations of the x and y intercepts?

3.2 RELATIONS AND FUNCTIONS

1	Relations, Domain, and Range
2	Functions and Functional Notation

1 Relations, Domain, and Range

A relationship may exist between two quantities in many situations. For instance, the price of an airplane ticket is related to the distance traveled. This is an example of a relation. In this section we begin the study of relations and functions, which are special types of relations.

A **relation** is any set of ordered pairs — that is, a relation is a rule that allows us to match elements in one set with elements in another set. For example, each student in an algebra class was born in a given month. Suppose that José was born in May, Lien was born in June, and Bill was born in August. In set notation this relation is written

$$\{(\text{José}, \text{May}), (\text{Lien}, \text{June}), (\text{Bill}, \text{August})\}$$

The set of first elements, {José, Lien, Bill}, is called the **domain, D**, of the relation. The set of second elements, {May, June, August}, is called the **range, R**, of the relation.

Relations in mathematics are commonly described with ordered pairs of numbers. For example, consider:

$$\{(3, 5), (0, -1), (6, 11)\}$$

The domain and range of this relation are $D = \{3, 0, 6\}$ and $R = \{5, -1, 11\}$.

> A **relation** is a set of ordered pairs. The set of all first coodinates is called the **domain** of the relation, and the set of all second coordinates is called the **range** of the relation.

EXAMPLE 1

Give the domain, D, and range, R, of the following relations.

a. $\{(2, 8), (3, 27), (-4, -64)\}$
b. $\{(0, 0), (4, 2), (4, -2) (9, 3), (9, -3)\}$

SOLUTION

a. $D = \{2, 3, -4\}$ and $R = \{8, 27, -64\}$
b. $D = \{0, 4, 9\}$ and $R = \{0, 2, -2, 3, -3\}$

Relations are often designated by letters such as S, T, f, and g. In this situation we conveniently use subscripts to write their domains and ranges.

For example,

$$S = \{(2, 5), (3, 7), (9, 11)\}$$
$$D_S = \{2, 3, 9\} \quad \text{and} \quad R_S = \{5, 7, 11\}$$

Each relation discussed to this point has been a list of ordered pairs. Usually a relation is described by a rule that assigns to each element in the domain one or more elements in the range. For example, the rule $y = 3x$ assigns to each real number y the real number $3x$. If we call this relation f, then the domain and range of f is the set of real numbers. Thus,

$$f = \{(x, y) \mid y = 3x\} \qquad D_f = R_f = \mathbb{R}$$

Frequently the domain or the range (or both) of a relation is a proper subset of the real numbers. For this situation we may often conveniently use interval notation. For example, let g be the relation with the rule $y = x^2$. Because $x^2 \geq 0$ for all real numbers x, the range of g is the set of all nonnegative real numbers:

$$g = \{(x, y) \mid y = x^2\}, \quad D_g = \mathbb{R}, \quad \text{and} \quad R_g = [0, \infty)$$

EXAMPLE 2

Express the domain and range of the following in interval notation.

a. $T = \{(x, y) \mid y = x^2 - 1\}$ **b.** $h = \{(x, y) \mid y = 2 + \sqrt{x}\}$

SOLUTION

a. $x^2 - 1$ is a real number for all real numbers x, so $D_T = \mathbb{R} = (-\infty, \infty)$. If x is a real number, then

$x^2 \geq 0$ Subtract 1 from both sides.
$x^2 - 1 \geq 0 - 1$
$x^2 - 1 \geq -1$, so the range of T is
$R_T = \{y \mid y \geq -1\} = [-1, \infty)$.

b. $\sqrt{x}$ is not a real number if $x < 0$. Thus, if y is to be real, then we need $x \geq 0$. Thus,
$D_h = [0, \infty)$.
To find the range, we know that
$\sqrt{x} \geq 0$ and $y = 2 + \sqrt{x} \geq 2$, so
$R_h = [2, \infty)$

When an equation involving x and y is given, and no limitations are placed on x, then we assume that the domain of the relation is the largest set of real numbers for which y is a real number. That is, $D = \{x \mid y$ is a real number$\}$.

Domain of a Relation

To ensure that y is real, the domain of a relation is the set of all real numbers x such that

1. We do not divide by 0.
2. We do not take the square root of a negative number.

Other restrictions are discussed in later chapters.

EXAMPLE 3

Find the domain of the following relations.

a. $y = \dfrac{3}{x^2 - 4}$ **b.** $y = \sqrt{6 - x}$ **c.** $y = \dfrac{x - 11}{\sqrt{2x - 10}}$

SOLUTION

a. We need to exclude the values of x for which $x^2 - 4 = 0$ or $x^2 = 4$. If $x = \pm 2$, then $x^2 = 4$. So $D = \{x \mid x \neq \pm 2\}$.

b. y is real if,

$$6 - x \geq 0 \qquad \text{Subtract 6.}$$
$$-x \geq -6 \qquad \text{Multiply by } -1;$$
$$x \leq 6, \quad \text{so} \quad \text{reverse} >.$$
$$D = \{x \mid x \leq 6\} = (-\infty, 6]$$

c. We have to satisfy both restrictions, so we need $2x - 10 \neq 0$ and $2x - 10 \geq 0$; that is, we need

$$2x - 10 > 0 \qquad \text{Add 10.}$$
$$2x > 10 \qquad \text{Divide by 2.}$$
$$x > 5, \quad \text{so}$$
$$D = \{x \mid x > 5\} = (5, \infty)$$

2 Functions and Functional Notation

For some relations a given first coordinate has more than one second coordinate, such as $\{(9, 3), (9, -3), (4, 2)\}$. For other relations a given element in the domain has exactly one element in the range. An example of this is

$$f = \{(-2, -8), (0, 0), (2, 8), (3, 27)\}$$

f is an example of a **function**, which is the most important type of relation because for a given x *exactly* one y exists.*

> A **function** is a relation such that for each first coordinate only one second coordinate exists. The **domain** of a function is the set of all first coordinates. The **range** of a function is the set of all second coordinates.

---

* "The keynote of Western culture is the function concept, a notion not even remotely hinted at by any earlier culture. And the function concept is anything but an extension or elaboration of previous number concepts — it is rather a complete emancipation from such notions." — *W. Schaaf (1930)*

EXAMPLE 4

Determine whether the following relations are functions. Find the domain and range of each.

a. $H = \{(1, 4), (6, 2), (6, 3)\}$　　**b.** $y = 2x + 4$
c. $F = \{(x, y) \mid x = 3\}$　　**d.** $f = \{(x, y) \mid y = -1\}$

SOLUTION

a. $(6, 2)$ and $(6, 3)$ are two ordered pairs with the same first coordinate and different second coordinates. Therefore, H is not a function. $D_H = \{1, 6\}$ and $R_H = \{4, 2, 3\}$.

b. $y = 2x + 4$ is graphed in Figure 3.4. From its graph we can see that exactly one y exists for each x. Thus, it is a function; $D = R = \mathbb{R}$.

c. $x = 3$ is graphed in Figure 3.6. $(3, -1)$ and $(3, 2)$ are elements of F, so it is not a function. $D_F = \{3\}$ and $R_F = \mathbb{R}$.

d. We can see from the grah of $y = -1$ (Figure 3.6) that for any value of x, $y = -1$. Thus, f is a function. $D_f = \mathbb{R}$ and $R_f = \{-1\}$.

Up to this point we have used two methods to describe a function. One method uses a rule of correspondence, such as $y = 2x + 4$, to indicate that y is a function of x. The second method uses set notation, such as $f = \{(1, 5), (2, 9), (7, 8)\}$. We may often conveniently combine these two methods. For example, let $f = \{(x, y) \mid y = 3x - 7\}$. Now replace y by the expression $f(x)$. Then,

$$y = 3x - 7 \qquad \text{and} \qquad f(x) = 3x - 7$$

have the same meaning. The expression $f(x) = 3x - 7$ means "the function f tells us to multiply x by 3 and then subtract 7."

The **functional notation** $f(x)$ is read "f of x." $f(x)$ does not mean f *times* x, it means "the functional value of f at x." That is, f represents a set of ordered pairs, and $f(x)$ represents the value of y for a given value of x. Thus, a point (x, y) can now be written as $(x, f(x))$ because $y = f(x)$.

EXAMPLE 5

Let $f(x) = 3x - 7$ and $g(x) = -x^2 - x + 3$. Find:

a. $g(2)$　　**b.** $f(-1)$　　**c.** $g(2) - f(-1)$　　**d.** $f(a + 6)$

SOLUTION

a. $g(2) = -2^2 - 2 + 3 = -4 - 2 + 3 = -6 + 3 = -3$
b. $f(-1) = 3(-1) - 7 = -3 - 7 = -10$
c. $g(2) - f(-1) = [-3] - [-10] = -3 + 10 = 7$
d. The function f tells us to multiply $a + 6$ by 3 and then subtract 7 from this result. That is, $f(a + 6) = 3(a + 6) - 7 = 3a + 18 - 7 = 3a + 11$

We will study several types of functions throughout this text. The main one, which we discussed in the last section, is the **linear function**, $f(x) = mx + b$. A special type of linear function is the **constant function**, $f(x) = C$, such as $f(x) = -1$. If $m = 1$ and $b = 0$, then we have the **identity function**, $I(x) = x$; that is, $I(x)$ is the same as x, such as $I(3) = 3$. Also, $f(x) = \mid x \mid$ is the **absolute value function**. When a function is defined by different rules over different parts of its domain, it is called a **piecewise function**. Note in our final examples that the y-axis is labeled as the f-axis because $y = f(x)$.

EXAMPLE 6

Graph $y = f(x) = \dfrac{|x|}{x}$ (see Figure 3.12).

SOLUTION   The domain of f is $D_f = \{x \mid x \neq 0\}$. Now consider f for $x < 0$ and $x > 0$:

If $x < 0$, then $y = \dfrac{|x|}{x} = \dfrac{-x}{x} = -1$.

If $x > 0$, then $y = \dfrac{|x|}{x} = \dfrac{x}{x} = 1$. Thus,

$$f(x) = \begin{cases} -1, & \text{if } x < 0 \\ \;\;1, & \text{if } x > 0 \end{cases}$$

Let $y_1 = -1$ for $x < 0$. $\{(-3, -1), (-1, -1)\}$ determines the graph of y_1. Graph $(0, -1)$ as an open circle because it is not a point on y_1. Let $y_2 = 1$ for $x > 0$. $\{(1, 1), (3, 1)\}$ determines the graph of y_2. **Graph** $(0, 1)$ **as an open circle.**

FIGURE 3.12

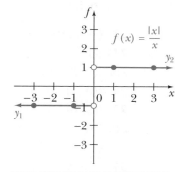

EXAMPLE 7

Graph the function f for the given values of x (see Figure 3.13).

$$f(x) = \begin{cases} -3, & \text{if } \quad\quad x < -1 \\ 2x, & \text{if } -1 \le x \le 1 \\ -x + 3, & \text{if } \quad\; 1 < x < 3 \end{cases}$$

FIGURE 3.13

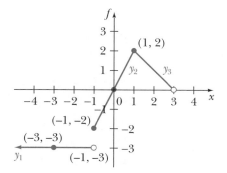

SOLUTION   We will call the three parts of the graph of f, y_1, y_2, and y_3:
1. $y_1 = -3$ for $x < -1$. We graph $(-1, -3)$ as an open circle because it is not on the ray $y_1 = -3$. $(-3, -3)$ is a point on the ray; the graph is determined by $\{(-3, -3), (-1, -3)\}$.

(continued)

2. $y_2 = 2x$ for $-1 \le x \le 1$. y_2 is determined by $\{(-1, -2), (0, 0), (1, 2)\}$. $(-1, -2)$ and $(1, 2)$ are graphed as closed circles because they are on y_2.

3. $y_3 = -x + 3$ for $1 < x < 3$. y_3 is determined by $\{(1, 2), (2, 1), (3, 0)\}$. $(1, 2)$ is graphed as a closed circle because it is on y_3. $(3, 0)$ is graphed as an open circle because it is not on y_3.

EXERCISE SET 3.2

A

1 Give the domain and range of the following in set notation.

1. $\{(4, 7), (8, 3)\}$

2. $\{(-1, 6), (0, -9)\}$

3. $\{(1, 9), (-2, 0), (3, 3)\}$

4. $\{(6, -2), (6, 0), (6, 4)\}$

5. $\{(3, 9), (-3, 9), (2, 9)\}$

6. $\{(0, 0), (3, 3), (5, 5)\}$

7. $\{(0, 1), (-2, 5), (-1, 2), (1, 2), (2, 5)\}$

8. $\{(0, 0), (1, 1), (1, -1), (16, 2), (16, -2)\}$

Express the domain and range of the following in interval notation.

9. $f = \{(x, y) \mid y = x + 1\}$

10. $g = \{(x, y) \mid y = -x\}$

11. $h = \{(x, y) \mid y = x^4\}$

12. $T = \{(x, y) \mid y = x^2 + 3\}$

13. $S = \{(x, y) \mid y = \sqrt{x - 2}\}$

14. $k = \{(x, y) \mid y = 1 + \sqrt{-x}\}$

Find the domain of the following.

15. $y = \dfrac{1}{x - 4}$

16. $y = \dfrac{x}{x + 5}$

17. $y = \dfrac{1}{x^2 + 1}$

18. $y = \dfrac{-2}{x^2 - 9}$

19. $s = \sqrt{8 - 2t}$

20. $v = \sqrt{t + 7}$

21. $h = \dfrac{1}{\sqrt{x - 3}}$

22. $P = \dfrac{c}{\sqrt{3c + 9}}$

2 Decide which of the following relations are functions. Give the domain, D, and range, R, of each relation and then graph each one. Note that some graphs are a finite number of points.

23. $\{(-2, 2), (-1, 4), (4, -3)\}$

24. $\{(1, 2), (1, 1), (2, 2), (3, 2)\}$

25. $\{(-2, 2), (-1, 2), (0, 1), (1, 0)\}$

26. $\{(0, 3), (0, -3), (3, 0), (-3, 0)\}$

27. $\{(0, 0), (1, 1) (1, -1), (4, 2), (4, -2)\}$

28. $\{(0, 0), (1, 1) (-1, 1), (2, 4), (-2, 4)\}$

29. $y = x + 1$ **30.** $y = -2x - 1$

31. $x = 4$ **32.** $y = 2$

Determine which of the following statements are true and which are false. Give an example that illustrates your answer to each one.

33. All functions are relations.

34. All relations are functions.

35. The range of $f(x) = mx + b$ is R.

36. All linear equations are relations, but some of them are not functions.

Let $f(x) = 2x - 4$, $g(x) = -3x + 2$, $h(x) = x^2$, and $k(x) = 3x^2 + 2x - 4$. Find:

37. $f(5)$ **38.** $-g(6)$

39. $h(-4)$ **40.** $g(4) - k(-1)$

41. $f(-2) + h(3)$ **42.** $3f(1) - 2g(0)$

43. $g(3) + 2$ **44.** $g(3 + 2)$

45. $g(x + h)$ **46.** $f(-3) \cdot g(0)$

47. $h(2) \cdot k(0)$ **48.** $[f(5)]^2$

49. $\dfrac{g(2)}{h(6)}$ **50.** $\dfrac{f(0)}{k(1)}$

51. $\dfrac{h(3)}{f(2)}$ **52.** $f(x + h)$

53. $-f(x)$ **54.** $f(x + h) - f(x)$

Graph the following piecewise functions.

55. $f(x) = \dfrac{|2x|}{x}$

56. $g(x) = \dfrac{|x - 1|}{x - 1}$

57. $f(x) = \begin{cases} 2, & \text{if } x < 0 \\ -2, & \text{if } x > 0 \end{cases}$

58. $h(x) = \begin{cases} x, & \text{if } x \le 0 \\ x + 1, & \text{if } x > 0 \end{cases}$

59. $G(x) = \begin{cases} 3, & \text{if } x < 1 \\ 2x, & \text{if } x \ge 1 \end{cases}$

60. $y = \begin{cases} x + 4, & \text{if } -4 \le x \le 0 \\ -x, & \text{if } 0 < x < 2 \end{cases}$

B

61. $f(x) = \begin{cases} 1, & \text{if } 1 \le x < 2 \\ 2, & \text{if } 2 \le x < 3 \\ 3, & \text{if } 3 \le x < 4 \end{cases}$

62. $y = \begin{cases} x, & \text{if } 0 < x \le 1 \\ x - 1, & \text{if } 1 < x \le 2 \\ x - 2, & \text{if } 2 < x \le 3 \end{cases}$

63. $y = \begin{cases} 0, & \text{if } x < -1 \\ 3x, & \text{if } -1 \le x < 1 \\ -2, & \text{if } x > 1 \end{cases}$

64. $y = \begin{cases} -3, & \text{if } x \le -2 \\ |x|, & \text{if } -2 < x \le 2 \\ 1, & \text{if } x > 2 \end{cases}$

Graph the following equations.

65. $x = |y|$ **66.** $x = |y| + 2$

67. $x = |y + 2|$ **68.** $x = -|y|$

69. $x = -3|y|$ **70.** $x = -|y| + 1$

C

Answer the following questions with complete sentences.

71. What is the difference between a relation and a function?

72. Explain why the domain of a relation is not always the entire set of real numbers.

73. What is meant by the term "piecewise function"?

74. What is meant by the term "constant function?"

75. What does the function $f(x) = 2x + 1$ tell us to do?

76. What does the function $g(x) = x^2 + x - 3$ tell us to do?

Graph the following equations. (*Hint:* Consider the graph in each quadrant.)

77. $|y| = |x|$

78. $|x| + |y| = 1$

79. $|x| - |y| = 1$

REVIEW EXERCISES

Simplify the following. (See Section 1.4.)

80. $(\sqrt{40})^2$ **81.** $\sqrt{125}$ **82.** $\sqrt{8}$

Find the hypotenuse, c, of the right triangle, given its legs a and b. (See Section 2.3.)

83. $a = 3, b = 4$

84. $a = 10, b = 5$

85. $a\sqrt{40}, b = \sqrt{8}$

3.3 DISTANCE AND SLOPE FORMULAS

1	**Distance Formula**
2	**Slope of a Line**

1   Distance Formula

In Section 2.3 we discussed the Pythagorean theorem. This section will use this theorem to find the distance between two points in the *xy*-plane. We begin by considering the distance between two points on the number line.

If A and B are two points on a line or in a plane, then the distance *d* from A to B is denoted by $d(A, B)$. If A = B, then $d(A, B) = 0$. If A ≠ B, then $d(A, B) > 0$ and $d(A, B) = d(B, A)$; that is, the distance from A to B is equal to the distance from B to A.

Let A and B be two points on a number line whose coordinates are 2 and 6, respectively; we denote this by A(2) and B(6). We can see from Figure 3.14 that the distance between A and B is 4 units. To have $d(A, B) = d(B, A)$, we use absolute value and define $d(A, B)$ and $d(B, A)$ to be:

$$d(A, B) = |6 - 2| = |4| = 4$$
$$d(B, A) = |2 - 6| = |-4| = 4$$

FIGURE 3.14

In general, let A(*a*) and B(*b*) represent two points on the number line with coordinates *a* and *b*, respectively.

Distance Formula

Let A(*a*) and B(*b*) be two points on the number line. Then the distance from A to B is

$$d(A, B) = |b - a|$$

We can use the distance formula for the number line and the Pythagorean theorem to find the distance between two points in the *xy*-plane. We begin with an example.

The points A(2, 1) and B(6, 4) are graphed in Figure 3.15. The horizontal broken line through A and the vertical broken line through B intersect at C(6, 1) and form a right triangle. The length of the hypotenuse, *c*, is the distance from A to B, $d(A, B)$. To find *c* we first have to determine *b* and *a*, the legs of the right triangle. The value of *b* is the distance between 2 and 6 on the *x*-axis, and the value of *a* is the distance between 1 and 4 on the *y*-axis; that is,

$$b = d(A, C) = |6 - 2| = |4| = 4$$
$$a = d(C, B) = |4 - 1| = |3| = 3$$

From the Pythagorean theorem,

$$c^2 = b^2 + a^2 = 16 + 9 = 25 \qquad \text{and} \qquad c = d(A, B) = \sqrt{25} = 5$$

B Let A and B be two points in the *xy*-plane. Find the domain and range of the following functions.

57. d, where $d(A, B)$ = the distance from A to B.

58. $g(A, B) = m$, where m is the slope of $\overleftrightarrow{AB}$.

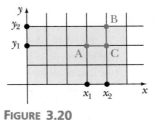

FIGURE 3.20

C

59. The *xy*-plane has more than one distance formula. If we live in a city that has perpendicular streets, then our distance formula would not give the shortest distance from A to B because buildings are in the way (Figure 3.20). To get from A to B we would travel from A to C and then from C to B. Find a formula, D(A, B), for this distance from A to B (which is called the "taxicab distance formula"). If A and B are the points A(6, 3) and B(10, 5), show that D(A, B) = D(B, A).

Answer the following questions with complete sentences.

60. Why is absolute value used in finding the distance between two points on the number line?

61. Why is absolute value *not* used in finding the distance between two points in the plane?

62. Why is the slope of a horizontal line zero?

63. Why is the slope of a vertical line undefined?

REVIEW EXERCISES

Graph the following. (See Section 3.2.)

64. $x = 4$ **65.** $y = 2x - 1$

66. $f(x) = -3x + 5$

Let $f(x) = 2x - 1$ and $g(x) = -3x + 5$. Find the following. (See Section 3.2.)

67. $f(x + 3)$

68. $f(x) + 3$

69. $f(x) + h$

70. $f(x + h)$

71. $-f(x)$

72. $f(x + h) - f(x)$

73. $g(4 + h)$

74. $-g(4)$

75. $g(4 + h) - g(4)$

3.4 EQUATION OF A LINE

1 Point–Slope Form: $y - y_1 = m(x - x_1)$

2 Slope–Intercept Form: $y = mx + b$

3 Parallel and Perpendicular Lines

4 Business Applications

1 Point–Slope Form: $y - y_1 = m(x - x_1)$

One of the main objectives of analytic geometry is to describe geometric figures with algebraic equations. We begin this topic with the simplest figure, a line. As mentioned in the preceding section, the first step in finding the equation of a line is to determine its slope. Once we know a line's slope and one of its points, we can find its equation.

Exactly one line passes through a fixed point with a given slope. Also, the slope of a line is independent of the points used to calculate it. These two facts allow us to describe a line algebraically. To illustrate this, we find the equation of the line through the point A(2, 1) with slope $m = 3$. Let P(x, y) represent any point on the line (Figure 3.21). Because the slope of a line is constant, P is on the line provided that the slope determined by P and A is 3. That is,

$$\frac{y - 1}{x - 2} = 3 \quad \text{or} \quad y - 1 = 3(x - 2)$$

The equation $y - 1 = 3(x - 2)$ expresses the relationship between x and y for every point on the line determined by A(2, 1) and $m = 3$.

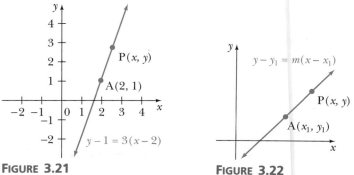

FIGURE 3.21   **FIGURE 3.22**

To generalize this example, let $A(x_1, y_1)$ be a fixed point on a nonvertical line with slope m (a vertical line does not have a slope). Let P(x, y) be any point on the line (Figure 3.22). Then the slope determined by A and P is equal to m; that is,

$$\frac{y - y_1}{x - x_1} = m \quad \text{or} \quad y - y_1 = m(x - x_1)$$

which is called the **point–slope form** of the equation of a line.

EXAMPLE 1

Find the equation of the line determined by the two given points.

a. A(3, 5), B(4, 2)   **b.** C(3, −2), D(3, 4)

SOLUTION

a. First, find the slope of $\overleftrightarrow{AB}$:

$$m = \frac{2 - 5}{4 - 3} = \frac{-3}{1} = -3$$

When we use A, the point–slope form is $y - 5 = -3(x - 3)$.
When we use B, the point–slope form is $y - 2 = -3(x - 4)$.

We might seem to have two different equations for $\overleftrightarrow{AB}$, depending on which point we use. We can show that these equations are equivalent by solving for y:

$$
\begin{aligned}
y - 5 &= -3(x - 3) & y - 2 &= -3(x - 4) \\
y - 5 &= -3x + 9 & y - 2 &= -3x + 12 \\
y &= -3x + 14 & y &= -3x + 14
\end{aligned}
$$

b. If we try to find the slope of $\overleftrightarrow{CD}$, we have $m = \dfrac{4 - (-2)}{3 - 3} = \dfrac{6}{0}$, which is undefined. $\overleftrightarrow{CD}$ does not have a slope; it is a vertical line, so its equation is $x = 3$ (see Figure 3.6).

2 Slope–Intercept Form: $y = mx + b$

Every nonvertical line has a slope, m, and a y-intercept, $(0, b)$. $(0, b)$ must satisfy the equation $y - y_1 = m(x - x_1)$. If we let $x_1 = 0$ and $y_1 = b$, then

$$y - y_1 = m(x - x_1)$$
$$y - b = m(x - 0)$$
$$y - b = mx$$
$$y = mx + b \quad \text{or} \quad f(x) = mx + b$$

This last equation is called the **slope–intercept form** of the equation of the line and is a convenient form to use when the y-intercept is known, as in the next example.

EXAMPLE 2

A linear function, g, has an x-intercept of 2 and a y-intercept of 3. Find its equation.

SOLUTION $A(2, 0)$ and $B(0, 3)$ are the points corresponding to the intercepts. Thus, the slope of g is $m = \dfrac{3 - 0}{0 - 2} = -\dfrac{3}{2}$. $b = 3$, so $g(x) = -\dfrac{3}{2}x + 3$

If we know the slope of a line and a point that is not its y-intercept, then we can use either of two methods to find the slope–intercept form of the equation. In the first one we express the equation in the point–slope form and then solve for y. In the second we find the value of b by substituting the coordinates of the point in the equation $y = mx + b$. Both methods require about the same amount of work, as illustrated in the following example.

EXAMPLE 3

Find the slope–intercept form of the equation of the line through the point $A(1, 3)$ with slope $m = 4$.

SOLUTION A   The point–slope form of the equation is
$$y - 3 = 4(x - 1)$$
$$y - 3 = 4x - 4$$
$$y = 4x - 1$$

SOLUTION B   In the form $y = mx + b$, $m = 4$. Thus, $y = 4x + b$. If $x = 1$ and $y = 3$, then
$$3 = 4 \cdot 1 + b$$
$$-1 = b, \quad \text{so}$$
$$y = 4x - 1$$

The following expression is important in advanced mathematics and in certain applied areas, such as business*:

$$\frac{f(x + h) - f(x)}{h}$$

If f is a linear function, then this quotient represents the slope of the line. For example, let $f(x) = 2x - 1$, whose slope is $m = 2$. Let A$(x, f(x))$ and B$(x + h, f(x + h))$ be two points on the graph of f (Figure 3.23). Then $f(x + h) - f(x)$ is the change in y, and $(x + h) - x = h$ is the change in x. Thus,

$$m = \frac{f(x + h) - f(x)}{(x + h) - x}$$

$$= \frac{f(x + h) - f(x)}{h} \qquad \frac{\text{change in } y}{\text{change in } x}$$

$$= \frac{[2(x + h) - 1] - [2x - 1]}{h}$$

$$= \frac{2x + 2h - 1 - 2x + 1}{h}$$

$$= \frac{2h}{h}$$

$$= 2$$

FIGURE 3.23

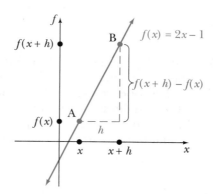

$f(x) = 2x - 1$

---

* Banks pay interest on saving accounts at a given rate for a given period of time. **Compound interest** is interest paid on interest. For example, if \$10,000 is invested at 12% compounded monthly, then in 20 years \$108,926 will be in the account (see Example 3, Section 10.5).

We may often find approximating the growth of an account to be more convenient. To do this we let A(t) be the amount in an account, at time $t \geq 0$, which is compounded over a period h, where $0 < h < 1$. Then a formula used in this approximation is

$$\frac{A(t + h) - A(t)}{h}$$

Math in Time

ALEXANDRIA, FOUNDED BY Alexander the Great in 325 B.C., was the greatest mathematical center in classical times. Upon Alexander's death two years later, control of Egypt fell to Ptolemy, one of his generals, who founded the University of Alexandria. Similar to the universities of today, it contained lecture rooms, laboratories, museums, and a library of more than 600,000 papyrus scrolls. The school opened in approximately 300 B.C. and was the intellectual center of the ancient world for almost 1000 years.

Ptolemy invited the best scholars of the day to staff the university, with Euclid being chosen to head the department of mathematics. Little is known about Euclid except that he probably received his education in Athens. He had a reputation for modesty and was known to display impatience with those who were not interested in mathematics for its own sake. When a student asked him of what practical use geometry was, he is reported to have said to his slave, "He wants profit from his learning — give him a penny."

The impact of Euclid's *Elements* as a model of mathematical reasoning was immense and lasting. It served as a basis for the study of plane geometry for 2300 years, and more than 1000 editions have appeared since its first printing in 1482. The *Elements* was an introductory textbook covering all elementary mathematics since the time of Pythagoras. Besides geometry, it covered the theory of numbers, irrational numbers, and algebraic topics written in geometric terms. Euclid also wrote books on advanced mathematics, optics, music, and astronomy.

A postulate is a statement accepted without proof, such as "Two points determine a line." One of the most important ideas in the *Elements* is the parallel postulate, which states "Exactly one line can be drawn through a point parallel to a given line." Failed attempts to reduce this postulate to a theorem (a statement that has been proved) led in the nineteenth century to a full appreciation of Euclid's genius in adopting it as a postulate and to the discovery of other, non-Euclidean, geometries. One of these was developed by Bernhard Riemann (1826–1866), a German mathematician, and was based on the postulate that parallel lines do not exist on a sphere. This geometry went on to describe the curvature of space in four dimensions, which was used by Albert Einstein (1879–1955) in his general theory of relativity. Today physicists use eleven space–time dimensions in their efforts to unify the fundamental forces of nature into one theory.

EXAMPLE 4

Let $g(x) = -3x + 5$. Evaluate $\dfrac{g(4 + h) - g(4)}{h}$.

SOLUTION

$$\frac{g(4 + h) - g(4)}{h} = \frac{[-3(4 + h) + 5] - [-3 \cdot 4 + 5]}{h}$$

$$= \frac{-12 - 3h + 5 - (-7)}{h}$$

$$= \frac{-12 - 3h + 12}{h}$$

$$= \frac{-3h}{h}$$

$$= -3$$

---

3   Parallel and Perpendicular Lines

The properties of parallel and perpendicular lines are of major importance in plane geometry. We will approach this material from the point of view of analytic geometry.

Recall that the slope of a line is a measure of its steepness. Because **parallel lines** do not intersect, they are equally steep, and thus their slopes are equal (Figure 3.24).

Perpendicular lines are two lines that meet at right angles. If two nonvertical lines are perpendicular, then the product of their slopes is -1; that is, let m_1 be the slope of the line L_1 and m_2 be the slope of the line L_2; if L_1 and L_2 are perpendicular, then

$$m_1 m_2 = -1 \quad \text{or} \quad m_2 = -\frac{1}{m_1}$$

This result is not obvious (it is proved in plane geometry), but we can illustrate it with an example. In Figure 3.25 two perpendicular lines, L_1 and L_2, intersect at the origin. As indicated, the slope of L_1 is $m_1 = 2/1 = 2$, and the slope of L_2 is $m_2 = \dfrac{1}{-2} = -\dfrac{1}{2}$. The product of the slopes is $m_1 m_2 = 2\left(-\dfrac{1}{2}\right) = -1$.

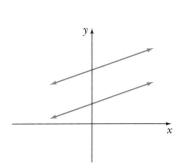

FIGURE 3.24

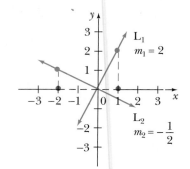

FIGURE 3.25

Parallel and Perpendicular Lines

1. Nonvertical lines are parallel if they have the same slope. Vertical lines are parallel.

2. Nonvertical lines are perpendicular if the product of their slopes is -1. A vertical line (no slope) is perpendicular to a horizontal line ($m = 0$).

We have discussed two forms of the equation of a line. A third one is called the **standard form**; it is defined as follows:

> **Standard form**: $Ax + By = C$, where A, B, and C are real numbers (A and B are not both zero).

EXAMPLE 5

Find the equation of the line through the point $A(3, -2)$ that is parallel to the line $4x + 2y = 5$. Write the answer in standard form.

SOLUTION

The slope of the required line is the same as the slope of $4x + 2y = 5$, because the lines are parallel. To find the slope of $4x + 2y = 5$, we write the equation in the form $y = mx + b$:

$$4x + 2y = 5$$
$$2y = -4x + 5$$
$$y = -2x + \frac{5}{2}, \quad \text{so } m = -2$$

Thus, the slope of both lines is -2. The point–slope form of the equation of the parallel line through A is

$$y - (-2) = -2(x - 3)$$
$$y + 2 = -2x + 6 \qquad \text{Subtract 2.}$$
$$y = -2x + 4 \qquad \text{Add } 2x.$$
$$2x + y = 4$$

EXAMPLE 6

Show that $C(0, 0)$, $A(2, -2)$, and $B(6, 2)$ are the vertices of a right triangle. Sketch the triangle (see Figure 3.26).

FIGURE 3.26

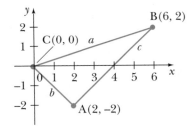

SOLUTION

In Example 2 in the last section (p. 121), we used the distance formula and the Pythagorean theorem to show that $\angle A$ is a right angle. A simpler way is to show that the product of the slopes of $\overleftrightarrow{AB}$ and $\overleftrightarrow{AC}$ is -1:

$$m_{AB} = \frac{2 - (-2)}{6 - 2} = 1, \quad m_{AC} = \frac{-2 - 0}{2 - 0} = -1, \quad \text{and}$$

$m_{AB} \cdot m_{AC} = 1(-1) = -1$. Thus, $\overleftrightarrow{AB}$ is perpendicular to $\overleftrightarrow{AC}$, so $\angle A$ is a right angle.

4   Business Applications

Linear equations have many applications in business. The function $C(x) = mx + b$, which gives the cost C of producing x items, is called a **cost equation** or **cost function** (m is called the *variable cost* per item and b the *fixed cost*).

EXAMPLE 7

A taxi company charges a fixed cost of $1.40 plus $1.60 per mile. The cost equation is $C(x) = 1.6x + 1.4$.

a. How much does it cost to travel 5 miles?
b. How far can one travel for $35?

SOLUTION

a. $x = 5$, so $C(5) = 1.6(5) + 1.4 = 8 + 1.4 = 9.4$; it costs $9.40 to travel 5 miles.

b. Let $C(x) = 35$. Then:
$$1.6x + 1.4 = 35$$
$$1.6x = 33.6$$
$$x = 21, \quad \text{so one can travel 21 miles for \$35.}$$

EXERCISE SET 3.4

A

1 Find the point–slope equation of the line through the given point with the given slope. Graph each line.

1. $(1, 2)$, $m = 3$ **2.** $(-3, 2)$, $m = 1$
3. $(-6, -4)$, $m = -2$ **4.** $(2, -3)$, $m = 4$
5. $(0, 2)$, $m = 1/2$ **6.** $(3, 0)$, $m = -2/5$

Find the point–slope equation of the line determined by the two points.

7. $(2, 1)$, $(3, 3)$ **8.** $(-3, 2)$, $(1, -6)$
9. $(1, 4)$, $(-2, -1)$ **10.** $(0, 0)$, $(-2, 5)$
11. $(0, -3)$, $(1, 0)$ **12.** $(-2, 0)$, $(-1, 6)$

2 Find the slope–intercept equation of the line through the given point with the given slope. Graph each line.

13. $(0, 2)$, $m = 3$
14. $(0, -1)$, $m = -2$
15. $(-2, -3)$, $m = -1$
16. $(3, 4)$, $m = 0$
17. $(4, 1)$, $m = -1/2$
18. $(-3, -2)$, $m = -4/3$

Find the slope–intercept equation of the line determined by the two points.

19. $(0, -3)$, $(1, -1)$ **20.** $(0, 4)$, $(2, 0)$
21. $(-2, 0)$, $(-1, -4)$ **22.** $(0, 0)$, $(6, -1)$

23. $(4, 2)$, $(-3, -6)$ **24.** $(1, -4)$, $(-2, 1)$

Find the equation of the line determined by the given points. Use any form of the equation.

25. $(1, 1)$, $(7, 8)$ **26.** $(-2, 3)$, $(0, 1)$
27. $(1, 4)$, $(3, 4)$ **28.** $(0, 0)$, $(-3, 3)$
29. $(-4, 0)$, $(0, -2)$ **30.** $(-4, -1)$, $(1, -1)$
31. $(2, 1)$, $(2, 4)$ **32.** $(1, -4)$, $(-2, 7)$
33. $(-3, 5)$, $(-3, 1)$ **34.** $(0, 3)$, $(-2, 3)$
35. $(0, -3)$, $(-1, 5)$ **36.** $(-5, 0)$, $(-5, -1)$

Find $\dfrac{f(x + h) - f(x)}{h}$ for the function f.

37. $f(x) = 3x + 1$ **38.** $f(x) = -2x - 3$
39. $f(x) = 4$ **40.** $f(x) = -5$
41. $f(x) = \dfrac{1}{2}x$ **42.** $f(x) = \dfrac{2}{3}x + 2$

Evaluate $\dfrac{g(a + h) - g(a)}{h}$ for the function g and value of a.

43. $g(x) = 6x - 2$; $a = 4$
44. $g(x) = -4x$; $a = -3$
45. $g(x) = x + 4$; $a = -6$
46. $g(x) = 7$; $a = 5$

3 Determine whether the following pairs of lines are parallel, perpendicular, or neither.

47. $y = 4x + 3$
    $y + 5 = 4(x - 2)$

48. $h(x) = x - 4$
    $k(x) = -x + 1$

49. $f(x) = 3x - 2$
    $g(x) = -3x + 4$

50. $x = 3$
    $y = 2$

51. $2x - 3y = -15$
    $3x + 2y = -6$

52. $-3x + 4y = -4$
    $6x - 8y = -2$

53. $x = -2$
    $x = 4$

54. $F(x) = 2x + 1$
    $2y = x$

Find the equation of the line through the given point that is a. parallel to the given line, b. perpendicular to the given line. Write the answers in standard form.

55. $(3, 1)$; $y - 7 = 2(x + 4)$
56. $(-1, 5)$; $f(x) = -6x$
57. $(-1, -4)$; $x + y = 3$
58. $(0, 0)$; $2x + 5y = 1$
59. $(4, -2)$; $x = -6$
60. $(-1, -7)$; $y = 0$

The line L is determined by the two given points. Find the equation of the line through the point P that is a. parallel to L, b. perpendicular to L.

61. $(1, 4), (2, 7)$; $P(-3, 6)$
62. $(1, 2), (-4, -1)$; $P(3, -2)$
63. $(-1, 6), (2, 6)$; $P(4, 3)$
64. $(1, 0), (1, 4)$; $P(-3, -5)$
65. $(-3, 6), (2, 5)$; $P(0, -4)$
66. $(-6, 0), (0, 3)$; $P(4, -1)$

Use the slope formula to determine whether the given points are vertices of a right triangle. Graph each triangle.

67. $(-2, -1), (6, -1), (2, 3)$
68. $(1, 1), (5, 3), (2, -1)$
69. $(-5, 1), (-7, -2), (-1, -2)$
70. $(-1, 4), (-4, -2), (9, -1)$

4 Solve the following cost-equation problems.

71. Suppose that the cost equation (in dollars) of producing x clocks is $C(x) = 10x + 15$.
    a. How much does it cost to produce 7 clocks?
    b. How many clocks can be produced for $145?

72. Suppose that the cost equation (in dollars) of producing x pairs of ski poles is $C(x) = 8.75x + 12.25$.
    a. How much does it cost to produce 6 pairs of ski poles?
    b. How many pairs of ski poles can be produced for $126?

B Many real-world situations can be described (approximately) with linear equations. For the following, use the two data points to find the slope–intercept form of the equation of the line relating the number of items, x, and the cost per item, y. Then answer the question.

73. A company can produce 8 boxes of candy for $12 and 15 boxes of candy for $18. What is the cost of producing 35 boxes of candy?

74. A company can produce 20 aluminum windows for $3600 and 40 of them for $6600. What is the cost of producing 70 windows?

75. Find the area in the first quadrant determined by the line $y = -2x + 4$.

76. Find the area in the second quadrant determined by the line $f(x) = 3x + 5$.

77. Find the area in the third quadrant determined by the lines $y = -2$ and $x = -3$.

78. Find the equations of the lines L_1 and L_2 in Figure 3.25.

C

Answer the following questions with complete sentences.

79. Compare and contrast the University of Alexandria and the college that you attend.

80. Discuss how you would derive the "slope–intercept form" of the equation of a line from the "standard form."

81. Given two points, discuss how you would find the equation of the line determined by them.

82. Why does the formula $m_1 m_2 = -1$ only apply to nonvertical perpendicular lines?

REVIEW EXERCISES

Graph the following sets on the number line (See Sections 2.6 and 2.7.)

83. $\{x \mid x \leq 1 \quad \text{and} \quad x > -2\}$

84. $|x + 1| > 2$

Graph the following lines. (See Section 3.2)

85. $y = 1$ **86.** $x = -3$

3.5 GRAPHING INEQUALITIES AND SYSTEMS OF INEQUALITIES

> **1** Graphing $\leq$ or $\geq$ Linear Inequalities
>
> **2** Graphing $<$ or $>$ Linear Inequalities
>
> **3** Solving Systems of Linear Inequalities by Graphing

1 Graphing $\leq$ or $\geq$ Linear Inequalities

In Section 2.6 we graphed inequalities in one variable, such as $x \leq 1$ and $x > -2$, on the number line. This section extends these ideas to graph inequalities in two variables, such as $y \leq x + 1$ and $y > -2x$, in the xy-plane. We begin with a discussion of the graph of $x \leq 1$.

Recall that A(1) represents the point A whose coordinate is 1. This point separates the number line into three sets of points: the point A; the set of points to the left of A, which is called a **half-line** and denoted $x < 1$; and the half-line to the right of A, $x > 1$. The inequality $x \leq 1$ represents the point A, which is graphed as a solid circle, and the half-line $x < 1$ (Figure 3.27).

FIGURE 3.27

Just as a point separates the number line into two half-lines, a line separates the xy-plane into two **half-planes**. A half-plane is the set of all the points in a plane on one side of a line. For example, the graph of $y = x + 1$ divides the plane into three sets of points:

1. The points on the line $y = x + 1$.

2. The points in the half-plane below the line, $y < x + 1$.

3. The points in the half-plane above the line, $y > x + 1$.

The line $y = x + 1$ is called the **boundary** of the two half-planes. The inequality $y \leq x + 1$ (graphed in Figure 3.28) represents the line $y = x + 1$, which is graphed as a solid line, and the half-plane $y < x + 1$.

The point P(3, 2) is in the half-plane $y < x + 1$, and (3, 2) satisfies the inequality $y < x + 1$; that is, $2 < 3 + 1$. In general, the coordinates of every point in a half-plane satisfy its inequality. This fact provides us with the following method for graphing an inequality that includes its boundary. Because only two half-planes exist, this procedure is fairly simple.

FIGURE 3.28

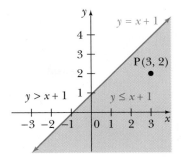

Graphing an Inequality Involving ≤ or ≥

1. Graph the corresponding equation as a solid line.

2. Pick a **test point** not on the line; (0, 0) is convenient if the line does not contain the origin.

3. The graph of the inequality is
   a. The half-plane containing the test point, if its coordinates satisfy the inequality
   b. The half-plane not containing the test point, if its coordinates do not satisfy the inequality

---

EXAMPLE 1

Graph $x - 2y \geq 2$ (see Figure 3.29).

SOLUTION

First, graph $x - 2y = 2$ as a solid line using $(0, -1)$ and $(2, 0)$. Because the line does not contain the origin, $(0, 0)$, this is a convenient test point. Letting $x = y = 0$ in $x - 2y > 2$, we have $0 - 0 > 2$, which is a false statement. Thus, the correct half-plane is the one not containing $(0, 0)$, so the region below the line $x - 2y = 2$ is colored.

FIGURE 3.29

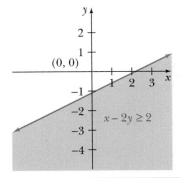

EXAMPLE 2

Graph the following inequalities (see Figures 3.30 and 3.31 on page 136).

a. $x \leq 1$ **b.** $y \geq 0$

(continued)

SOLUTION **a.** $x = 1$ is a vertical line through $(1, 0)$. $(0, 0)$ satisfies $x < 1$ as $0 < 1$. Thus, the half-plane is the one to the left of the line.

b. The line $y = 0$ is the x-axis. Because the line contains the origin, pick another point as the test point, say $A(1, 2)$. This point satisfies $y > 0$ as $2 > 0$, so the half-plane is the one above the x-axis.

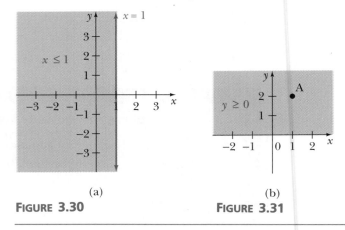

(a)   (b)

FIGURE 3.30   **FIGURE 3.31**

2   Graphing < or > Linear Inequalities

In Figure 3.27 $x = 1$ is graphed as a solid circle because it is in the set. When we graph $x > -2$ on the number line, $x = -2$ is graphed as an open circle because it is not in the set (Figure 3.32).

FIGURE 3.32

In a similar way the graph of the half-plane $y > -2x$ does not include its boundary line, $y = -2x$, so we graph it as an open, or broken, line. The graph contains the origin, so $P(1, 2)$ is a convenient test point. Because $2 > -2 \cdot 1$ is a true statement, the half-plane containing P is the correct one (see Figure 3.33).

FIGURE 3.33

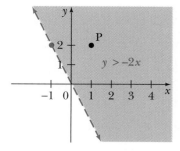

E X A M P L E 3   Graph $|y| < 1$ (see Figure 3.34).

SOLUTION Recall that $|a| < b$ if $-b < a < b$. Thus, if $|y| < 1$, then $-1 < y < 1$. Graph $y = 1$ and $y = -1$ as broken lines. The graph of $-1 < y < 1$ is the region in the plane between the lines $y = 1$ and $y = -1$. This can be determined by using $(0, 0)$ as a test point: $-1 < 0 < 1$.

FIGURE 3.34

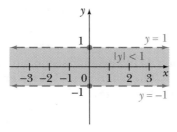

EXAMPLE 4

Graph $|x + 1| > 2$ (see Figure 3.35).

SOLUTION

If $|a| > b$, then $a > b$ or $a < -b$. $|x + 1| > 2$, if

$$x + 1 > 2 \quad \text{or} \quad x + 1 < -2$$
$$x > 1 \quad \text{or} \quad x < -3$$

$x = 1$ and $x = -3$ are the boundary lines. The test points A(2, 0) and B(-4, 0) are in the half-planes, because $2 > 1$ and $-4 < -3$.

FIGURE 3.35

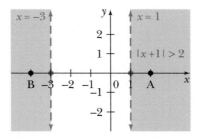

3 | **Solving Systems of Linear Inequalities by Graphing**

We now consider systems of two linear inequalities in two variables. The most efficient way to solve these systems is the **graphical method**. We graph each inequality on the same set of axes. The solution is the set of all ordered pairs that satisfies each inequality; that is, the intersection of the graphs of the individual inequalities.

As a first example, we consider the system

$$x + y \le 3$$
$$y > x + 1$$

In Figure 3.36, on page 138, both inequalities are graphed on the same set of axes. The two lines divide the plane into four regions, labeled A, B, C, and D. Let us use the following test points for the regions: A, (0, 0); B, (3, 1); C, (0, 4); D, (-1, 1). From these test points we have the following description of each region (for example, in A, $0 + 0 < 3$ is true and $0 > 0 + 1$ is false):

A: $x + y < 3$ is true and $y > x + 1$ is false.
B: $x + y < 3$ is false and $y > x + 1$ is false.
C: $x + y < 3$ is false and $y > x + 1$ is true.
D: $x + y < 3$ is true and $y > x + 1$ is true.

Thus the region D is the intersection of the two half-planes $x + y < 3$ and $y > x + 1$. The solution to this system is the region D and the heavily shaded portion of the line $x + y = 3$ adjacent to the region.

FIGURE 3.36

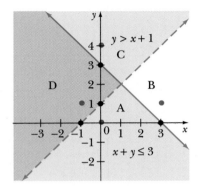

EXAMPLE 5

Graph the solution of the following system (see Figure 3.37).

$y > 2x + 1$
$y < 2x - 1$

SOLUTION $y = 2x + 1$ and $y = 2x - 1$ are graphed as broken lines. The test points A(-1, 1) and B(1, -1) determine the half-planes. Because the slope of both lines is 2, they are parallel. Thus, the intersection of the two graphs is the empty set, Ø; no solution exists for this system of inequalities.

FIGURE 3.37

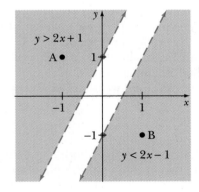

Math in Time

AN APPLICATION OF LINEAR INEQUALITIES

The graphs of systems of linear inequalities are used in an area of applied mathematics called *linear programming*. Many problems in fields such as business, economics, biology, and dietetics involve complicated relationships between capital, raw material, food supply, labor costs, and so on. In many cases the most cost-effective solution is required, such as maximizing sales or minimizing costs. In certain situations the relationships can be graphed as linear inequalities in two variables and then solved by the linear-programming technique. The following is an example of this type of problem.

Kane Manufacturing has a division that produces two models of hibachis, model A and model B. To produce each model A hibachi requires 3 pounds of cast iron and 6 minutes of labor. To produce each model B hibachi requires 4 pounds of cast iron and 3 minutes of labor. The profit for each model A hibachi is $2.00, and the profit for each model B hibachi is $1.50. If 1000 pounds of cast iron and 20 hours of labor are available for the production of hibachis per day, how many hibachis of each model should the division produce in order to help maximize the company's profits?

Answer: 120 model A, 160 model B, profit = $480.

Source: S. T. Tan, *Applied Finite Mathematics*, 3rd. ed. (Boston: PWS-KENT Publishing Company, 1990).

EXERCISE SET 3.5

A

1 Graph the following inequalities in the *xy*-plane.

1. $y \geq x + 1$ **2.** $y \leq -x + 3$
3. $x + y \geq -1$ **4.** $x - 2y \leq 2$
5. $x \geq 1$ **6.** $y \leq 0$

2

7. $y < -2x$ **8.** $y > x + 2$
9. $x + 3y > -3$ **10.** $x - y < 4$
11. $|y| > 1$ **12.** $|x + 1| < 2$

Graph the following in the *xy*-plane.

13. $y \geq x - 1$ **14.** $y > x - 1$
15. $y < -2x + 2$ **16.** $y \leq 3x - 3$

17. $x > 2$ **18.** $y \leq -3$
19. $2x + 3y \geq 6$ **20.** $2x - 5y < 3$
21. $y > x$ **22.** $y \leq -x$
23. $4y > 3x$ **24.** $-2y > 5x$
25. $\frac{x}{2} - \frac{y}{3} \geq 1$ **26.** $\frac{x}{3} + \frac{y}{6} < -\frac{1}{4}$
27. $|x| \leq 1$ **28.** $|y| < 2$
29. $|y + 2| < 3$ **30.** $|x - 3| \leq 4$
31. $|x + 4| \geq 1$ **32.** $|y - 1| > 2$

Graph the following **a.** on the number line; **b.** in the *xy*-plane.

33. $x \geq 2$ **34.** $x \leq -3$
35. $x < -1$ **36.** $x > 4$

37. $-1 < x < 2$

38. $1 \le x \le 5$

39. $-6 \le x < -2$

40. $-3 < x \le 4$

3 Graph the solution sets of the following systems of inequalities. If no solution exists, write Ø.

41. $y \le x + 2$
$y \le -x + 2$

42. $y \ge -x + 1$
$y \le 2x + 2$

43. $x - 2y < -2$
$x + y > 3$

44. $x - 3y > 0$
$x + 2y > 0$

45. $y \ge x + 1$
$y \le x - 1$

46. $y > x + 1$
$y > x - 1$

47. $x + y \ge -2$
$y > x - 2$

48. $2x + 3y < 6$
$y \le 2x - 2$

49. $y \le x + 2$
$x \ge -2$

50. $2x + 3y > 3$
$2x + 3y \le -6$

51. $y > x$
$x \ge 0$

52. $x + y > 0$
$y < 1$

53. $x > -2$
$y \ge -2$

54. $x \ge 3$
$x < -1$

55. $|x| \ge 2$
$|y| \le 1$

56. $|x| > 2$
$|y| > 1$

57. $|x| \le 1$
$|y| > 2$

58. $|x + 2| > 1$
$y \le 1$

59. $|y| \le 1$
$|y| > 2$

60. $|2x - 1| < 3$
$x + 2y \ge -1$

B

61. $x + y \ge 1$
$x \ge 0$
$y \ge 0$

62. $y < 2x + 1$
$x \le 0$
$y \ge 0$

63. $y > x - 2$
$x + y \ge -2$
$y \le 0$

64. $y \le x + 3$
$y < 2x + 3$
$y \ge -1$

C

Answer the following questions with complete sentences.

65. Describe how a test point is used to graph an inequality in the plane.

66. Is a linear inequality in two variables a function? Justify your answer.

REVIEW EXERCISES

Decide which of the following relations are functions. Give the domain, D, and range, R, of each one. (See Section 3.2.)

67. $S = \{(1, 5), (-3, 7), (6, 8), (-4, 7)\}$

68. $T = \{(6, -8), (7, 2), (-9, 0), (6, 2)\}$

Write the following in interval notation. (See Section 2.6)

69. $-2 \le x < 2$ **70.** $x < 4$ **71.** $x \ge -3$

Solve the following equations for y. (See Section 2.3.)

72. $x = 2y - 4$

73. $3x - 2y = 1$

74. $x = \dfrac{3y - 1}{4}$

75. $x = \dfrac{1}{6}y + \dfrac{3}{4}$

76. $x = \dfrac{4y + 1}{y}$

77. $x = \dfrac{2y - 1}{y + 5}$

3.6 INVERSE RELATIONS AND FUNCTIONS

1 Inverse Relations and Their Graphs

2 One-to-One Functions; Inverse of a Linear Function

1 Inverse Relations and Their Graphs

The concept of an inverse occurs frequently in mathematics. For example, subtraction $(8 - 3 = 5)$ is the inverse of addition $(5 + 3 = 8)$. This section introduces basic ideas about inverse relations and functions. Because a function is a relation, our comments about relations apply to functions.

Consider the relation

$$S = \{(-1, 0), (0, 2), (1, 3)\}$$

If we interchange the coordinates of each ordered pair of S, the resulting relation is called the **inverse** of S, which is denoted by S^{-1}. The symbol S^{-1} is read "S inverse." Thus,

$$S^{-1} = \{(0, -1), (2, 0), (3, 1)\}$$

Note that S^{-1} does not mean $1/S$, such as $2^{-1} = 1/2$.

We can usefully represent the domains and ranges of S and S^{-1} with Venn diagrams (see Section 1.1). In Figure 3.38 we can see that the domain of S is the same as the range of S^{-1}, and the range of S is equal to the domain of S^{-1}; that is, $D_S = R_{S^{-1}} = \{-1, 0, 1\}$ and $R_S = D_{S^{-1}} = \{0, 2, 3\}$. With the Venn diagrams we can visualize how S^{-1} "undoes" what S "does." For example, S "sends" 1 to 3 and S^{-1} "sends" 3 back to 1.

FIGURE 3.38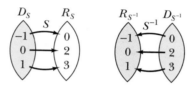

Inverse of a Relation

The inverse of a relation S is the set of all ordered pairs (b, a) where (a, b) is an element of S. The inverse of S is written S^{-1}.

$$\mathbf{D_S = R_{S^{-1}}} \qquad \text{and} \qquad \mathbf{R_S = D_{S^{-1}}}$$

EXAMPLE 1

Given $T = \{(-1, 2), (0, 0), (1, 2)\}$, find T^{-1}, D_T, R_T, $D_{T^{-1}}$, and $R_{T^{-1}}$.

SOLUTION $\quad T^{-1} = \{(2, -1), (0, 0), (2, 1)\}$

$$\mathbf{D}_T = \{-1, 0, 1\} = \mathbf{R}_{T^{-1}} \qquad \text{and} \qquad \mathbf{R}_T = \{2, 0\} = \mathbf{D}_{T^{-1}}$$

EXAMPLE 2

The domain of the relation U is the interval $[-2, 2)$, and the range of U is $[-8, 8)$. Find the domain and range of U^{-1}.

SOLUTION $\quad \mathbf{D}_{U^{-1}} = \mathbf{R}_U = [-8, 8) \qquad \text{and} \qquad \mathbf{R}_{U^{-1}} = \mathbf{D}_U = [-2, 2)$

We will now consider the relationship between the graph of a relation and the graph of its inverse. Suppose that the point $A(a, b)$ in Figure 3.39 on page 142 is an element of a relation S. Then the point $B(b, a)$ is an element of S^{-1}. With some basic geometry we can shown that the line $y = x$ is the perpendicular bisector of the line segment $\overline{AB}$; that is, $y = x$ and $\overline{AB}$ are perpendicular, and the points A and B are the same distance from the line $y = x$. As a result, A and B are mirror images of each other with respect to $y = x$, or they are **symmetric with respect to** $y = x$. In general, the graphs of any relation S and its inverse S^{-1} are symmetric with respect to the line $y = x$, which is illustrated in Figure 3.40. In Figure 3.41 the graph of our first example, $S = \{(-1, 0), (0, 2), (1, 3)\}$, and its inverse are graphed.

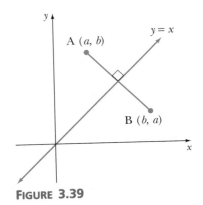

FIGURE 3.39

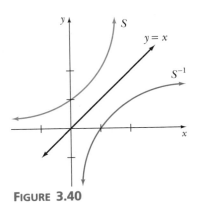

FIGURE 3.40

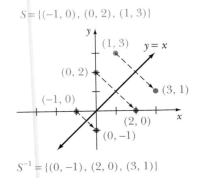

FIGURE 3.41

2   One-to-One Functions; Inverse of a Linear Function

At this point we can conveniently define the connective statement **if and only if**, which is abbreviated **iff**. Let p and q be two statements, such as "Today is Monday" or "Tomorrow is Tuesday." Suppose q is true whenever p is true, and p is true whenever q is true. Then we say "p if and only if q," or "p **iff** q." For example, because "If today is Monday, then tomorrow is Tuesday" and "If tomorrow is Tuesday, then today is Monday" are both true, we say "Today is Monday if and only if tomorrow is Tuesday." As another example, $a = b$ iff $a + c = b + c$.

By definition, a function has each element in its domain corresponding to *exactly one* element in its range. An important type of function has the additional property that to each element in its range there corresponds exactly one element in its domain. Such a function is called a **one-to-one function** or a **one-to-one correspondence**. Our first example (we will now call it f) is a one-to-one function:

$$f = \{(-1, 0), (0, 2), (1, 3)\} \quad \text{and} \quad f^{-1} = \{(0, -1), (2, 0), (3, 1)\}$$

We can see that f^{-1} is not only a function but also a one-to-one function. In Example 1 note that T is a function *but* it is not one-to-one; as a result, T^{-1} is not a function. One-to-one functions are significant because their inverses are one-to-one functions; that is, f^{-1} is a one-to-one function iff f is a one-to-one function.

To help visualize the concept of a one-to-one function, examine the functions $f(x) = 2x$ and $g(x) = |x|$ (see Example 5, page 110) in Figure

3.42. In part (a) two different values of x correspond to two different values of y; that is, if $x_1 \neq x_2$, then $f(x_1) \neq f(x_2)$. Therefore, f is a one-to-one function. However, in part (b) $x_1 \neq x_2$, but $g(x_1) = g(x_2)$. Thus, g is not a one-to-one function.

FIGURE 3.42

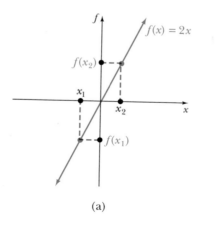

(a)

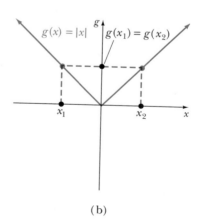

(b)

> A function f is a one-to-one function if, whenever $x_1 \neq x_2$, then $f(x_1) \neq f(x_2)$. Let f be a one-to-one function. Then f^{-1}, the inverse of f, is a one-to-one function.

Another way to view one-to-one functions is to say, "If $f(x_1) = f(x_2)$, then $x_1 = x_2$."

EXAMPLE 3

Determine whether the given function is one-to-one. If it is, give its inverse.

a. $f = \{(2, 7), (8, 6), (7, -2), (4, 4)\}$
b. $g = \{(3, 4), (1, 8), (6, 4), (5, 20)\}$

SOLUTION

a. f is one-to-one because no two ordered pairs have the same second element:
$$f^{-1} = \{(7, 2), (6, 8), (-2, 7) (4, 4)\}$$
b. g is not one-to-one because $3 \neq 6$, but $g(3) = g(6)$.

Now we will consider the inverse of a linear function. The inverses of the relations that we have considered were found by interchanging the x and y coordinates of each ordered pair. Now suppose that a relation is defined by an equation instead of a list of ordered pairs. We can obtain the equation of the inverse by interchanging x and y in the original equation. For example, suppose the relation S is defined by the equation $x^2 - y^2 = 1$. Then its inverse, S^{-1}, is determined by $y^2 - x^2 = 1$. For many one-to-one functions, $y = f(x)$, we can solve the new equation for y to find $y = f^{-1}(x)$.

Consider the following linear equation:

$$f(x) = 2x - 4 \qquad \text{Replace } f(x) \text{ by } y.$$

$$y = 2x - 4 \qquad \text{Interchange } x \text{ and } y.$$

$$x = 2y - 4 \qquad \text{Solve for } y.$$

$$x + 4 = 2y$$

$$\frac{x + 4}{2} = y \qquad \text{Replace } y \text{ by } f^{-1}(x).$$

$$f^{-1}(x) = \frac{x + 4}{2}$$

The functions $f(x) = 2x - 4$ and $f^{-1}(x) = \dfrac{x + 4}{2}$ are graphed in Figure 3.43. Notice their symmetry with respect to the line $y = x$. The function f has us multiply x by 2 and then subtract 4. f^{-1} has us "undo" this by adding 4 to x and then dividing by 2. To illustrate this, let $x = 1$. Then,

$$f(1) = 2 \cdot 1 - 4 = -2 \qquad \text{and} \qquad f^{-1}(-2) = \frac{-2 + 4}{2} = 1$$

Thus, f "sends" 1 to -2 and f^{-1} "sends" -2 back to 1.

FIGURE 3.43

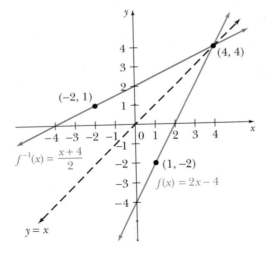

EXAMPLE 4

Find the inverse of $g(x) = \dfrac{1}{6}x + \dfrac{3}{4}$.

SOLUTION

$$g(x) = \frac{1}{6}x + \frac{3}{4} \qquad \text{Replace } g(x) \text{ by } y.$$

$$y = \frac{1}{6}x + \frac{3}{4} \qquad \text{Interchange } x \text{ and } y.$$

$$x = \frac{1}{6}y + \frac{3}{4} \qquad \text{Multiply by LCD} = 12.$$

$$12x = 12\left(\frac{1}{6}y + \frac{3}{4}\right)$$

$$12x = 2y + 9 \qquad \text{Solve for } y.$$

$$12x - 9 = 2y$$

$$\frac{12x - 9}{2} = y \qquad \text{Replace } y \text{ by } g^{-1}(x).$$

$$g^{-1}(x) = \frac{12x - 9}{2} = 6x - \frac{9}{2}$$

EXAMPLE 5

Find the inverse of the following.

a. $S = \{(x, y) \mid y = 3\}$ **b.** $T = \{(x, y) \mid y = (4x + 1)/x\}$

SOLUTION

a. Replace y by x in the equation $y = 3$. Thus, $S^{-1} = \{(x, y) \mid x = 3\}$. Note that $y = 3$ is not a one-to-one function (its graph is a horizontal line); thus, its inverse is not a function.

b.

$$y = \frac{4x + 1}{x} \qquad \text{Interchange } x \text{ and } y.$$

$$x = \frac{4y + 1}{y} \qquad \text{Multiply by } y.$$

$$xy = 4y + 1 \qquad \text{Solve for } y.$$

$$xy - 4y = 1$$

$$(x - 4)y = 1$$

$$y = \frac{1}{x - 4}$$

$$T^{-1} = \{(x, y) \mid y = 1/(x - 4)\}$$

> ### Finding $y = f^{-1}(x)$
>
> Let $y = f(x)$ be a one-to-one function.
>
> **1.** Replace $f(x)$ by y.
> **2.** Interchange x and y; this is the equation of f^{-1}.
> **3.** Solve the equation in step 2 for y, if possible.
> **4.** Replace y by $f^{-1}(x)$, if step 3 can be done.

As just indicated, for some functions solving the equation in step 2 is not possible. An example is $y = f(x) = 2^x$, whose inverse is $x = 2^y$. We will study this function in Chapter 10.

EXERCISE SET 3.6

A

1 Find the inverse of the given relation and represent its domain and range with a Venn diagram as in Figure 3.38. Graph the rela-tion, its inverse, and $y = x$ on the same axes as in Figure 3.41.

1. $S = \{(0, -2), (1, -1), (2, 1)\}$

2. $T = \{(-2, 3), (0, 3), (2, 3)\}$

3. $U = \{(4, 2), (4, 3), (1, 2)\}$

4. $V = \{(0, 0), (1, 1), (1, -1), (4, 2), (4, -2)\}$

5. $f = \{(-3, 1), (0, 3), (1, -2)\}$

6. $h = \{(-1, 1/2), (0, 1), (1, 2), (2, 4)\}$

The domain and range of a relation, S, is given in the following. Find the domain and range of S^{-1}.

7. $D_S = \{1, 7, -4\}, R_S = \{9, -6, 8\}$

8. $D_S = \{0, -6, 11, 20\}, R_S = \{5\}$

9. $D_S = [-1, 5], R_S = [2, 9]$

10. $D_S = (-\infty, \infty), R_S = (0, \infty)$

Of these four sets — $D_f, R_f, D_{f^{-1}},$ and $R_{f^{-1}}$ — two are given in interval notation. Find the remaining two sets.

11. $D_f = [1, 3], R_f = [2, 6]$

12. $D_{f^{-1}} = (-1, 1), R_{f^{-1}} = (-4, 8)$

13. $D_f = (0, 2], D_{f^{-1}} = (-5, 0]$

14. $R_f = [1, \infty), R_{f^{-1}} = [0, \infty)$

15. $D_{f^{-1}} = (-\infty, -1], R_{f^{-1}} = [-1, 0)$

16. $D_f = R_f = [0, 7]$

2 Determine whether the following *if and only if* statements are true or false. If one is false, state which part is incorrect.

17. This month is June iff the next month is July.

18. Susan lives in Ohio iff she does not live in Iowa.

19. The temperature is less than 50° F iff it is snowing.

20. A triangle has three equal sides iff it has three equal angles.

21. $a < b$ iff $b > a$.

22. Let L_1 and L_2 be nonvertical lines with slopes m_1 and m_2. L_1 is perpendicular to L_2 iff $m_1 m_2 = -1$.

23. Let L_1 and L_2 be two different lines with slopes m_1 and m_2. L_1 is parallel to L_2 iff $m_1 = m_2$.

24. Let $a, b,$ and c be real numbers. $a = b$ iff $ac = bc$.

Determine if the given relation is a function, a one-to-one function, or neither.

25. $\{(1, 4), (2, 8), (3, 4)\}$

26. $\{(3, 6), (1, 9), (3, 2)\}$

27. $\{(-1, 3), (1, -6), (2, 8)\}$

28. $\{(2, 2), (7, 7), (-3, -3)\}$

29. $y = 4x$

30. $y = -1$

31. $x = 6$

32. $y = |x| + 1$

Find the inverse of the following linear functions. Graph the function, its inverse, and $y = x$ on the same axes.

33. $f(x) = 2x$

34. $g(x) = -3x$

35. $h(x) = x + 1$

36. $g(x) = -2x - 2$

37. $2x + 3y = 6$

38. $x - 4y = 4$

Find $f^{-1}(x)$ for each function f.

39. $f(x) = \dfrac{2}{3}x + 1$

40. $f(x) = 3x - \dfrac{1}{2}$

41. $f(x) = \dfrac{3}{4}x - \dfrac{5}{6}$

42. $f(x) = \dfrac{1}{8} + \dfrac{7}{12}x$

43. $f(x) = \dfrac{1}{x}$

44. $f(x) = \dfrac{1}{x - 1}$

Find the inverses of the following.

45. $S = \{(x, y) \mid y = 5\}$

46. $T = \{(x, y) \mid x = -4\}$

47. $U = \{(x, y) \mid y = 3x\}$

48. $V = \{(x, y) \mid x^2 + y^2 = 1\}$

49. $f(x) = mx + b$

50. $g(x) = \dfrac{x - 6}{x + 4}$

B

51. $f(x) = \dfrac{2x - 3}{1 - 4x}$

52. $g(x) = \dfrac{a}{b - x}$

53. $h(x) = \dfrac{mx + b}{cx + d}$

54. $f(x) = \dfrac{t - 3x}{s + ux}$

C

Answer the following questions with complete sentences.

55. What are the relationships between the domains and ranges of a relation and its inverse?

56. Describe the relationship between the graph of a function and the graph of its inverse.

57. What is meant by the statement "Today is Friday if and only if tomorrow is Saturday"?

58. Let $y = f(x)$ be a one-to-one linear function. Describe how you would find $y = f^{-1}(x)$.

59. What does the function $g^{-1}(x) = 4x + 6$ tell us to do?

60. What does the function $f^{-1}(x) = \dfrac{x - 1}{2}$ tell us to do?

Chapter Summary

DEFINITIONS AND PROPERTIES

Cartesian coordinate system: **origin; quadrants; axes; intercepts; ordered pair, (a, b):** a is the x-coordinate, and b is the y-coordinate. A **linear,** or **first-degree, equation** in two variables is one that can be expressed in the form $Ax + By = C$ or $y = mx + b$. Its **graph** is a line (see Figure 3.44). (See Section 3.1.)

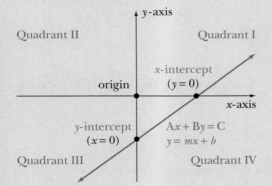

FIGURE 3.44

A **relation** is a set of ordered pairs. A **function** is a relation such that for each first coordinate only one second coordinate exists. The **domain** of a relation or a function is the set of the first coordinates. The **range** of a relation or a function is the set of all second coordinates. Types of functions: **linear function,** $f(x) = mx + b$; **constant function,** $f(x) = C$; **identity function,** $I(x) = x$; **absolute value function,** $f(x) = |x|$; **piecewise function,** a function defined by different rules over different parts of its domain. (See Section 3.2.)

Inverse Relations and Functions (See Section 3.6.)

The **inverse** of a relation S is the set of all ordered pairs (b, a) where (a, b) is an element of S. The inverse of S is written S^{-1}. $D_S = R_{S^{-1}}$ and $R_S = D_{S^{-1}}$. The graphs of S and S^{-1} are symmetric with respect to the line $y = x$. p **if and only if** q means that "q is true when p is true" and "p is true when q is true." A function f is said to be **one-to-one** if, whenever $x_1 \neq x_2$, then $f(x_1) \neq f(x_2)$. f^{-1} is a one-to-one function iff f is a one-to-one function.

Finding $y = f^{-1}(x)$ (See Section 3.6.)

Let $y = f(x)$ be a one-to-one function.

1. Replace $f(x)$ by y.

2. Interchange x and y; this is the equation of f^{-1}.

3. Solve the equation in step 2 for y, if possible.

4. Replace y by $f^{-1}(x)$, if step 3 can be done.

Let $A(x_1, y_1)$ and $B(x_2, y_2)$ be two points in the xy-plane. The **distance, d,** between A and B is

$$d(A, B) = \sqrt{(x_2 - x_1)^2 + (y_2 - y_1)^2}$$

The **slope, m,** of the line $\overleftrightarrow{AB}$ is

$$m = \frac{\text{change in } y}{\text{change in } x} = \frac{y_2 - y_1}{x_2 - x_1}$$

(See Section 3.3.)

Let $P(x, y)$ be any point on the nonvertical line through the fixed point $A(x_1, y_1)$; forms of the equation of the line are

$y - y_1 = m(x - x_1)$; **point–slope form**
$y = f(x) = mx + b$; **slope–intercept form**;
$b = y$-intercept

$Ax + By = C$; **standard form**; A, B, C are real numbers (A and B are not both 0). The equations of the vertical and horizontal lines through A are $x = x_1$ and $y = y_1$, respectively. Nonvertical lines are **parallel** if they have the same slope. Vertical lines are parallel. Nonvertical lines are **perpendicular** if the product of their slopes is -1. A vertical line (no slope) is perpendicular to a horizontal line ($m = 0$). (See Section 3.4.)

Graphing a Linear Inequality in Two Variables (See Section 3.5.)

1. Graph the corresponding equation as a
   a. Solid line if the inequality involves $\leq$ or $\geq$.
   b. Broken line if the inequality involves $<$ or $>$.
2. Pick a test point not on the line; (0, 0) is convenient if the line does not contain the origin.
3. The graph of the inequality is
   a. The half-plane containing the test point, if its coordinates satisfy the inequality.
   b. The half-line not containing the test point, if its coordinates do not satisfy the inequality.

Graphing a System of Inequalities (See Section 3.5.)

1. Graph all the inequalities on the same xy-plane.
2. The intersection of all the regions is the solution to the system of inequalities.

CHAPTER REVIEW EXERCISES

The answers to the following exercises are given in the answer section. If you have any trouble with them, review the material and exercises in the indicated sections.

Complete the following solutions for the given equation. (See Section 3.1.)

1. $y = 2x - 5$ (0,), (7,), (,3)

2. $3x - 2y = 12$ (0,), (,0), (,6)

Determine the x- and y-intercept for each of the following if they exist. Then graph each line. (See Section 3.1.)

3. $y = 3x - 6$ **4.** $3x + 4x = 12$ **5.** $y = 3$

Graph the following over the given interval. (See Section 3.1.)

6. $y = 2x - 3$, $[1, \infty)$

Express the domain and range of the following in interval notation. (See Section 3.2.)

7. $f = \{(x, y) \mid y = x^2 + 4\}$

Find the domains of the following. (See Section 3.2.)

8. $y = \sqrt{4x - 12}$ **9.** $y = \dfrac{x - 2}{x + 3}$

Graph the following (See Sections 3.1 and 3.2.)

10. $y = |\, 3x \,|$

11. $g(x) = |\, x \,| - 3$

12. $y = \dfrac{|\, x + 1 \,|}{x + 1}$

13. $y = \begin{cases} -x + 1, & \text{if } x < -1 \\ 2x, & \text{if } x \geq 1 \end{cases}$

14. $f(x) = \begin{cases} 3, & \text{if } x < 0 \\ -3, & \text{if } x > 0 \end{cases}$

15. $y = \begin{cases} x, & \text{if } 0 \leq x \leq 1 \\ -x + 2, & \text{if } 1 \leq x < 2 \\ -1, & \text{if } 2 \leq x \end{cases}$

For the following pairs of points, find a. the distance, d, between them, b. the slope, m of the line;

if the slope does not exist, write "undefined." (See Section 3.3.)

16. (1, 2), (3, 6)   **17.** (−3, 2), (−3, 7)

18. (−4, −1), (2, −3)

Find the point–slope equation of the line determined by the following. (See Section 3.4.)

19. (−2, 5), (1, −3)

Find the slope–intercept and standard forms of the equation of the line determined by the following. (See Section 3.4.)

20. (−2, 0), (1, 6)

Find the equation of the line determined by the given points. Use any form of the equation. (See Section 3.4.)

21. (−2, −1), (4, −1)   **22.** (1, 7), (1, 5)

Find the equation of the line through the given point that is parallel to the given line. (See Section 3.4.)

23. (5, −4), $y - 1 = -\frac{3}{4}(x + 4)$

The line L is determined by the two given points. Find the equation of the line through the point P that is perpendicular to L. (See Section 3.4.)

24. (−6, 1), (2, 5);   P(1, −4)

Use the slope formula to determine whether the given points are the vertices of a right triangle. (See Section 3.4.)

25. A(−2, 1), B(0, 0), C(1, 10)

Let $g(x) = -4x + 1$. Find the following. (See Section 3.4.)

26. $\dfrac{g(x + h) - g(x)}{h}$

Graph the following inequalities in the *xy*-plane. (See Section 3.5.)

27 $y \le 2x + 1$ **28.** $x + y > 3$

Graph the solution set of the following systems of inequalities. If there is no solution, write "undefined." (See Section 3.5.)

29. $y \le x + 1$ **30.** $y > -2$
    $x + 2y < 2$ $|x| \le 1$

Determine if the given relation, S, is a function, a one-to-one function, or neither. Find S^{-1}, D_S, R_S, $D_{S^{-1}}$, and $R_{S^{-1}}$. (See Section 3.6.)

31. $S = \{(-2, 16), (1, 1), (2, 16)\}$
32. $S = \{(-2, -8), (1, 1), (2, 8), (3, 27)\}$

Find the inverse of the following functions. Graph each function, its inverse, and $y = x$ on the same axes. (See Section 3.6.)

33. $f(x) = 2x - 1$ **34.** $g(x) = -\frac{1}{3}x + 2$

CHAPTER TEST

Treat this test as a class test and allow 50 minutes for completion. When finished, use the answer section for grading. If you have any wrong answers, refer to the corresponding problems in the review section.

Find the inverse of the following functions. Graph each function, its inverse, and $y = x$ on the same axes.

1. $f(x) = 2x + 1$
2. $g = \{(-3, 1), (0, 2), (1, 4)\}$

Find the domain of the following.

3. $y = \dfrac{1}{x - 4}$ **4.** $f(x) = \sqrt{6 - 3x}$

Graph the following lines.

5. $y = -2x + 4$ **6.** $3x - 2y = 6$
7. $x = -2$

Graph the following over the given interval.

8. $y = 3x + 1, (-1, \infty)$

Graph the following.

9. $f(x) = |x| + x - 1$

10. $y = |y - 3|$

11. $y = \begin{cases} 3, & \text{if } x < 1 \\ x, & \text{if } x \geq 2 \end{cases}$

12. $y = \begin{cases} x + 4, & \text{if } x < 0 \\ -2x + 1, & \text{if } x \geq 0 \end{cases}$

For the following pairs of points, find **a.** the distance, d, between them, **b.** the slope, m, of the line; if the slope does not exist, write "undefined."

13. $(-1, 1), (2, 7)$ **14.** $(-3, 2), (1, 2)$

Determine whether the points $A(-2, -2)$, $B(2, -1)$, and $C(0, 6)$ are the vertices of a right triangle by using the

15. Distance formula   **16.** Slope formula

Let $f(x) = 7x - 2$. Find

17. $\dfrac{f(x + h) - f(x)}{h}$

Find the equation of the line determined by the given points. Use any form of the equation.

18. $(-2, 0), (-2, -4)$ **19.** $(-1, 1), (6, 3)$

Find the equation of the line through the given point that is perpendicular to the given line.

20. $(-5, 3), y = \dfrac{2}{3}x + 6$

The line L is determined by the two given points. Find the equation of the line through the point P that is parallel to L.

21. $(5, 2), (1, -3);$ $P(-6, -7)$

Graph the following inequalities in the xy-plane.

22. $y > -3x + 2$ **23.** $2x - 3y \geq -12$

Graph the solution set of the following systems of inequalities. If no solution exists, write "undefined."

24. $y \leq 1$
$|x - 2| > 1$

25. $x + 4y > 8$
$-x - 4y \geq 4$

Cumulative Review

CHAPTERS 1–3

The answers to the following problems are given in the answer section. The section from which each question is taken is listed in brackets next to its answer. Therefore, if you have any wrong answers, you can review the material in the indicated section.

Simplify the following.

1. $8 - 2^2 + \sqrt{49}$

2. $6 + 28 \div 3 \cdot 2$

3. $6 + 4\,|\,5 - 3 \cdot 6\,|$

Solve the following for the indicated variables. For problem 7, write the solution in interval notation and graph it.

4. $x - (4 - x) = 7(x - 1)$

5. $|\,3x - 1\,| = 14$

6. $T = 2ab + 3bc + 4ac; \quad a$

7. $2(1 - 6x) \geq 14$

8. $\dfrac{y + 1}{4} + \dfrac{1}{6} = \dfrac{y - 2}{3}$

Let $f(x) = 3x - 1$ and $g(x) = 2x^2 - x + 5$. Find

9. $f(2) + g(-1)$

Find the domain of the following function.

10. $y = \dfrac{1}{x^2 - 4}$

Let $A = \{1, 2, 3\}$ and $B = \{3, 4\}$. Find the following union and intersection and illustrate them with Venn diagrams.

11. $A \cup B$ **12.** $A \cap B$

Find the inverse of the following function. Graph the function, its inverse, and $y = x$ on the same axes.

13. $f(x) = \dfrac{1}{2}x + 1$

Let $A = \{9, 0, \sqrt{3}, -5, 3/4, .\overline{23}, .23,$ $.2324252627 \ldots \}$. List all elements of A that are

14. Rational   **15.** Irrational

16. Integers   **17.** Natural numbers

For the following, find its a. opposite and b. reciprocal.

18. $-4/5$

Find the hypotenuse of the right triangle with the given legs.

19. 2 and $\sqrt{5}$

For the points $A(-1, 5)$ and $B(3, -2)$, find

20. $d(A, B)$, the distance between A and B

21. m, the slope of the line $\overleftrightarrow{AB}$

22. The point–slope equation of $\overleftrightarrow{AB}$

Find the slope of any line perpendicular to the following line.

23. $2x - 3y = 6$

Graph the solution set of the following system of inequalities.

24. $y \leq 3x + 2$
$\quad\;\; x + 3y < 6$

Solve the following word problems.

25. Sharon's age in 20 years will be the same as Ted's age now. In 10 years Ted's age will be twice Sharon's age. How old are they now?

26. The height, h, of a right circular cylinder is twice its radius, r. The surface area, S, is 54π cm². Find its radius and height. Use the formula $S = 2\pi r^2 + 2\pi rh$.

27. A number is multiplied by -3, then 1 is subtracted from this result, and the new number is divided by 2. The final number is between -5 and 7. Between what two numbers must the original number lie?

28. Cars A and B leave the same point at the same time and travel in the same direction. Car A travels 10 mph faster than car B. After 2.5 hours car A is 25 miles ahead of car B. Find the rate of car B.

29. Carmen mixes 10 liters of a 5% acid solution with an 11% acid solution to produce a 7% solution. How many liters of the 11% solution does she use?

30. The sum of the heights of Mt. McKinley and Mt. Shasta is 34,480 feet. If Mt. McKinley were 320 feet lower and Mt. Shasta were 850 feet higher, then Mt. Shasta would be 3/4 the height of Mt. McKinley. How high is each mountain?

FOUR

Systems of
Linear Equations

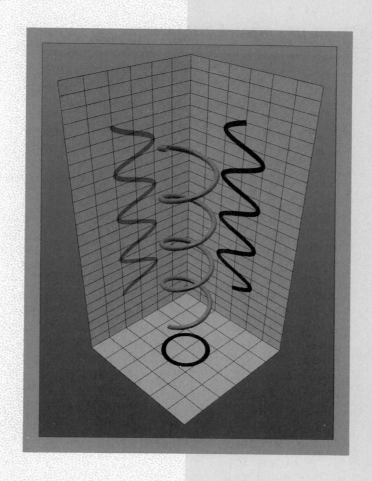

*When the line from a light source to a point on a plane is blocked
by an object, the point is in the object's shadow. Determining
the shadow requires solving a system of two linear equations:
one for the plane and one for the lines of light blocked.*

Chapter 3 examined linear equations in two variables. This chapter extends this material to systems of linear equations in two and three variables. Such systems are used to study kinship patterns in anthropology, equilibrium points in economics, and circuits in electrical engineering, among many other applications.

Word problems in algebra often involve quantities and can be described with a system of two equations in two variables. For example, the problem "find two numbers whose sum is 4 and whose difference is 2" can be represented by the system $x + y = 4$ and $x - y = 2$. The ordered pair (3, 1), which satisfies both equations, is the solution to this system. This chapter will consider such systems of equations and their applications.

4.1   SOLVING SYSTEMS OF LINEAR EQUATIONS IN TWO VARIABLES

1   **Solving a System by Graphing; Types of Equations**

2   **Solving a System by Substitution**

3   **Solving a System by Addition**

1   Solving a System by Graphing; Types of Equations

Chapter 3 showed that linear equations in two variables are equations in the form $y = mx + b$ or $Ax + By = C$ and that their graphs are straight lines. Two of these equations considered together are called a **system of linear equations**. Its **solution set** is the set of all ordered pairs that satisfy both equations.

Graphing is one method of solving a system. We graph both lines on the same axes, determine the coordinates of the point where the lines seem to intersect, and then see if the ordered pair satisfies both equations. To illustrate this, consider the system

$$y = x + 1$$
$$y = -x + 3$$

The two lines are graphed in Figure 4.1. The pair (1, 2) seems to be the point of intersection. To determine whether this is true, substitute 1 for x and 2 for y in both equations:

$$y = x + 1 \qquad\qquad\qquad y = -x + 3$$
$$2 = 1 + 1 \qquad\qquad\qquad 2 = -1 + 3$$

Thus (1, 2) is the solution to the system. We can also write the answer as "$x = 1$ and $y = 2$."

The equations $y = x + 1$ and $y = -x + 3$ represent two distinct lines that intersect in one point, (1, 2). A system of equations with one solution is called a **consistent system**.

FIGURE 4.1

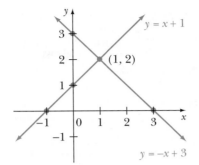

Two distinct lines can intersect in one point. However, they might be parallel instead and thus have no point of intersection. For example, the equations

$$y = 2x - 1$$
$$y = 2x + 1$$

represent different lines, but they have the same slope, $m = 2$, so they are parallel (see Figure 4.2). Therefore, no ordered pair satisfies both equations, so the solution is the empty set, Ø. A system of equations with no solution is called an **inconsistent system**.

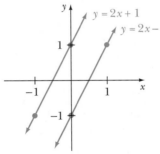

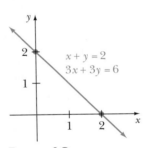

FIGURE 4.3

FIGURE 4.2

A system of equations has a third possible solution. Consider the equations

$$x + y = 2$$
$$3x + 3y = 6$$

The second equation, $3x + 3y = 6$, can be written as $3(x + y) = 3 \cdot 2$. Thus, the second equation is a multiple of the first: They both represent the same line (Figure 4.3) — that is, any ordered pair that satisfies one equation satisfies the other. The solution set of this system is the infinite set of all ordered pairs (x, y) such that $x + y = 2$ or $3x + 3y = 6$. A system of equations that represents the same line is called a **dependent system**. We write either equation to indicate the solution set.

Types of Solutions to a System of Linear Equations

1. **Consistent system:** one solution. The graphs intersect at one point, whose ordered pair is the solution (Figure 4.4).

2. **Inconsistent system:** no solution. The graphs are parallel lines, so Ø is the solution (Figure 4.5).

3. **Dependent system:** an infinite number of solutions. The graphs are the same line, so either equation is the solution (Figure 4.6).

1.   **2.**   **3.**

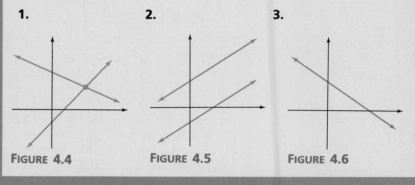

FIGURE 4.4   FIGURE 4.5   FIGURE 4.6

2   Solving a System by Substitution

Solving a system of equations by graphing allows us to visualize the three possible solutions. However, in most cases graphing is not a practical method. Although a solution such as (1, 2) can easily be found by this method, suppose the solution to a system is (100, 200) or (1.4, 2.3). Graphing is obviously impractical here. We will now develop algebraic methods of solving a system of equations that will work in all cases.

The first algebraic method is called the **substitution method**. It is a result of the substitution property of real numbers:

$$\text{If } a = b \text{ and } a = c, \text{ then } b = c.$$

For example, $12 = 2 \cdot 6$ and $12 = 3 \cdot 4$, so $2 \cdot 6 = 3 \cdot 4$. We will use this property to solve the system in Figure 4.1:

$$y = x + 1$$
$$y = -x + 3$$

If we let $a = y$, $b = x + 1$, and $c = -x + 3$, then

$$x + 1 = -x + 3 \quad {\scriptstyle b = c}$$
$$2x = 2$$
$$x = 1$$

To determine y, substitute $x = 1$ in either equation:

$$y = x + 1 = 1 + 1 = 2 \quad \text{or} \quad y = -x + 3 = -1 + 3 = 2$$

Thus, (1, 2) is the solution.

The substitution method is convenient when the coefficient of one of the variables is 1 or -1. In this situation we can avoid complicated work with fractions, as the first example illustrates.

EXAMPLE 1

Solve the system
$$3x - y = -10$$
$$5x + 2y = -2$$

SOLUTION

Because the coefficient of y in the first equation is -1, solve this equation for y.
$$3x - y = -10 \qquad \text{Add } -3x \text{ to both sides.}$$
$$-y = -3x - 10 \qquad \text{Multiply both sides by } -1.$$
$$y = 3x + 10$$

Now substitute $3x + 10$ for y in the second equation.
$$5x + 2y = -2 \qquad \text{and} \qquad y = 3x + 10$$
$$5x + 2(3x + 10) = -2$$
$$5x + 6x + 20 = -2$$
$$11x = -22$$
$$x = -2, \quad \text{and}$$
$y = 3x + 10 = 3(-2) + 10 = 4$, so the solution is $(-2, 4)$.

 CHECK

$$
\begin{array}{ll}
3x - y = -10 & \qquad 5x + 2y = -2 \\
3(-2) - 4 \overset{?}{=} -10 & \qquad 5(-2) + 2(4) \overset{?}{=} -2 \\
-6 - 4 = -10 & \qquad -10 + 8 = -2
\end{array}
$$

If we attempt to solve an inconsistent system such as the parallel lines in Figure 4.2, then we arrive at a false equation:
$$y = 2x + 1$$
$$y = 2x - 1$$
$$2x + 1 = 2x - 1$$
$$1 = -1$$

In general, if we try to solve a system and we obtain a

> **False equation** $a = b$,

then the system is inconsistent and the solution is Ø.

If we try to solve a dependent system such as the two equations representing the same line in Figure 4.3, then we arrive at a true equation:
$$x + y = 2$$
$$3x + 3y = 6$$

Solve the first equation for x: $\quad x = 2 - y$. Substitute this value of x in the second equation:
$$3(2 - y) + 3y = 6$$
$$6 - 3y + 3y = 6$$
$$6 = 6$$

In general, if we solve a system and we obtain a

> True equation $a = a,$

then the system is dependent and the solution is either equation.

In Chapter 3 we discussed linear functions and their inverses. Because f and f^{-1} form a system of linear equations, we can determine their point of intersection, which is illustrated in the following example.

EXAMPLE 2

Solve the system
$$f(x) = 2x - 4$$
$$f^{-1}(x) = \frac{x + 4}{2}$$

SOLUTION

The two functions are graphed in Figure 3.43, and we can see that their point of intersection is $(4, 4)$. To determine this algebraically, set f equal to f^{-1}:

$$f(x) = 2x - 4$$
$$f^{-1}(x) = \frac{x + 4}{2} \qquad f(x) = f^{-1}(x)$$
$$2x - 4 = \frac{x + 4}{2} \qquad \text{Multiply by 2.}$$
$$2(2x - 4) = 2\left(\frac{x + 4}{2}\right)$$
$$4x - 8 = x + 4$$
$$3x - 8 = 4$$
$$3x = 12$$
$$x = 4, \text{ and}$$
$$y = 2x - 4 = 2 \cdot 4 - 4 = 4, \quad \text{so the solution is } (4, 4).$$

3   Solving a System by Addition

The **addition method** is the second algebraic method of solving a system of equations. This method is convenient when none of the coefficients are 1 or -1 and results from the addition property of equality:

> If $a = b$ and $c = d,$ then $a + c = b + d.$

For example, to solve the system $2x + 3y = 8$ and $4x - 3y = 4$, we can add the equations to eliminate y:

$$
\begin{array}{r}
2x + 3y = 8 \\
\underline{4x - 3y = 4} \\
6x + 0 = 12 \\
x = 2
\end{array}
$$

Now substitute $x = 2$ in $2x + 3y = 8$:

$$2(2) + 3y = 8$$
$$y = 4/3$$

So $(2, 4/3)$ is the solution.

In many cases the coefficients of one of the variables will not have a sum of zero. We can deal with this problem by multiplying both sides of the equations by appropriate constants that will put the equations in this form.

EXAMPLE 3

Solve the following systems of equations:

a. $6x - 2y = -1$ **b.** $3x - 12 = 6y$ **c.** $\dfrac{3}{8}x - \dfrac{1}{2}y = 1$
    $8x - 4y = 1$ $5x - 4y = 3x + 8$ $-\dfrac{1}{3}x + \dfrac{4}{9}y = \dfrac{4}{3}$

SOLUTION

a. If we multiply the first equation by -2 and add it to the second, we eliminate y:

$$-2(6x - 2y) = -2(-1)$$
$$\begin{array}{r} -12x + 4y = 2 \\ 8x - 4y = 1 \\ \hline -4x + 0 = 3 \\ x = -3/4 \end{array}$$

Returning to the original equations, we eliminate x to find y. Multiply the first equation by -4 and the second by 3 and then add:

$$-4(6x - 2y) = -4(-1)$$
$$3(8x - 4y) = 3(1)$$
$$\begin{array}{r} -24x + 8y = 4 \\ 24x - 12y = 3 \\ \hline 0 - 4y = 7 \\ y = -7/4 \end{array}$$

So the solution is $(-3/4, -7/4)$.

b. First write the equations in the form $Ax + By = C$:

$$\begin{array}{ll} 3x - 12 = 6y & \\ 5x - 4y = 3x + 8 & \\ 3x - 6y = 12 & \text{Multiply by 2.} \\ 2x - 4y = 8 & \text{Multiply by } -3. \\ 2(3x - 6y) = 2(12) & \\ -3(2x - 4y) = -3(8) & \\ \end{array}$$
$$\begin{array}{r} 6x - 12y = 24 \\ -6x + 12y = -24 \\ \hline 0 + 0 = 0 \end{array}$$

Because $0 = 0$ is a true equation, the system is dependent; the solution is $3x - 12 = 6y$.

(continued)

c. First express the equations in the form $Ax + By = C$, where A, B, and C are integers:

$$8\left(\frac{3}{8}x - \frac{1}{2}y\right) = 8(1)$$

$$9\left(-\frac{1}{3}x + \frac{4}{9}y\right) = 9\left(\frac{4}{3}\right)$$

$$\begin{array}{r} 3x - 4y = 8 \\ -3x + 4y = 12 \\ \hline 0 + 0 = 20 \end{array}$$

Because $0 = 20$ is a false equation, the system is inconsistent; the solution is $\varnothing$.

EXERCISE SET 4.1

A

1 Solve the following systems with the graphing method.

1. $y = 2x + 5$
$y = -x + 2$

2. $y = x + 5$
$y = x + 3$

3. $y = -2x + 4$
$-2y = 4x - 8$

4. $x + y = 6$
$x - y = 2$

5. $x + y = 4$
$2x + 2y = -4$

6. $2x - 3y = 3$
$4x - 6y = 6$

2 Solve the following systems with the substitution method.

7. $y = 2x + 5$
$y = -x + 2$

8. $y = x + 5$
$y = x + 3$

9. $x - 2y = 2$
$3x - 6y = 6$

10. $5x + 3y = 70$
$-6x - y = 20$

11. $3x - y = 4$
$6x - 2y = -16$

12. $2x + 3y = 9$
$x - 6y = 2$

13. $f(x) = 4x + 5$
$g(x) = 4x - 7$

14. $f(x) = 3x - 2$
$f^{-1}(x) = \dfrac{x + 2}{3}$

3 Solve the following systems with the addition method.

15. $x + y = 6$
$x - y = 8$

16. $4x - 2y = -20$
$-4x + 5y = 26$

17. $x = 3$
$y = -4$

18. $2x - 6y = 10$
$-x + 3y = -4$

19. $3x - 6y = 12$
$2x - 4y = 8$

20. $5x - 2y = 4$
$2x + 3y = 13$

21. $6x + 2y = 1$
$-4x + 5y = 1$

22. $-4x + 6y = -6$
$6x - 9y = 9$

Solve the following systems of equations. Use the most convenient method.

23. $2x - y = 6$
$y = 5x$

24. $4x + 3y = 10$
$2x + y = 4$

25. $5x - 2y = 1$
$10x - 4y = -3$

26. $2x - 5y = 10$
$3x + y = 15$

27. $3x - 5y = -2$
$2x - 3y = 1$

28. $8x + 2y = 10$
$f(x) = -4x + 5$

29. $8x + 4y = 7$
$3x + 6y = 6$

30. $3x + 2y = -1$
$15x + 14y = -23$

31. $3x - 5y = -2$
$10y - 6x = 4$

32. $x - 11y - 2 = 0$
$.2x - y - .2 = 0$

33. $y - 3x + 2 = 0$
$.03x - .02y - .01 = 0$

34. $7x - 10y = x + 6$
$9x - 14y = y - 4$

35. $x + 4y = -14$
$\dfrac{x}{2} + \dfrac{y}{3} = -\dfrac{1}{3}$

36. $3x + 2y = 9$
$\dfrac{x}{3} + \dfrac{y}{5} = \dfrac{19}{15}$

37. $x = -1$
$F(x) = 2$

38. $f(x) = 4$
$g(x) = 1$

39. $f(x) = 2x + 1$
$g(x) = -2x + 1$

40. $F(x) = 3x + 2$
$G(x) = -x + 5$

41. $f(x) = -3x + 4$
$f^{-1}(x) = \dfrac{4 - x}{3}$

42. $g(x) = \dfrac{1}{6}x + \dfrac{3}{4}$
$g^{-1}(x) = 6x - \dfrac{9}{2}$

43. $\dfrac{1}{2}x + \dfrac{1}{3}y = 2$
$\dfrac{1}{6}y - \dfrac{1}{4}x = -1$

44. $y = \dfrac{2}{3}x + 4$
$\dfrac{1}{3}x - y = \dfrac{3}{4}$

45. $y = x + 3000$
$.10x + .08y = 600$

46. $x + y = 20$
$.6x + .45y = .5(20)$

B

47. $\dfrac{x - 2}{4} + \dfrac{y + 1}{3} = 2$

$\dfrac{x + 1}{7} + \dfrac{y - 3}{2} = \dfrac{1}{2}$

48. $\dfrac{x - 2}{3} - \dfrac{3y + 1}{6} = \dfrac{1}{6}$

$\dfrac{x - 1}{6} - \dfrac{y - 1}{7} = \dfrac{1}{21}$

49. $3(x - 1) + 2(y + 3) = 10$
$4(x + 6) + 3(y - 8) = 1$

50. $2(x - y) - 5(x + y) = 4$
$6(2x + y) - (3x - y) = -2$

C

Answer the following questions with complete sentences.

51. In general, why is solving a system of equations with the graphing method impractical?

52. How can we determine algebraically that a system of equations has no solution? What is the geometric relationship between the lines?

53. How can we determine algebraically that a system of equations has an infinite number of solutions? What is the geometric relationship between the lines?

54. When is it more convenient to use the addition method than the substitution method?

REVIEW EXERCISES

For the following, define your variables and write equations that represent the problems. Do not solve each equation.

55. The sum of two numbers is 42. The larger number is 6 more than the smaller number. Find the numbers. (See Section 2.2.)

56. A man has $3.05 in dimes and quarters. He has 6 more dimes than quarters. How many dimes and quarters does he have? (See Section 2.5.)

57. Alan flew his plane 314 miles with the wind in two hours. If the speed of the wind was 32 mph, find the speed of his plane in still air. (See Section 2.4.)

4.2 SOLVING WORD PROBLEMS

1	**Number Problems**
2	**Money Problems**
3	**Mixture Problems**
4	**Geometry Problems**
5	**Uniform Motion Problems**

---

1 **Number Problems**

In previous chapters we solved word problems using one variable. Many of these problems involved two unknowns, such as the length and width of a rectangle. In these cases using two variables and deriving a system of two equations is often an easier method. The system is then solved with the methods discussed in the last section.

Many of the applications covered in this section will be familiar, and some are just as readily solved with one variable. However, the objective of this section is to learn how to solve problems with systems of equations so that we can handle more difficult problems. The checks for all the examples except Example 1 are left as exercises. We begin with two number problems. (See Sections 2.2 and 2.4.)

EXAMPLE 1

One-third the sum of two numbers is 14. One-half the difference of the larger number and the smaller number is 3. Find the numbers.

SOLUTION

Let L = the larger number and S = the smaller number. $L + S$ = their sum, and $\frac{1}{3}(L + S) = 14$ is our first equation. $L - S$ = their difference, and $\frac{1}{2}(L - S) = 3$ is our second equation. The system is

$\frac{1}{3}(L + S) = 14$ Multiply both sides by 3.

$\frac{1}{2}(L - S) = 3$ Multiply both sides by 2.

$\begin{aligned} L + S &= 42 \qquad \text{Solve by addition.} \\ \underline{L - S} &= \underline{6} \\ 2L &= 48 \end{aligned}$

$L = 24$ and $S = 42 - L = 42 - 24 = 18.$
Thus $\{24, 18\}$ are the two numbers.

 CHECK $\frac{1}{3}(L + S) = \frac{1}{3}(24 + 18) = \frac{1}{3}(42) = 14$

$\frac{1}{2}(L - S) = \frac{1}{2}(24 - 18) = \frac{1}{2}(6) = 3$

EXAMPLE 2

The sum of the lengths of the Suez and Panama canals is 250 kilometers. If the Suez Canal were 4 kilometers shorter, then it would be twice the length of the Panama Canal. Find the length of each canal.

SOLUTION

Let s = the length of the Suez Canal and p = the length of the Panama Canal. Then $s + p = 250$ is the first equation. $s - 4 = 4$ km less than the length of the Suez Canal, $2p$ = twice the length of the Panama Canal, and $s - 4 = 2p$ or $s = 2p + 4$ is the second equation.

$s = 2p + 4$ Solve by substitution.
$s + p = 250$
$(2p + 4) + p = 250$
$p = 82 \text{ kilometers}$ and $s = 2p + 4 = 2 \cdot 82 + 4 = 168 \text{ kilometers.}$

Math in Time

GODFREY HARDY (1877–1947) was a leading specialist in number theory at Cambridge University in England. One day in 1913 he received a letter from an unknown Hindu clerk, Srinivasa Ramanujan (1887–1920), that contained some 120 theorems, without proofs, and a request that Hardy evaluate them. Hardy recognized some of the theorems as previous discoveries and was able to prove a few himself. The others, he said, "defeated me completely; I had never seen anything in the least like them before. A single look at them is enough to show that they could only be written down by a mathematician of the highest class. They must be true because, if they were not true, no one would have had the imagination to invent them." Hardy immediately made arrangements to bring Ramanujan to Cambridge.

Ramanujan was born in southern India and lived most of his life in poverty and obscurity. He started school at 5 and was transferred to a high school when he was 7. At 16 he was granted a scholarship to attend a local college, but because he only studied mathematics, he failed his other subjects and was expelled. From then until he went to England in 1914 he worked as a clerk in the port of Madras and studied mathematics on his own.

Ramanujan's only access to advanced mathematics was a text containing 6000 theorems from elementary mathematics and calculus. With this book and his genius for seeing quickly and deeply into intricate number relationships, he discovered more than 4000 theorems. He seems to have made a discovery by working out several examples on a slate (paper was too expensive) and then entering the general theorem in a notebook.

Srinivasa Ramanujan
The Granger Collection, New York

Ramanujan spent five years in England working closely with Hardy. Their collaboration was unique in the history of mathematics. Ramanujan's brilliant intuition combined with Hardy's formal training in mathematics produced several major discoveries. Hardy was very impressed with Ramanujan's memory of the properties of numbers, as illustrated by the following story. One day Hardy visited Ramanujan and mentioned that his taxicab's number was 1729, which seemed rather uninteresting. "No," Ramanujan replied, "it is a very interesting number; it is the smallest number expressible as a sum of two cubes in two different ways." That is, $1729 = 1^3 + 12^3 = 9^3 + 10^3$.

In 1917 Ramanujan contracted a mysterious incurable disease and spent the next two years in various nursing homes. Then, increasingly ill, he returned to India, where he died a year later at the age of 32. His widow recalled his last year: "He was only skin and bones. He often complained of severe pain. In spite of it, he was always busy doing his mathematics. That, evidently, helped him forget his pain."

2   Money Problems

We have covered a variety of money problems. The first example given here is a coin problem (Section 2.5). The second example is a business application, which is new material. From this point on we will not solve the systems of equations.

EXAMPLE 3   Solve the problem in the following cartoon.

PEANUTS reprinted by permission of UFS, Inc.

SOLUTION   Let d = the number of dimes the man has and q = the number of quarters he has. Then, $d + q = 20$ is our first equation. The value of the coins in cents is $10d + 25q$ (the money he has now). If the dimes were quarters and the quarters were dimes, then the value of the coins would be $10q + 25d$ (the money he would have). If we add 90 cents to the money he has now, then this is equal to the money he would have:

$(10d + 25q) + 90 = 10q + 25d$ Simplify.
$-15d + 15q = -90$ Divide by -15.
$d - q = 6$ is our second equation, and the system is
$d + q = 20$
$d - q = 6$ Add the equations.
$d = 13$ and $q = 7$, so he has 13 dimes and 7 quarters.

Recall from Section 3.4 that a cost function $C(x)$, gives the total cost, C, of producing x items. The **revenue function, $R(x)$**, is the total revenue, or income, R, from the sale of x items. $R(x)$ is equal to the product of the price per item and the number of items sold. A company makes a profit when $R > C$, and it has a loss when $R < C$. The point at which revenue equals cost, $R(x) = C(x)$, is called the **break-even point**.

EXAMPLE 4   If a firm's cost and revenue is given by the following systems of equations, find the break-even point.

$C(x) = 100x + 500$
$R(x) = 120x$

SOLUTION   Set $R(x) = C(x)$ and solve for x:
$R(x) = C(x)$
$120x = 100x + 500$
$20x = 500$
$x = 25$
Thus, the break-even point is at $x = 25$.

3 Mixture Problems

Recall that two types of mixture problems exist. The first deals with products, such as mixed nuts, at different prices. The second is concerned with mixing solutions, such as boric acid, of different concentrations (see Section 2.5). The following example is of the first type; the second type is covered in the exercises.

EXAMPLE 5

A grocer has two types of tea, one costing \$3 per kilogram and the other \$4 per kilogram. How many kilograms of each type must be used to produce a 20-kilogram mixture worth \$3.25 per kilogram?

SOLUTION

Let x = the number of kilograms of the \$3 tea used and y = the number of kilograms of the \$4 tea used. Then, $x + y = 20$ is the first equation. The value of the first tea, $3x$, plus the value of the second tea, $4y$, is equal to the value of the mixture, $3.25(20)$. Thus, the second equation is
$$3x + 4y = 3.25(20) = 65$$
and our system is
$$x + y = 20$$
$$3x + 4y = 65$$
The solution is $x = 15$ and $y = 5$. So, 15 kilograms of the \$3 tea and 5 kilograms of the \$4 tea are needed for the mixture.

4 Geometry Problems

Section 2.4 covered geometry problems that were solved with one variable. Recall that we can draw a diagram to visualize geometry problems.

EXAMPLE 6

An equilateral triangle (3 equal sides) and a square have the same perimeter. A side of the triangle is 2 meters longer than the side of the square. Find the dimensions of Figures 4.7 and 4.8.

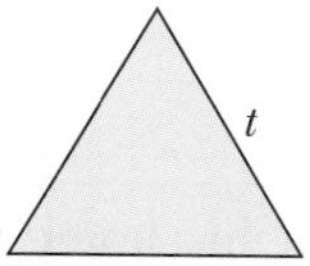

FIGURE 4.7

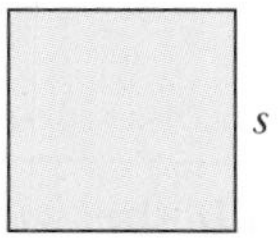

FIGURE 4.8

SOLUTION

Let t = the length of the side of the triangle and s = the length of the side of the square. Because t is 2 more than s, $t = s + 2$ is the first equation. The perimeter of the triangle, $3t$, is equal to the perimeter of the square, $4s$, so $3t = 4s$ is the second equation. The system of equations is
$$t = s + 2$$
$$3t = 4s$$
$s = 6$ and $t = 8$. Thus 8 meters is the length of one side of the triangle, and 6 meters is the length of one side of the square.

5   Uniform Motion Problems

Our first example is similar to Example 6 in Section 2.4.

EXAMPLE 7

Steve took 8 hours to drive 380 miles. During part of the trip he averaged 52 mph; the rest of the trip he averaged 40 mph. How long did he travel at each rate?

SOLUTION

Let t = the time spent traveling at 52 mph and T = the time spent traveling at 40 mph. Then $t + T = 8$. The information is organized in the following chart.

	rate $\cdot$	time =	distance
1st part	52	t	$52t$
2nd part	40	T	$40T$

Because the sum of the two distances is 380 miles, $52t + 40T = 380$, and the system of equations is

$$t + T = 8$$
$$52t + 40T = 380$$

$t = 5$ and $T = 3$. So Steve traveled for 5 hours at 52 mph and 3 hours at 40 mph.

Rates of travel are affected by such forces as wind and current. We have solved problems for which we were given the speed of the wind and asked to find the rate of the plane; or, conversely, we were given the rate of the plane and required to find the speed of the wind. With a system of equations we can solve a problem in which neither the speed of the wind nor the rate of the plane is known. This process is illustrated in the concluding example for this section.

EXAMPLE 8

Alan flew with the wind from his home to a ski resort in two hours, a distance of 314 miles. A week later he flew home against the wind, which was 10 mph faster than when he flew to the resort. After 3 hours he was 65 miles from home. Find the wind speed on the way to the resort and the speed of the plane in still air.

SOLUTION

Let r = the speed of the plane in still air and w = the speed of the wind going to the resort. Then, $w + 10$ = the speed of the wind on the return trip. $r + w$ = the rate traveling to the resort, and $r - (w + 10) = r - w - 10$ = the rate on the trip home. The information is organized in the following chart and the diagram in Figure 4.9 (let H = home and R = resort).

	rate · time = distance		
H to R	$r + w$	2	$2(r + w)$
R to H	$r - w - 10$	3	$3(r - w - 10)$

FIGURE 4.9

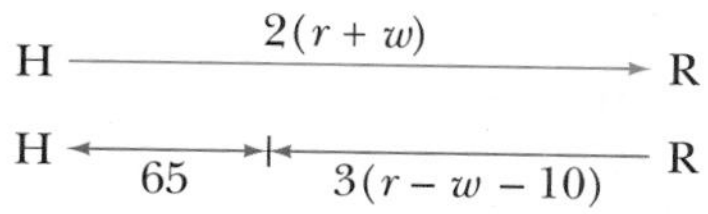

H $\xrightarrow{\hspace{1em} 2(r + w) \hspace{1em}}$ R

H $\xleftarrow{\hspace{1em}}$ $\underset{65}{\;}$ $\vert\!\leftarrow$ $\underset{3(r - w - 10)}{\hspace{3em}}$ R

The distance traveled from Alan's home to the resort is $2(r + w) = 314$. The distance traveled from the resort to his home is $3(r - w - 10) + 65 = 314$. The system of equations is

$$2(r + w) = 314$$
$$3(r - w - 10) + 65 = 314$$

$r = 125$ and $w = 32$. Thus the wind speed on the way to the resort was 32 mph, and the speed of the plane in still air was 125 mph.

EXERCISE SET 4.2

A

1 Use a system of equations to solve the following problems. Define each variable. Check the answers to the indicated examples.

1. Check the answer to Example 2 (p. 162).

2. The sum of two numbers is 26, and their difference is 2. Find the numbers.

3. The sum of two numbers is 3. Twice the larger minus the smaller is 24. Find the numbers.

4. Twice the sum of two numbers is -14, and 1/2 the difference of the larger and the smaller is 3. Find the numbers.

5. The denominator of a fraction is 6 more than the numerator. If 3 is added to the numerator and 1 is subtracted from the denominator, then the new fraction is 4/5. Find the original fraction.

6. The numerator of a fraction is one more than twice the denominator. If 5 is added to both the numerator and the denominator, then the new fraction is 5/3. Find the original fraction.

7. A carpenter has to cut a 19-foot board into two pieces so that the shorter piece is one more than one-half the longer piece. How long is each piece?

8. On a chemistry test the difference of the highest and lowest scores was 50, and the average of the two scores was 58. Find the two scores.

9. Leeann has twice as much money as Amy. If each had four more dollars, then they would have a total of $62. How much money do they each have?

2

10. Check the answer to Example 3 (p. 164).

11. Eric has 27 nickels and dimes. The number of dimes is three more than twice the number of nickels. How many nickels and dimes does he have?

12. Megan has 12 dimes and quarters. The sum of 4 times the number of dimes and 3 times the number of quarters is 43. How many dimes and quarters does she have?

13. Diana has 20 pennies and dimes worth 92¢. How many pennies and dimes does she have?

14. Mark has 15 nickels and quarters worth $2.15. How many nickels and quarters does he have?

15. Larry has 20 nickels and dimes. If the nickels were dimes and the dimes were nickels, then he would have 20 cents less than he has now. How many nickels and dimes does he have?

16. Sarah invested $6000, part at 7% and the rest at 9%. The total interest from the two investments was $490. How much did she invest at each rate?

17. Julio invested three times as much money at $8\frac{1}{4}\%$ as he did at $11\frac{1}{2}\%$. The interest earned in a year on the $8\frac{1}{4}\%$ investment was $530 more than the interest earned on the $11\frac{1}{2}\%$ investment. How much did he invest at each rate?

18. A company produces calculators. Its cost and revenue equations in dollars are $C(x) = 19x + 3800$ and $R(x) = 38x$.
  a. What is the cost of producing 150 calculators?
  b. What will be the revenue if 190 calculators are sold?
  c. Find the break-even point.

19. A firm produces radios. Its cost and revenue equations in dollars are $C(x) = 126x + 3700$ and $R(x) = 163x$.
  a. What is the cost of producing 80 radios?
  b. What will be the revenue if 120 radios are sold?
  c. Find the break-even point.

A firm's profit, P, is found by subtracting the cost, C, from the revenue, R. That is, the **profit function** is defined as

$$P(x) = R(x) - C(x)$$

20. What is the profit function for Exercise 18? Find the profit if 300 calculators are sold.

21. What is the profit function for Exercise 19? Find the profit if 250 radios are sold.

3

22. Check the answer to Example 5 (p. 165).

23. Craig mixes 6 pounds of cashews worth $8 per pound with pecans worth $9 per pound to produce a mixture worth $8.40 per pound. How many pounds of pecans are needed? How many pounds are in the mixture?

24. A merchant has two types of coffee, brand A worth $6 per pound and brand B worth $3.50 per pound. How many pounds of each brand should she mix together to obtain 12 pounds of a mixture worth $52?

25. A chemist has two acid solutions, one 5% and the other 15%. How much of each solution should be used to obtain 20 liters of a 12% solution?

26. A 40% alcohol solution is produced when 7.5 liters of a 30% solution are mixed with a 70% solution. How many liters of the 70% solution are used? How many liters are in the mixture?

27. A farmer has 70 gallons of a 60% disinfectant. How much water must she add to obtain a 50% solution? How many gallons are in the mixture?

28. A nurse has 12 liters of a 30% alcohol solution. How much pure alcohol must she add to produce a 50% alcohol solution? How many liters are in the mixture?

4

29. Check the answer to Example 6 (p. 165).

30. The width of a rectangle is the same length as the side of a square. The length of the rectangle is 1 more than 3 times its width. The combined perimeters of the two figures is 50. Find the dimensions of the two figures.

31. One side of a triangle is 9. The third side is 1 less than twice the second side, and the perimeter is 32. Find the two unknown sides of the triangle.

32. The length of a rectangular solid is 10, its width is 1 more than twice its height, and its surface area is 242. Find its width and height if their product is 21.

33. Two angles are supplementary, and the larger angle is twice the smaller angle. Find the angles.

34. Two angles are supplementary, and their difference is 86°. Find the angles.

35. Two angles are complementary, and the larger angle is 6° less than 5 times the smaller angle. Find the angles.

36. Two angles are complementary, and the sum of 1/2 the smaller angle and 1/4 the larger angle is 29°. Find the angles.

37. One angle of a triangle is 22°. Find the other two angles if their difference is 62°.

5

38. Check the answer to Example 7 (p. 166).

39. Check the answer to Example 8 (p. 166).

40. Roxann took 9 hours to drive 404 miles. During part of the trip she averaged 40 mph; during the remainder she averaged 48 mph. Find the length of time that she traveled at each rate.

41. A truck and a car leave Ashland at the same time heading in opposite directions. When they are 350 miles apart, the difference of their distances is 70 miles. If the truck travels at the slower rate, what is the distance that each travels?

42. A truck and a car leave Fresno at the same time heading in opposite directions. After 3 hours they are 315 miles apart, and the difference of their distances is 15 miles. If the truck travels at the faster rate, what is the speed of each vehicle?

43. José travels 32 miles down a river in 4 hours. On the return trip he travels 12 miles in 6 hours. Find the speed of the river and the speed of his boat in still water.

44. Brent's motorboat can travel 12 mph in still water. He travels down a river for 30 minutes and then returns in 1 hour. Find the rate of the river and the distance he travels each way.

45. A Coast Guard cutter traveling with the tide takes 20 minutes to reach a fishing boat that is 12 kilometers offshore. On the return trip the cutter is 6 kilometers from shore after 15 minutes. What is the speed of the cutter in still water? What is the rate of the tide?

B

46. On Saturday afternoon Dan took 4 hours to travel 32 miles down a stream. It rained that night, and on Sunday when he returned upstream the current was 1 mph faster than on Saturday. After 5 hours he was 17 miles from his starting point. Find the rate of the current on Saturday and the speed of his boat in still water.

Use a system of equations to solve the following miscellaneous exercises. Define each variable.

47. Two years from now Ted will be twice as old as Nancy was two years ago. The sum of their present ages is 30. How old are they now?

48. Susan and Betty are 20 miles apart. If they leave at the same time and cycle toward each other, they will meet in 2 hours. However, if they leave at the same time and cycle in the same direction, it will take Betty 10 hours to overtake Susan. How fast does each cycle?

C

49. David and Sarah went to Atlantic City, New Jersey, for gambling. They each cashed a check at the casino. If David bet $100 and won $100 and Sarah bet $100 and lost $100, David had twice the amount that Sarah had after the bets. However, if David bet $100 and lost $100 and Sarah bet $100 and won $100, Sarah had the same amount as David had after the bets. What was the value of each check?

 Answer the following questions with complete sentences.

50. Hardy and Ramanujan worked together and made several discoveries. Discuss the contributions of each man to the collaboration.

51. What is meant by the "break-even point"?

REVIEW EXERCISES

Find the *x*- and *y*-intercepts for the following exercises and graph them. (See Section 3.2.)

52. $x + y = 3$ **53.** $6x + 3y = 12$

Multiply both sides of each equation by the given number. (See Section 2.1.)

54. $3x - y - 4z = -5;$ 3

55. $x + 3y - 2z = 0;$ -1

Add the following pairs of equations. (See Section 4.2.)

56. $6x + 3y + 4z = 12$
$\underline{3x - y - 4z = -5}$

57. $-n - d - q = -10$
$\underline{n + 2d + 5q = 27}$

4.3 SOLVING SYSTEMS OF LINEAR EQUATIONS IN THREE VARIABLES

1	Using Geometric Interpretation
2	Solving a System by Addition and Substitution
3	Solving Word Problems

1 Using Geometric Interpretation

Chapter 1 introduced the number line and showed that the graph of an equation such as $x = 3$ is a point on the line. The *xy*-plane was discussed in Chapter 3, and a linear equation such as $x + y = 3$ was graphed as a line in the plane. This section extends the two-dimensional *xy*-plane to a **three-dimensional coordinate system** and represents an equation such as $x + y + z = 3$ as a plane in space. This material will be only introductory because our main objective here is to learn how to solve a system of three linear equations in three variables.

$Ax + By = C$ is called a **linear equation** because its graph is a line in a plane. $Ax + By + Cz = D$ is called a **linear equation in three variables**; its graph is a **plane** in space.

A solution to $x + y = 3$ is an ordered pair such as $(1, 2)$. In a similar way a solution to $x + y + z = 3$ is called an **ordered triple**, which is denoted (x, y, z); for example, the ordered triples $(1, 1, 1)$ and $(4, 0, -1)$ are solutions to $x + y + z = 3$ because

$$1 + 1 + 1 = 3 \quad \text{and} \quad 4 + 0 + (-1) = 3$$

The ordered triple $(2, 4, 6)$ is not a solution because $2 + 4 + 6 \neq 3$.

We constructed the *xy*-plane with two perpendicular number lines. Similarly, we describe space with three mutually perpendicular number lines, the *x, y,* and *z* axes. Their intersection is the origin, and the same unit of measure is used on the three axes (Figure 4.10). The angle between the positive *x* and *y* axes may not appear to be 90° because we are representing three-dimensional space on a two-dimensional piece of paper. To draw objects in perspective we must distort angles and foreshorten line segments.

The best way to visualize the portion of space called the **first octant**, which is determined by the positive axes, is to stand in a room facing a corner on the floor (the origin). The intersection of the floor (the *xy*-plane) and the wall on your left (the *xz*-plane) is the *x*-axis; the intersection of the

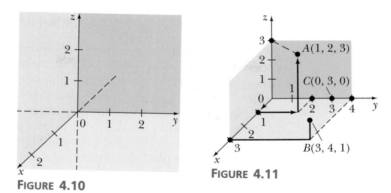

FIGURE 4.10

FIGURE 4.11

floor and the wall to your right (the yz-plane) is the y-axis; and the intersection of the two walls is the z-axis. The xy, xz, and yz planes are called the **coordinate planes** (Figure 4.11).

The method of graphing points in space is similar to the one for plotting points in the xy-plane. For example, to graph A(1, 2, 3) move one unit in the positive x-direction, two units in the positive y-direction, and three units in the positive z-direction. A, B(3, 4, 1), and C(0, 3, 0) are graphed in Figure 4.11.

We graph the plane $x + y + z = 3$ in the first octant by finding its intercepts. We find the x-intercept by letting $y = z = 0$ in the equation $x + y + z = 3$. Thus, $x + 0 + 0 = 3$ and $x = 3$. In a similar way we determine that the other intercepts are $y = 3$ and $z = 3$. Another point on the plane is A(1, 1, 1). The intersections of $x + y + z = 3$ and the coordinate planes are called **traces** and are graphed as line segments. These points and the traces are graphed in Figure 4.12. The portion of the axes that are beyond our line of sight behind the plane are graphed as broken line segments.

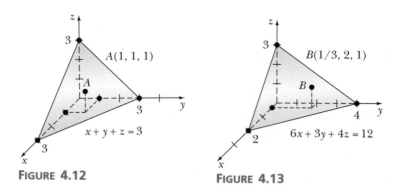

FIGURE 4.12

FIGURE 4.13

As another example, consider $6x + 3y + 4z = 12$. By letting $y = z = 0$, we have $6x = 12$ and $x = 2$, which is the x-intercept. In a similar way we can determine that $y = 4$ and $z = 3$ are the y- and z-intercepts. Another point on the plane is B(1/3, 2, 1). This plane is graphed in Figure 4.13.

2   Solving a System by Addition and Substitution

We have seen that a system of two equations in two variables has three possible solutions: one solution (intersecting lines), no solution (parallel lines), or infinitely many solutions (the same line). A similar situation exists with a system of three linear equations in three variables. The system describes three planes that can be related in a variety of ways.

First, the planes can intersect in one point, such as the floor and two adjacent walls of a room (the origin in Figure 4.11 is the intersection of the three coordinate planes). In this case the solution is the ordered triple that satisfies each equation, and the system is said to be *consistent*.

Second, no point of intersection exists, such as two parallel planes intersected by a third plane (Figure 4.14); the floor, ceiling, and wall of a room are an example. In this case we have an *inconsistent system*, and the empty set is the solution.

Third, we have a *dependent system*, that has infinitely many solutions, such as three planes that intersect in a line (Figure 4.15); three pages of a book constitute an example. Describing the solution set of a dependent system is beyond the level of this text, so we will just say that the system has "infinitely many solutions."

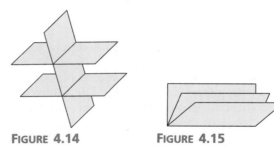

Figure 4.14   **Figure 4.15**

Now that we know the possible solutions to a system of three linear equations in three unknowns, we consider three examples to illustrate each case. We will use the addition method to reduce the system to two equations in two variables, which can then be solved with the methods covered in Section 4.1.

EXAMPLE 1

Solve the system

$$6x + 3y + 4z = 12 \quad (1)$$
$$3x - y - 4z = -5 \quad (2)$$
$$9x - 2y + 3z = 2 \quad (3)$$

SOLUTION

Let us select z as the variable to be eliminated. By adding equations (1) and (2) we produce an equation in x and y:

$$6x + 3y + 4z = 12 \quad (1)$$
$$\underline{3x - y - 4z = -5} \quad (2)$$
$$9x + 2y = 7 \quad (4)$$

To obtain another equation in x and y, we choose a different pair of the original equations. Add 3 times equation (2) to 4 times equation (3):

$$9x - 3y - 12z = -15 \quad \text{3 times (2)}$$
$$\underline{36x - 8y + 12z = 8 \qquad \text{4 times (3)}}$$
$$45x - 11y = -7 \qquad\qquad (5)$$

Our system of two equations in two variables is

$$9x + 2y = 7 \qquad (4)$$
$$45x - 11y = -7 \quad (5)$$

Add -5 times equation (4) to equation (5):

$$-45x - 10y = -35 \quad \text{-5 times (4)}$$
$$\underline{45x - 11y = -7 \qquad\quad (5)}$$
$$-21y = -42$$
$$y = 2$$

Substitute $y = 2$ in either (4) or (5). Choosing (4),

$$9x + 2 \cdot 2 = 7$$
$$x = 1/3$$

Substitute $x = 1/3$ and $y = 2$ in (1):

$$6(1/3) + 3(2) + 4z = 12$$
$$2 + 6 + 4z = 12$$
$$z = 1$$

so $\{(1/3, 2, 1)\}$ is the solution to the system. We check the answer by substituting $(1/3, 2, 1)$ in equations (1), (2), and (3). This check is left as an exercise.

EXAMPLE 2

Solve the system

$$2x - y + 3z = 4 \qquad (1)$$
$$-6x + 3y - 9z = 6 \qquad (2)$$
$$x - 5y + 2z = 8 \qquad (3)$$

SOLUTION   Add three times equation (1) to equation (2):

$$6x - 3y + 9z = 12 \quad \text{3 times (1)}$$
$$\underline{-6x + 3y - 9z = 6 \qquad\quad (2)}$$
$$0 = 18$$

The **false equation**, $0 = 18$, means that the system is inconsistent, so the solution set is $\emptyset$.

EXAMPLE 3

Solve the system

$$x + 3y - 2z = 0 \qquad (1)$$
$$x + 2y + 5z = 0 \qquad (2)$$
$$0 + y - 7z = 0 \qquad (3)$$

SOLUTION   Because equation (3) only contains y and z, we will use equations (1) and (2) to produce another equation in y and z. Add -1 times equation (1) to equation (2):

$$-x - 3y + 2z = 0 \quad \text{-1 times (1)}$$
$$\underline{x + 2y + 5z = 0 \qquad\quad (2)}$$
$$-y + 7z = 0 \qquad\qquad (4)$$

(continued)

Our system of two equations in two variables is (3) and (4). Add (3) to (4):

$$\begin{array}{ll} y - 7z = 0 & (3) \\ -y + 7z = 0 & (4) \\ \hline 0 = 0 \end{array}$$

The **true equation**, $0 = 0$, means that the system is dependent, so it has infinitely many solutions.

As a point of interest, this system represents distinct planes that intersect in a line that contains the origin $(0, 0, 0)$.

---

3   Solving Word Problems

Many applications of algebra involve three unknowns, such as the number of nickels, dimes, and quarters. Such problems can often be conveniently solved with a system of three linear equations in three variables. This process is illustrated in the concluding examples to this section.

EXAMPLE 4

Ted has 10 nickels, dimes, and quarters worth $1.35. He has 2 more dimes than quarters. How many nickels, dimes, and quarters does he have?

SOLUTION

Let n, d, and q be the number of nickels, dimes and quarters. With a total of 10 coins, $n + d + q = 10$. The difference of the dimes and quarters is 2, so $d - q = 2$. The value of the coins is 135 cents, so $5n + 10d + 25q = 135$; or, dividing by 5, $n + 2d + 5q = 27$. Thus, our system of equations is

$$\begin{array}{ll} n + d + q = 10 & (1) \\ 0 + d - q = 2 & (2) \\ n + 2d + 5q = 27 & (3) \end{array}$$

Adding -1 times (1) to (3) gives us the system

$$\begin{array}{ll} d + 4q = 17 & (4) \\ d - q = 2 & (2) \end{array}$$

Adding -1 times (2) to (4) gives us

$$5q = 15$$

$q = 3$. Then from (2),
$d = q + 2 = 3 + 2 = 5$, and from (1),
$n = 10 - d - q = 10 - 5 - 3 = 2$. Thus,
Ted has 2 nickels, 5 dimes, and 3 quarters.

EXAMPLE 5

The sum of three numbers is 0. Four times the first number, plus 2 times the second, plus the third is -1. The first number minus the second and plus the third is 8. Find the three numbers.

SOLUTION

Let $a =$ the first number, $b =$ the second number, and $c =$ the third number. The system of equations is

$$\begin{array}{ll} a + b + c = 0 & (1) \\ 4a + 2b + c = -1 & (2) \\ a - b + c = 8 & (3) \end{array}$$

We eliminate c in equations (2) and (3). By adding -1 times (1) to both (2) and (3) we have

$$3a + b = -1 \quad (4)$$
$$0 - 2b = 8 \quad (5)$$

$b = -4$ from (5). Substitute $b = -4$ in (4):

$$3a + (-4) = -1$$
$$a = 1$$

Substitute $a = 1$ and $b = -4$ in (1):

$$1 + (-4) + c = 0$$
$$c = 3$$

so the three numbers are 1, -4, and 3.

EXERCISE SET 4.3

A

1 For each of the following, draw a three-dimensional coordinate system and graph each set of points.

1. $\{(0, 0, 0), (0, 5, 0), (1, 2, 1), (4, 3, 2)\}$

2. $\{(4, 0, 0), (1, 3, 2), (0, 2, 3), (3, 1, 1)\}$

3. $\{(0, 0, 2), (3, 0, 1), (2, 2, 1), (1, 3, 4)\}$

4. $\{(4, 4, 0), (1, 4, 3), (3, 3, 2), (1, 1, 1)\}$

Graph the following planes in the first octant by plotting their intercepts and drawing their traces.

5. $x + y + z = 2$

6. $3x + 4y + 6z = 12$

7. $2x + 5y + 2z = 10$

8. $6x + 2y + 3z = 6$

9. $4x + 2y + z = 4$

2

10. Check the solution to Example 1 (p. 172).

Solve the following systems of equations. Check your solutions to Exercises 11 through 14.

11. $x + y + z = 2$
$0 + y - z = -3$
$x + y + 3z = 6$

12. $x + y - z = 3$
$2x - y + z = 3$
$x + 2y - 3z = 5$

13. $x + 2z = 1$
$2x - y + 3z = -1$
$4x + y + 8z = 2$

14. $3x + 5y + 7z = 1$
$x + 2y + 3z = -2$
$2x + 3y + 5z = 3$

15. $6x + 2y + 3z = 6$
$6x + 2y + 3z = 3$
$2x - y + 2z = 2$

16. $x + 2y + z = -1$
$2x - 3y + z = 1$
$3x - y + 3z = 4$

17. $x - y + z = 0$
$x + y - z = 0$
$2x - y = 0$

18. $x - y + 2z = 1$
$2x - 2y + 4z = 2$
$3x - 3y + 6z = 3$

19. $2x + 3y - z = 2$
$3x + y - 3z = 3$
$6x + 9y - 3z = 6$

20. $2x + 3y - z = 8$
$4x - y + 2z = -2$
$6x + y + z = 4$

21. $x + y + z = 0$
$\frac{1}{2}x + 2y - z = 12$
$x + \frac{1}{3}y + \frac{1}{5}z = 2$

22. $2x + y - 2z = 8$
$\frac{1}{8}x - \frac{1}{2}y + z = \frac{1}{2}$
$-x + \frac{5}{2}y + \frac{2}{3}z = -21$

23. $2x + y + z = 4$
$6x + 3y + 4z = 12$
$8x + 4y - 3z = 24$

24. $x - 2y + z = 1$
$x + 3y - z = 1$
$4x - 8y + 4z = 4$

25. $2x + 3y - 4z = 1$
$4x + 4z = 3$
$-3y + 8z = 1$

26. $2x - 4y + 6z = 2$
$x - 2y + 3z = 2$
$-x + 2y - 3z = 1$

27. $x + y + z = 1$
$y + z = 2$
$x - y + 3z = -1$

28. $x - y + z = 3$
$3x + y + z = -2$
$2x - z = 6$

29. $x + y = 5$
$x - z = 6$
$y + 2z = -5$

30. $2x - z = 1$
$3y + 2z = 0$
$x - y = -3$

3

31. Check the solution to Example 4 (p. 174).

32. Check the solution to Example 5 (p. 174).

Solve the following exercises using a system of three equations in three variables. Define each variable.

33. The sum of three numbers is 23. The second number is 27 more than the first number. The third number is 10 less than twice the second number. Find the numbers.

34. Given three numbers, the sum of the first two is 1. The second is 6 more than the third. The sum of the first and twice the third is 15. Find the numbers.

35. The perimeter of a triangle is 98 centimeters. The second side is 10 centimeters longer than the shortest side, and the third side is twice as long as the shortest side. Find the sides of the triangle.

36. The sum of the two smallest angles of a triangle is 100°. The difference of the largest and smallest angles is 50°. Find the three angles of the triangle.

37. The two smallest angles of a triangle are complementary. The largest angle is 10° less than 5 times the smallest angle. Find the three angles of the triangle.

38. Mousa has 61 nickels, dimes, and quarters that total $7.50. He has 9 more dimes than quarters. How many nickels, dimes, and quarters does he have?

39. Stephanie has 21 pennies, nickels, and quarters worth $2.13. The number of quarters is one more than the number of nickels. How many pennies, nickels, and quarters does she have?

40. Lisa invested $10,000. She put part of this amount in a savings account at 6%, part in bonds at 9%, and the rest in a money market at 12%. Her total yearly interest was $945. The amount invested at 12% is $1000 less than twice the amount invested at 6%. How much did she invest at each rate?

41. Ken invested $16,000, part at 7%, part at 8%, and the rest at 10%. The amount he invested at 8% was $3000 more than the amount he invested at 7%. The interest earned at 10% was $360 more than the combined interest earned at 7% and 8%. How much was invested at each rate?

42. A merchant wants to mix three types of tea to make 100 ounces of a mixture that will be worth $102. Brand A costs 90¢ per ounce, brand B costs $1.10 per ounce, and brand C costs $1.20 per ounce. She used 10 ounces more of brand B than brand C. How many ounces of each brand did she use?

43. The owner of a store mixes peanuts worth $3 per pound, cashews worth $9 per pound, and walnuts worth $6 per pound to get 30 pounds of a mixture worth $5.20 per pound. The number of pounds of peanuts is 2 more than twice the number of pounds of cashews. How many pounds of each kind of nut did he use?

44. Tickets for the San Francisco Opera cost $64 for the Grand Tier, $49 for the Dress Circle, and $21 for the Balcony Rear. One afternoon the box office sold 40 tickets for $1490. The number of balcony tickets sold was equal to the sum of the other tickets sold. How many of each type of ticket was sold?

B Solve the following systems of equations using the methods developed in this section.

45.
$$x + y + z + w = 5$$
$$x + 2y + z - w = 8$$
$$2x + y + z - w = 9$$
$$x + y - 3z - w = -5$$

46.
$$x + y - z + w = 4$$
$$3x - y + z + w = 8$$
$$x + 3y + z + 2w = 2$$
$$-x + 2y - z - 3w = -16$$

47.
$$x - y + z - 2w = -1$$
$$x - 2z + w = -4$$
$$2x + y - w = -3$$
$$x - 3y + z = 1$$

48.
$$x + y - z + w = 1$$
$$x - 2y + w = 4$$
$$3x - z + 3w = 6$$
$$x + 2y + 2z - w = 4$$

C

Answer the following questions with complete sentences.

49. Give the geometric interpretations of a system of three linear equations in three variables.

50. Let $x = 6$, $x + y = 6$, and $x + y + z = 6$. Discuss the geometric interpretations of these equations.

Solve the following system of equations. (See Section 4.1.)

51. $4x - 5y = 2$
$\quad\ 6x + 2y = -1$

52. $\quad 2x - 4y = 6$
$\quad -3x + 6y = -9$

53. $\qquad\qquad y = 2x + 3$
$\quad\ 6x - 3y = 7$

4.4 FINDING MATRIX SOLUTIONS TO SYSTEMS OF LINEAR EQUATIONS

> **1** Solving a System of Two Equations with Matrices
>
> **2** Solving a System of Three Equations with Matrices

1 Solving a System of Two Equations with Matrices

The addition–substitution method of solving a system of linear equations is convenient when only two or three equations are used. However, the method is impractical for larger systems; other techniques are needed. This and the next section introduce matrices and determinants, which can be used to solve larger systems. For the sake of simplicity we will stay with systems of two and three equations. Matrices and determinants are studied in detail in linear algebra, a branch of mathematics that is used in such fields as business, biology, and engineering. This section will introduce a matrix approach to solving systems of linear equations.

A **matrix** (plural: **matrices**) is a rectangular array of numbers arranged in rows and columns and placed in brackets. Examples are

$$A = \begin{bmatrix} 1 & 3 & 5 \\ 2 & 0 & 7 \end{bmatrix} \qquad B = [1 \ -1 \ 2 \ 4] \qquad C = \begin{bmatrix} 4 & 7 \\ 2 & 8 \end{bmatrix}$$

Because A has two rows and three columns, it is called a "two-by-three" matrix, which is written 2×3. B is a 1×4 matrix, and C is a 2×2 matrix. C is an example of a **square matrix**, which is one that has the same number of rows and columns.

With each system of linear equations we can associate a matrix of coefficients and constant terms. An example of a system and its matrix is

$$\begin{array}{r} 3x + 2y = 8 \\ x - 4y = -2 \end{array} \qquad \begin{bmatrix} 3 & 2 & \vdots & 8 \\ 1 & -4 & \vdots & -2 \end{bmatrix}$$

This matrix is called the **augmented matrix** of the system of equations. The dashed line is used to separate the coefficients from the constant terms.

Two systems of equations are **equivalent** if they have the same solution set. In Sections 4.1 and 4.3 we solved systems by transforming them into simpler systems. We did this by multiplying an equation by a nonzero constant and adding two equations. We can also interchange two equations without changing the solution set. These properties carry over to the augmented matrix that represents the system of equations. The following example illustrates these three properties.

$$3x + 2y = 8 \qquad \begin{bmatrix} 3 & 2 & | & 8 \\ 1 & -4 & | & -2 \end{bmatrix}$$
$$x - 4y = -2$$

1. Interchange the two equations and rows:

$$x - 4y = -2 \qquad \begin{bmatrix} 1 & -4 & | & -2 \\ 3 & 2 & | & 8 \end{bmatrix}$$
$$3x + 2y = 8$$

2. Multiply the first equation and row by -3:

$$-3x + 12y = 6 \qquad \begin{bmatrix} -3 & 12 & | & 6 \\ 3 & 2 & | & 8 \end{bmatrix}$$
$$3x + 2y = 8$$

3. Add the first equation and row to the second equation and row:

$$-3x + 12y = 6 \qquad \begin{bmatrix} -3 & 12 & | & 6 \\ 0 & 14 & | & 14 \end{bmatrix}$$
$$0 + 14y = 14$$

Now multiply the first equation and row by $-1/3$ and the second by $1/14$:

$$x - 4y = -2 \qquad \begin{bmatrix} 1 & -4 & | & -2 \\ 0 & 1 & | & 2 \end{bmatrix}$$
$$0 + y = 1$$

Because $y = 1$ and $x = -2 + 4y = -2 + 4 \cdot 1 = 2$, $\{(2, 1)\}$ is the solution set of all the systems of equations just considered.

When one of these properties is applied to a system of equations, it produces an equivalent system of equations. When it is applied to the corresponding augmented matrix, it is called a **row operation**, and it produces a **row-equivalent matrix**. Just three row operations are possible, but we often combine operations 2 and 3 into one step when solving a system. Therefore, for the sake of clarity, four row operations are given in the following summary.

Row Operations

An augmented matrix is transformed into a row-equivalent matrix if:

1. Any two rows are interchanged.

2. A row is multiplied by a nonzero constant.

3. Any two rows are added together.

4. A nonzero constant multiple of one row is added to a second row.

Using row operations on the augmented matrix of a system of equations allows us to solve it with matrices. Consider the following general system and its augmented matrix:

$$\begin{array}{c} a_1x + b_1y = c_1 \\ a_2x + b_2y = c_2 \end{array} \qquad \left[\begin{array}{cc|c} a_1 & b_1 & c_1 \\ a_2 & b_2 & c_2 \end{array} \right]$$

Row operations are applied to this matrix to produce

$$\left[\begin{array}{cc|c} 1 & p & q \\ 0 & 1 & r \end{array} \right]$$

which is row-equivalent to the original matrix. The corresponding system of equations is

$$\begin{aligned} x + py &= q \\ y &= r \end{aligned}$$

Substituting $y = r$ into the first equation gives us $x + pr = q$, or $x = q - pr$. Thus, $(q - pr, r)$ is the solution to the original system. These ideas are illustrated in the following example.

EXAMPLE 1

Solve the following systems with matrices.

a. $4x - 5y = 2$　　**b.** $2x - 4y = 6$　　**c.** $y = 2x + 3$
　　$6x + 2y = -1$　　　　$-3x + 6y = -9$　　　　$6x - 3y = 7$

SOLUTION　**a.** The augmented matrix is

$$\left[\begin{array}{cc|c} 4 & -5 & 2 \\ 6 & 2 & -1 \end{array} \right] \qquad \begin{array}{l} \text{Multiply row 1 by 3.} \\ \text{Multiply row 2 by } -2. \end{array}$$

$$\left[\begin{array}{cc|c} 12 & -15 & 6 \\ -12 & -4 & 2 \end{array} \right] \qquad \text{Add row 1 to row 2.}$$

$$\left[\begin{array}{cc|c} 12 & -15 & 6 \\ 0 & -19 & 8 \end{array} \right] \qquad \begin{array}{l} \text{Muliply row 1 by } 1/12. \\ \text{Multiply row 2 by } -1/19. \end{array}$$

$$\left[\begin{array}{cc|c} 1 & -\dfrac{5}{4} & \dfrac{1}{2} \\ 0 & 1 & -\dfrac{8}{19} \end{array} \right]$$

The corresponding system of equations is

$$x - \frac{5}{4}y = \frac{1}{2}$$

$$y = -\frac{8}{19}$$

Substitute this value of y in the first equation:

$$x = \frac{1}{2} + \frac{5}{4}y = \frac{1}{2} + \left(\frac{5}{4}\right)\left(-\frac{8}{19}\right) = \frac{1}{2} - \frac{10}{19} = \frac{19}{38} - \frac{20}{38} = -\frac{1}{38}, \text{ so}$$

$\left(-\dfrac{1}{38}, -\dfrac{8}{19}\right)$ is the solution.

b. $\left[\begin{array}{cc|c} 2 & -4 & 6 \\ -3 & 6 & -9 \end{array} \right] \qquad \begin{array}{l} \text{Multiply row 1 by 3.} \\ \text{Multiply row 2 by 2.} \end{array}$

$\left[\begin{array}{cc|c} 6 & -12 & 18 \\ -6 & 12 & -18 \end{array} \right] \qquad \text{Add row 1 to row 2.}$

$\left[\begin{array}{cc|c} 6 & -12 & 18 \\ 0 & 0 & 0 \end{array} \right]$

(continued)

Because $0 + 0 = 0$ is a true equation, the system is dependent, and the solution is $2x - 4y = 6$.

c. Write $y = 2x + 3$ as $-2x + y = 3$
                    $6x - 3y = 7$ $6x - 3y = 7$

$$\left[\begin{array}{rr:r} -2 & 1 & 3 \\ 6 & -3 & 7 \end{array}\right] \quad \text{Add 3 times row 1 to row 2.}$$

$$\left[\begin{array}{rr:r} -2 & 1 & 3 \\ 0 & 0 & 16 \end{array}\right]$$

Because $0 + 0 = 16$ is a false equation, the system is inconsistent, and the solution set is $\varnothing$.

2   Solving a System of Three Equations with Matrices

The matrix method of solving two equations in two unknowns can be applied to three linear equations in three variables. Consider the following general system and its augmented matrix:

$$\begin{array}{c} a_1x + b_1y + c_1z = d_1 \\ a_2x + b_2y + c_2z = d_2 \\ a_3x + b_3y + c_3z = d_3 \end{array} \qquad \left[\begin{array}{ccc:c} a_1 & b_1 & c_1 & d_1 \\ a_2 & b_2 & c_2 & d_2 \\ a_3 & b_3 & c_3 & d_3 \end{array}\right]$$

With row operations we can transform this matrix into

$$\left[\begin{array}{ccc:c} 1 & p & q & r \\ 0 & 1 & s & t \\ 0 & 0 & 1 & u \end{array}\right]$$

which is row-equivalent to the original matrix. The following corresponding system of equations is then solved by substitution:

$$x + py + qz = r$$
$$y + sz = t$$
$$z = u$$

EXAMPLE 2

Solve the system
$$3x - y + z = 6$$
$$x - y + z = 4$$
$$2x + 2y - 3z = -6$$

SOLUTION   The augmented matrix of this system is

$$\left[\begin{array}{rrr:r} 3 & -1 & 1 & 6 \\ 1 & -1 & 1 & 4 \\ 2 & 2 & -3 & -6 \end{array}\right] \qquad \text{Interchange rows 1 and 2.}$$

$$\left[\begin{array}{rrr:r} 1 & -1 & 1 & 4 \\ 3 & -1 & 1 & 6 \\ 2 & 2 & -3 & -6 \end{array}\right] \qquad \text{Multiply row 1 by } -3 \text{ and add the result to row 2.}$$

$$\left[\begin{array}{rrr:r} 1 & -1 & 1 & 4 \\ 0 & 2 & -2 & -6 \\ 2 & 2 & -3 & -6 \end{array}\right] \qquad \text{Multiply row 1 by } -2 \text{ and add the result to row 3.}$$

$$\begin{bmatrix} 1 & -1 & 1 & \vdots & 4 \\ 0 & 2 & -2 & \vdots & -6 \\ 0 & 4 & -5 & \vdots & -14 \end{bmatrix}$$ Multiply row 2 by -2 and add the result to row 3.

$$\begin{bmatrix} 1 & -1 & 1 & \vdots & 4 \\ 0 & 2 & -2 & \vdots & -6 \\ 0 & 0 & -1 & \vdots & -2 \end{bmatrix}$$ Multiply row 2 by 1/2.
Multiply row 3 by -1.

$$\begin{bmatrix} 1 & -1 & 1 & \vdots & 4 \\ 0 & 1 & -1 & \vdots & -3 \\ 0 & 0 & 1 & \vdots & 2 \end{bmatrix}$$

The corresponding system of equations is
$$x - y + z = 4$$
$$y - z = -3$$
$$z = 2$$

Substitute $z = 2$ into the second equation:
$$y = -3 + z = -3 + 2 = -1$$
Substitute $z = 2$ and $y = -1$ into the first equation:
$$x = 4 + y - z = 4 + (-1) - 2 = 1,$$
and $(1, -1, 2)$ is the solution to the system.

Examples 2 and 3 in the last section illustrated ways to determine when a system of three equations in three variables is inconsistent or dependent. These examples are repeated here so that we can compare the two methods of solving such a system.

EXAMPLE 3   Solve the system
$$2x - y + 3z = 4$$
$$-6x + 3y - 9z = 6$$
$$x - 5y + 2z = 8$$

SOLUTION $$\begin{bmatrix} 2 & -1 & 9 & \vdots & 4 \\ -6 & 3 & -9 & \vdots & 6 \\ 1 & -5 & 2 & \vdots & 8 \end{bmatrix}$$ Multiply row 1 by 3 and add the result to row 2.

$$\begin{bmatrix} 2 & -1 & 3 & \vdots & 4 \\ 0 & 0 & 0 & \vdots & 18 \\ 1 & -5 & 2 & \vdots & 8 \end{bmatrix} \longrightarrow 0x + 0y + 0z = 18, \text{ or } 0 = 18$$

Because $0 = 18$ is a false equation, the system is inconsistent, and the solution set is $\emptyset$.

EXAMPLE 4   Solve the system
$$x + 3y - 2z = 0$$
$$x + 2y + 5z = 0$$
$$y - 7z = 0$$

SOLUTION $$\begin{bmatrix} 1 & 3 & -2 & \vdots & 0 \\ 1 & 2 & 5 & \vdots & 0 \\ 0 & 1 & -7 & \vdots & 0 \end{bmatrix}$$ Multiply row 1 by -1 and add the result to row 2.

(continued)

$$\begin{bmatrix} 1 & 3 & -2 & \vdots & 0 \\ 0 & -1 & 7 & \vdots & 0 \\ 0 & 1 & -7 & \vdots & 0 \end{bmatrix}$$ Add row 2 to row 3.

$$\begin{bmatrix} 1 & 3 & -2 & \vdots & 0 \\ 0 & -1 & 7 & \vdots & 0 \\ 0 & 0 & 0 & \vdots & 0 \end{bmatrix} \longrightarrow 0x + 0y + 0z = 0, \quad \text{or} \quad 0 = 0$$

Because $0 = 0$ is a true equation, the system is dependent and has infinitely many solutions.

EXERCISE SET 4.4

A

1 Write the augmented matrix for each of the following systems.

1. $3x + y = 2$
$\quad 2x - y = 0$

2. $x - 5y = 7$
$\quad 6y = 5$

Write a system of equations that has the given augmented matrix.

3. $\begin{bmatrix} 1 & 3 & \vdots & 5 \\ 0 & 4 & \vdots & -3 \end{bmatrix}$

4. $\begin{bmatrix} 2 & -1 & \vdots & 0 \\ 1 & 8 & \vdots & 6 \end{bmatrix}$

Solve the following systems of equations using matrices.

5. $x + y = 7$
$\quad x - y = 5$

6. $x - 2y = -1$
$\quad 2x + 3y = 19$

7. $3x - 6y = 12$
$\quad 2x - 4y = 8$

8. $2x + 3y = 0$
$\quad 3x + 4y = 1$

9. $2x - y = 2$
$\quad 4x + 5y = -3$

10. $6x - 8y = 16$
$\quad -3x + 4y = 12$

11. $y = -x + 4$
$\quad 3x + 2y = 5$

12. $2x + 2 = -7y$
$\quad 5y + 3x = 8$

13. $\frac{1}{2}x + y = 1$
$\quad 2x + 7y = 1$

14. $\frac{2}{3}x + \frac{1}{2}y = 7$
$\quad .6x + y = 9.6$

2 Write the augmented matrices for the following systems.

15. $2x + 3y - z = 2$
$\quad x + 4y + 7z = 1$
$\quad 3x - 2y + z = 0$

16. $x + y + z = 13$
$\quad x - 2y + 4z = -1$
$\quad 7x - y = -2$

Write a system of equations that has the given augmented matrix.

17. $\begin{bmatrix} 3 & 2 & 1 & \vdots & 5 \\ 1 & 0 & -1 & \vdots & 8 \\ 1 & -7 & 4 & \vdots & 6 \end{bmatrix}$

18. $\begin{bmatrix} 2 & 1 & 0 & \vdots & -4 \\ 6 & -1 & 2 & \vdots & 0 \\ 1 & 12 & 1 & \vdots & -3 \end{bmatrix}$

Solve the following systems of equations using matrices.

19. $2x + y + 2z = 2$
$\quad 4x + 6y + z = 15$
$\quad 2x + 2y + 7z = -1$

20. $-2x + 3y + z = 2$
$\quad x - 2y + 3z = 9$
$\quad 3x + y - 5z = -8$

21. $x - 2y + z = 3$
$\quad -2x + 4y - 2z = 5$
$\quad 7x - 3y + 5z = 1$

22. $2x + 4y + 6z = 6$
$\quad 2x + 3y + 12z = 20$
$\quad x + y + 5z = 9$

23. $3x - 2y + z = 9$
$\quad 2x + 3y - z = 7$
$\quad -x - y + z = -2$

24. $-x + 2y - z = -1$
$\quad x + 3y - z = 1$
$\quad -2x + 4y - 2z = -2$

25. $x + y - 2z = -1$
$\quad x - 2y - z = 6$
$\quad 3y - z = -7$

26. $2x + y - 2z = 8$
$\quad\quad\quad y + 4z = 1$
$\quad x - 2y + 2z = -5$

27. $x + 3y = 3$
$\quad x - z = -2$
$\quad 3y + z = 5$

28. $y + 2z = -8$
$\quad x - z = 7$
$\quad x + 3y = 3$

B Use matrices to solve the following exercises from Section 4.3, (p. 176).

29. 41　　**30.** 42　　**31.** 43　　**32.** 44

C 🖊

Answer the following questions with complete sentences.

33. What is meant by a "3 × 3 square matrix?" Give an example.

34. What is meant by the "augmented matrix" of a system of linear equations?

REVIEW EXERCISES

Simplify the following. (See Section 1.4.)

35. $2 \cdot 6 - 4 \cdot 5$　　**36.** $(-1)(-8) - (1)(-2)$

37. $2(4 \cdot 5) - 3 \cdot 7) - 3(6 \cdot 5 - 0 \cdot 7) + 4(6 \cdot 3 - 0 \cdot 4)$

38. $3[4(-3) - (-6)1] - 6[1(-3) - 2(1)] + 1[1(-6) - 2 \cdot 4]$

4.5 USING DETERMINANTS AND CRAMER'S RULE

1	Evaluating 2 × 2 and 3 × 3 Determinants
2	Solving a System of Equations with Cramer's Rule

1　Evaluating 2 × 2 and 3 × 3 Determinants

In this section we will discuss Cramer's Rule, which is another method for solving systems of linear equations. This rule involves determinants, which are numbers closely related to square matrices. We begin with a discussion of determinants.*

In the last section a *square matrix* was identified as one that has the same number of rows and columns. A related special function called the **determinant function** associates a real number with every $n \times n$ (n by n) matrix with real entries. For every square matrix A, the **determinant** of A is denoted by the symbol det(A) or $| A |$. The 2 × 2 determinant (or "second-order determinant") of a 2 × 2 matrix is defined as follows.

---

* Determinants were first invented in 1683 by Japanese mathematician Seki Kōwa (1642–1708). German mathematician Gottfried Leibniz (1642–1716) independently developed the theory of determinants in 1693.

Definition of a 2 × 2 Determinant

The determinant of the square matrix $A = \begin{bmatrix} a_1 & b_1 \\ a_2 & b_2 \end{bmatrix}$ is the number

$$\det(A) = \begin{vmatrix} a_1 & b_1 \\ a_2 & b_2 \end{vmatrix} = a_1 b_2 - a_2 b_1$$

EXAMPLE 1

Find the value of the determinant associated with the given matrix.

a. $\begin{bmatrix} 2 & 5 \\ 4 & 6 \end{bmatrix}$ **b.** $\begin{bmatrix} -1 & 2 \\ 1 & -7 \end{bmatrix}$

SOLUTION

a. $\det\left(\begin{bmatrix} 2 & 5 \\ 4 & 6 \end{bmatrix}\right) = \begin{vmatrix} 2 & 5 \\ 4 & 6 \end{vmatrix} = 2 \cdot 6 - 4 \cdot 5 = 12 - 20 = -8$

b. $\det\left(\begin{bmatrix} -1 & 2 \\ 1 & -7 \end{bmatrix}\right) = \begin{vmatrix} -1 & 2 \\ 1 & -7 \end{vmatrix} = (-1)(-7) - 1 \cdot 2 = 5$

EXAMPLE 2

Find the value of x so that $\begin{vmatrix} 5 & x \\ 4 & x-2 \end{vmatrix} = 0$

SOLUTION

$$\begin{vmatrix} 5 & x \\ 4 & x-2 \end{vmatrix} = 0$$
$$5(x-2) - 4x = 0$$
$$5x - 10 - 4x = 0$$
$$x - 10 = 0$$
$$x = 10$$

A 3 × 3 matrix has a corresponding 3 × 3 determinant (or "third-order determinant"). A 3 × 3 determinant is evaluated by calculating three 2 × 2 determinants, which is defined as follows.

Definition of a 3 × 3 Determinant

The determinant of the square matrix

$\begin{bmatrix} a_1 & b_1 & c_1 \\ a_2 & b_2 & c_2 \\ a_3 & b_3 & c_3 \end{bmatrix}$ is the number

$$\begin{vmatrix} a_1 & b_1 & c_1 \\ a_2 & b_2 & c_2 \\ a_3 & b_3 & c_3 \end{vmatrix} = a_1 \begin{vmatrix} b_2 & c_2 \\ b_3 & c_3 \end{vmatrix} - b_1 \begin{vmatrix} a_2 & c_2 \\ a_3 & c_3 \end{vmatrix} + c_1 \begin{vmatrix} a_2 & b_2 \\ a_3 & b_3 \end{vmatrix}$$

The right side of this formula can be remembered as follows. The first term is the product of a_1 and the 2×2 determinant produced by deleting row 1 and column 1 from the left side of the formula. The second term is the product of $-b_1$ and the 2×2 determinant produced by deleting row 1 and column 2 from the left side. The third term is the product of c_1 and the 2×2 determinant produced by deleting row 1 and column 3 from the left side. For example,

$$\begin{vmatrix} 2 & 3 & 4 \\ 6 & 4 & 7 \\ 0 & 3 & 5 \end{vmatrix} = 2\begin{vmatrix} 2 & 3 & 4 \\ 6 & 4 & 7 \\ 0 & 3 & 5 \end{vmatrix} - 3\begin{vmatrix} 2 & 3 & 4 \\ 6 & 4 & 7 \\ 0 & 3 & 5 \end{vmatrix} + 4\begin{vmatrix} 2 & 3 & 4 \\ 6 & 4 & 7 \\ 0 & 3 & 5 \end{vmatrix}$$

$$= 2\begin{vmatrix} 4 & 7 \\ 3 & 5 \end{vmatrix} - 3\begin{vmatrix} 6 & 7 \\ 0 & 5 \end{vmatrix} + 4\begin{vmatrix} 6 & 4 \\ 0 & 3 \end{vmatrix}$$

$$= 2(20 - 21) - 3(30 - 0) + 4(18 - 0)$$

$$= -2 - 90 + 72$$

$$= -20$$

EXAMPLE 3

Find the determinant of the matrix

$$\begin{bmatrix} 4 & 1 & 3 \\ 2 & 0 & 7 \\ -1 & 3 & 2 \end{bmatrix}$$

SOLUTION

$$\begin{vmatrix} 4 & 1 & 3 \\ 2 & 0 & 7 \\ -1 & 3 & 2 \end{vmatrix} = 4\begin{vmatrix} 0 & 7 \\ 3 & 2 \end{vmatrix} - 1\begin{vmatrix} 2 & 7 \\ -1 & 2 \end{vmatrix} + 3\begin{vmatrix} 2 & 0 \\ -1 & 3 \end{vmatrix}$$

$$= 4(0 - 21) - (4 - (-7)) + 3(6 - 0)$$

$$= -77$$

2 Solving a System of Equations with Cramer's Rule

Determinants are defined in such a way that they can be used to solve systems of linear equations. The method considered here is called **Cramer's Rule**, which is named for the Swiss mathematician Gabriel Cramer (1704–1752). We begin by solving the general system of two equations in two variables for x and y.

$$a_1x + b_1y = c_1 \quad (1)$$
$$a_2x + b_2y = c_2 \quad (2)$$

To solve for x, multiply equation (1) by b_2, multiply equation (2) by $-b_1$, and then add the resulting equations:

$$a_1b_2x + b_1b_2y = c_1b_2$$
$$\underline{-a_2b_1x - b_1b_2y = -c_2b_1}$$
$$a_1b_2x - a_2b_1x + 0 = c_1b_2 - c_2b_1$$
$$(a_1b_2 - a_2b_1)x = c_1b_2 - c_2b_1$$
$$x = \frac{c_1b_2 - c_2b_1}{a_1b_2 - a_2b_1}$$

Now multiply equation (1) by $-a_2$, multiply equation (2) by a_1; then add the resulting equations:

$$-a_1a_2x - a_2b_1y = -a_2c_1$$
$$\underline{a_1a_2x + a_1b_2y = a_1c_2}$$
$$0 + a_1b_2y - a_2b_1y = a_1c_2 - a_2c_1$$
$$(a_1b_2 - a_2b_1)y = a_1c_2 - a_2c_1$$
$$y = \frac{a_1c_2 - a_2c_1}{a_1b_2 - a_2b_1}$$

Now let

$$D_x = c_1b_2 - c_2b_1 = \begin{vmatrix} c_1 & b_1 \\ c_2 & b_2 \end{vmatrix}, \quad D_y = a_1c_2 - a_2c_1 = \begin{vmatrix} a_1 & c_1 \\ a_2 & c_2 \end{vmatrix},$$

$$D = a_1b_2 - a_2b_1 = \begin{vmatrix} a_1 & b_1 \\ a_2 & b_2 \end{vmatrix};$$

so, $x = \dfrac{D_x}{D}$ and $y = \dfrac{D_y}{D}$.

The solution for x and y expressed in determinant form is Cramer's Rule. The following box summarizes the rule and the results that determine the three types of solutions.

Cramer's Rule

$$a_1x + b_1y = c_1$$
$$a_2x + b_2y = c_2$$

$$x = \frac{D_x}{D} \quad \text{and} \quad y = \frac{D_y}{D}, \text{ where}$$

$$D_x = \begin{vmatrix} c_1 & b_1 \\ c_2 & b_2 \end{vmatrix} \qquad D_y = \begin{vmatrix} a_1 & c_1 \\ a_2 & c_2 \end{vmatrix} \qquad D = \begin{vmatrix} a_1 & b_1 \\ a_2 & b_2 \end{vmatrix}$$

1. Consistent system (one solution): $D \neq 0$.

2. Inconsistent system (no solution): $D = 0$; $D_x, D_y \neq 0$.

3. Dependent system (infinitely many solutions):

$$D = D_x = D_y = 0.$$

Example 1 in Section 4.4 (p. 179) has three systems that illustrate the three types of solutions. The example is repeated here so that we can compare the matrix and determinant methods of solving a system of two equations in two variables.

EXAMPLE 4

Solve the following systems using Cramer's Rule.

a. $4x - 5y = 2$ **b.** $2x - 4y = 6$ **c.** $-2x + y = 3$
$\ 6x + 2y = -1$ $\ -3x + 6y = -9$ $\ 6x - 3y = 7$

SOLUTION   **a.** $a_1 = 4$ $b_1 = -5$ $c_1 = 2$
$\ a_2 = 6$ $b_2 = 2$ $c_2 = -1$

$$D_x = \begin{vmatrix} c_1 & b_1 \\ c_2 & b_2 \end{vmatrix} = \begin{vmatrix} 2 & -5 \\ -1 & 2 \end{vmatrix} = 4 - 5 = -1$$

$$D_y = \begin{vmatrix} a_1 & c_1 \\ a_2 & c_2 \end{vmatrix} = \begin{vmatrix} 4 & 2 \\ 6 & -1 \end{vmatrix} = -4 - 12 = -16$$

$$D = \begin{vmatrix} a_1 & b_1 \\ a_2 & b_2 \end{vmatrix} = \begin{vmatrix} 4 & -5 \\ 6 & 2 \end{vmatrix} = 8 - (-30) = 38$$

$$x = \frac{D_x}{D} = -\frac{1}{38} \quad \text{and} \quad y = \frac{D_y}{D} = -\frac{16}{38} = -\frac{8}{19},$$

so $\left(-\dfrac{1}{38}, -\dfrac{8}{19} \right)$ is the solution.

b. $a_1 = 2$ $b_1 = -4$ $c_1 = 6$
$\ a_2 = -3$ $b_2 = 6$ $c_2 = -9$

$$D_x = \begin{vmatrix} c_1 & b_1 \\ c_2 & b_2 \end{vmatrix} = \begin{vmatrix} 6 & -4 \\ -9 & 6 \end{vmatrix} = 36 - 36 = 0$$

$$D_y = \begin{vmatrix} a_1 & c_1 \\ a_2 & c_2 \end{vmatrix} = \begin{vmatrix} 2 & 6 \\ -3 & -9 \end{vmatrix} = -18 - (-18) = 0$$

$$D = \begin{vmatrix} a_1 & b_1 \\ a_2 & b_2 \end{vmatrix} = \begin{vmatrix} 2 & -4 \\ -3 & 6 \end{vmatrix} = 12 - 12 = 0$$

Because $D = D_x = D_y = 0$, the system is dependent, and the solution is $2x - 4y = 6$.

c. $a_1 = -2$ $b_1 = 1$ $c_1 = 3$
$\ a_2 = 6$ $b_2 = -3$ $c_2 = 7$

$$D_x = \begin{vmatrix} c_1 & b_1 \\ c_2 & b_2 \end{vmatrix} = \begin{vmatrix} 3 & 1 \\ 7 & -3 \end{vmatrix} = -9 - 7 = -16$$

$$D_y = \begin{vmatrix} a_1 & c_1 \\ a_2 & c_2 \end{vmatrix} = \begin{vmatrix} -2 & 3 \\ 6 & 7 \end{vmatrix} = -14 - 18 = -32$$

$$D = \begin{vmatrix} a_1 & b_1 \\ a_2 & b_2 \end{vmatrix} = \begin{vmatrix} -2 & 1 \\ 6 & -3 \end{vmatrix} = 6 - 6 = 0$$

Because $D = 0$, $D_x \neq 0$, and $D_y \neq 0$, the system is inconsistent, and the solution set is $\varnothing$.

The following box extends Cramer's Rule to three linear equations in three variables. Note that the determinant D_x is the determinant D with its first column replaced by the constant column with entries d_1, d_2, and d_3; D_y is D with its second column replaced with the constant column; and D_z is D with its third column replaced with the constant column. This is a convenient way to remember the formulas for D_x, D_y, and D_z.

Cramer's Rule

$$a_1x + b_1y + c_1z = d_1$$
$$a_2x + b_2y + c_2z = d_2$$
$$a_3x + b_3y + c_3z = d_3$$

$$x = \frac{D_x}{D}, \qquad y = \frac{D_y}{D}, \qquad z = \frac{D_z}{D}, \quad \text{where}$$

$$D_x = \begin{vmatrix} d_1 & b_1 & c_1 \\ d_2 & b_2 & c_2 \\ d_3 & b_3 & c_3 \end{vmatrix} \qquad D_y = \begin{vmatrix} a_1 & d_1 & c_1 \\ a_2 & d_2 & c_2 \\ a_3 & d_3 & c_3 \end{vmatrix}$$

$$D_z = \begin{vmatrix} a_1 & b_1 & d_1 \\ a_2 & b_2 & d_2 \\ a_3 & b_3 & d_3 \end{vmatrix} \qquad D = \begin{vmatrix} a_1 & b_1 & c_1 \\ a_2 & b_2 & c_2 \\ a_3 & b_3 & c_3 \end{vmatrix}$$

1. Consistent system: $D \neq 0$.
2. Inconsistent system: $D = 0$; $D_x, D_y, D_z \neq 0$.
3. Dependent system: $D = D_x = D_y = D_x = 0$.

This section concludes with a determinant solution to Example 2 from Section 4.4.

EXAMPLE 5

Solve the system
$$3x - y + z = 6$$
$$x - y + z = 4$$
$$2x + 2y - 3z = -6$$

SOLUTION

$$a_1 = 3 \qquad b_1 = -1 \qquad c_1 = 1 \qquad d_1 = 6$$
$$a_2 = 1 \qquad b_2 = -1 \qquad c_2 = 1 \qquad d_2 = 4$$
$$a_3 = 2 \qquad b_3 = 2 \qquad c_3 = -3 \qquad d_3 = -6$$

$$D_x = \begin{vmatrix} 6 & -1 & 1 \\ 4 & -1 & 1 \\ -6 & 2 & -3 \end{vmatrix} = 6\begin{vmatrix} -1 & 1 \\ 2 & -3 \end{vmatrix} - (-1)\begin{vmatrix} 4 & 1 \\ -6 & -3 \end{vmatrix} + 1\begin{vmatrix} 4 & -1 \\ -6 & 2 \end{vmatrix}$$

$$= 6(3 - 2) + (-12 + 6) + (8 - 6)$$
$$= 2$$

$$D_y = \begin{vmatrix} 3 & 6 & 1 \\ 1 & 4 & 1 \\ 2 & -6 & -3 \end{vmatrix} = 3\begin{vmatrix} 4 & 1 \\ -6 & -3 \end{vmatrix} - 6\begin{vmatrix} 1 & 1 \\ 2 & -3 \end{vmatrix} + 1\begin{vmatrix} 1 & 4 \\ 2 & -6 \end{vmatrix}$$

$$= 3(-12 + 6) - 6(-3 - 2) + (-6 - 8)$$
$$= -2$$

$$D_z = \begin{vmatrix} 3 & -1 & 6 \\ 1 & -1 & 4 \\ 2 & 2 & -6 \end{vmatrix} = 3\begin{vmatrix} -1 & 4 \\ 2 & -6 \end{vmatrix} - (-1)\begin{vmatrix} 1 & 4 \\ 2 & -6 \end{vmatrix} + 6\begin{vmatrix} 1 & -1 \\ 2 & 2 \end{vmatrix}$$

$$= 3(6 - 8) + (-6 - 8) + 6(2 + 2)$$
$$= 4$$

$$D = \begin{vmatrix} 3 & -1 & 1 \\ 1 & -1 & 1 \\ 2 & 2 & -3 \end{vmatrix} = 3 \begin{vmatrix} -1 & 1 \\ 2 & -3 \end{vmatrix} - (-1) \begin{vmatrix} 1 & 1 \\ 2 & -3 \end{vmatrix} + 1 \begin{vmatrix} 1 & -1 \\ 2 & 2 \end{vmatrix}$$

$$= 3(3 - 2) + (-3 - 2) + (2 + 2)$$
$$= 2$$

$$x = \frac{D_x}{D} = \frac{2}{2} = 1, \qquad y = \frac{D_y}{D} = \frac{-2}{2} = -1, \qquad z = \frac{D_z}{D} = \frac{4}{2} = 2$$

so $(1, -1, 2)$ is the solution to the system.

EXERCISE SET 4.5

A

1 Find det(A) for the following matrices.

1. $A = \begin{bmatrix} 2 & 3 \\ 1 & 4 \end{bmatrix}$ **2.** $A = \begin{bmatrix} -1 & 6 \\ -2 & 8 \end{bmatrix}$

Find the determinants of the following matrices.

3. $\begin{bmatrix} 6 & 0 \\ 9 & 3 \end{bmatrix}$ **4.** $\begin{bmatrix} 0 & 0 \\ 5 & 7 \end{bmatrix}$

5. $\begin{bmatrix} \sqrt{2} & -1 \\ 3 & \sqrt{8} \end{bmatrix}$ **6.** $\begin{bmatrix} 7 & \sqrt{6} \\ \sqrt{10} & 0 \end{bmatrix}$

7. $\begin{bmatrix} 1 & 1 \\ 3 & 2 \\ 4 & 6 \end{bmatrix}$ **8.** $\begin{bmatrix} 1 & 1 & 1 \\ 2 & 7 & -3 \\ 6 & -1 & 4 \end{bmatrix}$

9. $\begin{bmatrix} 2 & 4 & 3 \\ 1 & 2 & -1 \\ 0 & 5 & 1 \end{bmatrix}$ **10.** $\begin{bmatrix} 1 & -3 & 0 \\ 2 & 6 & -1 \\ 3 & 1 & 4 \end{bmatrix}$

11. $\begin{bmatrix} 0 & 0 & 0 \\ 2 & 7 & 9 \\ 1 & 4 & 8 \end{bmatrix}$ **12.** $\begin{bmatrix} 1 & 0 & 0 \\ 0 & 1 & 0 \\ 0 & 0 & 1 \end{bmatrix}$

Evaluate each determinant.

13. $\begin{vmatrix} x & 3 \\ -2 & x \end{vmatrix}$ **14.** $\begin{vmatrix} 6 & x + 2 \\ 4 & x - 3 \end{vmatrix}$

15. $\begin{vmatrix} x + y & 9 \\ x + y & 8 \end{vmatrix}$ **16.** $\begin{vmatrix} x - y & 7 \\ x - y & 3 \end{vmatrix}$

17. $\begin{vmatrix} a & 0 & 0 \\ 0 & b & 0 \\ 0 & 0 & c \end{vmatrix}$ **18.** $\begin{vmatrix} a & b & c \\ 1 & 2 & 1 \\ 0 & 1 & 3 \end{vmatrix}$

Solve the following for x.

19. $\begin{vmatrix} 3 & -4 \\ 5 & x \end{vmatrix} = 30$ **20.** $\begin{vmatrix} x + 3 & 5x \\ 3 & 2 \end{vmatrix} = -7$

21. $\begin{vmatrix} x & 3 \\ 2 & x \end{vmatrix} = 3$ **22.** $\begin{vmatrix} 2x & 1 \\ 1 & x \end{vmatrix} = 9$

23. $\begin{vmatrix} 0 & x & 0 \\ 2 & 5 & 3 \\ 1 & 4 & -2 \end{vmatrix} = 14$ **24.** $\begin{vmatrix} x & 0 & 0 \\ 0 & 3x & 0 \\ 0 & 0 & 4 \end{vmatrix} = 12$

2 Solve each system of equations using Cramer's Rule. If a system is inconsistent, write "Ø." If a system is dependent, write "infinitely many solutions."

25. $x + 2y = 8$
$3x - y = 3$

26. $3x + 2y = 5$
$9x + 4y = 7$

27. $x + y = 2$
$x + y = 3$

28. $x - y = 4$
$2x - 2y = 8$

29. $2x - \frac{1}{3}y = 0$
$6x + 2y = 9$

30. $\frac{4}{3}x - 2y = -6$
$x - .3y = 1.5$

31. $3x - 6y = 15$
$-2x + 4y = -10$

32. $2x - 5y = 0$
$-3x + 8y = 0$

33. $y = 2x - 3$
$y = -x + 4$

34. $2x - 3y = 12$
$6y = 4x + 12$

35. $x - 2y = 5$
$y = 3$

36. $3x - 2y = 10$
$x = 2$

37. $x + y + z = 3$
$x - y + 2z = 4$
$3x + 2y - 4z = 2$

38. $x - y + z = 0$
$2x - y - 2z = 0$
$x + y - 7z = 0$

39. $2x + 4y - 6z = 2$
$-x - 2y + 3z = 3$
$3x + 6y - 9z = 1$

40. $x + y - z = 6$
$x - y + 2z = -3$
$2y + 3z = 3$

41. $6x + 3y + 4z = 12$
$3x - y - 4z = -5$
$9x - 2y + 3z = 2$

42. $2x + 3y - z = 2$
$-3x - y + 3z = -3$
$6x + 9y - 3z = 6$

43. $x - 2y + z = 1$
$-x - 3y + z = -1$
$2x - 4y + 2z = 2$

44. $4x + 2y + z = -1$
$x + y + z = 0$
$x - y + z = 8$

45.
$$\begin{aligned} x + y + z &= 10 \\ y - z &= 2 \\ x + 2y + 5z &= 27 \end{aligned}$$

46.
$$\begin{aligned} -x + 2y - z &= -3 \\ 7x - 3y + 5z &= 1 \\ 2x - 4y + 2z &= -5 \end{aligned}$$

49. Show that $9 \begin{vmatrix} 1 & 2 \\ -1 & 4 \end{vmatrix} = \begin{vmatrix} 3 & 6 \\ -3 & 12 \end{vmatrix}$

B

47. Show that the following equation represents the slope–intercept form of the equation of a line.

$$\begin{vmatrix} y & x \\ m & 1 \end{vmatrix} = b$$

48. Show that $- \begin{vmatrix} b & a \\ d & c \end{vmatrix} = \begin{vmatrix} a & b \\ c & d \end{vmatrix}$

C

Answer the following questions with complete sentences.

50. What is the difference between a matrix and a determinant?

51. Discuss the method of evaluating a 3 by 3 determinant.

Chapter Summary

DEFINITIONS AND PROPERTIES

Definitions

Two or more equations in the same variables are called a **system of equations**. For two equations in two variables, the **solution set** is the set of all ordered pairs, (x, y), that satisfy both equations. For three equations in three variables the solution set is the set of all ordered triples, (x, y, z), that satisfy the three equations. (See Sections 4.1 and 4.3.)

Types of Solutions to a Linear System (see Sections 4.1 and 4.3):

1. Consistent system: one solution.

2. Inconsistent system: no solution. This is determined by arriving at a false equation, such as $0 = 1$.

3. Dependent system: infinitely many solutions. This is determined by arriving at a true equation, such as $0 = 0$.

Matrix Solutions to Systems of Linear Equations (see Section 4.4):

A **matrix** is a rectangular array of numbers. A **square matrix** has the same numbers of rows and columns. An **augmented matrix** represents a system of linear equations.

Row operations: An augmented matrix is transformed into a **row-equivalent matrix** if

1. Any two rows are interchanged

2. A row is multiplied by a nonzero constant

3. Any two rows are added together

4. A nonzero constant multiple of one row is added to a second row

Determinants and Cramer's Rule (see Section 4.5):

For a square matrix A, the **determinant** of A, $|A|$, is a real number:

$$\begin{vmatrix} a_1 & b_1 \\ a_2 & b_2 \end{vmatrix} = a_1 b_2 - a_2 b_1$$

$$\begin{vmatrix} a_1 & b_1 & c_1 \\ a_2 & b_2 & c_2 \\ a_3 & b_3 & c_3 \end{vmatrix} = a_1 \begin{vmatrix} b_2 & c_2 \\ b_3 & c_3 \end{vmatrix} - b_1 \begin{vmatrix} a_2 & c_2 \\ a_3 & c_3 \end{vmatrix} + c_1 \begin{vmatrix} a_2 & b_2 \\ a_3 & b_3 \end{vmatrix}$$

Cramer's Rule for a linear system of two equations:

$$\begin{aligned} a_1 x + b_1 y &= c_1 \\ a_2 x + b_2 y &= c_2 \end{aligned} \qquad x = \frac{D_x}{D} \quad \text{and} \quad y = \frac{D_y}{D}$$

$$D_x = \begin{vmatrix} c_1 & b_1 \\ c_2 & b_2 \end{vmatrix} \qquad D_y = \begin{vmatrix} a_1 & c_1 \\ a_2 & c_2 \end{vmatrix} \qquad D = \begin{vmatrix} a_1 & b_1 \\ a_2 & b_2 \end{vmatrix}$$

1. Consistent system: $D \neq 0$.

2. Inconsistent system: $D = 0$; D_x, $D_y \neq 0$.

3. Dependent system: $D = D_x = D_y = 0$.

Cramer's Rule for a linear system of three equations:

$$a_1x + b_1y + c_1z = d_1 \quad x = \frac{D_x}{D}, \quad y = \frac{D_y}{D}, \quad z = \frac{D_z}{D}$$

$$a_2x + b_2y + c_2z = d_2$$
$$a_3x + b_3y + c_3z = d_3$$

$$D_x = \begin{vmatrix} d_1 & b_1 & c_1 \\ d_2 & b_2 & c_2 \\ d_3 & b_3 & c_3 \end{vmatrix} \qquad D_y = \begin{vmatrix} a_1 & d_1 & c_1 \\ a_2 & d_2 & c_2 \\ a_3 & d_3 & c_3 \end{vmatrix}$$

$$D_z = \begin{vmatrix} a_1 & b_1 & d_1 \\ a_2 & b_2 & d_2 \\ a_3 & b_3 & d_3 \end{vmatrix} \qquad D = \begin{vmatrix} a_1 & b_1 & c_1 \\ a_2 & b_2 & c_2 \\ a_3 & b_3 & c_3 \end{vmatrix}$$

1. Consistent system: $D \neq 0$.

2. Inconsistent system: $D = 0$; D_x, D_y, $D_z \neq 0$.

3. Dependent system: $D = D_x = D_y = D_z = 0$.

CHAPTER REVIEW EXERCISES

The answers to the following exercises are in the answer section. If you have any trouble, then review the material and homework problems in the sections indicated.

Solve the following systems with the addition–substitution method. (See Sections 4.1 and 4.3.)

1. $2x - 3y = 12$
$4x + 5y = 2$

2. $y = 2x + 1$
$y = 2x - 1$

3. $\quad y = -3x + 1$
$6x + 2y = 2$

4. $\quad x + y + z = 0$
$2x + 2y - z = 9$
$3x - y + 2z = -5$

5. $x - 2y + z = 0$
$x + 3y - 2z = 0$
$5y - 3z = 0$

Solve Exercises 1–5 using matrices. (See Section 4.4.)

6. 1 **7.** 2 **8.** 4

Solve Exercises 6–8 using Cramer's Rule. (See Section 4.5.)

9. 3 **10.** 5

For the following, draw a three-dimensional coordinate system and graph the set of points. (See Section 4.3.)

11. $\{(0, 0, 0), (1, 3, 2), (3, 4, 1)\}$

Graph the following equation in the first octant by plotting its intercepts and drawing its traces. (See Section 4.3.)

12. $3x + 6y + 4z = 12$

Evaluate each determinant. (See Section 4.5.)

13. $\begin{vmatrix} 2 & 3 \\ -1 & 5 \end{vmatrix}$

14. $\begin{vmatrix} 3 & -1 & 2 \\ 2 & 0 & 1 \\ 0 & -2 & 3 \end{vmatrix}$

Solve the following for x. (See Section 4.5.)

15. $\begin{vmatrix} x & 4 \\ 25 & x \end{vmatrix} = 0$

Use a system of equations to solve the following word problems. Define each variable. (See Sections 4.2 and 4.3.)

16. A confectioner mixes nuts worth $1.30 per pound with candy worth 85¢ per pound to produce a 17-pound mixture worth $19.40. How many pounds of nuts and candy does she use?

17. The length of a rectangle is 3 less than twice its width. Its perimeter is 54. Find its length and width.

18. The difference of two numbers is 11. The smaller number is 1 more than 3 times the larger number. What are the numbers?

19. Chris has 56 pennies, nickels, and quarters worth $6.32. If he has twice as many nickels as pennies, how many coins of each kind does he have?

CHAPTER TEST

Treat this as a class test and allow 50 minutes for completion. When you have finished, use the answer section for scoring. For any wrong answers, refer to the corresponding exercises in the review section.

Solve the following systems with the addition–substitution method.

1. $4x - 6y = 6$
$\quad 2x - 3y = -6$

2. $3x - y = -10$
$\quad 2x + 3y = 8$

3. $\quad\quad y = 2x - 4$
$\quad 6x - 3y = 12$

4. $\quad x + y - z = -5$
$\quad 2x - y + z = 2$
$\quad x + 3y - 2z = -9$

5. $x - 2y + z = 5$
$\quad x - 2y + z = 4$
$\quad\quad\quad y + z = 6$

6. Solve Exercise 3 using matrices.

7. Solve Exercise 4 using matrices.

8. Solve Exercise 2 using Cramer's Rule.

9. Solve Exercise 5 using Cramer's Rule.

For the following exercise, draw a three-dimensional coordinate system and graph the set of points.

10. $\{(0, 0, 0), 1, 2, 3), (4, 4, 2)\}$

Graph the following equation in the first octant by plotting its intercepts and drawing its traces.

11. $x + y + 2z = 2$

Evaluate the following determinants.

12. $\begin{vmatrix} 8 & 1 \\ 7 & 2 \end{vmatrix}$

13. $\begin{vmatrix} 2 & 3 & -1 \\ 2 & 0 & 1 \\ 0 & 1 & 4 \end{vmatrix}$

Solve the following for x.

14. $\begin{vmatrix} 5 & x \\ x & 7 \end{vmatrix} = -1$

Use a system of equations to solve the following word problems. Define each variable.

15. The perimeter of a rectangle is 15. The length is 1/2 less than 3 times the width. Find the length and width of the rectangle.

16. The sum of the smallest and largest angles of a triangle is 132°. The third angle is 4 times the smallest angle. Find the three angles of the triangle.

17. A chemist has two solutions of boric acid; one solution is 6% and the other is 15%. How many liters of each solution does she need to mix together to produce 3 liters of a 12% boric acid solution?

18. Don travels 14 miles down a river in 2 hours and 9 miles up the river in 3 hours. Find the speed of the river and the speed of his boat.

F I V E

Polynomials

---

*If the deck of a swimming pool can be a source of equations, so too
can the water. The wave in the pool is a graph of the
"witch of Agnesi" function.*

Polynomials are expressions such as $3x + 4$, $a^2 + 7a - 8$, and $6k^4$. They are used extensively in both mathematics and the sciences. For example, the distance an object falls in t seconds under the force of gravity is $16t^2$ feet. Polynomials are as important to algebra as whole numbers are to arithmetic. Most of our work in arithmetic involves operations with whole numbers and fractions. In a similar way, most of our work in algebra deals with polynomials and their ratios.

A large portion of this chapter will be a review of topics covered in elementary algebra. We begin with integer exponents and then discuss operations with polynomials (such as addition) and factoring (such as the difference of two squares).

5.1 UNDERSTANDING INTEGER EXPONENTS

> **1** Using Natural Number Exponents
> **2** Using Integer Exponents

1 Using Natural Number Exponents

In Section 1.4 we introduced exponential notation, a^n, as a convenient way of expressing products, such as 3^4. Recall that n is called the *exponent* and a is called the *base*. Now we will discuss the methods for working with expressions containing integer exponents. We begin with a review of the ideas in Section 1.4.

> Let $n \in \mathbb{N}$ and $a \in \mathbb{R}$. Then
> $$a^1 = a \qquad \text{and} \qquad a^n = a \cdot a \cdot \ldots \cdot a, \; n \text{ factors of } a.$$
> $$0^n = 0 \qquad 1^n = 1 \qquad (-1)^n = \begin{cases} 1, & \text{if } n \text{ is even} \\ -1, & \text{if } n \text{ is odd} \end{cases}$$

For example, $(-1)^{41} = -1$, $(-3)^2 = (-3)(-3) = 9$, and $-3^2 = -3 \cdot 3 = -9$. *Note*: Do not confuse $-a^n$ with $(-a)^n$.

There are five rules of exponents that will be very useful in our work with polynomials. These rules apply *only* to multiplication and division; *there are no rules for addition or subtraction*. In the following discussion, m and n represent natural numbers.

The first rule allows us to express products with the same base in simpler form. For example,

$$2^3 \cdot 2^4 = (2 \cdot 2 \cdot 2)(2 \cdot 2 \cdot 2 \cdot 2)$$
$$= 2 \cdot 2 \cdot 2 \cdot 2 \cdot 2 \cdot 2 \cdot 2 \quad \text{Seven twos}$$
$$= 2^7$$
$$= 2^{3+4}$$

Rule 1: $a^m a^n = a^{m+n}$

An expression containing an exponent may commonly be raised to a second power such as $(2^4)^3$. We can simplify this expression by using the definition of a^n and Rule 1:

$$(2^4)^3 = 2^4 \cdot 2^4 \cdot 2^4 \quad \text{Three factors of } 2^4$$
$$= 2^{4+4+4} \quad \text{Rule 1}$$
$$= 2^{12}$$
$$= 2^{4 \cdot 3}$$

Rule 2: $(a^m)^n = a^{mn}$

The third rule of exponents deals with products raised to a power, such as $(5x)^2$. The commutative and associative properties allow us to express $(5x)^2$ as $5^2 x^2$:

$$(5x)^2 = (5x)(5x)$$
$$= (5 \cdot 5)(xx)$$
$$= 5^2 x^2 \quad \text{or} \quad 25x^2$$

Rule 3: $(ab)^n = a^n b^n$

EXAMPLE 1

Simplify the following:

a. $x^6 y^3 x$ **b.** $2^3 + 2^4$ **c.** $x^4(5x^2)^3$ **d.** $2^3 \cdot 3^2$
e. $-4^2(10)$ **f.** 2^{17}

SOLUTION

a. $x^6 y^3 x = x^6 x^1 y^3 = x^{6+1} y^3 = x^7 y^3$
Note: $x^7 y^3$ cannot be simplified.
b. $2^3 + 2^4 = 8 + 16 = 24$. Notice that $2^3 + 2^4 \neq 2^7$, because no rule exists for addition.
c. $x^4(5x^2)^3 = x^4(5^3)(x^2)^3 = 125x^4 x^6 = 125x^{10}$

(continued)

 d. $2^3 \cdot 3^2 = 8 \cdot 9 = 72$. Note that no rule of exponents applies to $2^3 \cdot 3^2$, because they have different bases.

 e. $-4^2(10) = -(4^2)(10) = -(16)(10) = -160$

 f. Use the y^x key on your calculator in the following sequence: Enter 2, press y^x, enter 17, and press $=$. Thus, $2^{17} = 131{,}072$.

The next rule is similar to $(ab)^n$ and involves quotients raised to a power, such as $(5/x)^2$. The definition of the product of two fractions allows us to simplify this expression:

$$\left(\frac{5}{x}\right)^2 = \frac{5}{x} \cdot \frac{5}{x} = \frac{5 \cdot 5}{x \cdot x} = \frac{5^2}{x^2} \quad \text{or} \quad \frac{25}{x^2}$$

> Rule 4: $\left(\dfrac{a}{b}\right)^n = \dfrac{a^n}{b^n}, \quad b \neq 0$

Our last rule deals with quotients of the form a^m/a^n, where $m > n$ ($m = n$ and $m < n$ are covered with integer exponents). For example,

$$\frac{x^5}{x^3} = \frac{xxxxx}{xxx} = \frac{xxx}{xxx} \cdot xx = 1x^2 = x^{5-3}$$

> Rule 5: $\dfrac{a^m}{a^n} = a^{m-n}$,   if $m > n$ and $a \neq 0$

EXAMPLE 2

Simplify the following:

 a. $\left(\dfrac{-5s^2}{t^5}\right)^3$ **b.** $\dfrac{(a^2)^{15}}{a^6 a^4}$

SOLUTION

 a. $\left(\dfrac{-5s^2}{t^5}\right)^3 = \dfrac{(-5s^2)^3}{(t^5)^3} = \dfrac{(-5)^3(s^2)^3}{t^{15}} = \dfrac{-125s^6}{t^{15}}$

 b. $\dfrac{(a^2)^{15}}{a^6 a^4} = \dfrac{a^{2 \cdot 15}}{a^{6+4}} = \dfrac{a^{30}}{a^{10}} = a^{30-10} = a^{20}$

  Note: $\dfrac{a^{30}}{a^{10}} \neq a^{30 \div 10} = a^3$

---

2 Using Integer Exponents

To use negative integers as exponents we must define a^0 and a^{-n}, for n a positive integer. We want to make these definitions in such a way that the preceding five rules will be valid for *all* integers; that is, we do not want to have one set of rules for positive exponents and another set for negative exponents.

Let us see how we should define a^0 so that Rule 1, $a^m a^n = a^{m+n}$, will hold. As an example,

$$3^0 \cdot 3^2 = 3^{0+2} = 3^2$$

Now we know that 1 is the only number such that $1 \cdot x = x$ for all x. Therefore, if $3^0 \cdot 3^2 = 3^2$ and $1 \cdot 3^2 = 3^2$, then we must define

$$3^0 = 1$$

In general,*   if $a \neq 0$,   then $a^0 = 1$.

Other examples of this definition are

$$(-469)^0 = 1, \qquad (8x)^0 = 1, \qquad \text{and} \qquad 8x^0 = 8 \cdot 1 = 8$$

Now we turn to the question of how to define a^{-n}. Consider the expression $3^{-2} \cdot 3^2$. If the first rule of exponents is to hold, then

$$3^{-2} \cdot 3^2 = 3^{-2+2} = 3^0 = 1$$

However, we know that $1/3^2$ is the only number such that

$$\frac{1}{3^2} \cdot 3^2 = \frac{1}{9} \cdot 9 = 1$$

Therefore, if $3^{-2} \cdot 3^2 = 1$ and $\dfrac{1}{3^2} \cdot 3^2 = 1$, then we must define

$$3^{-2} = \frac{1}{3^2}$$

In general,   if $a \neq 0$,   then $a^{-n} = \dfrac{1}{a^n}$.

Other examples of this definition are

$$(-2)^{-3} = \frac{1}{(-2)^3} = -\frac{1}{8}, \qquad 7^{-1} = \frac{1}{7}, \qquad \text{and} \qquad x^{-6} = \frac{1}{x^6}$$

With these definitions of a^0 and a^{-n}, the five rules of exponents hold for all integers.

We can use the definition of a^{-n} to evaluate fractions such as $1/5^{-2}$ and $1/a^{-n}$:

$$\frac{1}{5^{-2}} = \frac{1}{\dfrac{1}{5^2}} = \frac{1}{\dfrac{1}{5^2}} \cdot \frac{5^2}{5^2} = \frac{5^2}{1} = 5^2 = 25$$

$$\frac{1}{a^{-n}} = \frac{1}{\dfrac{1}{a^n}} = \frac{1}{\dfrac{1}{a^n}} \cdot \frac{a^n}{a^n} = \frac{a^n}{1} = a^n$$

---

* What about 0^0? We will investigate this by using the fact that $0^2 = 0$. Assume that $0^0 = c$, for some real number c. Then

$$0^0 \cdot 0^2 = c \cdot 0 = 0 \qquad \text{and} \qquad 0^0 \cdot 0^2 = 0^{0+2} = 0^2 = 0$$

Therefore, for any value of c we would have $0^0 \cdot 0^2 = 0$; that is, $0^0 = 1$, $0^0 = 17$, or any other value of c would be correct. Thus, 0^0 is not uniquely determined, so it is undefined ($0/0$ is undefined for the same reason). 0^0 and $0/0$ are also called *indeterminate*, because they could have any value.

In a similar way we can evaluate $(a/b)^{-1}$ and $(a/b)^{-n}$:

$$\left(\frac{a}{b}\right)^{-1} = \frac{1}{\dfrac{a}{b}} = \frac{1}{\dfrac{a}{b}} \cdot \frac{b}{b} = \frac{b}{a} \qquad\qquad \left(\frac{6}{7}\right)^{-1} = \frac{7}{6}$$

$$\left(\frac{a}{b}\right)^{-n} = \left(\frac{a}{b}\right)^{-1 \cdot n} = \left[\left(\frac{a}{b}\right)^{-1}\right]^n = \left(\frac{b}{a}\right)^n = \frac{b^n}{a^n} \qquad \left(\frac{x}{y}\right)^{-2} = \frac{y^2}{x^2}$$

Definitions and Properties of Exponents

Let a and b be real numbers and m and n be integers. Then, assuming nonzero denominators, if $a \neq 0$, then $a^0 = 1$; 0^0 is undefined.

$$a^{-n} = \frac{1}{a^n} \qquad\qquad \frac{1}{a^{-n}} = a^n$$

$$\left(\frac{a}{b}\right)^{-1} = \frac{b}{a} \qquad\qquad \left(\frac{a}{b}\right)^{-n} = \left(\frac{b}{a}\right)^n$$

$$a^m a^n = a^{m+n} \qquad\qquad (a^m)^n = a^{mn}$$

$$(ab)^n = a^n b^n \qquad\qquad \left(\frac{a}{b}\right)^n = \frac{a^n}{b^n}$$

$$\frac{a^m}{a^n} = a^{m-n}$$

EXAMPLE 3

Simplify the following and write the answers with positive exponents.

a. $x^{-7}x^7$ **b.** $(x^{-5})^2$ **c.** $(y^{-3}z^4)^{-5}$ **d.** 5^{-7}

e. $\dfrac{x^8}{x^8}$ **f.** $\left(\dfrac{k^{12}}{k^4}\right)^{-1}$ **g.** $\left(\dfrac{2}{x^{-6}}\right)^3$ **h.** $\dfrac{m^5 n^{-3}}{m^{-4}n^3}$

SOLUTION

a. $x^{-7}x^7 = x^{-7+7} = x^0 = 1$

b. $(x^{-5})^2 = x^{(-5)2} = x^{-10} = \dfrac{1}{x^{10}}$

c. $(y^{-3}z^4)^{-5} = (y^{-3})^{-5}(z^4)^{-5} = y^{15}z^{-20} = \dfrac{y^{15}}{z^{20}}$

 d. $5^{-7} = \dfrac{1}{5^7} = \dfrac{1}{78,125}$ Use the y^x key.

e. $\dfrac{x^8}{x^8} = x^{8-8} = x^0 = 1,$ or $\dfrac{x^8}{x^8} = 1$ because $\dfrac{a}{a} = 1, a \neq 0$

f. $\left(\dfrac{k^{12}}{k^4}\right)^{-1} = \dfrac{k^4}{k^{12}} = k^{4-12} = k^{-8} = \dfrac{1}{k^8}$

g. $\left(\dfrac{2}{x^{-6}}\right)^3 = (2x^6)^3 = 2^3(x^6)^3 = 8x^{18}$

h. $\dfrac{m^5 n^{-3}}{m^{-4}n^3} = m^{5-(-4)}n^{-3-3} = m^9 n^{-6} = \dfrac{m^9}{n^6}$

EXAMPLE 4

Simplify the following and write the answers without fractions.

a. $(32x^{-8})(2^{-3}x^4)$ **b.** $\left(\dfrac{h^3}{k^{-8}}\right)^{-2}$ **c.** $\left(\dfrac{x^{4n}}{x^{-2n}}\right)^3$

SOLUTION

a. $(32x^{-8})(2^{-3}x^4) = (2^5 \cdot 2^{-3})x^{-8}x^4 = 2^2x^{-4} = 4x^{-4}$

b. $\left(\dfrac{h^3}{k^{-8}}\right)^{-2} = \left(\dfrac{k^{-8}}{h^3}\right)^2 = \dfrac{(k^{-8})^2}{(h^3)^2} = \dfrac{k^{-16}}{h^6} = h^{-6}k^{-16}$

c. $\left(\dfrac{x^{4n}}{x^{-2n}}\right)^3 = (x^{4n-(-2n)})^3 = (x^{6n})^3 = x^{18n}$

Throughout this section we have indicated several mistakes that are commonly made with the rules of exponents. The following list shows a few other common errors made with this material. Others are given in some of the true–false questions in the exercises.

COMMON ERRORS

Right Solution	**Wrong Solution**
1. $2^{-3} = \dfrac{1}{2^3} = \dfrac{1}{8}$	$2^{-3} = -6$
2. $5^6 \cdot 5^2 = 5^8$	$5^6 \cdot 5^2 = 25^8$
3. $\dfrac{2^8}{2^2} = 2^6$	$\dfrac{2^8}{2^2} = 1^6$
4. $\dfrac{2^8}{2^{-2}} = 2^{10}$	$\dfrac{2^8}{2^{-2}} = 2^6$
5. $(3 + 4)^2 = 7^2 = 49$	$(3 + 4)^2 = 3^2 + 4^2 = 25$

EXERCISE SET 5.1

A

1 Simplify the following.

1. x^4x^5 **2.** $a^2a^3a^4$ **3.** $(x^4)^5$

4. $(4x)^2$ **5.** $(a^2b^3)^4$ **6.** $t^3(t^7)^2$

7. $\left(\dfrac{2}{x}\right)^3$ **8.** $\left(\dfrac{-4}{y^3}\right)^2$ **9.** $\dfrac{x^{10}}{x^2}$

Simplify the following. Express the answers as integers or rational numbers in reduced form.

10. -5^2

11. $(-5)^2$

12. $(2 + 4)^2$

13. $\dfrac{4y^{15}}{12y}$

14. $2^{30}\left(-\dfrac{1}{2}\right)^{30}$

15. $\dfrac{2^{12}}{2^6}$

16. 2^{21}

17. $(-3)^{16}$

18. $10^2 \cdot 11^4$

Determine whether the given expression is true or false. If it is false, give the correct answer.

19. $(1 + 5)^2 = 26$ **20.** $3^4 \cdot 3^5 = 9^9$

21. $3^2 + 3^3 = 36$ **22.** $-3^4 = -81$

23. $\dfrac{x^{12}}{x^3} = x^4$ **24.** $\dfrac{10^8}{10^5} = 1^3$

25. $3^2 \cdot 3^4 = 3^8$ **26.** $3^8 \cdot 5^8 = 15^8$

2

27. $x^7x^{-1} = x^6$ **28.** $3^0 = 3$

29. $2^{-2} + 2^{-3} = 2^{-5}$ **30.** $-2^{-4} = 8$

31. $(7x^{-3})^2 = 7x^{-6}$ **32.** $\dfrac{x^{12}}{x^{-4}} = x^{16}$

33. $\left(\dfrac{3}{2}\right)^{-2} = \dfrac{9}{4}$ **34.** $\dfrac{x^{-8}}{x^{-6}} = x^{-14}$

Simplify the following and write your answers with positive exponents; if no variables are involved, then write your answer as a rational number in reduced form.

35. 20^0

36. $(3x^{-4})^{-3}$

37. $x^3(x^4)^8$

38. $10^2 + 10^3$

39. $3^{-1} + 3^0 + 3^1$

40. $(374a^4b^7)^0$

41. 0^0

42. $(x^4)^3(x^{-2})^5$

43. $10a^3(2a^6)^5$

44. $\boxed{}\ (-4)^{-10}$

45. $\boxed{}\ -4^{-10}$

46. $\boxed{}\ 4^{12} + 6^8$

47. $\boxed{}\ 3^{-4} + 3^{-5}$

48. $\boxed{}\ 2^{-18} - 2^{-19}$

49. $\boxed{}\ 5^{-5} + 6^{-5}$

50. $\left(\dfrac{3}{4}\right)^{-1}$

51. $\dfrac{1}{x^{-4}}$

52. $\left(\dfrac{3}{x^2}\right)^{-4}$

53. $\dfrac{12x^8}{4x^{-3}}$

54. $(4x - 4x)^0$

55. $\dfrac{a^4b^{-3}}{a^8b^{-3}}$

56. $\left(\dfrac{4^0x^{-3}}{2}\right)^{-1}$

57. $\left(\dfrac{3x^2}{5y^{-3}}\right)^{-2}$

58. $\left(\dfrac{a^3b^{-1}}{c^4}\right)^{-3}$

59. $2^{-1} + 2^{-3}$

60. $3^{-3} - 3^{-2}$

61. $4^{-2} + 6^{-1}$

62. $\left(\dfrac{3}{2}\right)^{-2} + \left(\dfrac{3}{4}\right)^{-2}$

63. $\dfrac{(m^3)^2(n^{-1})^4}{(m^3n^{-4})^{-2}}$

64. $\left(\dfrac{x^{-7}x^{-3}}{x^{-6}y^{-7}}\right)^{-1}$

65. $x^{3n+1}x^{1-n}$

66. $x^{4n}(x^{3n+1})^2$

67. $\dfrac{a^{4n+2}}{a^{n-3}}$

68. $\dfrac{t^{6n}v^{m-6}}{t^{2n}v^{2-5n}}$

69. $\dfrac{1}{\left(\dfrac{3}{4}\right)^{-2}}$

70. $\dfrac{1}{\left(\dfrac{1}{10}\right)^{-3}}$

Simplify the following and write your answers without fractions.

71. $x^{-4}x^{-5}x^{-6}$

72. $(x^4y^{-3})^{-5}$

73. $(7x^{-3})^{-1}$

74. $x^6(x^4)^{-5}$

75. $\dfrac{(3x^5)^{-2}}{9xx^{-7}}$

76. $\dfrac{3^9}{2^9}\left(\dfrac{3}{2}\right)^{-9}$

77. $3^5 \cdot 2^5 \cdot 6^{-4}$

78. $4^7 \cdot 5^7 \cdot 20^{-6} + 20^0$

79. $\left(\dfrac{k^{4n-5}}{k^{8n-1}}\right)^3$

80. $\left(\dfrac{a^{-n}b^{2m}}{c^{-3n}b^{6m}}\right)^{-2}$

B

Simplify the following and write your answers with positive exponents.

81. $\left(\dfrac{a^4b^2c}{a^{-1}b^2c^{-4}}\right)^{-2}$

82. $\left(\dfrac{x^{-3}y^2}{z^{-4}}\right)^{-3}$

83. $3x^2y^3\left(\dfrac{3x^4y^{-1}}{2xy^{-8}}\right)^{-1}$

84. $8a^3b^{-2}\left(\dfrac{12a^{-2}b^{-3}}{24a^5b^{-5}}\right)^3$

85. $\dfrac{-4^2(x^{2n}y^{n-1})^2}{(-2x^ny^{2n})^3}$

86. $\left(\dfrac{x^{2n-1}y^{4n}}{x^ny^{3n+3}}\right)^{-2}$

87. 2^x3^{2x}

88. $2^{4x}5^{3x}$

89. $x^{3n}y^{3n}(xy)^{4n}$

90. $\dfrac{1}{\left(\dfrac{3a^2}{2b^3}\right)^{-4}}$

C 🖎

Answer the following questions with complete sentences.

91. Discuss the motivation for the definition of $a^{-0} = 1$, if $a \neq 0$.

92. Discuss the motivation for the definition of $a^{-n} = \dfrac{1}{a^n}$, if $a \neq 0$.

93. Explain the difference between 3^2 and 3^{-2}.

94. Explain the difference between -3^2 and $(-3)^2$.

R E V I E W E X E R C I S E S

Let $f(x) = 6x - 2$ and $g(x) = 2x^2 - 3x + 4$. Find the following (see Section 3.2):

95. $f(-3)$ **96.** $g(5)$ **97.** $f(2) + g(-1)$

Simplify the following expressions (see Section 2.1):

98. $5x - x$

99. $6a^2b - ab^2 + 5a^2b$

100. $6y - (y - 10)$

101. $(x - 4) - (3x - 7)$

We use the definition $a - b = a + (-b)$ to change the subtraction of two real numbers to the addition of a and the opposite of b. A similar process applies to the subtraction of polynomials. If b is a polynomial, then we can write $-b$ as $(-1)b$ and use the distributive property. This reduces the problem to adding like terms. For instance,

$$\begin{aligned}
(6x - 3) - (2x - 8) &= 6x - 3 + (-1)(2x - 8) \\
&= 6x - 3 + (-1)2x + (-1)(-8) \\
&= 6x - 3 - 2x + 8 \\
&= 4x + 5
\end{aligned}$$

Most of the steps in subtracting polynomials can be done mentally. Change the sign on each term of the polynomial being subtracted and then add like terms.

EXAMPLE 8

Simplify $(x^2 - 5) - (6 - 2x) - (1 + 7x - 3x^2)$.

SOLUTION

$$\begin{aligned}
(x^2 - 5) - (6 - 2x) - (1 + 7x - 3x^2) &= x^2 - 5 - 6 + 2x - 1 - 7x + 3x^2 \\
&= (x^2 + 3x^2) + (2x - 7x) + (-5 - 6 - 1) \\
&= 4x^2 - 5x - 12
\end{aligned}$$

EXERCISE SET 5.2

A

1 Classify the following according to their degrees and numbers of terms; write your answers in descending powers.

1. $4x^3$

2. $x^2 - 9$

3. $8x - 4$

4. $4t^2 - 6t^6 + 7t^9$

5. $8 - 3y + y^2$

6. $-14x^3$

7. 32

8. $a^3 - 27a^2 + a$

Classify the following functions as constant, linear, quadratic, or cubic.

9. $f(x) = 3x - 7$

10. $g(x) = 2x^2 - 3$

11. $h(t) = t^3 - 125$

12. $F(x) = -6$

13. $f(x) = 7x^2 - 6x + 2$

14. $k(x) = x$

Let $f(x) = 2x - 5$, $g(x) = x^2 - 6x + 1$, and $h(x) = x^3 + 2x - 3$. Find:

15. $f(4)$

16. $g(-2)$

17. $h(5)$

18. $f(-3) + g(2)$

19. $g(-1) - h(-1)$

20. $f(2) + h(4)$

2 Perform the indicated operations.

21. $(3x^8)(2x^5)$

22. $10x^3 + x^3$

23. $\dfrac{3x^9}{6x^3}$

24. $\dfrac{20m^3n^2}{30m^3n^8}$

25. $3x^2 - x^2 + 2x$

26. $(6a^4b^3)(-a^2b^7)$

27. $7x^4 - x^3 + 3x^4 + 5x^3$

28. $3r^4t + rt^3 - r^4t - 8rt^3$

29. $\left(\dfrac{3x^8y}{5}\right)\left(\dfrac{10xy^7}{12}\right)$

30. $\dfrac{15y^8z^6}{-5y^4z^9}$

31. $6 - (-9x) - 5 - x$

32. $4xy^2 + 6x^2y$

33. $(-a^4)^{20}$

34. $(-m^2n^3)^{41}$

35. $\dfrac{(8x^4)(-x^8)}{(-2x^6)^5}$

36. $\dfrac{(6a^3b^2)(-a^2b)^9}{(-3ab^{11})^4}$

37. $(2x^3)^6 + 5x^{18}$

38. $x^5 + 5x - x^5 - (-x)$

3

39. $(5x - 8) + (2x + 7)$

40. $(3x - 5y) - (2y - 6x)$

41. $x^2 - (6x^2 - 5)$

42. $x^3 - (3x^4 - 3x^2 + x)$

43. $(a^3 - 9b) + (4b^3 + b)$

44. $(4x^3 + 7x) + (8x - 3)$

Perform the indicated operations vertically.

45. $(3x^3 + 7x - 8) + (6x^3 - 3x^2 + 4)$

46. $(a^3 - 2a^2 + 4a) + (8 - 4a + 2a^2)$

47. $(x^2 + 3xy + 2y^2) + (3y^2 - 9xy - 8x^2)$
$+ (5x^2 - 3y^2)$

48. $(t^2 - 3t + 1) + (2 - 4t - 3t^2) - (5t^2 - t + 8)$

Perform the indicated operations either horizontally or vertically.

49. $(3t^2 - 7t + 1) - (4 - 5t) + (2t^2 + 6t - 3)$

50. $x - (3x - 1) + (x - 3) - [-(2 - 7x)]$

51. $(x - 2) - [3 - (x - 1)] - x$

52. $[2s^2 - (3s - 10)] - [7s^2 + (2s + 1) - 3]$

B

53. Subtract $3x - 1$ from the sum of $7x - 1$ and $6x - 4$.

54. Subtract $x^2 - 6$ from the sum of $2x^2 - 1$ and $x^2 + 5$.

55. Subtract the sum of $y^2 - 6y + 7$ and $3y^2 + 2y - 8$ from $10y^2 - 7y + 18$.

56. Subtract the sum of $z^3 - 6z + 4$ and $2z^2 - 3z - 1$ from $3z^3 - 6z^2 + 7z - 13$.

C

Answer the following questions with complete sentences.

57. What is the difference between a monomial and a polynomial?

58. What is the difference between a binomial and a trinomial?

59. What is meant by "the degree of a polynomial in one variable"?

60. What is the difference between a *quadratic* polynomial and a *quadratic* function? Give an example of each.

REVIEW EXERCISES

Simplify the following expressions. (See Section 2.1.)

61. $4 + 2(x + 6)$

62. $2x - 3(6 - 2x)$

63. $4(y - 2) - 5(3y + 4)$

64. $x(x + 3) + 4(x + 3)$

65. $a(a - 4) - 6(a - 4)$

66. $2x(4x - 5y) + 3y(4x - 5y)$

5.3   MULTIPLYING AND DIVIDING POLYNOMIALS

1   **Finding Products of Polynomials by the FOIL Method**

2   **Dividing a Polynomial by a Monomial**

3   **Dividing a Polynomial by a Polynomial**

1   **Finding Products of Polynomials by the FOIL Method**

This section continues our study of polynomial operations by covering products and quotients. This material is based on the preceding work with monomials.

The last section covered the product of two monomials. The next step in multiplying polynomials is to find the product of a monomial and a polynomial of two or more terms. We will use the distributive property to reduce the problem to the product of monomials. For example,

$$3x(2x + 4) = 3x(2x) + 3x(4) = 6x^2 + 12x$$

EXAMPLE 1

Find the following products.

a. $-2a^3(a^2 - 7a + 5)$ **b.** $m^4n^5(mn - m^2n^3 + 3m^7)$

SOLUTION   **a.** $-2a^3(a^2 - 7a + 5) = -2a^3(a^2) + (-2a^3)(-7a) + (-2a^3)(5)$
$$= -2a^5 + 14a^4 - 10a^3$$

b. $m^4n^5(mn - m^2n^3 + 3m^7) = m^4n^5(mn) - m^4n^5(m^2n^3) + m^4n^5(3m^7)$
$$= m^5n^6 - m^6n^8 + 3m^{11}n^5$$

By repeated use of the distributive property and the method of multiplying a monomial and a polynomial, we can find products such as $(x + 2)(y + 5)$. To express this in the form $(b + c)a$, let $b = x$, $c = 2$, and $a = y + 5$. Then

$$(b + c)(\quad a \quad) = b(\quad a \quad) + c(\quad a \quad)$$
$$(x + 2)(y + 5) = x(y + 5) + 2(y + 5) \qquad a(b + c) = ab + ac$$
$$= xy + x \cdot 5 + 2y + 2 \cdot 5$$
$$= xy + 5x + 2y + 10$$

This example illustrates that for the product of two polynomials, each term in the second polynomial is multiplied by each term in the first polynomial. Then we combine like terms.

EXAMPLE 2

Use the distributive property to find the product.
$(2x + 3y)(4x - 5y)$

SOLUTION $(2x + 3y)(4x - 5y) = 2x(4x - 5y) + 3y(4x - 5y)$
$$= 2x(4x) - 2x(5y) + 3y(4x) - 3y(5y)$$
$$= 8x^2 - 10xy + 12xy - 15y^2$$
$$= 8x^2 + 2xy - 15y^2$$

We must find the product of two binomials so frequently in algebra that a shortcut proves convenient. To illustrate this shortcut, return to $(x + 2)(y + 5)$:

$$(x + 2)(y + 5) = xy + x \cdot 5 + 2y + 2 \cdot 5$$

a. xy: the product of the **F**irst terms.
b. $x \cdot 5$:   the product of the **O**uter terms.
c. $2y$:   the product of the **I**nner terms.
d. $2 \cdot 5$:   the product of the **L**ast terms.

This procedure is called the **FOIL method**, from the first letter of the words **First**, **Outer**, **Inner**, and **Last**.

As another example of the FOIL method consider $(x + y)(x^2 + y^2)$ as in Figure 5.1:

FIGURE 5.1

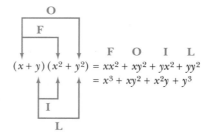

$$(x + y)(x^2 + y^2) = \overset{F}{xx^2} + \overset{O}{xy^2} + \overset{I}{yx^2} + \overset{L}{yy^2}$$
$$= x^3 + xy^2 + x^2y + y^3$$

EXAMPLE 3

Use the FOIL method to find the following products.

a. $(x + 3)(x + 3)$ **b.** $(x + 4)(x - 4)$

SOLUTION

a. $(x + 3)(x + 3) = x^2 + 3x + 3x + 3^2 = x^2 + 6x + 9$
b. $(x + 4)(x - 4) = x^2 - 4x + 4x - 4^2 = x^2 - 16.$

The form $(x + 3)(x + 3) = (x + 3)^2$ is an example of a **perfect square**. The general forms of perfect squares are $(a + b)^2$ and $(a - b)^2$. The form $(x + 4)(x - 4)$ is an example of the **difference of two squares**, $a^2 - b^2$.

> **Special Products**
>
> Perfect squares: $(a + b)^2 = a^2 + 2ab + b^2$
> $(a - b)^2 = a^2 - 2ab + b^2$
> Difference of squares: $(a + b)(a - b) = a^2 - b^2$

 **COMMON ERROR**   A common mistake is to think that $(a + b)^2$ is equal to $a^2 + b^2$.

$(x + 3)^2 \neq x^2 + 9$ $(x + 3)^2 = x^2 + 6x + 9$

We now consider products that involve a binomial and a trinomial. One method is to multiply them *horizontally*, as in the previous examples; this method is used in Example 4. A second method multiplies them *vertically*: We multiply each term in the second polynomial by each term in the first polynomial and then use the vertical method of addition covered in the last section. This method is illustrated in Example 5.

Math in Time

Leonardo Fibonacci
The Granger Collection, New York

THE GREATEST EUROPEAN mathematician in the time period between the fall of Rome (fifth century) to the Renaissance (fifteenth century) was the Italian Leonardo Fibonacci (ca. 1170–1250), who also was known as Leonardo of Pisa. Fibonacci had the opportunity to travel throughout the eastern Mediterranean region with his father, who was in the mercantile trade. In this way Fibonacci became familiar with the various arithmetic systems used by the merchants of the Middle East. He became convinced that the Hindu–Arabic numeration system, which we use today, was superior to the Roman numerals used in Europe at that time. Shortly after his return to Pisa in 1202, Fibonacci wrote his famous work *Liber Abaci* in which he strongly advocated the use of the Hindu–Arabic notation for calculations. Also included were methods of calculations with integers and fractions, computations with radicals, and the solutions of linear and higher-degree equations.

Fibonacci not only summarized Arabian algebra in his books but also made his own contributions to this field. He solved problems such as "find a rational number x such that $x^2 + 5$ and $x^2 - 5$ are squares of rational numbers." His answer was 41/12. His books contained many word problems; three are given below. The solution to the first problem led to the important set of numbers called the *Fibonacci sequence*: {1, 1, 2, 3, 5, 8, 13, 21, 34, 55, 89, 144, 233, . . . , a, b, $a + b$, . . . }. This sequence has applications in such fields as biology, business, statistics, archaeology, and psychology.

1. How many pairs of rabbits can be produced from a single pair in a year if every month each pair begets a new pair that from the second month on becomes productive? Answer: 233.

2. If Paul gets from Mark 7 denarii, then Paul's sum is fivefold Mark's. If Mark gets from Paul 5 denarii, then Mark's sum is sevenfold Paul's. How much does each have? (Names provided for clarity). Answer: Paul has 121/17 and Mark has 167/17.

3. A certain king sent 30 men into his orchard to plant trees. If they could set out 1000 trees in 9 days, in how many days would 36 men set out 4400 trees? Answer: 33 days.

"THIS MUST BE FIBONACCI'S."

EXAMPLE 4

SOLUTION

Find the product $(x - 2)^3$.

$(x - 2)^3 = (x - 2)(x - 2)^2$. First, find $(x - 2)^2$:

$(x - 2)^2 = x^2 - 4x + 4$ $(a - b)^2 = a^2 - 2ab + b^2$

$(x - 2)^3 = (x - 2)(x^2 - 4x + 4)$

$\qquad = x^3 - 4x^2 + 4x - 2x^2 + 8x - 8$

$\qquad = x^3 - (4x^2 + 2x^2) + (4x + 8x) - 8$

$\qquad = x^3 - 6x^2 + 12x - 8$

EXAMPLE 5

SOLUTION

Find $(2k + 3)(k^2 + 5k - 4)$ vertically.

$$
\begin{array}{r}
k^2 + 5k - 4 \\
2k + 3 \\
\hline
3k^2 + 15k - 12 \\
2k^3 + 10k^2 - 8k \\
\hline
2k^3 + 13k^2 + 7k - 12
\end{array}
$$

2 Dividing a Polynomial by a Monomial

To find the quotient of a polynomial and a monomial, we use the principle for adding fractions with the same denominator. For example, $\frac{2}{7} + \frac{3}{7} = \frac{2 + 3}{7}$. Also, $\frac{2 + 3}{7} = \frac{2}{7} + \frac{3}{7}$. In general, if a, b, and c represent real numbers, $c \neq 0$, then

$$\frac{a + b}{c} = \frac{a}{c} + \frac{b}{c}$$

We use this fact to convert the quotient of a polynomial and a monomial to the quotients of monomials. For example,

$$\frac{6x^9 + 8x^6}{2x^3} = \frac{6x^9}{2x^3} + \frac{8x^6}{2x^3} = 3x^6 + 4x^3$$

This procedure applies to polynomials with three or more terms. Simply divide each term in the polynomial by the monomial.

EXAMPLE 6

Find the following quotients.

a. $\dfrac{x^6 - 2x^5 + 4x}{2x^4}$ **b.** $\dfrac{a^4 - 3a^2b + 6ab^2 + b^4}{9ab}$

SOLUTION

a. $\dfrac{x^6 - 2x^5 + 4x}{2x^4} = \dfrac{x^6}{2x^4} - \dfrac{2x^5}{2x^4} + \dfrac{4x}{2x^4} = \dfrac{x^2}{2} - x + \dfrac{2}{x^3}$

b. $\dfrac{a^4 - 3a^2b + 6ab^2 + b^4}{9ab} = \dfrac{a^4}{9ab} - \dfrac{3a^2b}{9ab} + \dfrac{6ab^2}{9ab} + \dfrac{b^4}{9ab}$

$\qquad = \dfrac{a^3}{9b} - \dfrac{a}{3} + \dfrac{2b}{3} + \dfrac{b^3}{9a}$

3 Dividing a Polynomial by a Polynomial

When one polynomial is divided by another that is not a monomial, a long-division process is used. Subtraction is done vertically in this process.

To subtract two polynomials, change the sign of each term of the second polynomial and then add like terms. For example,

$$(8x - 3) - (2x - 7) = 8x - 3 - 2x + 7 = 6x + 4$$

To do this problem vertically, follow these three steps:

1. Place like terms in columns with $2x - 7$ below $8x - 3$.

2. Change all the signs in the second row.

3. Add like terms.

For example,

$$
\begin{array}{lll}
\textbf{1.} & 8x - 3 \\
& \underline{2x - 7}
\end{array}
\qquad
\begin{array}{ll}
\textbf{2.} & 8x - 3 \\
& \underline{-2x + 7}
\end{array}
\qquad
\begin{array}{ll}
\textbf{3.} & 8x - 3 \\
& \underline{-2x + 7} \\
& 6x + 4
\end{array}
$$

The following is a short way of doing this subtraction, with all steps done at once:

$$
\begin{array}{r}
8x - 3 \\
\underline{^-2x - {^+}7} \\
6x + 4
\end{array}
$$

EXAMPLE 7

Subtract the bottom polynomial from the top.

$$
\textbf{a.} \quad
\begin{array}{l}
6x^2 + 7x \\
6x^2 + 3x
\end{array}
\qquad
\textbf{b.} \quad
\begin{array}{l}
3y - 8 \\
-5y + 1
\end{array}
\qquad
\textbf{c.} \quad
\begin{array}{l}
2a^2 - 6a + 9 \\
2a^2 + 3a - 5
\end{array}
$$

SOLUTION

$$
\textbf{a.} \quad
\begin{array}{r}
6x^2 + 7x \\
\underline{^-6x^2 + {^-}3x} \\
4x
\end{array}
\qquad
\textbf{b.} \quad
\begin{array}{r}
3y - 8 \\
\underline{^-{^+}5 + {^-}1} \\
8y - 9
\end{array}
\qquad
\textbf{c.} \quad
\begin{array}{r}
2a^2 - 6a + 9 \\
\underline{^-2a^2 + {^-}3a - {^+}5} \\
-9a + 14
\end{array}
$$

The long-division process in dividing polynomials is very similar to the one used in arithmetic. Compare the two methods in the following examples:

$$\frac{679}{21}$$

$$21 \overline{)679}$$

Divide 67 by 21;
$3 \cdot 21 = 63$
Subtract:

$$
\begin{array}{r}
3 \\
21 \overline{)679} \\
\underline{63} \\
4
\end{array}
$$

$$\frac{6x^2 + 7x + 9}{2x + 1}$$

$$2x + 1 \overline{)6x^2 + 7x + 9}$$

Divide $6x^2$ by $2x$;
$3x(2x + 1) = 6x^2 + 3x$
Subtract:

$$
\begin{array}{r}
3x \\
2x + 1 \overline{)6x^2 + 7x + 9} \\
\underline{^-6x^2 + {^-}3x } \\
4x
\end{array}
$$

(continued)

Bring down the 9;
divide 49 by 21;
$2 \cdot 21 = 42$
Subtract:

$$\begin{array}{r} 32 \\ 21\overline{)679} \\ \underline{63} \\ 49 \\ \underline{42} \\ 7 \end{array}$$

$$\frac{679}{21} = 32 + \frac{7}{21}$$

Bring down the 9;
divide $4x$ by $2x$;
$2(2x + 1) = 4x + 2$
Subtract:

$$\begin{array}{r} 3x\ +\ 2 \\ 2x + 1\overline{)6x^2 + 7x + \quad 9} \\ \underline{6x^2 + 3x} \\ 4x +\quad 9 \\ \underline{^-4x +\ ^-2} \\ 7 \end{array}$$

$$\frac{6x^2 + 7x + 9}{2x + 1} = 3x + 2 + \frac{7}{2x + 1}$$

 CHECK

$679 \stackrel{?}{=} 32 \cdot 21 + 7$
$679 \stackrel{?}{=} 672 + 7$
$679 = 679$

$6x^2 + 7x + 9 \stackrel{?}{=} (3x + 2)(2x + 1) + 7$
$6x^2 + 7x + 9 \stackrel{?}{=} 6x^2 + 7x + 2 + 7$
$6x^2 + 7x + 9 = 6x^2 + 7x + 9$

⚠ **COMMON ERROR**

A common mistake in the division of polynomials is to add terms when they should be subtracted.

$$\begin{array}{r} 3 \\ 21\overline{)679} \\ \underline{63} \\ 130 \end{array}$$

$$\begin{array}{r} 3x \\ 2x + 1\overline{)6x^2 + 7x + 9} \\ \underline{6x^2 + 3x} \\ 10x \end{array}$$

130 ⟵————————— WRONG —————————⟶ 10x

Subtraction is done mentally in the concluding example.

EXAMPLE 8

Perform the indicated division.

a. $\dfrac{a^3 + 27}{a + 3}$ **b.** $\dfrac{x^4 - 2x^3 + 4x - 4}{x^2 - 1}$

SOLUTION   **a.** Let $a^3 + 27 = a^3 + 0a^2 + 0a + 27$; that is, $0 = 0a^2$ and $0 = 0a$ are placeholders.

$$\begin{array}{r} a^2 - 3a\ + 9 \\ a + 3\overline{)a^3 + 0a^2 + 0a + 27} \\ \underline{a^3 + 3a^2} \\ -3a^2 + 0a \\ \underline{-3a^2 - 9a} \\ 9a + 27 \\ \underline{9a + 27} \\ 0 \end{array}$$

Thus $\dfrac{a^3 + 27}{a + 3} = a^2 - 3a + 9$

b. $\dfrac{x^4 - 2x^3 + 4x - 4}{x^2 - 1} = \dfrac{x^4 - 2x^3 + 0x^2 + 4x - 4}{x^2 + 0x - 1}$

$$
\begin{array}{r}
x^2 - 2x + 1 \\
x^2 + 0x - 1 \overline{) x^4 - 2x^3 + 0x^2 + 4x - 4} \\
\underline{x^4 + 0x^3 - x^2} \\
-2x^3 + x^2 + 4x \\
\underline{-2x^3 + 0x^2 + 2x} \\
x^2 + 2x - 4 \\
\underline{x^2 + 0x - 1} \\
2x - 3
\end{array}
$$

Because $2x - 3$ is of lower degree than $x^2 - 1$, no monomial k exists such that $k(x^2) = 2x$. Thus, $2x - 3$ is the remainder and

$$\frac{x^4 - 2x^3 + 4x - 4}{x^2 - 1} = x^2 - 2x + 1 + \frac{2x - 3}{x^2 - 1}$$

EXERCISE SET 5.3

A

1 Find the following products using: a. the distributive property; and b. the FOIL method.

1. $(x + 3)(x + 4)$

2. $(x + 2)(x - 6)$

3. $(x + 2y)(x - 3y)$

4. $(2a + 3b)(a + 4b)$

5. $(x - 5)^2$

6. $(2x + 1)^2$

7. $(x + 6)(x - 6)$

8. $(3a - 2b)(3a + 2b)$

9. $(a + 2)(a^2 + 2a)$

10. $(x^2 - x)(3x^2 - 1)$

Find the following products using the vertical format.

11. $(x - 4)^2$

12. $(x - 4)^3$

13. $(x - 3y)(2x + 5y)$

14. $(x + 2)(x^2 - 3x + 2)$

15. $(a + 2)(a^2 - 2a + 4)$

16. $(x^2 - x + 3)(3x^2 + 2x - 1)$

Find the following products.

17. $3x(5x^2 - 6x + 4)$

18. $-2x^2(6x^3 + x^2 - 3x)$

19. $a^7(2a^6 - 3a^4 + a^3)$

20. $2a^3b^2(a^4 - a^2b^2 + 3b^4)$

21. $xy^2z^3(x^4y^2 - y^8z^6)$

22. $5ab^7c(2a^3b^4c + 3a^5b^7c^9)$

23. $(x + y)(2x + 3y)$

24. $(3y - 5)(2y - 2)$

25. $(a - 2)(a + 5)$

26. $(t - 3)(t + 3)$

27. $(4x + 5y)(4x - 5y)$

28. $(y - 2)^2$

29. $(2a + b)(3a - 2b)$

30. $(6x + y)(2x + 3y)$

31. $(2x + 3y)^2$

32. $(a^2 - 3b)^2$

33. $3x(3x^2 - 2)(2x^2 + 1)$

34. $-2x^2(1 - 3x)(5x - 2)$

35. $(x + 2)(x^2 - 3x + 5)$

36. $(2x - y)(x^2 - 3xy + 4y^2)$

37. $(x + 1)(x^2 - x + 1)$

38. $(y - 3z)(y^2 + 3yz + 9z^2)$

39. $(a - b)(a^2 + ab + b^2)$

40. $(a + b)(a^2 - ab + b^2)$

41. $(x - 1)^3$

42. $(x + 5)^3$

43. $(x^2 - x + 1)(3x^2 + x - 4)$

44. $(2y^3 + y - 3)(y^2 + 3y + 2)$

45. $(x + 1)^4$

46. $(a - b)^4$

2 Find the following quotients.

47. $\dfrac{6x^3 + 8x^2}{2x}$

48. $\dfrac{12x^6 - 9x^3}{-3x}$

49. $\dfrac{9y^8 + 6y^5 - 12y^2}{-4y}$

50. $\dfrac{6y^9 - 3y^2 + y}{y^2}$

51. $\dfrac{9y^{18} - 15y^{15} - 2y^2 + 1}{6y^3}$

52. $\dfrac{a^7 - 8a^4 + a^3 - 6}{4a^4}$

53. $\dfrac{2a^4b^5 - 6a^8b^9}{ab}$

54. $\dfrac{6x^8y^{12} + 4x^9y^{20}}{2xy^2}$

55. $\dfrac{30a^{12} - 25ab^{30} + ab}{5a^2b^3}$

56. $\dfrac{18m^6n^3 - mn + 12nm^{29}}{-6m^2n^3}$

3 Find the following quotients and check your answers.

57. $\dfrac{x^2 - 3x + 2}{x - 1}$

58. $\dfrac{x^2 + 7x + 12}{x + 3}$

59. $\dfrac{4y^2 - 16y + 15}{2y - 3}$

60. $\dfrac{6z^2 - 7z + 8}{3z + 1}$

61. $\dfrac{a + 3}{a + 2}$

62. $\dfrac{3x^2 - 2x + 4}{x^2 - 2}$

Find the following quotients and products.

63. $\dfrac{x^2 - x - 42}{x + 6}$

64. $\dfrac{x^2 - 3x - 28}{x - 7}$

65. $(x^2 - 2) \div (x + 4)$

66. $(x^2 + 5x + 8) \div (x + 2)$

67. $\dfrac{4y^2 - 8y + 3}{2y - 3}$

68. $\dfrac{4a^2 - 16a + 15}{2a - 3}$

69. $\dfrac{5m^2 - 24m - 25}{5m + 4}$

70. $\dfrac{x^3 - 1}{x - 1}$

71. $\dfrac{6n^3 + n^2 - 16n + 9}{2n - 1}$

72. $\dfrac{9x^3 - 21 - 6x^2 - 47x}{3x + 5}$

73. $\dfrac{3x^2 + 4 + x^3}{x^2 + 2x}$

74. $\dfrac{4z^3 - 2z^2 + 7z - 1}{z^2 - 2z + 3}$

75. $\dfrac{6x^4 + 5x^3 + x - 9}{3x^2 - 2x}$

76. $\dfrac{9t^4 - 13t^3 + 23t^2 - 9t + 2}{t^2 - t + 2}$

77. $\dfrac{9x^4 + 12x^2 + 4}{3x^2 + 2}$

78. $\dfrac{9 - 4x^3}{3 - 2x^2}$

B

79. $\dfrac{x - 10}{2x + 3}$

80. $\dfrac{5y^2 + 26y + 8}{5y + 4}$

81. $\dfrac{6x^3 + 2x^2 - 4x + 1}{2x - 1}$

82. $\dfrac{a^3 + 2a^2 - a + 2}{3a^2 + a}$

83. $(x^{2m} - 3)(x^{2m} + 3)$

84. $(2x^{3m} + 1)^2$

85. $(a^m + b^n)^2$

86. $(a^m + b^n)(a^m - b^2)$

Evaluate each determinant. (See Section 4.5.)

87. $\begin{vmatrix} x & x + 2 \\ 4 & x - 3 \end{vmatrix}$

88. $\begin{vmatrix} x + 1 & x - 2 \\ x + 2 & x - 1 \end{vmatrix}$

C

89. The first 13 numbers in the Fibonacci sequence are given on page 209. What are the next three numbers in the sequence?

90. The Lucas sequence is the set $\{1, 3, 4, 7, 11, 18, \ldots \}$. Give the next three numbers in this sequence.

Let $P_2 = \{ax^2 + bx + c \mid a, b,$ and c are real numbers$\}$. That is, P_2 is the set of all constant, linear, and quadratic polynomials in one variable. Justify your answer to the following with an example. Determine if P_2 is closed under:

91. addition **92.** subtraction

93. multiplication **94.** division

Answer the following questions with complete sentences.

95. Discuss the contributions Fibonacci made to European mathematics.

96. How is the seventh term of the Fibonacci sequence obtained?

REVIEW EXERCISES

Let $f(x) = 2x + 1$ and $g(x) = x^2 - 3x + 4$. Find the following. (See Section 4.2.)

97. $f(-2) + g(-2)$

98. $f(3) - g(3)$

99. $g(-1) - f(-1)$

Find $\dfrac{f(x + h) - f(x)}{h}$ for the function f. (See Section 3.4.)

100. $f(x) = 2x + 1$

101. $f(x) = 3x - 4$

102. $f(x) = 2 - 5x$

Find the following products. (See Section 5.3.)

103. $(x + 5)(x - 5)$

104. $(a - 3b)(a + 3b)$

105. $(x + 2)(x^2 - 2x + 4)$

106. $(x - 3)(x^2 + 3x + 9)$

5.4 UNDERSTANDING THE ALGEBRA OF FUNCTIONS AND INTRODUCTION TO FACTORING

1	Using the Algebra of Functions
2	Finding the Greatest Common Factor
3	Factoring $a^2 - b^2$
4	Factoring $a^3 + b^3$ and $a^3 - b^3$

1 Using the Algebra of Functions

This section continues our study of functions by combining polynomial functions with operations such as addition and multiplication. We will then examine factoring, which will be the main topic for the rest of the chapter.

In arithmetic we combine numbers with operations such as addition and multiplication to obtain new numbers. The process of combining functions to produce new functions is called the **algebra of functions**.

If $f(x) = x + 3$ and $g(x) = x + 4$, then the sum and product of f and $g, f + g$ and fg, are defined in a very natural way:

$$(f + g)(x) = f(x) + g(x) = (x + 3) + (x + 4) = 2x + 7$$
$$(fg)(x) = f(x)g(x) = (x + 3)(x + 4) = x^2 + 7x + 12$$

If f and g are two polynomial functions, then the domain of $f + g$, $f - g$, and fg is the set of real numbers. However, the domain of f/g is all values of x such that $g(x) \neq 0$. Using the two preceding functions,

$$\left(\frac{f}{g}\right)(x) = \frac{f(x)}{g(x)} = \frac{x + 3}{x + 4} \quad \text{and} \quad D_{f/g} = \{x \mid x \neq -4\}$$

In general:

> If f and g are polynomial functions, then
>
> $(f + g)(x) = f(x) + g(x)$ Sum
> $(f - g)(x) = f(x) - g(x)$ Difference
> $(fg)(x) = f(x)g(x)$ Product
> $\left(\dfrac{f}{g}\right)(x) = \dfrac{f(x)}{g(x)}, \quad g(x) \neq 0$ Quotient

EXAMPLE 1

Let $f(x) = 6x^2 + 8x + 9$ and $g(x) = 2x$. Find
a. $f - g$ **b.** g^2 **c.** f/g and its domain.

SOLUTION
a. $(f - g)(x) = f(x) - g(x)$
$= (6x^2 + 8x + 9) - (2x)$
$= 6x^2 + 6x + 9$

b. $(g^2)(x) = [g(x)]^2 = (2x)^2 = 4x^2$

c. $\left(\dfrac{f}{g}\right)(x) = \dfrac{f(x)}{g(x)} = \dfrac{6x^2 + 8x + 9}{2x} = 3x + 4 + \dfrac{9}{2x}$, $D_{f_g} = \{x \mid x \neq 0\}$

EXAMPLE 2

Let $f(a) = 4a - 1$ and $g(a) = 2a^2 - 9$. Find
a. $(f + g)(-2)$ **b.** $(fg)(3)$

SOLUTION
a. $(f + g)(-2) = f(-2) + g(-2)$
$= [4(-2) - 1] + [2(-2)^2 - 9]$
$= [-9] + [-1]$
$= -10$

b. $(fg)(3) = f(3)g(3) = [4 \cdot 3 - 1][2 \cdot 3^2 - 9] = [11][9]$
$= 99$

2   Finding the Greatest Common Factor

We have learned how to multiply two polynomials, such as $3x(2x + 4) = 6x^2 + 12x$. The reverse of multiplication is called **factoring**; that is, we start with a sum and write it as a product, such as $6^2 + 12x = 3x(2x + 4)$. Before we deal with polynomials, we will review some concepts from arithmetic.

Because $3 \cdot 5 = 15$,   3 and 5 are called **factors**, or divisors, of 15. They are also called **prime factors**, because they are only divisible by 1 and themselves. A number such as 6 is called **composite**, because it is divisible by a natural number other than 1 and itself (2 and 3). If **P** is the set of primes and **C** the set of composites, then

$$P = \{2, 3, 5, 7, 11, 13, 17, 19, \ldots\}$$
$$C = \{4, 6, 8, 9, 10, 12, 14, 15, \ldots\}$$

Every composite number can be expressed as the product of prime numbers, which is called the **prime factorization** of the number. When it is so factored, we say that the number is **factored completely**. For example,

$$30 = 2 \cdot 3 \cdot 5, \quad 105 = 3 \cdot 5 \cdot 7, \quad \text{and} \quad 121 = 11 \cdot 11$$

A factor of two or more integers is called a **common factor** of the integers. For example, 1, 2, 3, and 6 are common factors of 12 and 18. The **greatest common factor**, **GCF**, of a set of integers is the largest factor they have in common. Thus, 6 is the GCF of 12 and 18. A convenient way to find the GCF is to use prime factorization, as illustrated in the next example.

EXAMPLE 3

Find the GCF of each set of integers.

a. {30, 105}   **b.** {36, 60, 120}

SOLUTION **a.** $30 = 2 \cdot 3 \cdot 5 = 15 \cdot 2$ and $105 = 3 \cdot 5 \cdot 7 = 15 \cdot 7$, so GCF = 15
b. $36 = 2 \cdot 2 \cdot 3 \cdot 3 = 12 \cdot 3$, $60 = 2 \cdot 2 \cdot 3 \cdot 5 = 12 \cdot 5$, and $120 = 2 \cdot 2 \cdot 2 \cdot 3 \cdot 5 = 12 \cdot 10$, so GCF = 12

The concept of the greatest common factor also extends to monomials. The GCF of a set of monomials in one variable is the monomial with the GCF of the numerical coefficients and the variable raised to the smallest exponent. For example, the GCF of $10x^6$, $8x^4$, and $6x^3$ is $2x^3$ because

$$10x^6 = 2x^3(5x^3), \quad 8x^4 = 2x^3(4x), \quad \text{and} \quad 6x^3 = 2x^3(3)$$

To **factor out** the greatest common factor from a polynomial in one variable, we determine each polynomial term's GCF and then use the distributive property. For example,

$$10x^6 + 8x^4 + 6x^3 = 2x^3(5x^3) + 2x^3(4x) + 2x^3(3)$$
$$= 2x^3(5x^3 + 4x + 3)$$

Just as the GCF of 5 and 8 is 1, the GCF of $2x$ and 9 is 1. Therefore, we say that $2x + 9$ is **prime over the integers**, which means that $1(2x + 9)$ is the only factorization involving integers. When a polynomial is prime over the integers, we simply write "prime" and do not express it with a factor of 1.

EXAMPLE 4

Factor out the greatest common factor.

a. $14x^2 + 7x$ **b.** $16y - 9$ **c.** $36x^3 + 48x^2 - 24x$

SOLUTION **a.** $14x^2 + 7x = 7x(2x) + 7x(1)$ $a = a \cdot 1$
$\qquad\qquad\quad\; = 7x(2x + 1)$

(continued)

b. $16y - 9$ is prime.

c. The GCF of 36, 48, and 24 is 12. Thus,

$$36x^3 + 48x^2 - 24x = 12x(3x^2) + 12x(4x) - 12x(2)$$
$$= 12x(3x^2 + 4x - 2)$$

The greatest common factor of a polynomial in several variables is the monomial with the GCF of the numerical coefficients and each variable common to all terms raised to its smallest exponent. Once we determine the GCF of the polynomial, we factor it out with the distributive property. For instance,

$$18a^4b^3 + 81a^2b^7 = 9a^2b^3(2a^2) + 9a^2b^3(9b^4)$$
$$= 9a^2b^3(2a^2 + 9b^4)$$

EXAMPLE 5

Factor out the greatest common factor.

a. $-6x^3y + 21x^2y^2 - 15xy^3$ **b.** $9ab + 6xy - 4ab - xy$

SOLUTION

a. We commonly factor a negative sign out of a polynomial when the first term has a negative coefficient. Thus,

$$-6x^3y + 21x^2y^2 - 15xy^3 = -3xy(2x^2) - 3xy(-7xy) - 3xy(5y^2)$$
$$= -3xy(2x^2 - 7xy + 5y^2)$$

b. First simplify the polynomial:

$$9ab + 6xy - 4ab - xy = 5ab + 5xy = 5(ab + xy)$$

In Section 3.4 we evaluated $\dfrac{f(x + h) - f(x)}{h}$ for linear functions. Now that we have covered products of polynomials and factoring the GCF, we can simplify this expression for higher-degree polynomial functions.

EXAMPLE 6

Find $\dfrac{f(x + h) - f(x)}{h}$ for $f(x) = 3x^2 - 2x + 4$.

SOLUTION

$$\frac{f(x + h) - f(x)}{h} = \frac{3(x + h)^2 - 2(x + h) + 4 - (3x^2 - 2x + 4)}{h}$$

$$= \frac{3(x^2 + 2hx + h^2) - 2x - 2h + 4 - 3x^2 + 2x - 4}{h}$$

$$= \frac{3x^2 + 6hx + 3h^2 - 2h - 3x^2}{h}$$

$$= \frac{6hx + 3h^2 - 2h}{h} \qquad\qquad \text{GCF} = h$$

$$= \frac{h(6x + 3h - 2)}{h} \qquad\qquad h/h = 1$$

$$= 6x + 3h - 2$$

COMMON ERROR

Confusing $f(x + h)$ with $f(x) + h$ is a common mistake. If $f(x) = x^2 + x$, then

$$f(x + h) = (x + h)^2 + (x + h) = x^2 + 2hx + h^2 + x + h;$$
$$f(x) + h = x^2 + x + h$$

Thus, $f(x + h) \neq f(x) + h$.

3 Factoring $a^2 - b^2$

The expression $a^2 - b^2$ is called the **difference of two squares**, because

$$(a - b)(a + b) = a^2 + ab - ab - b^2 = a^2 - b^2$$

Difference of Two Squares

$$a^2 - b^2 = (a - b)(a + b)$$

Note that $a^2 + b^2$ is prime over the integers, unless a and b have a common factor other than 1. For example, $(2x)^2 + 6^2 = 4x^2 + 36 = 4(x^2 + 9)$, and $x^2 + 9$ is prime.

EXAMPLE 7

Factor the following.

a. $x^2 - 25$ **b.** $9m^2 - 100n^2$ **c.** $a^2 - (b - c)^2$

SOLUTION

a. $x^2 - 25 = x^2 - 5^2 = (x - 5)(x + 5)$
b. $9m^2 - 100n^2 = (3m)^2 - (10n)^2 = (3m - 10n)(3m + 10n)$
c. $a^2 - (b - c)^2 = [a - (b - c)][a + (b - c)]$
$$= (a - b + c)(a + b - c)$$

After factoring the GCF out of a polynomial, we may be left with the difference of two squares. For example,

$$3x^3 - 12x = 3x(x^2 - 4) = 3x(x - 2)(x + 2)$$

When different factoring methods are combined, we first factor out the GCF. When $3x^3 - 12x$ is expressed as $3x(x - 2)(x + 2)$, we say that it is *factored completely,* which means that it cannot be factored any further over the integers. Whenever we are asked to factor a polynomial, we understand that it is to be factored completely. The job is only half done if we leave $3x^3 - 12x$ as $3x(x^2 - 4)$.

EXAMPLE 8

Factor the following.

a. $2a^3b - 18ab$ **b.** $x - 81x^5$

SOLUTION

a. $2a^3b - 18ab = 2ab(a^2) - 2ab(9) = 2ab(a^2 - 9)$
$$= 2ab(a + 3)(a - 3) \quad a^2 - 9 = a^2 - 3^2$$

(continued)

b. $x - 81x^5 = x[1 - 81x^4]$
$$= x[1^2 - (9x^2)^2]$$
$$= x[1 - 9x^2][1 + 9x^2] \qquad \text{1 + 9}x^2 \text{ is prime.}$$
$$= x[1^2 - (3x)^2][1 + 9x^2]$$
$$= x(1 - 3x)(1 + 3x)(1 + 9x^2)$$

---

4   Factoring $a^3 + b^3$ and $a^3 - b^3$

We have just seen that the difference of two squares factors over the integers, although the sum of two squares is prime. However, both the sum *and* the difference of two cubes are factorable.

Consider the following product:

$$(a + b)(a^2 - ab + b^2) = a(a^2 - ab + b^2) + b(a^2 - ab + b^2)$$
$$= a^3 - a^2b + ab^2 + a^2b - ab^2 + b^3$$
$$= a^3 + b^3$$

Thus, $a^3 + b^3 = (a + b)(a^2 - ab + b^2)$. In a similar way we can show that $a^3 - b^3 = (a - b)(a^2 + ab + b^2)$. The term $a^3 + b^3$ is called the **sum of two cubes**, and $a^3 - b^3$ is called the **difference of two cubes**. Two examples are

$$x^3 + 8 = x^3 + 2^3$$
$$= (x + 2)(x^2 - x \cdot 2 + 2^2)$$
$$= (x + 2)(x^2 - 2x + 4)$$
$$x^3 - 8 = x^3 - 2^3$$
$$= (x - 2)(x^2 + x \cdot 2 + 2^2)$$
$$= (x - 2)(x^2 + 2x + 4)$$

Sum and Difference of Cubes

$$a^3 + b^3 = (a + b)(a^2 - ab + b^2)$$
$$a^3 - b^3 = (a - b)(a^2 + ab + b^2)$$

In remembering these formulas note that in each equation both binomials have the same sign between the terms: $a^3 + b^3$ and $a + b$; $a^3 - b^3$ and $a - b$. Also, several mistakes are common in using these formulas:

COMMON ERROR

Several mistakes can be made in factoring $a^3 + b^3$ and $a^3 - b^3$. The following are the most common:

$$a^3 + b^3 \neq (a + b)^3$$
$$a^3 + b^3 \neq (a + b)(a^2 + b^2)$$
$$a^3 + b^3 \neq (a + b)(a^2 - 2ab + b^2)$$
$$a^3 - b^3 \neq (a - b)(a^2 + 2ab + b^2)$$
$$a^3 - b^3 \neq (a - b)^3$$
$$a^3 - b^3 \neq (a - b)(a^2 + b^2)$$

EXAMPLE 9

Factor the following.

a. $8m^3 + 125n^3$ **b.** $a^6 - 1000$ **c.** $n^3 - (m - 1)^3$

SOLUTION   **a.** $8m^3 + 125n^3 = 2^3m^3 + 5^3n^3 = (2m)^3 + (5n)^3$
$$= (2m + 5n)[(2m)^2 - (2m)(5n) + (5n)^2]$$
$$= (2m + 5n)(4m^2 - 10mn + 25n^2)$$

b. $a^6 - 1000 = (a^2)^3 - 10^3 = (a^2 - 10)[(a^2)^2 + a^2 \cdot 10 + 10^2]$
$$= (a^2 - 10)(a^4 + 10a^2 + 100)$$

c. $n^3 - (m - 1)^3 = [n - (m - 1)][n^2 + n(m - 1) + (m - 1)^2]$
$$= (n - m + 1)(n^2 + nm - n + m^2 - 2m + 1)$$

As with previous problems, the sum and difference of two cubes are often combined with other types of factoring as illustrated in the concluding example for this section.

EXAMPLE 10

Factor the following.

a. $3k^4 + 3k$ **b.** $2x^5y^2 - 54x^2y^5$

SOLUTION   **a.** $3k^4 + 3k = 3k(k^3) + 3k(1)$ $a = a \cdot 1$
$$= 3k(k^3 + 1^3)$$ $1 = 1^3$
$$= 3k(k + 1)(k^2 - k + 1)$$

b. $2x^5y^2 - 54x^2y^5 = 2x^2y^2(x^3) - 2x^2y^2(27y^3)$
$$= 2x^2y^2[x^3 - 27y^3]$$
$$= 2x^2y^2[x^3 - (3y)^3]$$
$$= 2x^2y^2(x - 3y)[x^2 + x \cdot 3y + (3y)^2]$$
$$= 2x^2y^2(x - 3y)(x^2 + 3xy + 9y^2)$$

EXERCISE SET 5.4

A

1   Let $f(x) = 2x^2$, $g(x) = x - 1$, $h(x) = 3x^2 - x + 2$,   and $k(x) = x^3 - 1$. Find the following functions and give their domains.

1. $f + g$ **2.** $g + h$ **3.** $h + k$
4. $f - h$ **5.** $k - g$ **6.** $f - k$
7. fg **8.** gk **9.** f^2
10. k^2 **11.** h/f **12.** k/g

Let $f(x) = 3x - 1$, $g(x) = x^2 + 3x - 1$,   and $h(x) = 2x^3 - x + 3$. Find:

13. $(f + g)(2)$ **14.** $(g + h)(-1)$
15. $(f - h)(0)$ **16.** $(g - f)(4)$
17. $(fh)(1)$ **18.** $(gf)(-3)$
19. $\left(\dfrac{f}{h}\right)(2)$ **20.** $\left(\dfrac{h}{g}\right)(-2)$

2   Find the GCF of each set of integers.

21. $\{15, 45\}$ **22.** $\{16, 25\}$
23. $\{18, 24, -42\}$ **24.** $\{-8, 12, 28\}$
25. $\{24, 40, 32\}$ **26.** $\{6, 9, 27, 30\}$

Factor out the greatest common factor.

27. $3x + 9$
28. $12y - 18$
29. $4x^2 - 6x$
30. $5x^2 + 5x$
31. $6a^3 - 6a^2$
32. $6x + 25$
33. $4x^4 + 6x^3 - 10x$
34. $4xy^2 - 6x^2y$

35. $2x^3y + xy - 3xy^3$

36. $8a^3b^2c^4 - 12a^2b^7c^8$

37. $7ab + 4ab + 12cd - cd$

38. $5xy + xz - xy + 3xz$

Find $\dfrac{f(x + h) - f(x)}{h}$ for the following functions f.

39. $f(x) = 2x + 1$

40. $f(x) = 1 - 4x$

41. $f(x) = x^2 - 7$

42. $f(x) = 3x^2 + 2x$

43. $f(x) = 2x^2 - x + 3$

44. $f(x) = 3x^2 + 2x - 6$

45. $f(x) = x^3$

46. $f(x) = x^3 + 4$

3 Factor the following.

47. $y^2 - z^2$

48. $x^2 - 36$

49. $x^2 + 36$

50. $4a^2 - 49$

51. $4a^2 - 9b^2$

52. $25a^2b^4 - 1$

53. $(3x)^2 + 6^2$

54. $x^4 - 16$

55. $(x + 3)^2 - y^2$

56. $a^2 - (2b - 5)^2$

57. $3x^2 - 12$

58. $x^3y - xy^3$

59. $8x^3 - 18x$

60. $a^2bc - ab^3c$

61. $3x^5 - 3x$

62. $10y^6 - 810y^2$

63. $1 - x^4y^4$

64. $1 + x^4y^4$

4 Determine whether the given equation is true or false. If it is false, give the correct answer.

65. $x^3 + 8y^3 = (x + 2y)(x + 2y)(x + 2y)$

66. $x^3 + 125 = (x + 5)(x^2 - 5x + 25)$

67. $m^3 + 1000 = (m - 10)(m^2 + 10m + 100)$

68. $1 - a^3 = (1 - a)(1 + 2a + a^2)$

69. $a^3 + b^6 = (a + b^2)(a^2 - 2ab + b^4)$

70. $8x^3 - y^3 = (2x - y)(4x^2 + y^2)$

Factor the following.

71. $x^3 + 27$

72. $x^3 - 64$

73. $125x^3 - 8y^3$

74. $1000a^3 + b^3c^3$

75. $1 - x^3y^3$

76. $a^3b^6 + 1$

77. $a^6 + b^3c^6$

78. $64x^3 - y^{27}$

79. $2x^3 - 2y^3$

80. $3x^4y + 3xy^3$

81. $3x^5 + 24x^2y^3$

82. $a^7b - ab^4$

83. $a^9 - 1$

84. $x^9 + y^9$

85. $27x^6y^4 - 1$

86. $(x + 1)^3 - 1$

87. $a^3 - (b - c)^3$

88. $2x^4y + 2xy^3$

B

89. $m^3 + \dfrac{1}{27}$

90. $8x^3 - \dfrac{1}{8}$

91. $8 - (x^2 + 2)^3$

92. $x^4 - y^8$

93. $x^6 - y^{60}$

94. $36 - 4(a - b)^2$

95. $(a - b)^2 - (c - d)^2$

96. $x(x + y)^2 - x(m - n)^2$

97. $(a + b)^3 - (a - b)^3$

98. $(x - y)^3 + (x + y)^3$

C

Answer the following questions with complete sentences.

99. If f and g are polynomial functions, then the domain of fg is always the set of real numbers. Why is this not true for f/g?

100. What does saying that a polynomial is "prime over the integers" mean?

101. What does saying that a polynomial is "factored completely" mean?

102. What is the difference between a prime number and a composite number?

REVIEW EXERCISES

Find the following products. (See Section 5.3.)

103. $(a + c)(b + 7)$

104. $(x^2 + y)(z + 4)$

105. $(x + 3)(x + 4)$

106. $(x + 6y)(x - 3y)$

Solve the following equations. (See Section 2.3.)

107. $x^2 = 9$

108. $x^2 = 25$

5.5 FACTORING BY GROUPING AND $x^2 + bx + c$

> 1 **Factoring by Grouping**
>
> 2 **Factoring $x^2 + bx + c$ and $x^2 + bxy + cy^2$**
>
> 3 **Solving Equations**

1 Factoring by Grouping

In the last section we learned how to factor the greatest common monomial factor out of a polynomial. We begin this section with common factors that are binomials. This method of factoring then will be used to factor certain trinomials.

Sometimes a polynomial whose greatest common monomial factor is 1 has a common binomial factor. In this case the polynomial can be factored with the distributive property. For example, $x(x + 4) + 3(x + 4)$ has a common factor of $x + 4$. If we let $x + 4 = a$, then

$$x(x + 4) + 3(x + 4) = x(a) + 3(a)$$
$$= (x + 3)(a)$$
$$= (x + 3)(x + 4)$$

EXAMPLE 1

Factor the following.

a. $2x(4x - y) - 5y(4x - y)$ **b.** $(m - n)a + (m - n)b$

SOLUTION

a. $2x(4x - y) - 5y(4x - y) = (2x - 5y)(4x - y)$
b. $(m - n)a + (m - n)b = (m - n)(a + b)$

Frequently a polynomial is written without the common binomial factor being apparent, such as $rs + 7r + st + 7t$. However, by factoring r from the first two terms and t from the last two terms we are left with a common factor of $s + 7$:

$$rs + 7r + st + 7t = r(s + 7) + t(s + 7)$$
$$= (r + t)(s + 7)$$

EXAMPLE 2

Factor the following.

a. $x^2 - x + 3x - 3$ **b.** $mn^2 - 4n^2 + 2m - 8$

SOLUTION

a. $x^2 - x + 3x - 3 = x(x - 1) + 3(x - 1)$ $x = x \cdot 1$
$ = (x + 3)(x - 1)$
b. $mn^2 - 4n^2 + 2m - 8 = n^2(m - 4) + 2(m - 4)$
$ = (n^2 + 2)(m - 4)$

This factoring process is called **factoring by grouping**. Some polynomials can be factored by grouping, but not in the order in which their terms are written. In this case we regroup terms with common factors, which may be done in more than one way. For example,

$$x^2z + 4y + yz + 4x^2 = (x^2z + yz) + (4x^2 + 4y)$$
$$= z(x^2 + y) + 4(x^2 + y)$$
$$= (z + 4)(x^2 + y)$$

or

$$x^2z + 4y + yz + 4x^2 = (x^2z + 4x^2) + (4y + yz)$$
$$= x^2(z + 4) + y(4 + z)$$
$$= (x^2 + y)(z + 4)$$

EXAMPLE 3

Factor the following.

a. $x^3 - 18 + 2x^2 - 9x$ **b.** $xy + y - x + 1$
c. $a^2b^2c - abc^2 + a^2bc^2 - ab^2c$

SOLUTION

a. Group x^3 and $2x^2$, because their GCF is x^2:

$$x^3 - 18 + 2x^2 - 9x = (x^3 + 2x^2) - (9x + 18)$$
$$= x^2(x + 2) - 9(x + 2)$$
$$= (x^2 - 9)(x + 2) \qquad x^2 - 9 = x^2 - 3^2$$
$$= (x - 3)(x + 3)(x + 2)$$

b. $xy + y - x + 1 = y(x + 1) - 1(x - 1)$ No common factor
$$= (xy - x) + (y + 1)$$
$$= x(y - 1) + (y + 1)$$ No common factor

Thus, $xy + y - x + 1$ is prime.

c. $a^2b^2c - abc^2 + a^2bc^2 - ab^2c = abc[ab - c + ac - b]$ GCF $= abc$
$$= abc[(ab + ac) - (b + c)]$$ Group ab and ac.
$$= abc[a(b + c) - 1(b + c)]$$ $-x = -1x$
$$= abc(a - 1)(b + c)$$

2   Factoring $x^2 + bx + c$ and $x^2 + bxy + cy^2$

Expressing a trinomial as the product of two binomials is one of the most important types of factoring in algebra. Because factoring is the reverse of multiplication, we will start with a product, $(x + 3)(x + 4)$:

$$(x + 3)(x + 4) = x(x + 4) + 3(x + 4)$$
$$= x^2 + 4x + 3x + 3 \cdot 4$$
$$= x^2 + 7x + 12$$

To factor $x^2 + 7x + 12$ we must reverse the previous steps by expressing $7x$ as $4x + 3x$ and 12 as $3 \cdot 4$; that is, we must find integers, m and n, such that $m + n = 7$ and $mn = 12$. This process is done by finding the prime factorization of 12 and considering the possible products:

$$12 = 2 \cdot 2 \cdot 3$$
$$= 2 \cdot 6 \qquad \text{Will not work: } 2 + 6 \neq 7$$
$$= 4 \cdot 3 \qquad \text{Works: } 4 + 3 = 7$$

so $m = 4$ and $n = 3$.
Now we factor $x^2 + 7x + 12$ by grouping:

$$x^2 + 7x + 12 = x^2 + 4x + 3x + 3 \cdot 4$$
$$= x(x + 4) + 3(x + 4)$$
$$= (x + 3)(x + 4)$$

EXAMPLE 4

Factor $y^2 - y - 30$.

SOLUTION

We have to find m and n such that $m + n = -1$ and $mn = -30$. We can do this (if the numbers are not obvious) by setting up a table of all possible products that are -30 and their corresponding sums. Notice that we start with $m = 1$ and let m increase: $-30 = -1 \cdot 2 \cdot 3 \cdot 5 < 0$, so we need $m > 0$ and $n < 0$.

$mn = -30$	$m + n$
$1(-30) = -30$	$1 + (-30) = -29$
$2(-15) = -30$	$2 + (-15) = -13$
$3(-10) = -30$	$3 + (-10) = -7$
$5(-6) = -30$	$5 + (-6) = -1$

We are done. Thus
$m = 5$ and $n = -6$, so
$$y^2 - y - 30 = y^2 + 5y - 6y - 30$$
$$= y(y + 5) - 6(y + 5)$$
$$= (y - 6)(y + 5)$$
Note that we could have $m = -6$ and $n = 5$:
$$y^2 - y - 30 = y^2 - 6y + 5y - 30$$
$$= y(y - 6) + 5(y - 6)$$
$$= (y + 5)(y - 6)$$

EXAMPLE 5

Factor the following.
a. $x^2 + 16x - 17$ **b.** $a^2 + 7a + 15$

SOLUTION

a. $m + n = 16$ and $mn = -17 = -1 \cdot 17$; $m = -1$ and $n = 17$.
$$x^2 + 16x - 17 = x^2 - 1x + 17x - 17$$
$$= x(x - 1) + 17(x - 1)$$
$$= (x + 17)(x - 1)$$
b. $m + n = 7$ and $mn = 15 = 1 \cdot 3 \cdot 5$.

$mn = 15$	$m + n$
$1 \cdot 15 = 15$	$1 + 15 = 16$
$3 \cdot 5 = 15$	$3 + 5 = 8$

Because no other possible combinations of m and n exist, $a^2 + 7a + 15$ is prime.

The procedure for factoring $x^2 + bxy + cy^2$ is very similar to the one for $x^2 + bx + c$. We have to find integers m and n such that $m + n = b$ and $mn = c$. The values of m and n will be given in the remaining examples, because the general approach has been illustrated in Examples 4 and 5.

EXAMPLE 6

Factor the following.

a. $x^2 + 3xy - 18y^2$ **b.** $2a^3 + 18a^2b + 40ab^2$

SOLUTION

a. $m + n = 3$ and $mn = -18 = -2 \cdot 3 \cdot 3 = -3(6)$

$$x^2 + 3xy - 18y^2 = x^2 - 3xy + 6xy - 18y^2$$
$$= x(x - 3y) + 6y(x - 3y)$$
$$= (x + 6y)(x - 3y)$$

b. $2a^3 + 18a^2b + 40ab^2 = 2a(a^2 + 9ab + 20b^2)$

$m + n = 9$ and $mn = 20 = 4 \cdot 5$, so

$$a^2 + 9ab + 20b^2 = a^2 + 4ab + 5ab + 20b^2$$
$$= a(a + 4b) + 5b(a + 4b)$$
$$= (a + 5b)(a + 4b), \text{ so}$$
$$2a^3 + 18a^2b + 40ab^2 = 2a(a + 5b)(a + 4b)$$

3   Solving Equations

In Section 2.3 we solved quadratic equations in the form $x^2 = d, d > 0$. For instance, if $x^2 = 9$, then $x = \pm\sqrt{9} = \pm 3$. Other polynomial equations in one variable can be solved by means of a basic property of the real numbers. We know from arithmetic that if the product of two numbers is zero, then at least one of the numbers is zero. This property holds for algebraic expressions:

Zero-Factor Property

Let a and b represent real numbers.
If $ab = 0$, then $a = 0$ or $b = 0$.

We can use this fact to solve equations such as $x^2 - x - 6 = 0$:

$$x^2 - x - 6 = 0$$
$$(x - 3)(x + 2) = 0$$
$$x - 3 = 0 \quad \text{or} \quad x + 2 = 0$$
$$x = 3 \quad \text{or} \quad x = -2$$

so the solution set is $\{3, -2\}$

Note that we must write the equation in the form $ab = 0$; then we can use the zero-factor property.

EXAMPLE 7

Solve the following equations.
a. $(x - 4)(x - 5) = 20$ **b.** $3y^3 - 12y^2 = 15y$
c. $x^3 + x^2 - 9x - 9 = 0$

SOLUTION

a. $(x - 4)(x - 5) = 20$ Get 0 on one side.
$\qquad x^2 - 9x + 20 = 20$
$\qquad\qquad x^2 - 9x = 0$
$\qquad\qquad x(x - 9) = 0$
$\quad x = 0$ or $x - 9 = 0$
so $x = 0$ or 9

b. $\qquad\quad 3y^3 - 12y^2 = 15y$
$\quad 3y^3 - 12y^2 - 15y = 0$ GCF $= 3y$
$\quad\;\; 3y(y^2 - 4y - 5) = 0$ $m + n = -4$
$\quad 3y(y + 1)(y - 5) = 0$ $mn = -5 = 1(-5)$
$\quad 3y = 0, \quad y + 1 = 0, \quad$ or $\quad y - 5 = 0$
so $y = 0, \quad -1, \quad$ or 5

c. $\quad\; x^3 + x^2 - 9x - 9 = 0$ Factor by grouping.
$\quad x^2(x + 1) - 9(x + 1) = 0$
$\qquad\quad (x^2 - 9)(x + 1) = 0$
$\; (x - 3)(x + 3)(x + 1) = 0$
$\; x + 3 = 0, \quad x + 3 = 0, \quad$ or $\quad x + 1 = 0$
so $x = 3, \quad -3, \quad$ or -1

EXERCISE SET 5.5

A

1   Factor the following.

1. $x(x - 1) + 5(x - 1)$

2. $a(b + 3) - c(b + 3)$

3. $(r + 3)t - (r + 3)6$

4. $(x^2 + 1)y + (x^2 + 1)4$

5. $(5 + 5y)a - (5 + 5y)b$

6. $8a^2b(x - y) + 12ab^2(x - y)$

7. $x^2 + 5x + 6x + 30$

8. $x^2 + 6x + 5x + 30$

9. $y^2 - 3y + 7y - 21$

10. $a^2 - 4a - 5a + 20$

11. $3x^2 - 2xy - 12xy + 8y^2$

12. $10a^2 + 35ab - 6ab - 21b^2$

13. $x^3 + x^2 - x - 1$

14. $x^3 + 32 - 16x - 2x^2$

15. $xy - 12 - 3y + 4x$

16. $m^2t + ks^2 + kt + s^2m^2$

17. $3a + 3b - ca + cb$

18. $xy^2 + y - y^2 - xy$

19. $a^2bc - abc + a^2b - ab^2c$

20. $xy - 6 - 3x - 2y$

21. $2a + 2b + a^2 - b^2$

22. $n^2 - mt + mn - t^2$

2

23. $x^2 + 11x + 30$ **24.** $t^2 + t - 20$

25. $x^2 - 6x - 16$ **26.** $a^2 - 5a + 6$

27. $x^2 + 14x + 28$ **28.** $b^2 + 10b + 25$

29. $x^2 - 8x + 7$ **30.** $2x^3 + 2x^2 - 4x$

31. $x^2 + 13xy + 36y^2$ **32.** $y^2 - 4yz - 60z^2$

33. $12x^2 + 7xy + y^2$ **34.** $x^2 - 4xy + 6y^2$

35. $3y^3 + 3y^2 + 3y$ **36.** $x^2 + 3xy - 18y^2$

37. $x^2 - 14xy + 49y^2$

38. $r^2 - 14rs + 48s^2$

39. $x^2 - 21xy - 100y^2$

40. $2a^3b - 16a^2b^2 + 32ab^3$

41. $2x^3y^2 - 24x^2y^3 + 54xy^4$

42. $16a^2b^4 + 12ab^5 + 2b^6$

3   Solve the following equations.

43. $(x - 3)(x + 3) = 0$

44. $(x - 2)(x - 1) = 0$

45. $x^2 + 10x + 24 = 0$

46. $y^2 + 3y = 18$

47. $a^2 - 20 = 8a$

48. $z^2 = 5z + 6$

49. $6t^2 + 16t = t^3$

50. $y^2 = 16$

51. $y(y + 3) = 10$

52. $(x^2 - 1)(x - 3) = 0$

53. $k^2 - 49 = 0$

54. $(x - 1)^2 = 9$

55. $x^3 + 2x^2 - 4x - 8 = 0$

56. $2m^2 - 8 = 0$

57. $2n^3 = 18n$

58. $2x^3 + 64x = 24x^2$

B

59. $5x^3 - 10x^2 = -5x$ **60.** $x^4 = 72x^2 - x^3$

61. $x^4 - 9x = 9x^2 - x^3$ **62.** $12x^3 = 3x$

63. $x^4 - 5x^2 + 4 = 0$ **64.** $x^4 + 9 = 10x^2$

Factor the following.

65. $x^2 - (2y - 3)^2$

66. $x^2 + (m + n)^2$

67. $a(x - 4) + b(x - 4) - (x - 4)c$

68. $w(a - b) + x(a - b) - y(a - b) - 2z(a - b)$

Solve the following for x. (See Section 4.5.)

69. $\begin{vmatrix} x & 3 \\ 2 & x \end{vmatrix} = x$

70. $\begin{vmatrix} x & 2 \\ 5 & x + 3 \end{vmatrix} = 0$

C

Answer the following with complete sentences.

71. Describe the factoring process called "factoring by grouping."

72. How is the zero-factor property used to solve quadratic equations?

REVIEW EXERCISES

Find the following products. (See Section 5.3.)

73. $(3x + 5)(x + 2)$ **74.** $3ab(5a + 7)(a - 2b)$

75. $(2x + 3y)^2$ **76.** $3y(3y - 5)^2$

Evaluate the following functions for the given value of x. (See Section 3.2.)

77. $f(x) = x - 6; \quad x = 6$

78. $f(x) = x^2 + x - 12; \quad x = 3 \quad \text{and} \quad x = -4$

5.6 FACTORING $ax^2 + bx + c$ AND PERFECT SQUARES

1   Factoring $ax^2 + bx + c$ by Grouping

2   Factoring $ax^2 + bx + c$ by Trial and Error

3   Using a Shortcut (Optional)

4   Factoring Perfect Squares

5   Solving Equations; Roots of a Polynomial Function

1 Factoring $ax^2 + bx + c$ by Grouping

In the last section we learned how to factor $ax^2 + bx + c$, where $a = 1$. This section discusses the case when $a \neq 1$; we will see that the two procedures are very similar. Then perfect square trinomials are considered, which are a special case of $ax^2 + bx + c$.

We begin by seeing how $3x^2 + 11x + 10$ factors into $(3x + 5)(x + 2)$. First consider the product $(3x + 5)(x + 2)$:

$$(3x + 5)(x + 2) = 3x(x + 2) + 5(x + 2)$$
$$= 3x^2 + 6x + 5x + 10$$
$$= 3x^2 + 11x + 10$$

The key to factoring $3x^2 + 11x + 10$ is that $6 + 5 = 11$ and $6 \cdot 5 = 3 \cdot 10$; that is, if $m = 6$ and $n = 5$, then $m + n = 11$ and $mn = 3 \cdot 10$. Now we reverse the previous steps by expressing $11x$ as $6x + 5x$ and factor by grouping:

$$3x^2 + 11x + 10 = 3x^2 + 6x + 5x + 10$$
$$= 3x(x + 2) + 5(x + 2)$$
$$= (3x + 5)(x + 2)$$

In general, if $ax^2 + bx + c$ can be factored into the product of two binomials, then integers m and n exist such that

$$m + n = b \quad \text{and} \quad mn = ac$$

If $a = 1$, then $mn = c$, so $x^2 + bx + c$ is a special case of $ax^2 + bx + c$. To find m and n, first determine the prime factorization of ac. Then consider all possible products of the form $mn = ac$ and see whether any values of m and n have a sum of b. If not, then $ax^2 + bx + c$ is prime. If such values exist, then write bx as $mx + nx$ and factor by grouping.

EXAMPLE 1

Factor the following.

a. $10x^2 + 13x - 3$ **b.** $7x^2 + 8x + 2$
c. $2y^2 - 23y + 60$

SOLUTION   **a.** We have to find m and n such that $m + n = 13$ and $mn = 10(-3) = -30$. Set up a table of all possible products that are -30 and their corresponding sums, starting with $m = -1$. Because $-30 = -1 \cdot 2 \cdot 3 \cdot 5 < 0$ and $13 > 0$, we let $m < 0$ and $n > 0$.

$mn = -30$	$m + n$
$-1(30) = -30$	$-1 + 30 = 29$
$-2(15) = -30$	$-2 + 15 = 13$

We are done. Thus,
$m = -2$ and $n = 15$, so
$$10x^2 + 13x - 3 = 10x^2 - 2x + 15x - 3$$
$$= 2x(5x - 1) + 3(5x - 1)$$
$$= (2x + 3)(5x - 1)$$

(continued)

b. $m + n = 8$ and $mn = 7 \cdot 2$ $7 + 2 \neq 8$
$\qquad\qquad\qquad\qquad\quad\; = 1 \cdot 14$ $1 + 14 \neq 8$

Thus $7x^2 + 8x + 2$ is prime.

c. We need $m + n = -23$ and $mn = 2 \cdot 60 = 120$. Instead of writing down all possible combinations of mn, we can eliminate many of them mentally. For instance, we can quickly discard $-2(-60)$ and $-4(-30)$, because their sums are not close to -23. Because $120 = 1 \cdot 2 \cdot 2 \cdot 2 \cdot 3 \cdot 5 > 0$ and $-23 < 0$, we need $m < 0$ and $n < 0$.

$mn = 120$	$m + n$
$-6(-20) = 120$	$-6 + (-20) = -26$
$-10(-12) = 120$	$-10 + (-12) = -22$
$-8(-15) = 120$	$-8 + (-15) = -23$

$m = -8$ and $n = -15$, so
$$\begin{aligned} 2y^2 - 23y + 60 &= 2y^2 - 8y - 15y + 60 \\ &= 2y(y - 4) - 15(y - 4) \\ &= (2y - 15)(y - 4) \end{aligned}$$

The method of factoring $ax^2 + bxy + cy^2$ is very similar to the one for $ax^2 + bx + c$. We must find integers m and n such that $m + n = b$ and $mn = ac$. This search is illustrated in our next example; correct values of m and n are given, because the general approach has been illustrated.

EXAMPLE 2

Factor $16x^3 + 20x^2y + 6xy^2$.

SOLUTION

The GCF is $2x$, so
$$16x^3 + 20x^2y + 6xy^2 = 2x[8x^2 + 10xy + 3y^2]$$
$m + n = 10$ and $mn = 8 \cdot 3 = 24 = 4 \cdot 6$
$$\begin{aligned} 8x^2 + 10xy + 3y^2 &= 8x^2 + 4xy + 6xy + 3y^2 \\ &= 4x(2x + y) + 3y(2x + y) \\ &= (4x + 3y)(2x + y) \end{aligned}$$
Thus, $16x^3 + 20x^2y + 6xy^2 = 2x(4x + 3y)(2x + y)$

2   Factoring $ax^2 + bx + c$ by Trial and Error

We now consider the trial-and-error method of factoring trinomials. First let us multiply $(3x + 2)(x + 1)$ using the FOIL method; recall that FOIL stands for **First, Outer, Inner**, and **Last**; for example,

$$\overset{\text{F}\qquad\text{O}\qquad\text{I}\qquad\text{L}}{(3x + 2)(x + 1) = 3x \cdot x + 3x \cdot 1 + 2x + 2 \cdot 1 = 3x^2 + 5x + 2}$$

To factor $3x^2 + 5x + 2$, the product of the first terms must be $3x^2$, the product of the last terms must be 2, and the middle term, $5x$, must be the sum of the outer and inner terms. Because all the signs in $3x^2 + 5x + 2$ are

Math in Time

"ALL ABSTRACT SPECULATION . . . must be abandoned to the . . . solid mind of man. . . . For this reason women will never learn geometry." This statement by German philosopher Immanuel Kant (1724–1804) was typical of northern European attitudes toward women's ability in mathematics and the sciences in the eighteenth century. However, Italian men at this time were more enlightened, and many women in Italy made significant contributions to mathematics, the sciences, and the arts.

The most outstanding woman mathematician of Italy during this period was Maria Gaetana Agnesi (1718–1799). She was born into a wealthy and educated family, and her father was a professor of mathematics at the University of Bologna. She was recognized as a child prodigy, and by the age of 9 was fluent in Greek, Latin, Hebrew, and several modern languages. During her teenage years she studied the mathematics of Fermat, Descartes, Newton, Leibniz, and others.

At the age of 20 Maria began a textbook on calculus and analytic geometry. As a result of her linguistic ability, she was able to bring together the works of mathematicians throughout Europe. On several occasions she is reported to have worked unsuccessfully all day on a problem and then sleepwalked to her study and written out the solution to the problem. She spent 10 years on her textbook project; it was an instant success throughout Europe on its publication. She was honored by Empress Maria Theresa and Pope Benedict XIV and was appointed to a professorship at the University of Bologna.

One geometric topic discussed in her book is the graph of
$$y = \frac{a^3}{x^2 + a^2}.$$
This curve was called a *versiera*, meaning "to turn." However, versiera is also an abbreviation of *avversiera*, or "wife of the devil." The person who translated her work into English confused the two words and called the curve a "witch." Since then it has been known as the "Witch of Agnesi" (see illustration).

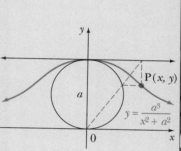

Maria Gaetana Agnesi
The Bettmann Archive

Witch of Agnesi

After her father's death in 1752, Maria withdrew from the academic world. A deeply religious person, she devoted the remainder of her life to the poor and sick of Milan by converting part of her house into a hospital and spending all her money on the needy.

Maria Agnesi has been remembered throughout Italy by the many streets and schools named for her. In addition, scholarships for underprivileged women have been donated in her honor.

---

positive, all the signs in the binomial factors must be positive. The product of the first terms is $3x^2 = 3x \cdot x$, so let

$$3x^2 + 5x + 2 = (3x + \quad)(x + \quad)$$

We then fill in the blanks with positive integers whose product is 2. We have two possibilities:

$$(3x + 1)(x + 2) \qquad \text{and} \qquad (3x + 2)(x + 1)$$

To determine which answer is correct, find the middle terms:

$$(3x + 1)(x + 2) = 3x^2 + 6x + x + 2$$
$$= 3x^2 + 7x + 2, \qquad \text{Wrong middle term}$$
$$(3x + 2)(x + 1) = 3x^2 + 3x + 2x + 2$$
$$= 3x^2 + 5x + 2 \qquad \text{Correct middle term}$$

Thus, the factors of $3x^2 + 5x + 2$ are $3x + 2$ and $x + 1$, so

$$3x^2 + 5x + 2 = (3x + 2)(x + 1)$$

Factoring $ax^2 + bx + c$ by Trial and Error

1. Write all pairs of factors of a.
2. Write all pairs of factors of c.
3. Try various combinations of these factors until the correct middle term is found. If all combinations fail, then the polynomial is prime.
4. If $a > 0$, then:
   a. If $c > 0$ and $b > 0$, then both factors of c will be positive.
   b. If $c > 0$ and $b < 0$, then both factors of c will be negative.
   c. If $c < 0$, then one factor of c will be positive and the other will be negative.

EXAMPLE 3

Factor $2x^2 - 11x + 15$.

SOLUTION

The only factors of 2 are 2 and 1. Thus,
$$2x^2 - 11x + 15 = (2x \quad)(x \quad)$$
The product of the last terms is positive, and the middle term is negative, so the factors of 15 must both be negative. Therefore, write

$$2x^2 - 11x + 15 = (2x - \quad)(x - \quad)$$

The possible factors and the corresponding middle terms are

Possible Factors	Middle Term = Outer + Inner Terms	
$(2x - 3)(x - 5)$	$-10x + (-3x) = -13x$	Wrong
$(2x - 5)(x - 3)$	$-6x + (-5x) = -11x$	Correct

Thus, $2x^2 - 11x + 15 = (2x - 5)(x - 3)$

EXAMPLE 4

Factor $10x^2 + 29xy - 21y^2$

SOLUTION

The pairs of factors of 10 are $2 \cdot 5$ and $1 \cdot 10$. We will try 2 and 5 (if these do not work, then we will try 1 and 10; if these do not work, then the polynomial is prime). Because $-21 < 0$, one of its factors will have to be positive and the other negative. Thus, the two possible factorizations are

$$(2x + \quad)(5x - \quad) \quad \text{and} \quad (2x - \quad)(5x + \quad)$$

The pairs of factors of -21 are $(3)(-7)$, $(7)(-3)$, $(1)(-21)$, and $(21)(-1)$. Because -21 has four factorizations and the polynomial has two, we can try eight separate combinations. The correct one is

$$10x^2 + 29xy - 21y^2 = (2x + 7)(5x - 3y)$$

3 Using a Shortcut (Optional)

By means of a little number theory we can eliminate some possibilities in certain factoring problems. For instance, consider $2x^2 + 9x + 8$. Using the grouping method, we need $m + n = 9$, which is an *odd* integer. When is the sum of two integers odd? When one is odd and the other is even, such as $7 + 4$. Now, $mn = 2 \cdot 2 \cdot 2 \cdot 2$, so we have no reason to consider products such as $2 \cdot 8$, because the sum of two even integers is even. Thus, the only possible values of m and n that can have an odd sum are 1 and 16. Because $1 + 16 \neq 9$, $2x^2 + 9x + 8$ is prime.

As another example, consider $10x^2 + 30x + 21$. We need $m + n = 30$, which is an *even* integer. The sum of two integers is even when they are both even (such as $2 + 8$) or both odd (such as $7 + 3$). So, $mn = 10 \cdot 21 = 2 \cdot 5 \cdot 3 \cdot 7$. Because only one factor of 2 is present m and n cannot both be even. They cannot both be odd because one has to contain the 2. Thus, $10x^2 + 30x + 21$ is prime. To summarize,

> $m + n$ is odd if one is odd and the other is even.
> $m + n$ is even if both are even or both are odd.

This shortcut is not only useful in determining when certain trinomials are prime, but also helpful if they can be factored. This is illustrated in the following example.

EXAMPLE 5

Factor the following.

a. $80x^2 + 43x - 3$ **b.** $4y^2 - 4yz - 15z^2$

SOLUTION

a. $m + n = 43$ and $mn = -2 \cdot 2 \cdot 2 \cdot 2 \cdot 3 \cdot 5 = -240$.

Because 43 is odd, we will only consider cases where one factor is odd and the other is even. Therefore, we express all the twos as one factor,

(continued)

16. Then

$$mn = -16 \cdot 3 \cdot 5$$
$$= -3(80) \qquad -3 \cdot 80 \neq 43$$
$$= -5(48) \qquad -5 + 48 = 43, \text{ so } m = -5 \text{ and } n = 48$$
$$80x^2 + 43x - 3 = 80x^2 - 5x + 48x - 3$$
$$= 5x(16x - 1) + 3(16x - 1)$$
$$= (5x + 3)(16x - 1)$$

b. $m + n = -4$ and $mn = 4(-15) = -2 \cdot 2 \cdot 3 \cdot 5 = -60$. Because both $m + n$ and mn are even, m and n must both be even. Thus, we will not consider cases such as $5(-12)$, whose sum is odd.

$$mn = -2 \cdot 2 \cdot 3 \cdot 5 = 6(-10), \quad \text{so}$$
$$4y^2 - 4yz - 15z^2 = 4y^2 + 6yz - 10yz - 15z^2$$
$$= 2y(2y + 3z) - 5(2y + 3z)$$
$$= (2y - 5z)(2y + 3z)$$

4   Factoring Perfect Squares

In Section 5.3 we discussed the perfect squares $(a + b)^2 = a^2 + 2ab + b^2$ and $(a - b)^2 = a^2 - 2ab + b^2$. This gives us the following factoring formulas.

Perfect Squares

$$a^2 + 2ab + b^2 = (a + b)^2$$
$$a^2 - 2ab + b^2 = (a - b)^2$$

    To use these formulas, first determine that two of the terms are in the form a^2 and b^2. If the third term is $2ab$ or $-2ab$, then the trinomial is a perfect square. If the trinomial is not a perfect square, do not assume that it is prime; it may factor with our $m + n$ method. And any trinomial that can be factored as a perfect square can also be factored with our $m + n$ procedure.

EXAMPLE 6

Factor the following.

a. $4x^2 - 12xy + 9y^2$ **b.** $16x^2 + 30x + 9$

SOLUTION   **a.** $4x^2 - 12xy + 9y^2 = (2x)^2 - 2(2x)(3y) + (3y)^2$
$$= (2x - 3y)^2$$

b. $16x^2 = (4x)^2$, $9 = 3^2$, but $30x \neq 2(4x)(3)$, so $16x^2 + 30x + 9$ is not a perfect square. Let $m + n = 30$ and $mn = 16 \cdot 9 = 2 \cdot 2 \cdot 2 \cdot 2 \cdot 3 \cdot 3 = 6 \cdot 24$

$$16x^2 + 30x + 9 = 16x^2 + 6x + 24x + 9$$
$$= 2x(8x + 3) + 3(8x + 3)$$
$$= (2x + 3)(8x + 3)$$

This text has presented many problems that required more than one method to factor the given polynomial. In the next example perfect squares and the difference of squares are used to factor the trinomials.

EXAMPLE 7

Factor the following.

a. $4y^2 - 25 + 4xy + x^2$ **b.** $z^2 - x^2 - y^2 + 2xy$

SOLUTION   **a.** The key to this problem is to group the **cross-product**, $4xy$, with the corresponding squares, $4y^2$ and x^2:

$$4y^2 - 25 + 4xy + x^2 = (4y^2 + 4xy + x^2) - 25$$
$$= (2y + x)^2 - 5^2$$
$$= (2y + x - 5)(2y + x + 5) \qquad \begin{array}{l} a^2 - b^2 = \\ (a - b)(a + b) \end{array}$$

b. After grouping $2xy$ with $-x^2$ and $-y^2$, we have to express the polynomial as the difference of two squares:

$$z^2 - x^2 - y^2 + 2xy = z^2 + (-x^2 + 2xy - y^2)$$
$$= z^2 - (x^2 - 2xy + y^2)$$
$$= z^2 - (x - y)^2$$
$$= [z - (x - y)][z + (x - y)]$$
$$= (z - x + y)(z + x - y)$$

---

5   Solving Equations; Roots of a Polynomial Function

We conclude this section by solving equations with the zero-factor property. Remember, the equation must be in the form $ab = 0$, then $a = 0$ or $b = 0$.

EXAMPLE 8

Solve the following equations.

a. $2x^2 + 7x = 4$ **b.** $27y^3 - 90y^2 + 75y = 0$

SOLUTION   **a.**
$$2x^2 + 7x = 4$$
$$2x^2 + 7x - 4 = 0 \qquad m + n = 7, mn = -1 \cdot 8$$
$$2x^2 - x + 8x - 4 = 0$$
$$x(2x - 1) + 4(2x - 1) = 0$$
$$(x + 4)(2x - 1) = 0$$
$$x + 4 = 0 \qquad \text{or} \qquad 2x - 1 = 0$$
$$x = -4 \qquad \text{or} \qquad x = 1/2$$

b.
$$27y^3 - 90y^2 + 75y = 0 \qquad \text{GCF} = 3y$$
$$3y[9y^2 - 30y + 25] = 0$$
$$3y[(3y)^2 - 2 \cdot 3y \cdot 5 + 5^2] = 0$$
$$3y(3y - 5)^2 = 0$$
$$3y = 0 \qquad \text{or} \qquad 3y - 5 = 0 \qquad 0^2 = 0$$
$$y = 0 \qquad \text{or} \qquad y = 5/3$$

Given a function f, a number a, for which $f(a) = 0$, is called a **root** or **zero** of f. For example, if $f(x) = x - 5$, then $f(5) = 0$, so 5 is the root of f.

EXAMPLE 9   Find the roots of $f(x) = x^2 + x - 12$.

SOLUTION $f(x) = 0$ if

$$x^2 + x - 12 = 0 \quad m + n = 1, mn = 4(-3)$$
$$(x + 4)(x - 3) = 0$$
$$x + 4 = 0 \quad \text{or} \quad x - 3 = 0, \text{ so}$$

-4 and 3 are the roots of f.

EXERCISE SET 5.6

A

1   Factor the following.

1. $x^2 + 8x + 12$

2. $y^2 - 12y + 35$

3. $3x^2 + 17x + 10$

4. $2a^2 + 11a - 6$

5. $6x^2 - 11x - 10$

6. $4x^2 + 2x + 1$

7. $12x^2 + 8xy + y^2$

8. $a^2 + 2ab - 15b^2$

2

9. $2x^2 + 5x + 3$

10. $x^2 + 6x + 10$

11. $x^2 - 2x - 15$

12. $3y^2 - 13y + 10$

13. $18x^2 - 19xy - 12y^2$

14. $6a^2 + 7ab - 2ab^2$

15. $9x^2 - 3xy + y^2$

16. $10x^2 - 37xy + 7y^2$

3

17. $2x^2 + 13x + 8$

18. $8x^2 - 21xy + 10y^2$

19. $4x^2 - 20xy + 21y^2$

20. $6x^2 - 36x + 55$

21. $32x^2 + 29x - 3$

22. $x^2 - 65x + 64$

23. $16x^2 + 97x + 64$

24. $a^2 - 13ab - 48b^2$

4

25. $x^2 + 8x + 16$

26. $y^2 - 14y + 49$

27. $9x^2 - 30xy + 25y^2$

28. $9x^2 - 60xy + 100y^2$

29. $25a^2 - 28ab + 8b^2$

30. $x^2 + 19x + 81$

31. $(x + 1)^2 - y^2$

32. $x^2 - t^2 + 6x + 9$

33. $36 - (x + y)^2$

34. $k^2 - s^2 - r^2 + 2rs$

Factor the following by using the most convenient method.

35. $3x^3 - 27x$

36. $m^4 - n^4$

37. $12n^2 - 17n - 40$

38. $15x^2 + 19x - 56$

39. $bx - 3x + 2by - 6y$

40. $xy + ac + cx + ay$

41. $x^3 + 3x^2 - 4x - 12$

42. $xy + 3y + xz + 6z$

43. $12a^2 - 8ab - 15b^2$

44. $16x^3y^2 - 12x^2y^3 - 2xy^4$

45. $3x^2 + 27x + 35$

46. $12k^3 - 12k^2 + 3k$

47. $a^2b - 2a^2b^2 + ab^3$

48. $a^2c - b^2c + a^2d - b^2d$

49. $4x^2 - 12xy - 9z^2 + 9y^2$

50. $a^2 - 4cd - c^2 - 4d^2$

51. $25 + 6xy - 9x^2 - y^2$
52. $x^4 - 10x^3 + 9x^2$
53. $x^4 - 2x^2y^2 + y^4$
54. $x^4 - 2x^2y^2 + y^4$

5 Find all rational solutions of the following equations.

55. $x^2 + 3x - 10 = 0$
56. $2x^2 - 9x + 4 = 0$
57. $3x^2 - 11x = 20$
58. $4y^2 = 15y - 14$
59. $5k = 4 - 6k^2$
60. $2(4z^2 + 5) = 19z$
61. $a(a - 5) = 14$
62. $x(x - 1)(x + 2) = 0$
63. $x^2 = 25$
64. $2x^2 = 18$
65. $3x^2 + 21x = 0$
66. $6y^2 = 8y$
67. $4x^2 - 20x = 0$
68. $6t = -4t^2$
69. $x^3 = x^2 - 6x$
70. $2y(10y^2 + 13y) = 6y$
71. $(x + 3)(x - 3) = x^2 - 9$
72. $x^2 + 4 = 0$
73. $x^2 + 5x = x^4 + 5x^3$
74. $x^4 - 5x^2 + 4 = 0$
75. $4x^4 + 9 = 37x^2$
76. $9x^4 - 13x^2 + 4 = 0$

Find the roots of the following functions.

77. $f(x) = x - 9$

78. $f(x) = x + 4$
79. $g(x) = 3x + 2$
80. $h(x) = 6 - 7x$
81. $f(x) = x^2 - 36$
82. $g(y) = 4y^2 - 9y$
83. $F(x) = x^2 + 6x - 7$
84. $G(x) = 2x^2 - 7x - 4$
85. $f(a) = a^3 - 25a$
86. $f(x) = x^3 + 9x^2 - x - 9$

B Factor the following.

87. $(a + b)^2 - (c - d)^2$
88. $x(w - 2)^2 - x(y + z)^2$
89. $(x - 3)^2 - a^2 + 2ab - b^2$
90. $a^2 - 2ab + b^2 - (m - 4)^2$
91. $(5x^2 - 9)^2 - (x^2 - 1)^2$
92. $(2x^2 + 1)^2 - (x^2 + 2)^2$

Solve the following for x. (See Section 4.5.)

93. $\begin{vmatrix} 2x & x + 1 \\ 3 & x - 2 \end{vmatrix} = 1$ **94.** $\begin{vmatrix} x & x - 1 \\ 3 & x^2 - 6 \end{vmatrix} = 3$

C

Answer the following questions with complete sentences.

95. How was Maria Agnesi's knowledge of languages useful in writing her calculus book?
96. What is meant by the "root" or "zero" of a function f?

REVIEW EXERCISES

Solve the following equations. (See Section 5.6.)

97. $x(2 - x) = -24$
98. $(3x - 4)^2 = x^2 + (2x + 4)^2$

99. $(2r)^2 + (2r + 2)^2 = 10^2$
100. $(s - 4)(s - 4)2 = 128$

5.7 SOLVING WORD PROBLEMS

1	Number Problems
2	Pythagorean Theorem
3	Geometry Problems

1   Number Problems

Many applications of algebra involve quadratic equations that can be solved by factoring. Several of the problems covered in this section involve familiar concepts, such as consecutive integers and the Pythagorean theorem. The methods developed in Chapter 2 for word problems, which led to linear equations, are just as appropriate for applications requiring quadratic equations. However, checking the solutions of the quadratic equation in the original problem is an important step because a solution may have no meaning in the context of the problem. For example, a negative number cannot represent the length of the side of a square. In this situation we simply discard meaningless solutions.

Many number problems have two solution sets, as illustrated in our first example.

EXAMPLE 1

The square of the sum of two consecutive odd integers is 30 more than the sum of their squares. Find the integers.

SOLUTION

Let x = the first consecutive odd integer and
$x + 2$ = the second consecutive odd integer. Then $x + (x + 2) = 2x + 2$ = their sum, and $(2x + 2)^2$ = the square of the sum of the two integers.
x^2 = the square of the first integer,
$(x + 2)^2$ = the square of the second integer, and
$x^2 + (x + 2)^2$ = the sum of their squares.
$(2x + 2)^2$ is 30 more than $x^2 + (x + 2)^2$, so

$$(2x + 2)^2 = x^2 + (x + 2)^2 + 30$$
$$4x^2 + 8x + 4 = x^2 + x^2 + 4x + 4 + 30$$
$$4x^2 + 8x + 4 = 2x^2 + 4x + 34$$
$$2x^2 + 4x - 30 = 0$$
$$2(x^2 + 2x - 15) = 0$$
$$2(x + 5)(x - 3) = 0$$
$$x + 5 = 0 \qquad \text{or} \qquad x - 3 = 0$$
$$x = -5 \qquad \text{or} \qquad x = 3$$

If $x = -5$, then $x + 2 = -3$. If $x = 3$, then $x + 2 = 5$. Thus, $\{-5, -3\}$ and $\{3, 5\}$ are the solutions.

 CHECK

$[-5 + (-3)]^2 = 64$, $(-5)^2 + (-3)^2 = 34$, and
$64 = 34 + 30$. $[5 + 3]^2 = 64$, $5^2 + 3^2 = 34$, and
$64 = 34 + 30$.

The checks for the rest of the examples in this section are left as exercises.

Recall that many number problems involve the sum or difference of two numbers (see Section 2.2 [4]). For example, if the sum of two numbers is 10 and one of them is x, then the other is $10 - x$, because $(10 - x) + x = 10$. On the other hand, if the difference of two numbers is 10 and the smaller is s, then the larger number is $10 + s$, because $(10 + s) - s = 10$. Our next example deals with the sum of two numbers; the difference of two numbers is covered in the exercises.

EXAMPLE 2

The sum of the two numbers is 2, and their product is -24. Find the numbers.

SOLUTION

Let $x =$ one of the numbers and
$2 - x =$ the other number. Then
$$x(2 - x) = -24$$
$$-x^2 + 2x + 24 = 0 \qquad \text{Multiply both sides by } -1.$$
$$x^2 - 2x - 24 = 0$$
$$(x - 6)(x + 4) = 0$$
$$x = 6 \quad \text{or} \quad x = -4$$
If $x = 6$, then $2 - x = -4$. If $x = -4$, then $2 - x = 6$. In either case, the two numbers are 6 and -4.

2 Pythagorean Theorem

Section 2.3 discussed the Pythagorean theorem, which states that

> In any right triangle, the square of the hypotenuse, c, is equal to the sum of the squares of the two legs, a and b: $c^2 = a^2 + b^2$.

Many problems requiring this theorem result in quadratic equations, as illustrated in the following examples.

EXAMPLE 3

The longer leg of a right triangle is 4 more than twice the shorter leg, and the hypotenuse is 4 less than 3 times the shorter leg. Find the three sides.

SOLUTION

Let $x =$ the length of the shorter leg. Then
$$2x + 4 = \text{the length of the longer leg,}$$
$$3x - 4 = \text{the length of the hypotenuse (see Figure 5.2), and}$$
$$(3x - 4)^2 = x^2 + (2x + 4)^2$$
$$9x^2 - 24x + 16 = x^2 + 4x^2 + 16x + 16$$
$$4x^2 - 40x = 0$$
$$4x(x - 10) = 0$$
$$x = 10 \quad (x = 0 \text{ is meaningless})$$
$$2x + 4 = 24 \quad \text{and} \quad 3x - 4 = 26$$
Thus, the lengths of the sides are 10, 24, and 26.

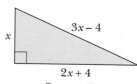

FIGURE 5.2

EXAMPLE 4

Robyn and Sheri leave the same point at the same time, Robyn walking due east and Sheri due north. After 2 hours they are 10 miles apart. Robyn's rate is 1 mph faster than Sheri's. Find their respective rates.

SOLUTION

Recall that distance = (rate)(time), $d = rt$. Let r = Sheri's rate   and $2r$ = her distance after 2 hours. Then, $r + 1$ = Robyn's rate   and $2(r + 1) = 2r + 2$ = her distance after 2 hours. The triangle in Figure 5.3 illustrates the problem after 2 hours. From the Pythagorean theorem,

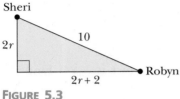

FIGURE 5.3

$$(2r)^2 + (2r + 2)^2 = 10^2$$
$$4r^2 + 4r^2 + 8r + 4 = 100$$
$$8r^2 + 8r - 96 = 0$$
$$8(r^2 + r - 12) = 0$$
$$8(r - 3)(r + 4) = 0$$
$$r = 3, \quad \text{so } r + 1 = 4 \quad (r = -4 \text{ is meaningless})$$

Thus, Sheri walks at 3 mph and Robyn at 4 mph.

3   Geometry Problems

We now turn to geometry problems; some have been covered in elementary algebra, but others are new.

EXAMPLE 5

A rectangular pool has a surface area of 240 square feet and is surrounded by a tiled walk with a uniform width. The walk's outside dimensions are 26 feet by 18 feet. Find the width of the walk and the length and width of the pool.

FIGURE 5.4

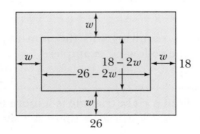

SOLUTION

Let w = the width of the walk,
$18 - 2w$ = the width of the pool, and
$26 - 2w$ = the length of the pool (see Figure 5.4). Then, because $LW = A$ is the area of a rectangle,

$$(26 - 2w)(18 - 2w) = 240$$
$$4w^2 - 88w + 468 = 240$$
$$4w^2 - 88w + 228 = 0 \qquad \text{GCF} = 4$$
$$4(w^2 - 22w + 57) = 0 \qquad \text{Divide by 4.}$$
$$(w - 19)(w - 3) = 0$$

Math in Time

WORD PROBLEMS HAVE been an integral part of algebra for at least 4000 years. An Egyptian papyrus from 1850 B.C. contains problems from earlier times, and a Babylonian tablet of 1700 B.C. asks, "How long will it take a certain sum of money to double itself at compound annual interest of 20%?" In Section 2.5 we saw Hindu word problems from A.D. 630 to A.D. 1150. The following are historical word problems from other countries.

1. A number and its 1/5 added together makes 21. Find the number. (Egypt, 1650 B.C.)

2. A mule and an ass went on their way with burdens of wineskins. Weighed down by its load, the ass was bitterly groaning. The mule, hearing its complaints, addressed it: "Friend, why do you complain? If you give me one measure of wine, then I will carry twice your burden; but if you take one measure from me, then our loads will be equal." Tell me the measure they bore, good sir, geometry's master. (Greece, 300 B.C. — Euclid)

3. There grows in the middle of a circular pond, 10 units in diameter, a reed which projects one unit out of the water. When it is drawn down, it just reaches the edge of the pond. How deep is the water? (China, 200 B.C.)

4. A dog is chasing a rabbit, which has a head start of 150 feet. The dog jumps 9 feet every time the rabbit jumps 7 feet. How many leaps does it take the dog to catch the rabbit? (England, A.D. 775)

5. A man hires a ship and asks the captain what the fare is. He replies, "The fare is the number of pesos which, when squared and added to this number, gives 1260." Find the fare. (Mexico, 1556)

$w = 19$ or $w = 3$
If $w = 19$, then $26 - 2w = -12$, which is impossible.
If $w = 3$, then $26 - 2w = 20$ and $18 - 2w = 12$.
Thus the tiled walk is 3 feet wide, and the pool is 20 feet by 12 feet.

EXAMPLE 6

An open box is to be constructed from a square piece of cardboard by cutting 2-inch squares from each corner and then turning up the resulting flaps. Find the side of the cardboard if the volume of the box is to be 128 cubic inches.

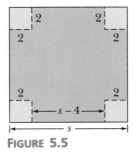

FIGURE 5.5   **FIGURE 5.6**

(continued)   **241**

SOLUTION   Let s = the length of each side of the cardboard, and $s - 4$ = the length of each flap (see Figures 5.5 and 5.6). Because $LWH = V$ is the volume of the box,

$$(s - 4)(s - 4)2 = 128 \quad \text{Divide by 2.}$$
$$s^2 - 8s + 16 = 64$$
$$s^2 - 8s - 48 = 0$$
$$(s - 12)(s + 4) = 0$$

$s = 12$ inches is the length of each side of the cardboard.

EXAMPLE 7   Find the radius of the sphere whose surface area is numerically equal to its volume.

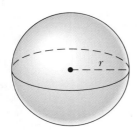

FIGURE 5.7

SOLUTION   Let r = the radius of the sphere in Figure 5.7. Then $V = \frac{4}{3}\pi r^3$ and $S = 4\pi r^2$ are its volume and surface area. If $V = S$, then

$$\frac{4}{3}\pi r^3 = 4\pi r^2$$

$$\frac{4}{3}\pi r^3 - 4\pi r^2 = 0$$

$$\frac{4}{3}\pi r^2(r) - \frac{4}{3}\pi r^2(3) = 0$$

$$\frac{4}{3}\pi r^2(r - 3) = 0$$

$r - 3 = 0 \quad (r = 0$ is meaningless), so

$r = 3$ is the radius of the sphere.

Calvin and Hobbes   by Bill Watterson

EXERCISE SET 5.7

A

1 Solve the following problems.

1. Find two consecutive integers such that the sum of their squares is 61.

2. Find two positive consecutive even integers such that the difference of their squares is 36.

3. Find three consecutive even integers such that the square of the smallest one is equal to the sum of the squares of the larger ones.

4. Find three consecutive odd integers such that the product of the largest two is 8 more than 3 times the square of the smallest one.

5. Check the solution to Example 2 (p. 239)

6. Find two numbers that have a sum of 20 and a product of 64.

7. The sum of two numbers is -5, and the sum of their squares is 73. Find the numbers.

8. The difference of two numbers is 10. When the square of the smaller one is added to twice the larger one, the result is 28. Find the two numbers.

9. The difference between two positive numbers is 7, and the difference between their squares is 91. Find the numbers.

10. Solve Problem 1 in the Math in Time section (p. 241).

11. The square of a number is equal to the number. Find all such numbers.

12. Two numbers have a product of 78, and one number is one more than twice the other. What are the numbers?

13. Two numbers have a product of 40, and one number is 2 less than 3 times the other. What are the numbers?

2

14. Check the solution to Example 3 (p. 239).

15. Solve the word problem in Example 4 (p. 240)

by letting R = Robyn's rate. Check your answer.

16. The lengths of the sides of a right triangle are consecutive integers. Find the three sides.

17. The longer leg and the hypotenuse of a right triangle are consecutive integers. The shorter leg is 7 less than the longer leg. Find the three sides.

18. Find the width of a rectangle that has a diagonal of 15 and a length of 12.

19. A ladder is leaning against a building, and the base of the ladder is 7 feet from the base of the building. The height of the top of the ladder is 1 foot less than the length of the ladder. Find the length of the ladder.

20. Solve Problem 3 in the Math in Time section (p. 241).

21. When a bamboo 18 cubits high was broken by the wind, its top touched the ground 6 cubits from the root. Tell the lengths of the segments of the bamboo. (India, A.D. 630)

22. Two hikers leave the same point at the same time, one walking due west at 3 mph and the other due south at 4 mph. How long will it take them to be 15 miles apart?

23. Two ships leave the same port at the same time, one heading due north and the other due east. After 2 hours they are 26 miles apart. The ship heading east travels 7 mph faster than the ship heading north. Find the speed of each ship.

3

24. Check the solution to Example 5 (p. 240).

25. Check the solution to Example 6 (p. 242).

26. Check the solution to Example 7 (p. 242).

27. A rectangle's width and length are consecutive even integers, and its area is 80 square feet. Find the rectangle's length, width, and perimeter.

28. The length of a rectangle is 1 centimeter less than 3 times its width. If the area is 70 square centimeters, what is its length, width, and perimeter?

29. The perimeter of a rectangle is 24 meters, and its area is 20 square meters. Find the rectangle's length and width.

30. The perimeter and area of a square are numerically equal. Find the side of the square.

31. The width of a rectangle is the same as the side of a square, and the length of the rectangle is 4 more than the side of the square. The area of the rectangle is 24 more than the area of the square. Find the side of the square and the width and length of the rectangle.

32. The area of a square is 3 less than the area of a rectangle. The width of the rectangle is 1 less than the side of the square, and the length is twice the side of the square. Find the dimensions of the square and the rectangle.

33. The base of a triangle is 4 times its height. The area is 32 square inches. Find the height and base of the triangle.

34. The base of a triangle is 1 centimeter more than its height. The area is numerically 4 times the base. Find the triangle's base, height, and area.

35. Find the radius of the circle whose area is numerically equal to its circumference.

36. A circular lawn is surrounded by a 4-meter wide dirt walk. If the walk were converted to lawn, the combined area of the two lawns would be 6π more than 3 times the area of the original lawn. Find the radius of the original lawn.

37. A rectangular pool is twice as long as it is wide and is surrounded by a walk 2 feet wide. The area of the walk is 112 square feet. Find the pool's width and length.

38. A picture has an area of 288 square inches and is surrounded by a border of uniform width. The outside dimensions of the border are 24 inches by 22 inches. Find the border's width and the picture's length and width.

39. An open box is to be constructed from a rectangular piece of tin by cutting 3-inch squares from each corner and then turning up the resulting flaps. Find the length and width of the original piece of tin if the box's volume is to be 360 cubic inches and its length to be 2 inches longer than its width.

40. Repeat Exercise 39 for 4-inch squares cut from each corner, a volume of 96 cubic inches, and a length twice the width.

41. A piece of cardboard is 11 inches by 20 inches. Squares are to be cut from each corner and the resulting edges folded up to make a box. How large a square should be cut so that the box will have a length that is twice its width?

42. Repeat Exercise 41 for a piece of cardboard 12 inches by 16 inches and a box length 3 times its width.

43. A **cube** is a rectangular solid for which $L = W = H$. Find:
   a. the formulas for the volume and surface area of a cube if the length of an edge is a.
   b. the volume and surface area of a cube with an edge of 4 inches.
   c. the edge of a cube whose volume is numerically equal to its surface area.

44. The height, h, of a right circular cylinder is 1 foot, and its surface area is 24π square feet. Find its radius.

45. The slant height, s, of a right circular cone is 3 centimeters, and its surface area is 10π square centimeters. Find its radius.

B Solve the following miscellaneous problems. Solve the following from the Math in Time section (p. 241).

46. Problem 2

47. Problem 4

48. Problem 5

49. Peter took a 28-mile bicycle ride. Numerically his time was 3 less than his average rate of travel. Find his average rate.

50. Jan went on a 24-mile hike. Numerically her rate was 2 more than her time. Find her time.

51. Chris is 2 years older than Andrew. In 3 years the product of their ages will be 80. Find their current ages.

52. Susan's age is twice Pat's age. The product of Susan's age in 1 year and Pat's age 2 years ago is 18. Find their current ages.

53. For the Calvin cartoon on page 242, assume that triangle ABC is a right triangle with angle A the right angle. Find the distance from B to A and from C to A.

54. The sum S, of the first n natural numbers is given by $S = 1 + 2 + 3 + \ldots + n = \dfrac{n(n + 1)}{2}$.

For example, $1 + 2 + 3 + 4 + 5 = \dfrac{5(6)}{2} = 15$

a. Find S if $n = 100$.
b. Find n so that $S = 55$.
c. Find n so that $S = 105$.

55. The number of diagonals, D, in a polygon of n sides (Figure 5.8) is given by: $D = \dfrac{n(n - 3)}{2}$

For example, a hexagon (6 sides) has $D = \dfrac{6(6 - 3)}{2} = \dfrac{18}{2} = 9$ diagonals.

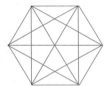

FIGURE 5.8

a. Find D if $n = 100$.
b. Find n if $D = 5$.
c. Find n if $D = 35$.

C

56. Show that for any four consecutive integers the product of the second and the third integers is 2 more than the product of the first and fourth integers. (*Hint:* Assume that the integers exist and arrive at a true equation.)

57. Show that no four consecutive integers exist such that the product of the smallest and the largest is equal to the product of the other two. (*Hint:* Assume that the integers exist and arrive at a false equation.)

58. Show that it is impossible for the sides of a right triangle to be consecutive odd integers.

Answer the following questions with complete sentences.

59. In solving a geometric problem, why is checking the solutions to the quadratic equation that represents the problem important?

60. Let x be the length of the longest side of a right triangle, and let w and t be the lengths of the other sides. What is the relationship between x, w, and t?

Chapter Summary

KEY WORDS, DEFINITIONS, AND PROPERTIES

Key Words

Monomial: a real number or the product of a real number and one or more variables raised to natural number exponents.

Polynomial: a finite sum of monomials.

Degree of a polynomial in one variable: its largest exponent.

Binomial: a polynomial with two unlike terms.

Trinomial: a polynomial with three unlike terms.

Linear: a first-degree polynomial in one variable.

Quadratic: a second-degree polynomial in one variable.

Quadratic function: $f(x) = ax^2 + bx + c$.

Cubic: a third-degree polynomial in one variable. (See Section 5.2.)

Zero-Factor Property (See Section 5.5.)

Let a and b represent real numbers. If $ab = 0$, then $a = 0$ or $b = 0$.

Definitions and Properties of Exponents
(See Section 5.1.)

Let a and b be real numbers and m and n be integers. Then, assuming nonzero denominators:

If $a \neq 0$, then $a^0 = 1$; 0^0 is undefined.

$$a^{-n} = \frac{1}{a^n} \qquad \frac{1}{a^{-n}} = a^n \qquad \left(\frac{a}{b}\right)^{-1} = \frac{b}{a}$$

$$\left(\frac{a}{b}\right)^{-n} = \left(\frac{b}{a}\right)^n \qquad a^m a^n = a^{m+n} \qquad (a^m)^n = a^{mn}$$

$$(ab)^n = a^n b^n \qquad \left(\frac{a}{b}\right)^n = \frac{a^n}{b^n} \qquad \frac{a^m}{a^n} = a^{m-n}$$

Algebra of Functions
(See Section 5.4.)

If f and g are polynomial functions, then

$(f + g)(x) = f(x) + g(x)$	Sum
$(f - g)(x) = f(x) - g(x)$	Difference
$(fg)(x) = f(x)g(x)$	Product
$\left(\dfrac{f}{g}\right)(x) = \dfrac{f(x)}{g(x)}, \quad g(x) \neq 0$	Quotient

Pythagorean Theorem
(See Section 5.7.)

In any right triangle, the square of the hypotenuse is equal to the sum of the squares of the two legs:
$c^2 = a^2 + b^2$.

Completely Factoring a Polynomial
(See Sections 5.4, 5.5, and 5.6.)

1. First factor out the greatest common factor (GCF):
$ab + ac = a(b + c)$

2. Check for the difference of two squares:
$a^2 - b^2 = (a - b)(a + b)$; $a^2 + b^2$ is prime.

3. Check for the sum or difference of two cubes:
$a^3 + b^3 = (a + b)(a^2 - ab + b^2)$
$a^3 - b^3 = (a - b)(a^2 + ab + b^2)$

4. Check for a perfect square:
$a^2 + 2ab + b^2 = (a + b)^2$
$a^2 - 2ab + b^2 = (a - b)^2$

5. To factor $ax^2 + bx + c$ or $ax^2 + bxy + cy^2$ by grouping, determine whether integers m and n exist such that $m + n = b$ and $mn = ac$. To factor by trial and error:
   a. Write all pairs of factors of a and of c.
   b. Try various combinations of these factors until the correct middle term is found.

6. If four or more terms exist, then try factoring by grouping.

CHAPTER REVIEW EXERCISES

The answers to the following problems are given in the answer section. If you have trouble, then review the material and homework problems in the indicated sections.

Simplify the following and write your answers with positive exponents. (See Sections 5.1 and 5.2.)

1. $x^6 x^{-8}$

2. $(3x^4)^2$

3. $(4x^8)(2x^4)^2$

4. $\left(\dfrac{x^{16}}{x^{-4}}\right)^{-1}$

5. $\dfrac{y^{-10}}{x^{-6}}$

6. $4^{-1} + 4^0 + 4^2$

7. $\dfrac{12x^6 y^3}{8x^2 y^{10}}$

8. $\left(\dfrac{2x^6}{y^4}\right)^3$

Let $f(x) = 3x^2 - 4x + 2$. Find the following. (See Section 5.2.)

9. $f(-2)$

Perform the indicated operations. (See Sections 5.2 and 5.3.)

10. $(a^3 + 2a - 6) + (5a^3 - 4a^2 - 10)$

11. $(6y^2 - 4y - 1) - (2y^4 - y + 7)$

12. $(x - 6)(x - 2)$

13. $(3x - 2y)(4x + 5y)$

14. $(x + 5)^3$

15. $\dfrac{15a^4b - 27ab^8 + 2b^8}{3a^2b}$

16. $(3x^2 + 4x - 1) \div (x + 2)$

Let $f(x) = 2x^2 - x + 4$ and $g(x) = x - 1$. Find the following. (See Section 5.4.)

17. $(f + g)(x)$ **18.** $(fg)(x)$

19. $\left(\dfrac{f}{g}\right)(x)$ **20.** $\dfrac{f(x + h) - f(x)}{h}$

Solve the following equations. (See Sections 5.5 and 5.6.)

21. $y^3 - 25y = 0$ **22.** $x^2 = 6x + 16$

Find the roots of the following functions. (See Section 5.6.)

23. $g(x) = 6x - 4$ **24.** $f(x) = x^2 - 1$

25. $h(x) = 6x^2 + 9x$

Factor the following if possible. If a polynomial cannot be factored, write "prime." (See Sections 5.4, 5.5, and 5.6.)

26. $6a^2b - 3ab$ **27.** $3x^3 - 6x^2 - 24x$

28. $ab - 2b + ac + 2c$ **29.** $x^3 - 27$

30. $4x^2 - 49$ **31.** $x^2 + 6xy + 9y^2$

32. $4a^2 + 13ab - 12b^2$ **33.** $a^4 - 81$

34. $y^2 + 4y - 32$ **35.** $x^3 + 3x^2 - 4x - 12$

36. $49a^2 - 14a + 1$ **37.** $3x^2 - 2xy - 5y^2$

Solve the following word problems. (See Section 5.7.)

38. Find two consecutive odd integers such that the square of their sum is 64.

39. Find the hypotenuse of the right triangle whose legs are 3 centimeters and 7 centimeters.

40. The perimeter of a rectangle is 28 centimeters, and its area is 48 square centimeters. Find the rectangle's length and width.

CHAPTER TEST

Treat this as a class test and allow 50 minutes for completion. When you have finished, use the answer section for grading. If you have any wrong answers, refer to the corresponding problems in the review section.

Perform the indicated operations and simplify your answers. For problems involving exponents, write the answers with positive exponents.

1. $x^2(x^3)^4$ **2.** $(2x^{-5})^6$

3. $(x^0y^{-4})^{-1}$ **4.** $\dfrac{21x^8y^4}{7x^4y^9}$

5. $\left(\dfrac{2x^4}{3y^{-5}}\right)^{-2}$ **6.** $(3x - y)^2$

7. $(3x^2 - 9x + 4) - (6x^2 + 5x - 3)$

8. $(3x - 2y)(4x + 6y)$

9. $\dfrac{16xy - 12x^3y^3 - 6x^9y^{12}}{8xy^3}$

10. $(2x^3 - 3x^2 + 4) \div (x - 3)$

Let $f(x) = x^2 - 3x + 2$ and $g(x) = 2x - 4$. Find:

11. $f(-3)$

12. $(fg)(x)$

13. $\dfrac{f(x + h) - f(x)}{h}$

Solve the following equations.

14. $2x^3 - 8x = 0$ **15.** $x^2 + 2x = 15$

Find the roots of the following function.

16. $f(x) = 2x^2 - 3x$.

Factor the following if possible. If a polynomial cannot be factored, write "prime."

17. $x^2 + 5x - 24$ **18.** $xy - 3y + xz - 3z$

19. $3x^4 + 24x$ **20.** $8x^2 - 10xy - 3y^2$

21. $2x^3y - 2xy^3$ **22.** $x^2 + 13x + 16$

Solve the following word problems.

23. Find two consecutive integers such that the sum of their squares is 41.

24. The lengths of the sides of a right triangle are consecutive even integers. Find the three sides.

25. The base of a triangle is twice its height. The area is 25 square feet. Find the triangle's height and base.

Rational Expressions

The effect of a weight in tilting a lever is proportional to its distance from the fulcrum, so objects with different weights may be arranged to balance a beam.

In Chapter 1 we studied the integers and their ratios, the rational numbers. The last chapter discussed polynomials and their properties. We are now ready to consider the ratios of polynomials, which are called *rational expressions* or algebraic fractions.

Rational expressions are as important in algebra as rational numbers are in arithmetic, and the methods for working with both types of fractions are very similar. For example, to reduce a rational number or a rational expression, we factor the numerator and denominator and divide out the common factors. After covering the basic operations with rational expressions, we will consider applications of this material in fields such as business and electronics.

6.1   SIMPLIFYING RATIONAL EXPRESSIONS

1	**Exploring Definitions and Vocabulary**
2	**Using the Domain of a Rational Function and Expression**
3	**Reducing Fractions to Lowest Terms**

1   Exploring Definitions and Vocabulary

Recall that any real number that can be expressed in the form a/b, $b \neq 0$, where a and b are integers, is called a *rational number*. If A and B are polynomials, $B \neq 0$,   then A/B is called a **rational expression** or an **algebraic fraction**. Examples of rational expressions are

$$\frac{2a^2b}{4ab^3}, \quad \frac{x - 6}{x^2 - 4}, \quad \text{and} \quad 3x + 8$$

because $3x + 8$ can be written as $\dfrac{3x + 8}{1}$. Just as integers are rational numbers, polynomials are rational expressions. For the sake of simplicity, we will use the word *fraction* to mean either a rational number or a rational expression.

In Section 5.2 we discussed polynomial functions. Two examples are $g(x) = x - 4$ and $h(x) = x^2 - 1$. A **rational function** is the ratio of two polynomial functions. Thus f is rational if

$$f(x) = \frac{g(x)}{h(x)}, \quad h(x) \neq 0$$

where $g(x)$ and $h(x)$ are polynomial functions. Two examples are

$$f(x) = \frac{x - 4}{x^2 - 1} \quad \text{and} \quad f(x) = \frac{1}{x - 2}$$

A rational function *can* represent a rational number when x is replaced by a real number, as illustrated in Example 1.

EXAMPLE 1

Evaluate $f(x) = \dfrac{x - 4}{x^2 - 1}$ for

a. $x = 4$ **b.** $x = 6$

SOLUTION   **a.** If $x = 4$, then $f(4) = \dfrac{4 - 4}{4^2 - 1} = \dfrac{0}{15} = 0$.

b. If $x = 6$, then $f(6) = \dfrac{6 - 4}{6^2 - 1} = \dfrac{2}{35}$.

2   Using the Domain of a Rational Function and Expression

As just mentioned, a rational function can represent a rational number for a given value of x. However, for certain values of x the denominator can be zero. For instance, if $x = 2$ and

$$f(x) = \frac{1}{x - 2}, \qquad \text{then} \qquad f(2) = \frac{1}{0}$$

which is undefined. Thus 2 is not in the domain of f.

Recall that the domain of a function $y = f(x)$ is the set of all real numbers x such that y is a real number (Section 3.2). Therefore, in our work with rational functions or expressions we cannot allow the variable to be replaced by numbers that make the denominator zero; that is,

Domain

The domain of a rational expression or function is the set of all real numbers for which the fraction is *defined*.

To determine the domain of a rational function or expression, first set the denominator equal to zero. Then solve the equation to find any numbers that make the denominator zero. These numbers are excluded from the domain. For example,

$$f(x) = \frac{x^2 - 9}{x^2 - 1}$$
$$x^2 - 1 = 0$$
$$(x + 1)(x - 1) = 0$$
$$x + 1 = 0 \qquad \text{or} \quad x - 1 = 0$$
$$x = -1 \quad \text{or} \qquad x = 1, \text{ so}$$
$$D_f = \{x \mid x \neq -1 \quad \text{or} \quad 1\}$$

EXAMPLE 2

Find the domain for the following fractions.

a. $\dfrac{x - 1}{x^2 + 2x - 8}$ **b.** $\dfrac{3}{x^2 + 1}$

SOLUTION

a. $x^2 + 2x - 8 = 0$
$(x - 2)(x + 4) = 0$
$x = 2 \quad \text{or} \quad x = -4, \text{ so}$
$D = \{x \mid x \neq 2 \quad \text{or} \quad -4\}$

b. If x is any real number, then $x^2 \geq 0$. Therefore, $x^2 + 1 > 0$, so no values of x exist for which $x^2 + 1 = 0$. Thus, $D = \mathbb{R}$, the set of real numbers.

3   Reducing Fractions to Lowest Terms

A fraction is said to be **reduced to lowest terms**, or **simplified**, if the greatest common factor (GCF) of its numerator and denominator is 1. The following is an example of reducing a fraction to lowest terms:

$$\frac{15}{35} = \frac{3 \cdot 5}{7 \cdot 5} = \frac{3}{7} \cdot \frac{5}{5} = \frac{3}{7} \cdot 1 = \frac{3}{7}$$

In simplifying this fraction, we used the definition of multiplication of fractions, $\dfrac{ac}{bd} = \dfrac{a}{b} \cdot \dfrac{c}{d}$, the property that $\dfrac{a}{a} = 1$, $a \neq 0$, and $a \cdot 1 = a$. In general,

$$\frac{ac}{bc} = \frac{a}{b} \cdot \frac{c}{c} = \frac{a}{b} \cdot 1 = \frac{a}{b} \qquad or \qquad \frac{a\cancel{c}}{b\cancel{c}} = \frac{a}{b}$$

where c is the GCF of the numerator and denominator. This property applies to rational expressions. For example,

$$\frac{15ab}{21bc} = \frac{3 \cdot 5ab}{3 \cdot 7bc} = \frac{5a \cdot 3b}{7c \cdot 3b} = \frac{5a \cdot \cancel{3b}}{7c \cdot \cancel{3b}} = \frac{5a}{7c}$$

Before considering other examples, two additional properties need to be covered. The first was discussed in Section 1.4. An example of each property is given.

$$-\frac{a}{b} = \frac{-a}{b} = \frac{a}{-b} \qquad\qquad \text{and} \qquad \frac{a - b}{b - a} = \frac{-1(b - a)}{b - a} = -1$$

$$-\frac{15}{3} = \frac{-15}{3} = \frac{15}{-3} = -5 \qquad\qquad \frac{3 - 5}{5 - 3} = \frac{-2}{2} = -1$$

The rules just discussed apply to rational expressions as well as to rational numbers:

Properties of Rational Expressions

Let A, B, and C be polynomials. Then, assuming nonzero denominators,

$$\frac{AC}{BC} = \frac{A}{B} \qquad -\frac{A}{B} = \frac{-A}{B} = \frac{A}{-B} \qquad \frac{A - B}{B - A} = -1$$

EXAMPLE 3

Simplify the following fractions.

a. $\dfrac{4x^2y}{8x^3y^2}$ **b.** $\dfrac{6-2x}{x-3}$ **c.** $\dfrac{4x-12}{x^2-9}$ **d.** $\dfrac{x^3-8}{x^2-4}$

SOLUTION

a. $\dfrac{4x^2y}{8x^3y^2} = \dfrac{1 \cdot 4x^2y}{2xy \cdot 4x^2y} = \dfrac{1}{2xy}$

b. $\dfrac{6-2x}{x-3} = \dfrac{2(3-x)}{x-3} = 2(-1) = -2 \qquad \dfrac{a-b}{b-a} = -1$

c. $\dfrac{4x-12}{x^2-9} = \dfrac{4(x-3)}{(x+3)(x-3)} = \dfrac{4}{x+3}$

d. $\dfrac{x^3-8}{x^2-4} = \dfrac{(x-2)(x^2+2x+4)}{(x-2)(x+2)} = \dfrac{x^2+2x+4}{x+2}$

One common mistake made in algebra is reducing fractions incorrectly. In Example 3d we are tempted to think that we can divide x^2 into x^3 and 4 into 8 to get $x-2$. To show that this is not correct, pick a value of x, say $x=3$. Then

$$\frac{x^3-8}{x^2-4} = \frac{3^3-8}{3^2-4} = \frac{27-8}{9-4} = \frac{19}{5} \qquad \text{but } x-2 = 3-2 = 1$$

Because $\dfrac{19}{5} \neq 1$, $x-2$ is not the answer.

COMMON ERROR

A common mistake in reducing fractions is to divide terms. The fraction must be in the form $\dfrac{AC}{BC}$ before we can divide out the common factor of C:

$$\frac{x^3-8}{x^2-4} \neq x-2 \qquad \text{and} \qquad \frac{x^2+x+1}{x+1} \neq \frac{x^2+x+1}{x+1}, \quad \text{or } x^2$$

EXERCISE SET 6.1

A

1 Evaluate the following for the given values of the indicated variables.

1. $f(x) = \dfrac{2x+4}{3x-5}; \quad x=6$

2. $f(x) = \dfrac{x+5}{x^2+x-2}; \quad x=-4$

3. $g(x) = \dfrac{x^3+2x-1}{3x^2+x-5}; \quad x=0$

4. $F(y) = \dfrac{y^{80}-1}{2y^{61}+2}; \quad y=-1$

5. $\dfrac{3x^2+y^2}{3x-2y}; \quad \begin{array}{l} x=2 \\ y=-1 \end{array}$

6. $\dfrac{a^2+2ab-b^2}{a^3-b^3}; \quad \begin{array}{l} a=-3 \\ b=-2 \end{array}$

2 Find the domains for the following.

7. $f(x) = \dfrac{3}{x-5}$

8. $g(x) = \dfrac{x-1}{x+6}$

9. $k(y) = \dfrac{1}{(y-2)(y+3)}$

10. $h(x) = \dfrac{x^2-1}{(2x-1)(3x+4)}$

11. $F(x) = \dfrac{3}{x^2-25}$

12. $G(x) = \dfrac{3x - 1}{7}$

13. $\dfrac{x^2 - x + 7}{x^2 + 3x + 2}$

14. $\dfrac{x - 14}{6x^2 + x - 2}$

15. $\dfrac{x}{x^2 + 4}$

16. $\dfrac{x - 1}{x^3 + 3x^2 - 4x}$

3   Determine whether the following are true or false. For false equations, give the correct answer.

17. $\dfrac{2a}{-b} = \dfrac{-2a}{b}$

18. $\dfrac{6x + 8}{4} = 6x + 2$

19. $\dfrac{x^2 - y^2}{x - y} = x - y$

20. $\dfrac{3x - y}{y - 3x} = -1$

21. $\dfrac{x^2 + 3x + 1}{x + 1} = x^2 + 3$

22. $-\dfrac{3x}{-y} = \dfrac{-3x}{y}$

23. $\dfrac{x(x + 2) + 3(x + 2)}{x + 2} = x + 3$

24. $\dfrac{x(x - 1) - 2(x + 1)}{(x - 1)(x + 1)} = x - 2$

Simplify the following. If a fraction is in reduced form, write "reduced."

25. $\dfrac{12}{27}$

26. $\dfrac{50}{-6}$

27. $\dfrac{-72}{-48}$

28. $-\dfrac{36}{55}$

29. $\dfrac{30x^4}{5x}$

30. $\dfrac{-8n^4}{20n^8}$

31. $\dfrac{6a^8b^4}{9a^6b^9}$

32. $\dfrac{-33x^2yz^8}{-6x^8y^4z^8}$

33. $\dfrac{(2a)^3}{(6a)^2}$

34. $\dfrac{54x^8y^9}{(3x^4)^4}$

35. $\dfrac{2x + 2}{x^2 - 1}$

36. $\dfrac{3x - 6}{2 - x}$

37. $\dfrac{6x - 12}{8x - 16}$

38. $\dfrac{x + 3}{3}$

39. $\dfrac{3x + 3}{3}$

40. $\dfrac{4x - 4}{5x - 5}$

41. $\dfrac{(6x^3)(3x^7)}{x^2(6x^3)^2}$

42. $\dfrac{(4x^2)^3}{(4x^2)(x^9)(2x^{11})}$

43. $\dfrac{a^2 - b^2}{a + b}$

44. $-\dfrac{4a^2 - 4a}{1 - a^2}$

45. $\dfrac{x^3 + 1}{x + 1}$

46. $\dfrac{a^3 - 27}{a^4 - 81}$

47. $\dfrac{x^2 + 2x + 1}{x + 1}$

48. $\dfrac{rt - st}{r^2 - 2sr + s^2}$

49. $\dfrac{x^2 - xy - 2y^2}{(x + y)^8}$

50. $\dfrac{2x^3 - 4x^2 + 8x}{x^3 + 8}$

51. $\dfrac{x^2 + 7x + 12}{x^2 - 2x - 15}$

52. $\dfrac{a^2 - ab - 2b^2}{a^2 - 3ab + 2b^2}$

53. $\dfrac{9 - x^2}{2x^2 - 7x + 3}$

54. $\dfrac{4x^3 - 25x}{6x^2 - 25x + 25}$

55. $\dfrac{8a^2 - 14ab + 3b^2}{12a^2 + 5ab - 2b^2}$

56. $\dfrac{6x^2 + 19xy + 3y^2}{3x^2 + 7xy - 6y^2}$

57. $\dfrac{n^2 - mt + mn - t^2}{mnt + n^2t + nt^2}$

58. $\dfrac{x^3 + x^2 - x - 1}{x^2 - 1}$

59. $\dfrac{3c^2 - 5c - 2}{ac + 2b - bc - 2a}$

60. $\dfrac{rt + st - sr - s^2}{rt + sr + st + s^2}$

B

61. $\dfrac{2x^3 + 2xy^3}{2x^3y - 4x^2y^2 + 4xy^3}$

62. $\dfrac{x^3 - 1}{3x^3 + 3x^2 + 3x}$

63. $\dfrac{a^4b^2 - a^2b^4}{a^4b + ab^4}$

64. $\dfrac{4y^2 - 25 + x^2 + 4xy}{20xy^2 + 10x^2y - 50xy}$

65. $\dfrac{ab^2c + abc^2 - a^2bc}{a^2 - c^2 + b^2 - 2ab}$

66. $\dfrac{x^3 + x^2 - 25x - 25}{x^3 + 5x^2 - x - 5}$

67. $\dfrac{4x^2 + 9y^2 + 12xy - 4}{6x^2y + 6xy + 9xy^2}$

68. $\dfrac{x^2 - y^2 + 25 + 10x}{x^2 + y^2 - 9 + 2xy}$

69. $\dfrac{2x^4 - 2x}{3x^3 + 3}$

70. $\dfrac{(x^3 - 1)^2}{(x^2 - 1)^2}$

Answer the following questions with complete sentences.

71. What is the difference between a rational ex-

pression and a rational function? Give an example of each.

72. What does it mean to say that a fraction is "reduced to lowest terms"?

R EVIEW E XERCISES

Let $f(x) = 2x - 6$ and $g(x) = x^2 - 4$. Find the following functions and give their domains. (See Section 5.4.)

73. fg **74.** f/g **75.** g/f

6.2 MULTIPLYING AND DIVIDING RATIONAL EXPRESSIONS

> **1** **Multiplying Rational Expressions**
>
> **2** **Dividing Rational Expressions**
>
> **3** **Using the Algebra of Functions; Roots of a Rational Function**

---

1 Multiplying Rational Expressions

This section reviews the rules for multiplication and division of rational numbers and then applies these rules to rational expressions. Just as the methods of reducing arithmetic and algebraic fractions are alike, the procedures for finding the products and quotients of rational numbers and expressions are similar.

The product of two or more fractions is the product of their numerators divided by the product of their denominators. For example,

$$\frac{2}{3} \cdot \frac{5}{7} = \frac{2 \cdot 5}{3 \cdot 7} = \frac{10}{21}$$

and, in general,

$$\frac{a}{b} \cdot \frac{c}{d} = \frac{ac}{bd}$$

Quite often the product of rational numbers will not be in reduced form. Before multiplying ac and bd, determine their GCF. If it is not 1, then continue the factorization of these numbers and simplify the fraction as in the last section. For instance,

$$\frac{20}{49} \cdot \frac{21}{25} = \frac{20 \cdot 21}{49 \cdot 25} = \frac{4 \cdot \cancel{5} \cdot \cancel{7} \cdot 3}{7 \cdot \cancel{7} \cdot \cancel{5} \cdot 5} = \frac{12}{35}$$

The procedure for multiplying rational numbers applies to rational expressions. For example,

$$\frac{2x}{y^2} \cdot \frac{5y}{2x^3} = \frac{2x \cdot 5y}{y^2 \cdot 2x^3} = \frac{2xy \cdot 5}{2xy \cdot x^2 y} = \frac{5}{x^2 y}$$

Product of Rational Expressions

If A, B, C, and D are polynomials with B and D nonzero, then

$$\frac{A}{B} \cdot \frac{C}{D} = \frac{AC}{BD}$$

E X A M P L E 1

Find the following products and simplify your answers.

a. $\dfrac{12a^3 b}{75} \cdot \dfrac{125}{8ab^3}$ **b.** $\dfrac{12 - 4x}{x^2 - 9} \cdot \dfrac{x^2 + 2x + 1}{x^2 - 1}$

SOLUTION **a.** $\dfrac{12a^3 b}{75} \cdot \dfrac{125}{8ab^3} = \dfrac{12a^3 b \cdot 125}{75 \cdot 8ab^3} = \dfrac{3 \cdot 4 \cdot 25 \cdot 5 \cdot ab \cdot a^2}{3 \cdot 25 \cdot 4 \cdot 2 \cdot ab \cdot b^2} = \dfrac{5a^2}{2b^2}$

b. $\dfrac{12 - 4x}{x^2 - 9} \cdot \dfrac{x^2 + 2x + 1}{x^2 - 1} = \dfrac{(12 - 4x)(x^2 + 2x + 1)}{(x^2 - 9)(x^2 - 1)}$

$= \dfrac{4(3 - x)(x + 1)(x + 1)}{(x + 3)(x - 3)(x + 1)(x - 1)}$ $\dfrac{3 - x}{x - 3} = -1$

$= \dfrac{-4(x + 1)}{(x + 3)(x - 1)}$

---

2   Dividing Rational Expressions

In Section 1.4 we stated that x divided by y is the same as x multiplied by the reciprocal of y; that is, if x and y are real numbers, $y \neq 0$, then

$$x \div y = x \cdot \frac{1}{y}$$

For example,

$$\frac{2}{3} \div \frac{5}{7} = \frac{2}{3} \cdot \frac{7}{5} = \frac{2 \cdot 7}{3 \cdot 5} = \frac{14}{15}$$

In general,

$$\frac{a}{b} \div \frac{c}{d} = \frac{a}{b} \cdot \frac{d}{c} = \frac{ad}{bc}$$

The method for dividing rational numbers also applies to rational expressions. For example,

$$\frac{x^2 - 4}{x} \div \frac{3x - 6}{2x} = \frac{x^2 - 4}{x} \cdot \frac{2x}{3x - 6}$$

$$= \frac{(x^2 - 4)2x}{x(3x - 6)}$$

$$= \frac{2x(x - 2)(x + 2)}{3x(x - 2)}$$

$$= \frac{2(x + 2)}{3}$$

Quotient of Rational Expressions

If A, B, C, and D are polynomials with B, D, and C nonzero, then

$$\frac{A}{B} \div \frac{C}{D} = \frac{A}{B} \cdot \frac{D}{C} = \frac{AD}{BC}$$

EXAMPLE 2

Perform the indicated operations and simplify your answers.

a. $\dfrac{x^2 + 5x - 14}{18x^{12}} \div \dfrac{x^2 - 49}{6x^3 - 12x^2}$

b. $\dfrac{3x^3 - 9x^2 + 27x}{3x^2 + 9x} \div (x^3 + 27)$

SOLUTION   **a.** $\dfrac{x^2 + 5x - 14}{18x^{12}} \div \dfrac{x^2 - 49}{6x^3 - 12x^2} = \dfrac{x^2 + 5x - 14}{18x^{12}} \cdot \dfrac{6x^3 - 12x^2}{x^2 - 49}$

$$= \frac{(x - 2)(x + 7)(6x^2)(x - 2)}{6x^2 \cdot 3x^{10}(x + 7)(x - 7)}$$

$$= \frac{(x - 2)^2}{3x^{10}(x - 7)}$$

b. $\dfrac{3x^3 - 9x^2 + 27x}{3x^2 + 9x} \div (x^3 + 27) = \dfrac{3x^3 - 9x^2 + 27x}{3x^2 + 9x} \cdot \dfrac{1}{x^3 + 27}$

$$= \frac{3x(x^2 - 3x + 9)}{3x(x + 3)(x + 3)(x^2 - 3x + 9)}$$

$$= \frac{1}{(x + 3)^2}$$

Some problems involve both multiplication and division. Recall that these operations are done in order from left to right. This is illustrated in our next example.

EXAMPLE 3

Perform the indicated operations and simplify.

$\dfrac{4a^2b}{55cd} \div \dfrac{b^2}{5c} \cdot \dfrac{d^2}{4a}$

(continued)

SOLUTION
$$\frac{4a^2b}{55cd} \div \frac{b^2}{5c} \cdot \frac{d^2}{4a} = \frac{4a^2b}{55cd} \cdot \frac{5c}{b^2} \cdot \frac{d^2}{4a}$$
$$= \frac{4a^2b \cdot 5c \cdot d^2}{55cd \cdot b^2 \cdot 4a}$$
$$= \frac{(4 \cdot 5abcd)ad}{(4 \cdot 5abcd)11b}$$
$$= \frac{ad}{11b}$$

3   Using the Algebra of Functions; Roots of a Rational Function

In Section 5.4 we discussed the algebra of functions. Recall that if f and g are polynomial functions, then their product and quotient are

$$(fg)(x) = f(x)g(x) \qquad \text{and} \qquad \left(\frac{f}{g}\right)(x) = \frac{f(x)}{g(x)}, \quad g(x) \neq 0$$

These definitions apply also to rational functions. For example, if $f(x) = \dfrac{x + 1}{x - 2}$ and $g(x) = \dfrac{x - 3}{x - 5}$, then

$$(fg)(x) = f(x)g(x) = \frac{x + 1}{x - 2} \cdot \frac{x - 3}{x - 5} = \frac{(x + 1)(x - 3)}{(x - 2)(x - 5)}$$

$$\left(\frac{f}{g}\right)(x) = \frac{f(x)}{g(x)} = f(x) \div g(x) = \frac{x + 1}{x - 2} \div \frac{x - 3}{x - 5}$$

$$= \frac{x + 1}{x - 2} \cdot \frac{x - 5}{x - 3} = \frac{(x + 1)(x - 5)}{(x - 2)(x - 3)}$$

The domain of fg cannot include 2, because $f(2)$ is undefined, or 5, because $g(5)$ is undefined. Thus, the domain of fg is

$$D_{fg} = \{x \mid x \neq 2 \quad \text{or} \quad 5\}$$

The domain of f/g has a further restriction: It cannot contain 3, because $g(3) = 0$. Thus,

$$D_{f/g} = \{x \mid x \neq 2, \quad 5, \quad \text{or} \quad 3\}$$

The domain of f/g is the set of all real numbers in the domain of f and in the domain of g and such that $g(x) \neq 0$.

EXAMPLE 4

Let $f(x) = \dfrac{5}{x}$ and $g(x) = \dfrac{x^2 - 9}{x^2 - 4}$. Find the following functions and their domains.

a. fg **b.** f/g

SOLUTION   **a.** $(fg)(x) = f(x)g(x) = \dfrac{5}{x} \cdot \dfrac{x^2 - 9}{x^2 - 4}$

$$= \frac{5(x + 3)(x - 3)}{x(x + 2)(x - 2)}$$

$D_f = \{x \mid x \neq 0\}$ and $D_g = \{x \mid x \neq -2 \quad \text{or} \quad 2\}$, so
$D_{fg} = \{x \mid x \neq 0, \quad -2, \quad \text{or} \quad 2\}$.

b. $\left(\dfrac{f}{g}\right)(x) = \dfrac{f(x)}{g(x)} = f(x) \div g(x) = \dfrac{5}{x} \div \dfrac{x^2 - 9}{x^2 - 4}$

$\qquad = \dfrac{5}{x} \cdot \dfrac{x^2 - 4}{x^2 - 9} = \dfrac{5(x + 2)(x - 2)}{x(x + 3)(x - 3)}$

Because $g(x) = 0$ if $x = -2$ or 2,

$D_{f/g} = \{x \mid x \neq 0, \ -3, \ 3, \ -2, \ \text{or} \ 2\}.$

In Section 5.6 we discussed the roots of polynomial functions. Recall that a is a root of a function f if $f(a) = 0$. For example, 6 is the root of $f(x) = x - 6$ because $f(6) = 6 - 6 = 0$. Now consider the rational function $f(x) = \dfrac{x - 2}{x + 3}$. Because $f(2) = \dfrac{2 - 2}{2 + 3} = \dfrac{0}{5} = 0$, $\ 2$ is the root of this function. In general, a is a root of the rational function

$$f(x) = \frac{g(x)}{h(x)} \quad \text{if} \quad g(a) = 0 \quad \text{and} \quad h(a) \neq 0$$

If $g(a) = h(a) = 0$, then we have $0/0$, which is undefined.

EXAMPLE 5

Find the roots of the following functions.

a. $f(x) = \dfrac{x^2 - 9}{x^2 - 1}$ **b.** $f(x) = \dfrac{6}{x + 7}$

SOLUTION **a.** $f(x) = 0$ if $x^2 - 9 = 0$; so, $x = 3$ or -3; that is, $f(3) = f(-3) = \dfrac{9 - 9}{9 - 1} = \dfrac{0}{8} = 0$. Thus, 3 and -3 are the roots.

b. $f(a) \neq 0$ for all values of a. Thus, f does not have any roots. Note that $f(-7) = \dfrac{6}{0} \neq 0; \ \dfrac{6}{0}$ is undefined.

EXERCISE SET 6.2

A

1 Perform the indicated operations and simplify your answers.

1. $\dfrac{4}{5} \cdot \dfrac{7}{6}$

2. $\dfrac{-5}{14} \cdot \dfrac{21}{-6}$

3. $\dfrac{25}{-16} \cdot \dfrac{88}{-15}$

4. $\dfrac{2}{3} \cdot \dfrac{3}{4} \cdot \dfrac{4}{5}$

5. $16 \cdot \dfrac{3}{2} \cdot \dfrac{-7}{20}$

6. $-\dfrac{21}{55} \cdot \dfrac{125}{-28} \cdot \dfrac{66}{15}$

7. $\dfrac{3y}{2x} \cdot \dfrac{y^4}{x^2}$

8. $\dfrac{9a^2}{b^3} \cdot \dfrac{2b}{6a^5}$

9. $-\dfrac{ac^9}{7b^6} \cdot \dfrac{2b^2}{-c^6} \cdot \dfrac{-14}{abc}$

10. $\dfrac{2x - 2}{3} \cdot \dfrac{x}{x^2 - 1}$

11. $\dfrac{3x - 9}{x^2} \cdot \dfrac{1}{9 - x^2}$

12. $\dfrac{x^3 + x^2}{21} \cdot \dfrac{49}{x^3 + 1}$

2

13. $\dfrac{5}{7} \div \dfrac{3}{2}$

14. $\dfrac{7}{6} \div \dfrac{-1}{12}$

15. $\dfrac{28}{27} \div \dfrac{14}{33}$

16. $\dfrac{24}{-5} \div \dfrac{36}{25}$

17. $\dfrac{3x^2}{2} \div \dfrac{9x}{y}$

18. $\dfrac{16a^8}{b^{12}} \div \dfrac{14a^7}{b^6}$

19. $\dfrac{55x^6y^2}{-5xy} \div -33x^4y^2$

20. $\dfrac{16x^2y}{24xy^3} \div \dfrac{9xy}{8x^2y^2}$

21. $\dfrac{x - x^3}{-x^3 x^9} \div \dfrac{2x^2}{(2x)^6}$

22. $\dfrac{2}{3} \cdot \dfrac{6}{5} \div \dfrac{8}{3}$

23. $\dfrac{4}{9} \div \dfrac{2}{21} \cdot \dfrac{1}{9}$

24. $\dfrac{3x}{2y} \div \dfrac{-x^7}{8y^6} \cdot \dfrac{xy}{21}$

25. $\dfrac{10x}{9y} \div \dfrac{x^2}{x - 3} \div \dfrac{xy^7}{x^2 - 9}$

26. $\dfrac{10x}{9y} \div \dfrac{x^2}{x - 3} \div \dfrac{xy^7}{x^2 - 9}$

27. $\dfrac{3x^8}{4y^2} \cdot \dfrac{20y^{10}}{-9x^{12}}$

28. $\dfrac{9z^2 - 4y^2}{27x^2} \cdot \dfrac{6x^7 - 15x^6}{4y^2 - 12yz + 9z^2}$

29. $\dfrac{(x - y)^2}{a^2 b} \div \dfrac{x^2 - y^2}{ab^2}$

30. $\dfrac{x^2 + 2x - 15}{8x^3 - y^3} \cdot \dfrac{4x^2 - y^2}{5x^3 + 25x^2}$

31. $\dfrac{a^{30}}{9a^2 - 1} \div \dfrac{a^3 - 3a^2}{6a^2 - 11a + 3}$

32. $\dfrac{y^2 - 2y - 8}{4y^2 + 8y} \cdot \dfrac{1}{2y^2 - 7y - 4}$

33. $\dfrac{15x}{3x^2 - 8x - 3} \div \dfrac{5x}{3x^2 + x}$

34. $\dfrac{x^2 + x - 2}{x + 2} \div \dfrac{x^2 + 2x - 3}{x + 3}$

35. $\dfrac{27x^3 + 125y^3}{x^2 + 2xy + y^2} \cdot \dfrac{x^3 y - xy^{3\cdot}}{3x^2 y + 5xy^2}$

36. $\dfrac{x^4 - 81}{4x^2 - 1} \cdot \dfrac{6x^2 + 5x - 4}{3x^2 + 13x + 12}$

37. $\dfrac{2}{3} \cdot \dfrac{9}{7} \div \dfrac{1}{5}$

38. $\dfrac{5}{7} \div \dfrac{20}{49} \cdot \dfrac{4}{5}$

39. $\dfrac{a^2}{b^2} \div \dfrac{2a}{3b} \cdot \dfrac{4a^6}{9b^8}$

40. $\dfrac{4 - 2a}{5} \cdot \dfrac{10a^{12}}{27} \div \dfrac{a^4 - 4a^2}{9}$

41. $\dfrac{a^2 b - 3ab}{a^2 - 5a + 6} \div \dfrac{ab}{a^2 - 2a + ab - 2b}$

42. $\dfrac{x^3 + x^2 + 3x + 3}{a^2 - 2ab + b^2} \cdot \dfrac{a^2 - 2b - ab + 2a}{x^2 + 7x + 6}$

3 Let $f(x) = \dfrac{x}{x - 1}$, $g(x) = \dfrac{x + 5}{x - 6}$, $h(x) = \dfrac{x - 8}{x}$,

and $k(x) = \dfrac{x - 7}{x + 9}$. Find the following functions and their domains.

43. fg **44.** fh **45.** fk

46. gh **47.** gk **48.** hk

49. f^2 **50.** g^2 **51.** f/g

52. g/f **53.** f/h **54.** h/f

55. f/k **56.** k/f **57.** g/h

58. g/k **59.** h/k **60.** k/h

Let $f(x) = \dfrac{x^2 - 1}{x^2 - 4}$, $g(x) = \dfrac{x^2 - 9}{x^2 - 25}$, $h(x) = \dfrac{x^2 - x - 12}{x^2 + x - 20}$, and $k(x) = \dfrac{2x - 1}{3x + 5}$. Find the following functions and their domains.

61. fg **62.** fh **63.** fk

64. gh **65.** gk **66.** hk

67. f/g **68.** g/f **69.** f/h

70. h/f **71.** f/k **72.** k/f

Find the roots for the following functions. If they do not exist, write "none."

73. $f(x) = \dfrac{x - 8}{x + 9}$

74. $f(x) = \dfrac{5}{x + 6}$

75. $f(x) = \dfrac{3x + 4}{2x - 1}$

76. $f(x) = \dfrac{x^2 - 1}{x + 3}$

77. $f(x) = \dfrac{-6}{x^2 - 1}$

78. $f(x) = \dfrac{x^2 - 3x}{x^3 - 1}$

79. $f(x) = \dfrac{x^2 - 5x + 6}{7}$

80. $f(x) = \dfrac{9x^2 - 25}{x + 3}$

B Perform the indicated operations and simplify your answers.

81. $\dfrac{3x^3 + 3x^2 + 3x}{x^2 - 2x + 1} \div \dfrac{x^3 - 1}{x^4 - 1}$

82. $\dfrac{8x^2 + 10x + 3}{48x^3 + 36x^2} \cdot \dfrac{27x^3 - 3x}{6x^2 + x - 1}$

83. $\dfrac{x^2 - 25}{3x + 6} \div \dfrac{x^2 + 10x + 25}{9x^2 - 36} \cdot \dfrac{4x^2 + 19x - 5}{2x^2 - 7x - 15}$

84. $\dfrac{a^4 - 16b^4}{ac - ad - a^2 + cd} \div \dfrac{a^2 - 2bc - 2ab + ac}{abcd} \div \dfrac{2a^3 b + 8ab^3}{a^2 - c^2}$

C 🖊

Answer the following questions with complete sentences.

85. Describe the process you would use to multiply and simplify two rational expressions.

86. Describe the process you would use to divide and simplify two rational expressions.

87. Let f and g be two rational functions. How would you find the domain of fg?

88. Let f and g be two rational functions. How would you find the domain of f/g?

What, if anything, is wrong with the following "proofs"?

89. $0 = 1$.   Proof:
Let $a = 1$,   and
$a^2 - a = a^2 - a$.   Then,
$$a^2 - a = a^2 - 1$$
$$a(a - 1) = (a + 1)(a - 1)$$
$$a = a + 1$$
$$-a + a = -a + a + 1$$
$$0 = 0 + 1$$
$$0 = 1$$

90. $1 = 2$.   Proof:
$$0 = 0$$
$$a^2 - a^2 = a^2 - a^2$$
$$a(a - a) = (a + a)(a - a)$$
$$a = a + a$$
$$1a = 2a$$
$$1 = 2$$

REVIEW EXERCISES

Find the prime factorizations for the following. (See Section 5.4.)

91. 210   **92.** 180   **93.** 100

Find the GCF of each set of integers. (See Section 5.4.)

94. $\{12, 18\}$ **95.** $\{10, 21\}$ **96.** $\{4, 25\}$

Simplify the following. (See Section 1.4.)

97. $6 + 4[1 - 3^2]$ **98.** $16 \div 4 - 2$

Let $f(x) = 3x^2 - 2x + 5$ and $g(x) = x^2 + 7x - 6$. Find the following functions and give their domains. (See Section 5.4.)

99. $f + g$ **100.** $f - g$

6.3 ADDING AND SUBTRACTING RATIONAL EXPRESSIONS

1	Adding and Subtracting Like Fractions
2	Finding the Least Common Denominator
3	Adding and Subtracting Unlike Fractions
4	Using the Order of Operations and the Algebra of Functions

1 Adding and Subtracting Like Fractions

Fractions that have the same denominator are called **like fractions**, and those with different denominators are called **unlike fractions**. The first part of this section covers the methods for adding and subtracting like fractions. Then we will discuss the least common denominator, which will allow us to combine unlike fractions.

To add or subtract fractions with a common denominator, we add or subtract the numerators and place this result over the common denominator. This procedure is a result of the distributive property and the fact that x divided by y is the same as x multiplied by the reciprocal of y. For example,

$$\frac{2}{7} + \frac{3}{7} = 2\left(\frac{1}{7}\right) + 3\left(\frac{1}{7}\right) \qquad \frac{x}{y} = x\left(\frac{1}{y}\right)$$

$$= (2 + 3)\left(\frac{1}{7}\right) \qquad ba + ca = (b + c)a$$

$$= 5\left(\frac{1}{7}\right)$$

$$= \frac{5}{7} \qquad x\left(\frac{1}{y}\right) = \frac{x}{y}$$

In general, if a/d and c/d represent rational numbers, then

$$\frac{a}{d} + \frac{c}{d} = \frac{a + c}{d} \qquad \text{and} \qquad \frac{a}{d} - \frac{c}{d} = \frac{a - c}{d}$$

Some subtraction problems are in the form $\dfrac{a}{d} - \dfrac{c}{-d}$, where the second denominator is the opposite of the first denominator. In this case we can use the convenient fact that $-\dfrac{a}{b} = \dfrac{a}{-b}$:

$$\frac{a}{d} - \frac{c}{-d} = \frac{a}{d} + \left(-\frac{c}{-d}\right) = \frac{a}{d} + \frac{c}{-(-d)} = \frac{a}{d} + \frac{c}{d} = \frac{a + c}{d}$$

Often the sum or difference of rational numbers must be reduced, as illustrated in the following example.

EXAMPLE 1

Perform the indicated operations and simplify the answers.

a. $\dfrac{5}{12} + \dfrac{11}{12}$ **b.** $-\dfrac{6}{11} - \dfrac{10}{11}$ **c.** $\dfrac{3}{10} - \dfrac{9}{-10}$

SOLUTION

a. $\dfrac{5}{12} + \dfrac{11}{12} = \dfrac{5 + 11}{12} = \dfrac{16}{12} = \dfrac{4 \cdot 4}{4 \cdot 3} = \dfrac{4}{3}$

b. $-\dfrac{6}{11} - \dfrac{10}{11} = \dfrac{-6}{11} - \dfrac{10}{11} = \dfrac{-6 - 10}{11} = \dfrac{-16}{11} = -\dfrac{16}{11}$

c. $\dfrac{3}{10} - \dfrac{9}{-10} = \dfrac{3}{10} + \dfrac{9}{-(-10)} = \dfrac{3}{10} + \dfrac{9}{10} = \dfrac{12}{10} = \dfrac{6 \cdot 2}{5 \cdot 2} = \dfrac{6}{5}$

The methods for adding and subtracting rational numbers apply to rational expressions. For example,

$$\frac{x}{x^2 - 1} - \frac{1}{x^2 - 1} = \frac{x - 1}{x^2 - 1} = \frac{1(x - 1)}{(x + 1)(x - 1)} = \frac{1}{x + 1}$$

> **Sum and Difference of Like Fractions**
>
> If A, C, and D are polynomials, $D \neq 0$, then
>
> $$\frac{A}{D} + \frac{C}{D} = \frac{A + C}{D}, \qquad \frac{A}{D} - \frac{C}{D} = \frac{A - C}{D}, \qquad \text{and}$$
>
> $$\frac{A}{D} - \frac{C}{-D} = \frac{A}{D} + \frac{C}{D} = \frac{A + C}{D}$$

EXAMPLE 2

Perform the indicated operations and simplify your answers.

a. $\dfrac{x^2 - x}{x^2 + 4x} - \dfrac{12 - 2x}{x^2 + 4x}$ b. $\dfrac{6a + 1}{8a} + \dfrac{2a + 5}{8a} + \dfrac{6a}{16a^2}$

c. $\dfrac{x + 1}{x - 6} - \dfrac{2}{6 - x}$

SOLUTION

a. $\dfrac{x^2 - x}{x^2 + 4x} - \dfrac{12 - 2x}{x^2 + 4x} = \dfrac{x^2 - x - (12 - 2x)}{x^2 + 4x} = \dfrac{x^2 + x - 12}{x^2 + 4x} =$

$\dfrac{(x - 3)(x + 4)}{x(x + 4)} = \dfrac{x - 3}{x}$

b. First, reduce the third fraction: $\dfrac{6a}{16a^2} = \dfrac{3 \cdot 2a}{8a \cdot 2a} = \dfrac{3}{8a}$

$\dfrac{6a + 1}{8a} + \dfrac{2a + 5}{8a} + \dfrac{6a}{16a^2} = \dfrac{6a + 1}{8a} + \dfrac{2a + 5}{8a} + \dfrac{3}{8a} =$

$\dfrac{6a + 1 + 2a + 5 + 3}{8a} = \dfrac{8a + 9}{8a}$

Note: $\dfrac{8a + 9}{8a} \neq \dfrac{8a + 9}{8a}$

c. This expression is in the form $\dfrac{A}{D} - \dfrac{C}{-D}$. Thus $\dfrac{x + 1}{x - 6} - \dfrac{2}{6 - x} =$

$\dfrac{x + 1}{x - 6} + \dfrac{2}{-(6 - x)} = \dfrac{x + 1}{x - 6} + \dfrac{2}{x - 6} = \dfrac{x + 3}{x - 6}$

2   Finding the Least Common Denominator

At the beginning of this section we showed that if two fractions have the same denominator, then the distributive property allows us to add them. This technique will not work if they have different denominators. However, without changing the value of the fractions, we can change their form so that they have a common denominator and can then be combined.

The smallest positive common denominator for a set of rational numbers is called their **least common denominator**, or **LCD**; that is, the LCD is the smallest natural number divisible by each denominator. For instance, the LCD for 1/6 and 1/4 is 12. When the LCD is not obvious, we can use prime factorization to construct it. For example, let us find the LCD of $\frac{2}{15} + \frac{5}{21} + \frac{1}{14}$. The prime factorizations of 15, 21, and 14 are

$$15 = 3 \cdot 5, \qquad 21 = 3 \cdot 7, \qquad \text{and} \qquad 14 = 7 \cdot 2$$

To be divisible by 15 the LCD must have factors of 3 and 5:

$$\text{LCD} = (3)(5)(\quad)$$

To be divisible by 21 the LCD must have a factor of 7:

$$\text{LCD} = (3)(5)(7)(\quad)$$

To be divisible by 14 the LCD must have a factor of 2:

$$\text{LCD} = (3)(5)(7)(2) = 210$$

This is the smallest natural number divisible by 15, 21, and 14. Note that $15 \cdot 21 \cdot 14 = 4410$ would be an awkward common denominator to use in this problem.

EXAMPLE 3

Find the LCD for the following.

a. $\frac{1}{12} - \frac{5}{18} + \frac{1}{30}$ **b.** $\frac{1}{4} + \frac{1}{25}$

SOLUTION

a. $12 = 2 \cdot 2 \cdot 3,\quad 18 = 2 \cdot 3 \cdot 3,\quad$ and $\quad 30 = 2 \cdot 3 \cdot 5.$

$$\begin{aligned}
\text{LCD} &= 2 \cdot 2 \cdot 3(\quad) && \text{Divisible by 12} \\
&= 2 \cdot 2 \cdot 3 \cdot 3(\quad) && \text{Divisible by 18} \\
&= 2 \cdot 2 \cdot 3 \cdot 3 \cdot 5 && \text{Divisible by 30} \\
&= 180
\end{aligned}$$

b. $4 = 2 \cdot 2\quad$ and $\quad 25 = 5 \cdot 5.$

$$\begin{aligned}
\text{LCD} &= 2 \cdot 2(\quad) && \text{Divisible by 4} \\
&= 2 \cdot 2 \cdot 5 \cdot 5 && \text{Divisible by 25} \\
&= 100
\end{aligned}$$

In Example 3b the GCF of 4 and 25 is 1, and the LCD is $4 \cdot 25$. In general:

> If the greatest common factor of two or more denominators is 1, then the least common denominator is their product.

The procedure for finding the LCD for rational numbers also applies to rational expressions. For example,

$$\frac{3}{5x^2 - 5x} + \frac{x - 2}{x^2 - 1}$$

$$5x^2 - 5x = 5x(x - 1) \qquad \text{and} \qquad x^2 - 1 = (x - 1)(x + 1)$$

$$\begin{aligned}
\text{LCD} &= 5x(x - 1)(\quad) && \text{Divisible by } 5x^2 - 5x. \\
&= 5x(x - 1)(x + 1) && \text{Divisible by } x^2 - 1
\end{aligned}$$

Leaving the LCD for rational expressions in factored form is convenient. In general:

> The least common denominator for a set of rational expressions is the polynomial of lowest degree that is divisible by each denominator.

As we have seen, the methods for finding the LCD for rational numbers and rational expressions are very similar. The following is a summary of the general approach.

> **Finding the Least Common Denominator**
> ——
> **1.** Find the prime factorization of each denominator.
> **2.** Form the product of each factor the greatest number of times that it appears in any single denominator.

EXAMPLE 4

Find the LCD for the following sets of fractions.

a. $\dfrac{y}{15x^2}, \quad \dfrac{x}{14y^3}$ **b.** $\dfrac{a}{a^2 - 36}, \quad \dfrac{a - 2}{a^2 - 2a - 24}$

SOLUTION

a. $15x^2 = 3 \cdot 5xx$ and $14y^3 = 2 \cdot 7yyy$.
Because the GCF = 1, the LCD = their product:
LCD = $15x^2 \cdot 14y^3 = 210x^2y^3$

b. $a^2 - 36 = (a + 6)(a - 6)$ and
$a^2 - 2a - 24 = (a - 6)(a + 4)$, so
LCD = $(a + 6)(a - 6)(a + 4)$

3   Adding and Subtracting Unlike Fractions

We have just discussed the method for finding the LCD for unlike fractions. The next step in adding or subtracting these fractions is to change them to like fractions without changing their value. Fractions that have the same value are called **equivalent fractions**. For example,

$$\frac{2}{3}, \quad \frac{6}{9}, \quad \text{and} \quad \frac{2c}{3c}, \quad c \ne 0, \text{ are equivalent fractions.}$$

Thus, we change a fraction to an equivalent fraction with the property $\dfrac{a}{b} = \dfrac{ac}{bc}$. We used this property to reduce fractions, and now we will use it to add them. For example, to find $\dfrac{1}{6} + \dfrac{1}{4}$, first determine that the LCD is $2 \cdot 2 \cdot 3 = 12$. Then multiply $\dfrac{1}{6}$ by $\dfrac{2}{2}$ and $\dfrac{1}{4}$ by $\dfrac{3}{3}$:

$$\frac{1}{6} + \frac{1}{4} = \frac{1}{6} \cdot \frac{2}{2} + \frac{1}{4} \cdot \frac{3}{3} = \frac{2}{12} + \frac{3}{12} = \frac{5}{12}$$

EXAMPLE 5

Perform the indicated operations and simplify your answers.

a. $\dfrac{7}{10} + \dfrac{3}{-10}$ **b.** $\dfrac{1}{12} - \dfrac{5}{18} + \dfrac{1}{30}$

SOLUTION   **a.** The LCD $= 10$, so multiply $\dfrac{3}{-10}$ by $\dfrac{-1}{-1}$:

$$\frac{7}{10} + \frac{3}{-10} = \frac{7}{10} + \frac{3}{-10} \cdot \frac{-1}{-1} = \frac{7}{10} + \frac{-3}{10} = \frac{4}{10} = \frac{2}{5}$$

b. LCD $= 2 \cdot 2 \cdot 3 \cdot 3 \cdot 5 = 180$ (see Example 3a), so

$$\frac{1}{12} - \frac{5}{18} + \frac{1}{30} = \frac{1}{12} \cdot \frac{15}{15} + \frac{-5}{18} \cdot \frac{10}{10} + \frac{1}{30} \cdot \frac{6}{6}$$

$$= \frac{15}{180} + \frac{-50}{180} + \frac{6}{180} = -\frac{29}{180}$$

These methods for adding and subtracting rational numbers extend to rational expressions. For example,

$$\frac{3}{5x^2 - 5x} + \frac{x - 2}{x^2 - 1} = \frac{3}{5x(x - 1)} + \frac{x - 2}{(x - 1)(x + 1)} \qquad \text{LCD} = 5x(x - 1)(x + 1)$$

$$= \frac{3}{5x(x - 1)} \cdot \frac{x + 1}{x + 1} + \frac{x - 2}{(x - 1)(x + 1)} \cdot \frac{5x}{5x}$$

$$= \frac{3x + 3}{5x(x - 1)(x + 1)} + \frac{5x^2 - 10x}{5x(x - 1)(x + 1)}$$

$$= \frac{5x^2 - 7x + 3}{5x(x - 1)(x + 1)}$$

EXAMPLE 6

Perform the indicated operations and simplify your answers.

a. $\dfrac{a}{a^2 - 36} - \dfrac{a - 2}{a^2 - 2a - 24}$ **b.** $x + \dfrac{x - y}{12x^3y^2} - \dfrac{5}{18x^2y^3}$

SOLUTION   **a.** The LCD $= (a + 6)(a - 6)(a + 4)$ from Example 4b. Note the use of the property $-\dfrac{a}{b} = \dfrac{-a}{b}$:

$$\frac{a}{a^2 - 36} - \frac{a - 2}{a^2 - 2a - 24} = \frac{a}{(a + 6)(a - 6)} + \frac{-(a - 2)}{(a - 6)(a + 4)}$$

$$= \frac{a}{(a + 6)(a - 6)} \cdot \frac{a + 4}{a + 4} + \frac{2 - a}{(a - 6)(a + 4)} \cdot \frac{a + 6}{a + 6}$$

$$= \frac{a^2 + 4a}{(a + 6)(a - 6)(a + 4)} + \frac{-a^2 - 4a + 12}{(a + 6)(a - 6)(a + 4)}$$

$$= \frac{12}{(a + 6)(a - 6)(a + 4)}$$

b. $12x^3y^2 = 2 \cdot 2 \cdot 3x^3y^2$, $18x^2y^3 = 2 \cdot 3 \cdot 3x^2y^3$, and the LCD $= 2 \cdot 2 \cdot 3 \cdot 3x^3y^3 = 36x^3y^3$

$$x + \frac{x - y}{12x^3y^2} - \frac{5}{18x^2y^3} = \frac{x}{1} \cdot \frac{36x^3y^3}{36x^3y^3} + \frac{x - y}{12x^3y^2} \cdot \frac{3y}{3y} + \frac{-5}{18x^2y^3} \cdot \frac{2x}{2x}$$

$$= \frac{36x^4y^3 + 3xy - 3y^2 - 10x}{36x^3y^3}$$

| **4** | **Using the Order of Operations and the Algebra of Functions** |

Many expressions involve two or more operations. In Section 1.4 we covered the order of operations for integers. The same rules apply to rational numbers and rational expressions, as the next example illustrates.

EXAMPLE 7

Perform the indicated operations and simplify your answers.

a. $\frac{2}{7} + \frac{3}{7}\left[1 - \left(\frac{2}{3}\right)^2\right]$ **b.** $\frac{16x^2}{x + 1} \div 4x - 2x$

SOLUTION   **a.** $\frac{2}{7} + \frac{3}{7}\left[1 - \left(\frac{2}{3}\right)^2\right] = \frac{2}{7} + \frac{3}{7}\left[\frac{9}{9} - \frac{4}{9}\right] = \frac{2}{7} + \frac{3}{7}\left[\frac{5}{9}\right] = \frac{2}{7} + \frac{5}{21} = \frac{11}{21}$

b. $\frac{16x^2}{x + 1} \div 4x - 2x = \frac{16x^2}{x + 1} \cdot \frac{1}{4x} - 2x = \frac{4x}{x + 1} - \frac{2x}{1} \cdot \frac{x + 1}{x + 1} =$

$\frac{4x - 2x^2 - 2x}{x + 1} = \frac{2x - 2x^2}{x + 1}$

Section 5.4 discussed the algebra of functions. Recall that if f and g are polynomial functions, then their sum and difference are

$$(f + g)(x) = f(x) + g(x) \quad \text{and} \quad (f - g)(x) = f(x) - g(x)$$

In the last section we saw that the definitions for the product and quotient of polynomial functions carry over to rational functions. This fact is also true for the sum and difference of polynomial functions. For example, if

$$f(x) = \frac{3}{x} \quad \text{and} \quad g(x) = \frac{2}{x - 1}, \text{ then}$$

$$(f + g)(x) = f(x) + g(x) = \frac{3}{x} + \frac{2}{x - 1} = \frac{5x - 3}{x(x - 1)},$$

$$(f - g)(x) = f(x) - g(x) = \frac{3}{x} - \frac{2}{x - 1} = \frac{x - 3}{x(x - 1)}, \quad \text{and}$$

$$D_{f+g} = D_{f-g} = \{x \mid x \neq 0 \quad \text{or} \quad 1\}$$

EXAMPLE 8

Let $f(x) = \dfrac{2}{x^2 - x}$ and $g(x) = \dfrac{5}{x^2 + 2x}$. Find $f + g$ and D_{f+g}.

SOLUTION $(f + g)(x) = f(x) + g(x) = \dfrac{2}{x^2 - x} + \dfrac{5}{x^2 + 2x}$

$$= \dfrac{2}{x(x - 1)} + \dfrac{5}{x(x + 2)} \qquad \text{LCD} = x(x - 1)(x + 2)$$

$$= \dfrac{2}{x(x - 1)} \cdot \dfrac{x + 2}{x + 2} + \dfrac{5}{x(x + 2)} \cdot \dfrac{x - 1}{x - 1}$$

$$= \dfrac{2x + 4}{x(x - 1)(x + 2)} + \dfrac{5x - 5}{x(x - 1)(x + 2)}$$

$$= \dfrac{7x - 1}{x(x - 1)(x + 2)}$$

Note: $\dfrac{7x - 1}{x(x - 1)(x + 2)} \neq \dfrac{7}{x(x + 2)}$

$D_f = \{x \mid x \neq 0 \ \text{ or } \ 1\}$ and $D_g = \{x \mid x \neq 0 \ \text{ or } \ -2\}$, so
$D_{f+g} = \{x \mid x \neq 0, \ 1, \ \text{ or } \ -2\}$.

EXAMPLE 9

Let $f(x) = \dfrac{1}{9x - 18}$ and $g(x) = \dfrac{1}{6 - 3x}$. Find:

a. $f + g$ **b.** $f - g$

SOLUTION   **a.** $(f + g)(x) = f(x) + g(x) = \dfrac{1}{9(x - 2)} + \dfrac{1}{3(2 - x)}$

$2 - x$ is the opposite of $x - 2$; that is,
$(2 - x)(-1) = x - 2$. LCD $= 9(x - 2)$, so multiply the second fraction by $-3/-3$.

$$(f + g)(x) = \dfrac{1}{9(x - 2)} + \dfrac{1}{3(2 - x)} \cdot \dfrac{-3}{-3}$$

$$= \dfrac{1}{9(x - 2)} + \dfrac{-3}{3(2 - x)(-1)(3)}$$

$$= \dfrac{1}{9(x - 2)} + \dfrac{-3}{9(x - 2)}$$

$$= \dfrac{-2}{9(x - 2)}$$

b. $(f - g)(x) = \dfrac{1}{9(x - 2)} - \dfrac{1}{3(2 - x)}$

$$= \dfrac{1}{9(x - 2)} + \dfrac{1}{-3(2 - x)}$$

$$= \dfrac{1}{9(x - 2)} + \dfrac{1}{3(x - 2)} \cdot \dfrac{3}{3}$$

$$= \dfrac{1}{9(x - 2)} + \dfrac{3}{9(x - 2)}$$

$$= \dfrac{4}{9(x - 2)}$$

Math in Time

BRILLIANT MATHEMATICIANS and scientists, it is generally believed, must begin serious studies at an early age, not be distracted by other commitments, and achieve their greatest successes early in life. An outstanding exception was German mathematician Karl Weierstrass (1815–1897), who taught high school for nearly 15 years, received his Ph.D. at age 41, and made major contributions to mathematics well into his 70s.

Karl was the eldest of four children of a domineering father, who was a customs officer at a salt mine. He did so well in high school that his father insisted he study law and finance at the University of Bonn. However, Karl had a strong dislike for these subjects and spent four years becoming an expert at fencing and beer drinking before returning home without a degree. He then attended the Academy of Münster for two years to prepare for a high school teaching career. While at the academy he became friends with a professor of mathematics and spent most of his time studying advanced mathematics.

During his years as a high school teacher, Weierstrass spent his nights in research. Unable to afford postage or books, he had no communication with other mathematicians and developed his ideas on his own. In 1854 he published a paper on Abelian functions that caused a sensation. Recognition was immediate; he was awarded a Ph.D. and a

Karl Weierstrass
The Bettmann Archive

professorship at the University of Berlin, where he spent the rest of his life.

The skills Weierstrass developed as a high school teacher carried over to his university career. He is considered by many to have been the greatest teacher of advanced mathematics in the nineteenth century, and many of his students became leading mathematicians in the early twentieth century. Weierstrass was a congenial man who often spent afternoons drinking beer and discussing mathematics with his devoted students. His one eccentricity was his strong dislike of all forms of music. He remained unmarried throughout his life.

Weierstrass's contributions to mathematics were so substantial that he became known as "the father of modern anaylsis." He made major advances in the theory of functions, improved our understanding of the real number system, and separated calculus from geometry by basing it on algebra. Perhaps Weierstrass's approach to his subject is revealed in his quote: "It is true that a mathematician who is not also something of a poet will never be a perfect mathematician."

EXERCISE SET 6.3

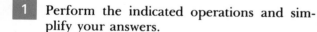
Perform the indicated operations and simplify your answers.

1. $\dfrac{3}{8} + \dfrac{1}{8}$

2. $-\dfrac{2}{10} + \dfrac{7}{10}$

3. $\dfrac{9}{11} - \dfrac{6}{11}$

4. $\dfrac{2}{5} - \dfrac{1}{-5}$

5. $-\dfrac{2}{15} - \dfrac{7}{-15}$

6. $-\dfrac{4}{9} - \dfrac{10}{18}$

7. $\dfrac{3}{z} + \dfrac{x}{z}$

8. $\dfrac{5}{2x} - \dfrac{1}{2x}$

9. $\dfrac{7}{x} - \dfrac{4}{-x}$

10. $\dfrac{7}{k-1} - \dfrac{k}{1-k}$

11. $\dfrac{6}{10mn} - \dfrac{-4}{10mn}$

12. $\dfrac{ab+3}{4a^2b^3} - \dfrac{6}{8a^2b^3}$

13. $\dfrac{3x+2}{x+1} + \dfrac{1}{x+1}$

14. $\dfrac{x}{x^2-4} + \dfrac{2}{x^2-4}$

15. $\dfrac{15x^2}{x-5x^2} - \dfrac{-3}{5x-1}$

16. $\dfrac{x^4}{x^3+x} - \dfrac{1}{x^3+x}$

17. $\dfrac{x^2-8x}{x^2-9} + \dfrac{7x-6}{x^2-9}$

18. $\dfrac{x}{x^3-1} - \dfrac{1}{x^3-1}$

2 Find the LCD for each set of fractions.

19. $\dfrac{1}{9}, \dfrac{2}{3}$

20. $\dfrac{2}{5}, \dfrac{1}{8}$

21. $\dfrac{1}{2}, \dfrac{2}{5}, \dfrac{3}{11}$

22. $\dfrac{2}{7}, \dfrac{1}{-7}$

23. $\dfrac{1}{6}, \dfrac{4}{9}$

24. $\dfrac{1}{12}, \dfrac{2}{15}$

25. $\dfrac{1}{21}, \dfrac{3}{14}, \dfrac{1}{35}$

26. $\dfrac{2}{15}, \dfrac{3}{20}, \dfrac{1}{25}$

27. $\dfrac{1}{x^2}, \dfrac{2}{x}$

28. $\dfrac{1}{x-2}, \dfrac{x+3}{x^2-4}$

29. $\dfrac{1}{2x-1}, \dfrac{3}{1-2x}$

30. $\dfrac{2}{3x-1}, \dfrac{7}{3x+1}$

31. $\dfrac{1}{x^2-1}, \dfrac{x}{x^2+x-2}$

32. $\dfrac{x}{3x+12}, \dfrac{1-x}{x^2+8x+16}$

33. $\dfrac{2}{5}, \dfrac{1}{x}, \dfrac{x-1}{x+3}$

34. $\dfrac{1}{x^2-4x}, \dfrac{2}{x^2-x}, \dfrac{3}{x^2+5x}$

35. $\dfrac{3}{x^3-1}, \dfrac{x}{x^2-1}$

36. $\dfrac{1}{y^3+8}, \dfrac{y-1}{y^2+4y+4}$

3 Perform the indicated operations and simplify your answers.

37. $\dfrac{3}{7} + \dfrac{2}{-7}$

38. $\dfrac{1}{16} - \dfrac{7}{-4}$

39. $\dfrac{1}{12} - \dfrac{5}{6} + \dfrac{3}{8}$

40. $\dfrac{2}{15} - \dfrac{1}{18} - \dfrac{-1}{30}$

41. $\dfrac{x}{y} + \dfrac{y}{x}$

42. $\dfrac{2}{15a^3} - \dfrac{1-b}{12b^2}$

43. $\dfrac{x-1}{10x^2y^4} + \dfrac{y+1}{15x^6y^2}$

44. $\dfrac{1}{a^2bc} + \dfrac{2}{ab^2c} - \dfrac{3}{abc^2}$

45. $\dfrac{3}{x-1} - \dfrac{2-x}{x^2-1}$

46. $\dfrac{2}{x^2-x} + \dfrac{x}{3-3x}$

47. $x + \dfrac{1}{x} - \dfrac{3}{x^2}$

48. $\dfrac{b}{a^2+ab} - \dfrac{a}{b^2+ab}$

49. $\dfrac{a}{ab-b^2} - \dfrac{-b}{ab-a^2}$

50. $x - 2 + \dfrac{x-1}{x+2}$

51. $\dfrac{6}{2x^2+2} + \dfrac{2}{x^2+x+1}$

52. $\dfrac{x^2}{x^3+x} - \dfrac{1}{x^4-1}$

53. $\dfrac{1}{x^2-1} - \dfrac{1-x}{x^2+4x+3}$

54. $\dfrac{x}{x^2-2xy+y^2} + \dfrac{y}{x^2-y^2}$

55. $\dfrac{3}{x^3-1} + \dfrac{x}{x^2-1}$

56. $\dfrac{1}{x^3+8} - \dfrac{2}{2x+4}$

57. $\dfrac{a}{a+2} - \dfrac{3}{a^4-16} + \dfrac{1}{2-a}$

58. $\dfrac{x-1}{x^2+x-6} + \dfrac{3-x}{2x^2+7x+3}$

59. $\dfrac{x}{x^3+1} - \dfrac{1}{x^2+x}$

60. $\dfrac{2}{x} + \dfrac{x+3}{x^2-x} - \dfrac{x}{1-x^2}$

4

61. $\dfrac{3}{5} + \dfrac{2}{5} \cdot \dfrac{3}{4}$

62. $\dfrac{1}{4} + \dfrac{11}{4} \div \dfrac{5}{6}$

Often a term of an algebraic expression is a complex fraction. The first step in simplifying such an expression is to express the complex fraction as a simple fraction. This step is illustrated in the following example.

EXAMPLE 4

Simplify $3 + \dfrac{2}{x - \dfrac{1}{4}}$

SOLUTION

$$3 + \frac{2}{x - \dfrac{1}{4}} = 3 + \frac{2}{x - \dfrac{1}{4}} \cdot \frac{4}{4} = 3 + \frac{8}{4x - 1}$$

$$= \frac{3(4x - 1)}{4x - 1} + \frac{8}{4x - 1} = \frac{12x + 5}{4x - 1}$$

3 **Simplifying Complex Fractions with Negative Exponents**

Complex fractions often involve negative exponents. The first step in simplifying one of these fractions is to rewrite it without negative exponents by using $a^{-n} = 1/a^n$. For example,

$$\frac{a^{-1} + a^{-2}}{3a} = \frac{\dfrac{1}{a} + \dfrac{1}{a^2}}{3a} \cdot 1 = \frac{\dfrac{1}{a} + \dfrac{1}{a^2}}{3a} \cdot \frac{a^2}{a^2} = \frac{a + 1}{3a^3}$$

Recall that the rules for exponents apply only to multiplication and division. Thus, we cannot write $a^{-1} + a^{-2}$ as a^{-3}. These rules are often misused with complex fractions.*

 COMMON ERROR

A common mistake is to apply rules of exponents to expressions containing addition or subtraction.

$$\frac{x + y^2}{y^{-1}} \neq x + y^{2 - (-1)} = x + y^3$$

$$\frac{x + y^2}{y^{-1}} = \frac{x + y^2}{\dfrac{1}{y}} \cdot \frac{y}{y} = xy + y^3$$

---

* A "howler" is a method that obtains a correct result by incorrect means. Students are sources of many howlers, but mathematicians also produce them by being too hasty. Below are two howlers for the same problem; the mistakes and correct solution are left as exercises.

Simplify $\dfrac{x^{-1} + y}{y^{-1} + x}$.

a. $\dfrac{x^{-1} + y}{y^{-1} + x} = \dfrac{y + y}{x + x} = \dfrac{2y}{2x} = \dfrac{y}{x}$

b. $\dfrac{x^{-1} + y}{y^{-1} + x} = \dfrac{x^{-1}}{y^{-1}} + \dfrac{y}{x} = \left(\dfrac{x}{y}\right)^{-1} + \dfrac{y}{x} = \dfrac{y}{x} + \dfrac{y}{x} = \dfrac{y + y}{x + x} = \dfrac{2y}{2x} = \dfrac{y}{x}$

THE FAR SIDE   By GARY LARSON

"Yes, yes, I *know* that, Sidney ... *everybody* knows *that*! ... But look: Four wrongs *squared*, minus two wrongs to the fourth power, divided by this formula, do make a right."

THE FARSIDE copyright 1987 UNIVERSAL PRESS SYNDICATE. Reprinted with permission. All rights reserved.

EXAMPLE 5

Simplify the following expressions.

a. $\dfrac{2^{-2} + 6}{2^0 - 6^{-1}}$ **b.** $\dfrac{a^{-1} + b^{-1}}{a + b}$ **c.** $(x^{-1} - y^{-2})^{-1}$

SOLUTION

a. Recall that $b^0 = 1$, if $b \neq 0$.

$$\frac{2^{-2} + 6}{2^0 - 6^{-1}} = \frac{\dfrac{1}{2^2} + 6}{1 - \dfrac{1}{6}} = \frac{\dfrac{1}{4} + 6}{1 - \dfrac{1}{6}} \cdot \frac{12}{12} = \frac{3 + 72}{12 - 2} = \frac{75}{10} = \frac{15}{2}$$

b. $\dfrac{a^{-1} + b^{-1}}{a + b} = \dfrac{\dfrac{1}{a} + \dfrac{1}{b}}{a + b} \cdot \dfrac{ab}{ab} = \dfrac{b + a}{(a + b)ab} = \dfrac{1}{ab}$

c. $(x^{-1} - y^{-2})^{-1} = \left(\dfrac{1}{x} - \dfrac{1}{y^2}\right)^{-1}$ $\text{LCD} = xy^2$

$= \left(\dfrac{y^2 - x}{xy^2}\right)^{-1}$ $\left(\dfrac{a}{b}\right)^{-1} = \dfrac{b}{a}$

$= \dfrac{xy^2}{y^2 - x}$

4 Simplifying Functions and Solving Word Problems

Section 6.1 defined a rational function to be the ratio of two polynomial functions; that is, f is rational if $f(x) = g(x)/h(x)$, $h(x) \neq 0$, where g and h are polynomial functions. These functions can involve complex fractions for certain values of x, as illustrated in our next example.

EXAMPLE 6

Evaluate $f(x) = \dfrac{x - 1}{x^2 + 2}$ for $x = \dfrac{2}{3}$.

SOLUTION $\quad f\left(\dfrac{2}{3}\right) = \dfrac{\dfrac{2}{3} - 1}{\left(\dfrac{2}{3}\right)^2 + 2} = \dfrac{\dfrac{2}{3} - 1}{\dfrac{4}{9} + 2} \cdot \dfrac{9}{9} = \dfrac{6 - 9}{4 + 18} = -\dfrac{3}{22}$

In Sections 3.4 and 5.4 we evaluated $\dfrac{f(x + h) - f(x)}{h}$ for polynomial functions. If f is a rational function, then this expression will be a complex fraction, which can be simplified with the methods just discussed.

EXAMPLE 7

Find $\dfrac{f(x + h) - f(x)}{h}$ for $f(x) = \dfrac{1}{x}$.

SOLUTION

$$\dfrac{f(x + h) - f(x)}{h} = \dfrac{\dfrac{1}{x + h} - \dfrac{1}{x}}{h} \cdot \dfrac{x(x + h)}{x(x + h)}$$

$$= \dfrac{\dfrac{1}{x + h} \cdot x(x + h) - \dfrac{1}{x} \cdot x(x + h)}{hx(x + h)}$$

$$= \dfrac{x - (x + h)}{hx(x + h)}$$

$$= \dfrac{-h}{hx(x + h)} \qquad h/h = 1$$

$$= \dfrac{-1}{x(x + h)}$$

This section concludes with two applications of complex fractions. The first application finds the **average speed** in a uniform motion problem. Recall that $d = rt$ gives the distance traveled at a uniform speed (or rate) r for t units of time. Thus $t = d/r$ and $r = d/t$ gives the time and speed. In most situations speed varies with time. In this case,

$$\text{average speed} = \dfrac{\text{total distance}}{\text{total time}}$$

EXAMPLE 8

Jill drove the first 20 miles to her office at 40 mph. Then she joined rush-hour traffic and drove the last 10 miles at 30 mph. Find her average speed for the trip.

SOLUTION

Jill's time for the first part of the trip is

$$t = \frac{d}{r} = \frac{20}{40} = \frac{1}{2} \text{ of an hour.}$$

Her time for the second part of the trip is

$$t = \frac{d}{r} = \frac{10}{30} = \frac{1}{3} \text{ of an hour.}$$

Thus her

$$\text{average speed} = \frac{20 + 10}{\frac{1}{2} + \frac{1}{3}} = \frac{30}{\frac{1}{2} + \frac{1}{3}} \cdot \frac{6}{6} = \frac{180}{5} = 36 \text{ mph.}$$

Our second application of complex fractions is from business and deals with changing prices. The key to this type of problem is that if C = the cost of x items at $\$y$ per item, then

$$C = xy, \qquad y = \frac{C}{x}, \qquad \text{and} \qquad x = \frac{C}{y}$$

EXAMPLE 9

If a certain number of postcards can be purchased for $6, how many can be purchased for $6 after the price has been increased by 25¢ per postcard?

SOLUTION

If x = the number of postcards purchased for $6, then they cost $\$6/x$ per postcard. If the price is increased by 25¢ = $\$1/4$, then the new price is $6/x + 1/4$ dollars each. The cost, $6, divided by the price per postcard gives the number that can be purchased at the new cost:

$$\frac{6}{\frac{6}{x} + \frac{1}{4}} = \frac{6}{\frac{6}{x} + \frac{1}{4}} \cdot \frac{4x}{4x} = \frac{24x}{24 + x}$$

To illustrate this problem, suppose the postcards cost $.50 each; then we could buy 12 for $6. If the price were increased 25¢ to $.75 each, then we could buy 8 because $x = 12$ and

$$\frac{24 \cdot 12}{24 + 12} = \frac{288}{36} = 8.$$

EXERCISE SET 6.4

A

1   Simplify the following complex fractions.

1. $\dfrac{\frac{2}{7}}{\frac{5}{3}}$

2. $\dfrac{-\frac{3}{5}}{-\frac{7}{8}}$

3. $\dfrac{-\frac{3}{10}}{\frac{9}{25}}$

4. $\dfrac{\frac{6}{x}}{\frac{7}{y}}$

5. $\dfrac{\frac{12a^2}{11b}}{\frac{9a}{22b^3}}$

6. $\dfrac{\frac{2x^4}{9y}}{\frac{8x^2}{15y^8}}$

7. $\dfrac{\frac{x-1}{2x}}{\frac{x+1}{x}}$

8. $\dfrac{\dfrac{x^2-4}{x+3}}{\dfrac{x-2}{x^2-9}}$ **9.** $\dfrac{\dfrac{1}{x-y}}{\dfrac{1}{x^2-y^2}}$

33. $(a^{-2}+a^{-3})^{-2}=a^4+a^6$

34. $(2^{-1}+3^{-1})^{-1}=5$

35. $\dfrac{3^{-1}+4}{3^{-1}}=13$

2

10. $\dfrac{2+\dfrac{1}{4}}{1-\dfrac{1}{3}}$ **11.** $\dfrac{\dfrac{5}{6}-\dfrac{3}{8}}{\dfrac{1}{2}+\dfrac{3}{4}}$ **12.** $\dfrac{3\frac{1}{2}}{2\frac{5}{6}}$

36. $(x+6)^{-2}=\dfrac{1}{x^2}+\dfrac{1}{36}$

37. $(x^{-4}x^{-1})^{-1}=x^5$

38. $\dfrac{x^{-1}-y^{-1}}{x^{-2}-y^{-2}}=\dfrac{x^2-y^2}{x-y}$

13. $\dfrac{3-\dfrac{1}{x}}{2+\dfrac{1}{y}}$ **14.** $\dfrac{x+\dfrac{3}{xy}}{\dfrac{1}{x}-\dfrac{1}{y}}$

For Exercises 39 through 41, refer to the footnote on "howlers" on page 275. What is wrong with the following solutions?

39. Solution a?   **40.** Solution b?

15. $\dfrac{\dfrac{1}{2a}+\dfrac{2}{3b^2}}{4-\dfrac{1}{ab}}$ **16.** $\dfrac{\dfrac{1}{2}-\dfrac{2}{x^2}}{1+\dfrac{2}{x}}$

41. Find a correct solution for $\dfrac{x^{-1}+y}{y^{-1}+x}$.

42. List the mistakes in the following "howler" and then give a correct solution.

$$\dfrac{(x+3)^3}{(x+3)^2}=\dfrac{x^3+3^3}{x^2+3^2}=\dfrac{x^3+27}{x^2+9}=\dfrac{x^3}{x^2}+\dfrac{27}{9}=x+3$$

17. $\dfrac{\dfrac{1}{y}-\dfrac{4y}{x^2}}{\dfrac{1}{y^2}-\dfrac{2}{xy}}$ **18.** $\dfrac{\dfrac{1}{xy^3}-\dfrac{1}{x^3y}}{\dfrac{1}{x^2y^3}-\dfrac{1}{x^3y^2}}$

Simplify the following.

43. $3^{-1}+4^{-1}$ **44.** $x^{-2}-x^{-3}$

19. $\dfrac{3+\dfrac{2}{m-2}}{1-\dfrac{4}{m-2}}$ **20.** $\dfrac{4-\dfrac{2}{x-6}}{2+\dfrac{6}{x-6}}$

45. $(3^{-1}-4^{-1})^{-1}$ **46.** $(x^{-1}-y^{-1})^{-1}$

47. $\dfrac{a^{-1}-b^2}{a-b^{-2}}$ **48.** $\dfrac{pq^{-1}-1}{p^2q^{-2}-1}$

21. $\dfrac{1-\dfrac{4}{1-x}}{2+\dfrac{8}{x-1}}$ **22.** $\dfrac{1-\dfrac{1}{m+1}}{1+\dfrac{1}{m-1}}$

49. $\dfrac{2}{a^{-1}+b^{-1}}$ **50.** $\dfrac{ab^{-1}-ba^{-1}}{b-a}$

51. $ba^{-2}+ab^{-3}$ **52.** $x^2y^{-1}-x^{-3}y^2$

23. $\dfrac{\dfrac{1}{x+h}-\dfrac{1}{x}}{h}$ **24.** $\dfrac{\dfrac{2}{x+h}+\dfrac{2}{x}}{h}$

25. $\dfrac{abc}{\dfrac{1}{a}+\dfrac{1}{b}-\dfrac{1}{c}}$ **26.** $\dfrac{m^2}{1-\dfrac{v^2}{c^2}}$

4

53. Evaluate $f(x)=\dfrac{1}{x+2}$ for:

a. $x=\dfrac{1}{5}$ **b.** $x=-\dfrac{4}{3}$

27. $1+\dfrac{1}{1+\dfrac{1}{3}}$ **28.** $2-\dfrac{3}{4-\dfrac{1}{5}}$

54. Evaluate $f(x)=\dfrac{x-2}{2x+3}$ for:

a. $x=-\dfrac{1}{2}$ **b.** $x=2\dfrac{2}{3}$

29. $x-\dfrac{x}{1+\dfrac{1}{x}}$ **30.** $x+\dfrac{1}{x-\dfrac{1}{x}}$

55. Evaluate $g(t)=\dfrac{4t}{t^2-1}$ for:

a. $t=-2.1$ **b.** $t=0.6$

3 Determine whether the following are true or false. For false equations, give the correct solution.

56. Evaluate $F(y)=\dfrac{3y-6}{2y^2-y}$ for:

31. $\dfrac{x^{-1}+y}{x^{-1}}=1+y$ **32.** $\dfrac{a^{-1}+a}{a^{-1}+a^2}=\dfrac{1+a^2}{1+a^3}$

a. $y=\dfrac{1}{6}$ **b.** $y=-0.2$

Find $\dfrac{f(x + h) - f(x)}{h}$ for the following functions.

57. $f(x) = \dfrac{3}{x}$ **58.** $f(x) = -\dfrac{1}{x}$

59. $f(x) = \dfrac{3x}{x - 1}$ **60.** $f(x) = \dfrac{2x}{x + 3}$

61. $f(x) = \dfrac{x - 3}{x + 2}$ **62.** $f(x) = \dfrac{1 - x}{4 + x}$

63. $f(x) = \dfrac{1}{x^2}$ **64.** $f(x) = \dfrac{-2}{x^2}$

Solve the following.

65. Towns A and B are 60 miles apart. Carmen drove from A to B at 60 mph. On the return trip she drove at 30 mph. Is her average speed for the trip 45 mph?

66. Steve cycled 10 kilometers at 5 km/h and 5 kilometers at 10 km/h. Find his average speed.

67. Susan traveled 1 mile at 60 mph, 2 miles at 40 mph, and 3 miles at 30 mph. Find her average speed.

68. Hasan drove the first 30 miles to his office at 50 mph and the last 10 miles at 30 mph. If he drove home at 35 mph, find his average speed correctly to one decimal place.

69. Maria drove d kilometers at 60 km/h and returned the same distance at 40 km/h. Find her average speed.

70. Jan drove to Mt. Hood, Oregon, for a ski weekend. She drove there at 52 mph and returned home at 36 mph. Find her average speed for the trip correctly to two decimal places.

71. If a certain number of items can be purchased for $10, how many can be purchased for $10 after the price has been increased by 50¢?

72. If a certain number of items can be purchased for $30, how many can be purchased for $24 after the price has been increased by $3.50?

73. If a certain number of items can be purchased for $16, how many can be purchased for $16 after the price has been reduced by $1.20?

74. If a certain number of items can be purchased for $8, how many can be purchased for $10 after the price has been reduced by 75¢?

B

75. Find the reciprocal of $\dfrac{1}{x} - \dfrac{1}{x + 1}$.

76. Find the reciprocal of $\dfrac{1}{a - b} + \dfrac{1}{a + b}$.

77. Find the average of $\dfrac{1}{a - b}$ and $\dfrac{1}{a + b}$.

78. Find the average of x, $\dfrac{1}{x}$, and $\dfrac{1}{x + 1}$.

Simplify the following.

79. $\dfrac{\dfrac{n + 1}{5^{n + 1}}}{\dfrac{n}{5^n}}$

80. $t + \dfrac{1 - \dfrac{1 - t}{1 - t}}{1 + \dfrac{1 + t}{1 - t}}$

81. $\dfrac{\dfrac{a}{a + b} + \dfrac{b}{a - b}}{\dfrac{b}{a + b} - \dfrac{a}{a - b}}$

82. $\dfrac{\dfrac{1}{abc^2} + \dfrac{1}{ab^2c} - \dfrac{1}{a^2bc}}{\dfrac{a}{bc} - \dfrac{b}{a^2c} + \dfrac{c}{ab^2}}$

C

Answer the following questions with complete sentences.

83. How does a complex fraction differ from a simple fraction?

84. Explain how to simplify a complex fraction using the LCD method.

85. What would be your first step in simplifying $\dfrac{a^{-2} + a^{-1}}{4a}$?

86. What is meant by a "howler"?

REVIEW EXERCISES

Solve the following equations. (See Section 2.2.)

87. $\dfrac{x}{6} + \dfrac{x}{4} = 2$ **88.** $\dfrac{x - 1}{12} - \dfrac{x}{9} = \dfrac{1}{18}$

Solve the following for the indicated variables. (See Section 2.3.)

89. $w - xw = 1 + x$; w **90.** $dD = fD + df$; D

91. $\dfrac{x}{2} - \dfrac{y}{5} = 1$; y **92.** $V = \dfrac{1}{3}\pi r^2 h$; π

Solve the following equations. (See Section 5.6.)

93. $x^2 + 2x - 15 = 0$ **94.** $2x^2 + 7x = 4$

Find the domain for the following. (See Section 6.1.)

95. $\dfrac{x^2 + 3x}{5x + 25}$ **96.** $\dfrac{x}{x^2 - 4}$

6.5   SOLVING FRACTIONAL EQUATIONS AND FORMULAS

1	Solving Fractional Equations
2	Solving Proportions
3	Solving Formulas and Literal Equations

1   Solving Fractional Equations

Many formulas and equations contain fractions, both simple and complex. In Section 2.2 we solved fractional equations that contained integer denominators. In this section we will solve fractional equations whose denominators contain variables. Then we will consider formulas that contain fractions.

Recall that the procedure for solving a fractional equation is to multiply both sides by the LCD of all the denominators. This procedure results in an equation involving only integers. This material is reviewed in the first example of this section.

EXAMPLE 1

Solve $\dfrac{1}{6} + \dfrac{x}{2} = \dfrac{29 - x}{9}$ for x.

SOLUTION   The LCD is 18. Thus

$$\frac{1}{6} + \frac{x}{2} = \frac{29 - x}{9}$$

$$18\left(\frac{1}{6} + \frac{x}{2}\right) = 18\left(\frac{29 - x}{9}\right) \quad a(b + c) = ab + ac$$

$$18 \cdot \frac{1}{6} + 18 \cdot \frac{x}{2} = 2(29 - x)$$

$$3 + 9x = 58 - 2x$$

$$3 + 11x = 58$$

$$11x = 55$$

$$x = 5$$

✔ CHECK $\dfrac{1}{6} + \dfrac{x}{2} = \dfrac{1}{6} + \dfrac{5}{2} = \dfrac{1}{6} + \dfrac{15}{6} = \dfrac{16}{6} = \dfrac{8}{3}$, and

$$\frac{29 - x}{9} = \frac{29 - 5}{9} = \frac{24}{9} = \frac{8}{3}.$$

The procedure illustrated in Example 1 applies to a fractional equation that contains a variable in one or more of its denominators. We multiply both sides by the LCD to eliminate the denominators. For example,

$$\frac{2}{x} - \frac{3}{4} = \frac{1}{2x} \qquad \text{LCD} = 4x$$

$$4x\left(\frac{2}{x} - \frac{3}{4}\right) = 4x\left(\frac{1}{2x}\right)$$

$$4x \cdot \frac{2}{x} - 4x \cdot \frac{3}{4} = 2$$

$$8 - 3x = 2$$

$$-3x = -6$$

$$x = 2$$

An equation that contains a variable in its denominator(s) has a potential problem: We might obtain a value of the variable that makes a denominator zero. In this case we must discard that number as a possible solution. For instance,

$$\frac{x}{x - 4} + \frac{4}{5} = \frac{4}{x - 4} \qquad \text{LCD} = 5(x - 4)$$

$$5(x - 4)\left(\frac{x}{x - 4} + \frac{4}{5}\right) = 5(x - 4)\left(\frac{4}{x - 4}\right)$$

$$5x + (x - 4)4 = 5 \cdot 4$$

$$5x + 4x - 16 = 20$$

$$9x = 36$$

$$x = 4$$

If $x = 4$, then $\dfrac{x}{x - 4} = \dfrac{4}{4 - 4} = \dfrac{4}{0}$, which is undefined.

Because $x \neq 4$ in the original equation, the solution set is Ø, the empty set.

The best way to avoid getting the wrong answer to this type of equation is to determine its domain. If one of the solutions is a number that is not in its domain, then that number must be excluded from the solution set.

Many fractional equations simplify to quadratic equations. Recall that we solve a quadratic equation by writing it with zero on one side of the equation and then using the zero-factor property: If $ab = 0$, then $a = 0$ or $b = 0$. This solution is illustrated in the next example; the checks are left as exercises.

EXAMPLE 2

Solve the following equations.

a. $\dfrac{x^2 + 3x}{5x + 25} - \dfrac{2}{x + 5} = \dfrac{1}{5}$ **b.** $2x + \dfrac{\dfrac{1}{3} - \dfrac{1}{10}}{\dfrac{1}{30}} = \dfrac{4}{x}$

SOLUTION **a.** $\dfrac{x^2 + 3x}{5(x + 5)} - \dfrac{2}{x + 5} = \dfrac{1}{5}$

$\text{LCD} = 5(x + 5)$ and $D = \{x \mid x \neq -5\}$. Then

$$5(x + 5)\left[\dfrac{x^2 + 3x}{5(x + 5)} - \dfrac{2}{x + 5}\right] = 5(x + 5)\left[\dfrac{1}{5}\right]$$

$$x^2 + 3x - 10 = x + 5$$

$$x^2 + 2x - 15 = 0$$

$$(x + 5)(x - 3) = 0$$

$$x + 5 = 0 \quad \text{or} \quad x - 3 = 0$$

$$x = -5 \quad \text{or} \quad x = 3$$

$-5 \notin D$ so $x = 3$ is the solution.

b. $D = \{x \mid x \neq 0\}$. First simplify the complex fraction:

$$2x + \dfrac{\dfrac{1}{3} - \dfrac{1}{10}}{\dfrac{1}{30}} \cdot \dfrac{30}{30} = \dfrac{4}{x}$$

$$2x + \dfrac{10 - 3}{1} = \dfrac{4}{x}$$

$$2x + 7 = \dfrac{4}{x}$$

$$x(2x + 7) = x \cdot \dfrac{4}{x}$$

$$2x^2 + 7x = 4$$

$$2x^2 + 7x - 4 = 0 \qquad m + n = 7$$

$$2x^2 + 8x - x - 4 = 0 \qquad mn = 2(-4)$$

$$2x(x + 4) - 1(x + 4) = 0 \qquad\quad = 8(-1)$$

$$(2x - 1)(x + 4) = 0$$

$$2x - 1 = 0 \quad \text{or} \quad x + 4 = 0$$

$x = 1/2 \quad \text{or} \quad -4$, which are both in D. Thus, the solution set is $\{-4, 1/2\}$.

E X A M P L E 3

Solve for x:

$$\dfrac{2}{x} + \dfrac{3}{x + 2} = \dfrac{4}{5x}$$

SOLUTION $\text{LCD} = 5x(x + 2)$ and $D = \{x \mid x \neq -2 \text{ or } 0\}$.

$$5x(x + 2)\left[\dfrac{2}{x} + \dfrac{3}{x + 2}\right] = 5x(x + 2)\left[\dfrac{4}{5x}\right]$$

$$10(x + 2) + 5x \cdot 3 = (x + 2)4$$

$$10x + 20 + 15x = 4x + 8$$

$$25x + 20 = 4x + 8$$

$$21x = -12$$

$$x = -\dfrac{12}{21} = -\dfrac{4}{7}$$

EXAMPLE 4

Combine and simplify

$$\frac{2}{x} + \frac{3}{x + 2} - \frac{4}{5x}$$

SOLUTION

$$\frac{2}{x} + \frac{3}{x + 2} - \frac{4}{5x} \qquad\qquad LCD = 5x(x + 2)$$

$$\frac{2}{x} \cdot \frac{5(x + 2)}{5(x + 2)} + \frac{3}{x + 2} \cdot \frac{5x}{5x} + \frac{-4}{5x} \cdot \frac{x + 2}{x + 2}$$

$$\frac{10x + 20}{5x(x + 2)} + \frac{15x}{5x(x + 2)} + \frac{-4x - 8}{5x(x + 2)}$$

$$\frac{21x + 12}{5x(x + 2)}$$

Confusing an equation (such as Example 3) with an expression (such as Example 4) is one of the most common mistakes made in algebra. The multiplication property of equality allows us to eliminate the denominators of an equation, but we cannot do this with the sum, difference, or both of rational expressions. Changing the equal sign in Example 3 to the subtraction sign in Example 4 completely changes the problem!

COMMON ERROR

A common mistake is to confuse the method of solving a fractional equation with the method of combining rational expressions.

Right

$$\frac{x}{x - 6} + \frac{1}{x}$$

$$\frac{x}{x - 6} \cdot \frac{x}{x} + \frac{1}{x} \cdot \frac{x - 6}{x - 6}$$

$$\frac{x^2}{x(x - 6)} + \frac{x - 6}{x(x - 6)}$$

$$\frac{x^2 + x - 6}{x(x - 6)}$$

Wrong

$$\frac{x}{x - 6} + \frac{1}{x}$$

$$x(x - 6)\left[\frac{x}{x - 6} + \frac{1}{x}\right]$$

$$x^2 + x - 6$$

This is like saying,

$$\frac{2}{7} + \frac{3}{7} = 5$$

2   Solving Proportions

A **ratio**, a/b, is the quotient of two numbers (or quantities), such as $\frac{3}{4}$ and $\frac{x + 1}{x + 2}$. A **proportion** is an equation stating that two ratios are equal. A proportion is usually written: $\frac{a}{b} = \frac{c}{d}$, $b \neq 0$ and $d \neq 0$.

Cross-multiplication is a convenient method for solving some proportions. We justify it as follows:

$$\frac{a}{b} = \frac{c}{d} \qquad\qquad LCD = bd$$

$$bd\left(\frac{a}{b}\right) = bd\left(\frac{c}{d}\right)$$

$$ad = bc$$

> **Cross-Multiplication Property of Proportions**
>
> If $\dfrac{a}{b} = \dfrac{c}{d}$, $b \neq 0$ and $d \neq 0$, then $ad = bc$.

EXAMPLE 5

Solve the following proportions.

a. $\dfrac{n + 5}{n + 10} = \dfrac{3}{4}$ **b.** $\dfrac{3}{x} = \dfrac{11}{x^2}$ **c.** $\dfrac{h}{30} = \dfrac{7}{6}$

SOLUTION   **a.** $\dfrac{n + 5}{n + 10} = \dfrac{3}{4}$, $D = \{n \mid n \neq -10\}$. Cross-multiply

$$(n + 5)4 = (n + 10)3$$
$$4n + 20 = 3n + 30$$
$$n = 10$$

b. $\dfrac{3}{x} = \dfrac{11}{x^2}$, $D = \{x \mid x \neq 0\}$. Cross-multiply

$$3x^2 = 11x$$
$$3x^2 - 11x = 0$$
$$x(3x - 11) = 0$$

$x = 0$ or $3x - 11 = 0$; $x \neq 0$, so the solution is

$x = 11/3$

c. The simplest way to solve this proportion is to multiply both sides of the equation by 30.

$$\frac{h}{30} = \frac{7}{6}$$
$$30 \cdot \frac{h}{30} = 30 \cdot \frac{7}{6}$$
$$h = 5 \cdot 7 = 35$$

3   Solving Formulas and Literal Equations

Section 2.3 discussed formulas and literal equations, such as $P = 2L + 2W$ and $3x - 2y = 6$, and used the methods for solving linear equations to solve them for a given variable. We will now repeat this process for fractional formulas. Multiplying both sides of a formula by the LCD of all its denominators simplifies it to an equation like the ones in Section 2.3. We begin with a formula from astronomy.

Solve $\dfrac{1}{S} = \dfrac{1}{E} - \dfrac{1}{P}$ for E. The LCD $= SEP$, so

$$SEP\left(\frac{1}{S}\right) = SEP\left(\frac{1}{E} - \frac{1}{P}\right)$$

$$EP = SP - SE \qquad \text{Add } SE \text{ to both sides.}$$
$$SE + EP = SP \qquad \text{Factor.}$$
$$E(S + P) = SP \qquad \text{Divide by } S + P.$$
$$E = \frac{SP}{S + P}$$

Many formulas describe relationships between different masses, velocities, and so forth. Conveniently, we can use subscripts in these situations. Recall that a subscript is a number or letter written below and to the right of a variable, such as m_1 or F_x. These are read, "m sub one" and "F sub x." An example of a formula involving subscripts is

$$F = \frac{Gm_1m_2}{d^2}$$

This equation describes the force of gravitational attraction between two bodies, such as the earth and the moon, with masses m_1 and m_2 separated by the distance d between their centers. G is called the "gravitational constant." The formula was discovered by English mathematician and physicist Sir Isaac Newton (1642–1727).

We conclude this section with examples of solving formulas for a specified variable. In the next section we will consider applications of fractional formulas.

EXAMPLE 5

Solve the following for the variables listed after each equation.

a. $F = \frac{Gm_1m_2}{d^2}$; m_2 Newton's law of gravitation

b. $\frac{V_1}{P_f} = \frac{V_f}{P_i}$; P_i Chemistry — Boyle's Law

c. $C = \frac{36x}{108 - x}$; x An equation from business

d. $V^2 = \dfrac{B + \frac{4}{3}G}{d}$; G Geology — an earthquake formula

SOLUTION   **a.** $F = \dfrac{Gm_1m_2}{d^2} = \dfrac{Gm_1}{d^2} \cdot m_2$ Multiply by $\dfrac{d^2}{Gm_1}$.

$\dfrac{d^2}{Gm_1} \cdot F = \dfrac{\not{d^2}}{\not{Gm_1}} \cdot \dfrac{\not{Gm_1}}{\not{d^2}} \cdot m_2$

$\dfrac{d^2 F}{Gm_1} = m_2$

b.
$\dfrac{V_i}{P_f} = \dfrac{V_f}{P_i}$ Cross-multiply.

$V_i P_i = P_f V_f$ Divide by V_i.

$P_i = \dfrac{P_f V_f}{V_i}$

c. $C = \dfrac{36x}{108 - x}$ Multiply by $108 - x$.

$C(108 - x) = 36x$ $a(b - c) = ab - ac$

$108C - Cx = 36x$ Add Cx.

$108C = Cx + 36x$ $ba + ca = (b + c)a$

$108C = (C + 36)x$ Divide by $C + 36$.

$\dfrac{108C}{C + 36} = x$

d. First simplify the complex fraction.

$$V^2 = \frac{B + \frac{4}{3}G}{d} \cdot \frac{3}{3}$$

$$V^2 = \frac{3B + 4G}{3d} \qquad \text{Multiply by } 3d.$$

$$3dV^2 = 3B + 4G \qquad \text{Subtract } 3B.$$

$$3dV^2 - 3B = 4G \qquad \text{Divide by } 4.$$

$$\frac{3dV^2 - 3B}{4} = G$$

EXERCISE SET 6.5

A

1

1. Check the solution to Example 2 (p. 282).

2. Check the solution to Example 3 (p. 283).

Solve the following equations and check the solutions to Exercises 3 through 10.

3. $\dfrac{x}{6} - \dfrac{x}{4} = 1$

4. $\dfrac{3x}{2} - \dfrac{1}{5} = 4 - \dfrac{x}{10}$

5. $\dfrac{x + 3}{4} + \dfrac{4x - 5}{5} = 5$

6. $n^2 = \dfrac{1}{6} - \dfrac{n}{6}$

7. $\dfrac{3}{4t} + \dfrac{6}{5t} = \dfrac{13}{20}$

8. $\dfrac{2}{3x} - 25 = \dfrac{9}{x}$

9. $\dfrac{x - 2}{x} - \dfrac{5}{2} = \dfrac{8 - x}{2x}$

10. $\dfrac{a - 5}{3a} + \dfrac{5}{6} = \dfrac{a + 5}{a}$

11. $\dfrac{3x}{x - 2} + 4 = \dfrac{6}{x - 2}$

12. $\dfrac{-4}{x} - \dfrac{2 - x}{x^2} = -\dfrac{2}{x}$

13. $x - 1 = \dfrac{30}{x}$

14. $\dfrac{x}{x - 6} + \dfrac{6}{7} = \dfrac{6}{x - 6}$

15. $\dfrac{y + 2}{y - 2} + \dfrac{7}{y^2 - 4} = \dfrac{y^2 - 10}{y^2 - 4}$

16. $k + \dfrac{1}{k} = \dfrac{17}{4}$

17. $\dfrac{3}{3 - n} = 5 - \dfrac{n}{n - 3}$

18. $\dfrac{6}{x - 5} + \dfrac{2}{5 - x} = 8$

19. $\dfrac{1}{x - 1} + \dfrac{2}{x + 1} = -\dfrac{2}{3}$

20. $\dfrac{5}{x + 2} + \dfrac{1}{x - 2} = \dfrac{4}{x^2 - 4}$

21. $\dfrac{x}{x + 5} + \dfrac{5}{4} = -\dfrac{5}{x + 5}$

22. $\dfrac{4}{t^2 - 4t} - \dfrac{t - 3}{t - 4} = \dfrac{1}{t}$

23. $\dfrac{2}{k - 5} + \dfrac{1}{k + 5} = \dfrac{11}{k^2 - 25}$

24. $\dfrac{1}{x + 4} = \dfrac{x + 12}{x^2 - 16} - \dfrac{3}{x - 4}$

25. $\dfrac{1}{x - 1} = \dfrac{2}{x^2 - 1}$

26. $\dfrac{x}{x + 3} + \dfrac{5}{x} = \dfrac{3}{2}$

27. $\dfrac{\frac{x}{2} - 2}{3} + \dfrac{1}{4} = x$

28. $\dfrac{\frac{x}{6} + \frac{1}{2}}{\frac{1}{3}} - \dfrac{x}{6} = 1$

29. $\dfrac{2}{x} + \dfrac{\frac{1}{x}}{1 - \frac{1}{x}} = 2$

30. $1 - \dfrac{1}{\frac{1}{2} + \frac{3}{2x}} = \dfrac{4}{x + 4}$

For each of the following, either solve the equation or perform the indicated operations and simplify.

31. $\dfrac{4}{x} + \dfrac{7}{2x} - \dfrac{1}{5}$

32. $\dfrac{4}{x} + \dfrac{7}{2x} = \dfrac{1}{5}$

33. $\dfrac{x + 3}{2} = \dfrac{x + 2}{2} + \dfrac{1}{x}$

34. $\dfrac{t}{t + 1} + \dfrac{2}{t - 1} - \dfrac{t}{t^2 - 1}$

35. $\dfrac{3}{2x - 6} - \dfrac{x - 1}{x^2 - 3x}$ **36.** $\dfrac{x + 1}{6} - \dfrac{3}{4} = \dfrac{1 - x}{3}$

37. $\dfrac{1}{2x^3} + \dfrac{1}{2x^2} = \dfrac{1}{8x} + \dfrac{1}{8}$ **38.** $\dfrac{1}{10} + \dfrac{5}{2y} = \dfrac{y}{10} + \dfrac{5}{2y^2}$

2   Solve the following proportions.

39. $\dfrac{x}{6} = \dfrac{3}{7}$ **40.** $\dfrac{-4}{11} = \dfrac{2}{x}$

41. $\dfrac{2}{x - 1} = \dfrac{3}{x}$ **42.** $\dfrac{9}{5} = \dfrac{t - 1}{t}$

43. $\dfrac{2x - 1}{3x + 4} = \dfrac{3}{4}$ **44.** $\dfrac{1}{9} = \dfrac{1}{x^2}$

45. $\dfrac{x}{3} = \dfrac{x + 4}{x + 2}$ **46.** $\dfrac{2 - x}{x + 4} = \dfrac{2x}{3}$

3   Solve the following for the indicated variables.

47. $\dfrac{x}{6} + \dfrac{y}{8} = 1; \quad x$ **48.** $\dfrac{x}{6} + \dfrac{y}{8} = 1; \quad y$

49. $\dfrac{2x}{3} - \dfrac{y}{4} = \dfrac{1}{2}; \quad y$ **50.** $\dfrac{x}{5} - \dfrac{3y}{2} = \dfrac{1}{10}; \quad x$

51. $\dfrac{P_i V_i}{T_i} = \dfrac{P_f V_f}{T_f}; \quad T_f$ **52.** $K = \dfrac{n + 3}{m}; \quad n$

53. $y = \dfrac{n + sf}{s}; \quad s$ **54.** $A = \dfrac{R}{R - s}; \quad R$

55. $\dfrac{y - b}{x} = m; \quad y$ **56.** $\dfrac{4}{x + 3} = \dfrac{5}{y - 2}; \quad x$

57. $\dfrac{A}{B} = \dfrac{C}{B + C}; \quad B$ **58.** $\dfrac{A}{B} = \dfrac{C}{B + C}; \quad C$

59. $\dfrac{a + b}{b} = \dfrac{c + d}{d}; \quad a$ **60.** $\dfrac{a - b}{b} = \dfrac{c - d}{d}; \quad d$

61. $S = \dfrac{w}{2} - \dfrac{wy}{t}; \quad y$ **62.** $y = \dfrac{a}{b}x - \dfrac{c}{d}; \quad x$

63. $\dfrac{1}{f} = \dfrac{1}{f_1} + \dfrac{1}{f_2}; \quad f_2$ **64.** $\dfrac{1}{f} = \dfrac{1}{f_1} + \dfrac{1}{f_2}; \quad f$

65. $T = \dfrac{v + v_0}{v - v_1}; \quad v$ **66.** $C = \dfrac{an}{R + nr}; \quad n$

67. $A = \dfrac{4a_1}{a_1 + a_2}; \quad a_1$ **68.** $A = \dfrac{4a_1}{a_1 + a_2}; \quad a_2$

B

69. $M = \dfrac{\dfrac{1}{m}}{1 + \dfrac{1}{n}}; \quad m$ **70.** $T = \dfrac{1 + \dfrac{1}{x}}{1 - \dfrac{1}{y}}; \quad y$

71. $A = \dfrac{x - \dfrac{4}{5}y}{z}; \quad x$ **72.** $M^2 = \dfrac{m^2}{1 - \dfrac{v^2}{c^2}}; \quad c^2$

73. $R = \dfrac{1}{\dfrac{1}{R_1} + \dfrac{1}{R_2}}; \quad R_1$ **74.** $C = \dfrac{3}{\dfrac{1}{a} - \dfrac{2}{b}}; \quad b$

C

Answer the following questions with complete sentences.

75. Why should we check our solutions to a fractional equation that contains a variable in its denominator?

76. Discuss the difference between the method of solving the equation $\dfrac{1}{2} + \dfrac{1}{x + 1} = \dfrac{2}{3}$ and the method of simplifying the expression $\dfrac{1}{2} + \dfrac{1}{x + 1} - \dfrac{2}{3}$.

REVIEW EXERCISES

Solve the following proportions for the indicated variable.

77. $\dfrac{h}{29} = \dfrac{4}{5}$ **78.** $\dfrac{4}{h} = \dfrac{5}{29}$

79. $\dfrac{V_1}{P_2} = \dfrac{V_2}{P_1}; \quad V_2$

Solve the following geometry problems. (See Section 2.3.)

80. The length of a rectangle is 42 centimeters, and its width is 24 centimeters. Find its perimeter.

81. The sides of a triangle are 4, 12, and 14 inches. Find its perimeter.

6.6 SOLVING RATIO AND PROPORTION PROBLEMS

1	**Understanding Ratio Problems**
2	**Applying Proportion Problems**
3	**Applying Formulas**

1 Understanding Ratio Problems

In the last section we defined a proportion to be a statement of equality between two ratios: $a/b = c/d$. In this section we will consider applications of ratios and proportions.*

If a and b are two numbers, $b \neq 0$, then the ratio of a to b is written $\frac{a}{b}$ or $a : b$. A ratio provides a way of comparing two quantities. For example, if a class of 45 students has 20 women and 25 men, then the ratio of women to men is

$$20 \text{ to } 25 = \frac{20}{25} = \frac{4}{5} = 4 : 5$$

In words, the class has 4 women for every 5 men.

The symbol, :, is particularly useful when comparing three or more quantities. For instance, if Rubina spends \$600 per month for rent, \$300 for food, and \$200 for utilities, then her expenses are in the ratio

$$600 : 300 : 200 = 6 : 3 : 2$$

In a typical ratio problem we are asked to find unknown quantities that are in a given ratio. Enough information is provided to allow us to use the ratio to write an equation. For example, suppose that we are told that two numbers are in the ratio 3 to 4, or 3/4. An infinite number of pairs of numbers are in this ratio: 3/4, 6/8, and so on. In general, any two numbers in the form $3x$ and $4x$ are in the ratio 3 to 4. If we are told that their sum is 49, then we can find the numbers as follows:

$$3x + 4x = 49$$
$$7x = 49$$
$$x = 7$$
$$3x = 21 \quad \text{and} \quad 4x = 28, \quad \text{so the numbers are 21 and 28.}$$

---

* The word *ratio* comes from the latin verb *ratus*, meaning "to reckon" or "to reason." In the Middle Ages the word meant "computation." The symbols :, for ratio, and ::, for proportion, originated in early seventeenth-century England. Our equation $\frac{a}{b} = \frac{c}{d}$ was written then as $a : b :: c : d$, which was later changed to $a : b = c : d$. These earlier forms are still occasionally used.

EXAMPLE 1

The length and width of a rectangle are in the ratio of 7 to 4. The perimeter is 132 centimeters. Find the rectangle's length and width.

SOLUTION

Let $L = 7x$ = the length of the rectangle and $W = 4x$ = the width of the rectangle. $2L + 2W = P$ is the formula for the perimeter. Then

$$2(7x) + 2(4x) = 132$$
$$22x = 132$$
$$x = 6$$

$L = 7 \cdot 6 = 42$ centimeters   and $W = 4 \cdot 6 = 24$ centimeters are the rectangle's dimensions.

EXAMPLE 2

The gold solder used by a jeweler has gold, silver, and copper in the ratio $10 : 6 : 5$. How much gold, silver, and copper are in 31.5 grams of solder?

SOLUTION

Let $10x$ = the amount of gold, $6x$ = the amount of silver, and $5x$ = the amount of copper. Then

$$10x + 6x + 5x = 31.5$$
$$21x = 31.5$$
$$x = 1.5, \text{ so}$$

$10(1.5) = 15$ grams of gold,
$6(1.5) = 9$ grams of silver, and
$5(1.5) = 7.5$ grams of copper.

2   Applying Proportion Problems

The proportion $a/b = c/d$ is read "a is to b as c is to d." Proportions can be used to solve a wide variety of problems. For example:

> A 4-foot stick casts a 5-foot shadow when a tree casts a 29-foot shadow. How tall is the tree to the nearest foot?

Let h = the tree's height. Then the ratio of the tree's height to its shadow, $h/29$, is equal to the ratio of the stick's height to its shadow, 4/5. Thus

$$\frac{h}{29} = \frac{4}{5}$$

$$h = 29 \cdot \frac{4}{5} = \frac{116}{5} = 23.2 \approx 23 \text{ feet.}$$

We could use any of four proportions to solve this problem:

$$\frac{h}{29} = \frac{4}{5}, \qquad \frac{29}{h} = \frac{5}{4}, \qquad \frac{h}{4} = \frac{29}{5}, \qquad \text{and} \qquad \frac{4}{h} = \frac{5}{29}$$

In each proportion the ratios are equivalent because, by cross-multiplying, they all result in $5h = 4 \cdot 29$.

We have no difficulty as long as we use equivalent ratios in a proportion problem. However a common mistake is to use ratios that are not equivalent, such as

$$\frac{h}{29} \neq \frac{5}{4}$$

The ratio of the tree's height to its shadow is not the same as the stick's shadow to its height.

 COMMON ERROR Using ratios that are not equivalent is a common mistake in a proportion problem:

$$\frac{\text{height}}{\text{shadow}} = \frac{\text{height}}{\text{shadow}} \qquad \text{but} \qquad \frac{\text{height}}{\text{shadow}} \neq \frac{\text{shadow}}{\text{height}}$$

EXAMPLE 3

A sum of \$1250 was divided between Ted and Steve in the ratio of 2 to 3. How much did each receive?

SOLUTION

Let t = the amount that Ted received. Then $1250 - t$ = the amount that Steve received. Then t is to $1250 - t$ as 2 is to 3; that is,

$$\frac{t}{1250 - t} = \frac{2}{3} \qquad \text{Cross-multiply.}$$

$$3t = 2(1250 - t)$$
$$3t = 2500 - 2t$$
$$5t = 2500$$
$$t = 500 \quad \text{and}$$
$$1250 - t = 1250 - 500 = 750.$$

Therefore, Ted received \$500 and Steve received \$750.

Englishman Robert Boyle (1627–1691) was one of the first experimental scientists. He had a wide range of interests and discovered the part taken by air in the propagation of sound and, as an alchemist, tried to turn lead into gold. He is mainly remembered today for his study of the relationship between the pressure and volume of a gas. This equation, known as **Boyle's Law**, states that if P_1 and V_1 represent the initial pressure and volume of a gas and P_2 and V_2 the final pressure and volume of the gas at the same temperature, then

$$\frac{V_1}{P_2} = \frac{V_2}{P_1}$$

EXAMPLE 4

If the volume of a balloon is 2.0 liters when the pressure is 0.98 atmospheres, what will the volume be when the balloon rises to a point at which the pressure is 0.75 atmospheres?

SOLUTION

Let V_2 = the volume when pressure P_2 is .75.
If $V_1 = 2$ and $P_1 = .98$, then

$$\frac{V_2}{P_1} = \frac{V_1}{P_2}$$

$$\frac{V_2}{.98} = \frac{2}{.75}$$

$$V_2 = \frac{.98(2)}{.75} = \frac{1.96}{.75} = 2.61\overline{3}, \quad \text{or approximately 2.6 liters.}$$

3 Applying Formulas

Section 3.4 discussed cost functions that involved linear equations. We will now consider a cost function described by a rational expression.

A mathematical description of an event is called a **model**. Rational functions can be used to model the cost of removing a given percentage of a pollutant from the environment; these functions are called **cost–benefit models**. As illustrated in our last example, the cost of removing 100% of a pollutant from air or water is considerably higher than removing 90%.

EXAMPLE 5

A ship accidentally spilled fuel oil into a harbor. The cost–benefit model for removing the oil is given by the function

$$C(x) = \frac{36x}{108 - x}$$

where C is in thousands of dollars and x is a percent; $0 \leq x \leq 100$. Determine the approximate cost of removing the following amounts of oil from the harbor.

a. 100%   **b.** 90%   **c.** 50%

SOLUTION

a. $C(100) = \dfrac{36(100)}{108 - 100} = \dfrac{3600}{8} = 450$

Removing all of the oil would cost $450,000.

b. $C(90) = \dfrac{36(90)}{108 - 90} = \dfrac{3240}{18} = 180$

Removing 90% of the oil would cost $180,000.

c. $C(50) = \dfrac{36(50)}{108 - 50} = \dfrac{1800}{58} \approx 31$

Removing 50% of the oil would cost $31,000.

EXERCISE SET 6.6

A

1 Express each ratio as a fraction in reduced form.

1. $3 : 11$ **2.** $8 : 12$
3. 45 to 30   **4.** 500 to 750

Express each ratio as a fraction in reduced form; use the same unit of measure when possible.

5. 62 miles to 2 gallons

6. 40 men to 55 women

7. 18 feet to 30 feet

8. 6 feet to 4 inches

9. $3 to 50¢

10. 4 hours to 20 minutes

Solve the following ratio problems.

11. Two numbers are in the ratio of 6 to 5. Their sum is 33. Find the numbers.

12. Three numbers are in the ratio $2 : 3 : 5$. Their sum is 15. Find the numbers.

13. The sides of a triangle are in the ratio $2 : 6 : 7$. The perimeter is 45 centimeters. Find the three sides.

14. The angles of a triangle are in the ratio $2 : 3 : 5$. Find the three angles.

15. The width and length of a rectangle are in the

ratio of 3 to 4. The perimeter is 35 meters. Find the rectangle's width and length.

16. The sides of a rectangle are in the ratio 5 : 4. The area is 320 square centimeters. Find the length and width.

17. The ratio of a triangle's height to its base is 4 : 5. The area is 250 square feet. Find the triangle's height and base.

18. Two complementary angles are in the ratio of 7 to 11. Find the angles.

19. Two supplementary angles are in the ratio 1 : 8. Find the angles.

20. Jan has $3.90 worth of nickels and dimes, which are in the ratio 3 : 5. How many nickels and dimes does she have?

21. Ken has $11.50 in nickels, dimes, and quarters, which are in the ratio 3 : 4 : 7. How many of each type of coin does he have?

22. Renee cycled 96 kilometers. The ratio of her time to her rate was 3 : 8. Find her time and rate.

23. Luis drove 270 miles. The ratio of his rate to his time was 15 : 2. Find his rate and time.

24. A profit of $1050 is divided among three employees in the ratio 3 : 5 : 6. How much does each person receive?

2 Use cross-multiplication to determine whether the following proportions are true or false.

25. $\dfrac{3}{5} = \dfrac{18}{30}$ **26.** $\dfrac{4}{7} = \dfrac{60}{112}$

27. $\dfrac{22}{7} = \dfrac{223}{71}$ **28.** $\dfrac{62}{155} = \dfrac{2}{5}$

Solve the following proportion problems.

29. A 6-foot man casts a 7-foot shadow when a tree casts a 52-foot shadow. How tall is the tree to the nearest foot?

30. On a map, $1\frac{1}{4}$ inches represents 4 miles. If the map shows $3\frac{1}{2}$ inches between San Mateo and Palo Alto, how many miles apart are the two cities?

31. On a map, 1 inch represents 17.3 miles. If Seattle and Portland are 160 miles apart, how many inches are between their map locations?

32. A recipe for oatmeal bread requires $6\frac{3}{4}$ cups of

flour for 2 loaves. How many cups of flour are needed for 7 loaves?

33. If 2 pounds of coffee will make 155 cups of coffee, how many pounds of coffee, to the nearest pound, are needed to serve 690 cups of coffee at a wedding reception?

34. If 1 meter = 1.09 yards, how many yards equal 17 meters?

35. If 2.2 pounds = 1 kilogram, how many kilograms are in 90 pounds?

36. The ratio of an object's weight on earth to its weight on the moon is 6 : 1. How much does an astronaut weigh on the earth if she would weigh $20\frac{1}{3}$ pounds on the moon?

37. The ratio of an object's weight on Mars to its weight on earth is 2 : 5. How much would a payload weighing 2200 pounds on earth weigh on Mars?

38. An inheritance of $93,000 is divided between a son and a cancer fund in the ratio of 7 to 3. How much does each receive?

39. If a home valued at $240,000 is assessed $1200 in real estate taxes, what would be the tax on a $320,000 home in the same area?

40. The tax on Pat's house was $825 per year, based on the square footage. After she built a 650-square-foot addition, her new tax was $1150. What was the original square footage of her house?

Use Boyle's law to solve the following problems:
$$\frac{V_1}{P_2} = \frac{V_2}{P_1}.$$

41. Twelve liters of a gas are under 2.0 atmospheres of pressure. What will the new volume be if the new pressure is 3.0 atmospheres?

42. Five hundred milliliters of oxygen at a pressure of 1.0 atmosphere is to be compressed to a volume of 450 milliliters. What pressure is needed to do this?

43. One hundred milliliters of a gas is compressed to a pressure of 1.05 atmospheres and a volume of 92.30 milliliters. Find the initial pressure.

44. Two liters of gaseous oxygen is allowed to expand to a new volume of 25 liters and a pressure of 0.4 atmosphere. Find the initial pressure.

○3 From Example 5 (p. 292), find the cost of removing the following amounts of oil from the harbor.

45. 🔲 96%   **46.** 🔲 30%

A pesticide accidentally spills into a lake. The cost–benefit model for removing the pesticide is given by

$$C(x) = \frac{18x}{106 - x}$$

where C is in thousands of dollars and x is a percent; $0 \le x \le 100$. Find the cost of removing the following amounts of pesticide from the lake.

47. 🔲 100%   **48.** 🔲 94%

49. 🔲 70%   **50.** 🔲 20%

The relationship between R, the radius of curvature of a spherical mirror; S, the distance from the mirror to the object; and s, the distance from the mirror to the image is given by $\frac{2}{R} = \frac{1}{S} + \frac{1}{s}$.

51. Find s, if $S = 20$ centimeters and $R = 30$ centimeters.

52. Find R correct to one decimal place if $S = 25$ centimeters and $s = 55$ centimeters.

Resistance is a property of metallic objects that conduct electricity such as lamps and power saws. A resistor is indicated by the symbol ─╲╱╲╱╲─ and resistance is measured in **ohms**. Let R_1 and R_2 denote two resistors connected in parallel, as indicated in Figure 6.1. If R is the total resistance of R_1 and R_2, then

$$\frac{1}{R} = \frac{1}{R_1} + \frac{1}{R_2}$$

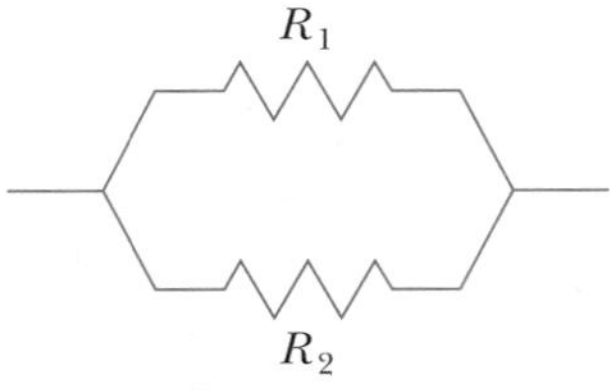

R_1

R_2

FIGURE 6.1

53. A 14-ohm power drill is connected in parallel to a 105-ohm lamp. Find the total resistance of the circuit.

54. Two resistors are connected in parallel, one of them with a resistance of 8 ohms. If the total resistance is 6 ohms, find the value of the other resistor.

55. If $R_1 = R_2$, find R in terms of R_2.

56. If $R_2 = 4R$, find R_1 in terms of R.

B Let R_1, R_2, and R_3 be three resistors connected in parallel. If R is the total resistance, then

$$\frac{1}{R} = \frac{1}{R_1} + \frac{1}{R_2} + \frac{1}{R_3}$$

57. Three resistors of 6, 8, and 12 ohms are connected in parallel. Find the total resistance of the circuit.

58. The total resistance of three resistors connected in parallel is 36/13 ohms. If two of the resistors are 9 and 12 ohms, find the third resistor.

Solve the following problems.

59. The numerical ratio of a rectangle's perimeter to its area is 11 : 15. Its length is 6 meters. Find its width.

60. The sides of a rectangle are in the ratio 3 : 2. If the perimeter is 50 cm, find its length and width.

61. Two doctors perform an operation and share the fee of $18,000 in the ratio 11 : 25. How much does each doctor receive?

62. A 6-foot man is 20 feet from the point directly beneath a street light, which is 22 feet above the street. What is the length of his shadow?

63. A county ordinance requires a 3% "fall" for a sewage pipe from a house to the main pipe under the street. How much vertical drop is required for a horizontal distance of 80 feet?

64. The "grade" of a road expressed as a percent is the number of feet of vertical change for each 100 feet of horizontal change. If a highway has an 8% grade, what is the change in elevation for 1 mile of horizontal change (1 mile = 5280 feet)?

C

Answer the following questions with complete sentences.

65. What is the difference between a ratio and a proportion? Give an example of each.

66. What is the origin of the word *ratio*?

REVIEW EXERCISES

Solve the following problems. (See Sections 2.2, 2.3, and 2.4.)

67. Find two consecutive integers whose sum is 37.

68. Find three consecutive even integers whose sum is -18.

69. Elda travels 24 miles downstream in 3 hours. Find the speed of her boat in still water if the speed of the river is 2 mph.

70. Steve travels 20 miles upstream in 4 hours. Find the speed of the river if the speed of his boat in still water is 8 mph.

71. How long does it take Stavroula to drive 60 miles if she can average 40 mph?

72. Ramon drives 156 miles in 3 hours. Find his average speed.

6.7 SOLVING WORD PROBLEMS

1	Exploring Number Problems
2	Applying Uniform Motion Problems
3	Solving Work Problems

1   Exploring Number Problems

Fractional equations have many applications. In this section we return to two familiar topics, number and uniform motion problems. We then consider a new type known as "work problems."

We begin with number problems. The following example uses the concepts of reciprocal and consecutive integers. Recall that the reciprocal of a number x, $x \neq 0$, is $1/x$. We can represent consecutive integers by x, $x + 1, x + 2$, and so on. Consecutive odd or even integers can be expressed as $x, x + 2, x + 4$, and so on.

EXAMPLE 1

The reciprocal of the smaller of two consecutive even integers is subtracted from the reciprocal of the larger. The result is $-1/24$. Find both numbers.

SOLUTION

Let $x =$ the smaller integer and $x + 2 =$ the larger one. Then their reciprocals are $\dfrac{1}{x}$ and $\dfrac{1}{x + 2}$. When $\dfrac{1}{x}$ is subtracted from $\dfrac{1}{x + 2}$ the result is $-1/24$; that is,

$$\frac{1}{x + 2} - \frac{1}{x} = -\frac{1}{24} \qquad \text{LCD} = 24x(x + 2)$$

$$24x(x + 2)\left[\frac{1}{x + 2} - \frac{1}{x}\right] = 24x(x + 2)\left[-\frac{1}{24}\right]$$

$$24x - 24(x + 2) = -x(x + 2)$$

$$24x - 24x - 48 = -x^2 - 2x$$

$$x^2 + 2x - 48 = 0$$

$$(x + 8)(x - 6) = 0$$

$$x + 8 = 0 \qquad \text{or} \quad x - 6 = 0$$

$$x = -8 \quad \text{or} \qquad x = 6$$

If $x = -8$, then $x + 2 = -6$. If $x = 6$, then $x + 2 = 8$. Thus, we have two answers: $\{-8, -6\}$ and $\{6, 8\}$.

In many number problems one fraction is changed to another fraction. One type changes an initial unknown fraction to a known fraction, and we are required to find the original fraction; this procedure is illustrated in Example 2. Variations on this type of problem are covered in the exercises.

EXAMPLE 2

The denominator of a fraction is 7 more than the numerator. If 3 is added to the denominator and 5 is added to the numerator, then the new fraction is 3/4. Find the original fraction.

SOLUTION   Let n = the numerator of the original fraction and $n + 7$ = its denominator. Then $\dfrac{n}{n + 7}$ represents the original fraction, and $\dfrac{n + 5}{(n + 7) + 3} = \dfrac{n + 5}{n + 10}$ represents the new fraction. So,

$$\dfrac{n + 5}{n + 10} = \dfrac{3}{4} \quad \text{Cross-multiply.}$$
$$4(n + 5) = 3(n + 10)$$
$$4n + 20 = 3n + 30$$
$$n = 10, \quad \text{so } n + 7 = 17 \quad \text{and } 10/17 \text{ is the original fraction.}$$

 CHECK   If $n = 10$, then $\dfrac{n + 5}{n + 10} = \dfrac{10 + 5}{10 + 10} = \dfrac{15}{20} = \dfrac{3}{4}$.

2   Applying Uniform Motion Problems

We now return to uniform motion problems. From the equation $rt = d$ we have the formulas $r = d/t$ and $t = d/r$, which allow us to solve certain problems requiring fractions. In a typical problem of this type the total time for a trip is equal to the sum of the times at different rates. This is illustrated in Example 3, which also reviews the concept of adding and subtracting rates. Recall that rates of travel are affected by such forces as wind and current. Thus, when a boat travels downriver we add the rate of the current to the rate of the boat in still water, whereas we subtract it when the boat moves upriver.

EXAMPLE 3

Jeff traveled 20 miles upstream to a store and returned to his camp in 7 hours. If the speed of the river was 3 mph, what was the speed of his boat in still water?

SOLUTION   Let r = the rate of his boat in still water. Then $r - 3$ = the rate going up the river, and $r + 3$ = the rate going down the river. The information is organized in the following chart.

	distance	rate	$t = d/r$
up	20	$r - 3$	$\dfrac{20}{r - 3}$
down	20	$r + 3$	$\dfrac{20}{r + 3}$

Because the total travel time is 7 hours, $\dfrac{20}{r-3} + \dfrac{20}{r+3} = 7$, which simplifies to $7r^2 - 40r - 63 = 0$,   and this factors into
$(r - 7)(7r + 9) = 0$
$r - 7 = 0$ or $7r + 9 = 0$
$\quad r = 7$ or $\qquad r = -9/7$
which is meaningless. Thus, the speed of his boat in still water is 7 mph.

EXAMPLE 4

A car and a truck travel at the same rate. The car travels for 3 hours and the truck for 5 hours. If the truck travels 104 more miles than the car, how far does the car travel?

SOLUTION

Let $x =$ the distance the car travels. Then $x + 104 =$ the distance the truck travels.

	distance	time	$r = d/t$
car	x	3	$\dfrac{x}{3}$
truck	$x + 104$	5	$\dfrac{x + 104}{5}$

Because they both travel at the same rate, $\dfrac{x}{3} = \dfrac{x + 104}{5}$. The solution to this equation is $x = 156$, so the car travels 156 miles.

---

3   Solving Work Problems

We now turn to a set of problems of some antiquity called **work problems**. These occur in such fields as construction, manufacturing, and so forth. The following is a typical example.

> If Bruce can paint a fence in 6 hours and Chris can paint it in 4 hours, how long would it take them to paint the fence if they work together?

First, assume that they work at a constant rate. Then let $t =$ the number of hours they work together. In one hour Bruce does 1/6 of the job; that is, his rate is 1/6 of the fence per hour. If he works for t hours, then the amount of work he does is

$$\frac{1}{6} \cdot t = \frac{t}{6}$$

For example, if Bruce works for $t = 3$ hours, then he paints 3/6 or 1/2 of the fence. Similarly, Chris's rate is 1/4 of the fence per hour, and in t hours the amount of work that he does is

$$\frac{1}{4} \cdot t = \frac{t}{4}$$

Together Bruce and Chris paint one fence, so the equation is

$$\frac{t}{6} + \frac{t}{4} = 1 \qquad \text{One fence painted; LCD} = 12$$

$$12\left(\frac{t}{6} + \frac{t}{4}\right) = 12(1)$$

$$2t + 3t = 12$$

$$5t = 12$$

$$t = \frac{12}{5} = 2\frac{2}{5} \text{ hours}$$

The following are general guidelines for solving work problems. A, B, C, and so on represent people working together, pipes filling tanks, and so forth. These guidelines are then illustrated in the concluding examples.

1. The jobs in question are either the same or equivalent. Assume that the work is done at a constant rate.

2. The units of measure must be the same: hours, days, and so on. Do not mix units such as hours and minutes.

3. The work A does is equal to the rate times the time:

$$\text{rate} \cdot \text{time} = \text{work, and}$$

$$\frac{\text{work}}{\text{A does}} + \frac{\text{work}}{\text{B does}} = 1 \qquad \text{One job done}$$

4. A chart is often useful for organizing the information.

EXAMPLE 5

Susan requires $1\frac{2}{3}$ hours more to type a paper than does Betty. Working together they can type the paper in 2 hours. How long does it take Betty to type the paper alone?

SOLUTION   Let $t = $ the time Betty takes to type the paper alone; her rate is $1/t$.
$t + 1\frac{2}{3} = t + \frac{5}{3} = $ the time for Susan to type the paper alone; her rate is $\dfrac{1}{t + \dfrac{5}{3}}$.

	rate	· time =	work
Betty	$\dfrac{1}{t}$	2	$\dfrac{2}{t}$
Susan	$\dfrac{1}{t + \dfrac{5}{3}}$	2	$\dfrac{2}{t + \dfrac{5}{3}}$

Math in Time

THE GREEKS AND Hindus were fond of work problems, which evidently were intended for mental recreation. Although many of these problems are easily solved today with our modern algebra, they would have been quite challenging in these earlier periods. One of our sources of Greek algebra problems is the *Greek Anthology,* a collection of problems compiled by Metrodorus (A.D. 500). Some of them are as old as Plato's time (fifth century B.C.), and others are similar to problems found in the Egyptian Rhind papyrus (1650 B.C.). The first two problems given below are from Metrodorus, and the third is a Hindu problem from Brahmagupta (A.D. 628).

1. Brickmaker, I am in a hurry to erect this house. Today is cloudless, and I do not require many more bricks, for I have all I want but 300. Thou alone in one day couldst make as many, thy son 200, and thy son-in-law 250. Working all together, in how many days can thou make these bricks?

2. I am a brazen lion; my spouts are my two eyes, my mouth, and the flat of my right foot. My right eye fills a jar in two days (1 day = 12 hours), my left eye in three, and my foot in four. My mouth is capable of filling it in six hours. Tell me how long all four together will take to fill it.

3. In what time will four fountains, being let loose together, fill a cistern, which they would severally fill in a day, in half a day, in a quarter of a day, and in a fifth part of a day?

$$\frac{2}{t} = \frac{2}{t + \frac{5}{3}} = 1 \qquad \text{Simplify the complex fraction.}$$

$$\frac{2}{t} = \frac{2}{t + \frac{5}{3}} \cdot \frac{3}{3} = 1$$

$$\frac{2}{t} + \frac{6}{3t + 5} = 1 \qquad \text{Simplify this equation; LCD} = t(3t + 5)$$

$$3t^2 - 7t - 10 = 0$$

$$(t + 1)(3t - 10) = 0$$

$$t + 1 = 0 \quad \text{or} \quad 3t - 10 = 0$$

$t = -1$ is meaningless, so $t = \frac{10}{3} = 3\frac{1}{3}$ hours is the time Betty needs to type the paper alone.

EXAMPLE 6

Pipe A fills a pool in 15 hours, pipe B fills it in 12 hours, and pipe C drains it in 10 hours. Pipes A and B were turned on at the same time to fill the pool, but pipe C was accidentally left open. After 45 minutes the mistake was found and pipe C was closed. How long did it take to fill the pool?

(continued)

SOLUTION   Let t = the time to fill the pool, and express 45 minutes as 3/4 of an hour.

	rate · time = work		
pipe A	$\frac{1}{15}$	t	$\frac{t}{15}$
pipe B	$\frac{1}{12}$	t	$\frac{t}{12}$
pipe C	$\frac{1}{10}$	$\frac{3}{4}$	$\frac{3}{40}$

Because pipe C is draining the pool, we subtract the work it does from the sum of the work done by pipes A and B:

$$\frac{t}{15} + \frac{t}{12} - \frac{3}{40} = 1 \qquad \text{LCD = 120}$$

Simplify this equation.

$$18t = 129$$

$$t = \frac{129}{18} = 7\frac{1}{6} \text{ hours are needed to fill the pool.}$$

EXERCISE SET 6.7

A

1

1. Check the solutions to Example 1 (p. 295).

Solve the following number problems.

2. The sum of a number and its reciprocal is 53/14. Find the number.

3. The sum of a number and one-third of its reciprocal is −13/6. Find the number.

4. The reciprocal of the larger of two consecutive odd integers is subtracted from the reciprocal of the smaller one. The result is 2/15. Find the numbers.

5. The denominator of a fraction is 2 more than 3 times the numerator, and the fraction is equal to 5/16. Find the fraction.

6. The numerator of a fraction is 2 less than 5 times the denominator, and the fraction is equal to 9/2. Find the fraction.

7. The denominator of a fraction is 6 more than the numerator. If 10 is added to the numerator and 1 is subtracted from the denominator, then the new fraction is 3/2. Find the original fraction.

8. A number is added to both the numerator and denominator of 4/7, and the result is 4/5. What is the number?

9. The numerator of 6/5 is multiplied by a number, and the same number is added to the denominator. The new fraction is 13/3. Find the number.

10. A number is subtracted from the numerator of 9/14 and added to its denominator. The new fraction is 2 divided by 3 times the number. Find all such numbers.

11. The sum of two numbers is 90. When the larger number is divided by the smaller, the quotient is 3 and the remainder is 10. Find the two numbers.

12. The difference of two numbers is 41. When the larger is divided by the smaller, the quotient is 4 and the remainder is 5. Find the numbers.

2

13. Check the solution to Example 3 (p. 296).

14. Check the solution to Example 4 (p. 297).

Solve the following uniform motion problems.

15. Jane can cycle 16 miles in the same time that she can walk 6 miles. If she rides 5 mph faster than she walks, how fast does she walk?

16. Ted's motorboat has a speed of 28 km/h in still water. He can travel 100 kilometers down a river in the same time that he can travel 72 kilometers up the river. Find the speed of the river correctly to one decimal place.

17. The speed of a river is 4 mph. A boat goes 24 miles upstream and back in 8 hours. Find the speed of the boat in still water.

18. The speed of a motorboat in still water is 9 mph. The boat travels 12 miles upstream and back in 3 hours. What is the speed of the current?

19. A truck travels 2 hours longer and 78 more miles than a car. The truck's speed is 46 mph and the car's speed is 50 mph. Find the distance and time that each travels.

20. A truck and a car travel at the same rate, and the car travels 42 miles less than twice the distance the truck travels. The truck travels for 4 hours and the car for 7 hours. Find the distance each travels and its rate.

21. Two cars travel at the same speed. Car A travels 72 miles, while car B travels 168 miles. If car B travels for 3 hours longer than car A, find the length of time that each travels and its speed.

22. Carol can jog twice as fast as she can walk. She walks 15 kilometers and jogs for 18 kilometers. If she walks for 1 hour longer than she jogs, find her time and rate for walking and jogging.

23. A truck takes 2 hours longer to travel 300 kilometers than a car takes to travel 280 kilometers. The car travels 20 km/h faster than the truck. Find the rate and time for both the truck and the car.

24. Ira had to drive 80 kilometers in one hour to be on time for a meeting. After driving 32 kilometers, she had to increase her speed by 32 km/h for the remaining distance. Find her speed for the first part of the trip.

3 Solve the following work problems.

25. Bob can tile a floor in 8 hours, while Bruce takes 12 hours to tile the floor. How long would it take them to tile the floor working together?

26. Maria can paint a room in 4 hours, while Janice can paint it in 8 hours. How long would it take them working together?

27. Jorge can paint a fence in 5 hours, while Ilan can paint it in 8 hours. They start painting the fence together, but after 2 hours Ilan leaves to go windsurfing. How long does Jorge take to finish the fence?

28. Helen can stack a cord of wood in 2 hours, while Kathy can do it in 3 hours. Kathy works for 15 minutes and then is joined by Helen. How long does it take them working together to finish the job?

29. Pipe A can fill a tank in 6 hours, and pipe B can fill it in 9 hours. If the tank is empty and both pipes are turned on at the same time, how long does it take to fill two-thirds of the tank?

30. Working together Ed and Kathy can paint their house in 6 days. Working alone Ed can paint it in 10 days. How long would it take Kathy to paint their house working alone?

31. Pipe A can fill a tank in 6 hours, and pipe B can drain it in 8 hours. How long would filling the tank take if both pipes are open?

32. In Example 6 (p. 299), how much time would be needed to fill the pool if the mistake had not been found?

33. Pipe A can fill a pool in 8 hours, and pipe B can drain it in 12 hours. If the pool is one-half full when both pipes are opened, how long will it take to fill the pool?

34. Pipe A fills a tank in 6 hours, pipe B drains it in 8 hours, and pipe C drains it in 10 hours. If the tank is empty and all three pipes are opened, how much time will be needed to fill the tank?

B   Solve the following problems in the Math in Time section (p. 299).

35. 1   **36.** 2   **37.** 3

38. Ted can paint a house in 18 days. Ted and Sam paint 3/5 of the house in 6 days. Working alone, how long would it take Sam to finish painting the house?

39. Find two consecutive even integers such that the sum of their reciprocals is −9/40.

40. On Friday morning Barbara averaged 24 mph driving from her home to work. That evening she averaged 36 mph driving home. On Saturday morning she averaged 48 mph driving to work. If the three trips took 1 hour and 5 minutes, what is the distance from her home to work?

Solve the following Greek problems from Metrodorus' *Greek Anthology*.

41. How many apples are needed if four persons of six receive one-third, one-eighth, one-fourth, and one-fifth, respectively, of the total number, while the fifth receives 10 apples, and one apple remains for the sixth person?

42. "After staining the holy chaplet of fair-eyed Justice that I might see thee, all-subduing gold, grow so much, I have nothing; for I gave 40 talents under evil auspices to my friends in vain, while, O ye varied mischances of men, I see my enemies in possession of the half, the third, and the eighth of my fortune." How many talents of gold did the man once possess?

C

Answer the following questions with complete sentences.

43. How is the rate of travel of a boat affected by the current of a river?

44. Discuss the method of solving a work problem.

Chapter Summary

DEFINITIONS AND PROPERTIES

Definitions

Rational expression: the ratio of two polynomials.

Rational function: the ratio of two polynomial functions. (See Section 6.1.)

Domain of a rational expression or function: the set of all real numbers for which the fraction is defined. (See Section 6.1.)

LCD: the least common denominator for a set of rational expressions is the polynomial of lowest degree that is divisible by each denominator. (See Section 6.3.)

Complex fraction: a fraction whose numerator, denominator, or both contains one or more simple fractions. (See Section 6.4.)

Ratio: the ratio of a to b is $\dfrac{a}{b}$ or $a : b$. (See Section 6.6.)

Proportion: $\dfrac{a}{b} = \dfrac{c}{d}$, "$a$ is to b as c is to d." (See Section 6.6.)

Properties of Rational Expressions (See Sections 6.1, 6.2, and 6.3.)

Let $A, B, C,$ and D be polynomials.

$$\frac{AC}{BC} = \frac{A}{B}$$

$$\frac{A - B}{B - A} = -1$$

$$\frac{A}{B} \div \frac{C}{D} = \frac{A}{B} \cdot \frac{D}{C} = \frac{AD}{BC}$$

$$\frac{A}{D} - \frac{C}{D} = \frac{A - C}{D}$$

$$-\frac{A}{B} = \frac{-A}{B} = \frac{A}{-B}$$

$$\frac{A}{B} \cdot \frac{C}{D} = \frac{AC}{BD}$$

$$\frac{A}{D} + \frac{C}{D} = \frac{A + C}{D}$$

$$\frac{A}{D} - \frac{C}{-D} = \frac{A}{D} + \frac{C}{D} = \frac{A + C}{D}$$

Algebra of Functions
(See Sections 6.2 and 6.3.)

If f and g are rational functions, then

$(f + g)(x) = f(x) + g(x)$

$(f - g)(x) = f(x) - g(x)$

$(fg)(x) = f(x)g(x)$

$\left(\dfrac{f}{g}\right)(x) = \dfrac{f(x)}{g(x)}, \quad g(x) \neq 0$

Finding the Least Common Denominator
(See Section 6.3.)

1. Find the prime factorization of each denominator.

2. Form the product of each factor the greatest number of times it appears in any single denominator.

Simplifying a Complex Fraction
(See Section 6.4.)

Method 1: Express the numerator and denominator of the complex fraction as simple fractions. Then perform the indicated division and simplify your answer.

Method 2: Multiply the numerator and denominator of the complex fraction by the LCD of its simple fractions. Simplify your answer.

CHAPTER REVIEW EXERCISES

The answers to the following problems are given in the answer section. If you have trouble, then review the material and homework problems in the sections indicated.

Evaluate the following for the given values of the variables. (See Sections 6.1 and 6.4.)

1. $f(x) = \dfrac{3x - 2}{4x + 5}; \quad x = -3$

2. $f(x) = \dfrac{x}{x - 3}; \quad x = \dfrac{2}{5}$

Find the domain and roots of the following functions. (See Sections 6.1 and 6.2.)

3. $f(x) = \dfrac{x + 4}{3x - 15}$

4. $g(x) = \dfrac{x^2 - 25}{x^2 - 36}$

Simplify the following. (See Section 6.1.)

5. $\dfrac{25a - a^3}{a^2 - 3a - 10}$

6. $\dfrac{8x^3 + y^3}{2x^2y + 2xy^2}$

Perform the indicated operations and simplify your answers. (See Sections 6.2 and 6.3.)

7. $\dfrac{27a^5}{2b^4} \cdot \dfrac{4b}{15a^2}$

8. $\dfrac{10x^2}{9y} \div \dfrac{25x}{15yw}$

9. $\dfrac{x^2y}{x + 3} \div \dfrac{xy^2}{x^2 - 9}$

10. $\dfrac{x^2 + 6x + 5}{9x - 54} \cdot \dfrac{3x - 18}{x^2 + 2x + 1}$

11. $\dfrac{5}{6a} + \dfrac{7}{4b}$

12. $\dfrac{4}{15x^2} - \dfrac{1 - x}{12x}$

13. $\dfrac{2y}{x^2 + xy} - \dfrac{xy}{x^2 - y^2}$

14. $\dfrac{x - 1}{x^2 + 5x + 6} + \dfrac{x + 1}{x^2 + 4x + 4}$

Find the LCD for each set of fractions. (See Section 6.3.)

15. $\dfrac{2}{21}, \quad \dfrac{1}{15}, \quad \dfrac{5}{24}$

16. $\dfrac{1}{x^2 - 1}, \quad \dfrac{x}{x^2 - 4}, \quad \dfrac{x - 6}{x^2 - x - 2}$

Simplify the following complex fractions. (See Section 6.4.)

17. $\dfrac{\dfrac{4}{9}}{\dfrac{8}{27}}$

18. $\dfrac{\dfrac{1}{x + y}}{\dfrac{1}{x^2 - y^2}}$

19. $\dfrac{\dfrac{1}{6} - \dfrac{2}{a}}{\dfrac{1}{4} + \dfrac{1}{a^2}}$

20. $\dfrac{1 - \dfrac{1}{x + y}}{1 + \dfrac{1}{x - y}}$

21. $x^{-3} + x^{-2}$ **22.** $(3^{-1} - 2^{-1})^{-1}$

Let $f(x) = \dfrac{1}{x - 2}$, $g(x) = \dfrac{x}{x - 3}$,   and $h(x) = \dfrac{2}{x^2 - 9}$.

Find the following functions and their domains. (See Sections 6.2 and 6.3.)

23. $f + g$ **24.** $g - h$ **25.** $g - f$

26. fg **27.** f/g

Solve the following equations and formulas for the indicated variables. (See Section 6.5.)

28. $\dfrac{1}{3x} - \dfrac{3}{4} = \dfrac{5}{6}$ **29.** $\dfrac{4}{t^2 - 4t} - \dfrac{t - 3}{t - 4} = \dfrac{1}{t}$

30. $\dfrac{2}{x - 1} = \dfrac{3}{2x + 1}$ **31.** $\dfrac{2x}{3} - \dfrac{y}{5} = 1$; y

32. $I = \dfrac{nE}{R + nr}$; r **33.** $I = \dfrac{nE}{R + nr}$; n

Solve the following problems. (See Sections 6.4, 6.6, and 6.7.)

34. Steve traveled 2 miles at 50 mph and 3 miles at 42 mph. Find his average speed to the nearest mph.

35. A 16-ohm power sander is connected in parallel to a 120-ohm lamp. Find the total resistance of the circuit to the nearest ohm; $\dfrac{1}{R} = \dfrac{1}{R_1} + \dfrac{1}{R_2}$.

36. The numerator of a fraction is 2 more than its denominator. If 7 is added to the numerator and 4 is added to the denominator, the new fraction is 4/3. Find the original fraction.

37. A truck and a car travel at the same rate. The truck travels for 1.5 hours, and the car travels for 3.5 hours. The car travels 18 miles more than twice the distance the truck travels. Find the distance they travel and their rates.

38. Machine A can cap 30 bottles per minute, while machine B can cap 40 bottles per minute. Working together, how long would it take them to cap 24,000 bottles to the nearest hour?

39. The sides of a triangle are in the ratio 3 : 4 : 5. The perimeter is 24 centimeters. Find the three sides.

40. The ratio of the complement of an angle to the supplement of the angle is 13 : 31. Find the three angles.

CHAPTER TEST

Treat this as a class test and allow 50 minutes for completion. When you have finished, use the answer section for scoring. If you have any wrong answers, refer to the corresponding problems in the review section.

Evaluate the following function for the given value of x.

1. $f(x) = \dfrac{x + 4}{x}$; $x = -\dfrac{2}{3}$

Find the domain and roots of the following function.

2. $f(x) = \dfrac{x^2 - 1}{x^2 - 9}$

Perform the indicated operations and simplify your answers.

3. $\dfrac{x^3 - 1}{2x - 2}$

4. $\dfrac{2x - 8}{x^2 - 4x - 21} \cdot \dfrac{2x^2 + 2x + 3}{16 - x^2}$

5. $\dfrac{27x^6}{16y} \div \dfrac{18x^4}{y^8}$

6. $\dfrac{5}{12x^2y} - \dfrac{x - y}{18xy^2}$

7. $\dfrac{x}{x^2 - 25} + \dfrac{x + 1}{x^2 - x - 20}$

8. $(x^{-1} + y^{-1})^{-1}$

9. $\dfrac{1 + \dfrac{x}{y}}{\dfrac{x}{y} - \dfrac{y}{x}}$

10. $2x + \dfrac{x}{2 - \dfrac{3}{x}}$

Find $\dfrac{f(x + h) - f(x)}{h}$ for the following function.

11. $f(x) = 5/x$

Find the LCD for the following set of fractions.

12. $\dfrac{x}{x^4 - 1}$, $\dfrac{3}{x^3 + 1}$, $\dfrac{x + 2}{x^3 - x^2 + x}$

Let $f(x) = \dfrac{1}{x}$, $g(x) = \dfrac{x}{x + 1}$, and $h(x) = \dfrac{3}{x^2 - 1}$.
Find the following functions and their domains.

13. $f + h$ **14.** $f - g$ **15.** fg **16.** h/g

Solve the following equations and formulas for the indicated variables.

17. $\dfrac{2}{y} = \dfrac{3}{4} + \dfrac{1}{2y}$ **18.** $\dfrac{1}{3} = \dfrac{4}{x^2 - 4} - \dfrac{1}{x - 2}$

19. $\dfrac{V_1}{P_2} = \dfrac{V_2}{P_1}$; P_1 **20.** $y = \dfrac{a + bx}{x}$; x

Solve the following problems.

21. The volume of a rectangular solid is 810 cubic centimeters. Find its dimensions if they are in the ratio 2 : 3 : 5.

22. If a home valued at $68,000 is assessed $720 in real estate taxes, what would be the tax on a $51,000 home in the same area?

23. Pipe A can fill a tank in 8 hours, and pipe B can fill it in 6 hours. The tank is empty and pipe A is turned on. After one hour pipe B is turned on. How long does it take to fill the tank?

24. The sum of the reciprocals of two consecutive odd integers is $-8/15$. Find the integers.

25. An airplane flies 350 mph in still air. It travels 830 miles with the wind in the same time that it travels 570 miles against the wind. What is the speed of the wind?

Cumulative Review

The answers to the following problems are given in the answer section. The section from which each question is taken follows the answer. If you have any wrong answers, you can review the material in the indicated section.

Perform the indicated operations and simplify your answers.

1. $2 \mid -6 \mid - 7 \mid 1 - (-9) \mid$

2. $4 + 8 \div 4 - 5^2$

3. $2^{-3} + 2^0$

4. $2x^2(6x^{-3})^{-1}$

5. $\left(\dfrac{2x^3}{5x^{-2}} \right)^2$

6. $\dfrac{10}{x^2 - 9} \div \dfrac{15}{x^2 + 6x + 9}$

7. $\dfrac{2}{x^3 - 1} + \dfrac{x}{x^2 - 1}$

8. $\dfrac{1 - \dfrac{a}{b}}{\dfrac{a}{b} - \dfrac{b}{a}}$

Solve the following equations and inequalities for the indicated variables. Write the answers to the inequalities in interval notation and graph them on a number line.

9. $2(3x - 1) = 8 - (1 - x)$

10. $6x^2 - 7x - 3 = 0$

11. $\dfrac{1}{x + 3} + \dfrac{5}{x - 3} = \dfrac{x}{x^2 - 9}$

12. $\dfrac{1}{4} = \dfrac{1}{x^2}$

13. $5x - 3y = 15; \quad y$

14. $\dfrac{a}{b} = \dfrac{c}{b - c}; \quad b$

15. $\mid 4x - 1 \mid = 7$

16. $\mid 3x + 1 \mid < 10$

17. $8 - 3x \geq 20$

Solve the following systems of equations by addition and substitution.

18. $\begin{aligned} 2x - 5y &= 1 \\ 8x - 2y &= -1 \end{aligned}$ **19.** $\begin{aligned} y &= 3x - 2 \\ 6x - 2y &= 5 \end{aligned}$

20. $\begin{aligned} 4x + 8y + z &= 2 \\ -x - 7y + 3z &= 14 \\ 2x - 3y + 2z &= 3 \end{aligned}$

Solve the system $\begin{aligned} 3x + y &= 7 \\ 2x + 5y &= 9 \end{aligned}$

21. with matrices   **22.** with Cramer's Rule

Graph the solution set of the following system of inequalities.

23. $\begin{aligned} y &\leq x + 2 \\ 2x + 3y &> 6 \end{aligned}$

Graph the following equations.

24. $y = 2x + 4$ **25.** $x = -2$ **26.** $y = \mid x \mid - 1$

Given the points $A(-1, 3)$ and $B(1, 7)$, find

27. the distance from A to B

28. the slope–intercept form of the equation of the line $\overleftrightarrow{AB}$

Find the slope of any line perpendicular to the following line.

29. $2x - 3y = 1$

Find the domain and range of the following relation.

30. $\{(1, 2), (3, 7), (1, 8)\}$

Let $f(x) = x^2 - 3x + 1$. Find

31. $\dfrac{f(x + h) - f(x)}{h}$

Let $f(x) = 4x - 1$ and $g(x) = 2x + 3$. Find

32. $f^{-1}(x)$ **33.** fg

Factor the following.

34. $2x^3 - 8x$ **35.** $ac - 2b + bc - 2a$

Let $f(x) = x^3 - 9x$. Find

36. the domain of f **37.** the roots of f

Let $A = \{-2, 0, 1, 2/3, \sqrt{5}, .27, .\overline{27}, .272829 \ldots \}$.
List all elements of A that are

38. rational   **39.** irrational

40. whole numbers

Solve each of the following word problems with a system of equations.

41. Jan has two acid solutions; one is 6% and the other is 15% pure acid. How many liters of each solution must she mix together to produce 3 liters of a 12% solution?

42. Konsin has 24 pennies, nickels, and dimes worth $1.79. The number of dimes is 6 more than the sum of the number of pennies and nickels. How many pennies, nickels, and dimes does she have?

Solve the following word problems.

43. For three consecutive integers, the sum of the first two is less than four times the third one. Find all such integers.

44. The ratio of the complement of an angle to its supplement is 2/5. Find the measure of the angle.

45. The longer leg of a right triangle is 2 more than the shorter leg, and the hypotenuse is 4 more than the shorter leg. Find the three sides.

46. The area of a circle is 25π square centimeters. Find the circle's radius, diameter, and circumference.

47. The sum of two numbers is 10, and the sum of their squares is 52. Find the two numbers.

48. Tanya invested some money at 8% and twice that amount at 12%. The total interest earned was $96. How much had she invested at each rate?

49. Eric drove 205 miles in 6 hours. During the first part of the trip his rate was 26 mph, and during the second part it was 40 mph. How long did he drive at 26 mph?

50. David is 4 years older than Rachel. Three years ago the sum of their ages was 22 years. How old are they now?

SEVEN

Rational Exponents and Radicals

The path of a satellite through a gravitational field is charted by a method of graphing. The strength of the force of gravity is modeled with combined variation.

In this chapter we extend several topics introduced in earlier chapters and then use this new material in various places in later chapters.

Section 5.1 discussed integer exponents and showed how to simplify expressions such as $x^{-3}x^7$ by adding exponents. This chapter extends the rules for integer exponents to rational exponents, before simplifying $x^{-3/5}x^{7/5}$ with the same procedure.

Square roots were introduced in Section 1.4. Recall that 5 is a square root of 25 because 5 squared is 25. In a similar manner, 2 is the *cube root* of 8 because 2 cubed is 8. In this chapter we will generalize square roots to cube and *n*th roots.

In Section 2.3 we learned how to solve equations in the form $x^2 = d$, $d > 0$. For instance, the solutions of $x^2 = 9$ are 3 and -3, because $3^2 = (-3)^2 = 9$. However, $x^2 = -9$ has no *real* solution, because $x^2 \geq 0$ for every real number x. This chapter concludes with a discussion of a new number system that will allow us to solve equations such as $x^2 = -9$. With these new numbers we will be able to solve every equation of the form $ax^2 + bx + c = 0$, which we will cover in Chapter 8.

7.1 RADICALS

1	**Review of Integer Exponents**
2	**Definitions and Properties of *n*th Roots**
3	**Irrational Roots**

1   Review of Integer Exponents

In this section we will extend the concepts of square roots to cube and higher-order roots. Then in Section 7.2 we will discuss rational exponents. Because the properties for fractional and integer exponents are the same, this section begins with a review of integer exponents (see Section 5.1). For example,

$$x^{-3}x^7 = x^{-3+7} = x^4$$

$$(x^{-4})^{-6} = x^{(-4)(-6)} = x^{24}$$

$$\frac{x^7}{x^{-3}} = x^{7-(-3)} = x^{10}$$

$$\frac{5^0}{4^{-3}} = \frac{1}{4^{-3}} = 4^3 = 64$$

Definitions and Properties of Integer Exponents

Let a and b be real numbers and m and n be integers. Then, assuming nonzero denominators:

If $a \neq 0$, then $a^0 = 1$; 0^0 is undefined.

$$a^{-n} = \frac{1}{a^n} \qquad\qquad \frac{1}{a^{-n}} = a^n$$

$$\left(\frac{a}{b}\right)^{-1} = \frac{b}{a} \qquad\qquad \left(\frac{a}{b}\right)^{-n} = \left(\frac{b}{a}\right)^n$$

$$a^m a^n = a^{m+n} \qquad\qquad (a^m)^n = a^{mn}$$

$$(ab)^n = a^n b^n \qquad\qquad \left(\frac{a}{b}\right)^n = \frac{a^n}{b^n}$$

$$\frac{a^m}{a^n} = a^{m-n}$$

---

2 Definitions and Properties of *n*th Roots

Recall that finding a square root is the inverse of squaring a number; that is, if $b^2 = a$, then b is a **square root** of a. For instance, $7^2 = (-7)^2 = 49$, so 7 and -7 are the square roots of 49. These are written $\sqrt{49} = 7$, which is the **principal square root** of 49, and $-\sqrt{49} = -7$, which is the **negative square root** of 49. Every positive number a has two square roots, $\sqrt{a}$ and $-\sqrt{a}$. A negative number does not have a real square root, because $b^2 \geq 0$, if b is real; for example, $\sqrt{-9}$ is not a real number. In general,

$$\sqrt{a} = b, \quad b \geq 0, \quad \text{if } b^2 = a$$

The symbol $\sqrt{}$ is called the **radical sign**, a is called the **radicand**, and $\sqrt{a}$ is called a **radical**.

As just mentioned, finding a square root is the inverse of squaring a number. In a similar way, finding a **cube root** is the inverse of cubing a number. For example, because $2^3 = 8$, 2 is the real cube root of 8, which is written $\sqrt[3]{8} = 2$. Also, $\sqrt[3]{-27} = -3 = -\sqrt[3]{27}$, because $(-3)^3 = -27$. In general, $\sqrt[3]{a} = b$ if $b^3 = a$. Also, $\sqrt[3]{-a} = -\sqrt[3]{a}$. Note that $\sqrt[3]{a}$ is a real number for all real values of a, but $\sqrt{a}$ is real only for $a \geq 0$.

We can generalize the concept of square and cube roots to *n*th roots. For example, $\sqrt[4]{81} = 3$ because $3^4 = 81$, and $\sqrt[5]{-32} = -2$ because $(-2)^5 = -32$. In general, $\sqrt[n]{a}$ is called the **principal *n*th root** of a, and $\sqrt[n]{a} = b$ if $b^n = a$; n is called the **index**. In our discussions involving *n*th roots, we understand that n is a natural number greater than 1 and that a and b are nonnegative when n is even.

$$nth \text{ Roots}$$

1. Let n be even. Then
   a. Every positive real number has two real nth roots that are opposites of each other. For example, the real fourth roots of 81 are 3 and -3.
   b. Negative real numbers do not have real nth roots.
2. Let n be odd. Then
   a. Every real number has one real nth root.
   b. The real nth root of a positive number is positive. For example, $\sqrt[5]{32} = 2$.
   c. The real nth root of a negative number is negative, and $\sqrt[n]{-a} = -\sqrt[n]{a}$. For example, $\sqrt[5]{-32} = -\sqrt[5]{32} = -2$.

EXAMPLE 1

Find the following roots.

a. $\sqrt[6]{64}$ b. $\sqrt[n]{0}$ c. $-\sqrt[9]{-1}$ d. $\sqrt[4]{\dfrac{1}{81}}$

SOLUTION   a. $\sqrt[6]{64} = 2$, because $2^6 = 64$
b. $\sqrt[n]{0} = 0$, because $0^n = 0$
c. $-\sqrt[9]{-1} = -(-1) = 1$, because $(-1)^9 = -1$
d. $\sqrt[4]{\dfrac{1}{81}} = \dfrac{1}{3}$, because $\left(\dfrac{1}{3}\right)^4 = \dfrac{1}{81}$

The expressions $(\sqrt[n]{a})^n$ and $\sqrt[n]{a^n}$ are common in mathematics. Let us consider an example of $(\sqrt{a})^2$:

$$\sqrt{25} = 5 \qquad \text{so} \qquad (\sqrt{25})^2 = (5)^2 = 25$$

In general, if $b^2 = a$, $b \geq 0$, then $\sqrt{a} = b$, so $(\sqrt{a})^2 = (b)^2 = a$. Also, $(\sqrt[3]{27})^3 = (3)^3 = 27$, and $(\sqrt[4]{16})^4 = (2)^4 = 16$. Thus,

$$(\sqrt[n]{a})^n = a; \quad \text{if } n \text{ is even, then } a \geq 0.$$

EXAMPLE 2

Simplify the following radicals.

a. $(\sqrt{7})^2$ b. $(\sqrt[7]{-6})^7$ c. $\sqrt{7x}\sqrt{7x}, \quad x \geq 0$
d. $(-\sqrt[4]{3})^4$ e. $(2\sqrt[3]{7x^2})^3$

SOLUTION   a. $(\sqrt{7})^2 = 7$ b. $(\sqrt[7]{-6})^7 = -6$
c. $\sqrt{7x}\sqrt{7x} = (\sqrt{7x})^2 = 7x$
d. Because $(-b)^4 = b^4$, $(-\sqrt[4]{3})^4 = (\sqrt[4]{3})^4 = 3$
e. $(2\sqrt[3]{7x^2})^3 = 2^3(\sqrt[3]{7x^2})^3$ $(ab)^n = a^n b^n$
$\qquad = 8(7x^2)$
$\qquad = 56x^2$

To evaluate $\sqrt[n]{a^n}$, we start with the case in which n is odd. Two examples that illustrate this case are

$$\sqrt[3]{5^3} = \sqrt[3]{125} = 5 \quad \text{and} \quad \sqrt[5]{(-2)^5} = \sqrt[5]{-32} = -2$$

Thus,

$$\sqrt[n]{a^n} = a, \quad \text{if } n \text{ is odd}$$

The case in which n is even is more complicated. We start with $\sqrt{a^2}$. Because $a^2 \geq 0$, $\sqrt{a^2} \geq 0$ for all a. For example, let

$a = 7$: $\quad \sqrt{7^2} = \sqrt{49} = 7 \quad$ and $\quad \sqrt{a^2} = a, \quad \text{if } a \geq 0$

$a = -7$: $\quad \sqrt{(-7)^2} = \sqrt{49} = 7 = -(-7) \quad$ and $\quad \sqrt{a^2} = -a, \quad \text{if } a < 0$

Thus, $\sqrt{a^2}$ is defined to be the absolute value of a: $\sqrt{a^2} = |a|$. In a similar way, $\sqrt[4]{(2)^4} = \sqrt[4]{16} = 2 = |2|$, and $\sqrt[4]{(-2)^4} = \sqrt[4]{16} = 2 = |-2|$. In general,

$$\sqrt[n]{a^n} = |a| = \begin{cases} a, & \text{if } a \geq 0 \\ -a, & \text{if } a < 0 \end{cases}, \quad \text{if } n \text{ is even}$$

EXAMPLE 3

Simplify the following radicals.

a. $\sqrt[3]{(-2)^3}$ **b.** $\sqrt[5]{x^5 y^{10}}$ **c.** $\sqrt{(-6)^2}$

d. $\sqrt{9x^4 y^6}$ **e.** $\sqrt[6]{5^6 x^{12}}$

SOLUTION

a. $\sqrt[3]{(-2)^3} = -2$

b. $\sqrt[5]{x^5 y^{10}} = \sqrt[5]{x^5 (y^2)^5} = \sqrt[5]{(xy^2)^5} = xy^2, \quad a^n b^n = (ab)^n$

c. $\sqrt{(-6)^2} = |-6| = -(-6) = 6$

d. $\sqrt{9x^4 y^6} = \sqrt{3^2 (x^2)^2 (y^3)^2} = \sqrt{(3x^2 y^3)^2} = |3x^2 y^3|$

We cannot write the answer as $3x^2 y^3$ because we do not know whether y^3 is positive or negative.

e. $\sqrt[6]{5^6 x^{12}} = \sqrt[6]{5^6 (x^2)^6} = \sqrt[6]{(5x^2)^6} = |5x^2| = 5x^2$, because $5x^2 \geq 0$ for all values of x.

Properties of nth Roots

$\sqrt[n]{a} = b$ if $b^n = a$;   if n is even, then a and b are nonnegative.

1. Let n be even. Then

    a. $(\sqrt[n]{a})^n = a$ for $a \geq 0$

    b. $\sqrt[n]{a^n} = |a| = \begin{cases} a, & \text{if } a \geq 0 \\ -a, & \text{if } a < 0 \end{cases}$

2. Let n be odd and a be any real number. Then

    $(\sqrt[n]{a})^n = a, \qquad \sqrt[n]{a^n} = a, \qquad \text{and} \qquad \sqrt[n]{-a} = -\sqrt[n]{a}$

3   Irrational Roots

If a is the square of a natural number, then it has rational square roots. For example, let $a = 9$; then $\sqrt{9} = \sqrt{3^2} = 3$ and $-\sqrt{9} = -\sqrt{3^2} = -9$. However, if a is not a square, then its square roots are irrational. For instance, if $a = 7$, then its square roots, $\sqrt{7}$ and $-\sqrt{7}$, are irrational. In general, if $a \neq b^n$, for some rational number b, then $\sqrt[n]{a}$ is irrational, so it is a nonterminating, nonrepeating decimal. For instance, $\sqrt[3]{-5}$ and $\sqrt[4]{17}$ are irrational, and $\sqrt[4]{17} = 2.0305432\ldots$.

A calculator offers a convenient way to approximate nth roots.* In addition to a $\sqrt{x}$ key, most calculators have an inverse key, INV, and a y-to-the-x key, y^x. The usual order of entry to find $\sqrt[x]{y}$ is: y, INV, y^x, and x. The y value cannot be negative, but it can be fractional. Recall that $\approx$ means "is approximately equal to." An example of an irrational root correct to seven places from a calculator is

$$\sqrt[5]{9} \approx 1.5518456: \quad \text{Enter } \mathbf{9}, \text{ press } \mathbf{INV}, \text{ press } \mathbf{y^x},$$
$$\text{enter } \mathbf{5}, \text{ press } \mathbf{=}.$$

EXAMPLE 4   Approximate the following to three decimal places.

   a. $6\sqrt{29}$ **b.** $\sqrt[7]{-15}$ **c.** $2 + \sqrt{3}$

SOLUTION   **a.** Use the $\sqrt{x}$ key to find the square root.
   $6\sqrt{29} \approx 6(5.3851648) = 32.310989 \approx 32.311$
   b. $\sqrt[7]{-15} = -\sqrt[7]{15} \approx -1.4723567 \approx -1.472$
   c. $2 + \sqrt{3} \approx 2 + 1.7320508 \approx 2 + 1.732 = 3.732$

EXERCISE SET 7.1

A

1   Simplify the following and write your answers with positive exponents; write constants as rational numbers in reduced form.

1. 27^0 **2.** $(2x^{-5})^{-3}$

3. $x^4(x^3)^9$ **4.** $(5xy^4)^2$

5. $(3^{-2})(3^{-4})$ **6.** $3^{-2} + 3^{-4}$

7. $(3x^{-2}y^6)^3$ **8.** $x^{-5}x^{-6}$

9. $(x^5y^{-2})^{-4}$ **10.** $\dfrac{16x^9}{4x^{-3}y^{-1}}$

11. $\left(\dfrac{3x^3}{5y^{-4}}\right)^{-2}$ **12.** $\dfrac{1}{7^{-2}}$

13. $\dfrac{1}{\left(\dfrac{3}{4}\right)^{-1}}$ **14.** $\dfrac{37^0}{\left(\dfrac{2}{5}\right)^{-3}}$

2   Simplify the following radicals. Assume the variables represent positive numbers.

15. $\sqrt{100}$ **16.** $-\sqrt{64}$

17. $\sqrt[8]{0}$ **18.** $\sqrt[4]{81}$

19. $-\sqrt[3]{-27}$ **20.** $2\sqrt[3]{-125}$

21. $\sqrt[16]{1}$ **22.** $\sqrt[17]{-1}$

23. $\sqrt{49x^2}$ **24.** $\sqrt[3]{1000x^3}$

25. $\sqrt[4]{x^8}$ **26.** $\sqrt[5]{-32}$

---

  * On many calculators the square of the rational number 66,922/47,321 is 2 (check your calculator). Because $\sqrt{a} = b$, $b \geq 0$,   if $b^2 = a$, why is $\sqrt{2}$ not a rational number and equal to 66,922/47,321?

27. $\sqrt{\dfrac{x^2}{25}}$ **28.** $6\sqrt[3]{\dfrac{y^3}{27}}$

29. $-\sqrt[4]{\dfrac{a^{12}}{16}}$ **30.** $\sqrt{\dfrac{x^2 y^8}{25 z^6}}$

31. $\sqrt{x^{-2}}$ **32.** $\sqrt[3]{x^{-6}}$

33. $\sqrt[4]{81 a^{-8}}$ **34.** $\sqrt{x^4 y^6 z^8}$

35. $(\sqrt{5x})^2$ **36.** $(\sqrt[3]{3ab})^3$

37. $\sqrt[3]{-8 x^6 y^9}$ **38.** $\sqrt{(5x)^2}$

39. $\sqrt[7]{x^7}$ **40.** $\sqrt[4]{(ab)^4}$

41. $(6x\sqrt{6x})^2$ **42.** $\sqrt[8]{(abc)^8}$

Simplify the following. Make no assumptions about the variables.

43. $\sqrt{x^2}, \quad x \ge 0$ **44.** $\sqrt{x^2}, \quad x < 0$

45. $\sqrt[4]{a^4}, \quad a < 0$ **46.** $\sqrt{25 a^2}$

47. $\sqrt[3]{27 a^3}$ **48.** $\sqrt[4]{16 t^4}$

49. $\sqrt[3]{x^3 y^6}$ **50.** $\sqrt[4]{x^4 y^8}$

51. $\sqrt[5]{x^5 y^{10}}$ **52.** $\sqrt{(x+1)^2}$

53. $\sqrt{x^2 + 6x + 9}$ **54.** $\sqrt[3]{(x+1)^3}$

3 🖩

Approximate the following to two decimal places.

55. $\sqrt{10}$ **56.** $-\sqrt{31}$

57. $\sqrt[3]{25}$ **58.** $1 + \sqrt{5}$

59. $3 - \sqrt{2}$ **60.** $\sqrt{7} + \sqrt{11}$

61. $\sqrt[3]{-18}$ **62.** $4\sqrt[4]{86}$

63. $2\sqrt[5]{701}$ **64.** $\sqrt[7]{-683}$

65. $\sqrt{2}\sqrt[3]{3}$ **66.** $\sqrt{2} + \sqrt[3]{3}$

67. $\sqrt{.81}$ **68.** $\sqrt[3]{.008}$

69. $\sqrt[4]{.0081}$

B

Solve the following problems.

70. Find the radius of a circle whose area is 4225 square centimeters.

71. The volume of a cube is 55 cubic inches. Find the cube's side correctly to one decimal place.

72. Find the radius and surface area of a sphere whose volume is 36π cubic inches.

73. Find the surface area of a sphere whose volume is 288π cubic centimeters.

Simplify the following. Assume that the variables represent positive numbers.

74. $(\sqrt[3n]{xy})^{3n}$ **75.** $\sqrt[2n]{x^{2n}}$

76. $\sqrt[3n]{a^{3n}}$ **77.** $\sqrt[3n]{2^{9n}}$

78. $\sqrt[4n]{5^{8n}}$ **79.** $\sqrt{4 x^{6y}}$

C

80. Find the mistake in the following "proof" that all real numbers are equal.
Proof: Let a and b be any two real numbers. Then
$$a - b = -(b - a)$$
$$(a - b)^2 = [-(b - a)]^2$$
$$(a - b)^2 = (b - a)^2$$
$$\sqrt{(a - b)^2} = \sqrt{(b - a)^2}$$
$$a - b = b - a$$
$$2a = 2b, \quad \text{so}$$
$$a = b,$$
and all real numbers are equal.

✎   Answer the following questions with complete sentences.

81. Explain why the square root of a negative number is not real, but the cube root of a negative number is real.

82. When is $\sqrt{a}$ a rational number?

83. Explain why $\sqrt{a^2} \ne a$.

84. Answer the question in the footnote on page 314.

REVIEW EXERCISES

Graph the following. Give their x- and y-intercepts. (See Section 3.2.)

85. $y = x$ **86.** $y = x - 1$ **87.** $y = -2x + 4$

Find the domain, D, and range, R, of the following functions. (See Section 3.2.)

88. $\{(0, 0), (1, 1), (4, 2)\}$ **89.** $f(x) = -2x + 4$

90. $g(x) = 3$ **91.** $f(x) = |x|$

Find the domain and range of the function f. Find f^{-1}, $D_{f^{-1}}$, and $R_{f^{-1}}$. (See Section 3.6.)

92. $f = \{(0, 0), (.5, .7), (1, 1), (4, 2)\}$

Find the inverse of the following functions. Graph each function and its inverse and $y = x$ on the same axes. (See Section 3.6.)

93. $f(x) = -\dfrac{1}{3}x$ **94.** $g(x) = 2x + 1$

Graph the following equations. (See Section 3.1).

95. $y = -|x + 2|$ **96.** $y = 2|x| + 1$

7.2 RATIONAL EXPONENTS

1 Using Rational Exponents and Radicals

2 Graphing a Radical Function and Its Inverse

1 Using Rational Exponents and Radicals

To extend the rules for natural number exponents to integer exponents we had to define a^0 and a^{-n} appropriately. We now repeat this process for rational exponents; that is, we will define $a^{1/n}$ in such a way that the rules reviewed in the last section will apply to exponents that are fractions. This definition will tie together the concepts of *exponent* and *root*.

To illustrate the definition of $a^{1/n}$ we can use the property that $(\sqrt[n]{a})^n = a$ and require that $(a^m)^n = a^{mn}$ holds for $m = 1/n$. Let us compare the following results.

$$(\sqrt{6})^2 = 6 \quad \text{and} \quad (6^{1/2})^2 = 6^{(1/2)2} = 6^1 = 6$$

The only positive number whose square is 6 is $\sqrt{6}$.
Thus, $6^{1/2}$ and $\sqrt{6}$ must be the same number: $6^{1/2} = \sqrt{6}$.

$$(\sqrt[3]{8})^3 = 8 \quad \text{and} \quad (8^{1/3})^3 = 8^{(1/3)3} = 8^1 = 8$$

The only real number whose cube is 8 is $\sqrt[3]{8} = 2$.
Thus, $8^{1/3}$ and $\sqrt[3]{8}$ must be the same number: $8^{1/3} = \sqrt[3]{8}$.

If the rule $(a^m)^n = a^{mn}$ is going to hold for fractional exponents, then we must define $a^{1/n}$ as follows.

Let a be a real number when n is odd and a nonnegative real number when n is even. Then

$$a^{1/n} = \sqrt[n]{a}$$

Math in Time

THE DEVELOPMENT OF the properties and notation of rational exponents was a long and difficult process, one that stretched from the third to the seventeenth century and involved many mathematicians from several countries.

The Greek Diophantus (ca. 250) was the first person to use exponential notation. He used Δ^Y, K^Y, $\Delta^Y\Delta$, ΔK^Y, and $K^Y K$ for x^2 up to x^6. Evidently he didn't need to write powers greater than 6.

The first known use of fractional exponents was by French bishop and mathematician Nicole Oresme (1323–1382), who wrote $\frac{1}{2}\, 2^P$ for $2^{1/2}$ and $1^P \frac{1}{2}\, 4$ for $4^{1+1/2} = 4^{3/2}$.

He also discovered the rules of exponents that we now express as $a^r a^s = a^{r+s}$ and $(a^r)^s = a^{rs}$.

The first use of integer exponents was by another French mathematician, Nicolas Chuquet (?–1500), who wrote $.10.^3$ for $10x^3$, $.9.^0$ for $9x^0$, and $.9.^{2.m.}$ for $9x^{-2}$. He also discovered the rule for $a^r/a^s = a^{r-s}$. Our present notation of x^2, x^3, and so on was introduced in 1637 by French philosopher and mathematician René Descartes (1596–1650).

The general theory of rational exponents was completed by Englishman John Wallis (1616–1703), who showed that $a^0 = 1$, $a^{-r} = 1/a^r$, and $a^{1/n} = \sqrt[n]{a}$. He also established the common use of negative and fractional exponents. Wallis's contributions were used by one of his countrymen, Sir Isaac Newton (1642–1727), in the development of calculus.

EXAMPLE 1

Write the following as radicals and then simplify them.

a. $36^{1/2}$ **b.** $(-27)^{1/3}$ **c.** $-16^{1/4}$

SOLUTION

a. $36^{1/2} = \sqrt{36} = 6$ **b.** $(-27)^{1/3} = \sqrt[3]{-27} = -3$

c. $-16^{1/4} = -\sqrt[4]{16} = -2$

Note that $(-16)^{1/4} = \sqrt[4]{-16}$ is not a real number.

With this definition of $a^{1/n}$, the properties of integer exponents apply to exponents that are fractions. Using these rules, we can express $a^{m/n}$ in two radical forms: m is a nonzero integer, and n is a positive integer greater than 1. Each result is illustrated with an example:

$$8^{2/3} = 8^{2(1/3)} = (8^2)^{1/3} = \sqrt[3]{8^2} = \sqrt[3]{64} = 4, \text{ and}$$
$$a^{m/n} = a^{m(1/n)} = (a^m)^{1/n} = \sqrt[n]{a^m}$$
$$8^{2/3} = 8^{(1/3)2} = (8^{1/3})^2 = (\sqrt[3]{8})^2 = (2)^2 = 4, \text{ and}$$
$$a^{m/n} = a^{(1/n)m} = (a^{1/n})^m = (\sqrt[n]{a})^m$$

The following is a summary of the properties of rational exponents.

317

Definitions and Properties of Rational Exponents

Let a and b be real numbers, r and s rational numbers, and m and n integers with $m \neq 0$ and $n > 1$. Then, assuming nonzero denominators and that $\sqrt[n]{a} \in \mathbb{R}$, if $a \neq 0$, then $a^0 = 1$; 0^0 is undefined.

$$a^{1/n} = \sqrt[n]{a} \quad \text{and} \quad a^{m/n} = \sqrt[n]{a^m} = (\sqrt[n]{a})^m$$

$$a^{-r} = \frac{1}{a^r} \qquad \frac{1}{a^{-r}} = a^r \qquad \left(\frac{a}{b}\right)^{-1} = \frac{b}{a}$$

$$\left(\frac{a}{b}\right)^{-r} = \left(\frac{b}{a}\right)^r \qquad a^r a^s = a^{r+s} \qquad (a^r)^s = a^{rs}$$

$$(ab)^r = a^r b^r \qquad \left(\frac{a}{b}\right)^r = \frac{a^r}{b^r} \qquad \frac{a^r}{a^s} = a^{r-s}$$

EXAMPLE 2

Write each of the following with one radical.

a. $6y^{5/8}$ **b.** $x^{3/-5}$ **c.** $a^{1/4}b^{3/4}$ **d.** $a^{1/2}b^{1/6}$

SOLUTION

a. $6y^{5/8} = 6(y^5)^{1/8} = 6\sqrt[8]{y^5}$ or
$6y^{5/8} = 6(y^{1/8})^5 = 6(\sqrt[8]{y})^5$

b. The denominator cannot be negative, so let $\dfrac{3}{-5} = \dfrac{-3}{5}$:

$x^{3/-5} = x^{-3/5} = \sqrt[5]{x^{-3}}$ or $(\sqrt[5]{x})^{-3}$

c. $a^{1/4}b^{3/4} = a^{1/4}(b^3)^{1/4} = (ab^3)^{1/4} = \sqrt[4]{ab^3}$

d. $a^{1/2}b^{1/6} = a^{3/6}b^{1/6} = (a^3b)^{1/6} = \sqrt[6]{a^3b}$

EXAMPLE 3

Write the following with rational exponents. Simplify when possible.

a. $\sqrt{ab}$ **b.** $\sqrt[4]{x^2b^3}$ **c.** $\sqrt[3]{x^6y^{15}}$

SOLUTION

a. $\sqrt{ab} = (ab)^{1/2} = a^{1/2}b^{1/2}$

b. $\sqrt[4]{x^2y^3} = (x^2y^3)^{1/4} = (x^2)^{1/4}(y^3)^{1/4} = x^{1/2}y^{3/4}$

c. $\sqrt[3]{x^6y^{15}} = (x^6y^{15})^{1/3} = x^2y^5$

We have seen that $8^{2/3}$ can be simplified by writing it as either $\sqrt[3]{8^2}$ or $(\sqrt[3]{8})^2$. Both methods require about the same amount of work. However, to simplify $125^{2/3}$ we could more easily express it as $(\sqrt[3]{125})^2$ rather than as $\sqrt[3]{125^2}$. We also have the option of simplifying these expressions with the rules of exponents, which is often the simplest of the three methods. For example,

$$8^{2/3} = (2^3)^{2/3} = 2^{3(2/3)} = 2^2 = 4$$

EXAMPLE 4

Simplify the following.

a. $125^{2/3}$ **b.** $(-32)^{-3/5}$ **c.** $\sqrt[6]{27}$ **d.** $\left(\dfrac{27}{5}\right)^{-1/3}$

SOLUTION   **a.** $125^{2/3} = (\sqrt[3]{125})^2 = (5)^2 = 25$ or
$125^{2/3} = (5^3)^{2/3} = 5^2 = 25$

b. $(-32)^{-3/5} = [(-2)^5]^{-3/5} = (-2)^{-3} = \dfrac{1}{(-2)^3} = \dfrac{1}{-8} = -\dfrac{1}{8}$

c. $\sqrt[6]{27} = (27)^{1/6} = (3^3)^{1/6} = 3^{1/2}$ or $\sqrt{3}$

d. $\left(\dfrac{27}{5}\right)^{-1/3} = \left(\dfrac{5}{27}\right)^{1/3}$ $\left(\dfrac{a}{b}\right)^{-r} = \left(\dfrac{b}{a}\right)^{r}$

$= \dfrac{5^{1/3}}{(3^3)^{1/3}}$ $\left(\dfrac{a}{b}\right)^{r} = \dfrac{a^r}{b^r}$

$= \dfrac{5^{1/3}}{3}$ or $\dfrac{\sqrt[3]{5}}{3}$

In the last section we used a calculator to approximate irrational numbers such as $\sqrt[5]{9}$. Many numbers in the form $a^{m/n}$ are also irrational and can be approximated with a calculator. For example, to approximate $9^{3/5}$, first write 3/5 as the decimal .6. Then $9^{3/5}$ to seven places is

 $9^{3/5} = 9^{.6} \approx 3.7371928$:   Enter **9**, press y^x, enter **.6**, press **=**.

EXAMPLE 5

Approximate the following to three decimal places.

a. $\sqrt[5]{9}$ **b.** $17^{2/3}$ **c.** $(-10)^{1/25}$

SOLUTION   **a.** $\sqrt[5]{9} = 9^{1/5} = 9^{.2} \approx 1.5518456 \approx 1.552$

b. $2/3 = .6\overline{6} \approx .6667$. Thus,
$17^{2/3} \approx 17^{.6667} \approx 6.6121134 \approx 6.612$

c. $(-10)^{1/25} = \sqrt[25]{-10} = -\sqrt[25]{10} = -(10)^{1/25}$.
$10^{1/25} = 10^{.04} \approx 1.0964782 \approx 1.096$. Thus,
$(-10)^{1/25} \approx -1.096$
In general, if n is odd, then $(-a)^{1/n} = -(a)^{1/n}$.

The rules of exponents allow us to simplify algebraic expressions containing rational exponents, as the next example illustrates.

EXAMPLE 6

Simplify the following. Express your answers with positive exponents.

a. $\left(\dfrac{a^{-1/2}}{b^{1/3}}\right)^6$ **b.** $x^{1/2}(5x^{2/3})^2$ **c.** $\left(\dfrac{2x^{1/3}}{3xy^{1/4}}\right)^{-1}$

SOLUTION   **a.** $\left(\dfrac{a^{-1/2}}{b^{1/3}}\right)^6 = \dfrac{(a^{-1/2})^6}{(b^{1/3})^6} = \dfrac{a^{-3}}{b^2} = \dfrac{1}{a^3b^2}$

b. $x^{1/2}(5x^{2/3})^2 = x^{1/2}(5)^2(x^{4/3}) = 25x^{1/2+4/3}$
$= 25x^{11/6}$

c. $\left(\dfrac{2x^{1/3}}{3xy^{1/4}}\right)^{-1} = \dfrac{3x^1y^{1/4}}{2x^{1/3}} = \dfrac{3x^{1-1/3}y^{1/4}}{2} = \dfrac{3x^{2/3}y^{1/4}}{2}$

Many equations in mathematics and the sciences either originate in the form $x^{m/n} = k$, where k is a constant, or can be reduced to this form. We solve this equation by raising both sides to the n/m power (we assume that $x^{m/n}$ and $k^{n/m}$ are real numbers):

$$x^{m/n} = k$$
$$(x^{m/n})^{n/m} = k^{n/m} \qquad \frac{m}{n} \cdot \frac{n}{m} = 1$$
$$x^1 = k^{n/m}$$
$$x = k^{n/m}$$

EXAMPLE 7   Solve the following equations.

a. $x^{3/2} = 8$ **b.** $x^{1/4} - 3 = 0$ **c.** $2x^{-1/5} + 4 = 0$

SOLUTION   **a.** $x^{3/2} = 8$
$$(x^{3/2})^{2/3} = 8^{2/3}$$
$$x = (2^3)^{2/3} = 2^2 = 4$$

b. $x^{1/4} - 3 = 0$ Add 3 to both sides.
$$x^{1/4} = 3$$
$$(x^{1/4})^4 = 3^4$$
$$x = 81$$

c. $2x^{-1/5} + 4 = 0$ Subtract 4.
$$2x^{-1/5} = -4$$ Divide by 2.
$$x^{-1/5} = -2$$
$$(x^{-1/5})^{-5} = (-2)^{-5}$$
$$x = \frac{1}{(-2)^5} = \frac{1}{-32} = -\frac{1}{32}$$

2   Graphing a Radical Function and Its Inverse

In Chapter 3 we graphed linear functions such as $f(x) = 2x - 4$ by plotting two ordered pairs that were solutions to the equation. Then we used a third point as a check for arithmetic errors.

We will now graph **radical functions**, such as $f(x) = \sqrt{x}$. Because the only function whose graph is a line is $f(x) = mx + b$, we have to find more than two points to determine these curves. Finding the domain of a radical function is important, because the even root of a negative number is not real. The following are guidelines for graphing these curves.

1. Determine the domain of the function.

2. Determine a set of ordered pairs that satisfy the function. Approximate irrational values of $f(x)$ with a calculator to one decimal place.

3. Plot the ordered pairs and connect the points with a smooth curve.

EXAMPLE 8   Graph $f(x) = \sqrt{x}$.

SOLUTION   Because x must be nonnegative, $D_f = \{x \mid x \geq 0\}$. Therefore, we will only use these values of x. Now find $f(x)$ for $x = 0, .5, 1, 4,$ and 6:

$$f(0) = \sqrt{0} = 0 \qquad f(.5) = \sqrt{.5} \approx .7 \qquad f(1) = \sqrt{1} = 1$$
$$f(4) = \sqrt{4} = 2 \qquad f(6) = \sqrt{6} \approx 2.4$$

Now plot $\{(0, 0), (.5, .7), (1, 1), (4, 2), (6, 2.4)\}$ and connect this set of points with a smooth curve (see Figure 7.1).

FIGURE 7.1

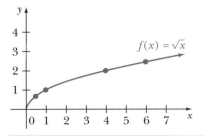

The range of a radical function can be found from its graph. For instance, in Example 8 the minimum value of y is $y = 0$, which occurs when $x = 0$. For any other value of x the value of y is greater than zero. Thus, the range of $f(x) = \sqrt{x}$ is $R_f = \{y \mid y \geq 0\} = [0, \infty)$.

We now return to inverse functions and relations. In Section 3.6 we discovered that if we know quite a bit about a one-to-one function, f, then we know quite a bit about its inverse, f^{-1}. For instance, f^{-1} is a one-to-one function, and its graph is found by reflecting the graph of f through the line $y = x$. Also, if we know the domain and range of f, then we know the domain and range of f^{-1}: $D_{f^{-1}} = R_f$ and $R_{f^{-1}} = D_f$. Finally, the equation for f^{-1} is found by interchanging x and y in the equation for f.

Recall that a function f is one-to-one if, whenever $x_1 \neq x_2$, then $f(x_1) \neq f(x_2)$. From the graph of $f(x) = \sqrt{x}$ (Example 8) we can see that f is one-to-one; two different values of x (1 and 4) correspond to two different values of y (1 and 2). Thus, f^{-1} is a one-to-one function. Because $D_f = R_f = [0, \infty)$, it follows that $D_{f^{-1}} = R_{f^{-1}} = [0, \infty)$. The equation for f^{-1} is found as follows (recall from elementary algebra that if $a = b$, then $a^2 = b^2$):

$f(x) = \sqrt{x}$	Replace $f(x)$ by y.
$y = \sqrt{x}$	Interchange x and y.
$x = \sqrt{y}$	If $a = b$, then $a^2 = b^2$.
$x^2 = (\sqrt{y})^2$	$(\sqrt{a})^2 = a$.
$x^2 = y$	Replace y by $f^{-1}(x)$.
$f^{-1}(x) = x^2, \quad D_{f^{-1}} = R_{f^{-1}} = [0, \infty)$	

Remember that when a function f is a list of ordered pairs, we find f^{-1} by interchanging the coordinates of each ordered pair of f. This concept can be used to determine the graph of f^{-1} from the ordered pairs that give us the graph of f. The graph of $f(x) = \sqrt{x}$ (Example 8) is determined by the ordered pairs.

$$\{(0, 0),\ (.5, .7),\ (1, 1),\ (4, 2)\}$$

Thus,

$$\{(0, 0),\ (.7, .5),\ (1, 1),\ (2, 4)\}$$

determines the graph of $f^{-1}(x) = x^2$, $x \geq 0$. Figure 7.2 shows the graphs of f and f^{-1}; note that they are symmetric with respect to the line $y = x$.

FIGURE 7.2

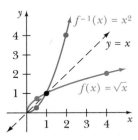

EXAMPLE 9

Let $g(x) = -\sqrt{x - 1}$. Graph g and g^{-1} and find their domains and ranges. Find the equation of g^{-1}.

SOLUTION   We need $x - 1 \geq 0$ or $x \geq 1$. Thus, $D_g = [1, \infty)$. Let $x = 1, 2, 5$. Then
$g(1) = -\sqrt{1 - 1} = -\sqrt{0} = 0$
$g(2) = -\sqrt{2 - 1} = -\sqrt{1} = -1$
$g(5) = -\sqrt{5 - 1} = -\sqrt{4} = -2$
Thus $\{(1, 0), (2, -1), (5, -2)\}$ determines the graph of g, so $\{(0, 1), (-1, 2), (-2, 5)\}$ determines the graph of g^{-1}. From the graphs of g and g^{-1} in Figure 7.3, we can see that $D_g = R_{g^{-1}} = [1, \infty)$ and $R_g = D_{g^{-1}} = (-\infty, 0]$. Because $y = g(x) = -\sqrt{x - 1}$ is the equation of g, $x = -\sqrt{y - 1}$ is the equation of g^{-1}. Solving for y (see Section 7.5, Example 6c), $y = g^{-1}(x) = x^2 + 1, x \leq 0$.

FIGURE 7.3

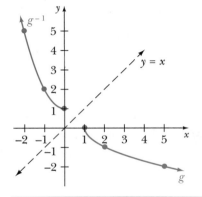

In Section 3.1 [4] we graphed functions involving absolute value. These functions are not one-to-one, so their inverses are not functions; they are relations. Our last example considers one of these functions and its inverse.

EXAMPLE 10   Let $S = \{(x, y) \mid y = 2 \mid x \mid + 1\}$. Find the inverse of S. Graph S and S^{-1} and find their domains and ranges.

SOLUTION   To find S^{-1}, interchange x and y in the equation of S: $S^{-1} = \{(x, y) \mid x = 2 \mid y \mid + 1\}$

Because $\{(-1, 3), (0, 1), (1, 3)\}$ determines the graph of S, $\{(3, -1), (1, 0), (3, 1)\}$ determines the graph of S^{-1}. From their graphs (Figure 7.4) we can see that $D_s = R_{s^{-1}} = \mathbb{R}$ and $R_s = D_{s^{-1}} = [1, \infty)$.

FIGURE 7.4

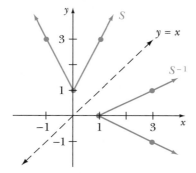

EXERCISE SET 7.2

A

1   Write each of the following with one radical. Simplify when possible. Variables represent positive numbers.

1. $x^{1/2}$ **2.** $y^{1/3}$

3. $3z^{1/7}$ **4.** $(ab)^{1/2}$

5. $ab^{1/2}$ **6.** $(5ab)^{1/3}$

7. $x^{3/4}$ **8.** $(16a^4)^{1/4}$

9. $x^{2/5}y^{3/5}$ **10.** $a^{1/3}b^{2/3}$

11. $4^{3/-2}$ **12.** $(-32)^{2/-5}$

13. $x^{1/2}y^{3/4}$ **14.** $a^{2/3}b^{5/6}$

15. $a^{1/2}b^{1/3}$ **16.** $a^{1/4}b^{5/6}$

Write the following with rational exponents. Simplify when possible. Variables represent positive numbers.

17. $\sqrt{ab^2}$ **18.** $4\sqrt[3]{xy^3}$

19. $\sqrt[4]{a^2b^6}$ **20.** $\sqrt[5]{a^2b^4}$

21. $2x\sqrt{x^2y}$ **22.** $x^4\sqrt[3]{x^3y}$

23. $a\sqrt[4]{ab}$ **24.** $ab\sqrt[3]{ab^2}$

25. $\sqrt{a + b}$ **26.** $\sqrt{a} + \sqrt{b}$

27. $\sqrt{(a - b)^4}$ **28.** $\sqrt[3]{(x - y)^3}$

Simplify the following.

29. $25^{1/2}$ **30.** $64^{1/3}$

31. $-9^{3/2}$ **32.** $32^{2/5}$

33. $36^{-1/2}$ **34.** $-8^{-1/3}$

35. $(-32)^{-3/5}$ **36.** $81^{-3/4}$

37. $\left(\dfrac{1}{9}\right)^{1/2}$ **38.** $\left(\dfrac{-8}{27}\right)^{1/3}$

39. $\left(\dfrac{125}{8}\right)^{2/3}$ **40.** $\left(\dfrac{1}{64}\right)^{5/6}$

41. $\left(\dfrac{1}{4}\right)^{-1/2}$ **42.** $\left(\dfrac{1}{8}\right)^{-2/3}$

43. $\left(\dfrac{-1}{27}\right)^{-5/3}$ **44.** $\left(\dfrac{16}{81}\right)^{-3/4}$

45. $(3^6)^{1/3}$ **46.** $(2^{2/3})^6$

47. $(9^4)^{3/8}$ **48.** $(8^{5/6})^2$

49. $(3^{-8})^{-3/8}$ **50.** $(4^{3/4})^{-2}$

51. $(25)^{1/2}(27)^{1/3}$ **52.** $(9)^{-1/2}(16)^{1/4}$

53. $(-8)^{2/3}(4)^{3/2}$ **54.** $(81)^{-1/2}(-27)^{1/3}$

55. $(10^8)^{-1/8}(16)^{-1/4}$ **56.** $(10^6)^{1/2}(125)^{-2/3}$

🖩   Approximate the following to three decimal places.

57. $10^{1/2}$ **58.** $8^{1/4}$

59. $14^{3/4}$ **60.** $(-7)^{1/5}$

61. $6^{1/3}$ **62.** $(-12)^{2/3}$

63. $4 + 5^{1/6}$ **64.** $2 - 3^{8/5}$

65. $(2^{1/4})(3^{1/5})$ **66.** $(6^{2/5})(7^{1/7})$

67. $(-2)^{1/3} + 6^{5/4}$ **68.** $3^{5/8} - (-4)^{3/5}$

For the following exercises, simplify and express your answers with positive exponents. Variables represent positive numbers.

69. $(3x^{1/5})(2x^{4/5})$ **70.** $(2x^{3/4})(-x^{1/6})$

71. $a^{2/3}a^{-1/4}$ **72.** $(x^{3/5})^{15}$

73. $(x^{-1/6}y^{3/4})^{12}$ **74.** $(5x^{1/2}y^{-1})^2$

75. $x^2(x^{1/4})^8$ **76.** $3x^3(2x^{1/2})^3$

77. $ab^2(a^{1/2}b^{-1/3})^6$ **78.** $(-3a^{1/4}b^2)(4a^{-1/4}b^{-5})$

79. $(8x^6y^{-3})^{1/3}$ **80.** $(16x^2y^8)^{1/4}$

81. $\dfrac{a^{2/3}}{a^{1/6}}$ **82.** $\dfrac{9a^{3/4}}{3a^{-1/2}}$

83. $\dfrac{12x^2}{-4x^{1/2}y^{-1/5}}$ **84.** $\left(\dfrac{x^{1/6}}{y^{-3}}\right)^6$

85. $\left(\dfrac{a^{-2/3}}{b^2}\right)^{-1}$ **86.** $\left(\dfrac{5x^{2/5}}{6x^{1/3}}\right)^2$

87. $\left(\dfrac{y^{-12}}{16x^8}\right)^{1/4}$ **88.** $\left(\dfrac{4a^{-1/3}}{9a^{-1/4}}\right)^{-1/2}$

Solve the following equations.

89. $x^{1/2} = 2$ **90.** $x^{5/2} = 32$

91. $x^{-1/2} - 2 = 0$ **92.** $2x^{1/3} - 8 = 0$

93. $x^{-1/3} + 3 = 0$ **94.** $4x^{-3/5} + 32 = 0$

2   Find the equation of the inverse of each relation (do not solve for y). Graph the relation, its inverse, and $y = x$ on the same axes. Give the domains and ranges of each relation and its inverse.

95. $f(x) = 2\sqrt{x}$ **96.** $g(x) = \sqrt{-x}$

97. $y = -\sqrt{x}$ **98.** $g(x) = \sqrt{x - 1}$

99. $y = \sqrt{x} - 1$ **100.** $g(t) = 1 - \sqrt{t}$

101. $f(x) = \sqrt{4 - x}$

102. $g(x) = 3\sqrt{x} + 1$

103. $f(s) = -\sqrt{2s} - 2$

104. $S = \{(x, y) \mid y = |x|\}$

105. $T = \{(x, y) \mid y = |3x|\}$

106. $U = \{(x, y) \mid y = 2|x - 3|\}$

107. $V = \{(x, y) \mid y = -|2x|\}$

108. $S = \{(x, y) \mid y = -|x + 2|\}$

109. $T = \{(u, v) \mid v = -3|u|\}$

110. $W = \{(x, P) \mid P = 2|x| + 2\}$

B   Graph the following functions and give the domain and range of each.

111. $v = -\sqrt{t + 3} + 1$ **112.** $a = \sqrt{t - 2} - 2$

113. $y = 2\sqrt{1 - x} - 1$ **114.** $y = \sqrt[3]{x}$

115. $g(x) = \sqrt[3]{-x}$ **116.** $f(x) = \sqrt[3]{x} - 1$

117. $y = \sqrt[4]{x}$ **118.** $y = \sqrt{x} + x$

C ✏️

Answer the following questions with complete sentences.

119. How does the definition of $a^{1/n}$ tie together the concepts of exponent and root?

120. Describe how you would approximate $2^{3/4}$ to two decimal places.

121. Describe how you would use the ordered pairs that determine the graph of f to graph f^{-1}.

122. Discuss the contributions the French made to the theory of exponents.

REVIEW EXERCISES

Simplify the following radicals. (See Section 7.1.)

123. $\sqrt{(-6)^2}$ **124.** $\sqrt{x^2}$

125. $\sqrt[3]{x^3}$ **126.** $\sqrt[4]{y^4}$

Use the properties of exponents to simplify the following radicals. (See Section 7.2.)

127. $\sqrt[4]{25}$ **128.** $\sqrt[6]{125}$

129. $\sqrt[12]{81}$ **130.** $\sqrt[12]{8}$

7.3 PROPERTIES OF RADICALS

1	Product Rule
2	Quotient Rule
3	Reduction Rule

1 Product Rule

The last two sections used properties of radicals and exponents to simplify expressions such as $\sqrt[3]{5^3} = 5$ and $\sqrt[6]{27} = \sqrt{3}$. This section will explore three results of the properties of exponents that allow us to simplify radicals such as $\sqrt{12}$, $\sqrt{7}/\sqrt{3}$, and $\sqrt{5}\,\sqrt[3]{2}$.

The following examples illustrate the **product rule** for radicals:

$$\sqrt{4 \cdot 25} = \sqrt{100} = 10 \quad \text{and} \quad \sqrt{4}\,\sqrt{25} = 2 \cdot 5 = 10, \quad \text{so}$$
$$\sqrt{4 \cdot 25} = \sqrt{4}\,\sqrt{25}$$
$$\sqrt[3]{8 \cdot 27} = \sqrt[3]{216} = 6 \quad \text{and} \quad \sqrt[3]{8}\,\sqrt[3]{27} = 2 \cdot 3 = 6, \quad \text{so}$$
$$\sqrt[3]{8 \cdot 27} = \sqrt[3]{8}\,\sqrt[3]{27}$$

In general, the nth root of a product is the product of the nth roots, which can be proved with the properties of exponents:

$$\sqrt[n]{ab} = (ab)^{1/n} = a^{1/n}b^{1/n} = \sqrt[n]{a}\,\sqrt[n]{b}$$

Product Rule for Radicals

$$\sqrt[n]{ab} = \sqrt[n]{a}\,\sqrt[n]{b}$$

If n is even, then a and b must be nonnegative.

We use the product rule to remove squares from square roots, cubes from cube roots, and so on. We also use the product rule to write the product of two or more radicals as one radical that can then be simplified. These ideas are illustrated in the first two examples.

EXAMPLE 1

Simplify the following radicals.

a. $5\sqrt{12}$ **b.** $\sqrt{48x^2}$ **c.** $\sqrt[3]{8x^4}$ **d.** $\sqrt{9x^2 + 9y^2}$

SOLUTION

a. $5\sqrt{12} = 5\sqrt{4 \cdot 3} = 5\sqrt{4}\sqrt{3} = 5 \cdot 2\sqrt{3} = 10\sqrt{3}$

b. Because 16 is the largest square that is a factor of 48,

$$\sqrt{48x^2} = \sqrt{16x^2 \cdot 3} = \sqrt{16x^2}\sqrt{3} = \sqrt{(4x)^2}\sqrt{3} = |4x|\sqrt{3}$$

because $\sqrt{a^2} = |a|$.

c. Because $8x^3$ is the largest cube in $8x^4$,

$$\sqrt[3]{8x^4} = \sqrt[3]{8x^3 \cdot x} = \sqrt[3]{(2x)^3}\sqrt[3]{x} = 2x\sqrt[3]{x}$$

d. $\sqrt{9x^2 + 9y^2} = \sqrt{9(x^2 + y^2)} = \sqrt{9}\sqrt{x^2 + y^2} = 3\sqrt{x^2 + y^2}$

Notice in Example 1d that $\sqrt{x^2 + y^2}$ cannot be simplified to $x + y$. Confusing $\sqrt[n]{a + b}$ with $\sqrt[n]{ab}$ is a common mistake; the properties of radicals and exponents only apply to multiplication and division.

COMMON ERROR

A common mistake is to think that $\sqrt[n]{a + b}$ can be simplified to $\sqrt[n]{a} + \sqrt[n]{b}$. In general,

$$\sqrt[n]{a + b} \neq \sqrt[n]{a} + \sqrt[n]{b}$$

$$\sqrt{9 + 16} = \sqrt{25} = 5 \quad \text{but} \quad \sqrt{9} + \sqrt{16} = 3 + 4 = 7$$

EXAMPLE 2

Simplify the following radicals. Assume that the variables are nonnegative.

a. $\sqrt{6xy}\sqrt{3xz}$ **b.** $\sqrt{x^3}\sqrt{x^3}\sqrt{x^5}$ **c.** $\sqrt[3]{54x^6}\sqrt[3]{x^5}$

SOLUTION

a. $\sqrt{6xy}\sqrt{3xz} = \sqrt{6xy \cdot 3xz} = \sqrt{18x^2yz} = \sqrt{9x^2}\sqrt{2yz} = 3x\sqrt{2yz}$

b. $\sqrt{x^3}\sqrt{x^3}\sqrt{x^5} = \sqrt{x^3x^3x^5} = \sqrt{x^{11}}$; x^{10} is the largest square in x^{11}, because $x^{10} = (x^5)^2$. Thus,

$$\sqrt{x^3}\sqrt{x^3}\sqrt{x^5} = \sqrt{x^{11}} = \sqrt{x^{10}}\sqrt{x} = \sqrt{(x^5)^2}\sqrt{x} = x^5\sqrt{x}$$

c. x^9 is the largest cube in x^{11}, because $x^9 = (x^3)^3$, so

$$\sqrt[3]{54x^6}\sqrt[3]{x^5} = \sqrt[3]{54x^6x^5} = \sqrt[3]{54x^{11}} = \sqrt[3]{27x^9 \cdot 2x^2}$$
$$= \sqrt[3]{3^3(x^3)}\sqrt[3]{2x^2} = 3x^3\sqrt[3]{2x^2}$$

2   **Quotient Rule**

The **quotient rule** for radicals is similar to the product rule, as illustrated by the following example:

$$\sqrt{\frac{4}{9}} = \sqrt{\left(\frac{2}{3}\right)^2} = \frac{2}{3} \quad \text{and} \quad \frac{\sqrt{4}}{\sqrt{9}} = \frac{2}{3}, \quad \text{so} \quad \sqrt{\frac{4}{9}} = \frac{\sqrt{4}}{\sqrt{9}}$$

In general, the *n*th root of a quotient is the quotient of the *n*th roots, which is proved as follows:

$$\sqrt[n]{\frac{a}{b}} = \left(\frac{a}{b}\right)^{1/n} = \frac{a^{1/n}}{b^{1/n}} = \frac{\sqrt[n]{a}}{\sqrt[n]{b}}$$

Quotient Rule for Radicals

$$\sqrt[n]{\frac{a}{b}} = \frac{\sqrt[n]{a}}{\sqrt[n]{b}}$$

$b \neq 0$,   and if n is even, then a and b must be nonnegative.

EXAMPLE 3

Simplify the following radicals. Assume that $x > 0$.

a. $\sqrt{\dfrac{7}{16}}$ **b.** $\sqrt[3]{\dfrac{16}{125}}$ **c.** $\dfrac{\sqrt{50x^3}}{\sqrt{2x}}$ **d.** $\dfrac{\sqrt[4]{64x}}{\sqrt[4]{2x}}$

SOLUTION

a. $\sqrt{\dfrac{7}{16}} = \dfrac{\sqrt{7}}{\sqrt{16}} = \dfrac{\sqrt{7}}{4}$

b. $\sqrt[3]{\dfrac{16}{125}} = \dfrac{\sqrt[3]{16}}{\sqrt[3]{125}} = \dfrac{\sqrt[3]{8}\,\sqrt[3]{2}}{\sqrt[3]{5^3}} = \dfrac{2\sqrt[3]{2}}{5}$

c. $\dfrac{\sqrt{50x^3}}{\sqrt{2x}} = \sqrt{\dfrac{50x^3}{2x}} = \sqrt{25x^2} = 5x$

d. $\dfrac{\sqrt[4]{64x}}{\sqrt[4]{2x}} = \sqrt[4]{\dfrac{64x}{2x}} = \sqrt[4]{32} = \sqrt[4]{16}\,\sqrt[4]{2} = 2\sqrt[4]{2}$

When $\sqrt{\dfrac{7}{16}}$ is written as $\dfrac{\sqrt{7}}{4}$, we say that it is *simplified* because its denominator is a rational number. However, when $\sqrt{\dfrac{7}{3}}$ is written as $\dfrac{\sqrt{7}}{\sqrt{3}}$, we need to **rationalize the denominator** to finish simplifying it. This rationalization is done by multiplying it by $\sqrt{3}/\sqrt{3}$:

$$\sqrt{\frac{7}{3}} = \frac{\sqrt{7}}{\sqrt{3}} = \frac{\sqrt{7}}{\sqrt{3}} \cdot 1 = \frac{\sqrt{7}}{\sqrt{3}} \cdot \frac{\sqrt{3}}{\sqrt{3}} = \frac{\sqrt{21}}{(\sqrt{3})^2} = \frac{\sqrt{21}}{3} \quad \text{or}$$

$$\sqrt{\frac{7}{3}} = \sqrt{\frac{7}{3} \cdot \frac{3}{3}} = \sqrt{\frac{21}{9}} = \frac{\sqrt{21}}{\sqrt{9}} = \frac{\sqrt{21}}{3}$$

EXAMPLE 4

Simplify the following radicals. Assume that $x > 0$.

a. $\dfrac{9}{\sqrt{18x}}$ **b.** $\dfrac{1}{\sqrt[3]{5x^2}}$ **c.** $\dfrac{1}{\sqrt[4]{8x}}$

SOLUTION   **a.** $\dfrac{9}{\sqrt{18x}} = \dfrac{9}{\sqrt{9}\,\sqrt{2x}} = \dfrac{9}{3\sqrt{2x}} \cdot \dfrac{\sqrt{2x}}{\sqrt{2x}} = \dfrac{3\sqrt{2x}}{(\sqrt{2x})^2} = \dfrac{3\sqrt{2x}}{2x}$

b. The smallest cube for which $5x^2$ is a factor is 5^3x^3. Thus, we must multiply $5x^2$ by 5^2x to produce 5^3x^3:

$$\frac{1}{\sqrt[3]{5x^2}} = \frac{1}{\sqrt[3]{5x^2}} \cdot \frac{\sqrt[3]{5^2x}}{\sqrt[3]{5^2x}} = \frac{\sqrt[3]{25x}}{\sqrt[3]{5^3x^3}} = \frac{\sqrt[3]{25x}}{5x}$$

c. $\dfrac{1}{\sqrt[4]{8x}} = \dfrac{1}{\sqrt[4]{2^3x}} \cdot \dfrac{\sqrt[4]{2x^3}}{\sqrt[4]{2x^3}} = \dfrac{\sqrt[4]{2x^3}}{\sqrt[4]{2^4x^4}} = \dfrac{\sqrt[4]{2x^3}}{2x}$

---

3 Reduction Rule

In many situations we have to change the index of a radical. Our ability to express a radical in exponential form allows us to do this. In Example 4c of the last section we changed $\sqrt[6]{27}$ to $\sqrt{3}$ by writing $\sqrt[6]{27}$ as $(3^3)^{1/6} = 3^{1/2} = \sqrt{3}$. A second way to simplify $\sqrt[6]{27}$ is to write it as the square root of the cube root of 27:

$$\sqrt[6]{27} = \sqrt{\sqrt[3]{27}} = \sqrt{3}$$

As another example,

$$\sqrt[4]{25} = (25)^{1/4} = (5^2)^{1/4} = 5^{2/4} = 5^{1/2} = \sqrt{5} \quad \text{or}$$
$$\sqrt[4]{25} = \sqrt{\sqrt{25}} = \sqrt{5}$$

In general,

$$\sqrt[mn]{a} = a^{1/mn} \qquad \frac{1}{mn} = \frac{1}{n} \cdot \frac{1}{m}$$
$$= (a^{1/n})^{1/m}$$
$$= (\sqrt[n]{a})^{1/m}$$
$$= \sqrt[m]{\sqrt[n]{a}}$$

This result is called the **reduction rule** for radicals, which allows us to simplify a radical whose index can be reduced to a smaller number. In applying this rule, we can either convert the radical to exponential notation or stay with the radical form. Example 5 illustrates both methods.

Reduction Rule for Radicals

$$\sqrt[mn]{a} = a^{1/mn} = \sqrt[m]{\sqrt[n]{a}}$$

If m or n is even, then a must be nonnegative.

EXAMPLE 5

Simplify the following.

a. $\sqrt[6]{25}$ **b.** $\sqrt[12]{x^4}$

SOLUTION   **a.** $\sqrt[6]{25} = (25)^{1/6} = (5^2)^{1/6} = 5^{1/3} = \sqrt[3]{5}$,   or
$$\sqrt[6]{25} = \sqrt[3 \cdot 2]{25} = \sqrt[3]{\sqrt{25}} = \sqrt[3]{5}$$
b. $\sqrt[12]{x^4} = (x^4)^{1/12} = x^{1/3} = \sqrt[3]{x}$,   or
$$\sqrt[12]{x^4} = \sqrt[3 \cdot 4]{x^4} = \sqrt[3]{\sqrt[4]{x^4}} = \sqrt[3]{x}$$

The product rule allows us to simplify $\sqrt[3]{5}\,\sqrt[3]{2}$ to $\sqrt[3]{10}$ because both radicals have the same index, 3. But consider $\sqrt{5}\,\sqrt[3]{2}$; it cannot be simplified in this form with the product rule because the indices are different. To write $\sqrt{5}\,\sqrt[3]{2}$ as one radical we must change the indices of 2 and 3 to the common index of 6:

$$\sqrt{5}\,\sqrt[3]{2} \qquad\qquad \text{or} \quad \sqrt{5}\,\sqrt[3]{2}$$

$$= 5^{1/2}2^{1/3} \qquad\qquad\qquad = \sqrt{\sqrt[3]{5^3}}\;\sqrt[3]{\sqrt{2^2}}$$

$$= 5^{3/6}2^{2/6} \qquad\qquad\qquad = \sqrt[2\cdot3]{5^3}\;\sqrt[3\cdot2]{2^2}$$

$$= (5^3)^{1/6}(2^2)^{1/6} \qquad\qquad = \sqrt[6]{5^3}\,\sqrt[6]{2^2}$$

$$= (5^3 \cdot 2^2)^{1/6} \qquad\qquad\;\; = \sqrt[6]{5^3 \cdot 2^2}$$

$$= \sqrt[6]{125 \cdot 4} \qquad\qquad\quad = \sqrt[6]{125 \cdot 4}$$

$$= \sqrt[6]{500} \qquad\qquad\qquad\;\; = \sqrt[6]{500}$$

EXAMPLE 6   Write the following as single radicals. Assume that x and y are positive.

a. $5\sqrt{3}$ **b.** $\sqrt[3]{2}\,\sqrt[4]{2}$ **c.** $\sqrt[6]{x}\,\sqrt[4]{y}$

SOLUTION   **a.** $5\sqrt{3} = \sqrt{5^2}\,\sqrt{3} = \sqrt{25 \cdot 3} = \sqrt{75}$

b. $\sqrt[3]{2}\,\sqrt[4]{2} = (2)^{1/3}(2)^{1/4} = (2)^{1/3 + 1/4} = 2^{7/12} = \sqrt[12]{2^7} = \sqrt[12]{128}$
With a common base of 2, this is the simplest method.

c. Because the least common multiple of 6 and 4 is 12, let us convert both radicals to a 12th root:

$$\sqrt[6]{x}\,\sqrt[4]{y} = (x)^{1/6}(y)^{1/4} = (x)^{2/12}(y)^{3/12} = (x^2)^{1/12}(y^3)^{1/12} = [x^2y^3]^{1/12}$$

$$= \sqrt[12]{x^2y^3} \quad \text{or}$$

$$\sqrt[6]{x}\,\sqrt[4]{y} = \sqrt[6]{\sqrt{x^2}}\,\sqrt[4]{\sqrt[3]{y^3}} = \sqrt[12]{x^2}\,\sqrt[12]{y^3} = \sqrt[12]{x^2y^3}$$

EXAMPLE 7   Simplify the following. Assume that x and y are positive.

a. $\dfrac{\sqrt{5}}{\sqrt[3]{5}}$ **b.** $\dfrac{\sqrt[6]{x}}{\sqrt[4]{y^3}}$

SOLUTION   **a.** $\dfrac{\sqrt{5}}{\sqrt[3]{5}} = \dfrac{5^{1/2}}{5^{1/3}} = 5^{1/2 - 1/3} = 5^{1/6} = \sqrt[6]{5}$

b. Rationalize the denominator; then use Example 6c:

$$\frac{\sqrt[6]{x}}{\sqrt[4]{y^3}} = \frac{\sqrt[6]{x}}{\sqrt[4]{y^3}} \cdot \frac{\sqrt[4]{y}}{\sqrt[4]{y}} = \frac{\sqrt[6]{x}\,\sqrt[4]{y}}{\sqrt[4]{y^4}} = \frac{\sqrt[12]{x^2y^3}}{y}$$

EXERCISE SET 7.3

A

1 Simplify the following radicals. Assume that the variables are positive. Express your answers in radical form.

1. $\sqrt{18}$ **2.** $2\sqrt{75x}$

3. $-\sqrt{45x^2}$ **4.** $\sqrt[3]{81}$

5. $\sqrt[3]{8} + 16$ **6.** $\sqrt[3]{8} + \sqrt[3]{16}$

7. $3\sqrt[4]{32x^4}$ **8.** $\sqrt{x^2y^3}$

9. $\sqrt{20x^4y^7}$ **10.** $-\sqrt[3]{54x^3}$

11. $a^2b\sqrt[3]{a^4b^7}$ **12.** $\sqrt{9x^2 + 9}$

13. $\sqrt[3]{a^4 + a^3b^2}$ **14.** $\sqrt[5]{-64x^5y^8}$

15. $\sqrt{8a^3b^7c^8}$ **16.** $(6\sqrt{6})(5\sqrt{15})$

17. $\sqrt{xy^3}\,\sqrt{xy}$ **18.** $\sqrt{5a^2b}\,\sqrt{10ab^5}$

19. $\sqrt[3]{2x}\,\sqrt[3]{-4x^5}$ **20.** $\sqrt[3]{-ab}\,\sqrt[3]{a^2b^3}$

21. $\sqrt[7]{4x^3}\,\sqrt[7]{32x^5}$ **22.** $\sqrt[4]{a^2b^3}\,\sqrt[4]{a^3b^2}$

23. $\sqrt{2}\,\sqrt{10}\,\sqrt{15}$ **24.** $\sqrt[3]{3}\,\sqrt[3]{6}\,\sqrt[3]{12}$

2

25. $\sqrt{\dfrac{5}{9}}$ **26.** $\sqrt{\dfrac{28}{25}}$

27. $\sqrt[3]{\dfrac{3}{8}}$ **28.** $5\sqrt[4]{\dfrac{x^5}{81}}$

29. $\sqrt{\dfrac{a}{4b^2}}$ **30.** $\sqrt[3]{-\dfrac{ab^2}{a^4b^8}}$

31. $\dfrac{\sqrt{75x^3}}{\sqrt{3x}}$ **32.** $\dfrac{\sqrt[3]{-16a^4}}{\sqrt[3]{-2ab^3}}$

33. $\dfrac{4\sqrt{40x^3y^6}}{\sqrt{2}}$ **34.** $\dfrac{\sqrt{49}}{\sqrt{2}}$

35. $\dfrac{\sqrt{5a^3}}{\sqrt{3}}$ **36.** $10\sqrt{\dfrac{63}{5}}$

37. $\sqrt{\dfrac{2}{7}}$ **38.** $\sqrt[3]{\dfrac{2}{7}}$

39. $\sqrt[4]{\dfrac{2}{7}}$ **40.** $\dfrac{8}{\sqrt[3]{4}}$

41. $\dfrac{9x^3}{\sqrt[3]{9x}}$ **42.** $\dfrac{1}{\sqrt[3]{12x^2}}$

43. $\dfrac{1}{\sqrt[4]{12x^2}}$ **44.** $\dfrac{1}{\sqrt[5]{12x^2}}$

45. $\dfrac{12x}{\sqrt[4]{18x}}$ **46.** $\sqrt{\dfrac{7}{3}}\,\sqrt{\dfrac{25}{7}}$

47. $\sqrt[3]{\dfrac{4x}{3y}}\,\sqrt[3]{\dfrac{81y^5}{8x^2}}$ **48.** $\dfrac{\sqrt[3]{40a^5}}{\sqrt[3]{5a^8}}$

Simplify the following radicals. Make no assumptions about the variables except that denominators are nonzero.

49. $\sqrt{27x^2}$ **50.** $\sqrt[3]{8x^3}$

51. $\sqrt{x^4y^6}$ **52.** $\sqrt{8a^4b^8}$

53. $\sqrt[5]{-64x^6}$ **54.** $\sqrt[4]{81a^4b^6}$

55. $\sqrt{\dfrac{a^2}{2b^4}}$ **56.** $\sqrt{\dfrac{18a^4}{50b^{12}}}$

3

For the following problems, assume that variables are positive.

Simplify the following.

57. $\sqrt[4]{9}$ **58.** $\sqrt[4]{100}$ **59.** $\sqrt[6]{8}$

60. $\sqrt[6]{16}$ **61.** $\sqrt[9]{27}$ **62.** $\sqrt[8]{81}$

63. $\sqrt[8]{25}$ **64.** $\sqrt[15]{-125}$ **65.** $\sqrt[12]{25}$

66. $\sqrt[12]{27}$ **67.** $\sqrt[12]{64}$ **68.** $\sqrt[12]{625}$

Express the following as 12th roots.

69. $\sqrt{a}$ **70.** $\sqrt[3]{b}$ **71.** $\sqrt[4]{c}$ **72.** $\sqrt[6]{d}$

Write the following as single radicals.

73. $3\sqrt{2}$ **74.** $5\sqrt[3]{2}$

75. $\sqrt{3}\,\sqrt[3]{3}$ **76.** $\sqrt[3]{5}\,\sqrt[4]{5}$

77. $\dfrac{5}{\sqrt{7}}$ **78.** $\dfrac{\sqrt{2}}{3}$

79. $\dfrac{\sqrt{7}}{\sqrt[3]{7}}$ **80.** $\dfrac{\sqrt[6]{2}}{\sqrt[8]{2}}$

81. $\sqrt{3}\,\sqrt[4]{5}$ **82.** $\sqrt[3]{2}\,\sqrt[6]{3}$

83. $\sqrt[8]{x}\,\sqrt[4]{y}$ **84.** $\sqrt{2}\,\sqrt[3]{3}$

85. $\sqrt{3}\,\sqrt[3]{2}$ **86.** $\sqrt[6]{a}\,\sqrt[8]{b}$

87. $\sqrt[3]{x}\,\sqrt[5]{y}$ **88.** $\sqrt[3]{a^2}\,\sqrt[4]{b^3}$

89. $\dfrac{\sqrt{6}}{\sqrt[4]{3}}$ **90.** $\dfrac{\sqrt[6]{5}}{\sqrt[3]{2}}$

91. $\dfrac{\sqrt[3]{x}}{\sqrt{y}}$ **92.** $\dfrac{\sqrt[6]{a^5}}{\sqrt[4]{b}}$

B

93. $\sqrt{a}\,\sqrt[3]{a}\,\sqrt[4]{a}$ **94.** $\sqrt{a}\,\sqrt[3]{a^2}\,\sqrt[4]{a^3}$

95. $\sqrt{a}\,\sqrt[4]{a^3}\,\sqrt[6]{a^5}$

Use rational exponents to simplify the following.

96. $\sqrt[3]{5\sqrt{5}}$ **97.** $\sqrt{7\sqrt[3]{7}}$

98. $\sqrt{3\sqrt{3\sqrt{3}}}$

C	

Answer the following questions with complete sentences.

99. Find a value of a such that $\sqrt{a+b} = \sqrt{a} + \sqrt{b}$. Justify your answer.

100. What does it mean to "rationalize the denominator" of a fraction?

REVIEW EXERCISES

Find the following products. (See Section 5.3.)

101. $2x(x + 4y)$

102. $(x + 3)(x + 4)$

103. $(1 + x)(1 - x)$

104. $(1 + x)(1 - x + x^2)$

7.4 SIMPLIFYING RADICALS

1	Adding and Subtracting Radicals
2	Multiplying Radicals
3	Rationalizing Binomial Denominators

1 Adding and Subtracting Radicals

In the last three sections we developed rules that allowed us to simplify individual radicals. In this section we will use these rules and properties such as the distributive and commutative laws to add and multiply radical expressions. These operations are very similar to the methods of adding and multiplying polynomials.

Recall that the distributive property allows us to combine like terms. For example, $2x + 5x = (2 + 5)x = 7x$, where x is any real number. Therefore, if $x = \sqrt{3}$, then

$$2\sqrt{3} + 5\sqrt{3} = (2 + 5)\sqrt{3} = 7\sqrt{3}$$

Just as $2x + 5y$ cannot be simplified because they are unlike terms, $2\sqrt{3} + 5\sqrt{7}$, $2\sqrt{3} + 5\sqrt[3]{3}$, and $2 + 5\sqrt{7}$ cannot be simplified. In general, to be added or subtracted, radicals must have the same index and the same radicand. Example 1 illustrates this concept.

EXAMPLE 1

Simplify the following.

a. $14\sqrt{7} + 4 - 8\sqrt{7}$ **b.** $2\sqrt[5]{6} + 3\sqrt[4]{6} - \sqrt[5]{6}$

SOLUTION   **a.** $14\sqrt{7} + 4 - 8\sqrt{7} = 4 + 14\sqrt{7} - 8\sqrt{7} = 4 + (14 - 8)\sqrt{7} = 4 + 6\sqrt{7}$. Note that $4 + 6\sqrt{7} \neq 10\sqrt{7}$.

b. $2\sqrt[5]{6} + 3\sqrt[4]{6} - \sqrt[5]{6} = (2\sqrt[5]{6} - \sqrt[5]{6}) + 3\sqrt[4]{6} = \sqrt[5]{6} + 3\sqrt[4]{6}$

We often have to simplify individual radicals before they are in a form in which they can be combined. For example,

$$6\sqrt{2} + 2\sqrt{50} = 6\sqrt{2} + 2\sqrt{25}\sqrt{2} = 6\sqrt{2} + 10\sqrt{2} = 16\sqrt{2}$$

EXAMPLE 2

Simplify the following.

a. $\sqrt[3]{81} - \sqrt[3]{24}$ **b.** $\sqrt[4]{9} + 5\sqrt{3}$ **c.** $\dfrac{1}{\sqrt{3}} + \dfrac{\sqrt{12}}{5} - \sqrt{3}$

(continued)

SOLUTION   **a.** $\sqrt[3]{81} - \sqrt[3]{24} = \sqrt[3]{27 \cdot 3} - \sqrt[3]{8 \cdot 3} = 3\sqrt[3]{3} - 2\sqrt[3]{3} = \sqrt[3]{3}$

b. $\sqrt[4]{9} + 5\sqrt{3} = \sqrt{\sqrt{9}} + 5\sqrt{3} = \sqrt{3} + 5\sqrt{3} = 6\sqrt{3}$

c. $\dfrac{1}{\sqrt{3}} + \dfrac{\sqrt{12}}{5} - \sqrt{3} = \dfrac{1}{\sqrt{3}} \cdot \dfrac{\sqrt{3}}{\sqrt{3}} + \dfrac{\sqrt{4 \cdot 3}}{5} - \sqrt{3} = \dfrac{\sqrt{3}}{3} + \dfrac{2\sqrt{3}}{5} - 1\sqrt{3}$

$$= \left(\dfrac{1}{3} + \dfrac{2}{5} - 1\right)\sqrt{3} = \dfrac{-4\sqrt{3}}{15}$$

The process of simplifying radicals that contain variables is similar to the method just discussed. For simplicity, we will assume that all variables represent positive numbers.

EXAMPLE 3

Simplify the following.

a. $3\sqrt{4x} - \sqrt{9x} + \sqrt{32x}$ **b.** $\sqrt[3]{3x^4} + x\sqrt[3]{24x}$

SOLUTION   **a.** $3\sqrt{4x} - \sqrt{9x} + \sqrt{32x} = 3\sqrt{4}\sqrt{x} - \sqrt{9}\sqrt{x} + \sqrt{16}\sqrt{2x}$

$$= 6\sqrt{x} - 3\sqrt{x} + 4\sqrt{2x} = 3\sqrt{x} + 4\sqrt{2x}$$

b. $\sqrt[3]{3x^4} + x\sqrt[3]{24x} = \sqrt[3]{x^3}\sqrt[3]{3x} + x\sqrt[3]{8}\sqrt[3]{3x} = x\sqrt[3]{3x} + 8x\sqrt[3]{3x}$

$$= (1 + 8)x\sqrt[3]{3x} = 9x\sqrt[3]{3x}$$

2   Multiplying Radicals

We have just seen that the procedure for adding like radicals is similar to the method of adding like terms with polynomials. Also, the process of multiplying radical expressions is similar to finding products of polynomials. For example, to find $2\sqrt{3}(\sqrt{3} + 4\sqrt{5})$ or $2x(x + 4y)$, we use the distributive property and then simplify the resulting terms:

$2\sqrt{3}(\sqrt{3} + 4\sqrt{5})$ $2x(x + 4y)$

$= 2\sqrt{3}(\sqrt{3}) + 2\sqrt{3}(4\sqrt{5})$ $= 2x(x) + 2x(4y)$

$= 2(\sqrt{3})^2 + 8\sqrt{3}\sqrt{5}$ $= 2x^2 + 8xy$

$= 6 + 8\sqrt{15}$

Note: $6 + 8\sqrt{15} \neq 14\sqrt{15}$!

As another example, we multiply $(\sqrt{7} + 3)(\sqrt{7} + 4)$ just as we would $(x + 3)(x + 4)$:

$(\sqrt{7} + 3)(\sqrt{7} + 4)$ $(x + 3)(x + 4)$

$= (\sqrt{7} + 3)\sqrt{7} + (\sqrt{7} + 3)4$ $= (x + 3)x + (x + 3)4$

$= (\sqrt{7})^2 + 3\sqrt{7} + 4\sqrt{7} + 12$ $= x^2 + 3x + 4x + 12$

$= 7 + 7\sqrt{7} + 12$ $= x^2 + 7x + 12$

$= 19 + 7\sqrt{7}$

EXAMPLE 4

Find the following products and simplify.

a. $(\sqrt{a} + \sqrt{b})^2$ **b.** $(1 + \sqrt[3]{2})(1 - \sqrt[3]{2} + \sqrt[3]{4})$

c. $(2 + \sqrt{3})(2 - \sqrt{3})$

SOLUTION **a.** $(\sqrt{a} + \sqrt{b})^2 = (\sqrt{a} + \sqrt{b})(\sqrt{a} + \sqrt{b})$
$$= (\sqrt{a})^2 + \sqrt{ab} + \sqrt{ab} + (\sqrt{b})^2 = a + 2\sqrt{ab} + b$$

Note: $(\sqrt{a} + \sqrt{b})^2 \ne (\sqrt{a})^2 + (\sqrt{b})^2 = a + b$

b. $(1 + \sqrt[3]{2})(1 - \sqrt[3]{2} + \sqrt[3]{4})$
$$= 1(1 - \sqrt[3]{2} + \sqrt[3]{4}) + \sqrt[3]{2}(1 - \sqrt[3]{2} + \sqrt[3]{4})$$
$$= 1 - \sqrt[3]{2} + \sqrt[3]{4} + \sqrt[3]{2} - \sqrt[3]{4} + \sqrt[3]{8}$$
$$= 1 + (-\sqrt[3]{2} + \sqrt[3]{2}) + (\sqrt[3]{4} - \sqrt[3]{4}) + 2$$
$$= 3$$

c. $(2 + \sqrt{3})(2 - \sqrt{3}) = 4 - 2\sqrt{3} + 2\sqrt{3} - \sqrt{9} = 4 - 3 = 1$

Mathematics and the sciences present many situations in which expressions that contain rational exponents must be multiplied. The procedure is similar to finding the product of polynomials. For example,

$$x^{2/3}(x^{4/3} + x^{1/3}) = x^{2/3}x^{4/3} + x^{2/3}x^{1/3}$$
$$= x^{6/3} + x^{3/3}$$
$$= x^2 + x$$

EXAMPLE 5

Find the following products.

a. $(a^{3/2} + 2^{3/2})(a^{3/2} - 2^{3/2})$ **b.** $(x^{1/2} - 3)^2$

SOLUTION **a.** $(a^{3/2} + 2^{3/2})(a^{3/2} - 2^{3/2})$
$$= (a^{3/2})^2 - 2^{3/2}a^{3/2} + 2^{3/2}a^{3/2} - (2^{3/2})^2$$
$$= a^3 + 0 - 2^3$$
$$= a^3 - 8$$

b. $(x^{1/2} - 3)^2 = (x^{1/2} - 3)(x^{1/2} - 3)$
$$= (x^{1/2})^2 - 3x^{1/2} - 3x^{1/2} + 9$$
$$= x - 6x^{1/2} + 9 \quad \text{or} \quad x - 6\sqrt{x} + 9$$

3   Rationalizing Binomial Denominators

Many fractions have binomial denominators that contain radicals, such as $\dfrac{1}{2 + \sqrt{3}}$. We rationalize this denominator by using the result of Example 4c: $(2 + \sqrt{3})(2 - \sqrt{3}) = 1$. Thus,

$$\frac{1}{2 + \sqrt{3}} = \frac{1}{2 + \sqrt{3}} \cdot \frac{2 - \sqrt{3}}{2 - \sqrt{3}} = \frac{2 - \sqrt{3}}{1} = 2 - \sqrt{3}$$

The expressions $2 + \sqrt{3}$ and $2 - \sqrt{3}$ are called **conjugates** of each other. These numbers are in the form $a + b$ and $a - b$, where a, b, or both contain square roots. Because $(a + b)(a - b) = a^2 - b^2$, the difference of two squares, conjugates have the property that their product is a rational number. We use this fact to rationalize binomial denominators that contain square roots, as illustrated in our concluding example. A summary of the requirements for a simplified radical expression follows the example.

EXAMPLE 6   Simplify the following fractions.

$$\textbf{a.}\ \frac{2}{\sqrt{10} - 3} \qquad \textbf{b.}\ \frac{\sqrt{2}}{\sqrt{6} + \sqrt{2}} \qquad \textbf{c.}\ \frac{x - 25}{\sqrt{x} - 5}$$

SOLUTION   **a.** $\dfrac{2}{\sqrt{10} - 3} = \dfrac{2}{\sqrt{10} - 3} \cdot \dfrac{\sqrt{10} + 3}{\sqrt{10} + 3}$

$$= \frac{2(\sqrt{10} + 3)}{(\sqrt{10})^2 - 3\sqrt{10} + 3\sqrt{10} - 3^2} = \frac{2(\sqrt{10} + 3)}{10 - 9}$$

$$= 2\sqrt{10} + 6$$

b. $\dfrac{\sqrt{2}}{\sqrt{6} + \sqrt{2}} = \dfrac{\sqrt{2}}{\sqrt{6} + \sqrt{2}} \cdot \dfrac{\sqrt{6} - \sqrt{2}}{\sqrt{6} - \sqrt{2}} = \dfrac{\sqrt{12} - (\sqrt{2})^2}{(\sqrt{6})^2 - (\sqrt{2})^2} = \dfrac{\sqrt{4 \cdot 3} - 2}{6 - 2} =$

$$\frac{2\sqrt{3} - 2}{4} = \frac{2(\sqrt{3} - 1)}{2 \cdot 2} = \frac{\sqrt{3} - 1}{2}$$

c. $\dfrac{x - 25}{\sqrt{x} - 5} = \dfrac{x - 25}{\sqrt{x} - 5} \cdot \dfrac{\sqrt{x} + 5}{\sqrt{x} + 5} = \dfrac{(x - 25)(\sqrt{x} + 5)}{(\sqrt{x})^2 - 5^2}$

$$= \frac{(x - 25)(\sqrt{x} + 5)}{x - 25} = \sqrt{x} + 5$$

Summary

A radical expression is simplified if:

1. A square root does not contain a factor that is a square, a cube root does not contain a factor that is a cube, and so on.
2. No fractions are under the radical sign.
3. No radicals are in the denominator of a fraction.
4. The index of a radical is reduced to the smallest possible natural number.
5. Like radicals are combined.

EXERCISE SET 7.4

A

1 Simplify the following. Assume that the variables represent positive numbers.

1. $5\sqrt{2} + 3\sqrt{2}$

2. $6\sqrt{7x} - 2\sqrt{7x}$

3. $7\sqrt[3]{5x} - 2\sqrt[3]{5x}$

4. $9\sqrt{11} + \sqrt[3]{11} + 2\sqrt{11}$

5. $\sqrt[3]{3x} + \sqrt[3]{5x} + 8\sqrt[3]{3x}$

6. $2\sqrt{13} + \sqrt[4]{16} - \sqrt{13}$

7. $\sqrt{81} + 5\sqrt{3}$

8. $9\sqrt{45x} - 2\sqrt{20x}$

9. $\sqrt[3]{24y^2} - 8\sqrt[3]{81y^2}$

10. $8\sqrt{25} - 2\sqrt{5} + 7\sqrt{45}$

11. $x\sqrt[4]{32} + 5x\sqrt[4]{2} - x\sqrt[4]{162}$

12. $5\sqrt{2x^2} - 3x\sqrt{8} + \sqrt{18x^2}$

13. $6\sqrt[3]{27x^4} - 12\sqrt[3]{-8x}$

14. $2b\sqrt[4]{a^5b} + 7a\sqrt[4]{ab^5}$

15. $\sqrt{x^5} + 2x\sqrt{9x^3} - 8x^2\sqrt{25x}$

16. $5a\sqrt{b^2c^2} + 3a\sqrt{ab^3c} - ab\sqrt{abc}$

17. $\frac{1}{4}\sqrt{2} + \frac{1}{6}\sqrt{50}$

18. $\frac{2}{3}\sqrt[3]{x^4} - \frac{x}{8}\sqrt[3]{8x}$

19. $\frac{1}{\sqrt{3}} + \frac{5\sqrt{3}}{3}$

20. $\frac{\sqrt{2}}{2} + \frac{1}{\sqrt{2}}$

21. $\frac{1}{\sqrt[3]{4}} + \frac{6\sqrt[3]{-2}}{5}$

22. $\frac{1}{\sqrt[3]{3}} + \frac{3\sqrt[3]{72}}{4}$

23. $\sqrt{\frac{1}{5}} + \sqrt{20} - \frac{2\sqrt{125}}{3}$

24. $\sqrt[4]{25} + \frac{1}{\sqrt{5}}$

25. $\sqrt[4]{4} + 2\sqrt{18}$

26. $\sqrt[6]{4} - 2\sqrt[3]{250}$

27. $3\sqrt[6]{8} + 4\sqrt[8]{16}$

28. $\sqrt[4]{36} - \sqrt[6]{216}$

2

29. $\sqrt{2}(\sqrt{2} + \sqrt{3})$

30. $\sqrt{3}(\sqrt{6} - 4\sqrt{3})$

31. $2\sqrt{5}(\sqrt{10} + 5\sqrt{15})$

32. $\sqrt[3]{6}(\sqrt[3]{4} - \sqrt[3]{45})$

33. $\sqrt{ab}(2\sqrt{ab} - \sqrt{a^3b})$

34. $\sqrt{3x}(\sqrt{6xy} - \sqrt{3y})$

35. $(\sqrt{3} + 2)(\sqrt{2} + 5)$

36. $(2\sqrt{3} - 5)(\sqrt{3} + 2)$

37. $(\sqrt{2} - \sqrt{3})(\sqrt{6} + \sqrt{3})$

38. $(\sqrt{x} + 2)(\sqrt{x} - 4)$

39. $(\sqrt{a} + \sqrt{5})(\sqrt{a} - \sqrt{10})$

40. $(2\sqrt{x} - \sqrt{y})(3\sqrt{x} + 2\sqrt{y})$

41. $(\sqrt{3} + 5)^2$

42. $(\sqrt{5} - \sqrt{2})^2$

43. $(\sqrt{x} - 4)^2$

44. $(3 - 2\sqrt{a})^2$

45. $(\sqrt{5} - 2)(\sqrt{5} + 2)$

46. $(3 + \sqrt{2})(3 - \sqrt{2})$

47. $(\sqrt{6} + \sqrt{5})(\sqrt{6} - \sqrt{5})$

48. $(\sqrt{x} + 4)(\sqrt{x} - 4)$

49. $(\sqrt{a} - \sqrt{b})(\sqrt{a} + \sqrt{b})$

50. $(\sqrt[3]{2} + 3)(\sqrt[3]{4} - 2)$

51. $x^{3/4}(x^{1/4} - x^{5/4})$

52. $x^{1/3}(x^{8/3} + x^{2/3})$

53. $(a^{1/2} - 2)(a^{1/2} - 3)$

54. $(a^{1/3} + a^{1/2})(a^{2/3} - a^{1/2})$

55. $(x^{1/2} + 4)^2$

56. $(a^{1/2} - b^{1/2})^2$

3

57. $\dfrac{1}{\sqrt{5} - 2}$ **58.** $\dfrac{1}{3 + \sqrt{2}}$

59. $\dfrac{\sqrt{3}}{1 - 2\sqrt{3}}$ **60.** $\dfrac{2\sqrt{2}}{\sqrt{6} + 2}$

61. $\dfrac{1}{\sqrt{6} + \sqrt{5}}$ **62.** $\dfrac{8}{\sqrt{7} - \sqrt{3}}$

63. $\dfrac{\sqrt{5} + 3}{\sqrt{5} + 2}$ **64.** $\dfrac{\sqrt{7}}{x - \sqrt{7}}$

65. $\dfrac{\sqrt{3}}{y + 2\sqrt{3}}$ **66.** $\dfrac{2}{3 + \sqrt{x}}$

67. $\dfrac{y - 1}{\sqrt{y} - 1}$ **68.** $\dfrac{1 - \sqrt{2}}{1 + \sqrt{2}}$

B

69. $\dfrac{\sqrt{6} + \sqrt{2}}{3\sqrt{2} - 2\sqrt{3}}$ **70.** $\dfrac{\sqrt{10} - \sqrt{5}}{2\sqrt{5} + 5\sqrt{3}}$

71. $\dfrac{x^2 - y^2}{\sqrt{x} + \sqrt{y}}$ **72.** $\dfrac{a^2 - 2ab + b^2}{\sqrt{a} - \sqrt{b}}$

73. $\dfrac{8a - 18b}{2\sqrt{a} - 3\sqrt{b}}$ **74.** $\dfrac{4x^2 - xy}{2\sqrt{x} + \sqrt{y}}$

C

We simplified $\dfrac{1}{2 + \sqrt{3}}$ by letting $2 + \sqrt{3} = a + b$ in the formula $(a + b)(a - b) = a^2 - b^2$. In a similar way we can simplify $\dfrac{1}{1 + \sqrt[3]{2}}$ by letting

$1 + \sqrt[3]{2} = a + b$ in the formula $(a + b)(a^2 - ab + b^2) = a^3 + b^3$. Using the result of Example 4b and $a^2 - ab + b^2 = 1^2 - 1 \cdot \sqrt[3]{2} + (\sqrt[3]{2})^2 = 1 - \sqrt[3]{2} + \sqrt[3]{4}$ we have

$$\frac{1}{1 + \sqrt[3]{2}} = \frac{1}{1 + \sqrt[3]{2}} \cdot \frac{1 - \sqrt[3]{2} + \sqrt[3]{4}}{1 - \sqrt[3]{2} + \sqrt[3]{4}} = \frac{1 - \sqrt[3]{2} + \sqrt[3]{4}}{3}$$

Rationalize the denominators of the following.

75. $\dfrac{4}{1 + \sqrt[3]{3}}$

76. $\dfrac{6}{2 - \sqrt[3]{5}}$

77. $\dfrac{1}{2 - \sqrt[3]{9}}$

78. $\dfrac{2}{\sqrt[3]{2} - \sqrt[3]{4}}$

79. $\dfrac{1}{1 + \sqrt[3]{2} + \sqrt[3]{4}}$

80. $\dfrac{1}{4 + 2\sqrt[3]{x} + \sqrt[3]{x^2}}$

Answer the following questions with complete sentences.

81. How is the addition of radicals similar to the addition of monomials?

82. Discuss the steps in rationalizing the binomial denominator of a radical expression.

REVIEW EXERCISES

Solve the following for the indicated variables. (See Sections 5.6 and 6.5.)

83. $x^2 - 25 = 0$

84. $y^2 - 4y + 4 = 2y - 4$

85. $k = \dfrac{x}{3m + M}; \quad m$

86. $\dfrac{2x}{3} - \dfrac{4y}{5} = 1; \quad y$

87. $c = \dfrac{2ab}{d}; \quad d$

7.5 RADICAL EQUATIONS AND FORMULAS

1	Solving Radical Equations in One Variable; Roots of a Radical Function
2	Solving Formulas and Literal Equations
3	Applying Radical Equations

1 Solving Radical Equations in One Variable; Roots of a Radical Function

Many equations and formulas contain radicals. The first part of this section shows how to solve radical equations by converting them to familiar polynomial equations. Then we solve radical formulas for a given variable and consider certain applications, such as the change in mass described in Einstein's special theory of relativity.

Equations containing radicals with variables in the radicand are called radical equations. Examples are

$$\sqrt{2x^2 - 25} = x, \qquad \sqrt{x + 6} = 2 + \sqrt{x}, \qquad \text{and} \qquad \sqrt[3]{4x} = 2$$

To solve such an equation we need the property of equality, which states that if two quantities are equal, then their nth powers are equal; that is,

$$\text{If } a = b, \text{ then } a^n = b^n.$$

For example, if $x = 4$, then $x^2 = 16$. However, the solution set of $x = 4$ is $\{4\}$, but the solution set of $x^2 = 16$ is $\{4, -4\}$. Thus, $x = -4$ is not a solution of the first equation; it is called an **extraneous solution** or **root** of $x = 4$. In general, the solution set of $a^n = b^n$ contains all the solutions of $a = b$, but it may contain extra values that do not satisfy $a = b$. Therefore, part of the solution of a radical equation is to check the answers to $a^n = b^n$ in $a = b$ to find any extraneous roots.

EXAMPLE 1

Solve $\sqrt{2x^2 - 25} = x$.

SOLUTION

$$\sqrt{2x^2 - 25} = x \qquad\qquad \text{Square both sides.}$$
$$(\sqrt{2x^2 - 25})^2 = x^2 \qquad\qquad (\sqrt{a})^2 = a$$
$$2x^2 - 25 = x^2$$
$$x^2 - 25 = 0$$
$$(x - 5)(x + 5) = 0$$
$$x - 5 = 0 \quad \text{or} \quad x + 5 = 0$$
$$x = 5 \quad \text{or} \qquad\quad x = -5$$

 CHECK $x = 5$:

$$\sqrt{2 \cdot 5^2 - 25} \overset{?}{=} 5 \qquad \sqrt{2(-5)^2 - 25} \overset{?}{=} -5$$
$$\sqrt{50 - 25} \overset{?}{=} 5 \qquad\qquad \sqrt{50 - 25} \overset{?}{=} -5$$
$$\sqrt{25} = 5 \qquad\qquad\qquad \sqrt{25} \neq -5$$

$x = -5$:

Thus, $x = -5$ is an extraneous root, and the solution set is $\{5\}$.

EXAMPLE 2

Solve $\sqrt[3]{5t - 1} = \sqrt[3]{3t + 13}$.

SOLUTION

$$\sqrt[3]{5t - 1} = \sqrt[3]{3t + 13} \qquad \text{Cube both sides.}$$
$$(\sqrt[3]{5t - 1})^3 = (\sqrt[3]{3t + 13})^3 \quad (\sqrt[3]{a})^3 = a$$
$$5t - 1 = 3t + 13$$
$$2t = 14$$
$$t = 7$$

 CHECK $\sqrt[3]{5 \cdot 7 - 1} \overset{?}{=} \sqrt[3]{3 \cdot 7 + 13}$

$\sqrt[3]{34} = \sqrt[3]{34}$, so $t = 7$ is the solution.

EXAMPLE 3

Solve $2 + \sqrt{2y - 4} = y$.

SOLUTION

The first step in solving this equation is to isolate $\sqrt{2y - 4}$ on the left side of the equation:

$2 + \sqrt{2y - 4} = y$ Subtract 2 from both sides.

$\sqrt{2y - 4} = y - 2$ Square both sides.

$(\sqrt{2y - 4})^2 = (y - 2)^2$

$2y - 4 = y^2 - 4y + 4$

$0 = y^2 - 6y + 8$

$0 = (y - 2)(y - 4)$

$y = 2 \quad \text{or} \quad y = 4$

 CHECK

$y = 2$:

$2 + \sqrt{2 \cdot 2 - 4} \overset{?}{=} 2$

$2 + \sqrt{0} = 2$

$y = 4$:

$2 + \sqrt{2 \cdot 4 - 4} \overset{?}{=} 4$

$2 + \sqrt{4} = 4$

Thus, the solution set is $\{2, 4\}$.

In Example 3 notice that we isolated the radical on one side of the equation before we squared both sides. If we had correctly squared both sides of the given equation, then we would have produced

$$4 + 4\sqrt{2y - 4} + 2y - 4 = y^2 \quad (a + b)^2 = a^2 + 2ab + b^2$$

which is far more complicated than the original equation. Also, a common mistake is to square both sides incorrectly and obtain $4 + 2y - 4 = y^2$. To square both sides of an equation does not mean that we square each term.

 COMMON ERROR

A common mistake is to improperly square (or raise to the nth power) both sides of an equation.

$$(2 + \sqrt{x})^2 \neq 4 + x \quad \text{because} \quad (a + b)^2 \neq a^2 + b^2$$

Many equations contain two or more radicals, such as $\sqrt{x + 6} = 2 + \sqrt{x}$. In this case isolating each radical is impossible, so we square both sides of the equation to produce an equation that contains one radical.

EXAMPLE 4

Solve $\sqrt{x + 6} = 2 + \sqrt{x}$.

SOLUTION

$\sqrt{x + 6} = 2 + \sqrt{x}$ Square both sides.

$(\sqrt{x + 6})^2 = (2 + \sqrt{x})^2$ $(a + b)^2 = a^2 + 2ab + b^2$

$x + 6 = 2^2 + 2 \cdot 2\sqrt{x} + (\sqrt{x})^2$

$x + 6 = 4 + 4\sqrt{x} + x$ Isolate $4\sqrt{x}$.

$2 = 4\sqrt{x}$ Square both sides.

$2^2 = (4\sqrt{x})^2$

$4 = 16x$

$\dfrac{1}{4} = x$

CHECK $\quad \sqrt{\dfrac{1}{4} + 6} \stackrel{?}{=} 2 + \sqrt{\dfrac{1}{4}}$

$$\sqrt{\dfrac{25}{4}} \stackrel{?}{=} 2 + \dfrac{1}{2}$$

$$\dfrac{5}{2} = \dfrac{5}{2}, \quad \text{so } x = \dfrac{1}{4} \text{ is the solution.}$$

In Sections 5.6 and 6.2 we discussed the roots of polynomial and rational functions. The following example illustrates the method of finding the roots of a radical function if they exist.

EXAMPLE 5

Find the roots of the given function.

a. $f(x) = \sqrt{x^2 - 3} - 1$ **b.** $g(x) = \sqrt{2x + 1} + 3$

SOLUTION

a. We need to find x so that $f(x) = 0$; that is,

$$\sqrt{x^2 - 3} - 1 = 0 \qquad \text{Add 1 to both sides.}$$
$$\sqrt{x^2 - 3} = 1 \qquad \text{Square both sides.}$$
$$(\sqrt{x^2 - 3})^2 = 1^2 \qquad (\sqrt{a})^2 = a$$
$$x^2 - 3 = 1 \qquad \text{Add 3 to both sides.}$$
$$x^2 = 4$$
$$x = \pm 2$$

CHECK $\quad \sqrt{2^2 - 3} - 1 = 1 - 1 = 0 \quad$ and $\quad \sqrt{(-2)^2 - 3} - 1 = 0$
Thus, $\{2, -2\}$ are the roots of f.

b. We need to find x so that $\sqrt{2x + 1} + 3 = 0$.
$\sqrt{2x + 1} + 3 = 0$ if $\sqrt{2x + 1} = -3$. However, $\sqrt{2x + 1} \geq 0$ and $-3 < 0$. Therefore, $\sqrt{2x + 1} + 3 = 0$ has no solution, so g does not have a root. If we had solved the equation as in part (a) and checked the answer, then we would have found that the equation has no solution. This method would tell us that the function g does not have a root.

2 **Solving Formulas and Literal Equations**

Many formulas and literal equations involving radicals occur in mathematics and the sciences. The technique for solving one of these for a given variable is similar to the method used in solving a radical equation. If necessary we isolate the radical, raise both sides of the equation to the appropriate power, and then solve the resulting equation for the required variable.

For instance, the formula $c = \sqrt{2GM/R}$ is used in astronomy. The constant c is the escape velocity of a black hole, which is the speed of light, and R is the radius of the black hole. For example, if the earth and the sun became black holes, then their radii would be 1 centimeter and 3 kilometers, respectively. This formula is solved for R in the following example.

EXAMPLE 6

Solve the following for the indicated variables.

a. $c = \sqrt{\dfrac{2GM}{R}}$; R escape velocity of a black hole

b. $r = \sqrt[3]{\dfrac{3V}{\pi}}$; V radius of a cone, $r = h$

c. $x = -\sqrt{y - 1}$; y

d. $x = 3 + \sqrt{y - x}$; y

SOLUTION   **a.** $c = \sqrt{\dfrac{2GM}{R}}$ Square both sides.

$c^2 = \left(\sqrt{\dfrac{2GM}{R}}\right)^2$

$c^2 = \dfrac{2GM}{R}$ Multiply by R.

$c^2 R = 2GM$ Divide by c^2.

$R = \dfrac{2GM}{c^2}$

b. $r = \sqrt[3]{\dfrac{3V}{\pi}}$ Cube both sides.

$r^3 = \left(\sqrt[3]{\dfrac{3V}{\pi}}\right)^3$

$r^3 = \dfrac{3V}{\pi}$ Multiply by π.

$\pi r^3 = 3V$ Divide by 3.

$\dfrac{\pi r^3}{3} = V$

c. $x = -\sqrt{y - 1}$ Square both sides.

$x^2 = (-\sqrt{y - 1})^2$ $(-a)^2 = a^2$

$x^2 = y - 1$ Add 1.

$x^2 + 1 = y$

d. $x = 3 + \sqrt{y - x}$ Isolate $\sqrt{y - x}$.

$x - 3 = \sqrt{y - x}$ Square both sides.

$(x - 3)^2 = (\sqrt{y - x})^2$

$x^2 - 6x + 9 = y - x$ Add x to both sides.

$x^2 - 5x + 9 = y$

3   Applying Radical Equations

In Albert Einstein's special theory of relativity (see Math in Time, page 341), time, length, and mass (or weight, which is proportional to mass) vary with speed. If an object moves at a velocity close to the speed of light, then three things happen, as observed by a person at rest: Mass increases, length in the direction of motion decreases, and time slows down (time intervals increase in length). For example, suppose you saw your 120-pound mother traveling at close to 90% of the speed of light in a spaceship that was 100 feet long before the trip started. You would observe that the spaceship was nearly 50 feet long, her weight was approximately 240 pounds, and her

Math in Time

IN THE SEVENTEENTH century Sir Isaac Newton (1642–1727) presented a picture of the universe in which time was absolute; that is, the passage of time for a traveler would be the same as that for a stationary observer. For nearly 200 years this viewpoint was consistent with observations. However, experiments in the 1880s showed that the speed of light was constant, regardless of the motion of the source of light or the motion of the observer. This result was not consistent with Netwon's concept of absolute time. The conflict was resolved at the turn of the century by Albert Einstein (1879–1955). At the age of 14 he asked himself, "What would the world look like if I rode on a beam of light?" After 12 years of consideration, he published, in 1905, his special theory of relativity, which held that time, length, and mass are not absolutes but vary according to velocity.

"For Newton, time and space formed an absolute framework, within which the material events of the world ran their course in imperturbable order. His is a God's eye view of the world: it looks the same to every observer, wherever he is and however he travels. By contrast, Einstein's is a man's eye view, in which what you see and what I see is relative to each of us, that is, to our place and speed. And this relativity cannot be removed. We cannot know what the world is like in itself, we can only compare what it looks like to each of us, by the practical procedure of exchanging messages" —(*Bronowski, 1973*).

Calvin and Hobbes

by Bill Watterson

watch and general aging process had slowed to almost half of yours. Einstein's theories seem bizarre at first, but they have been verified with experiments in atomic physics and by astronomical observations.

The following equations relate the mass, time, and length at rest (M_0, T_0, L_0) to the mass, time, and length (M, T, L) for a velocity v. The speed of light, c, is approximately 186,000 miles per second (mps).

$$M = \frac{M_0}{\sqrt{1 - \dfrac{v^2}{c^2}}}, \qquad T = \frac{T_0}{\sqrt{1 - \dfrac{v^2}{c^2}}}, \qquad L = L_0 \sqrt{1 - \frac{v^2}{c^2}} \qquad (1)$$

341

EXAMPLE 7

Sue's weight is 125 pounds. Find the speed at which she would have to travel for her weight to increase to 250 pounds. Use $c = 186,000$ mps.

SOLUTION

In (1), let $M_0 = 125$ and $M = 250$. Then

$$250 = \frac{125}{\sqrt{1 - \dfrac{v^2}{c^2}}} \qquad \text{Divide both sides by 125.}$$

$$2 = \frac{1}{\sqrt{1 - \dfrac{v^2}{c^2}}} \qquad \text{Square both sides.}$$

$$4 = \frac{1}{1 - \dfrac{v^2}{c^2}} \qquad \text{Simplify the complex fraction.}$$

$$4 = \frac{1}{1 - \dfrac{v^2}{c^2}} \cdot \frac{c^2}{c^2}$$

$$4 = \frac{c^2}{c^2 - v^2} \qquad \text{Multiply by } c^2 - v^2.$$

$$4(c^2 - v^2) = c^2$$
$$4c^2 - 4v^2 = c^2$$
$$-4v^2 = -3c^2$$
$$v^2 = \frac{3}{4}c^2$$
$$v = \frac{\sqrt{3}}{2}c \approx 0.866c = 0.866(186,000) = 161,076 \text{ mps.}$$

Thus, if Sue could travel at 86.6% of the speed of light, or 161,076 miles per second, her weight would double.

EXERCISE SET 7.5

A

1 Solve the following equations.

1. $\sqrt{3x} = 6$
2. $\sqrt{2x} = -4$
3. $\sqrt[3]{2x} = -4$
4. $\sqrt[3]{4x} = 2$
5. $1 + \sqrt{t + 2} = 6$
6. $\sqrt{2s - 1} - 7 = 0$
7. $\sqrt{2y^2 - 9} - y = 0$
8. $2z + \sqrt{25z^2 - 49} = 5z$
9. $3\sqrt{x + 2} = 4$
10. $2\sqrt[4]{x - 1} = 3$
11. $\sqrt{x^2 - 4x - 5} = x - 5$
12. $\sqrt[3]{x^3 - 4x + 1} - x = 0$
13. $x - 1 + \sqrt{x - 1} = 0$

14. $x = 7 + \sqrt{2x + 1}$
15. $\sqrt{8x - 2} = \sqrt{4x - 1}$
16. $\sqrt[4]{9x - 1} = \sqrt[4]{x + 11}$
17. $\sqrt[4]{x + 8} - \sqrt[4]{2x} = 0$
18. $\sqrt[3]{7x - 1} - \sqrt[3]{x - 13} = 0$
19. $\sqrt{3x} - 3 = x - 9$
20. $x + \sqrt{x + 7} = 2x + 1$
21. $\sqrt{\dfrac{4t - 1}{3}} = \sqrt{\dfrac{3t - 5}{2}}$
22. $\sqrt{\dfrac{y + 3}{2}} = \sqrt{\dfrac{2y + 1}{3y}}$
23. $\sqrt{m - 3} = \sqrt{m} - 1$
24. $\sqrt{x + 4} = \sqrt{x} + 4$

25. $\sqrt{k + 7} = \sqrt{2k} + 1$

26. $\sqrt{x} = 2 + \sqrt{x - 12}$

27. $\sqrt{5x + 6} + \sqrt{3x + 4} = 2$

28. $\sqrt{3x + 4} - \sqrt{2x - 4} = 2$

29. $\sqrt{y - 5} - \sqrt{y - 8} = 3$

30. $\sqrt{2x} + \sqrt{x + 4} = 2$

Find the roots of the given function. If a root does not exist, write "none."

31. $f(x) = \sqrt{7x} - 2$

32. $g(x) = 2\sqrt{x^2 - 8} - 2$

33. $k(x) = 3\sqrt{x^2 + 2} - 12$

34. $h(x) = 4 + \sqrt{5 + x}$

35. $f(x) = 1 - x + \sqrt{2x + 1}$

36. $g(x) = \sqrt{x^2 - x - 2}$

2 Solve the following for the indicated variables.

37. $x = 3\sqrt{y - 5};\quad y$

38. $x = -\sqrt{y + 3} + 1;\quad y$

39. $x = 2\sqrt{1 + y} - 1;\quad y$

40. $x = \sqrt[3]{y - 1};\quad y$

41. $c = \sqrt{\dfrac{6GM}{R}};\quad M$ — last stable orbit of a black hole

42. $T = 2\pi\sqrt{\dfrac{L}{32}};\quad L$ — period of a pendulum of length L

43. $r = \dfrac{\sqrt{A}}{\sqrt{P}} - 1;\quad P$ — interest formula

44. $v = r\sqrt{\dfrac{g}{r + h}};\quad h$ — orbital velocity formula

45. $r = \sqrt{\dfrac{S - 2\pi rs}{\pi}};\quad s$ — surface area of a cone

46. $s = \sqrt[3]{V};\quad V$ — volume of a cube of side s

47. $V = \sqrt{\dfrac{4gH}{3}};\quad H$

48. $V = \sqrt{\dfrac{hd}{kL}};\quad L$

49. $y = \sqrt{r^2 - x^2};\quad x$

50. $S = 2\pi r\sqrt{X^2 + Y^2};\quad X$

51. $x = 1 + \sqrt{x + y};\quad y$

52. $a = 3 + 2\sqrt{a - b};\quad b$

53. $4\sqrt[3]{a + b} = b;\quad a$

54. $\sqrt[5]{3xy} = y;\quad x$

55. $\sqrt[4]{2x + 3y} = 3;\quad y$

3 Use Equations (1) (page 341) to solve the following relativity problems. Use $c = 186{,}000$ mps.

56. How fast would an electron have to travel to have a relativistic mass 3 times its rest mass? In other words, find v so that $M = 3M_0$.

57. Suppose a 100-pound boy could travel at 3/5 the speed of light; that is, $v = 3c/5$ or $v/c = 3/5$. Find M.

58. Suppose that a clock is traveling at 4/5 the speed of light, so that $v/c = 4/5$. What would a 3-second time interval become at this speed? In other words, find T when $T_0 = 3$.

59. How fast would a clock have to travel so that 1 second of rest time ($T_0 = 1$) would change to 4 seconds of relativistic time ($T = 4$)?

60. Compute the velocity for which an object would shrink to three-fourths its length in the direction of motion; that is, find v so that $L = (3/4)L_0$.

61. Suppose a 1-foot ruler travels at 12/13 the speed of light; $v/c = 12/13$. Find L, its relativistic length, to the nearest 10th of an inch.

62. Suppose a 1-foot ruler could travel at the speed of light. What would its length become?

The formula $s = 30\sqrt{x/y}$ allows the police to estimate the speed, s, of a car involved in an accident; x is the length of the skid marks left at the accident site. A police officer drives a car of the same make and model as the car in the accident at 30 mph under road conditions similar to those at the accident and then skids to a stop. In the police test y is the length of the skid marks. Find s to the nearest mph for the values of x and y, which are in feet.

63. $x = 400,\ y = 100$ **64.** $x = 405,\ y = 45$

65. $x = 24,\ y = 30$ **66.** $x = 56,\ y = 32$

The formula $d = \sqrt{6h}/2$ is used to approximate the distance, d, in miles that one can see to the horizon from a height of h feet above the ground. For example, a 6-foot man standing at the edge of an ocean can see $d = \sqrt{6 \cdot 6}/2 = 3$ miles out to sea. How far, to the nearest 10th of a mile, can one see from the following distances above the ground?

67. 75 feet   **68.** 800 feet

What is the height above the ground, to the nearest foot, of a person who can see the following distances to the horizon?

69. 27 miles   **70.** 8 miles

If x is the length of each leg of an isosceles right triangle, then $\sqrt{2x}$ is the length of the hypotenuse. Find x if

71. The perimeter is 12.   **72.** The area is 14.

Find the number(s) described in the following problems.

73. The square root of the sum of a number and 8 is 7.

74. The square root of 6 times a number is the same as the number.

75. The square root of 1 more than twice a number is twice the square root of 3.

76. One more than a number is the same as the square root of one less than five times the number.

77. The cube root of 1 less than 4 times a number is 3.

78. The fourth root of 6 more than the square of a number is equal to the fourth root of 5 times the number.

B

Solve the following equations. (*Hint*: Simplify the radicals.)

79. $\sqrt{3x} + \sqrt{12x} = 18$

80. $7y\sqrt{2y} = 16 + \sqrt{18y^3}$

81. $3 + \sqrt{45x} - \sqrt{20x} = 2x - 2$

82. $\sqrt[3]{16x} = 2 + \sqrt[3]{54x}$

Solve the following equations. (*Hint*: In Exercise 87 raise both sides of the equation to the fourth power.)

83. $\sqrt{x + 5} + \sqrt{x - 3} = \sqrt{4x}$

84. $2\sqrt{y - 1} = \sqrt{y + 4} + \sqrt{y - 4}$

85. $\sqrt{y + 4} - \sqrt{2} = \sqrt{y - 6}$

86. $\sqrt{4t + 1} - \sqrt{t - 2} = \sqrt{t + 3}$

87. $\sqrt{3x} = \sqrt[4]{28x - 3}$ **88.** $\sqrt[6]{7x + 2} = \sqrt[3]{2x}$

89. $\sqrt{3x} = \sqrt[3]{5x}$ **90.** $\sqrt[3]{3y} = \sqrt{2y}$

Solve the following: a. for v; b. for c.

91. $L = L_0 \sqrt{1 - \dfrac{v^2}{c^2}}$

92. $T = \dfrac{T_0}{\sqrt{1 - \dfrac{v^2}{c^2}}}$

Answer the following questions with complete sentences.

93. What is an extraneous solution to a radical equation?

94. What would be your first step in solving the equation $3 + \sqrt{x} = x + 1$?

95. What would be your first step in solving the equation $3 + \sqrt{x} = \sqrt{x + 1}$?

96. Discuss the differences between Newton's and Einstein's views of the universe.

REVIEW EXERCISES

Values for all but one of the variables are given for each of the following equations. Find the value of the remaining variable. (See Section 2.3.)

97. $y = kx$; $x = 6$, $y = 9$

98. $y = kx^3$; $k = 4$, $y = 32$

99. $r = \dfrac{60}{t}$; $r = 15$

100. $y = \dfrac{kxz}{w}$; $y = 30$, $x = 2$, $z = 25$, $w = 9$

7.6 VARIATION

1	Direct Variation
2	Inverse Variation
3	Joint and Combined Variation

1 Direct Variation

Many situations involve the concept of variation. For instance, pressure on an object submerged in water varies directly with its depth, and the volume of a gas at a constant temperature varies inversely as the pressure. This section will discuss these two basic types of variation and then present problems involving more than two variables.

When *y varies directly as x*, a change in x produces a corresponding change in y. For example, if Steve earns \$9 per hour, then in 1 hour he earns $9 \cdot 1 = \$9$, in 2 hours he earns $9 \cdot 2 = \$18$, and in x hours he earns $y = 9x$ dollars. In general:

Direct Variation

y varies directly as x if a nonzero constant k exists such that

$$y = kx$$

That y is **directly proportional** to x is another way of saying that y varies directly as x. The constant k is called the **constant of variation** or the **constant of proportionality**.

In a variation problem we are given enough information to find k. Having done this, we can find the value of one of the variables given the value of the others. This procedure is illustrated in the following example.

EXAMPLE 1

y varies directly as x. When $x = 6$, $y = 9$. Find y when $x = -10$.

SOLUTION $y = kx$ is the equation of variation. If $x = 6$ and $y = 9$, then

$$9 = k \cdot 6, \quad k = \frac{9}{6} = \frac{3}{2}, \quad \text{and} \quad y = \frac{3}{2}x.$$

If $x = -10$, then

$$y = \frac{3}{2}(-10) = -15$$

Several types of direct variation besides $y = kx$ exist. Some are familiar, such as "the area of a circle varies directly as the square of its radius,"

$A = \pi r^2$, where π is the constant of variation. The following example illustrates other types of direct variation.

EXAMPLE 2   Express the following as equations.

a. y varies directly as the cube of x.
b. a varies directly as the nth power of b, $\quad n > 0$.
c. r is directly proportional to the cube root of V.

SOLUTION   **a.** $y = kx^3$ **b.** $a = kb^n$ **c.** $r = k\sqrt[3]{V}$

The technique for solving a variation problem using one of these equations or $y = kx$ is the same. The following example illustrates the technique.

EXAMPLE 3   The distance (in miles), d, that a person can see to the horizon varies directly as the square root of the height (in feet), h, above the ground. At a height of 600 feet one can see 30 miles to the horizon. Find the elevation necessary to see 15 miles to the horizon.

SOLUTION $k\sqrt{h} = d$ is the equation; $\quad d = 30$ when $h = 600$, so

$$k\sqrt{600} = 30$$
$$k \cdot 10\sqrt{6} = 30$$
$$k = \frac{30}{10\sqrt{6}} = \frac{3}{\sqrt{6}} \cdot \frac{\sqrt{6}}{\sqrt{6}} = \frac{3\sqrt{6}}{6} = \frac{\sqrt{6}}{2}, \quad \text{so}$$

$\frac{\sqrt{6}}{2}\sqrt{h} = d$. Let $d = 15$:

$$\frac{\sqrt{6}}{2}\sqrt{h} = 15$$
$$\sqrt{6}\,\sqrt{h} = 30 \qquad\qquad \text{Square both sides.}$$
$$(\sqrt{6}\,\sqrt{h})^2 = (30)^2$$
$$6h = 900$$
$$h = 150$$

Thus, one must be 150 feet above the ground to see 15 miles to the horizon.

2   Inverse Variation

The second basic type of variation is called **inverse variation**. In this case the product of two variables is constant. As an example, suppose that Pat has to drive 60 miles. The relationship between her rate, time, and distance is

$$rt = 60 \qquad \text{or} \qquad r = \frac{60}{t}$$

To complete the trip in 1 hour, Pat would have to drive 60 mph; to complete it in 2 hours, $r = 30$ mph; to complete it in 3 hours, $r = 20$ mph; and so on. As Pat's time increases, her rate decreases; we say that r varies inversely as t, or r is inversely proportional to t. As with direct variation, 60 is called the constant of variation or the constant of proportionality. In general:

Inverse Variation
---
y varies inversely as *x* if a nonzero constant *k* exists such that

$$y = \frac{k}{x} \quad \text{or} \quad xy = k$$

EXAMPLE 4

y varies inversely as *x*. When $x = -12$, $y = 1/3$. Find *x* when $y = 2/5$.

SOLUTION   In $k = xy$, let $x = -12$ and $y = 1/3$:

$k = -12 \cdot \frac{1}{3} = -4$. Thus,

$xy = -4$ or $y = \dfrac{-4}{x}$ is the equation of variation.

Let $y = 2/5$ in $xy = -4$:

$\frac{2}{5}x = -4$

$x = \frac{5}{2}(-4) = -10$

As with direct variation, several types of inverse variation exist, as shown in the next example.

EXAMPLE 5

Express the following as equations.

a. *y* is inversely proportional to the *n*th power of *x*.
b. *r* varies inversely as the fourth root of *t*.

SOLUTION   **a.** $y = \dfrac{k}{x^n}$ or $yx^n = k$ **b.** $r = \dfrac{k}{\sqrt[4]{t}}$ or $r\sqrt[4]{t} = k$

EXAMPLE 6

The resistance of a wire of fixed length varies inversely with the square of its diameter. If 25 meters of wire with a diameter of .03 centimeter has a resistance of 12 ohms, what is the diameter of 25 meters of wire of the same material with a resistance of 16 ohms?

SOLUTION   Let $R = $ the resistance and $d = $ the diameter. Then

$R = \dfrac{k}{d^2}$ or $k = Rd^2$

$R = 12$ and $d = .03,$ so
$k = 12(.03)^2 = .0108,$ and
$Rd^2 = .0108$

(continued)

Let $R = 16$ and solve for d:

$$d^2 = \frac{.0108}{R} = \frac{.0108}{16} = .000675$$

$$d = \sqrt{.000675} \approx .0259808 \approx .026 \text{ centimeter}$$

Note that the length of 25 meters did not enter into the calculations because the equation represents the resistance for a fixed length.

3   Joint and Combined Variation

Many variation problems involve more than two variables. For instance, one quantity may vary directly as the product of two or more other quantities. This type of variation is called **joint variation**. For example, "w varies jointly as x and the square of y" means

$$w = kxy^2$$

EXAMPLE 7

If a flat surface of area, A, is submerged horizontally at a depth, h, in a liquid, then the force, F, on the surface varies jointly as h and A; that is,

$$F = khA$$

The constant k is the density of the liquid (weight per unit volume). For example, the density of water is 62.4 pounds per cubic foot.

A child's circular wading pool is 8 feet in diameter and 2 feet deep. Find the force on the bottom of the pool, to the nearest pound. Use $\pi \approx 3.14$.

SOLUTION $F = 62.4hA$, $\quad h = 2$, $\quad A = \pi r^2$, $\quad$ and $\quad r = 8/2 = 4$. Then

$$\begin{aligned} F &= 62.4(2)(\pi)(4^2) \\ &\approx 62.4(2)(3.14)(16) \\ &= 6269.952 \\ &\approx 6270 \text{ lb} \end{aligned}$$

In many situations direct and inverse variation are combined in the same equation. The following example illustrates **combined variation**.

EXAMPLE 8

Express the following as equations.

a. z varies directly as x and inversely as y.
b. F varies jointly as m_1 and m_2 and inversely as the square of d; G is the constant of variation (Newton's law of gravitation).
c. A is directly proportional to B and inversely proportional to the cube root of C.

SOLUTION   **a.** $z = \dfrac{kx}{y}$ **b.** $F = \dfrac{Gm_1m_2}{d^2}$ **c.** $A = \dfrac{kB}{\sqrt[3]{C}}$

EXAMPLE 9

y varies jointly as *x* and the square of *z* and inversely as *w*; $y = 15$ when $x = 3$, $z = 5$, and $w = 10$. Find the constant of variation.

SOLUTION $y = \dfrac{kxz^2}{w}$ is the equation of variation.

$y = 15$ when $x = 3$, $z = 5$, and $w = 10$. Thus,

$$15 = \frac{k(3)(5^2)}{10} = \frac{15k}{2}$$

$$\frac{2}{15} \cdot 15 = \frac{2}{15} \cdot \frac{15k}{2}$$

$$2 = k$$

The constant of variation is 2.

EXERCISE SET 7.6

A

1 Express each of the following as an equation, find the constant of variation, *k*, and then solve the equation for the indicated variable.

1. *y* varies directly as *x*. When $x = 7, y = 28$. Find *y* when $x = -3$.

2. *y* varies directly as *x*. When $x = -1/6, y = 1/2$. Find *x* when $y = 21$.

3. *y* varies directly as x^2. When $x = 5, y = 75$. Find *x* when $y = 26$.

4. *y* is directly proportional to the cube of *x*. $y = 9$ when $x = 3$. Find *y* when $x = -6$.

5. *r* is directly proportional to the square root of *s*. When $s = 16, r = 2$. Find *s* when $r = 3$.

6. The cube of *y* varies directly as the square of *x*. $y = 2$ when $x = 3$. Find *x* when $y = 6$.

2

7. *y* varies inversely as *x*. $y = 1/5$ when $x = 10$. Find *y* when $x = 12$.

8. *y* varies inversely as *x*. $y = 2$ when $x = -15$. Find *x* when $y = 10$.

9. *A* varies inversely as the square of *B*. $A = 2/5$ when $B = 5$. Find *B* when $A = 8$.

10. *m* is inversely proportional to the cube of *n*. $m = -8$ when $n = 1/2$. Find *m* when $n = -3$.

11. *y* is inversely proportional to the cube root of *x*. $y = 2$ when $x = 27$. Find *y* when $x = -4$.

12. *y* is inversely proportional to the square root of *x*. $y = 1$ when $x = 2$. Find *x* when $y = 1/5$.

3

13. *A* varies jointly as *L* and *W*. $A = 6$ when $L = 3$ and $W = 2$. Find *A* when $L = 7$ and $W = 5$.

14. *w* varies jointly with *x* and the square of *y*. $w = 90$ when $x = 5$ and $y = 3$. Find *w* when $x = 1/2$ and $y = 5$.

15. *a* varies jointly as *b*, *c*, and *d*. $a = 8$ when $b = 2$, $c = 3$, and $d = 4$. Find *c* when $a = -2, b = 6$, and $d = -5$.

16. *z* varies directly as *x* and inversely as *y*. $z = 1$ when $x = 2$ and $y = 10$. Find *y* when $x = 3$ and $z = 7$.

17. *y* varies jointly as *x* and *w* and inversely as the square of *t*. $y = 6$ when $x = 4, w = 30$, and $t = \sqrt{2}$. Find *x* when $w = 3, y = 6$, and $t = 2$.

18. *a* varies jointly as *b* and *c* and inversely as the product of *d* and *e*. $a = 75$ when $b = 25, c = 9$, $d = 2$, and $e = 3$. Find *d* when $a = 7, b = 4$, $c = 14$, and $e = 8$.

Express the following as equations. Use *k* as the constant of variation.

19. The volume, *V*, of a sphere varies directly as the cube of its radius, *r*.

20. Froude's law says that the velocity, v, that a fish swims is directly proportional to the square root of its length, L.

21. Geologists have found that the amount of sediment, S, that a river can carry is directly proportional to the sixth power of its speed, v.

22. German astronomer Johann Kepler (1571–1630) discovered that the square of the time, t, required for a planet to make one revolution about the sun varies directly as the cube of its average distance, d, from the sun.

23. Anthropologists use the cephalic index in their study of race and genetics. The cephalic index, C, varies directly as the width, W, of the head and inversely as the length, L, of the head.

24. The work, W, done by a force in moving an object varies jointly as the mass, m, of the object and distance, d, that it is moved.

25. Sociologists have discovered that the number of telephone calls, N, made between two cities varies jointly as the populations, P_1 and P_2, of the cities and inversely as the distance, d, between them.

Solve the following problems.

26. At a fixed rate (in mph) distance varies directly as the time of travel. In 30 minutes Jill traveled 24 miles. How far would she travel in 2 hours?

27. The distance (in feet), d, that an object falls from rest (ignoring air resistance) varies directly as the square of the time (in seconds) that it falls. In 1/2 second a rock falls 4 feet. How far would it fall in 3 seconds?

28. The length of a rectangle of constant area varies inversely as the width. A rectangle has a width of 3 and a length of 8. What is the length of another rectangle of the same area if its width is 4?

29. The volume of a gas at a constant temperature is inversely proportional to its pressure. If a volume of 50 cubic feet is under a pressure of 48 pounds per square inch, what would be the pressure when the volume expands to 60 cubic feet?

30. The velocity, v, of a meteor varies inversely as the square root of its distance, d, from the

center of the earth. If the velocity of a meteor is 4 kilometers per second when $d = 10{,}000$ kilometers, find d when v increases to 5 kilometers per second.

31. The force, F, of the wind on a vertical surface varies jointly as the area, A, of the surface and the square of the velocity, v, of the wind. $F = 100$ pounds when $A = 1$ square foot and $v = 40$ mph. The side of the first-aid room at the top of Heavenly Valley ski resort is 9 feet high and 20 feet long. Find the force on this surface when $v = 60$ mph.

32. The resistance, R, of a wire is directly proportional to its length, L, and inversely proportional to the square of its diameter, d. If 50 feet of wire with a diameter of 0.01 inch has a resistance of 5 ohms, find the resistance of 12 feet of wire of the same material if its diameter is 0.03 inch.

33. A triangular plate is submerged horizontally in water at a depth of 20 feet. The base of the triangle is 16 feet and the height is 12 feet. Find the force on the plate. (See Example 7.)

B

34. y varies directly as the cube of x. How does y change if x is doubled?

35. y varies inversely as the square of x. How does y change if x is tripled?

36. The surface area, S, of a sphere varies directly as the square of its radius, r. How does S change if r is replaced by $10r$?

37. The volume of a rectangular solid varies jointly as the length, L, width, W, and height, H. How does the volume change if each dimension is multiplied by 3?

C

Answer each question with complete sentences.

38. What does it mean to say that "y varies directly as x"?

39. What does it mean to say that "y is inversely proportional to x"?

40. What is meant by "combined variation"?

41. What is meant by "joint variation"?

REVIEW EXERCISES

Evaluate the following.

42. 10^2 **43.** 10^6

44. 10^{-3} **45.** 10^{-5}

46. $(4.1)(100)$ **47.** $(2.61)(1,000,000)$

48. $\dfrac{2.64}{1000}$ **49.** $\dfrac{7.934}{100,000}$

7.7 SCIENTIFIC NOTATION

1	Conversion Between Scientific and Decimal Notation
2	Applications
3	Calculators and Scientific Notation

1 Conversion Between Scientific and Decimal Notation

Very large and very small numbers occur throughout mathematics and the sciences. For example, the numbers

$$82,000,000,000 \quad \text{and} \quad 0.000\ 001\ 36 \text{ centimeters}$$

are the approximate number of particles of tar and other pollutants in one cubic inch of cigarette smoke and the wavelength of ultraviolet light, respectively. Written in this notation these numbers are difficult to use without making arithmetic mistakes. To help us work with this type of number, we use a system called *scientific notation*.

Scientific notation is based on the fact that every positive number in decimal notation can be written as the product of a number between 1 and 10 and a power of 10. Two examples are 4.72×10^3 and 1.9×10^{-2}.

Scientific Notation

A number is in scientific notation if it is written in the form

$$a \times 10^n$$

where $1 \le a < 10$, and n is an integer.

To convert from scientific to decimal notation we use the definitions of 10^n and 10^{-n}. For example,

4.72×10^3

$= 4.72 \times 10 \times 10 \times 10$
$= 47.2 \times 10 \times 10$
$= 472 \times 10$
$= 4720$

1.9×10^{-2}

$= 1.9 \times \dfrac{1}{10^2}$

$= 1.9 \times \dfrac{1}{10} \times \dfrac{1}{10}$

$= .19 \times \dfrac{1}{10}$

$= .019$

In general, when a decimal is multiplied by 10^n, with n being a positive integer, the decimal point is moved n places to the right. When the decimal is multiplied by 10^{-n}, the decimal point is moved n places to the left.

EXAMPLE 1

Express the following numbers in decimal notation.

a. 1.47×10^7;   the area of the moon in square miles
b. 2.95×10^{-5} inch;   the diameter of a red blood cell

SOLUTION

a. Move the decimal point seven places to the right: $1.47 \times 10^7 = 14{,}700{,}000$

b. Move the decimal point five places to the left: $2.95 \times 10^{-5} = 0.000\ 029\ 5$ inch

To write a number in scientific notation, we must express it as $a \times 10^n$, $1 \le a < 10$ and n is an integer. For example,

$273 = 273 \times 1$

$= 273 \times \dfrac{10^2}{10^2}$

$= \dfrac{273}{100} \times 10^2$

$= 2.73 \times 10^2$

$0.0078 = 0.0078 \times 1$

$= 0.0078 \times 10^3 \times 10^{-3}$

$= (0.0078 \times 1000) \times 10^{-3}$

$= 7.8 \times 10^{-3}$

In general, to move the decimal point in a number n places to the left, multiply it by $1 = 10^n/10^n$. The $1/10^n$ repositions the decimal point, and the 10^n keeps the value of the number. To move the decimal point in a number n places to the right, multiply the number by $10^n \times 10^{-n}$. The 10^n repositions the decimal point, and the 10^{-n} keeps the value of the number because $10^n \times 10^{-n} = 10^0 = 1$.

EXAMPLE 2

Write the following numbers in scientific notation.

a. 120,000,000 grams;   the weight of a blue whale
b. 100,000,000,000;   the number of stars in a galaxy
c. 2.54;   the number of centimeters in 1 inch
d. 0.000 02 centimeter;   the length of a bacterium
e. 0.000 001 59 ounce;   the relativistic increase in mass of a 25,000-ton ocean liner traveling at 30 mph

SOLUTION

a. $120,000,000 = 120,000,000 \times \dfrac{10^8}{10^8} = 1.2 \times 10^8$ grams

b. $100,000,000,000 = 1 \times 10^{11}$

c. Because $1 \le 2.54 < 10$, we can use $10^0 = 1$ and write
$2.54 = 2.54 \times 10^0$

d. $0.000\ 02 = 0.000\ 02 \times 10^5 \times 10^{-5} = 2 \times 10^{-5}$ centimeter

e. $0.000\ 001\ 59 = 1.59 \times 10^{-6}$ ounce

---

2   Applications

One application of scientific notation is simplifying numerical calculations. Suppose we need to find the product

$$(200,000,000,000)(0.000\ 000\ 004)$$

Using this notation, we might easily put the decimal point in the wrong place. With scientific notation we can avoid this problem with a much simpler computation:

$$(200,000,000,000)(0.000\ 000\ 004)$$
$$= (2 \times 10^{11})(4 \times 10^{-9})$$
$$= 8 \times 10^2 \quad \text{or} \quad 800$$

EXAMPLE 3

Use scientific notation to evaluate the following; write your answers in scientific notation.

a. $(87,000,000)^2$ **b.** $\dfrac{(1600)(0.000\ 015)}{(.5)(800,000)}$

SOLUTION

a. $(87,000,000)^2$

$\quad = (8.7 \times 10^7)^2$ $(ab)^n = a^n b^n$

$\quad = (8.7)^2(10^7)^2$ $(a^m)^n = a^{mn}$

$\quad = 75.69 \times 10^{14}$

$\quad = 7.569 \times 10^1 \times 10^{14}$ $a^m a^n = a^{m+n}$

$\quad = 7.569 \times 10^{15}$

b. $\dfrac{(1600)(0.000\ 015)}{(.5)(800,000)}$

$\quad = \dfrac{1.6 \times 10^3 \times 1.5 \times 10^{-5}}{5 \times 10^{-1} \times 8 \times 10^5}$

$\quad = \dfrac{1.6}{8} \times \dfrac{1.5}{5} \times \dfrac{10^3 \times 10^{-5}}{10^{-1} \times 10^5}$

$\quad = (.2)(.3) \times \dfrac{10^{-2}}{10^4}$ $\dfrac{a^m}{a^n} = a^{m-n}$

$\quad = .06 \times 10^{-6}$

$\quad = 6 \times 10^{-2} \times 10^{-6}$

$\quad = 6 \times 10^{-8}$

One predicted result of Einstein's special theory of relativity is that the speed of light (approximately 186,000 miles per second) is the maximum velocity possible in the universe. Because the speed of light is finite, we look back in time when we look out into space. For example, if we observe a star that is 18 light-years from earth (a light-year is the distance light travels in a year), then we are not seeing how the star looks now but how it looked 18 years ago.

EXAMPLE 4

When the earth and Mars are in opposition (in line with the sun), they are approximately 48,000,000 miles apart. If a radio message is received from a spaceship on Mars, how long ago was it sent?

SOLUTION

Radio waves travel at the speed of light, 186,000 mps = 1.86×10^5 mps. 48,000,000 miles = 4.8×10^7 miles.
From the formula $d = rt$, we have

$$t = \frac{d}{r} = \frac{4.8 \times 10^7 \text{ miles}}{1.86 \times 10^5 \text{ mps}} \approx 2.58 \times 10^2 = 258 \text{ sec} \quad \text{or}$$

$\frac{258}{60} \approx 4.3$ minutes. Thus, the message was sent approximately 4.3 minutes ago.

 ## 3 Calculators and Scientific Notation

In Section 5.1 we used a calculator to evaluate 2^{17} ($2^{17} = 131,072$). However, calculators cannot display numbers that contain more than approximately eight digits. Therefore, many calculators have the ability to work with numbers in scientific notation. For example, to evaluate 2^{40} enter **2**, press **y^x**, enter **40**, and press **=**. The display is

$$\boxed{1.0995 \quad 12}$$

which means 1.0995×10^{12}. If a calculator does not have this ability, then this type of calculation will result in "Error" being displayed.

EXAMPLE 5

Evaluate $(.000\ 005)^3$:

a. with scientific notation.   **b.** with a calculator.

SOLUTION

a. $(.000\ 005)^3 = (5 \times 10^{-6})^3 = 5^3 \times (10^{-6})^3 = 125 \times 10^{-18}$
$= 1.25 \times 10^2 \times 10^{-18} = 1.25 \times 10^{-16}$
b. Use the y^x key in the following sequence: Enter **.000 005**, press **y^x**, enter **3**, and press **=**.

The display is $\boxed{1.25 \quad -16}$, so the answer is 1.25×10^{-16}.

EXAMPLE 6

Use a calculator to evaluate the following.

a. $(12,000,000)^2$ **b.** 2^{-40}

SOLUTION

a. Enter **12,000,000** and press the **x^2** key. $(12,000,000)^2 = 1.44 \times 10^{14}$

b. Note the use of the 1/x key in this problem.

$$2^{-40} = (2^{40})^{-1} \qquad \text{Evaluate } 2^{40}.$$
$$= (1.0995 \times 10^{12})^{-1} \quad a^{-1} = 1/a$$
$$= \frac{1}{1.0995 \times 10^{12}} \qquad \text{Press } 1/x.$$
$$= 9.0949 \times 10^{-13}$$

The above steps are the algebraic solution, but all we have to do is enter **2**, press y^x, enter **40**, press **=**, and press **1/x**.

Calculators with scientific notation capability allow us to enter numbers in this form and to perform calculations. Different calculators have different "enter the exponent" keys; the most common are EE, EXP, SCI, and E EX (check the manual for your calculator).

EXAMPLE 7

Enter the following numbers in a calculator.

a. 2.7×10^{13} **b.** 1.91×10^{-4}

SOLUTION **a.** Enter **2.7**, press **EE**, and enter **13**. The display is $\boxed{2.7 \quad 13}$

b. Enter **1.91**, press **EE**, press the **+/−** key, and enter **4**. The display is $\boxed{1.91 \quad -04}$

EXAMPLE 8

Use a calculator to evaluate the following.

a. $(2 \times 10^4)(3 \times 10^7)$ **b.** $\dfrac{320{,}000{,}000}{0.000\ 16}$

SOLUTION **a.** Enter **2**, press **EE**, enter **4**, press **×**, enter **3**, press **EE**, enter **7**, and press **=**. The display is $\boxed{6 \quad 11}$, so the answer is 6×10^{11}.

b. $\dfrac{320{,}000{,}000}{0.000\ 16} = \dfrac{3.2 \times 10^8}{1.6 \times 10^{-4}}$

Enter **3.2**, press **EE**, enter **8**, press **÷**, enter **1.6**, press **EE**, press **+/−**, enter **4**, and press **=**. The display is $\boxed{2 \quad 12}$, so the answer is 2×10^{12}.

EXERCISE SET 7.7

A

1 Express the following numbers in decimal notation.

1. 4×10^4; the number of characters in the Chinese alphabet

2. 6.227×10^9; the number of different ways the 13 cards in a bridge hand can be arranged

3. 2.5×10^8 years; the age of the oceans

4. 4.5×10^{12}; the number of grams of matter converted into pure energy each second by the sun (the approximate mass of a small mountain)

5. 4×10^{33} ergs;   the amount of pure energy produced in the sun each second

6. 1.609×10^0;   the number of kilometers in 1 mile

7. 6×10^{-7} meter;   the wavelength of yellow light

8. 10^{-8} mph;   the speed at which human hair grows

9. 10^{-13} centimeter;   the diameter of an electron

10. 9.1×10^{-28} gram;   the mass of an electron

Express the following numbers in scientific notation.

11. 82,000,000,000;   the number of particles of pollutants in 1 cubic inch of cigarette smoke

12. 5,866,000,000,000 miles;   a light-year, the distance light travels in a year

13. 30,000,000,000;   the speed of light in centimeters per second

14. 10,000,000,000 years;   the probable age of the universe

15. 638,000,000 centimeters;   the radius of the earth

16. 1,800,000,000,000,000,000,000   ergs; the total energy contained in a two-gram penny

17. 1.0936;   the number of yards in 1 meter

18. 0.000 001 36 centimeter;   the wavelength of ultraviolet light

19. 0.000 002 2 second;   the life of a meson particle

20. 0.000 000 000 066 7;   Newton's gravitational constant, G

2 ▦

Simplify the following and write your answers in scientific notation. Approximate irrational numbers to two decimal places.

21. $(2 \times 10^5)(4.1 \times 10^4)$

22. $(3 \times 10^{-8})(7 \times 10^5)$

23. $\dfrac{3.4 \times 10^{-3}}{2 \times 10^8}$

24. $\dfrac{2.34 \times 10^8}{5 \times 10^{-4}}$

25. $(3,000,000)^2$

26. $(0.000\ 04)^3$

27. $(.02)(.003)(4000)$

28. $(6000)(1000)(.000\ 05)$

29. $\dfrac{80,000,000}{0.000\ 2}$

30. $\dfrac{0.000\ 006}{30,000}$

31. $\dfrac{(.01)(.000\ 14)}{.000\ 05}$

32. $\dfrac{(.000\ 03)^2}{(60,000)(200,000)}$

33. $(90,000)^{3/2}$

34. $(0.000\ 008)^{2/3}$

Use scientific notation to solve the following problems and write your answers in scientific notation.

35. Venus is 67,000,000 miles from the sun. How many seconds does it take for light to travel from the sun to Venus? How many minutes?

36. Repeat Exercise 35 for Neptune, which is 2,800,000,000 miles from the sun.

37. A certain computer can perform 8,300,000 calculations in one second. How many calculations can it perform in 8 hours?

38. The mass of an elephant is 4000 kilograms, and the mass of a flea is 0.000 3 kilogram. How many times heavier is an elephant than a flea?

39. A radio wave has a wavelength of 50,000 centimeters, and an X ray a wavelength of 0.000 000 01 centimeter. How many times longer is a radio wave than an X ray?

40. Find c^2 in Einstein's formula $E = mc^2$, using the value of c given in Exercise 13.

41. One kiloparsec = 3260 light-years. Find this distance in miles, correctly to three decimal places. (See Exercise 12.)

42. The supernova 1987A was first observed on February 23, 1987, in the Large Magellanic Cloud, 170,000 light-years from the earth. Find this distance in miles. (See Exercise 12.) How many years ago did this star explode?

3 ▦

Use a calculator to evaluate the following. Write your answers in scientific notation.

43. $(5,000,000)^3$

44. $(0.000\ 07)^2$

45. $(4 \times 10^8)(2 \times 10^4)$

46. $\dfrac{6 \times 10^{15}}{2 \times 10^3}$

47. $(2400)(16,000)$

48. $(0.000\ 9)(0.000\ 002)$

49. $(24,000)(0.003)$

50. $(0.000\ 000\ 4)(80,000,000)$

51. $\dfrac{15,000}{0.005}$

52. $\dfrac{0.000\ 001\ 8}{60,000}$

53. $\dfrac{0.000\ 000\ 012}{0.000\ 06}$

54. $\dfrac{0.000\ 21}{0.000\ 000\ 007}$

55. 2^{50} **56.** 2^{-50} **57.** 3^{100}

58. 3^{-100} **59.** $(-3)^{25}$ **60.** $(-5)^{20}$

61. $(-5)^{-20}$ **62.** $(-7)^{-25}$

B

Use scientific notation to solve the following problems and write your answers in scientific notation.

63. The sun's mass is 2×10^{30} kilograms, and its radius is 7×10^{8} meters. The earth's mass is 6×10^{24} kilograms, and its radius is 6.4×10^{6} meters. Show that the earth's density is approximately four times the sun's density. Density is mass divided by volume (consider the sun and earth to be spheres).

64. The distance, d, between the earth and the sun is 1.5×10^{11} meters. Use Newton's law of gravitation,
$$F = \frac{Gm_1 m_2}{d^2}$$
to find the force, F, of attraction between the sun and earth (G is given in Exercise 20, and m_1 and m_2 are given in Exercise 63). F is measured in newtons, N (the force needed to give a mass of 1 kilogram an acceleration of 1 meter per second per second).

C

Answer the following with complete sentences.

65. Explain how you would write the following in decimal notation.
  a. 2.35×10^{6} **b.** 2.35×10^{-6}

66. Explain how you would write the following in scientific notation.
  a. 789,000   **b.** .000 789

REVIEW EXERCISES

Solve the following equations. (See Section 2.3.)

67. $x^2 = 9$ **68.** $x^2 - 2 = 0$

69. $3x^2 = 25$ **70.** $2x^2 = 54$

Let $A = \{8,\ -3,\ \sqrt{2},\ .6\overline{6},\ -4/5,\ 0,\ \sqrt[3]{-5}\}$ be a subset of R. List all the elements of A that are (see Section 1.2):

71. Natural numbers   **72.** Integers

73. Rational numbers   **74.** Irrational numbers

7.8 COMPLEX NUMBER SYSTEM

  1   **Using Complex Numbers and the Complex Plane**

  2   **Operating with Complex Numbers**

  3   **Solving $x^2 = -d$ and Simplifying Radicals**

1   Using Complex Numbers and the Complex Plane

Throughout the history of mathematics new numbers have been invented to deal with deficiencies in the existing number system. For example, the equation $3x = -2$ does not have a solution in the integers, but when we extend the integers to the rational numbers, the equation has the solution

$x = -2/3$. In a similar way the irrational numbers were invented to solve equations such as $x^2 = 2$, which have no solutions in the rational numbers. The limitation of the real number system is that we cannot take the even root of a negative number. As a result, equations such as $x^2 = -1$ have no real solutions because $x^2 \geq 0$ for all real numbers x. We will now extend the real numbers to a larger set of numbers that will allow us to solve every quadratic equation.

One solution to $x^2 = 2$ is $x = \sqrt{2}$. Sixteenth-century mathematicians generalized this concept and let $x = \sqrt{-1}$ be a solution to $x^2 = -1$. The introduction of expressions such as $\sqrt{-1}$ and $5 + \sqrt{-15}$ led to their designation as "fictitious" or "imaginary." Today such numbers are still called **imaginary numbers**, but they are just as respectable as real numbers. Leonhard Euler (1707–1783) called them "impossible" numbers, and from this word the letter i is used as an abbreviation for $\sqrt{-1}$; that is, i is defined to be a solution to $x^2 = -1$. Thus

$$i = \sqrt{-1} \qquad \text{and} \qquad i^2 = -1$$

Imaginary numbers and real numbers are also called **complex numbers**. The set of complex numbers, $\mathbb{C}$, consists of all numbers that can be expressed as $a + bi$, where a and b are real numbers. The term $a + bi$ is called the **standard form** of a complex number; a is called the **real part** of the complex number, and b (not bi) is called the **imaginary part**. Examples of complex numbers are

$$3 + 4i, \qquad 5 - \sqrt{15}i, \qquad 6i, \qquad \text{and} \qquad 9, \quad \text{because } 9 = 9 + 0i$$

Complex numbers, such as $6i = 0 + 6i$, where $a = 0$ and $b \neq 0$, are called **pure imaginary numbers**. The equation $9 = 9 + 0i$ illustrates the fact that every real number a is a complex number, because it can be written as $a = a + 0i$. Thus, $\mathbb{R}$ is a subset of $\mathbb{C}$, and the set of complex numbers is the union of the set of real numbers and the set of imaginary numbers, as illustrated in Figure 7.5.

Calvin and Hobbes   by Bill Watterson

FIGURE 7.5 $\mathbb{C} = \{a + bi \mid a, b \in \mathbb{R}; \ i = \sqrt{-1}, \ i^2 = -1\}$

Imaginary: $b \neq 0$ Real: $b = 0$
$7i, 3 - 8i, \ldots$ $9, -8, 3/4, \pi, \ldots$

EXAMPLE 1

Let $A = \{\pi, -17, -7i, 6 - i, .\overline{81}, \sqrt{-5}, \sqrt[3]{-5}\}$ be a subset of $\mathbb{C}$. List all the elements of A that are:

a. integers   **b.** rational   **c.** irrational
d. real   **e.** imaginary   **f.** pure imaginary

SOLUTION

a. $\{-17\}$ **b.** $\{-17, .\overline{81}\}$
c. $\{\pi, \sqrt[3]{-5}\}$ **d.** $\{\pi, -17, .\overline{81}, \sqrt[3]{-5}\}$
e. $\{-7i, 6 - i, \sqrt{-5}\}$ **f.** $\{-7i, \sqrt{-5}\}$

Recall that real numbers are represented geometrically as points on a horizontal number line. As a result, they are called "one-dimensional numbers." Imaginary numbers, such as $3 + 2i$, involve two real numbers, so they are called "two-dimensional numbers" and are represented as points in a coordinate plane, called the **complex plane**. The horizontal axis is called the **real axis**, denoted by r; and the vertical axis is called the **imaginary axis**, denoted by i.

Graphing $a + bi$ in the complex plane is very similar to graphing the ordered pair (a, b) in the xy-plane. The r-axis represents the real numbers a ($b = 0$); thus, a number such as $-4 = -4 + 0i$ is graphed on this axis. The i-axis represents the pure imaginary numbers bi ($a = 0$); so a number such as $4i = 0 + 4i$ is graphed on this axis. If $a \neq 0$ and $b \neq 0$, then $a + bi$ is graphed as a point off the axes. For example, the number $3 + 2i$ is graphed as the point with coordinates $(3, 2)$. $3 + 2i$ and other complex numbers are graphed in Figure 7.6.

FIGURE 7.6

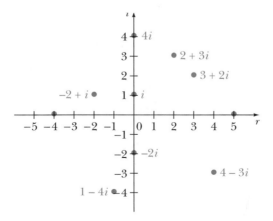

2 Operating with Complex Numbers

The real numbers are ordered, in the sense that, given any two real numbers a and b, exactly one of the following is true:

$$a < b \quad \text{or} \quad a = b \quad \text{or} \quad a > b$$

For instance, if $a = 5$ and $b = 3$, then $5 > 3$. This property is called the **trichotomy postulate**. We can see from Figure 7.6 that $3 + 2i \neq 2 + 3i$, but we cannot say that one is greater than or less than the other. Therefore, the complex numbers are not ordered. As a result, no inequalities are found in mathematics that involve imaginary numbers. All the other properties of the real numbers carry over to the complex numbers. This fact allows us to add, subtract, multiply, and divide complex numbers.

Addition and subtraction of complex numbers is similar to these operations with binomials. We use the commutative, associative, and distributive properties to group and combine like terms. For example,

$$(2 + 3i) + (4 + 5i) = (2 + 4) + (3i + 5i)$$
$$= 6 + (3 + 5)i$$
$$= 6 + 8i$$

EXAMPLE 2

Perform the indicated addition and subtraction.

a. $(6 - 8i) + (-2 + 10i)$ **b.** $(1 - 3i) - (4 - 7i)$

SOLUTION   **a.** $(6 - 8i) + (-2 + 10i) = (6 - 2) + (-8i + 10i)$
$$= 4 + 2i$$

b. $(1 - 3i) - (4 - 7i) = 1 - 3i - 4 + 7i = -3 + 4i$

We multiply complex numbers by using the distributive property and the fact that $i^2 = -1$. For instance,

$$2i(3 + 4i) = 2i(3) + 2i(4i)$$
$$= 6i + 8i^2$$
$$= 6i + 8(-1)$$
$$= -8 + 6i$$

EXAMPLE 3

Perform the indicated operations.

a. $(1 + 2i)^2$ **b.** $(1 + 2i)^3$ **c.** $(2 + 3i)(2 - 3i)$

SOLUTION   **a.** $(1 + 2i)^2 = (1 + 2i)(1 + 2i)$ $a^2 = aa$
$$= 1 + 2i + 2i + 4i^2 \qquad i^2 = -1$$
$$= 1 + 4i - 4$$
$$= -3 + 4i$$

b. $(1 + 2i)^3 = (1 + 2i)^2(1 + 2i)$ $a^3 = a^2a$
$$= (-3 + 4i)(1 + 2i)$$
$$= -3 - 6i + 4i + 8i^2$$
$$= -3 - 2i - 8$$
$$= -11 - 2i$$

c. $(2 + 3i)(2 - 3i) = 4 - 6i + 6i - 9i^2 = 4 + 0 + 9 = 13$

Notice in Example 3c that the product of $2 + 3i$ and $2 - 3i$ is a real number. These numbers are called *complex conjugates* or simply *conjugates*.

Math in Time

BEFORE THE EARLY nineteenth century, imaginary numbers had a mystical quality. Swiss mathematician Leonhard Euler (1707–1783) said that "they are neither nothing, nor greater than nothing, nor less than nothing, which necessarily constitutes them impossible or imaginary." German mathematician and theologian Gottfried Leibniz (1646–1716) called imaginary numbers "sort of amphibian, halfway between existence and nonexistence, resembling in this respect the Holy Ghost in Christian theology" (Boyer, 1968). However, Leibniz did not hesitate to use these numbers, and he achieved results such as

$$\sqrt{6} = \sqrt{1 + \sqrt{3}i} + \sqrt{1 - \sqrt{3}i}$$

Complex numbers have a long history, beginning with Greek mathematics. Heron of Alexandria (ca. A.D. 50) encountered $\sqrt{81 - 144}$ and quickly changed it to $\sqrt{144 - 81}$. Diophantus (ca. 250) tried to find a right triangle with a perimeter of 12 and an area of 7. The resulting equation involved the square root of -2672, so he said that no solution existed. Hindu mathematician Mahavira (ca. 850) said that "as in the nature of things a negative number is not a square, it has no square root." Italians Girolamo Cardano (1501–1576) and Rafael Bombelli (1526–1573) were the first people to use imaginary numbers. Cardano showed that $5 + \sqrt{15}i$ and $5 - \sqrt{15}i$ had a sum of 10 and a product of 40, and Bombelli developed the first algebraic theory of imaginary numbers.

The first attempt at a geometric interpretation of complex numbers came in 1676 when Englishman John Wallis suggested that pure imaginary numbers might be represented by an axis perpendicular to the real axis. Strangely, he did not think of using both axes to graph numbers such as $3 + 2i$. More than 100 years later, in 1797, Caspar Wessel, a Norwegian surveyor, developed the first modern geometric theory of complex numbers. Imaginary numbers began to lose their ethereal quality when they could be visualized as points in a coordinate plane.

Several people contributed to our present-day vocabulary and notation. The terms "real" and "imaginary" were introduced by Descartes (1637); Euler (1748) established the use of i for $\sqrt{-1}$; Cauchy (1821) suggested the term "conjugate"; Gauss (1832) gave us the name "complex number"; and, at the end of the nineteenth century, Weierstrass called $\sqrt{a^2 + b^2}$ the "absolute value" of $a + bi$ and represented it by $|a + bi|$.

Perhaps the best way to approach imaginary numbers, or any new mathematical idea, is to follow the advice of Lewis Carroll, the logician and author of *Alice in Wonderland:* "I pay them extra and make them mean what I like."

In general, the complex numbers $a + bi$ and $a - bi$ are called complex conjugates, and

$$(a + bi)(a - bi) = a^2 - abi + abi - b^2i^2 = a^2 + b^2$$

Note that the sum of two squares, $a^2 + b^2$, factors over the complex numbers (see the B exercises on p. 365). Recall that we rationalize the denominator of an expression such as $1/(2 + \sqrt{3})$ by multiplying it by its conjugate, $2 - \sqrt{3}$. In a similar way we convert the denominator of $1/(2 + 3i)$ to a rational number by multiplying it by its conjugate, $2 - 3i$.

For comparison, these two expressions are simplified together:

$$\frac{1}{2 + 3i} = \frac{1}{2 + 3i} \cdot \frac{2 - 3i}{2 - 3i} \qquad\qquad \frac{1}{2 + \sqrt{3}} = \frac{1}{2 + \sqrt{3}} \cdot \frac{2 - \sqrt{3}}{2 - \sqrt{3}}$$

$$= \frac{2 - 3i}{13} \qquad\qquad\qquad\qquad = \frac{2 - \sqrt{3}}{4 - 3}$$

$$= \frac{2}{13} - \frac{3i}{13} \qquad\qquad\qquad\quad = 2 - \sqrt{3}$$

In general, if the denominator of a fraction is $a + bi$, $a \neq 0$, then we perform the indicated division by using its conjugate, $a - bi$. If the denominator is $a - bi$, then we use $a + bi$. If the denominator is bi, then we can produce a real denominator by multiplying it by i.

EXAMPLE 4

Perform the indicated operations and write your answers in standard form.

a. $\dfrac{1 + i}{2 - i}$ **b.** $(4 + \sqrt{5}i)^{-1}$ **c.** $\dfrac{-5}{6i}$

SOLUTION   **a.** $\dfrac{1 + i}{2 - i} = \dfrac{1 + i}{2 - i} \cdot \dfrac{2 + i}{2 + i} = \dfrac{2 + i + 2i + i^2}{4 + 2i - 2i - i^2} = \dfrac{2 + 3i - 1}{4 - (-1)} = \dfrac{1 + 3i}{5} = \dfrac{1}{5} + \dfrac{3}{5}i$

b. $(4 + \sqrt{5}i)^{-1} = \dfrac{1}{4 + \sqrt{5}i} = \dfrac{1}{4 + \sqrt{5}i} \cdot \dfrac{4 - \sqrt{5}i}{4 - \sqrt{5}i} = \dfrac{4 - \sqrt{5}i}{16 - (\sqrt{5})^2i^2}$

$$= \dfrac{4 - \sqrt{5}i}{16 + 5} = \dfrac{4}{21} - \dfrac{\sqrt{5}i}{21}$$

c. $\dfrac{-5}{6i} = \dfrac{-5}{6i} \cdot \dfrac{i}{i} = \dfrac{-5i}{6i^2} = \dfrac{-5i}{-6} = \dfrac{5i}{6} = 0 + \dfrac{5}{6}i$

---

3 Solving $x^2 = -d$ and Simplifying Radicals

In Section 2.3 we worked with quadratic equations in the form $x^2 = d$, for $d > 0$. Recall that $x = \pm\sqrt{d}$ are the solutions to this equation. For example, if $x^2 = 9$, then $x = \pm\sqrt{9} = \pm3$. If $x^2 = -9$, then we define $\sqrt{-9} = \sqrt{9}\sqrt{-1} = 3i$ and $x = \pm\sqrt{-9} = \pm3i$. In general:

$$\text{If } x^2 = -d, \quad d > 0, \quad \text{then } x = \pm\sqrt{d}i.$$

EXAMPLE 5

Solve the following equations.

a. $2x^2 = -54$ **b.** $3x^2 + 75 = 0$

SOLUTION   **a.** $2x^2 = -54$ Divide by 2.

$$x^2 = -27$$

$$x = \pm\sqrt{-27} = \pm\sqrt{27}\sqrt{-1} = \pm\sqrt{9}\sqrt{3}i = \pm3\sqrt{3}i$$

A common practice is to write $3i\sqrt{3}$, rather than $3\sqrt{3}i$ to avoid confusing it with $\sqrt{3i}$. Either $3\sqrt{3}i$ or $3i\sqrt{3}$ is correct, however; just be careful not to write $\sqrt{di}$.

b. $3x^2 + 75 = 0$ Subtract 75.
$$3x^2 = -75$$ Divide by 3.
$$x^2 = -25$$
$$x = \pm\sqrt{-25} = \pm\sqrt{25}i = \pm5i$$

Recall that $\sqrt{a}\,\sqrt{b} = \sqrt{ab}$ provided that a and b are nonnegative. If a and b are negative, then we cannot use the product rule directly. However, we can use the definition $\sqrt{-d} = \sqrt{d}i$ first and then use the product rule. For example,

$$\sqrt{-2}\,\sqrt{-8} = \sqrt{2}i\,\sqrt{8}i = \sqrt{16}i^2 = 4(-1) = -4, \quad \text{and}$$
$$\sqrt{(-2)(-8)} = \sqrt{16} = 4, \quad \text{so}$$
$$\sqrt{-2}\,\sqrt{-8} \neq \sqrt{(-2)(-8)}$$

We can also get into trouble with the quotient rule, $\sqrt{\dfrac{a}{b}} = \dfrac{\sqrt{a}}{\sqrt{b}}$, if the variables are negative. For example,

$$\sqrt{\frac{-4}{9}} = \sqrt{\frac{4}{-9}} \qquad \frac{-a}{b} = \frac{a}{-b}$$
$$\frac{\sqrt{-4}}{\sqrt{9}} = \frac{\sqrt{4}}{\sqrt{-9}} \qquad \text{Wrong!}$$
$$\frac{2i}{3} = \frac{2}{3i} \qquad \text{Cross-multiply.}$$
$$6i^2 = 6$$
$$-6 = 6$$

COMMON ERROR   A common mistake is to use the product and quotient rules for negative values of the variable. If a and b are nonnegative, then

$$\sqrt{ab} = \sqrt{a}\,\sqrt{b} \qquad \text{and} \qquad \sqrt{\frac{a}{b}} = \frac{\sqrt{a}}{\sqrt{b}}, \quad b \neq 0$$

EXAMPLE 6

Simplify the following.

a. $\sqrt{-45}$ **b.** $\sqrt{2}\,\sqrt{-3}\,\sqrt{-6}$ **c.** $\sqrt{\dfrac{4}{-9}}$ **d.** $\dfrac{\sqrt{32}}{\sqrt{-8}}$

SOLUTION   **a.** $\sqrt{-45} = \sqrt{45}i = \sqrt{9 \cdot 5}i = \sqrt{9}\,\sqrt{5}i = 3\sqrt{5}i$

b. $\sqrt{2}\,\sqrt{-3}\,\sqrt{-6} = \sqrt{2}\,\sqrt{3}i\,\sqrt{6}i = \sqrt{2 \cdot 3 \cdot 6}i^2 = \sqrt{36}(-1) = -6$

c. $\sqrt{\dfrac{4}{-9}} = \sqrt{-\dfrac{4}{9}} = \sqrt{\dfrac{4}{9}}i = \dfrac{\sqrt{4}}{\sqrt{9}}i = \dfrac{2}{3}i$

d. $\dfrac{\sqrt{32}}{\sqrt{-8}} = \dfrac{\sqrt{32}}{\sqrt{8}i} = \sqrt{\dfrac{32}{8}} \cdot \dfrac{1}{i} \cdot \dfrac{i}{i} = \sqrt{4} \cdot \dfrac{i}{i^2} = \dfrac{2i}{-1} = -2i$

In Section 7.4 we simplified radicals to put them in a form where they could be added or subtracted. For example,

$$\sqrt{8} + \sqrt{50} = \sqrt{4}\,\sqrt{2} + \sqrt{25}\,\sqrt{2} = 2\sqrt{2} + 5\sqrt{2} = 7\sqrt{2}$$

A similar procedure applies to imaginary numbers. For instance,

$$\sqrt{-8} + \sqrt{-50} = \sqrt{8}i + \sqrt{50}i = (\sqrt{8} + \sqrt{50})i = 7\sqrt{2}i$$

EXAMPLE 7

Simplify the following.

a. $3\sqrt{-75} - \sqrt{-27}$ **b.** $\sqrt[3]{-8} - \sqrt[3]{-27}$

SOLUTION

a. $3\sqrt{-75} - \sqrt{-27} = 3\sqrt{75}i - \sqrt{27}i = 3\sqrt{25}\sqrt{3}i - \sqrt{9}\sqrt{3}i$
$= 15\sqrt{3}i - 3\sqrt{3}i = (15 - 3)\sqrt{3}i = 12\sqrt{3}i$

b. $\sqrt[3]{-8} - \sqrt[3]{-27} = -2 - (-3) = 1$
Remember that $\sqrt[3]{a}$ is a real number for all real values of a. Imaginary numbers occur with even roots of negative numbers.

EXERCISE SET 7.8

A

1 Let $A = \{.25, .\overline{25}, .252627 \ldots, \sqrt{-4}, \sqrt[3]{-8}, 3 + 4i, 0, -1, i\}$. List all the elements of A that are

1. Whole numbers
2. Integers
3. Rational
4. Real
5. Imaginary
6. Pure imaginary

Let $B = \{\sqrt{7}, \sqrt{-7}, \sqrt[5]{-7}, 4, .\overline{7}, .7, \pi, -6, -6i, 1 - i, -i^2\}$. List all the elements of B that are

7. Natural numbers
8. Irrational
9. Complex
10. Real
11. Imaginary
12. Pure imaginary

Classify the following as true or false.

13. Every real number is a complex number.
14. Every complex number is a real number.
15. Every pure imaginary number is a complex number.
16. Every irrational number is a complex number.
17. Every rational number is an imaginary number.
18. Some numbers are both rational and imaginary.
19. Some numbers are both rational and integers.
20. Every integer can be written in the form $a + bi$.

21. The square root of a negative number is real.
22. The cube root of a negative number is real.

Graph each set of numbers on a complex plane.

23. $\{3, -2, 2i, -3i, 4 + i, -3 + 2i, -5 - i, 3 - 3i\}$
24. $\{-3, 2, -i, 3i, -3 - 2i, 1 + 4i, -2 + 2i, 2 - 4i\}$

2 Perform the indicated operations and write your answer in standard form.

25. $(2 + 5i) + (1 + 4i)$
26. $(6 - 7i) + (5 - 3i)$
27. $(3 - i) - (2 + 9i)$
28. $(-5 + 2i) - (-8 - 7i)$
29. $8 + (6 - 4i)$
30. $5i - (7 - 11i)$
31. $5i - (1 - 3i) + (6 - i)$
32. $10 + (3 + i) - (7 - 8i)$
33. $\left(\frac{1}{3} - \frac{1}{4}i\right) + \left(\frac{2}{5} + \frac{1}{3}i\right)$
34. $\left(\frac{3}{8} + \frac{2}{3}i\right) - \left(\frac{3}{4} - \frac{1}{5}i\right)$
35. $(-2i)(5i)$ **36.** $(4i)^3$
37. $3(2 + 4i)$ **38.** $3i(2 + 4i)$

39. $-2i(6 - 8i)$ **40.** $(2 + 3i)(4 + 5i)$

41. $(1 + 2i)(3 + i)$ **42.** $(2 - i)(7 + 2i)$

43. $(4 - 6i)(2 - 3i)$ **44.** $(1 - i)(2 - i)$

45. $(1 + i)^2$ **46.** $(1 + i)^3$

47. $(1 + i)^4$ **48.** $(2 - i)^2$

49. $(2 - i)^3$ **50.** $(3 - 2i)^2$

51. $(2 + 5i)(2 - 5i)$ **52.** $(4 - i)(4 - i)$

53. $\dfrac{1}{2 + 5i}$ **54.** $\dfrac{i}{4 - i}$

55. $\dfrac{1 + i}{1 - i}$ **56.** $\dfrac{8i}{3 + 5i}$

57. $\dfrac{1}{\sqrt{2} + i}$ **58.** $\dfrac{10}{\sqrt{3} - \sqrt{2}i}$

59. $(2 + 3i)^{-1}$ **60.** $(5 - 2i)^{-1}$

61. $\dfrac{2}{5i}$ **62.** $\dfrac{1 + i}{i}$

63. $\dfrac{1 - i}{2i}$ **64.** $\dfrac{2 + 6i}{-4i}$

3 Solve the following equations.

65. $x^2 = 16$ **66.** $x^2 = -16$

67. $3x^2 = -12$ **68.** $-5x^2 = -30$

69. $-2y^2 = 14$ **70.** $x^2 - 2 = -10$

71. $5x^2 + 100 = 0$ **72.** $3z^2 - 1 = -82$

73. $2x^2 + 5 = -20$ **74.** $4x^2 + 18 = 3$

75. $3x^2 - 6x = 0$ **76.** $2x^2 = 7x$

Simplify the following.

77. $\sqrt{-2}\sqrt{-18}$ **78.** $\sqrt{(-2)(-18)}$

79. $2\sqrt{-3}\sqrt{-6}$ **80.** $\sqrt{2}\sqrt{-10}$

81. $\sqrt{-1}\sqrt{-2}\sqrt{-3}$ **82.** $\sqrt[3]{-2}\sqrt[3]{-8}$

83. $\dfrac{\sqrt{-5}}{\sqrt{9}}$ **84.** $\dfrac{\sqrt{5}}{\sqrt{-9}}$

85. $\dfrac{\sqrt{-4}}{\sqrt{-25}}$ **86.** $\dfrac{\sqrt{-48}\sqrt{-3}}{\sqrt{-2}}$

87. $\sqrt{\dfrac{-2}{25}}$ **88.** $\sqrt{\dfrac{3}{-7}}$

89. $\sqrt{-12} + \sqrt{-3}$

90. $\sqrt{-63} - 2\sqrt{-28}$

91. $4\sqrt{-80} + 3\sqrt{-20}$

92. $\sqrt[3]{-27} - 2i\sqrt{-9}$

93. $i\sqrt{18} + \sqrt{-8}$

94. $4i\sqrt{-128} - \sqrt{50}$

B

Use the fact that $a^2 + b^2 = (a + bi)(a - bi)$ to factor the following over the complex numbers.

95. $a^2 + 25$ **96.** $x^2 + 9y^2$

97. $x^3 + 100x$ **98.** $12y^2 + 3$

99. $x^4 - 1$ **100.** $x^4 - 16$

Recall that a set A is closed under addition if $a + b$ is an element of A whenever a and b are in A. Determine whether $A = \{1, -1, i, -i\}$ is closed under

101. Addition **102.** Subtraction

103. Multiplication **104.** Division

C

We can use the properties of exponents to simplify i^n, where n is an integer. For example,

$$i^5 = i^{4+1} = i^4 i^1 = (i^2)^2 i = (-1)^2 i = (1)i = i, \quad \text{and}$$

$$i^{-6} = \frac{1}{i^6} = \frac{1}{(i^2)^3} = \frac{1}{(-1)^3} = \frac{1}{-1} = -1$$

Simplify the following; when possible, use $i^4 = 1$.

105. i^3 **106.** i^7 **107.** i^8

108. i^{11} **109.** i^{20} **110.** i^{-1}

111. i^{-2} **112.** i^{-3} **113.** i^{-9}

114. i^{-12}

From the reduction rule, $\sqrt[4]{-1} = \sqrt{\sqrt{-1}} = \sqrt{i}$. Advanced mathematics shows that $\sqrt{i} = \dfrac{\sqrt{2}}{2} + \dfrac{\sqrt{2}}{2}i$; this equation can be proved by showing that $\left(\dfrac{\sqrt{2}}{2} + \dfrac{\sqrt{2}}{2}i\right)^2 = i$ ($\sqrt{a} = b$ if $b^2 = a$). Show that

115. $\sqrt{i} = \dfrac{\sqrt{2}}{2} + \dfrac{\sqrt{2}}{2}i$

116. $\sqrt{-i} = \dfrac{\sqrt{2}}{2} - \dfrac{\sqrt{2}}{2}i$

117. $\sqrt[3]{i} = -i$

118. $\sqrt[6]{-1} = i$

119. Show that the following determinant represents the complex number $a + bi$. (See Section 4.5.)

$$\begin{vmatrix} a & -b \\ i & 1 \end{vmatrix}$$

120. Find a determinant that represents the complex conjugate of $a + bi$.

✎ Answer the following questions with complete sentences.

121. Explain why a real number is a complex number.

122. When is the complex conjugate of a complex number equal to itself?

123. Compare the methods of squaring $1 + 2i$ and $1 + 2x$.

124. Discuss the contributions the Italians made to the development of complex numbers.

Chapter Summary

KEY WORDS, DEFINITIONS, AND PROPERTIES

Key Words and Definitions

$\sqrt[n]{a} = b$ if $b^n = a$; if n is even, then a and b are nonnegative. $\sqrt{}$ is called the **radical sign**, a is called the **radicand**, and $\sqrt[n]{a}$ is called a **radical**. (See Section 7.1.)

Conjugate radicals: $a + b$ and $a - b$ where a, b, or both contain square roots. **Complex conjugates:** $a + bi$ and $a - bi$; $(a + bi)(a - bi) = a^2 + b^2$. (See Sections 7.4 and 7.8.)

Variation: k is the **constant of variation** or the **constant of proportionality.** $y = kx$: y varies directly as x. $y = k/x$ or $xy = k$: y varies **inversely** as x. $y = kwx$: y varies **jointly** as w and x. $y = kw/x$: **combined** variation; y varies directly as w and inversely as x. (See Section 7.6.)

Scientific notation: $a \times 10^n$, $1 \leq a < 10$, $n \in \mathbb{Z}$. (See Section 7.7.)

Complex numbers, $\mathbb{C}$. (See Section 7.8.)
$\mathbb{C} = \{z = a + bi \mid a, b \in \mathbb{R}; \; i = \sqrt{-1}, \; i^2 = -1\}$. z is **real** if $b = 0$; z is **imaginary** if $b \neq 0$; z is **pure imaginary** if $a = 0$ and $b \neq 0$. a is the **real part** and b is the **imaginary part.** If $x^2 = -d$, $d > 0$, then $x = \pm\sqrt{d}\,i$. The **complex plane** is the coordinate plane determined by the horizontal r-axis and the vertical i-axis; $a + bi$ is graphed as the point (a, b).

Properties of nth Roots (See Sections 7.1 and 7.3.)

1. Let n be even. Every positive real number has two real nth roots. The nth roots of a negative number are imaginary. $(\sqrt[n]{a})^n = a$.

$$\sqrt[n]{a^n} = |a| = \begin{cases} a, & \text{if } a \geq 0 \\ -a, & \text{if } a < 0 \end{cases}$$

2. Let n be odd and a be real. Every real number has one real nth root, which is positive if a is positive and negative if a is negative. $\sqrt[n]{-a} = -\sqrt[n]{a}$, $(\sqrt[n]{a})^n = a$, and $\sqrt[n]{a^n} = a$.

3. The product, quotient, and reduction rules. We assume that each radical is a real number.

$$\sqrt[n]{ab} = \sqrt[n]{a}\,\sqrt[n]{b};$$

$$\sqrt[n]{\frac{a}{b}} = \frac{\sqrt[n]{a}}{\sqrt[n]{b}};$$

$$\sqrt[mn]{a} = a^{1/mn} = \sqrt[m]{\sqrt[n]{a}}$$

Simplifying Radical Expressions (See Section 7.4.)

A radical expression is simplified if

1. A square root does not contain a factor that is a square, a cube root does not contain a factor that is a cube, and so on.

2. No fractions are under the radical sign.

3. No radicals are in the denominator of a fraction.

4. The index of a radical is reduced to the smallest possible natural number.

5. Like radicals are combined.

Graphing a radical function (See Section 7.2.)

To graph a radical function:

1. Determine the domain of the function.

2. Determine a set of ordered pairs that satisfy the function. Approximate irrational values of $f(x)$ with a calculator to one decimal place.

3. Plot the ordered pairs and connect the points with a smooth curve.

Solving a Radical Equation (See Section 7.5.)

To solve a radical equation:

1. Isolate the radical if necessary.

2. Raise both sides of the equation to the nth power, where n is the order of the radicals involved.

3. Check for extraneous roots.

Properties of Rational Exponents (See Section 7.2.)

Let a and b be real, r and s rational, and m and n integers with $m \neq 0$ and $n > 1$. Then, assuming nonzero denominators and that $\sqrt[n]{a} \in \mathbb{R}$:

If $a \neq 0$, then $a^0 = 1$; 0^0 is undefined.

$$a^{1/n} = \sqrt[n]{a} \quad \text{and} \quad a^{m/n} = \sqrt[n]{a^m} = (\sqrt[n]{a})^m.$$

$$a^{-r} = \frac{1}{a^r} \qquad \frac{1}{a^{-r}} = a^r \qquad \left(\frac{a}{b}\right)^{-1} = \frac{b}{a}$$

$$\left(\frac{a}{b}\right)^{-r} = \left(\frac{b}{a}\right)^r \qquad a^r a^s = a^{r+s} \qquad (a^r)^s = a^{rs}$$

$$(ab)^r = a^r b^r \qquad \left(\frac{a}{b}\right)^r = \frac{a^r}{b^r} \qquad \frac{a^r}{a^s} = a^{r-s}$$

CHAPTER REVIEW EXERCISES

The answers to the following problems are given in the answer section. If you have trouble, review the material and homework problems in the sections indicated.

Simplify the following and write your answers with positive exponents. Assume that variables represent positive numbers. (See Sections 7.1, 7.2, and 7.8.)

1. $(3x^{-4})^{-2}$ **2.** $a^5(a^2)^9$

3. $16^{3/4}$ **4.** $(18^0 x^8 y^{-1})^2$

5. $\left(\frac{1}{9}\right)^{-1/2}$ **6.** $\frac{8a^{1/4}}{2a^{-1/2}}$

7. $(3x^{1/2}y^{-1})^2$ **8.** $-\sqrt{16}$

9. $\sqrt{-16}$

Simplify the following. Make no assumptions about the variables. (See Section 7.1.)

10. $\sqrt[3]{8a^3}$ **11.** $\sqrt[4]{16b^4}$

Perform the indicated operations. Assume that variables represent positive numbers. (See Sections 7.3, 7.4, 7.7, and 7.8.)

12. $\sqrt{8x^3}$ **13.** $\sqrt[3]{3} + \sqrt[6]{9}$

14. $5\sqrt{45x} - 3\sqrt{20x}$ **15.** $\dfrac{\sqrt{10}}{2 + \sqrt{5}}$

16. $\dfrac{-15i}{3 - 4i}$ **17.** $\sqrt{-\dfrac{3}{5}}$

18. $\sqrt[3]{-\dfrac{3}{5}}$ **19.** $3i(2 - 4i)$

20. $(2 + \sqrt{6})(3 - \sqrt{3})$ **21.** $\sqrt{-4}\sqrt{-9}$

22. 7^{-20} **23.** $(3 + 2i)(5 - 6i)$

Solve the following equations and formulas. (See Sections 7.2, 7.5, and 7.8.)

24. $2x^2 = -16$

25. $5 + \sqrt[3]{3x - 10} = 7$

26. $\sqrt{3t + 7} = \sqrt{t - 5} + 4$

27. $a = 5 - 3\sqrt{a + b}; \quad b$

28. $X = \sqrt{Z^2 - R^2}; \quad R$

29. $x^{3/4} + 1 = 28$

Graph each relation and its inverse on the same axes. (See Section 7.2.)

30. $f(x) = \sqrt{x + 2}$ **31.** $S = \{(x, y) \mid y = |x + 2|\}$

Simplify the following and write your answer in scientific notation. (See Section 7.7.)

32. $\dfrac{810,000,000}{0.000\ 3}$

Find the roots of the following function. (See Section 7.5.)

33. $f(x) = \sqrt{5x} - 4$

Solve the following. (See Section 7.5.)

34. The square root of 1 more than twice a number is 1 less than the number. Find the number(s).

Graph the following set of numbers on a complex plane. (See Section 7.8.)

35. $\{2, i, -4, -i, -3i, -2 + i, -1 - 2i, 2 - 2i, 3 + 2i\}$

Solve the following variation problems. (See Section 7.6.)

36. z varies directly as x and inversely as y. $z = 3/5$ when $x = 2$ and $y = 10$. Find x when $z = -3$ and $y = -36$.

37. Geologists have found that the amount of sediment, S, that a stream can carry is directly proportional to the sixth power of the velocity, v, of the water. If a stream carries 1 unit of sediment when the current is 2 mph, how many units of sediment will it carry when the current is 6 mph?

CHAPTER TEST

Treat this test as a class test and allow 50 minutes for completion. When you have finished, use the answer section for scoring. If you have any wrong answers, refer to the corresponding problems in the review section.

Perform the indicated operations. Assume that variables represent positive numbers.

1. $x^{-4}(x^3)^{-2}$

2. $32^{-2/5}$

3. $x^2(x^{1/4})^2$

4. $\left(\dfrac{a^{-1/3}}{b^3}\right)^{-1}$

5. $\dfrac{6x^4}{\sqrt[3]{-9x}}$

6. $(-3)^{29}$

7. $\sqrt{-5}\,\sqrt{-10}$

8. $\dfrac{14}{3 - \sqrt{2}}$

9. $\dfrac{8i}{3 + 5i}$

10. $3\sqrt{5} + \sqrt[4]{25}$

11. $(3 + \sqrt{5})^2$

12. $\sqrt[3]{-27} + 4i\sqrt{-25}$

13. $4i - (1 - 6i)$

14. $\sqrt[3]{16x^5}$

15. $8^0 + 8^{2/3}$

Solve the following equations and formulas.

16. $2x^{2/3} = 18$

17. $3 + \sqrt{x - 1} = x$

18. $x^2 + 12 = 0$

19. $f = \dfrac{1}{2\pi\sqrt{LC}}$; L

Find the following product.

20. $(2^x + 2^{-x})^2$

Graph the following function, its inverse, and $y = x$ on the same axes. Give their domains and ranges.

21. $f(x) = \sqrt{1 - x}$

Find the roots of the following function.

22. $f(x) = \sqrt{x^2 - 8} - 1$

Use scientific notation to solve the following problem.

23. The greatest distance of the moon from the earth is 249,000 miles. How many seconds does it take for light to travel from the moon to the earth (correctly to two decimal places)? The speed of light is 186,000 miles per second.

Solve the following variation problems.

24. y is inversely proportional to the square of x; $y = 2$ when $x = 3$. Find x when $y = 12$.

25. The wattage, W, of an appliance varies jointly as the resistance, R, and the square of the current, I. $W = 1$ watt when $R = 100$ ohms and $I = 0.1$ ampere. Find W when $R = 240$ ohms and $I = 0.38$ ampere.

E I G H T

Quadratic Equations and Inequalities

Sections of a parabolic surface show the variation possible in the shape of parabolas.

In Chapter 5 we learned how to solve quadratic equations that have rational solutions, such as $9x^2 - 4 = 0$. In the last chapter we studied certain equations with imaginary solutions, such as $9x^2 + 4 = 0$. In this chapter we will develop methods for solving all quadratic equations and inequalities.

Chapter 3 introduced the Cartesian coordinate system and discussed the graph of the linear function $f(x) = mx + b$. This chapter will investigate the graph of the quadratic function $f(x) = ax^2 + bx + c$ in detail.

8.1 QUADRATIC EQUATIONS

> **1**   **Solving Quadratic Equations by Completing the Square**
>
> **2**   **Using the Quadratic Formula**

1   Solving Quadratic Equations by Completing the Square

In previous chapters we solved quadratic equations that could either be factored over the integers or written as $x^2 = d$. In this section we will learn how to write an equation that cannot be factored in the form $(x + k)^2 = d$; this equation can then be solved as a general case of $x^2 = d$. We begin with an example of solving equations that are expressed as $(x + k)^2 = d$.

EXAMPLE 1

Solve the following equations.

   a. $(x + 2)^2 = 7$ **b.** $(y - 4)^2 = 9$ **c.** $(x - 3)^2 = -9$

SOLUTION   **a.** $(x + 2)^2 = 7$

$$x + 2 = \pm\sqrt{7}$$
$$x = -2 \pm \sqrt{7}$$

  b. $(y - 4)^2 = 9$

$$y - 4 = \pm\sqrt{9}$$
$$y = 4 \pm 3$$
$$y = 4 + 3 \quad \text{or} \quad y = 4 - 3$$
$$y = 7 \qquad \text{or} \quad y = 1$$

  c. $(x - 3)^2 = -9$

$$x - 3 = \pm\sqrt{-9}$$
$$x = 3 \pm \sqrt{9}i$$
$$x = 3 \pm 3i$$

A definition of the **standard form** of a quadratic equation is now in order.

Standard Form of a Quadratic Equation

$$ax^2 + bx + c = 0$$

where a, b, and c are real numbers, $a \neq 0$.

We now discuss the method of writing an equation that cannot be factored over the integers, such as $x^2 + 6x + 4 = 0$; we are going to put it in the form $(x + k)^2 = d$. During this process, called **completing the square**, we will be referring to the individual terms of $ax^2 + bx + c = 0$. The term ax^2 is called the **quadratic term**; bx, the **linear term**; and c, the **constant term**.

The type of perfect squares that we will consider will have quadratic terms with $a = 1$, such as $x^2 + 6x + 9 = (x + 3)^2$. Notice the relationship between the coefficient of the linear term, 6, and the constant term, 9:

$$\left[\frac{1}{2}(6)\right]^2 = [3]^2 = 9$$

In all perfect squares with $a = 1$, the square of one-half the coefficient of the linear term is equal to the constant term. For example,

$$x^2 + 10x + 25 = (x + 5)^2 \qquad \left[\frac{1}{2}(10)\right]^2 = 25$$

$$x^2 - 20x + 100 = (x - 10)^2 \qquad \left[\frac{1}{2}(-20)\right]^2 = 100$$

We use this relationship to construct a perfect square from $x^2 + bx$; that is, we add $\left[\frac{1}{2}b\right]^2 = \frac{b^2}{4}$ to $x^2 + bx$ to produce the square

$$x^2 + bx + \frac{b^2}{4} = x^2 + bx + \left[\frac{b}{2}\right]^2 = \left(x + \frac{b}{2}\right)^2$$

EXAMPLE 2

Add the constant term to the following expressions to produce perfect squares.

a. $x^2 - 12x$ **b.** $x^2 + 3x$

SOLUTION   **a.** The constant we need is $\left[\frac{1}{2}(-12)\right]^2 = [-6]^2 = 36$:

$$x^2 - 12x + 36 = x^2 - 12x + (-6)^2 = (x - 6)^2$$

b. The constant is $\left[\frac{1}{2}(3)\right]^2 = \left[\frac{3}{2}\right]^2 = \frac{9}{4}$. Thus,

$$x^2 + 3x + \frac{9}{4} = x^2 + 3x + \left(\frac{3}{2}\right)^2 = \left(x + \frac{3}{2}\right)^2$$

We can use the technique of completing the square to express $x^2 + bx + c = 0$ as $(x + k)^2 = d$. Then we can solve the equation as in Example 1. As a first example, let's return to the equation $x^2 + 6x + 4 = 0$; notice that our first step is to subtract 4 from both sides of the equation:

$$x^2 + 6x + 4 = 0$$
$$x^2 + 6x = -4 \qquad \text{Add } \left[\frac{1}{2}(6)\right]^2 = 9 \text{ to both sides.}$$
$$x^2 + 6x + 9 = -4 + 9$$
$$(x + 3)^2 = 5$$
$$x + 3 = \pm\sqrt{5}$$
$$x = -3 \pm \sqrt{5}$$

In general, to solve $x^2 + bx + c = 0$ by completing the square, we write it as $x^2 + bx = -c$ and then add $\left[\frac{1}{2}b\right]^2$ to both sides of the equation. The equation can now be written as $(x + k)^2 = d$; we then take the square root of both sides of the equation and solve for x.

EXAMPLE 3

Solve the following by completing the square.

a. $x^2 - 14x + 50 = 0$ **b.** $y^2 = 1 - y$

SOLUTION **a.** $x^2 - 14x + 50 = 0$ Subtract 50 from both sides.

$$x^2 - 14x = -50$$

$$x^2 - 14x + 49 = -50 + 49 \qquad \left[\frac{1}{2}(-14)\right]^2 = 49$$

$$(x - 7)^2 = -1$$

$$x - 7 = \pm\sqrt{-1}$$

$$x = 7 \pm i$$

b. $\qquad\qquad y^2 = 1 - y$ Add y to both sides.

$$y^2 + y = 1$$

$$y^2 + 1y + \left[\frac{1}{2}\right]^2 = 1 + \frac{1}{4} \qquad \left[\frac{1}{2}(1)\right]^2 = \left[\frac{1}{2}\right]^2 = \frac{1}{4}$$

$$\left(y + \frac{1}{2}\right)^2 = \frac{5}{4}$$

$$y + \frac{1}{2} = \pm\sqrt{\frac{5}{4}}$$

$$y = -\frac{1}{2} \pm \frac{\sqrt{5}}{2}$$

$$y = \frac{-1 \pm \sqrt{5}}{2}$$

To solve $ax^2 + bx + c = 0$, where $a \neq 1$, first move c to the other side of the equation. Then multiply both sides by $\frac{1}{a}$ to produce a coefficient of 1 on x^2. Then we proceed as in the last example.

EXAMPLE 4

Solve $3x^2 + 6x + 2 = 0$ by completing the square.

SOLUTION $3x^2 + 6x + 2 = 0$ Subtract 2.

$$3x^2 + 6x = -2$$ Multiply by $\frac{1}{3}$.

$$\frac{1}{3}(3x^2 + 6x) = \frac{1}{3}(-2)$$

$$x^2 + 2x = -\frac{2}{3} \qquad \left[\frac{1}{2}(2)\right]^2 = 1$$

$$x^2 + 2x + 1 = -\frac{2}{3} + 1$$

$$(x + 1)^2 = \frac{1}{3}$$

$$x + 1 = \pm\sqrt{\frac{1}{3}}$$

$$x = -1 \pm \frac{\sqrt{3}}{3} \qquad -1 \pm \frac{\sqrt{3}}{3} = \frac{-3}{3} \pm \frac{\sqrt{3}}{3}$$

$$x = \frac{-3 \pm \sqrt{3}}{3}$$

2   Using the Quadratic Formula

Although every quadratic equation can be solved by completing the square, the arithmetic can become rather complicated. We can avoid this problem by using the **quadratic formula**. The formula is derived by solving $ax^2 + bx + c = 0$, which is done by completing the square. Compare the derivation with the solution of $3x^2 + 6x + 2 = 0$ in Example 4; instead of 3, 6, and 2, we have a, b, and c. The following derivation is for $a > 0$; the proof for $a < 0$ is similar and is omitted.

$$ax^2 + bx + c = 0, \quad a > 0 \qquad \text{Subtract } c.$$

$$ax^2 + bx = -c \qquad \text{Multiply by } \frac{1}{a}.$$

$$\frac{1}{a}(ax^2 + bx) = \frac{1}{a}(-c)$$

$$x^2 + \frac{b}{a}x = \frac{-c}{a} \qquad \left[\frac{1}{2} \cdot \frac{b}{a}\right]^2 = \frac{b^2}{4a^2}$$

$$x^2 + \frac{b}{a}x + \left(\frac{b}{2a}\right)^2 = \left(\frac{b}{2a}\right)^2 + \frac{-c}{a} \qquad \text{LCD} = 4a^2$$

$$\left(x + \frac{b}{2a}\right)^2 = \frac{b^2}{4a^2} + \frac{-c}{a} \cdot \frac{4a}{4a}$$

$$\left(x + \frac{b}{2a}\right)^2 = \frac{b^2 - 4ac}{4a^2}$$

$$x + \frac{b}{2a} = \pm\sqrt{\frac{b^2 - 4ac}{4a^2}}$$

$$x + \frac{b}{2a} = \pm\frac{\sqrt{b^2 - 4ac}}{\sqrt{4a^2}} \qquad \sqrt{4a^2} = |2a| = 2a; \quad a > 0.$$

$$x = -\frac{b}{2a} \pm \frac{\sqrt{b^2 - 4ac}}{2a}$$

$$x = \frac{-b \pm \sqrt{b^2 - 4ac}}{2a}$$

Quadratic Formula

The solutions of $ax^2 + bx + c = 0$, $\quad a \neq 0$, $\quad$ are

$$x = \frac{-b \pm \sqrt{b^2 - 4ac}}{2a}$$

In using the quadratic formula, we must write the equation in the standard form $ax^2 + bx + c = 0$ to identify a, b, and c. The next example is a solution to Example 4 using the quadratic formula.

EXAMPLE 5

SOLUTION

Solve $3x^2 + 6x + 2 = 0$ with the quadratic formula.

$a = 3$, $b = 6$, and $c = 2$, so

$$x = \frac{-6 \pm \sqrt{6^2 - 4 \cdot 3 \cdot 2}}{2 \cdot 3} = \frac{-6 \pm \sqrt{36 - 24}}{6} = \frac{-6 \pm \sqrt{12}}{6}$$

$$= \frac{-6 \pm 2\sqrt{3}}{6} = \frac{\cancel{2}(-3 \pm \sqrt{3})}{\cancel{2} \cdot 3} = \frac{-3 \pm \sqrt{3}}{3}$$

Section 6.1 mentioned that reducing fractions incorrectly is one of the most common mistakes made in algebra. For instance,

$$\frac{-6 + x}{6} \neq \frac{-\cancel{6} + x}{\cancel{6}}, \quad \text{or} \quad -1 + x$$

This mistake is often made with fractions involving radicals. In Example 5 we cannot divide the 6 into the -6.

  COMMON
ERROR

A common mistake in reducing fractions is to divide terms:

$$\frac{-6 \pm 2\sqrt{3}}{6} \neq \frac{-\cancel{6} \pm 2\sqrt{3}}{\cancel{6}}, \quad \text{or} \quad -1 \pm 2\sqrt{3}$$

EXAMPLE 6

SOLUTION

Solve $\frac{1}{x} + \frac{x}{x + 1} = \frac{2}{3}$ with the quadratic formula.

Multiply both sides by the LCD, $3x(x + 1)$, and then write the equation in the standard form. Note that $x \neq 0$ or -1 (why?).

$$3x(x + 1)\left[\frac{1}{x} + \frac{x}{x + 1}\right] = 3x(x + 1) \cdot \frac{2}{3}$$

$$3(x + 1) + 3x \cdot x = 2x(x + 1)$$

$$3x + 3 + 3x^2 = 2x^2 + 2x$$

$$x^2 + x + 3 = 0 \qquad a = b = 1, \quad c = 3$$

$$x = \frac{-1 \pm \sqrt{1^2 - 4 \cdot 1 \cdot 3}}{2 \cdot 1} = \frac{-1 \pm \sqrt{-11}}{2}$$

$$= \frac{-1 \pm \sqrt{11}i}{2}$$

The quadratic formula applies to equations where any a, b, or c is irrational or imaginary, as illustrated in the next two examples.

EXAMPLE 7

SOLUTION

Solve $x^2 - \sqrt{8}x - 7 = 0$.

$x^2 - \sqrt{8}x - 7 = 0$ \hfill $a = 1$, $b = -\sqrt{8}, c = -7$

Math in Time

QUADRATIC EQUATIONS

The topic of quadratic equations is one of the earliest in algebra. In Iraq in the mid-nineteenth century, an ancient Babylonian library was discovered that contained some 500,000 tablets, which were small unbaked-clay bricks the size of a human hand. Approximately 1200 of these tablets dealt with mathematics and astronomy. As a result of this discovery, historians determined that by 2000 B.C. the Babylonians could solve any three-term quadratic equation with positive roots. They used both the method of completing the square and verbal directions that are equivalent to our quadratic formula. Quadratic equations were used to solve a particular socioeconomic problem: the distribution of farmland after periodic floods by the Tigris and Euphrates rivers.

Babylonian mathematics most probably were transmitted to Greece and India. However, the Greeks developed geometric rather than algebraic methods of solving quadratic equations. They used two approaches, which probably originated with the Pythagoreans (ca. 500 B.C.): the theory of proportions and the study of areas of polygons. By the seventh century A.D. the Hindus could solve any quadratic equation with real roots using a technique of completing the square called "The Hindu Method" (see Exercise section C), which is similar to ours. This was the first time that zero and negative numbers were used as solutions of equations.

The Arabs of the ninth to twelfth centuries used both the Greek geometric and the Indian algebraic methods of solving quadratic equations. Islamic algebra was used to help astronomers find the direction from any point in the Arab world to Mecca, the holy city toward which Muslims face during prayer. Islamic algebra was also used to solve monetary problems, such as religious donations and inheritance sharing.

Medieval Europeans acquired their knowledge of quadratic equations from the Arabic writers, and no advancement on this material was made until the end of the sixteenth century. Englishman Thomas Harriot (1560–1621) established the method of solving quadratic equations by factoring. At the same time Frenchman François Viète (1540–1603) used modern notation and gave an algebraic derivation of the quadratic formula. Today this formula is used throughout mathematics and the sciences.

$$x = \frac{-(-\sqrt{8}) \pm \sqrt{(-\sqrt{8})^2 - 4(1)(-7)}}{2 \cdot 1}$$

$$= \frac{\sqrt{8} \pm \sqrt{8 + 28}}{2}$$

$$= \frac{\sqrt{4}\sqrt{2} \pm \sqrt{36}}{2}$$

$$= \frac{2\sqrt{2} \pm 6}{2} \qquad \frac{2\sqrt{2} \pm 6}{2} \neq \sqrt{2} + 6$$

$$= \frac{2(\sqrt{2} \pm 3)}{2}$$

$$= \sqrt{2} \pm 3$$

375

EXAMPLE 8

Solve $3iy^2 + 2i = 5y$.

SOLUTION

$3iy^2 + 2i = 5y$

$3iy^2 - 5y + 2i = 0$ $a = 3i, \quad b = -5, \quad c = 2i$

$$y = \frac{-(-5) \pm \sqrt{(-5)^2 - 4(3i)(2i)}}{2 \cdot 3i}$$

$$= \frac{5 \pm \sqrt{25 - 24i^2}}{6i} \qquad\qquad -24i^2 = -24(-1) = 24$$

$$= \frac{5 \pm \sqrt{49}}{6i}$$

$$= \frac{5 \pm 7}{6i}, \quad \text{so}$$

$$y = \frac{5 + 7}{6i} = \frac{12}{6i} = \frac{2}{i} \cdot \frac{i}{i} = \frac{2i}{i^2} = \frac{2i}{-1} = -2i, \quad \text{and}$$

$$y = \frac{5 - 7}{6i} = \frac{-2}{6i} = \frac{-1}{3i} \cdot \frac{i}{i} = \frac{-i}{3i^2} = \frac{-i}{-3} = \frac{i}{3}$$

Thus, $\{-2i, i/3\}$ is the solution set.

EXERCISE SET 8.1

A

1   Solve the following equations.

1. $x^2 = 25$ **2.** $x^2 = -25$

3. $y^2 = -18$ **4.** $y^2 = 75$

5. $9x^2 - 4 = 0$ **6.** $9x^2 + 4 = 0$

7. $(x - 2)^2 = 5$ **8.** $(y + 5)^2 = 20$

9. $(a + 1)^2 = -100$ **10.** $(a - 4)^2 = -20$

11. $\left(x - \frac{1}{3}\right)^2 = \frac{7}{9}$ **12.** $\left(x + \frac{4}{5}\right)^2 = \frac{1}{2}$

13. $(2x - 1)^2 = 10$ **14.** $(3x + 4)^2 = -1$

15. $2(x + 6)^2 = -4$ **16.** $4(5x - 2)^2 = 1$

Add the constant term to the following expressions to produce a perfect square and write it as $(x + k)^2$.

17. $x^2 + 20x$ **18.** $x^2 + 2x$

19. $y^2 - 4y$ **20.** $a^2 - 16a$

21. $x^2 + 7x$ **22.** $x^2 - 5x$

23. $x^2 - \frac{2}{3}x$ **24.** $y^2 + \frac{1}{2}y$

Solve the following equations by completing the square.

25. $x^2 - 2x = 3$ **26.** $x^2 + 8x = 2$

27. $y^2 - 6y = -10$

28. $x^2 - 10x + 30 = 0$

29. $x^2 + 12x - 4 = 0$

30. $a^2 - 11 = 2a$

31. $x^2 + 4x = 0$

32. $y^2 = 6y$

33. $3x - 1 = -x^2$

34. $-x^2 + x - 1 = 0$

35. $x^2 - \frac{2}{5}x = 1$

36. $t^2 + \frac{1}{3}t = 2$

37. $2x^2 + 4x = 4$

38. $3x^2 - 12x + 5 = 0$

39. $2x^2 + 3x + 1 = 0$

40. $4x^2 - 2x - 1 = 0$

2   Solve the following equations by using the quadratic formula.

41. $x^2 + 5x + 3 = 0$ **42.** $x^2 - 6x + 7 = 0$

43. $x^2 + 2x + 4 = 0$ **44.** $3x^2 - x + 2 = 0$

45. $2x^2 + 5x = 3$ **46.** $x^2 = 2x - 2$

47. $x^2 - 6x + 9 = 0$ **48.** $4x^2 + 12x + 9 = 0$

49. $x^2 + 12x + 34 = 0$ **50.** $x^2 + x + 1 = 0$

51. $x^2 + 4 = 2x$ **52.** $9x^2 = -3x - 1$

53. $9x^2 - 4 = 0$ **54.** $3x^2 - 5x = 0$

55. $\frac{1}{2}x^2 + 3x - 1 = 0$ **56.** $\frac{x^2}{6} + \frac{3x}{4} = \frac{2}{3}$

57. $x = \dfrac{7}{2} + \dfrac{2}{x}$

58. $\dfrac{5}{x + 2} + \dfrac{1}{x - 2} = \dfrac{4}{x^2 - 4}$

59. $\dfrac{x^2 + 3x}{x + 5} - 1 = \dfrac{10}{x + 5}$

60. $\dfrac{2}{3} + \dfrac{1}{y - 1} + \dfrac{2}{y + 1} = 0$

61. $x^2 - \sqrt{5}x - 5 = 0$

62. $x^2 + \sqrt{12}x = 1$

63. $3x^2 + 2x = \sqrt{5}$

64. $x^2 + ix - 3 = 0$

65. $2x^2 + 5 = 4ix$

66. $ix^2 + 3i = 2x$

B

Solve the following equations.

67. $\dfrac{1}{4} + \dfrac{1}{x} = \dfrac{1}{3x^2} + \dfrac{1}{12x}$

68. $\dfrac{1}{18x} - \dfrac{3}{2x^2} = \dfrac{1}{6x} + \dfrac{2}{3}$

69. $(x + 1)(x^2 - x + 1) = 0$

70. $(x - 2)(x^2 + 2x + 4) = 0$

71. $3x^2 + \sqrt{2}x + \sqrt{7} = 0$

72. $\sqrt{2}x^2 + \sqrt{10}x = \sqrt{8}$

73. $x^2 - (2 + 3i)x + (-1 + 3i) = 0$

74. $ix^2 - (2 + 2i)x + 2 = 0$

C

The following process is the "Hindu Method" (seventh century) of solving $ax^2 + bx + c = 0$:

$$ax^2 + bx = -c$$
$$4a(ax^2 + bx) = 4a(-c)$$
$$4a^2x^2 + 4abx = -4ac$$
$$(2ax)^2 + 4abx + b^2 = b^2 - 4ac \quad u^2 + 2uv + v^2 =$$
$$(2ax + b)^2 = b^2 - 4ac \quad (u + v)^2$$
$$2ax + b = \pm\sqrt{b^2 - 4ac}$$
$$2ax = -b \pm \sqrt{b^2 - 4ac}$$
$$x = \dfrac{-b \pm \sqrt{b^2 - 4ac}}{2a}$$

Use the above method of completing the square to solve the following equations.

75. $x^2 + 5x = 1$ **76.** $3x^2 + x + 2 = 0$

77. $2x^2 + 3x + 6 = 0$ **78.** $4x^2 - 7x = 0$

Answer the following questions with complete sentences.

79. Describe the steps that you would use to solve $x^2 + 6x - 2 = 0$ by the method of completing the square.

80. Why must we write a quadratic equation in the form $ax^2 + bx + c = 0$ before we can use the quadratic formula?

81. Answer the question in Example 6 (p. 374).

82. Discuss the Babylonian and Islamic applications of quadratic equations.

REVIEW EXERCISES

Solve the given formula for the indicated variable. (See Section 7.5.)

83. $c = \sqrt{\dfrac{E}{m}};\quad E$ **84.** $r = \sqrt{\dfrac{V}{\pi h}};\quad h$ **85.** $r = \dfrac{\sqrt{A}}{\sqrt{P}} - 1;\quad P$ **86.** $S = 2\pi r^2 + 2\pi rh;\quad h$

8.2 ADDITIONAL MATERIAL ON QUADRATIC EQUATIONS

1	Solving a Quadratic Equation
2	Finding the Roots of a Quadratic Equation
3	Solving Equations That Are Quadratic in Form
4	Solving Formulas and Word Problems

1   Solving a Quadratic Equation

In this section we will cover several topics involving quadratic equations. In many applications of algebra we need to determine only the type of solutions of a quadratic equation rather than providing the solutions themselves. Here we will learn how to determine whether the roots are rational, imaginary, and so on. We will also return to two familiar topics: solving a formula for a given variable and word problems. We begin with a discussion of the best method of solving a quadratic equation.

We have covered several methods for solving quadratic equations. The most efficient method depends on the equation. The general approach is to try factoring first. If the equation cannot be factored or is too hard to factor, then the quadratic formula and completing the square are the two alternatives. Enough equations also are in the form $x^2 = d$ or $(x + k)^2 = d$ to make knowing the square root method worthwhile. Guidelines and examples follow to help you decide which method is best for solving a quadratic equation.

Factoring   If the equation is in the form $ax^2 + bx = 0$ or $a^2x^2 - c^2 = 0$, or if the factors can be easily found, then use the factoring method.

$$2x^2 + 7x = 0 \qquad\qquad\qquad\qquad 4x^2 - 9 = 0$$
$$x(2x + 7) = 0 \qquad\qquad\qquad (2x + 3)(2x - 3) = 0$$
$$x = 0 \quad \text{or} \quad -\frac{7}{2} \qquad\qquad\qquad\qquad x = \pm\frac{3}{2}$$

$$x^2 + x - 6 = 0$$
$$(x + 3)(x - 2) = 0$$
$$x = -3 \quad \text{or} \quad 2$$

Using Square Roots   If the equation is in the form $ax^2 + c = 0$, $x^2 = d$,   or $(x + k)^2 = d$, then use the square root method.

$$4x^2 - 5 = 0 \qquad\qquad\qquad\qquad (x + 2)^2 = 7$$
$$x^2 = \frac{5}{4} \qquad\qquad\qquad\qquad x + 2 = \pm\sqrt{7}$$
$$\qquad\qquad\qquad\qquad\qquad\qquad x = -2 \pm \sqrt{7}$$
$$x = \pm\frac{\sqrt{5}}{2}$$

Completing the Square   If the equation is in the form $x^2 + bx + c = 0$ and b is divisible by 2, then use the method of completing the square.

$$x^2 + 8x + 25 = 0 \qquad\qquad\qquad (x + 4)^2 = -9$$
$$x^2 + 8x = -25 \qquad\qquad\qquad x + 4 = \pm\sqrt{-9}$$
$$x^2 + 8x + 16 = -25 + 16 \qquad\qquad\qquad x = -4 \pm 3i$$

Applying the Quadratic Formula   If the equation is in the form $ax^2 + bx + c = 0$, $a \neq 1$,   and cannot be factored, then use the quadratic formula.

$$3x^2 + 5x + 4 = 0$$

$$x = \frac{-5 \pm \sqrt{5^2 - 4 \cdot 3 \cdot 4}}{2 \cdot 3}$$

$$= \frac{-5 \pm \sqrt{25 - 48}}{6}$$

$$= \frac{-5 \pm \sqrt{-23}}{6}$$

$$= \frac{-5 \pm \sqrt{23}i}{6}$$

EXAMPLE 1

Solve $x^2 + 2x - 8 = 0$ by:

a. Factoring   **b.** Completing the square
c. The quadratic formula

SOLUTION

a.
$$x^2 + 2x - 8 = 0$$
$$x^2 + 4x - 2x - 8 = 0$$
$$x(x + 4) - 2(x + 4) = 0$$
$$(x - 2)(x + 4) = 0$$
$$x - 2 = 0 \quad \text{or} \quad x + 4 = 0$$
$$x = 2 \quad \text{or} \qquad x = -4$$

   $m + n = 2$
   $mn = -8 = 4(-2)$

b. $x^2 + 2x - 8 = 0$
$$x^2 + 2x = 8$$
$$x^2 + 2x + 1 = 8 + 1$$
$$(x + 1)^2 = 9$$
$$x + 1 = \pm\sqrt{9}$$
$$x = -1 \pm 3, \quad \text{so}$$
$$x = -1 + 3 = 2 \quad \text{or} \quad x = -1 - 3 = -4$$

   Add 8.
   $[1/2(2)]^2 = 1$

c. $x^2 + 2x - 8 = 0$

   $a = 1, \quad b = 2, \quad c = -8$

$$x = \frac{-2 \pm \sqrt{2^2 - 4(1)(-8)}}{2 \cdot 1}$$

$$x = \frac{-2 \pm \sqrt{4 + 32}}{2}$$

$$x = \frac{-2 \pm \sqrt{36}}{2}$$

$$x = \frac{-2 \pm 6}{2}, \quad \text{so}$$

$$x = \frac{-2 + 6}{2} = 2 \quad \text{or} \quad x = \frac{-2 - 6}{2} = -4$$

---

2   Finding the Roots of a Quadratic Equation

In certain applications of quadratic equations we must know only the type of solutions of an equation. For example, the equation $2x^2 + 4x + 3 = 0$ describes the possible points of intersection of a line and a circle. Because the solutions of this equation are imaginary numbers, we conclude that the two curves do not intersect. We could more conveniently reach this conclusion without solving the equation, as the following material shows.

The expression $b^2 - 4ac$ that occurs under the radical sign in the quadratic formula is called the **discriminant** because it discriminates between the different number and type of roots. For example, the discriminant of $2x^2 + 4x + 3 = 0$ is

$$b^2 - 4ac = 4^2 - 4 \cdot 2 \cdot 3 = 16 - 24 = -8 < 0$$

so the equation has two imaginary roots. The following box describes the **discriminant test** for quadratic equations.

Discriminant Test

Let $ax^2 + bx + c = 0$,   where $a, b,$ and c are real numbers, $a \neq 0$.

1. If $b^2 - 4ac < 0$, then two unequal imaginary roots that are complex conjugates exist.
2. If $b^2 - 4ac = 0$, then two equal real roots exist, $x = -b/2a$.
3. If $b^2 - 4ac > 0$, then two unequal real roots that are radical conjugates exist.

EXAMPLE 2

Use the discriminant test to describe the number and type of roots of each equation.

a. $x^2 + 6x + 9 = 0$ **b.** $x^2 + x + 1 = 0$
c. $x^2 - 3x - 10 = 0$ **d.** $4x^2 + 4\sqrt{2}x + 1 = 0$

SOLUTION

a. $b^2 - 4ac = 6^2 - 4 \cdot 1 \cdot 9 = 0$,   so two equal real roots exist, $x = -\dfrac{6}{2} \cdot 1 = -3$.

b. $b^2 - 4ac = 1^2 - 4 \cdot 1 \cdot 1 = -3 < 0$, so two unequal imaginary roots exist.

c. $b^2 - 4ac = (-3)^2 - 4(1)(-10) = 49$, so two unequal real roots exist (both are rational).

 d. $b^2 - 4ac = (4\sqrt{2})^2 - 4 \cdot 4 \cdot 1 = 32 - 16 = 16$, so two unequal real roots exist (both are irrational).

---

3   Solving Equations That Are Quadratic in Form

Many equations are not quadratic, but with appropriate substitution they can be written in the form $au^2 + bu + c = 0$. Such equations are said to be **quadratic in form**. We begin with a fourth-degree polynomial equation that is quadratic in form.

EXAMPLE 3

Solve $(x^2 - 1)^2 - 7(x^2 - 1) + 12 = 0$.

SOLUTION

Let $u = x^2 - 1$. Then, $u^2 = (x^2 - 1)^2$. Thus,

$$(x^2 - 1)^2 - 7(x^2 - 1) + 12 = 0$$
$$u^2 - 7u + 12 = 0 \qquad\qquad m + n = -7$$
$$(u - 3)(u - 4) = 0 \qquad\qquad mn = 12 = (-4)(-3)$$
$$u - 3 = 0 \quad \text{or} \quad u - 4 = 0$$
$$u = 3 \quad \text{or} \qquad u = 4 \quad \text{Replace } u \text{ by } x^2 - 1.$$
$$x^2 - 1 = 3 \quad \text{or} \quad x^2 - 1 = 4$$
$$x^2 = 4 \qquad\qquad x^2 = 5 \quad \text{Use } x^2 = d.$$
$$x = \pm 2 \quad \text{or} \qquad x = \pm\sqrt{5}$$

and the solution set is $\{2, -2, \sqrt{5}, -\sqrt{5}\}$.

EXAMPLE 4

Solve $x + 3\sqrt{x} - 10 = 0$.

SOLUTION

Let $u = \sqrt{x}$. Then, $u^2 = (\sqrt{x})^2 = x$.

$$x + 3\sqrt{x} - 10 = 0$$
$$u^2 + 3u - 10 = 0$$
$$(u + 5)(u - 2) = 0$$
$$u = -5 \quad \text{or} \quad u = 2$$
$$\sqrt{x} = -5 \qquad\qquad \sqrt{x} = 2$$
$$(\sqrt{x})^2 = (-5)^2 \qquad (\sqrt{x})^2 = 2^2$$
$$x = 25 \quad \text{or} \quad x = 4$$

 CHECK

$x = 25$	$x = 4$
$x + 3\sqrt{x} - 10 = 0$	$x + 3\sqrt{x} - 10 = 0$
$25 + 3\sqrt{25} - 10 \stackrel{?}{=} 0$	$4 + 3\sqrt{4} - 10 \stackrel{?}{=} 0$
$25 + 15 - 10 \neq 0$	$4 + 6 - 10 = 0$

Thus, 25 is an extraneous root, so the solution set is $\{4\}$. Note that this equation could be solved by writing it as $3\sqrt{x} = 10 - x$ and then squaring both sides of the equation, as in Section 7.5.

As the equations become more complicated, the choice of substitution is not always clear. However, there are only two alternatives. If the first one doesn't work, we try the second. This is illustrated in the following example.

EXAMPLE 5

Solve $18x^{-2/3} - x^{-4/3} - 81 = 0$.

SOLUTION

Let $u = x^{-4/3}$. Then $u^2 = (x^{-4/3})^2 = x^{-8/3}$. Because the equation does not contain $x^{-8/3}$, this alternative was the wrong one. Therefore, let $u = x^{-2/3}$ and

$u^2 = (x^{-2/3})^2 = x^{-4/3}$. Thus,

$$18x^{-2/3} - x^{-4/3} - 81 = 0$$
$$18u - u^2 - 81 = 0 \qquad\qquad \text{Multiply by } -1.$$
$$u^2 - 18u + 81 = 0 \qquad\qquad a^2 - 2ab + b^2 = (a - b)^2$$
$$(u - 9)^2 = 0$$
$$u = 9 \quad \text{and} \quad u = x^{-2/3}, \text{ so}$$
$$x^{-2/3} = 9 \qquad\qquad \text{Raise both sides to the}$$
$$(x^{-2/3})^{-3/2} = (3^2)^{-3/2} \qquad\qquad -\tfrac{3}{2} \text{ power.}$$
$$x = 3^{-3} = \frac{1}{27}$$

4   Solving Formulas and Word Problems

Many formulas and literal equations contain the square of a variable, such as $E = mc^2$. This equation can be solved for c, the speed of light, by isolating c^2 on one side of the equation and then taking the positive square root of E/m, because $c > 0$:

$$mc^2 = E$$
$$c^2 = E/m$$
$$c = \sqrt{E/m}$$

EXAMPLE 6

Solve the following equations for the indicated variables.

a. $A = P(r + 1)^2$; r interest formula
b. $h = rt - 5t^2$; t physics — motion formula

SOLUTION
a. $P(r + 1)^2 = A$ Divide by P.
      $(r + 1)^2 = A/P$ Take the square root.
         $r + 1 = \sqrt{A/P}$ $r > 0$
           $r = \sqrt{A/P} - 1$

b. $h = rt - 5t^2$ Use the quadratic formula.
     $5t^2 - rt + h = 0$
    $5t^2 + (-r)t + h = 0$ $a = 5$, $b = -r$, and $c = h$

$$t = \frac{-(-r) + \sqrt{(-r)^2 - 4(5)(h)}}{2(5)}, \quad t > 0$$

$$= \frac{r + \sqrt{r^2 - 20h}}{10}$$

We have solved many word problems by using quadratic equations and the factoring method. As a result, the solutions to these problems are rational numbers. We now can handle applications where the solutions are irrational or imaginary. The last example is the problem solved by Cardano (1501–1576). It contained the first known use of imaginary numbers (see Math in Time section on p. 383).

EXAMPLE 7

The length of a rectangle is twice its width, and its area is 4 square meters. Find the rectangle's width and length.

SOLUTION
Let w = the width of the rectangle.
Then $2w$ = its length (Figure 8.1), and its area is

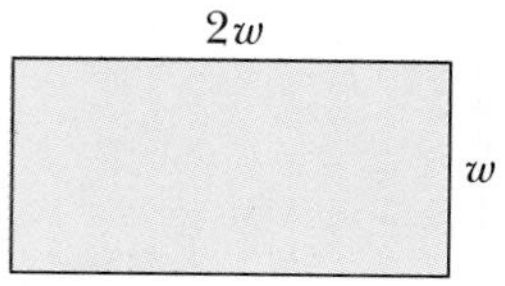

$$2w(w) = 4$$
$$w^2 = 2$$
$$w = \sqrt{2} \quad \text{and} \quad 2w = 2\sqrt{2}$$

Thus, the width is $\sqrt{2}$ meters and the length is $2\sqrt{2}$ meters.

FIGURE 8.1

Math in Time

ALTHOUGH EARLY CIVILIZATIONS had considerable success with linear and quadratic equations, their results with higher-degree polynomials were more limited. The Babylonians, Greeks, and Arabs solved certain third- and fourth-degree equations, but Italians of the sixteenth century discovered the general solutions to these equations.

The story is more like a lurid novel than an academic pursuit. It began around 1515, when Antonio Fior was given the solution to $x^3 + ax = b$ by his professor. The solution was a secret between the two men, but it did Fior little good when he encountered Nicolo Tartaglia (1499–1557).

Nicolo of Bresica received the nickname Tartaglia (meaning "the stammerer") because as a small boy he was caught in a battle between French and Italian soldiers and received a saber cut to the mouth that left him with a speech impairment. According to one story he was too poor to buy paper when he was a student, so he used the tombstones in a cemetery as slates.

Around 1535 Tartaglia, who was a far better mathematician than Fior, discovered the solutions to $x^3 + ax = b$ and $x^3 + ax^2 = b$. A bitter rivalry developed between Fior and Tartaglia, which resulted in a public contest of solving cubic equations. Fior was defeated because he didn't know the solution to $x^3 + ax^2 = b$. By 1541 Tartaglia had developed a method of solving any cubic equation, which he kept secret because he planned to publish it in an algebra book.

We now encounter Girolamo Cardano (1501–1576), the illegitimate son of a lawyer and the father of a murderer. One of his sons poisoned his own wife; and, while in a fit of rage, Cardano is reputed to have cut off the ears of another son. A doctor by training,

Nicolo Tartaglia
The Bettmann Archive

Cardano was interested in mathematics and astrology. He was once imprisoned for publishing a horoscope of Christ's life, but he later became an astrologer to a pope. Cardano is said to have died by his own hand in fulfillment of an astrological prediction of the date of his death.

By repeated requests and a promise of secrecy, Cardano obtained the solution to the cubic equation from Tartaglia. A few years later, in 1545, Cardano included this material in his book *Ars Magna*

Girolamo Cardano
North Wind Picture Archives

("great art"), just before Tartaglia's book was to be published. Cardano gave full credit to Tartaglia, but the method is still known as "Cardano's rule," and Tartaglia died in despair. *Ars Magna* also includes the solution to the fourth-degree equation, discovered by Cardano's pupil Ludovico Ferrari, who was poisoned by his sister at the age of 43.

For the next two centuries mathematicians tried to solve the fifth-degree equation. Finally, in 1824, the Norwegian Niels Abel (1802–1829) showed that no general algebraic solution exists for equations of degree greater than four.

EXAMPLE 8   The sum of two numbers is 10, and their product is 40. Find the numbers.

SOLUTION   Let x and y represent the two numbers. Then $x + y = 10$ and $xy = 40$. From the first equation $y = 10 - x$; we can substitute this value of y in the second equation:

$$xy = 40$$
$$x(10 - x) = 40$$
$$10x - x^2 = 40 \qquad \text{Multiply by } -1.$$
$$x^2 - 10x = -40 \qquad \text{Complete the square.}$$
$$x^2 - 10x + 25 = -40 + 25$$
$$(x - 5)^2 = -15$$
$$x - 5 = \pm\sqrt{-15}$$
$$x = 5 + \sqrt{15}i$$

If $x = 5 + \sqrt{15}i$,   then $y = 10 - (5 + \sqrt{15}i) = 5 - \sqrt{15}i$.
If $x = 5 \pm \sqrt{15}i$,   then $y = 10 - (5 - \sqrt{15}i) = 5 + \sqrt{15}i$.
Thus, the two numbers are $5 + \sqrt{15}i$ and $5 - \sqrt{15}i$.

✔ CHECK $x + y = (5 + \sqrt{15}i) + (5 - \sqrt{15}i) = 10$
$xy = (5 + \sqrt{15}i)(5 - \sqrt{15}i)$
$\quad = 25 - 5\sqrt{15}i + 5\sqrt{15}i - (\sqrt{15})^2i^2 \quad i^2 = -1$
$\quad = 25 + 0 + 15$
$\quad = 40$

EXERCISE SET 8.2

A

1 Solve each of the following by: a. Factoring; b. Completing the square; and c. Applying the quadratic formula.

1. $x^2 + 4x + 3 = 0$
2. $x^2 - 6x = -5$
3. $x^2 + 12 = 8x$
4. $x^2 = 2x + 8$
5. $x^2 + 8x = 0$
6. $2x^2 = 12x$
7. $a^2 - 3a - 10 = 0$
8. $2x^2 - x - 1 = 0$

Solve the following; use whichever method seems best.

9. $x^2 - 7 = 0$
10. $x^2 + 6x - 16 = 0$
11. $x^2 + 7x + 2 = 0$
12. $25y^2 - 16 = 0$
13. $(x - 3)(x + 2) = 9$
14. $(2x - 3)^2 = 18$
15. $\dfrac{x}{2} = 1 - \dfrac{5}{x}$
16. $\dfrac{1}{x} + \dfrac{3}{x^3} = \dfrac{1}{x^2}$
17. $y^2 + 8y + 873 = 0$
18. $2x^2 + 11 = 0$
19. $a^2 = \sqrt{3}a$
20. $x^2 - x - 6 = 0$
21. $5(1 + 4y)^2 = -10$
22. $x^2 - 10x = 462$

2 Use the discriminant test to describe the number and type of roots of each equation. Do not solve the equations.

23. $x^2 + 4x + 4 = 0$
24. $x^2 - x + 1 = 0$
25. $3x^2 + x - 1 = 0$
26. $x^2 - \sqrt{2}x - 8 = 0$
27. $x^2 + 2x = -4$
28. $3x^2 + 1 = 6x$
29. $3x^2 + 4x = 0$
30. $2y^2 = 5$
31. $\sqrt{3}x^2 + x + \sqrt{3} = 0$
32. $x^2 = 3x - 10$

3 Solve the following equations.

33. $2(2x^2)^2 + 9(2x^2) - 5 = 0$

34. $(x + 3)^2 + 2(x + 3) = 3$

35. $(y^2 + 2)^2 + 4 = 5(y^2 + 2)$

36. $(x^2 - x)^2 = 4(x^2 - x) + 5$

37. $x^4 - 3x^2 - 28 = 0$

38. $x^4 + 8x^2 = 9$

39. $x^4 + 26x^2 + 25 = 0$

40. $4x^4 + 7x^2 = 2$

41. $x^4 - 7x^2 = 8$

42. $x^{-2} - 4x^{-1} = 0$

43. $x^{-2} = x^{-1} + 20$

44. $x^{-4} - 8x^{-2} + 15 = 0$

45. $11x^{-2} = x^{-4} + 28$

46. $x + \sqrt{x} = 2$

47. $x + \sqrt{x + 7} = 2x + 1$

48. $x^{1/6} + 2 = x^{1/3}$

49. $x^{2/3} - 4x^{1/3} = 5$

50. $x^{-2/3} - x^{-1/3} = 0$

51. $x^{-2/3} + 2x^{-1/3} + 1 = 0$

52. $x^{-1} + 9 = 6x^{-1/2}$

4 Solve the following equations for the indicated variable.

53. $c^2 = a^2 + b^2$; c Pythagorean theorem

54. $d^2 = W^2 + L^2$; W diagonal of a rectangle

55. $d^2 = 3s^2$; s diagonal of a cube

56. $h = rt - 16t^2$; t motion formula

57. $d = 16t^2$; t

58. $A = \pi r^2$; r

59. $mv^2/r = F$; v

60. $V/r^2 = \pi h$; r

61. $1 + \sqrt{x^2 - y^2} = z$; x

62. $1 + \sqrt{x^2 - y^2} = z$; y

63. $V = \frac{1}{3}\pi r^2 h$; r

64. $S = 4\pi r^2$; r

65. $S = \pi r^2 + \pi rs$; r

66. $x^2 - 3x + 1 = y$; x

67. $hv^2 = r^2 g - v^2 r$; v

68. $hv^2 = r^2 g - v^2 r$; r

Find all numbers that satisfy the following conditions.

69. The sum of a number and its reciprocal is $\dfrac{4\sqrt{3}}{3}$.

70. The sum of a number and twice its reciprocal is 4.

71. The sum of a number and its reciprocal is $\dfrac{1}{2}$.

72. The difference of a number and its reciprocal is $\dfrac{13i}{6}$.

73. A number is equal to its reciprocal.

74. The opposite of a number is equal to the reciprocal of the number.

75. The sum of two numbers is 6, and their product is 25.

76. The sum of two numbers is 4, and their product is 1.

Solve the following word problems.

77. One leg of a right triangle is twice as long as the other. The hypotenuse is $\sqrt{15}$. Find the two legs.

78. One leg of a right triangle is $-3 + 6\sqrt{5}$. The hypotenuse is 3 more than the other leg. Find the two sides.

79. The base of a triangle is 4 times its height. The area is 56. Find the triangle's base and height.

80. The length of a rectangle is 4 more than its width, and the area is 2. Find the rectangle's length and width.

81. The length of a rectangle is 1 less than 3 times its width. The diagonal is $\sqrt{29}$. Find the rectangle's length and width.

82. The surface area of a right circular cylinder is 12π, and its height is $2\sqrt{2}$. Find the cylinder's radius.

B

Use the discriminant test to justify your answers to the following. Can $ax^2 + bx + c = 0$ have

83. two equal imaginary roots?

84. one real and one imaginary root?

Solve the following equations for the indicated variable.

85. $L^2 - LW - W^2 = 0$; L

86. $\dfrac{x + y}{x} = \dfrac{x}{y}$; x

87. $3x^2 + 2xy + y^2 = 1$; x

88. $3x^2 + 2xy + y^2 = 1$; y

Let x_1 and x_2 be the solutions of $ax^2 + bx + c = 0$; that is,

$$x_1 = \frac{-b + \sqrt{b^2 - 4ac}}{2a} \quad \text{and} \quad x_2 = \frac{-b - \sqrt{b^2 - 4ac}}{2a}$$

89. Show that the sum of the roots, $x_1 + x_2$, is $-\dfrac{b}{a}$.

90. Show that the product of the roots, $x_1 x_2$, is $\dfrac{c}{a}$.

The sum and product relationships allow us to check the potential solutions of a quadratic equation. For example, $x = \dfrac{-3 \pm \sqrt{3}}{3}$ are the solutions to $3x^2 + 6x + 2 = 0$. The following is the check for this answer:

SUM: $x_1 + x_2 = \dfrac{-3 + \sqrt{3}}{3} + \dfrac{-3 - \sqrt{3}}{3} = \dfrac{-6}{3}$

$$= -2 \quad \text{and} \quad -\frac{b}{a} = -\frac{6}{3} = -2$$

PRODUCT: $x_1 x_2 = \left(\dfrac{-3 + \sqrt{3}}{3}\right)\left(\dfrac{-3 - \sqrt{3}}{3}\right)$

$$= \frac{6}{9} = \frac{2}{3} \quad \text{and} \quad \frac{c}{a} = \frac{2}{3}$$

Use the sum and product relationships to determine whether the given set of numbers is the solution to the given equation.

91. $x^2 + 2x - 15 = 0$ $\{3, -5\}$

92. $6x^2 + x - 2 = 0$ $\left\{\dfrac{1}{2}, -\dfrac{2}{3}\right\}$

93. $x^2 + 10 = 6x$ $\{-3 \pm i\}$

94. $x^2 + 8x = -25$ $\{-4 \pm 3i\}$

95. $2x^2 = 2 - 5x$ $\left\{\dfrac{-5 \pm \sqrt{41}}{4}\right\}$

96. $9x^2 + 2 = 12x$ $\left\{\dfrac{2 \pm \sqrt{2}}{3}\right\}$

Solve the following equations. *Hint*: A third-degree equation has three roots, a fourth-degree equation has four roots, and so on.

97. $x^3 + 1 = 0$ **98.** $x^3 - 8 = 0$

99. $8x^3 = 27$ **100.** $x^4 + 125x = 0$

101. $x^4 - 1 = 0$ **102.** $x^5 = 16x$

C 🖉

Answer the following questions with complete sentences.

103. When is it best to use the method of "completing the square" to solve a quadratic equation?

104. When is it best to use the quadratic formula to solve a quadratic equation?

105. What does it mean for an equation to be "quadratic in form"?

106. Discuss Tartaglia's contributions to mathematics.

REVIEW EXERCISES

Write the following in interval notation. (See Section 2.6.)

107. $y \geq 0$ **108.** $y \leq 0$

109. $y \leq 3$ **110.** $y \geq -1$

Find the roots of the following functions. (See Section 5.6.)

111. $g(x) = x - 6$ **112.** $f(x) = 2x + 1$

113. $h(x) = -x^2 + 1$ **114.** $f(x) = 4x^2 - 1$

Graph f, f^{-1}, and $y = x$ on the same axes. Give their domains and ranges. (See Sections 3.6 and 7.2.)

115. $f(x) = 2x + 1$ **116.** $f(x) = -x + 1$

117. $f(x) = \sqrt{x} + 1$ **118.** $f(x) = \sqrt{2x - 4}$

8.3   QUADRATIC FUNCTION $f(x) = ax^2 + c$

> **1**   **Graphing $f(x) = ax^2$**
>
> **2**   **Graphing $f(x) = ax^2 + c$ and Its Inverse**

1   **Graphing $f(x) = ax^2$**

In Chapter 3 we graphed linear functions such as $f(x) = 4x - 1$. The graph of this type of equation is a line, which is determined by two points. This section examines the graphs of the quadratic functions $f(x) = ax^2$ and $f(x) = ax^2 + c$, and the next section considers the general case of $f(x) = ax^2 + bx + c$. To sketch one of these equations we need more than two points because the graph is a curve. We begin with the simplest quadratic, $f(x) = x^2$.

To graph $y = f(x) = x^2$ we select values of x close to the origin. For example, if $x = -2$, then $y = (-2)^2 = 4$. The following chart lists ordered pairs that satisfy the equation.

x	-2	-1	$-\dfrac{1}{2}$	0	$\dfrac{1}{2}$	1	2
y	4	1	$\dfrac{1}{4}$	0	$\dfrac{1}{4}$	1	4

By plotting these points and drawing a smooth curve through them, we produce the graph in Figure 8.2, which is called a **parabola**. The graph of any pair of points with the same y-coordinate, such as $(-2, 4)$ and $(2, 4)$, are the same distance from the y-axis. For this reason the y-axis is called the **axis of symmetry** of $y = x^2$.

From the graph of $y = f(x) = x^2$ we can see that if x is any real number, then $y \geq 0$. Thus, the domain of f is the set of all real numbers, $D_f = \mathbb{R}$, and the range is $R_f = [0, \infty)$, in interval notation. The point $(0, 0)$ is the **minimum** point on the curve and is called the **vertex**. We will use the letter V for the vertex.

FIGURE 8.2

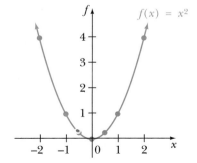

EXAMPLE 1

Graph the following parabolas on the same set of axes. Give their vertex, V, their domain, D, and range, R.

a. $y = f(x) = 4x^2$ **b.** $y = \frac{1}{4}x^2$

SOLUTION   **a.** Let $x = -1, -\frac{1}{2}, 0, \frac{1}{2},$ and 1. Then

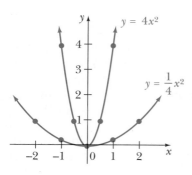

$$f(-1) = 4(-1)^2 = 4 \qquad f\left(-\frac{1}{2}\right) = 4\left(-\frac{1}{2}\right)^2 = 4 \cdot \frac{1}{4} = 1$$

$$f(0) = 4(0)^2 = 0 \qquad f\left(\frac{1}{2}\right) = 4\left(\frac{1}{2}\right)^2 = 4 \cdot \frac{1}{4} = 1$$

$$f(1) = 4(1)^2 = 4 \qquad V(0, 0), \quad D_f = \mathbb{R}, \; R_f = [0, \infty)$$

Thus, the set $\{(-1, 4), \left(-\frac{1}{2}, 1\right), (0, 0), \left(\frac{1}{2}, 1\right), (1, 4)\}$ determines the graph of $y = 4x^2$.

FIGURE 8.3

b. The following set of points determines the graph: $\{(-2, 1), \left(-1, \frac{1}{4}\right),$

$(0, 0), \left(1, \frac{1}{4}\right), (2, 1)\}; \quad V(0, 0), D = \mathbb{R}, \quad \text{and} \quad R = [0, \infty).$

These parabolas are graphed in Figure 8.3.

The number a plays an important part in the graph of $y = ax^2 + bx + c$. Comparing the graphs of $y = 4x^2$ and $y = 1x^2$ we can see that $y = 4x^2$ "closes in" on the axis of symmetry, and $4 > 1$. However, the graph of $y = \frac{1}{4}x^2$ "opens away" from the y-axis compared with the graph of $y = 1x^2$,

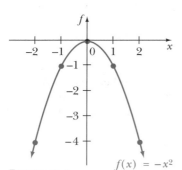

and $0 < \frac{1}{4} < 1$. In general, if $a > 1$, then the graph of $y = ax^2 + bx + c$ has a shape similar to that of $y = 4x^2$; if $0 < a < 1$, then its shape resembles that of $y = \frac{1}{4}x^2$. Also, if $a > 0$, then the parabola **opens upward**.

However, if $a < 0$, then the parabola **opens downward**, as we now illustrate.

In graphing $y = f(x) = -x^2$ note that $-x^2 \neq (-x)^2 = x^2$. For example, if $x = -2$, then $f(-2) = -(-2)^2 = -4$. Thus, $(-2, -4)$ is a point on the graph of $y = -x^2$. Other points on the parabola are $\{(-1, -1), (0, 0), (1, -1), (2, -4)\}$. The parabola is graphed in Figure 8.4.

FIGURE 8.4

From the graph of $y = f(x) = -x^2$ we can see that if x is any real number, then $y \leq 0$. Thus, the domain of f is the set of all real numbers, $D_f = \mathbb{R}$, and the range is $R_f = (-\infty, 0]$. The vertex, $V(0, 0)$, is now the **maximum** point on the curve. In general, the domain of $f(x) = ax^2 + bx + c$ is $\mathbb{R}$, but its range varies, depending on the values of $a, b,$ and c. In Example 2 the range of each function is $(-\infty, 0]$.

EXAMPLE 2

Graph the following parabolas on the same set of axes. Give their vertex.

a. $y = f(x) = -\frac{1}{4}x^2$ **b.** $y = -4x^2$

SOLUTION   **a.** Let $x = -2, -1, 0, 1,$ and 2. Then,

$$f(-2) = -\frac{1}{4}(-2)^2 = -1 \qquad f(-1) = -\frac{1}{4}(-1)^2 = -\frac{1}{4}$$

$$f(0) = -\frac{1}{4}(0)^2 = 0 \qquad f(1) = -\frac{1}{4}(1)^2 = -\frac{1}{4}$$

$$f(2) = -\frac{1}{4}(2)^2 = -1$$

The set $\{(-2, -1), \left(-1, -\frac{1}{4}\right), V(0, 0), \left(1, -\frac{1}{4}\right), (2, -1)\}$ determines the graph of $y = -\frac{1}{4}x^2$.

b. The following set of points determines the graph: $\{(-1, -4), \left(-\frac{1}{2}, -1\right), V(0, 0), \left(\frac{1}{2}, -1\right), (1, -4)\}$.
The parabolas are graphed in Figure 8.5.

FIGURE 8.5

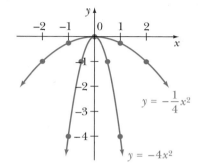

Compared with $y = -x^2$, the graph of $y = -4x^2$ is "narrower," $-4 < -1$, whereas the graph of $y = -\frac{1}{4}x^2$ is "wider," $-1 < -\frac{1}{4} < 0$.

---

2   Graphing *f(x) = ax² + c* and Its Inverse

The graph of $y = ax^2 + c$ has the same shape as $y = ax^2$ and opens in the same direction: upward if $a > 0$ and downward if $a < 0$. The number c moves the parabola $y = ax^2$ "up" the y-axis c units if $c > 0$ and "down" the y-axis $-c$ units if $c < 0$ ($-c > 0$).

As a first example, we will graph $y = 4x^2 - 1$. If $x = 0$, then $y = -1$, and the vertex is the point $V(0, -1)$. The parabola opens upward as $a = 4 > 0$, so the vertex is the minimum point on the curve, and $y \geq -1$ for all values of x. Therefore, the range of the function is $R = [-1, \infty)$.

Other ordered pairs that satisfy the equation are $\{(-1, 3), \left(-\frac{1}{2}, 0\right), \left(\frac{1}{2}, 0\right), (1, 3)\}$. The values of $x = \frac{1}{2}$ and $-\frac{1}{2}$ are the roots of the equation $4x^2 - 1 = 0$ and are the x-intercepts of the parabola $y = 4x^2 - 1$. The parabola is graphed in Figure 8.6; notice its relationship with $y = 4x^2$ (Figure 8.3).

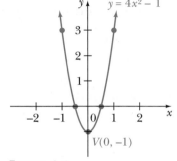

FIGURE 8.6

E X A M P L E   3

Sketch the graph of $g(x) = x^2 + 1$. Find its vertex, roots, x-intercepts, and range.

SOLUTION

Let $x = -2, -1, 0, 1,$ and 2. Then

$$g(-2) = (-2)^2 + 1 = 5 \qquad g(-1) = (-1)^2 + 1 = 2$$
$$g(0) = 0^2 + 1 = 1 \qquad g(1) = 1^2 + 1 = 2$$
$$g(2) = 2^2 + 1 = 5 \qquad V(0, 1)$$

To find the roots, let $x^2 + 1 = 0$; thus, $x^2 = -1$ and $x = \pm i$. Because the roots are imaginary, no x-intercepts exist, and the parabola does not cross the x-axis. $V(0, 1)$, is the minimum point on the curve, so $R_g = [1, \infty)$. The curve is determined by the set $\{(-2, 5), (-1, 2), (0, 1), (1, 2), (2, 5)\}$; it is graphed in Figure 8.7.

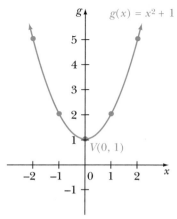

FIGURE 8.7

Notice that the vertices of $y = 4x^2 - 1$, $V(0, -1)$, and $y = x^2 + 1$, $V(0, 1)$, both involve the number c. In general:

> The vertex of $y = ax^2 + c$ is $V(0, c)$.

As other examples, the vertex of $y = -2x^2 + 3$ is $V(0, 3)$, and the vertex of $y = -\frac{1}{2}x^2 - 2$ is $V(0, -2)$. The following example discusses these parabolas.

E X A M P L E   4

Sketch the graphs of the following equations. Find the vertex, roots, x-intercepts, and range of each function.

a. $y = -2x^2 + 3$ **b.** $y = -\frac{1}{2}x^2 - 2$

SOLUTION   **a.** The vertex is $V(0, 3)$, which is the maximum point on the curve, because $a = -2 < 0$. Therefore, the range is $R = (-\infty, 3]$. To find the roots, let
$$-2x^2 + 3 = 0$$
$$x^2 = \frac{3}{2} = \frac{6}{4}$$
$$x = \pm\frac{\sqrt{6}}{2} \approx \pm\frac{2.449}{2} \approx \pm 1.2; \quad \text{the } x\text{-intercepts are } \pm\frac{\sqrt{6}}{2}.$$

For graphing purposes we will use $x = \pm 1.2$. The following points determine the graph: $\{(-1.2, 0), (-1, 1), (0, 3), (1, 1), (1.2, 0)\}$. **(See Figure 8.8.)**

b. The vertex is $V(0, -2)$, which is the maximum point on the graph, because $a = -1/2 < 0$. Thus, the range is $R = (-\infty, -2]$. To find the roots, let

$$-\frac{1}{2}x^2 - 2 = 0$$
$$x^2 = -4$$
$$x = \pm 2i.$$

Because the roots are imaginary, no x-intercepts exist, and the parabola does not cross the x-axis. The points $\{(-2, -4), (0, -2), (2, -4)\}$ determine the parabola. (See Figure 8.9.)

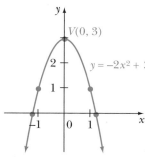

FIGURE 8.8

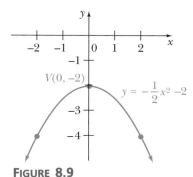

FIGURE 8.9

Summary of $f(x) = ax^2 + c$

1. The domain of f is $D_f = \mathbb{R}$, all real numbers.

2. The parabola opens upward if $a > 0$ and downward if $a < 0$.

3. The parabola is "narrower" than $y = x^2$ if $a > 1$ or $a < -1$, and "wider" if $-1 < a < 1$, $a \neq 0$.

4. The vertex is $V(0, c)$. It is the minimum point if $a > 0$, and the range of f is $R_f = [c, \infty)$. It is the maximum point if $a < 0$, and the range of f is $R_f = (-\infty, c]$.

5. If the roots of f are real, then they are the x-intercepts. If they are imaginary, then the parabola does not cross the x-axis.

We now consider the inverse of $f(x) = ax^2 + c$. Because this is not a one-to-one function, its inverse is not a function; it is a relation. Recall from Section 7.2 that we can determine the graph of an inverse relation, S^{-1}, by interchanging the coordinates of the ordered pairs that give us the graph of S.

EXAMPLE 5

Let $S = \left\{(x, y) \mid y = \frac{1}{2}x^2 + 2\right\}$. Find the inverse of S. Graph S and S^{-1} and find their domains and ranges.

SOLUTION

To find S^{-1}, interchange x and y in the equation of S:
$$S^{-1} = \left\{(x, y) \mid x = \frac{1}{2}y^2 + 2\right\}$$
The set $\{(-2, 4), (0, 2), (2, 4)\}$ determines the graph of S, so
$\{(4, -2), (2, 0), (4, 2)\}$ determines the graph of S^{-1}.
From their graphs in Figure 8.10, we can see that $D_s = R_{s^{-1}} = \mathbb{R}$, and $R_s = D_{s^{-1}} = [2, \infty)$.

FIGURE 8.10

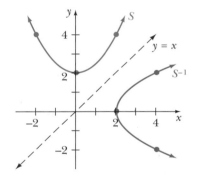

EXERCISE SET 8.3

A

1   Sketch the graphs of the following functions.
Give their vertices and ranges.

1. $y = 2x^2$ **2.** $y = 3x^2$

3. $y = 6x^2$ **4.** $f(x) = \frac{1}{2}x^2$

5. $f(x) = \frac{1}{3}x^2$ **6.** $g(x) = \frac{2}{5}x^2$

7. $F(x) = \frac{2}{3}x^2$ **8.** $G(x) = \frac{3}{2}x^2$

9. $H(x) = \frac{5}{4}x^2$ **10.** $y = -2x^2$

11. $u = -3w^2$ **12.** $y = -6x^2$

13. $f(x) = -\frac{1}{2}x^2$ **14.** $f(x) = -\frac{1}{3}x^2$

15. $k(x) = -\frac{3}{5}x^2$ **16.** $y = -\frac{3}{4}x^2$

17. $y = -\frac{5}{2}x^2$ **18.** $y = -\frac{1}{6}x^2$

2 Sketch the graphs of the following functions. Find the vertex, roots, *x*-intercepts (if they exist), and the range of each function. If the *x*-intercepts are irrational, then use a one-decimal-place approximation to graph them.

19. $y = x^2 - 1$ **20.** $y = x^2 - 4$

21. $y = x^2 + 1$ **22.** $y = -x^2 + 1$

23. $f(x) = -x^2 + 4$ **24.** $s = -t^2 - 2$

25. $f(z) = 2z^2 - 6$ **26.** $y = 3x^2 - 1$

27. $y = 4x^2 + 1$ **28.** $y = -2x^2 + 1$

29. $y = -3x^2 - 2$ **30.** $k(a) = -5a^2$

31. $g(x) = \frac{5}{3}x^2$ **32.** $v = \frac{1}{2}t^2 - 2$

33. $y = \frac{1}{4}x^2 + 1$ **34.** $y = -2x^2 + \frac{1}{2}$

35. $y = -3x^2 - \frac{2}{3}$ **36.** $y = x^2 - \frac{3}{4}$

37. $y = 2x^2 + \frac{3}{4}$ **38.** $y = -\frac{1}{6}x^2 - 2$

39. $y = \frac{2}{3}x^2 + \frac{1}{3}$ **40.** $y = -\frac{1}{3}x^2 + \frac{4}{3}$

41. $C(x) = -\frac{4}{7}x^2 - 1$ **42.** $y = \frac{1}{2}x^2 - \frac{1}{2}$

Graph the following; give their vertices and roots.

43. $v = 2t^2$ **44.** $a = t^2 - 1$

45. $h = -t^2$ **46.** $C = -t^2 + 4$

Find the equation of the inverse of the relation *S*. Graph *S*, S^{-1}, and $y = x$ on the same axes. Find their domains and ranges.

47. $S = \{(x, y) \mid y = x^2\}$

48. $S = \{(x, y) \mid y = -x^2\}$

49. $S = \{(x, y) \mid y = -4x^2\}$

50. $S = \{(x, y) \mid y = 3x^2\}$

51. $S = \{(x, y) \mid y = 4x^2 - 1\}$

52. $S = \{(x, y) \mid y = x^2 + 1\}$

53. $S = \{(x, y) \mid y = -x^2 + 1\}$

54. $S = \{(x, y) \mid y = -2x^2 - 1\}$

55. $S = \left\{(x, y) \mid y = \frac{1}{3}x^2 + 1\right\}$

56. $S = \left\{(x, y) \mid y = -\frac{1}{4}x^2 + 2\right\}$

B

57. $S = \left\{(x, y) \mid y = \frac{3}{4}x^2 + \frac{1}{2}\right\}$

58. $S = \left\{(x, y) \mid y = -\frac{5}{6}x^2 + \frac{1}{3}\right\}$

59. $S = \left\{(x, y) \mid y = \frac{2}{3}x^2 - \frac{1}{4}\right\}$

60. $S = \{(x, y) \mid y = .8x^2 - .5\}$

61. $S = \{(x, y) \mid y = 1.2x^2\}$

62. $S = \{(x, y) \mid y = -.5x^2 + .4\}$

C

Answer the following questions with complete sentences.

63. How can you tell when a parabola opens upward and when it opens downward?

64. How does the number *a* affect the shape of the graph of $y = ax^2 + c$?

65. How can you determine whether the vertex is the minimum or the maximum point on $y = ax^2 + c$?

66. What is the relationship between the roots and the *x*-intercepts of a parabola?

REVIEW EXERCISES

Add the constant term to each of the following to produce a perfect square; write your answer as $(x + h)^2$. (See Section 8.1.)

67. $x^2 - 6x$ **68.** $x^2 + 4x$ **69.** $x^2 - 2x$

Solve the following by completing the square (See Section 8.1.)

70. $x^2 - 6x + 8 = 0$

71. $-x^2 + 2x + 1 = 0$

72. $-x^2 - 2x - 2 = 0$

73. $2x^2 - 12x + 16 = 0$

8.4 QUADRATIC FUNCTION $f(x) = ax^2 + bx + c$

> **1**   **Graphing $f(x) = x^2 + bx + c$**
>
> **2**   **Graphing $f(x) = -x^2 + bx + c$**
>
> **3**   **Graphing $f(x) = ax^2 + bx + c$**

1   **Graphing $f(x) = x^2 + bx + c$**

This section continues our study of $f(x) = ax^2 + bx + c$ and its inverse. If $b = 0$, then this equation reduces to $f(x) = ax^2 + c$, whose vertex is on the y-axis at $V(0, c)$. If $b \neq 0$, then the vertex is off the y-axis. However, the graph of $y = ax^2 + bx + c$ has the same shape as $y = ax^2$ and opens in the same direction. Also, the domain of f is $\mathbb{R}$, the set of all real numbers.

We will use the following step-by-step procedure for graphing these parabolas.

Graphing $y = f(x) = ax^2 + bx + c$

1. Determine the direction in which the parabola opens. If $a > 0$, then it opens upward, and the vertex, V, is the minimum point on the curve. If $a < 0$, then the parabola opens downward, and V is the maximum point on the curve.

2. Complete the square on $ax^2 + bx$ to find the vertex.

3. Find two convenient points on opposite sides of the axis of symmetry (the vertical line through V). The x-intercepts are often used, if they exist.

4. Find the y-intercept (let $x = 0$) and use the point $(0, c)$, if it is convenient.

We now consider several examples to illustrate this procedure. We begin with the perfect square

$$y = f(x) = x^2 - 6x + 9 = (x - 3)^2$$

1. The parabola opens upward because $a = 1 > 0$. Thus, its vertex is the minimum point on the curve.

2. Because $(x - 3)^2 \geq 0$, 0 is the smallest value that y can have; it occurs when $x = 3$; that is, if $x = 3$, then $y = (3 - 3)^2 = (0)^2 = 0$. Thus, the vertex is $V(3, 0)$.

3. Replace x by 2 and 4 in the equation $y = (x - 3)^2$:
If $x = 2$, then $y = (2 - 3)^2 = (-1)^2 = 1$;   (2, 1) is on the curve.
If $x = 4$, then $y = (4 - 3)^2 = 1^2 = 1$;   (4, 1) is on the curve.

4. If $x = 0$, then the y-intercept is 9, but (0, 9) is inconvenient. Thus, $\{(2, 1), (3, 0), (4, 1)\}$ determines the graph of the parabola. Both $y = x^2 - 6x + 9$ and $y = x^2$ have the same shape; $b = -6$ and $c = 9$ move the graph of $y = x^2$ three units along the x-axis in the positive direction. Both equations are graphed in Figure 8.11.

Now consider $y = x^2 - 6x + 8$, which is not a perfect square.

1. The parabola opens upward $(a = 1)$; V is the minimum point.

2. To find the parabola's vertex, we complete the square on $x^2 - 6x$ by adding 9. However, we can only add 0 to an expression without changing its value. Therefore, if we add 9, then we must subtract 9, to add zero:

$$y = x^2 - 6x + 8 \qquad\qquad \left[\tfrac{1}{2}(-6)\right]^2 = 9$$
$$y = (x^2 - 6x + 9) - 9 + 8 \qquad 9 - 9 = 0$$
$$y = (x - 3)^2 - 1$$

Because $(x - 3)^2 \geq 0$, $(x - 3)^2 - 1 \geq -1$. Therefore, the smallest value that y can have is -1, which occurs when $x = 3$; that is, if $x = 3$, then $y = (3 - 3)^2 - 1 = -1$. Thus, $V(3, -1)$ is the vertex.

3. To find the x-intercepts (and the roots), let $y = 0$:

$$x^2 - 6x + 8 = 0$$
$$(x - 4)(x - 2) = 0$$
$$x = 4 \text{ and } 2 \text{ are the } x\text{-intercepts.}$$

4. The y-intercept is 8, but the point (0, 8) is not convenient. The points $\{(2, 0), (3, -1), (4, 0)\}$ determine the graph of $y = x^2 - 6x + 8$ (Figure 8.12).

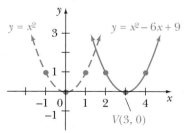

FIGURE 8.11

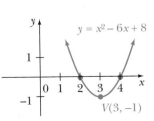

FIGURE 8.12

EXAMPLE 1

Sketch the graph of $y = x^2 + 4x$ and find its range.

SOLUTION

1. $a = 1$, so the parabola opens upward.

2. To find the vertex, complete the square on $x^2 + 4x$:

$$y = x^2 + 4x$$
$$y = (x^2 + 4x + 4) - 4$$
$$y = (x + 2)^2 - 4$$

$$\left[\frac{1}{2}(4)\right]^2 = 4$$
$$4 - 4 = 0$$

$(x + 2)^2 \geq 0$ for all x, so
$y = (x + 2)^2 - 4 \geq -4$;   if $x = -2$, then $y = -4$, so $V(-2, -4)$ is the vertex. Because $y \geq -4$, the range is $\{y \mid y \geq -4\} = [-4, \infty)$.

3. To find the x-intercepts, let $y = 0$:

$$x^2 + 4x = 0$$
$$x(x + 4) = 0$$

$x = 0$ and -4 are the x-intercepts.

4. If $x = 0$, then $y = 0$ is the y-intercept.

The set $\{(-4, 0), (-2, -4), (0, 0)\}$ determines the graph (Figure 8.13).

Notice that $x = 0$ is a root of $y = x^2 + 4x$, so the parabola passes through the origin. In general, $y = ax^2 + bx$ has a root of 0, and its graph contains the origin.

FIGURE **8.13**

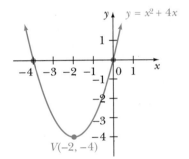

$V(-2, -4)$

---

2   **Graphing $f(x) = -x^2 + bx + c$**

For the first example of this type of equation, consider $y = -x^2 + 2x + 1$.

1. Because $a = -1 < 0$, the parabola opens downward, and the vertex is the maximum point on the curve.

2. Recall that when we solve an equation such as $-x^2 + 2x + 1 = 0$ by completing the square, we write it as $x^2 - 2x = 1$ so that we can complete the square on $x^2 - 2x$. To find the vertex of $y = -x^2 + 2x + 1$ we only work on the right side of the equation, because the left side is not 0. To complete the square on $-x^2 + 2x$ we write the equation as $y = -(x^2 - 2x) + 1$ and then add 1 to $x^2 - 2x$ to produce $-(x^2 - 2x + 1)$. However, the negative sign before the parentheses means that we have actually added -1 to the right side of the equation. Therefore, we must add $+1$ to give us a sum of $-1 + 1 = 0$:

$$y = -x^2 + 2x + 1$$
$$y = -(x^2 - 2x) + 1$$
$$y = -(x^2 - 2x + 1) + 1 + 1$$
$$y = -(x - 1)^2 + 2$$

$$-x^2 + 2x =$$
$$-x^2 - (-2x) =$$
$$-(x^2 - 2x)$$
$$-(x^2 - 2x + 1)$$
$$\uparrow\underline{\qquad -1 \qquad}\uparrow$$

Now, for all x, $-(x - 1)^2 \le 0$, because $(x - 1)^2 \ge 0$. Thus, $y = -(x - 1)^2 + 2 \le 2$, so the largest value that y can have is $y = 2$, which occurs when $x = 1$, as $-(1 - 1)^2 + 2 = 2$. Thus, $V(1, 2)$ is the vertex.

3. Solving $-x^2 + 2x + 1 = 0$ gives $x = 1 \pm \sqrt{2}$ as the roots. For graphing purposes we can use

$$x = 1 \pm \sqrt{2} \approx 1 \pm 1.4 = -.4 \quad \text{and} \quad 2.4$$

for the x-intercepts.

4. If $x = 0$, then $y = 1$ is the y-intercept and $(0, 1)$ is a convenient point to use.

The set $\{(-.4, 0), (0, 1), (1, 2), (2, 1), (2.4, 0)\}$ determines the graph of $y = -x^2 + 2x + 1$ (Figure 8.14).

Recall from the last section that the axis of symmetry of $y = x^2$ is the y-axis. This axis is the vertical line through its vertex $(0, 0)$. In general, if $V(h, k)$ is the vertex of a parabola, then the axis of symmetry is the vertical line through h, and its equation is $x = h$. This concept is illustrated in the following example.

FIGURE 8.14

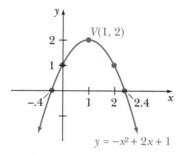

$$y = -x^2 + 2x + 1$$

EXAMPLE 2

Graph $y = -x^2 - 2x - 2$ and its axis of symmetry. Give the range of the equation.

SOLUTION

1. $a = -1 < 0$, so the parabola opens downward. The vertex is the maximum point on the parabola.

2. $y = -x^2 - 2x - 2$
$y = -(x^2 + 2x) - 2$
$y = -(x^2 + 2x + 1) + 1 - 2 \qquad -1 + 1 = 0$
$y = -(x + 1)^2 - 1$
$V(-1, -1)$ is the vertex, and $x = -1$ is the equation of the axis of symmetry. Because V is the maximum point on the parabola, $y \le -1$ and $(-\infty, -1]$ is the range.

(continued)

3. To find the roots, let $y = 0$:
$$0 = -(x + 1)^2 - 1 \quad \text{Add } -(x + 1)^2 \text{ to both sides.}$$
$$(x + 1)^2 = -1$$
$$x + 1 = \pm\sqrt{-1}$$
$$x = -1 \pm i$$
so no x-intercepts exist. If $x = -2$, then $y = -(-2 + 1)^2 - 1 = -1 - 1 = -2$, and $(-2, -2)$ is a point on the curve.

4. The y-intercept is -2, and $(0, -2)$ is on the curve. The set $\{(-2, -2), (-1, -1), (0, -2)\}$ determines the graph of the parabola; see Figure 8.15.

FIGURE 8.15

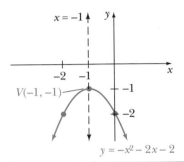

$$y = -x^2 - 2x - 2$$

---

3   Graphing $f(x) = ax^2 + bx + c$

We now turn to the general case, $y = ax^2 + bx + c$. In the following example notice that by adding 9 to $x^2 - 6x$, we have actually added $2 \cdot 9 = 18$ to the right side of the equation. Therefore, we must add -18 so that $18 - 18 = 0$.

EXAMPLE 3

Graph $y = 2x^2 - 12x + 16$ and its axis of symmetry. Find the range of the function.

SOLUTION **1.** $a = 2 > 0$, so the parabola opens upward and the vertex is the minimum point on the curve.

2. $y = 2x^2 - 12x + 16$
$y = 2(x^2 - 6x) + 16$
$y = 2(x^2 - 6x + 9) - 18 + 16$
$y = 2(x - 3)^2 - 2$

$\left[\frac{1}{2}(-6)\right]^2 = 9$
$2 \cdot 9 - 18 = 0$

If $x = 3$, then $y = -2$, and $V(3, -2)$ is the vertex. $x = 3$ is the equation of the axis of symmetry. $y \geq -2$, so $[-2, \infty)$ is the range.

3. $2x^2 - 12x + 16 = 0$
$2(x - 2)(x - 4) = 0$
so $x = 2$ and 4 are the x-intercepts.

4. $y = 16$ is the y-intercept, but $(0, 16)$ is not a convenient point to graph. The set $\{(2, 0), (3, -2), (4, 0)\}$ determines the graph in Figure 8.16.

FIGURE 8.16

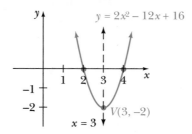

$y = 2x^2 - 12x + 16$

$V(3, -2)$

$x = 3$

As we have just seen, the first step in finding the vertex is to factor a out of $ax^2 + bx$. When a is not a factor of b, we can use the fact that $1 = a\left(\dfrac{1}{a}\right)$ and proceed as follows:

$$y = ax^2 + bx + c = ax^2 + a \cdot \frac{1}{a} \cdot bx + c = a\left(x^2 + \frac{b}{a}x\right) + c$$

Then we complete the square on $x^2 + \dfrac{b}{a}x$.

EXAMPLE 4

Find the vertex of $y = 3x^2 + 2x + 1$.

SOLUTION

$y = 3x^2 + 2x + 1$

$\quad = 3x^2 + 3 \cdot \dfrac{1}{3} \cdot 2x + 1$

$\quad = 3\left(x^2 + \dfrac{2}{3}x\right) + 1$

$\quad = 3\left(x^2 + \dfrac{2}{3}x + \dfrac{1}{9}\right) - \dfrac{3}{9} + 1$

$\quad = 3\left(x + \dfrac{1}{3}\right)^2 + \dfrac{2}{3}, \quad$ so $V\left(-\dfrac{1}{3}, \dfrac{2}{3}\right)$ is the vertex.

$2x = 1 \cdot 2x$

$1 = 3 \cdot \dfrac{1}{3}$

$\left[\dfrac{1}{2}\left(\dfrac{2}{3}\right)\right]^2 = \dfrac{1}{9}$

$3 \cdot \dfrac{1}{9} - \dfrac{3}{9} = 0$

We now consider the inverse of $f(x) = ax^2 + bx + c$. As in the last section, we interchange the ordered pairs that give us the graph of $S = \{(x, y) \mid y = ax^2 + bx + c\}$ to determine the graph of S^{-1}.

EXAMPLE 5

$S = \{(x, y) \mid y = x^2 - 6x + 8\}$. Find the inverse of S. Graph S and S^{-1} and find their domains and ranges.

(continued)

SOLUTION $S^{-1} = \{(x, y) \mid x = y^2 - 6y + 8\}$. S is graphed in Figure 8.17, and its vertex is $(3, -1)$. S^{-1} is a parabola, and its vertex is $(-1, 3)$. The set $\{(2, 0), (3, -1), (4, 0)\}$ determines the graph of S, so $\{(0, 2), (-1, 3), (0, 4)\}$ determines the graph of S^{-1}. From their graphs we can see that $D_s = R_{s^{-1}} = \mathbb{R}$ and $R_s = D_{s^{-1}} = [-1, \infty)$.

FIGURE 8.17

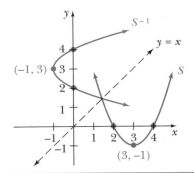

In Section 3.4 we found the equation of the line determined by two given points. Three noncollinear points in a plane determined a parabola. We will consider those parabolas whose equations are $y = ax^2 + bx + c$ or $x = ay^2 + by + c$. The equation is found by solving three linear equations in a, b, and c (see Section 4.3).

EXAMPLE 6   Find the equation of the parabola determined by $(1, 0)$, $(2, -1)$, and $(-1, 8)$.

SOLUTION $y = ax^2 + bx + c$ is the equation of the parabola. By substituting $(1, 0)$, $(2, -1)$, and $(-1, 8)$ in $ax^2 + bx + c = y$ we produce the system
$$a + b + c = 0$$
$$4a + 2b + c = -1$$
$$a - b + c = 8$$
This system of equations was solved in Example 5 of Section 4.3. The solution is $a = 1$, $b = -4$, and $c = 3$. Substitute these values in $y = ax^2 + bx + c$: $y = x^2 - 4x + 3$ is the equation of the parabola.

EXERCISE SET 8.4

A

1 For each of the following, find the: a. vertex; b. range; c. roots; d. x-intercepts, if they exist; e. y-intercept; and f. equation of the axis of symmetry. Then graph the vertex, x-intercepts, y-intercept (if it is a convenient point), and the parabola. In Exercises 1 through 14 graph the axis of symmetry.

1. $y = (x - 2)^2$

2. $y = (x + 1)^2$

3. $y = (x + 2)^2 - 1$

4. $y = x^2 - 2x + 1$

5. $f(x) = x^2 + 6x + 9$ **6.** $g(t) = t^2 - 4t + 3$
7. $v = u^2 + 6u + 10$ **8.** $y = x^2 + 2x - 1$
9. $y = x^2 - 4x$ **10.** $y = x^2 + 5x$

2

11. $y = -(x - 1)^2$ **12.** $y = -(x + 3)^2$
13. $y = -(x - 4)^2 + 1$ **14.** $y = -x^2 - 4x - 3$
15. $y = -x^2 + x$
16. $P(x) = -x^2 + 10x - 26$
17. $f(x) = -x^2 - 2x + 2$
18. $g(x) = -x^2 + 2x + 1$
19. $a = -t^2 + 4t - 6$
20. $y = -x^2 + 3x - 2$

3

21. $y = 2(x - 1)^2$
22. $y = -3(x + 2)^2$
23. $y = 3(x + 1)^2 - 3$
24. $y = -2(x + 3)^2 + 2$
25. $f(x) = 4x^2 + 16x + 12$
26. $h(x) = -5x^2 - 10x - 6$
27. $y = 2x^2 - 4$
28. $y = -3x^2 + 2$
29. $y = -2x^2 - 12x - 20$
30. $y = 3x^2 - 6x + 1$
31. $y = -3x^2 + 2x + 1$
32. $y = 2x^2 + 2x - 2$

Find the vertices for the following parabolas.

33. $y = 3x^2 - 4x + 1$ **34.** $y = -2x^2 + 3x - 1$

35. $y = -\frac{2}{5}x^2 + x$ **36.** $y = \frac{7}{4}x^2 - x$

37. $y = 5x^2 + \frac{3}{2}x - 2$

38. $y = -3x^2 - \frac{5}{4}x - 1$

39. $f(t) = -16t^2 + 128t$
40. $C(x) = .01x^2 - 4x + 2000$
41. $A(x) = -x^2 + 10x$
42. $P(S) = 6S^2 + 60S$

Graph the following; give their vertices and roots.
43. $v = t^2 - 2t + 2$
44. $a = t^2 - 3t$
45. $A(x) = -x^2 + 2x$
46. $P(s) = -s^2 + 2s + 2$

Find the equation of the inverse of the relation S. Graph S, S^{-1}, and $y = x$ on the same axes. Find their domains and ranges.

47. $S = \{(x, y) \mid y = x^2 - 6x + 9\}$
48. $S = \{(x, y) \mid y = x^2 + 4x\}$
49. $S = \{(x, y) \mid y = -x^2 - 2x - 2\}$
50. $S = \{(x, y) \mid y = 2x^2 - 12x + 16\}$
51. $S = \{(x, y) \mid y = -x^2 + 2x\}$
52. $S = \{(x, y) \mid y = 2x^2 + 12x + 17\}$
53. $S = \{(x, y) \mid y = -2x^2 - 4x - 1\}$
54. $S = \{(x, y) \mid y = 3x^2 - 1\}$

Find a, b, and c so that the parabola $y = ax^2 + bx + c$ contains the following points.

55. $\{(-1, 0), (0, -1), (1, 0)\}$
56. $\{(-2, 0), (2, 4), (3, 10)\}$
57. $\{(1, 1), (2, 3), (-1, 9)\}$
58. $\{(-5, 7), (-2, 10), (1, -5)\}$

Find a, b, and c so that the parabola $x = ay^2 + by + c$ contains the following points.

59. $\{(0, -1), (0, 1), (2, 0)\}$
60. $\{(0, -3), (-1, -2), (0, -1)\}$
61. $\{(0, 2), (1, 3), (-3, 5)\}$
62. $\{(1, -1), (3, 0), (9, 1)\}$

B

Use the discriminant test (Section 8.2) to determine whether each parabola has any x-intercepts. If it does not, then determine whether the parabola is completely above or completely below the x-axis. (*Hint*: Determine whether it opens upward or downward.)

63. $y = x^2 - 4x - 3$ **64.** $y = x^2 + 2x + 2$
65. $y = -x^2 + 6x - 10$ **66.** $y = -2x^2 - 2x - 1$

67. $y = 3x^2 + 12x + 13$ **68.** $y = -x^2 - 2x + 1$

69. $y = 3x^2 + 4x$ **70.** $y = 3x^2 + 4$

Answer the following questions with complete sentences.

71. What is the relationship between the x-intercepts and the axis of symmetry of a parabola?

72. How does the vertex of $y = ax^2 + c$ differ from the vertex of $y = ax^2 + bx + c$, $b \neq 0$?

REVIEW EXERCISES

Graph the following. (See Section 3.1.)

73. $C = 2x - 1$ **74.** $a = t - 1$

75. $h = -t + 2$

Evaluate each function for the given value of the variable. (See Section 5.2.)

76. $f(t) = -16t^2 + 128t;$ $t = 4$

77. $C(x) = .01x^2 - 4x + 2000;$ $x = 200$

8.5 MAXIMUM AND MINIMUM PROBLEMS

| 1 | Solving Problems for Which the Functions Are Given |
| 2 | Solving Problems for Which the Functions Are Derived |

1 Solving Problems for Which the Functions Are Given

Many applications of mathematics deal with finding a maximum or minimum value of a function. For instance, a physician needs to find the dosage of a drug that provides maximum effectiveness, and a manufacturer wants to know the production level that will result in minimum cost. Many of these problems are described by quadratic functions. The vertex of such a function, $V(h, k)$, gives the maximum value of the function if the parabola opens downward ($a < 0$) and the minimum value if the parabola opens upward ($a > 0$); that is, h indicates where the maximum or minimum occurs, and k is the maximum or minimum value of the function.

The first example uses the function

$$h = f(t) = -16t^2 + rt$$

which was discovered by Newton. This function gives the height in feet, h, that an object will reach in t seconds (ignoring air resistance) if it is projected straight upward with an initial velocity (speed) of r feet per second.

Math in Time

GALILEO GALILEI (1564–1642) was a brilliant Italian astronomer and physicist. In approximately 1590 he discovered the equation for free fall. From various heights on the leaning tower of Pisa, according to legend, Galileo dropped small cannon balls and measured their time and distance of travel. He determined that if an object is dropped from rest and air resistance is ignored, then the number of feet, d, that it falls in t seconds is given by the equation $d = 16t^2$. He also demonstrated that a heavier object does not fall faster than a lighter one. For example, in two seconds a marble and a bowling ball both fall $d = 16 \cdot 2^2 = 64$ feet.

Sir Isaac Newton (1642–1727) was born on Christmas Day in the year of Galileo's death. He is considered by many scientists to be the greatest physicist to have ever lived. He extended Galileo's equation for free fall to general laws of gravitation and motion. One of these laws is $h = -16t^2 + rt$.

© 1992 by Sidney Harris. Reprinted with permission.

EXAMPLE 1

An arrow is shot vertically upward with an initial velocity of 128 feet per second. Find the maximum height the arrow will reach and at what time. When will it hit the ground?

SOLUTION

$r = 128$ in the function $f(t) = -16t^2 + rt$. Thus,

$$\begin{aligned} f(t) &= -16t^2 + 128t \\ &= -16(t^2 - 8t) \\ &= -16(t^2 - 8t + 16) + 16 \cdot 16 \\ &= -16(t - 4)^2 + 256 \end{aligned}$$

$128 = -16(-8)$
$[1/2(-8)]^2 = 16$
$-16 \cdot 16 + 16 \cdot 16 = 0$

$V(4, 256)$ is the vertex. Four seconds after being shot, the arrow will reach a maximum height of 256 feet. To find when it will land, we need the roots:

$$-16t^2 + 128t = 0$$
$$-16t(t - 8) = 0$$

$t = 0$ or $t = 8$. The arrow leaves the ground at $t = 0$, and it hits the ground at $t = 8$. This information is shown in Figure 8.18. The parabola gives the height, h, for any time, t, $0 \le t \le 8$ (the graph is not to scale).

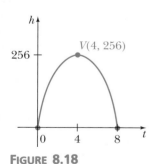

FIGURE 8.18

403

EXAMPLE 2

A manufacturer estimates that the total cost of producing x items per day is given by the function $C(x) = .01x^2 - 4x + 2000$, with C in dollars. How many items should be produced each day so that the cost will be a minimum? What will be the cost?

SOLUTION

$$C(x) = .01x^2 - 4x + 2000$$
$$= .01x^2 - .01(1/.01)4x + 2000$$
$$= .01(x^2 - 400x) + 2000$$
$$= .01[x^2 - 400x + (200)^2] - .01(200)^2 + 2000$$
$$= .01(x - 200)^2 + 1600$$

$$1 = a \cdot 1/a$$
$$[1/2(-400)]^2 = (200)^2$$

$V(200, 1600)$ is the vertex (Figure 8.19). Thus, if 200 items are produced each day, then the minimum cost will be $C(200) = \$1600$ per day. Also, $C(0) = \$2000$.

FIGURE 8.19

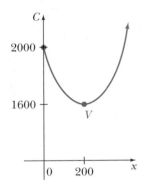

2   Solving Problems for Which the Functions Are Derived

In many maximum–minimum problems we have to derive the required function. This process is illustrated in Examples 3 and 4.

The oldest known maximum–minimum problem is in Euclid's *Elements* (300 B.C.). It states, "The square, of all rectangles of a given perimeter, has maximum area." The proof is an exercise in the B section on page 407. Example 3 is a specific case of this theorem.

EXAMPLE 3

Find the dimensions of the rectangle that has a perimeter of 20 and an area as large as possible.

SOLUTION

Let x = the width of the rectangle, y = its length, and A = its area (see Figure 8.20). Then its perimeter is

$$2x + 2y = 20$$
$$x + y = 10$$
$$y = 10 - x$$

Now $A = xy$, and the area as a function of x is

$$A(x) = x(10 - x)$$

FIGURE 8.20

$$= -x^2 + 10x$$
$$= -(x^2 - 10x)$$
$$= -(x^2 - 10x + 25) + 25 \quad -25 + 25 = 0$$
$$= -(x - 5)^2 + 25$$

$V(5, 25)$ is the vertex. Thus, $x = 5, y = 10 - x = 10 - 5 = 5$, and the area is $A(5) = 25$ (see Figure 8.21).

FIGURE 8.21

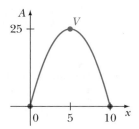

Note that the function $A(x) = -x^2 + 10x$ gives the area of every rectangle whose perimeter is 20. The one with the largest area is a square.

EXAMPLE 4

Two numbers have a difference of 10; the product of twice the smaller number and three times the larger number is as small as possible. What are the numbers? Also find the minimum product.

SOLUTION

Let S = the smaller number, L = the larger number, and P = the product. Then $L - S = 10$ and $L = S + 10$. $2S$ = twice the smaller number, and $3L$ = three times the larger number. The product is $P = (2S)(3L) = 6SL$. The product as a function of S is

$$P(S) = 6S(S + 10) \qquad \text{0 and } -10 \text{ are the } x\text{-intercepts.}$$
$$= 6S^2 + 60S$$
$$= 6(S^2 + 10S)$$
$$= 6(S^2 + 10S + 25) - 6 \cdot 25$$
$$= 6(S + 5)^2 - 150$$

$V(-5, -150)$ is the vertex (Figure 8.22). Thus, $S = -5, L = S + 10 = -5 + 10 = 5$, and the minimum product is $P(-5) = -150$.

FIGURE 8.22

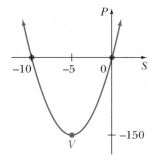

EXERCISE SET 8.5

A

1   Solve the following problems.

1. An arrow is shot vertically upward with an initial velocity of 32 feet per second. Find the maximum height the arrow will reach and at what time. When will it land? ($h = -16t^2 + rt$)

2. Repeat Exercise 1 for $r = 64$.

3. Repeat Exercise 1 for $r = 48$.

4. Effectiveness of a drug, y, depends on the dosage size, x, according to the equation $y = 1000x - x^2$. Find the dosage that gives maximum effectiveness.

5. Insulin affects the blood sugar level of some diabetics according to the function $f(x) = -.2x^2 + 450$, where $f(x)$ is the blood sugar level one hour after x units of insulin are injected (this function is valid for $x \le 40$). What is the value of x that will result in the maximum level of blood sugar? Find $f(40)$.

6. A company's daily costs in dollars in producing x items is given by $C(x) = .001x^2 - 2x + 20,000$. Find the production level that will minimize cost; find the minimum cost.

7. A company's daily profit, P, in hundreds of dollars, is given by $P(x) = -x^2 + 8x - 7$, where x is the number of items produced each day. How many items must be produced to have maximum profit? What is the maximum profit?

8. The total daily profit in dollars, P, on the production of x lamps is $P(x) = -2x^2 + 64x - 10$. How many lamps have to be made each day to achieve maximum profit? What is the maximum profit?

2

9. Find two positive numbers whose sum is 30 and product is as large as possible. What is the maximum value?

10. Two positive numbers have a sum of 10, and the product of 3 times the first and 2 times the second is as large as possible. What are the numbers? What is the maximum value?

11. Two numbers have a sum of 20, and the sum of the square of one number plus 12 times the other number is minimum. What are the numbers? What is the minimum value?

12. Two numbers have a difference of 20, and the square of the smaller number minus 8 times the larger number is minimum. What are the numbers? What is the minimum value?

13. Find two numbers whose difference is 30 and whose product is as small as possible. What is the minimum value?

14. Jill wants to fence in a rectangular garden next to her house. She has 100 feet of fencing and will not fence the side of the garden by her house. What are the dimensions of the largest possible garden? What is its area?

15. Monique is building a rectangular pen next to a straight river. The side next to the river does not require fencing. She has 120 yards of fencing. What dimensions will give the pen a maximum area? What is its area?

16. A rectangular field is to be fenced in with two types of fencing. Two opposite sides will use fencing costing $3 per foot, and the other two sides will use fencing costing $2 per foot. What are the dimensions of the largest area if only $600 can be spent for the fencing? What is the area?

17. The sum of a triangle's height and base is 40 centimeters. Find the height and base so that the area will be a maximum; also find the maximum area.

18. Each point $P(x,y)$ on the line $y = -3x + 12$ in the first quadrant determines a rectangle with dimensions x and y. Find the coordinates of P that will produce the rectangle of maximum area. What is its area?

Use the equation $d = 16t^2$ to solve the following problems; see the brief biography of Galileo on page 403. A rock falls off a cliff. How far does it fall in

19. 4 seconds?

20. 5 seconds?

21. A rock falls from the top of a 144-foot cliff. How long before it reaches the ground?

22. A dime is dropped from a 49-foot bridge. How long before the coin hits the water?

B

Solve the following problems.

23. Two vertices of a rectangle are on the x-axis, and the other two are on the sides of a triangle determined by the x-axis and the lines $y = 2x$ and $y = -3x + 30$. Find the dimensions and the area of the largest rectangle possible.

24. A long rectangular sheet of metal is 8 inches wide. It will be made into a rain gutter by turning up two sides of height x inches so that they are perpendicular to the sheet. What should x be to maximize the capacity of the gutter?

25. A farmer wants to build a fence around a rectangular field and then subdivide it into three rectangular pieces of land by building two fences parallel to the shorter side. He has 400 yards of fencing. Find the length and width of the field that will give him the maximum area. What is the maximum area?

26. Prove Euclid's theorem: "The square, of all rectangles of a given perimeter, has maximum area."

27. The annual revenue and cost functions for a manufacturer of oak desks are

$R(x) = 500x - .02x^2$ and
$C(x) = 300x + 90,000$

where x is the number of desks made per year. Find the maximum annual profit. (*Hint*: Profit = revenue − cost.)

28. In Exercise 27, find the break-even point (see Section 4.2).

29. A 1-meter wire is cut into two pieces. One piece, of x meters length, is bent to form a square, and the other piece is bent to form a circle.

   a. Derive a function, $A(x)$, that represents the combined area of the two figures.

   b. Find the value of x for which the combined area is minimum. What is the minimum area?

30. A Norman window, which has a rectangular base and a semicircular top (see Section 2.3, Example 4), has a perimeter of 50 feet. Let r be the radius of the semicircle.

   a. Derive a function $A(r)$, that represents the area of the window.

   b. Find the value of r for which the area of the window will be maximum. Find the maximum area.

C

Answer the following questions with complete sentences.

31. What type of parabola will give a maximum value for a function?

32. What type of parabola will give a minimum value for a function?

REVIEW EXERCISES

Use the discriminant test to determine the types of roots of each equation. (See Section 8.2.)

33. $x^2 + x - 2 = 0$ **34.** $3x^2 - 2x + 5 = 0$

Find the domains of the following functions. (See Sections 6.1 and 7.2.)

35. $f(x) = \dfrac{1}{x + 5}$ **36.** $g(x) = \dfrac{x}{x^2 - 9}$

37. $f(x) = \sqrt{x - 9}$ **38.** $h(x) = \sqrt{4 - 6x}$

Solve the following inequalities and graph their solutions. (See Section 2.6.)

39. $\dfrac{x}{2} > 1$ **40.** $\dfrac{x}{-2} > 1$ **41.** $\dfrac{x}{-5} \le -1$

8.6 QUADRATIC INEQUALITIES

1	**Solving Quadratic Inequalities Geometrically**
2	**Solving Fractional Inequalities Geometrically**
3	**Solving Inequalities Algebraically**

1   Solving Quadratic Inequalities Geometrically

Section 2.6 discussed linear inequalities, such as $3x - 1 > 0$. In this section we will consider **quadratic inequalities**, which are expressions in the form $ax^2 + bx + c > 0$, or with $>$ replaced by $\geq$, $<$, or $\leq$. We will use our knowledge of the graph of $y = ax^2 + bx + c$ to solve these inequalities. In the second part of this section, we will solve fractional inequalities by converting them to quadratic inequalities. This section concludes with an algebraic method for solving inequalities.

The graphical representation of $y > 0$ is the half-plane above the x-axis; that is, any point above the x-axis has a positive y-coordinate. Therefore, the solution of the inequality $ax^2 + bx + c > 0$ is the set of all values of x for which the graph of the equation $y = ax^2 + bx + c$ lies above the x-axis.

For example, consider $x^2 - 1 > 0$. First, let $y = x^2 - 1$. Next find the x-intercepts of this equation:

$$x^2 - 1 = 0$$
$$(x + 1)(x - 1) = 0$$
$$x = -1 \quad \text{and} \quad x = 1 \text{ are the } x\text{-intercepts.}$$

Now sketch the graph of $y = x^2 - 1$, using the points $\{(-1, 0), (0, -1), (1, 0)\}$ (Figure 8.23). Note that the x-intercepts are graphed as open circles, because $y > 0$. From Figure 8.23 we can see that if x is less than -1 or greater than 1, then the graph of $y = x^2 - 1$ lies above the x-axis and $y > 0$. Therefore, the solution of $x^2 - 1 > 0$ is the set $\{x \mid x < -1 \quad \text{or} \quad x > 1\}$. Note that y is just another name for $x^2 - 1$; $y > 0$ and $x^2 - 1 > 0$ have the same solution.

FIGURE 8.23

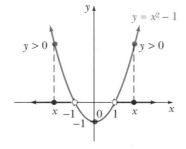

Because we are using the equation $y = ax^2 + bx + c$ to solve quadratic inequalities, we are not interested in the exact shape of the graph. We only need to find the x-intercepts and where the curve is above and below the x-axis. Therefore, we don't usually bother to find the vertex.

EXAMPLE 1

Solve $-x^2 + 3x > 0$.

SOLUTION   Let $y = -x^2 + 3x$ and find the x-intercepts:
$$-x^2 + 3x = 0$$
$$-x(x - 3) = 0$$
$$x = 0 \quad \text{and} \quad x = 3$$
are the x-intercepts.

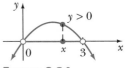

FIGURE 8.24

Because $a = -1 < 0$, the parabola opens downward (Figure 8.24). Therefore, the vertex is above the x-axis between 0 and 3. From the graph of $y = -x^2 + 3x$ we can see that if x is between 0 and 3, then $y > 0$. Thus, the solution of $-x^2 + 3x > 0$ is $\{x \mid 0 < x < 3\}$.

The graphical representation of $y < 0$ is the half-plane below the x-axis; that is, any point below the x-axis has a negative y-coordinate. Therefore, the solution of the inequality $ax^2 + bx + c < 0$ is the set of all values of x for which the graph of the equation $y = ax^2 + bx + c$ lies below the x-axis. This concept is illustrated in the following example.

EXAMPLE 2

Solve $x^2 \le 2 - x$.

SOLUTION $x^2 \le 2 - x$. Produce 0 on one side of the inequality:
$x^2 + x - 2 \le 0$. Now let $y = x^2 + x - 2$ and find the x-intercepts.
$$x^2 + x - 2 = 0$$
$$(x + 2)(x - 1) = 0$$
$$x = -2 \quad \text{and} \quad x = 1$$
are the x-intercepts, which are graphed as closed circles, as $y \le 0$. Because $a = 1 > 0$, the parabola opens upward. Therefore, the vertex is below the x-axis between -2 and 1. From the graph of $y = x^2 + x - 2$ in Figure 8.25, we can see that if x is between -2 and 1, inclusive, then $y \le 0$. Thus, the solution of $x^2 \le 2 - x$ is $\{x \mid -2 \le x \le 1\}$.

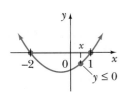

FIGURE 8.25

Recall that if the roots of a quadratic equation are imaginary numbers, then the parabola has no x-intercepts. In this case the parabola is either completely above or completely below the x-axis. The corresponding inequality either has no solution, Ø, or the solution is the entire set of real numbers, $\mathbb{R}$. If the equation does not factor, then the discriminant test is a convenient way to determine if the roots are imaginary. These ideas are illustrated in the following example.

EXAMPLE 3

Solve $3x^2 + 5 \le 2x$.

SOLUTION $3x^2 + 5 \le 2x$
$3x^2 - 2x + 5 \le 0$. Let $y = 3x^2 - 2x + 5$. Use the discriminant test to determine the type of roots of $3x^2 - 2x + 5 = 0$:
$$b^2 - 4ac = (-2)^2 - 4 \cdot 3 \cdot 5 = 4 - 60 = -56 < 0$$

(continued)

so the roots are imaginary. Because $a = 3 > 0$, the parabola opens upward (see Figure 8.26). Therefore, the parabola is completely above the x-axis, as the graph indicates. Thus, for all values of x, $y > 0$. In other words, no value of x exists such that $y = 3x^2 - 2x + 5 \leq 0$. Therefore, the solution set of $3x^2 + 5 \leq 2x$ is $\emptyset$, the empty set.

FIGURE 8.26

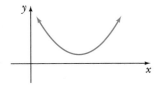

Note that $y = 3x^2 - 2x + 5 \geq 0$ is a true statement for all real numbers x, so the solution set of $3x^2 - 2x + 5 \geq 0$ is $\mathbb{R}$.

One application of this material is finding the domain of a radical function.

EXAMPLE 4

Find the domain of $f(x) = \dfrac{1}{\sqrt{x^2 - 9}}$

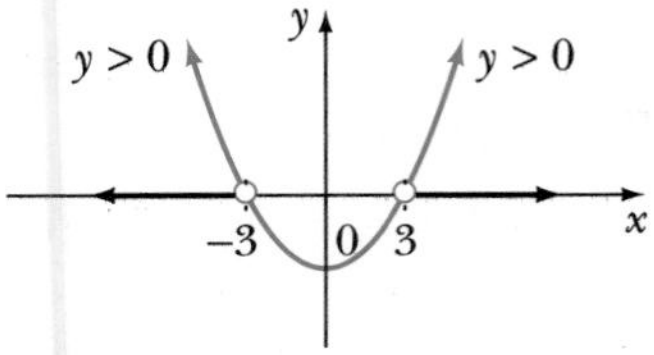

SOLUTION $x^2 - 9$ cannot be zero or negative. Thus,
$$x^2 - 9 > 0$$
$$y = x^2 - 9$$
$$x^2 - 9 = 0$$
$$(x + 3)(x - 3) = 0$$
$x = \pm 3$ are the x-intercepts. From the graph of $y = x^2 - 9$ (Figure 8.27), we can see that $y > 0$ if $x < -3$ or $x > 3$. Thus, $D_f = \{x \mid x < -3$ or $x > 3\}$.

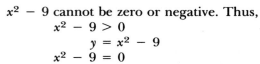

FIGURE 8.27

---

2   Solving Fractional Inequalities Geometrically

In Section 2.6 we solved fractional linear inequalities with denominators that did not contain variables. Recall that when we multiply such an inequality by a positive number, c, then we don't change the inequality symbol. However, if c is negative, then we must reverse the inequality symbol. For example,

$$\frac{x}{3} > 1 \qquad\qquad\qquad \frac{x}{-3} > 1$$

$$3 \cdot \frac{x}{3} > 3 \cdot 1 \qquad\qquad -3 \cdot \frac{x}{-3} < -3 \cdot 1$$

$$x > 3 \qquad\qquad\qquad x < -3$$

If we tried to solve an inequality such as $\dfrac{3}{x} > 1$ by multiplying both sides by x, then we would run into problems. If $x > 0$, then we would keep the order of the inequality, but if $x < 0$, then we would reverse $>$. However, $x^2 > 0$ for all $x \neq 0$. Therefore, if we multiply both sides of $\dfrac{3}{x} > 1$ by x^2, then we are using a positive number, so we keep the order of the inequality:

Math in Time

SONYA KOVALEVSKY (1850–1891) was "perhaps the most dazzling mathematicial genius to surface among women during the past two centuries" (Osen, 1974). The daughter of an authoritarian Russian general, Sonya grew up believing that her parents loved her less than they loved her brother and sister. Her resulting emotional insecurities made personal relationships very difficult, causing her to alternate between extreme affection and overwhelming jealousy.

Sonya was attracted to mathematics at an early age. The walls of a room in her house were covered with copies of calculus lectures. As a result she already knew many of the formulas and concepts from her wallpaper; and when she had her first lessons in this subject at the age of 15, her teacher was astonished at her ability.

Russian universities were closed to women at this time, and single women were not allowed to travel abroad to study. Sonya used a common device to get around these restrictions; she entered into a "marriage of convenience" with a young student when she was 18 and prompty left for Germany.

Sonya spent two years at the University of Heidelberg, where she studied mathematics, physics, and astronomy with the leading professors of the day. She made a sensation in this small university town, because she was not only brilliant in mathematics, but also fluent in several languages, a gifted writer (she wrote three novels), and a remarkable beauty.

Sonya Kovalevsky
The Bettmann Archive

In 1870 Sonya went to Berlin to try to study with Karl Weierstrass, a leading mathematician of the nineteenth century. The University of Berlin did not admit women, but Weierstrass was so impressed with her ability that he asked the administration if she could audit his lectures. This request was denied, so he tutored her every Sunday afternoon for four years until she received her Ph.D. in differential equations.

Unable to find a university position in either Germany or Russia, Sonya accepted a lectureship at the University of Stockholm, where she became a popular teacher and a distinguished researcher. On Christmas Eve, 1888, she won the prestigious Prix Bordin of the French Academy of Science. The prize was nearly doubled in value owing to the "quite extraordinary service rendered to mathematical physics by this . . . remarkable work" (Mozans, 1913). Unfortunately, Sonya's life was soon to meet an untimely end.

In the winter of 1891 she traveled to Moscow to visit her dying sister. On the return trip she was in one of her depressed, hopeless moods and spent several cold nights in deserted train stations. She arrived at Stockholm in an exhausted, feverish state and died a few days later from influenza.

$$\frac{3}{x} > 1 \qquad x^2 > 0 \quad \text{for} \quad x \neq 0$$

$$x^2 \cdot \frac{3}{x} > x^2 \cdot 1$$

$$3x > x^2$$

$$-x^2 + 3x > 0 \qquad \text{and} \qquad 0 < x < 3 \text{ is the solution}$$

The inequality $-x^2 + 3x > 0$ was solved in Example 1.

In general, if the denominator of a fractional inequality contains a variable, then we multiply both sides by the square of the denominator and keep the order of the inequality. This process converts the original inequality into a polynomial inequality.

EXAMPLE 5

Solve $\dfrac{x - 1}{x + 2} \le 0$.

SOLUTION   For $x \ne -2$, $(x + 2)^2 > 0$. Thus,

$$\frac{x - 1}{x + 2} \le 0$$

$$(x + 2)^2 \cdot \frac{x - 1}{x + 2} \le (x + 2)^2 \cdot 0$$

$$(x + 2)(x - 1) \le 0$$

Let $y = (x + 2)(x - 1) = x^2 + x - 2$. From Example 2 the solution of $x^2 + x - 2 \le 0$ is $-2 \le x \le 1$. However, if $x = -2$, then $\dfrac{x - 1}{x + 2}$ is undefined

Therefore, the solution of $\dfrac{x - 1}{x + 2} \le 0$ is $\{x \mid -2 < x \le 1\}$.

An inequality such as $\dfrac{6x + 7}{x + 3} \ge 3$ can be solved by multiplying both sides by $(x + 3)^2$. However, this approach often results in an equation that is difficult to factor. We can avoid this result by producing 0 on one side of the inequality and proceeding as in the last example.

EXAMPLE 6

Solve $\dfrac{6x + 7}{x + 3} \ge 3$.

SOLUTION

$$\frac{6x + 7}{x + 3} \ge 3$$

$$\frac{6x + 7}{x + 3} - 3 \ge 0$$

$$\frac{6x + 7}{x + 3} + \frac{-3(x + 3)}{x + 3} \ge 0$$

$$\frac{3x - 2}{x + 3} \ge 0$$

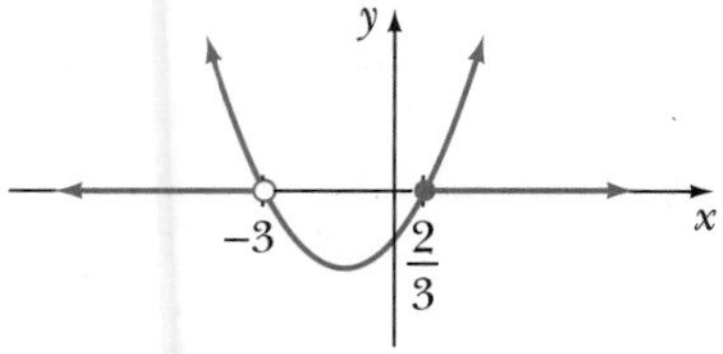

If $x \ne -3$, then $(x + 3)^2 > 0$,   and

$$(x + 3)^2 \cdot \frac{3x - 2}{x + 3} \ge (x + 3)^2 \cdot 0$$

$$(x + 3)(3x - 2) \ge 0$$

Let $y = (x + 3)(3x - 2) = 3x^2 + 7x - 6$, whose x-intercepts are -3 and $\dfrac{2}{3}$. Because $a = 3 > 0$, the parabola opens upward. Therefore, the vertex is below the x-axis. From the graph of $y = 3x^2 + 7x - 6$ in Figure 8.28, we

FIGURE 8.28

can see that $y > 0$ if x is less than -3 or greater than $\frac{2}{3}$. Because x cannot be equal to -3 but can equal $\frac{2}{3}$, the solution of $\frac{6x+7}{x+3} \geq 3$ is $\left\{ x \mid x < -3 \right.$ or $\left. x \geq \frac{2}{3} \right\}$.

---

3 Solving Inequalities Algebraically

The second method of solving quadratic inequalities is similar to the first, although it is more algebraic in nature. Instead of using the *xy*-plane, we will use the number line.

We begin with the first example in this section, $x^2 - 1 > 0$. The first step is to solve the corresponding equation $x^2 - 1 = 0$:

$$x^2 - 1 = 0$$
$$(x + 1)(x - 1) = 0$$
$$x = -1 \quad \text{or} \quad x = 1$$

We now graph -1 and 1 on the number line as open circles, because they are not included in the solution set (Figure 8.29). These numbers divide the number line into three intervals:

A. the numbers less than -1, $(-\infty, -1)$
B. the numbers between -1 and 1, $(-1, 1)$
C. the numbers greater than 1, $(1, \infty)$

FIGURE 8.29

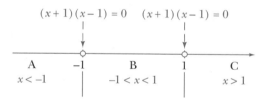

We are looking for the interval(s) where $(x + 1)(x - 1) > 0$; that is, where the product of $x + 1$ and $x - 1$ is positive. When is the product of two numbers positive? When they are both positive or both negative.

We now pick a **test number** in each interval. If one number in an interval satisfies the inequality, then all the numbers in that interval satisfy the inequality. In interval A, choose $x = -2$ as the test number. Then

$$x + 1 = -2 + 1 = -1 < 0, \qquad x - 1 = -2 - 1 = -3 < 0, \qquad \text{and}$$
$$(x + 1)(x - 1) = (-1)(-3) = 3 > 0$$

In interval B, let $x = 0$. Then $x + 1 = 1$, $x - 1 = -1$, and $(x + 1)(x - 1) = -1 < 0$. In interval C, let $x = 2$. Then $x + 1 = 3$, $x - 1 = 1$, and $(x + 1)(x - 1) = 3 > 0$. This information is organized in Figure 8.30.

FIGURE 8.30

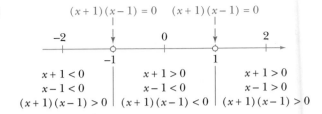

We can see that $(x + 1)(x - 1) > 0$ for x less than -1 or x greater than 1. Therefore, the solution of $x^2 - 1 > 0$ is $\{x \mid x < -1 \quad \text{or} \quad x > 1\} = (-\infty, -1) \cup (1, \infty)$.

EXAMPLE 7

Solve $x^2 \leq 2 - x$ (see Example 2).

SOLUTION

$$x^2 \leq 2 - x$$
$$x^2 + x - 2 \leq 0$$
$$(x + 2)(x - 1) \leq 0$$
$$(x + 2)(x - 1) = 0 \quad \text{if} \quad x = -2 \text{ or } 1$$

Place closed circles at -2 and 1, because these numbers are included in the solution set. Let -3, 0, and 2 be the test numbers for the three intervals determined by the roots -2 and 1. The signs of $x + 2$, $x - 1$, and $(x + 2)(x - 1)$ are indicated in Figure 8.31.

FIGURE 8.31

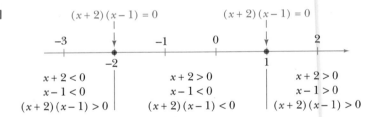

The solution set is $\{x \mid -2 \leq x \leq 1\} = [-2, 1]$.

This algebraic method of solving quadratic inequalities is useful in solving higher-degree polynomial and fractional inequalities and is illustrated in the concluding examples.

EXAMPLE 8

Solve $x(x - 3)^2 \leq 0$.

SOLUTION

$$x(x - 3)^2 \leq 0$$
$$x(x - 3)^2 = 0 \quad \text{if} \quad x = 0 \text{ or } 3$$

Place closed circles at 0 and 3. Let -1, 1, and 4 be the test numbers for the three intervals (Figure 8.32).

FIGURE 8.32

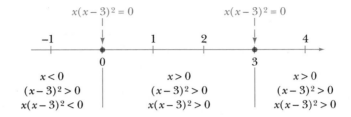

The solution set is $\{x \mid x \leq 0 \quad \text{or} \quad x = 3\} = (-\infty, 0] \cup \{3\}$.

EXAMPLE 9

Solve $x^3 > x$.

SOLUTION

$$x^3 > x$$
$$x^3 - x > 0 \qquad\qquad x^3 - x = x(x^2 - 1)$$
$$x(x + 1)(x - 1) > 0$$
$$x(x + 1)(x - 1) = 0 \quad \text{if} \quad x = 0, -1, \text{ or } 1.$$

Place open circles at -1, 0, and 1. Let -2, $-\dfrac{1}{2}$, $\dfrac{1}{2}$, and 2 be the text numbers for the four intervals determined by the roots -1, 0, and 1.

FIGURE 8.33

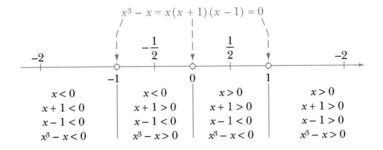

From Figure 8.33 we can see that the solution set of $x^3 > x$ and $x^3 - x > 0$ is $\{x \mid -1 < x < 0 \quad \text{or} \quad x > 1\} = (-1, 0) \cup (1, \infty)$.

Note that the solutions to Examples 10 and 7 are very similar; that is, the solutions to $(x + 2)(x - 1) < 0$ and $\dfrac{x - 1}{x + 2} < 0$ are the same. Also, Examples 10 and 5 are the same.

EXAMPLE 10

Solve $\dfrac{x-1}{x+2} \leq 0$.

SOLUTION   This fraction is negative if either $x - 1$ or $x + 2$ is positive and the other is negative. We use the numbers 1 and -2 to find the required values of x.
For $x = 1$, the fraction is equal to zero; for $x = -2$, the fraction is undefined. Graph 1 as a closed circle, because it is a solution to the inequality; graph -2 as an open circle, because it is not a solution to the inequality. The numbers 1 and -2 divide the number line into three intervals. Let $-3, 0$, and 2 be the test numbers for these intervals. The signs of $x + 2$, $x - 1$, and $\dfrac{x-1}{x+2}$ are indicated in Figure 8.34.

FIGURE 8.34

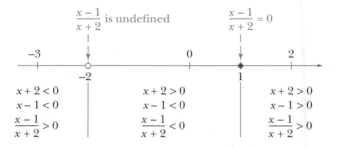

The solution set is $\{x \mid -2 < x \leq 1\} = (-2, 1]$.

EXERCISE SET 8.6

A

1 Solve the following inequalities

1. $x(x - 2) > 0$

2. $x(x - 2) < 0$

3. $(x + 1)(x - 3) \leq 0$

4. $(x + 1)(x - 3) \geq 0$

5. $x^2 - 4 \geq 0$

6. $x^2 + 5x < 0$

7. $-2x^2 + 6x \geq 0$

8. $-3x^2 - 12x \leq 0$

Find the domains of the following functions.

9. $f(x) = \sqrt{x - 1}$

10. $f(x) = \sqrt{x^2 - 1}$

11. $g(x) = \sqrt[3]{x^2 - 1}$

12. $h(x) = \sqrt{x^2 - x - 6}$

13. $k(x) = \dfrac{1}{\sqrt{4 - x}}$

14. $f(x) = \dfrac{x}{\sqrt[3]{4 - x^2}}$

2 Solve the following inequalities.

15. $\dfrac{x}{2} < 1$

16. $\dfrac{x}{-2} < 1$

17. $\dfrac{x - 3}{x - 7} > 0$

18. $\dfrac{x - 2}{x + 3} > 0$

19. $\dfrac{x + 3}{2x} \geq 1$

20. $\dfrac{x + 1}{x + 3} < 3$

3 Use the algebraic method to solve

21. Exercise 1

22. Exercise 2

23. Exercise 3

24. Exercise 4

25. Exercise 5

26. Exercise 6

27. Exercise 7

28. Exercise 8

29. Exercise 17

30. Exercise 18

31. Exercise 19

32. Exercise 20

Solve the following using either the geometric or the algebraic method. Write each answer in interval notation.

33. $x^2 > x + 6$ **34.** $-x^2 + 5x > 4$

35. $x^2 + 2 \geq 0$ **36.** $2x^2 + 1 \leq 0$

37. $x^2 < 3x$ **38.** $2x^2 > x + 3$

39. $x^3 - x \leq 0$ **40.** $9x - x^3 > 0$

41. $x(x - 1)^2 < 0$ **42.** $(1 - x)(x + 2)^2 > 0$

43. $x^2 \geq 3$ **44.** $x^2 + 6x + 9 > 0$

45. $-2x^2 + x - 4 > 0$ **46.** $-x^2 + x \geq 0$

47. $(x + 2)(1 - x)(x - 3) \geq 0$

48. $(x + 2)(1 - x)(x - 3) < 0$

49. $x^2(x + 3) \leq 0$ **50.** $(2 - x)(x - 1)^2 > 0$

51. $x^2 + 16 \leq 8x$ **52.** $6x^2 \leq x + 1$

53. $\dfrac{x + 1}{x + 2} \leq 0$ **54.** $\dfrac{-3x}{x - 4} \leq 0$

55. $\dfrac{1 - x}{2x + 5} \geq 0$ **56.** $\dfrac{2}{x - 3} \geq -4$

57. $\dfrac{3x}{6 - x} \geq -2$ **58.** $\dfrac{x + 2}{x - 2} + 1 \geq 7$

59. $\dfrac{5}{x} \leq \dfrac{2}{3}$ **60.** $\dfrac{2}{x} \leq -\dfrac{1}{5}$

61. $\dfrac{(x - 1)(x - 4)}{x} > 0$ **62.** $\dfrac{(x + 1)(x + 3)}{x - 2} < 0$

63. $\dfrac{x(x + 2)}{x - 3} \leq 0$ **64.** $\dfrac{(x - 4)(x + 2)}{x + 3} \geq 0$

65. $\dfrac{(x - 1)^2}{4x} \geq 0$ **66.** $\dfrac{1}{x - 3} > \dfrac{1}{6}$

67. $\dfrac{x^2 - 9}{x + 2} > 0$ **68.** $\dfrac{1 - x^2}{x - 4} < 0$

B

69. $\dfrac{x^2 - 9}{(x - 1)^2} > 0$ **70.** $\dfrac{x^2 + x - 20}{(x - 6)^2} < 0$

71. $\dfrac{x^2 - 1}{x(x - 2)^2} > 0$ **72.** $\dfrac{x^2 - 9}{(x + 1)(x + 5)^2} < 0$

73. $x^3 \leq 1$ **74.** $1 - x^4 \geq 0$

C

Answer the following questions with complete sentences.

75. Discuss the difficulties that Sonya Kovalevsky faced in her pursuit of mathematics.

76. In Example 5, why did we multiply the fraction by $(x + 2)^2$ instead of by $x + 2$?

Chapter Summary

KEY WORDS, DEFINITIONS, AND PROPERTIES

Definitions

Completing the square: Write $ax^2 + bx + c = 0$ as $(x + k)^2 = d$.

Quadratic formula: If $ax^2 + bx + c = 0$, $a \neq 0$, then $x = \dfrac{-b \pm \sqrt{b^2 - 4ac}}{2a}$.

Discriminant: $b^2 - 4ac$. (See Sections 8.1 and 8.2.)

Methods for Solving a Quadratic Equation (See Section 8.2.)

1. Factoring: $ax^2 + bx = 0$, $a^2x^2 - c^2 = 0$, or it can be easily factored.

2. Using square roots: $ax^2 + c = 0$, $x^2 = d$, or $(x + k)^2 = d$.

3. Completing the square: $x^2 + bx + c = 0$, b divisible by 2.

4. Applying the quadratic formula: $ax^2 + bx + c = 0$ does not factor.

Discriminant Test: $ax^2 + bx + c = 0$; a, b, c rational. (See Section 8.2.)

1. $b^2 - 4ac < 0$: two imaginary roots.

2. $b^2 - 4ac = 0$: one rational root, $x = \dfrac{-b}{2a}$.

3. $b^2 - 4ac > 0$, a square: two rational roots.

4. $b^2 - 4ac > 0$, not a square: two irrational roots.

Equation Quadratic in Form

An equation that is quadratic in form can be written in the form $au^2 + bu + c = 0$. (See Section 8.2.)

Parabola

The graph of $y = ax^2 + bx + c$. The parabola opens upward if $a > 0$ and the vertex is the minimum point; the parabola opens downward if $a < 0$ and the vertex is the maximum point. The vertex of $y = ax^2 + c$ is $V(0, c)$. The axis of symmetry is the vertical line through the vertex. If the roots are real, then they are the x-intercepts; if they are imaginary, then the parabola does not cross the x-axis. See Sections 8.3 and 8.4.)

CHAPTER REVIEW EXERCISES

The answers to the following exercises are given in the answer section. If you have trouble, review the material and homework problems in the sections indicated.

Solve $x^2 + 2x = 15$ by (Section 8.1):

1. Factoring

2. Completing the square

3. Applying the quadratic formula

Solve the following equations and formulas for the indicated variables. (See Section 8.2.)

4. $x^2 - 11 = 0$
5. $2x^2 + 3 = x$
6. $x^2 + 6x = 80$
7. $x^3 + 16x = 0$
8. $x^4 + 13x^2 + 36 = 0$
9. $9x^{-1} = x^{-2} + 8$
10. $K = \frac{1}{2}mv^2;\quad v$
11. $s = \frac{1}{2}gt^2 + vt;\quad t$

Use the discriminant test to describe the types of roots of each equation. Don't solve the equations. (See Section 8.2.)

12. $x^2 + x = 1$
13. $3x^2 = x - 4$
14. $x^2 - 8x + 16 = 0$

Sketch the graph of the following. Give their vertices, intercepts, and ranges. (See Sections 8.3 and 8.4.)

15. $y = 5x^2$
16. $y = -2x^2$
17. $y = 3x^2 - 2$
18. $y = -x^2 + 1$

19. $y = 2x^2 - 4x$
20. $y = -x^2 - 6x - 8$

Solve the following inequalities. (See Section 8.6.)

21. $x^2 - 5x > 0$
22. $x^2 \leq 9$
23. $\dfrac{x - 1}{x + 4} \geq 0$
24. $\dfrac{x^2 + 1}{x} \leq 2$
25. $x(x + 2)(3 - x) > 0$

Find the equation of the inverse of the relation S. Graph S, S^{-1}, and $y = x$ on the same axes. Find their domains and ranges. (See Section 8.3.)

26. $S = \{(x, y) \mid y = x^2 - 1\}$

Solve the following word problems. (See Sections 8.2 and 8.5.)

27. The sum of a number and its reciprocal is $3i/2$. Find all such numbers.

28. The length of a rectangle is 2 more than its width, and the area is 1. Find the length and width.

29. The profit, P, on the production of x items is given by $P(x) = -x^2 + 10x + 105$. How many items should be made to have maximum profit?

30. Two numbers have a difference of 6 and a product as small as possible. What are the numbers? What is the minimum product?

CHAPTER TEST

Treat this test as a class test and allow 50 minutes for completion. When you have finished, use the answer section for scoring. If you have any wrong answers, refer to the corresponding problems in the review section.

Solve $x^2 + 4x = 5$ by

1. Factoring

2. Completing the square

3. The quadratic formula

Solve the following equations, inequalities, and formulas for the indicated variables.

4. $x^3 = 4x$

5. $5x^3 + 125x = 0$

6. $5 + x^{-2/3} = 6x^{-1/3}$

7. $x^2 + 10x = 95$

8. $3x^2 - 2x + 5 = 0$

9. $x^2 \geq 9$

10. $F = g\dfrac{m_1 m_2}{d^2}; \quad d$

11. $\dfrac{x^2}{a^2} + \dfrac{y^2}{b^2} + \dfrac{z^2}{c^2} = 1; \quad z$

12. $x^3 \geq 9x$

13. $\dfrac{x - 2}{x + 1} \leq 0$

Use the discriminant test to describe the types of roots of each equation. Don't solve the equations.

14. $2x^2 + 3x = 2$

15. $3x^2 + x = 5$

16. $x^2 + x + 1 = 0$

Sketch the graphs of the following. Give their vertices, intercepts, and ranges.

17. $y = 3x^2$

18. $y = -\dfrac{1}{4}x^2$

19. $y = x^2 - 1$

20. $y = -3x^2 + 2$

21. $y = -x^2 + 4x$

Find the equation of the inverse of the relation S. Graph S, S^{-1}, and $y = x$ on the same axes. Find their domains and ranges.

22. $S = \{(x, y) \mid y = x^2 + 6x + 9\}$

Solve the following word problems.

23. The sum of two numbers is 4, and their product is 13. Find the numbers.

24. One leg of a right triangle is twice as long as the other leg. The hypotenuse is 5. Find the two legs.

25. Find the dimensions of the rectangle with a perimeter of 12, whose area is as large as possible. What is the maximum area?

Conic Sections

We can obtain conic sections by intersecting a double-napped right circular cone with a plane. By varying the position of the plane, we obtain a circle, an ellipse, a parabola, or a hyperbola.

Chapter 8 discussed the parabola, which is one example of a conic section. This chapter will consider the other conic sections and their inverses. As we will see, quadratic equations in two variables are used in the study of all the conic sections.

In Chapter 4 we solved systems of linear equations; Section 9.3 will consider nonlinear systems, such as the intersection of a line and a parabola. Also, the concepts of systems of linear inequalities will be extended to systems of quadratic inequalities.

We begin with the simplest conic section, the circle.

9.1 CIRCLES

| 1 | **Circles with Their Centers at the Origin** |
| 2 | **Circles with Their Centers Off the Origin** |

1   Circles with Their Centers at the Origin

Section 8.4 examined the parabola, whose equation is $y = ax^2 + bx + c$. This equation has one second-degree term, ax^2. We now begin the study of curves whose equations contain two second-degree terms. In this section we consider the simplest of these curves, the circle. This material depends on the distance formula (see Section 3.3). We briefly review this formula before looking at a precise definition of a circle.

Let $A(x_1, y_1)$ and $B(x_2, y_2)$ be two points in the xy-plane. Then the distance, d, between A and B is given by

$$d(A, B) = \sqrt{(x_2 - x_1)^2 + (y_2 - y_1)^2}$$

For example, if A and B are the points $A(-1, 2)$ and $B(5, 4)$, then

$$d(A, B) = \sqrt{[5 - (-1)]^2 + (4 - 2)^2} = \sqrt{36 + 4} = \sqrt{40} = 2\sqrt{10}$$

Definition of a Circle

A **circle** is the set of all points in a plane that lie a fixed distance from a fixed point. The fixed distance, r, is called the **radius**; the fixed point, C, is called the **center**.

Because the definition of a circle involves the distance between the center and a point on the circle, we use the distance formula to find its equation. For example, consider the circle with center at the origin, $C(0, 0)$, and radius $r = 3$ (Figure 9.1). Let $P(x, y)$ represent any point on the circle.

Then the distance between P and C is 3 units. Thus,

$$d(P, C) = 3$$
$$\sqrt{(x - 0)^2 + (y - 0)^2} = 3 \quad \text{Distance formula}$$
$$\sqrt{x^2 + y^2} = 3 \quad \text{Square both sides}$$
$$(\sqrt{x^2 + y^2})^2 = 3^2 \quad (\sqrt{a})^2 = a$$
$$x^2 + y^2 = 9$$

Notice that the x and y intercepts are 3 and -3. Also, $x^2 + y^2 = 9$ is a relation but not a function, because $(0, 3)$ and $(0, -3)$ are two points on the circle with the same first coordinate but different second coordinates. The domain and range of $x^2 + y^2 = 9$ is the interval $[-3, 3]$.

In general, let the origin, $C(0, 0)$, be the center of a circle with radius r (Figure 9.2). If $P(x, y)$ is any point on the circle, then

$$d(P, C) = r$$
$$\sqrt{(x - 0)^2 + (y - 0)^2} = r$$
$$\sqrt{x^2 + y^2} = r \quad \text{Square both sides.}$$
$$x^2 + y^2 = r^2$$

> The **standard form** of the equation of a circle with center at the origin and radius r is
>
> $$x^2 + y^2 = r^2$$

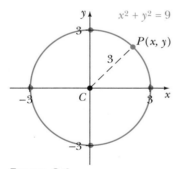

FIGURE 9.1

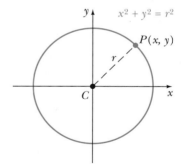

FIGURE 9.2

EXAMPLE 1

Find the equation of the circle with center at the origin and radius $\sqrt{6}$.

SOLUTION $x^2 + y^2 = r^2$
$x^2 + y^2 = (\sqrt{6})^2$
$x^2 + y^2 = 6$

**COMMON
ERROR** A common mistake is failing to square the radius when finding the equation of a circle. In Example 1, $x^2 + y^2 \neq \sqrt{6}$.

In certain problems we are given the center of a circle and a point on the circle. From this information we can find its radius and then its equation, as illustrated in the following example.

EXAMPLE 2 $A(2, -1)$ is a point on the circle whose center is the origin. Find its equation, sketch its graph, and give its domain and range.

SOLUTION $r^2 = x^2 + y^2$. Let $x = 2$ and $y = -1$. Then $r^2 = 2^2 + (-1)^2 = 5$ and $r = \sqrt{5} \approx 2.3$. Thus, $x^2 + y^2 = 5$ is the equation of the circle. From the graph of $x^2 + y^2 = 5$ in Figure 9.3, we can see that its domain and range is $D = R = [-\sqrt{5}, \sqrt{5}]$.

FIGURE 9.3

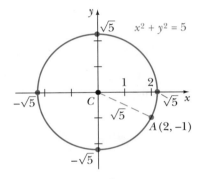

2   Circles with Their Centers Off the Origin

We now consider the case where the center of a circle is not the origin. Let $C(h, k)$ be the center of a circle of radius r, and let $P(x, y)$ be an arbitrary point on the circle (Figure 9.4). Now we use the distance formula

$$d(P, C) = r \qquad \text{Definition of radius}$$
$$\sqrt{(x - h)^2 + (y - k)^2} = r \qquad \text{Distance formula}$$
$$(x - h)^2 + (y - k)^2 = r^2 \qquad \text{Square both sides.}$$

For example, the equation of the circle with center $C(-1, 1)$ and radius $r = 2$ is (Figure 9.5).

$$[x - (-1)]^2 + (y - 1)^2 = 2^2$$
$$(x + 1)^2 + (y - 1)^2 = 4$$

The **standard form** of the equation of a circle with center $C(h, k)$ and radius r is

$$(x - h)^2 + (y - k)^2 = r^2$$

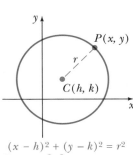

$(x - h)^2 + (y - k)^2 = r^2$
FIGURE 9.4

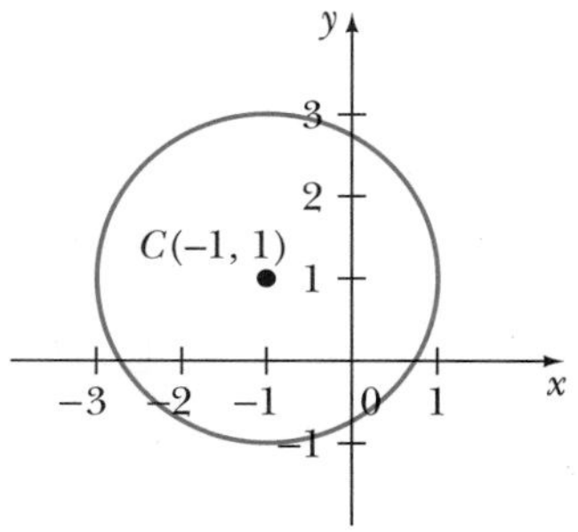

$(x + 1)^2 + (y - 1)^2 = 4$
FIGURE 9.5

If the standard form of the equation, $(x - h)^2 + (y - k)^2 = r^2$, is expanded and simplified, we have

$$x^2 + y^2 + Dx + Ey + F = 0$$

which is called the **general form** of the equation of a circle. In this form the center and radius cannot be found by inspection. By completing the square on the x and y terms, we can write the equation in standard form and then determine the center and radius.

EXAMPLE 3

Find the center and radius of the circle whose equation is $x^2 + y^2 + 6x - 4y + 6 = 0$.

SOLUTION

$$x^2 + y^2 + 6x - 4y + 6 = 0$$
$$(x^2 + 6x) + (y^2 - 4y) = -6$$
$$(x^2 + 6x + 9) + (y^2 - 4y + 4) = -6 + 9 + 4$$
$$(x + 3)^2 + (y - 2)^2 = 7$$
$$[x - (-3)]^2 + (y - 2)^2 = (\sqrt{7})^2 \qquad a = (\sqrt{a^2})$$

$C(-3, 2)$ is the center, and $r = \sqrt{7}$ is the radius.

In the following example we consider the graphs of a circle and its inverse.

EXAMPLE 4

$S = \{(x, y) \mid (x - 3)^2 + (y - 1)^2 = 1\}$. Find the inverse of S. Graph S, S^{-1}, and $y = x$. Find their domains and ranges.

SOLUTION

Interchange x and y in the equation of S:
$$S^{-1} = \{(x, y) \mid (y - 3)^2 + (x - 1)^2 = 1\}$$
$$= \{(x, y) \mid (x - 1)^2 + (y - 3)^2 = 1\}$$
The center of the circle S is $(3, 1)$, so the center of the circle S^{-1} is $(1, 3)$. The radius of each circle is 1. From their graphs in Figure 9.6, we can see that $D_s = R_{s^{-1}} = [2, 4]$ and $R_s = D_{s^{-1}} = [0, 2]$.

FIGURE 9.6

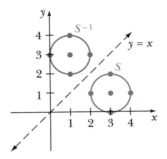

EXERCISE SET 9.1

A

1 Find the equation of the circle with center $C(0, 0)$ and the given radius r.

1. $r = 1$ **2.** $r = 4$ **3.** $r = 7$

4. $r = \sqrt{2}$ **5.** $r = \sqrt{10}$ **6.** $r = \sqrt{2}/2$

7. $r = 1/6$ **8.** $r = 3/5$

Find the center and radius of each circle and then sketch its graph.

9. $x^2 + y^2 = 1$ **10.** $x^2 + y^2 = 36$

11. $x^2 + y^2 = 12$ **12.** $x^2 + y^2 = 8$

13. $2x^2 + 2y^2 = 8$ **14.** $\dfrac{x^2}{3} + \dfrac{y^2}{3} = 2$

The center for each of the following circles is $C(0, 0)$, and the given point is on the circle. Find the equation of the circle and sketch its graph.

15. $(4, 3)$ **16.** $(-3, 1)$ **17.** $(-2, -2)$

18. $(3, -1)$ **19.** $(2, 0)$ **20.** $(0, 4)$

21. $(-3, 0)$ **22.** $(0, -1)$

Identify the graph of the given equation as a circle or a parabola and then sketch its graph.

23. $x^2 + y^2 = 9$ **24.** $x^2 + y = 9$

25. $x^2 + y = -1$ **26.** $x^2 + y^2 = 1$

27. $x^2 = 4 - y^2$ **28.** $y = x^2 - 1$

2 Find the standard form of the equation of the circle given its center and radius. Sketch its graph.

29. $C(2, 3)$, $r = 1$

30. $C(-3, 1)$, $r = 2$

31. $C(-3, -4)$, $r = \sqrt{3}$

32. $C(5, -2)$, $r = \sqrt{2}$

33. $C(4, 0)$, $r = 1/2$

34. $C(0, -3)$, $r = 4/9$

35. $C(-2, 1)$, $r = 1$

36. $C(2, 3)$, $r = 2$

Find the center and radius of each circle and then sketch its graph. Note in Exercise 41 that $x^2 = (x - 0)^2$.

37. $(x - 3)^2 + (y - 2)^2 = 4$
38. $(x - 2)^2 + (y + 1)^2 = 9$
39. $(x + 4)^2 + (y + 5)^2 = 1$
40. $(x + 3)^2 + (y - 4)^2 = 2$
41. $x^2 + (y - 3)^2 = 1$
42. $(x - 4)^2 + y^2 = 3$
43. $x^2 + y^2 = 3$
44. $x^2 + y^2 = 9/4$

Write the following equations in general form.

45. $(x - 3)^2 + (y - 2)^2 = 4$
46. $(x - 2)^2 + (y + 1)^2 = 9$
47. $(x + 1)^2 + (y + 2)^2 = 7$
48. $x^2 + (y - 6)^2 = 2$

Find the center and radius of the circle with the given equation.

49. $x^2 + y^2 - 2y = 3$
50. $x^2 + y^2 + 4x = -3$
51. $x^2 + y^2 - 2x - 8y + 8 = 0$
52. $x^2 + y^2 + 6x + 8y + 22 = 0$
53. $x^2 + y^2 + 6x - 2y = -8$
54. $x^2 + y^2 - 6x + 8y = -20$
55. $x^2 + y^2 = 3x + 2y - \dfrac{5}{4}$
56. $x^2 + 4x = -y^2 - 5y - \dfrac{17}{4}$

Find the standard form of the equation of the circle with the given center C and given point A on the circle.

57. $C(-1, 3)$, $A(2, 4)$

58. $C(-1, 4)$, $A(1, 2)$
59. $C(-2, 0)$, $A(1, -3)$
60. $C(0, 3)$, $A(1, 4)$
61. $C(3, 4)$, $A(0, 0)$
62. $C(-1, 5)$, $A(0, 0)$

Find the equation of the inverse of S. Graph S, S^{-1}, and $y = x$ on the same axes. Find their domains and ranges.

63. $S = \{(x, y) \mid x^2 + y^2 = 9\}$
64. $S = \{(x, y) \mid x^2 + y^2 = 5\}$
65. $S = \{(x, y) \mid (x + 3)^2 + (y + 1)^2 = 1\}$
66. $S = \{(x, y) \mid (x - 1)^2 + (y + 3)^2 = 1\}$
67. $S = \{(x, y) \mid (x + 1)^2 + (y - 1)^2 = 4\}$
68. $S = \{(x, y) \mid (x + 4)^2 + y^2 = 2\}$
69. $S = \{(x, y) \mid x^2 + y^2 + 4x + 4y + 7 = 0\}$
70. $S = \{(x, y) \mid x^2 + y^2 - 6x - 6y + 14 = 0\}$

B

Find the equation of the following circles with center C.

71. $C(1, 4)$ and tangent to the y-axis.
72. $C(-3, -2)$ and tangent to the x-axis.
73. $C(2, -1)$ and tangent to the line $y = 1$.
74. $C(-1, -4)$ and tangent to the line $x = 3$.

C

Answer the following questions with complete sentences.

75. Let $S = \{(x, y) \mid x^2 + y^2 = r^2\}$. What is the relationship between S and S^{-1}? Justify your answer.

76. Is the equation of a circle a function? Justify your answer.

REVIEW EXERCISES

Find the domains of the following equations. (See Section 8.6.)

77. $y = \sqrt{x}$ **78.** $y = \sqrt{x^2 - 1}$
79. $y = \sqrt{25 - x^2}$

Graph the following equations. (See Section 3.1.)

80. $y = -x$ **81.** $y = 2x$ **82.** $y = -\dfrac{3}{4}x$

9.2 ELLIPSES AND HYPERBOLAS

1	**Ellipses with Their Centers at the Origin**
2	**Hyperbolas with Their Centers at the Origin**
3	**Conic Sections**

1 Ellipses with Their Centers at the Origin

In the last section we saw that the graph of $x^2 + y^2 = 9$ is a circle with its center at the origin. In general, any circle with its center at the origin has an equation in the form $Ax^2 + By^2 = C$, where $A = B$ and $A, B,$ and C are nonzero constants with the same sign. For instance, $2x^2 + 2y^2 = 8$ is equivalent to $x^2 + y^2 = 2^2$, the standard form of the equation of a circle with its center at the origin. The equation $Ax^2 + By^2 = C$, where $A \neq B$, describes two important curves with their centers at the origin. The case of centers off the origin is left to more advanced courses.

An **ellipse** with its center at the origin is a curve whose equation is $Ax^2 + By^2 = C$, where $A, B,$ and C have the same sign but $A \neq B$. As an example, consider

$$4x^2 + 25y^2 = 100$$

The first step in graphing this equation is finding the x- and y-intercepts by letting y and x be 0:

$$4x^2 + 25(0)^2 = 100 \qquad\qquad 4(0)^2 + 25y^2 = 100$$
$$4x^2 = 100 \qquad\qquad\qquad 25y^2 = 100$$
$$x^2 = 25 \qquad\qquad\qquad\quad y^2 = 4$$
$$x = \pm 5 \qquad\qquad\qquad\quad y = \pm 2$$

Thus, $(5, 0)$, $(-5, 0)$, $(0, 2)$, and $(0, -2)$ are the points where the ellipse crosses the x- and y-axes. These points are called the **vertices** of the ellipse. Now let x be 3 or -3. Then

$$4x^2 + 25y^2 = 100$$
$$4 \cdot 9 + 25y^2 = 100$$
$$25y^2 = 64$$
$$y^2 = 64/25$$
$$y = \pm 8/5 = \pm 1.6$$

Therefore, $(3, 1.6)$, $(3, -1.6)$, $(-3, 1.6)$, and $(-3, -1.6)$ are four other points on the curve. These points and the ellipse are graphed in Figure 9.7. Note that the domain and range are $D = [-5, 5]$ and $R = [-2, 2]$.

Now that we know the general shape of an ellipse, simply using the intercepts is sufficient, as in Example 1.

FIGURE 9.7

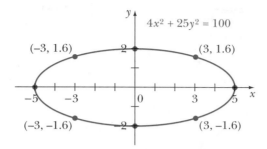

$4x^2 + 25y^2 = 100$

$(-3, 1.6)$
$(3, 1.6)$
$(-3, -1.6)$
$(3, -1.6)$

EXAMPLE 1

Sketch the graph of $9x^2 + 2y^2 = 18$. What is its domain and range?

SOLUTION

To find the x- and y-intercepts, let y and x be zero:

$$9x^2 + 2(0)^2 = 18 \qquad\qquad 9(0)^2 + 2y^2 = 18$$
$$9x^2 = 18 \qquad\qquad 2y^2 = 18$$
$$x^2 = 2 \qquad\qquad y^2 = 9$$
$$x = \pm\sqrt{2} \approx 1.4 \qquad\qquad y = \pm 3$$

Thus, $(\sqrt{2}, 0)$, $(-\sqrt{2}, 0)$, $(0, 3)$, and $(0, -3)$ are the vertices. From the graph of $9x^2 + 2y^2 = 18$ in Figure 9.8, we can see that $D = [-\sqrt{2}, \sqrt{2}]$ and $R = [-3, 3]$.

FIGURE 9.8

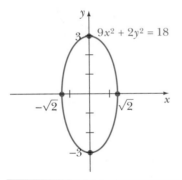

$9x^2 + 2y^2 = 18$

$-\sqrt{2}$
$\sqrt{2}$

---

2 Hyperbolas with Their Centers at the Origin

A **hyperbola** with its center at the origin is a curve whose equation is $Ax^2 + By^2 = C$, where A and B have different signs and $C \neq 0$; for example, consider

$$x^2 - y^2 = 1$$

If $y = 0$, then $x^2 = 1$ and $x = \pm 1$ are the x-intercepts. The points $(1, 0)$ and $(-1, 0)$ are called the **vertices** of the hyperbola. If $x = 0$, then $y^2 = -1$, which has no real solution, so no y-intercepts exist.

To find other points on the graph of $x^2 - y^2 = 1$, we first solve the equation for y:

$$x^2 - y^2 = 1$$
$$-y^2 = -x^2 + 1$$
$$y^2 = x^2 - 1$$
$$y = \pm\sqrt{x^2 - 1}$$

Because the radicand, $x^2 - 1$, must be nonnegative, the domain of this relation is

$$D = \{x \mid x^2 - 1 \geq 0\} = \{x \mid x \leq -1 \quad \text{or} \quad x \geq 1\}$$

The inequality $x^2 - 1 > 0$ was solved in Section 8.6 (see Figure 8.23). The following table gives several points on the graph of $x^2 - y^2 = 1$ (see Figure 9.9).

x	± 1	± 2	± 3
y	0	$\pm\sqrt{3} \approx \pm 1.7$	$\pm\sqrt{8} \approx \pm 2.8$

FIGURE 9.9

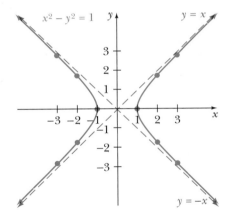

Each branch of the hyperbola in Figure 9.9 *appears* to be a parabola, but these curves are quite different. For instance, each branch of the hyperbola approaches the lines $y = x$ and $y = -x$, which are called **asymptotes** (a parabola does not have an asymptote). In general, an asymptote (as'-simp-tōht) is a line that a curve approximates more and more closely (but never meets) as its distance from the origin increases.

To sketch the graph of the hyperbola $Ax^2 + By^2 = C$, we need to find only its vertices and asymptotes. Fortunately, finding the equations of the asymptotes is very easy; we simply replace C by zero and solve for y. (The reason why this procedure works is discussed in calculus.) Thus, to find the asymptotes in Figure 9.9, let

$$x^2 - y^2 = 1 \qquad \text{Replace 1 by 0.}$$
$$x^2 - y^2 = 0$$
$$-y^2 = -x^2$$
$$y^2 = x^2$$
$$y = \pm\sqrt{x^2} = \pm x$$

$y = x$ and $y = -x$ are the asymptotes of $x^2 - y^2 = 1$.

EXAMPLE 2

Graph $y^2 - 4x^2 = 4$ and its asymptotes. Find the equations of the asymptotes.

SOLUTION

Let $x = 0$; then
$$y^2 - 4(0)^2 = 4$$
$$y^2 = 4$$
$$y = \pm 2$$
so $(0, 2)$ and $(0, -2)$ are the vertices. If $y = 0$, then $x^2 = -1$, so no x-intercepts exist. Now find the asymptotes:
$$y^2 - 4x^2 = 4 \qquad \text{Replace 4 by 0.}$$
$$y^2 - 4x^2 = 0$$
$$y^2 = 4x^2$$
$$y = \pm 2x.$$
The asymptote $y = 2x$ is determined by $\{(0, 0), (1, 2), (-1, -2)\}$. The asymptote $y = -2x$ is determined by $\{(0, 0), (1, -2), (-1, 2)\}$. **(See Figure 9.10)**.

FIGURE 9.10

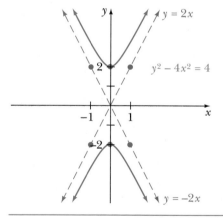

In section 7.6 we used the equation

$$y = k/x \quad \text{or} \quad xy = k, \quad k \neq 0$$

to solve inverse variation problems. The graph of this equation is a hyperbola whose *asymptotes* are the x- and y-axes. From this knowledge, we can sketch its graph by finding a table of coordinates, as illustrated in the following example.

EXAMPLE 3

Graph the following hyperbolas.

a. $y = \dfrac{1}{x}$ **b.** $y = -\dfrac{2}{x}$

SOLUTION   **a.** If $x = \dfrac{1}{3}$, then $y = 1 \div \dfrac{1}{3} = 3$.

If $x = \dfrac{1}{2}$, then $y = 1 \div \dfrac{1}{2} = 2$.

If $x = 1$, then $y = 1$.

If $x = 2$, then $y = \dfrac{1}{2}$.

If $x = 3$, then $y = \dfrac{1}{3}$.

In a similar manner we obtain points in the third quadrant. These points are summarized in the following table and are graphed in Figure 9.11.

x	$\dfrac{1}{3}$	$\dfrac{1}{2}$	1	2	3	$-\dfrac{1}{3}$	$-\dfrac{1}{2}$	-1	-2	-3
y	3	2	1	$\dfrac{1}{2}$	$\dfrac{1}{3}$	-3	-2	-1	$-\dfrac{1}{2}$	$-\dfrac{1}{3}$

FIGURE 9.11

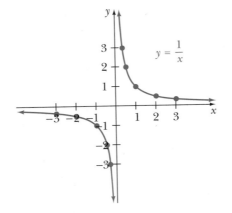

$$y = \frac{1}{x}$$

b. The values in the following table determine the graph of $y = -2/x$ (Figure 9.12).

x	-3	-2	-1	$-\dfrac{1}{2}$	$\dfrac{1}{2}$	1	2	3
y	$\dfrac{2}{3}$	1	2	4	-4	-2	-1	$-\dfrac{2}{3}$

FIGURE 9.12

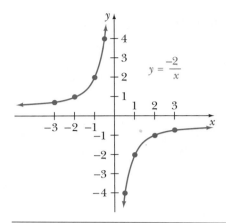

The method used in the last section to graph the inverse of a circle also applies to an ellipse or a hyperbola. The following example shows the graph of the inverse of the hyperbola discussed in Example 2. The inverses of ellipses are covered in the exercises.

EXAMPLE 4

$S = \{(x, y) \mid y^2 - 4x^2 = 4\}$. Find the inverse of S. Graph S^{-1} and its asymptotes. Find the equations of the asymptotes.

SOLUTION $S^{-1} = \{(x, y) \mid x^2 - 4y^2 = 4\}$. Because $(0, 2)$ and $(0, -2)$ are the vertices of $y^2 - 4x^2 = 4$, $(2, 0)$ and $(-2, 0)$ are the vertices of $x^2 - 4y^2 = 4$. Because $y = \pm 2x$ are the asymptotes of $y^2 - 4x^2 = 4$, $x = \pm 2y$ or $y = \pm\frac{1}{2}x$ are the asymptotes of $x^2 - 4y^2 = 4$. (See Figure 9.13.)

FIGURE 9.13

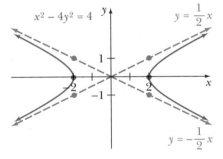

3 Conic Sections

Appendix E shows a diagram of one part of a **right circular cone**, which is like an ice-cream holder. To produce both parts of this geometric figure (Figure 9.14), we start with a circle, called the **base**, B, and a point, called the **vertex**, V, that lies directly over the center of the circle, C. The cone is the surface formed by all the lines that pass through V and a point on the circle; L and s are two such lines. The **axis**, h, is the line through V and C.

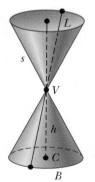

FIGURE 9.14

FIGURE 9.15

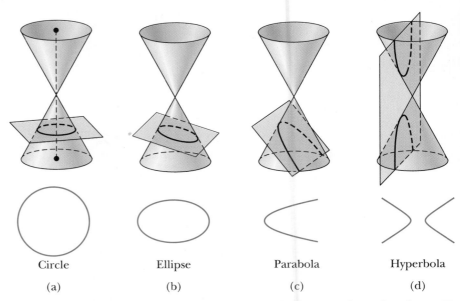

| Circle | Ellipse | Parabola | Hyperbola |
| (a) | (b) | (c) | (d) |

A **conic section** is the curve formed by the intersection of a plane, H, and a right circular cone. When H is perpendicular to h, the conic section is a circle (Figure 9.15a). When H intersects one part of the cone and is not perpendicular to h, the section is an ellipse (Figure 9.15b). If H is parallel to the slant height, s, then the curve is a parabola (Figure 9.15c). If H intersects both parts of the cone and is parallel to h, then the conic section is a hyperbola (Figure 9.15d).

A second geometric definition of the conic sections involving distance in the xy-plane leads to the algebraic equations we have thus far studied. The last section showed that the definition of a circle led to the equation $x^2 + y^2 = r^2$. We leave the derivations of the other equations to a more advanced course, but we will provide the definitions so that we can make a few concluding remarks about some applications of the conic sections.

A parabola is the set of all points in the plane that are equidistant from a fixed line, the **directrix**, d, and a fixed point, the **focus**, F (Figure 9.16). An ellipse is the set of all points in a plane the sum of whose distance from two fixed points, the foci (plural of focus), F_1 and F_2, is a constant, c (Figure 9.17). A hyperbola is the set of all points in a plane the difference of whose distance from two fixed points, the foci, is a positive constant (Figure 9.18).

The conic sections have a wide range of applications. For example, the path of a projectile, such as a baseball or a lava projectile from a volcano, is

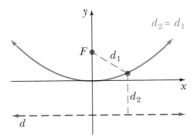

FIGURE 9.16

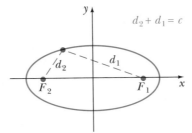

FIGURE 9.17

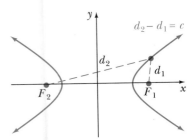

FIGURE 9.18

Math in Time

MENAECHMUS (ca. 350 B.C.) OF ATHENS, a pupil of Plato's, is credited with discovering the conic sections, possibly because of his work with sundials. Euclid (ca. 300 B.C.) wrote four books on the subject at an elementary level.

Apollonius of Perga (ca. 262–190 B.C.) wrote eight books on the conics (seven have survived) that went so far beyond his predecessors' work that he was called "The Great Geometer." Little is known of his life; he was born in Perga in southern Asia Minor and spent most of his life in Alexandria, first as a student and then as a professor. He is reported to have written 13 other books on mathematics and optics, and he was a noted astronomer.

Apollonius gave us the names "ellipse," "parabola," and "hyperbola." In the solutions of quadratic equations through the application of areas, he placed the base of a rectangle on a line segment. He said the result was an ellipse (a deficiency), a parabola (a placing beside or an equality), or a hyperbola (a throwing beyond or an excess), depending on whether the base was shorter than, equal to, or greater than the line segment.

Apollonius's *Conic Sections* contained 487 theorems and was more complete than the usual present-day college course on the subject. He also anticipated many later developments in mathematics. His discussion of maximum and minimum distances from a point to a conic was similar to Newton's work on tangents and normals to curves. By using the asymptotes of $xy = k$ as axes, he foreshadowed the coordinate geometry of Descartes.

In Apollonius's time, just as today, students asked about the "usefulness" of pure mathematics. Referring to his theorems, Apollonius asserted, "They are worthy of acceptance for the sake of the demonstrations themselves, . . . for this and for no other reason" (Boyer, 1968). His students couldn't have known, of course, that his work on hyperbolas would lead to Boyle's Law and the general theory of gases or that his study of ellipses would be essential to modern astronomy.

a parabola. If a reflecting surface is parabolic, then parallel rays of light are reflected to its focus. As a result of this principle, a reflecting telescope uses a parabolic mirror with the astronomer's instruments placed at the focus. Flashlights and automobile headlights use this principle by having a light source at the focus.

In approximately 1600 Johann Kepler (1571–1630) discovered that the path of the earth and the other planets around the sun form an ellipse with the sun at one focus. Dentists use elliptical reflectors with the light source at one focus and the patient's mouth at the other focus. Ellipses also occur in gears and camshafts, orbits of satellites, and the domes of buildings.

Hyperbolas are used in the long-range navigation (loran) system. When transmitters are placed at the foci of two hyperbolas, the position of a ship can be determined by the intersections of the two curves. If a cable, such as a telephone line, is suspended between two points at the same height, then the equation of the cable involves a hyperbolic function. Such a hyperbolic function is used in the construction of suspension bridges, for example the Golden Gate Bridge in San Francisco, California. Hyperbolas are also used in problems involving optics, comets and meteors, and market-area analysis.

BIZARRO   By DAN PIRARO

The "Bizarro" cartoon by Dan Piraro is reproduced by permission of Chronicle Feature, San Francisco, CA.

EXERCISE SET 9.2

A

1   Sketch the graph of each ellipse and label its vertices. Give its domain and range.

1. $x^2 + 4y^2 = 16$ **2.** $4x^2 + y^2 = 16$

3. $9x^2 + y^2 = 36$ **4.** $x^2 + 25y^2 = 25$

5. $3x^2 + y^2 = 3$ **6.** $x^2 + 12y^2 = 12$

7. $9x^2 + 4y^2 = 36$ **8.** $4x^2 + 9y^2 = 36$

9. $16x^2 + 9y^2 = 144$ **10.** $4x^2 + 3y^2 = 12$

11. $9x^2 + 5y^2 = 45$ **12.** $6x^2 + 25y^2 = 150$

13. $2x^2 + 9y^2 = 18$ **14.** $3x^2 + 2y^2 = 6$

15. $5x^2 + 7y^2 = 35$ **16.** $x^2 + \dfrac{y^2}{25} = \dfrac{1}{25}$

17. $\dfrac{x^2}{9} + \dfrac{y^2}{4} = \dfrac{1}{36}$ **18.** $\dfrac{x^2}{25} + \dfrac{9y^2}{4} = 1$

2   Sketch the graph of each hyperbola and its asymptotes. Label its vertices. Find the equations of the asymptotes.

19. $x^2 - 4y^2 = 4$ **20.** $4x^2 - y^2 = 4$

21. $4x^2 - 4y^2 = 36$ **22.** $y^2 - x^2 = 1$

23. $4y^2 - x^2 = 4$ **24.** $16y^2 - 9x^2 = 144$

25. $y^2 - 9x^2 = 16$ **26.** $4x^2 - y^2 = 8$

27. $9y^2 - x^2 = 27$ **28.** $\dfrac{x^2}{4} - \dfrac{y^2}{25} = 1$

29. $x^2 - \dfrac{y^2}{2} = 1$ **30.** $\dfrac{y^2}{4} - \dfrac{3x^2}{4} = 1$

Graph the following hyperbolas.

31. $y = \dfrac{2}{x}$ **32.** $y = -\dfrac{1}{x}$ **33.** $y = -\dfrac{3}{x}$

34. $y = \dfrac{4}{x}$ **35.** $2xy = 1$ **36.** $xy = -1$

37. $3xy = -2$ **38.** $2xy = 3$

Identify the graph of the given equation as a circle, ellipse, parabola, or hyperbola and then sketch its graph.

39. $x^2 + 9y^2 = 36$ **40.** $xy = 1$

41. $y = 3x^2$ **42.** $x^2 + y^2 = 4y$

43. $y = x^2 + 4x + 3$ **44.** $25x^2 + y^2 = 25$

45. $x^2 - y = 4$

46. $y^2 = 25x^2 + 25$

47. $x^2 + y^2 + 2x = 8$

48. $x^2 + y^2 = 5$

49. $x^2 - y = 4x$

50. $x^2 - 9y^2 = 36$

51. $x^2 + y = 1$

52. $4x^2 + 4y^2 = 1$

53. $xy = -2$

54. $x^2 + y^2 - 4x + 6y + 9 = 0$

Find the inverses of the following conics and graph them. For the hyperbolas, find the equations of the asymptotes and graph them.

55. $4x^2 + 25y^2 = 100$

56. $9x^2 + 2y^2 = 18$

57. $x^2 - y^2 = 1$

58. $y^2 - x^2 = 4$

59. $9y^2 + 16x^2 = 144$

60. $xy = 2$

61. $xy = -2$

62. $x^2 + 4y^2 = 4$

63. $y = -2x^2 - 1$

64. $x^2 + y^2 = 1$

65. $25y^2 - 4x^2 = 100$

66. $y = x^2 - 4x + 3$

67. $x^2 + y^2 + 6x = -8$

68. $xy = 1$

69. $9x^2 + y^2 = 9$

70. $9x^2 - 16y^2 = 144$

B

Graph the following equations.

71. $y = \dfrac{1}{x^2}$

72. $y = -\dfrac{1}{x^2}$

73. $y = -\dfrac{2}{x^2}$

74. $y^2 = \dfrac{1}{x^2}$

75. $y^2 = \dfrac{4}{x^2}$

76. $y^2 = \dfrac{9}{x^2}$

C

Answer the following questions with complete sentences.

77. Describe an application of each of the conic sections.

78. From their equations, how can you tell an ellipse from a hyperbola?

79. Describe how to find the equations of the asymptotes of a hyperbola.

80. Why did the Greeks call Apollonius "The Great Geometer"?

81. An accurate ellipse can be constructed with a loop of string and two thumbtacks. Tie the ends of the string to the tacks and place them on a sheet of paper so that the distance between them is less than the length of the string (Figure 9.19). Use a pencil to pull the string taut and move the pencil around the loop of string.

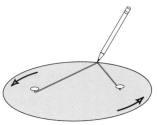

FIGURE 9.19

82. A parabola can be constructed with straight lines. Draw a V (Figure 9.20) and mark off equally spaced points on each side of the V, approximately 1/4 inch apart. On one side of the V label the points $1, 2, \ldots, n$. On the other side label the points $n, n - 1, \ldots, 1$. Now draw line segments from 1 to 1, 2 to 2, $\ldots$, and n to n. The closer the points are, the more accurate the parabola that results.

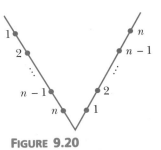

FIGURE 9.20

REVIEW EXERCISES

Graph the following lines. (See Section 3.1.)

83. $4x - y = 5$ **84.** $y = 3x$

Graph the following parabolas. (See Section 8.3.)

85. $y = x^2 - 1$ **86.** $y = -2x^2 + 3$

Simplify the following. (See Section 7.8.)

87. $(2 + i) + (2 - i)$ **88.** $(2 + i)(2 - i)$

89. $\sqrt{-25}$ **90.** $\sqrt{-1/4}$

9.3 NONLINEAR SYSTEMS OF EQUATIONS IN TWO VARIABLES

> **1** Solving a System with a Quadratic and a Linear Equation
>
> **2** Solving a System with Two Quadratic Equations
>
> **3** Solving Nonlinear Systems with Complex Solutions
>
> **4** Solving Word Problems

1 Solving a System with a Quadratic and a Linear Equation

Up to this point we have studied systems that contained only linear equations. A **nonlinear system of equations** is one that has at least one equation that is not linear. We now consider systems that contain quadratic equations. To help visualize the solutions, we will graph the equations. The ordered pairs, however, will be found with the addition–substitution approach that we used with the systems of linear equations.

We begin with systems that consist of one linear and one quadratic equation. First we solve one of the equations for x or y. We then substitute this expression in the other equation to give us an equation in one variable. See the following examples for the details.

EXAMPLE 1

Solve the system $y = x^2 - 1$
$$y = 4x - 5$$

SOLUTION

Substitute $y = x^2 - 1$ in the second equation:
$$y = 4x - 5$$
$$x^2 - 1 = 4x - 5$$
$$x^2 - 4x + 4 = 0$$
$$(x - 2)^2 = 0$$
$$x = 2$$

Then $y = 4x - 5 = 4 \cdot 2 - 5 = 3$. Thus, $A(2, 3)$ is the solution to the system.

From the graphs of the equations in Figure 9.21, we can see that the line is tangent to the parabola at $A(2, 3)$.

FIGURE 9.21

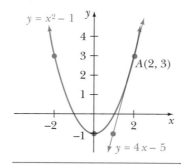

EXAMPLE 2

Solve the system $x^2 + y^2 = 1$
$$x + y = 0$$

SOLUTION $x + y = 0$, so $y = -x$. Then
$$x^2 + y^2 = 1 \qquad \text{Substitute } y = -x.$$
$$x^2 + (-x)^2 = 1$$
$$2x^2 = 1$$
$$x^2 = \frac{1}{2} = \frac{2}{4}$$
$$x = \pm\frac{\sqrt{2}}{2}$$

If $x = \frac{\sqrt{2}}{2}$, then $y = -x = -\frac{\sqrt{2}}{2}$.

If $x = -\frac{\sqrt{2}}{2}$, then $y = -x = -\left(-\frac{\sqrt{2}}{2}\right) = \frac{\sqrt{2}}{2}$. Thus,

$A\left(\frac{\sqrt{2}}{2}, -\frac{\sqrt{2}}{2}\right)$ and $B\left(-\frac{\sqrt{2}}{2}, \frac{\sqrt{2}}{2}\right)$ are the solutions (**see Figure 9.22**).

FIGURE 9.22

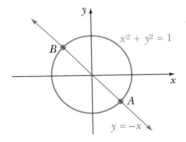

In Example 2 we substituted $x = \frac{\sqrt{2}}{2}$ in the linear equation to find the value of y. If we had substituted it in $x^2 + y^2 = 1$, then we would have obtained the extraneous root $y = \frac{\sqrt{2}}{2}$, that is, $\left(\frac{\sqrt{2}}{2}, \frac{\sqrt{2}}{2}\right)$ is not a solution to the system. In general, the best approach is to substitute the solutions to the quadratic equation in the linear equation to find the values of the other variable.

2 Solving a System with Two Quadratic Equations

We now consider systems in which both equations are quadratic. In most problems the addition method is just as easy to use as the substitution method. In Example 3 the substitution method is used; note that x^2 is substituted, not x.

EXAMPLE 3

Solve the system $y = -\frac{1}{2}x^2 + 1$
$$x^2 + 4y^2 = 4$$

(continued)

SOLUTION Solve the first equation for x^2 and substitute this expression in the second equation.

$$y = -\frac{1}{2}x^2 + 1 \qquad \text{Multiply both sides by } -2;$$

$$-2y + 2 = x^2 \qquad \text{then add 2 to both sides.}$$

$$x^2 + 4y^2 = 4$$

$$(-2y + 2) + 4y^2 = 4$$

$$4y^2 - 2y - 2 = 0 \qquad \text{Multiply both sides by } \frac{1}{2}.$$

$$2y^2 - y - 1 = 0$$

$$(y - 1)(2y + 1) = 0$$

$y = 1$ or $-\frac{1}{2}$. Substitute these values in $x^2 = -2y + 2$.

If $y = 1$, then $x^2 = -2y + 2 = -2 \cdot 1 + 2 = 0$ and $x = 0$. Thus, $A(0,1)$ is one solution.

If $y = -\frac{1}{2}$, then $x^2 = -2\left(-\frac{1}{2}\right) + 2 = 3$ and $x = \pm\sqrt{3}$. So

$B\left(\sqrt{3}, -\frac{1}{2}\right)$ and $C\left(-\sqrt{3}, -\frac{1}{2}\right)$ are the other solutions (See Figure 9.23).

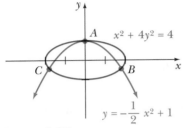

FIGURE 9.23

A system that consists of one linear and one quadratic equation can have a maximum of two real solutions, and a system of two quadratic equations can have a maximum of four real solutions. The case of four real solutions is illustrated in the following example.

E X A M P L E 4

Solve the system $4y^2 - x^2 = 4$

$$x^2 + y^2 = 6$$

SOLUTION To eliminate x^2, add the two equations:

$$4y^2 - x^2 = 4$$

$$\underline{y^2 + x^2 = 6}$$

$$5y^2 + 0 = 10$$

$$y^2 = 2$$

$$y = \pm\sqrt{2}$$

$x^2 + y^2 = 6$;   replace y^2 in this equation by 2:

$$x^2 + 2 = 6$$

$$x^2 = 4$$

$$x = \pm 2$$

The four points of intersection of the hyperbola and the circle are $A(2, \sqrt{2})$, $B(-2, \sqrt{2})$, $C(-2, -\sqrt{2})$, and $D(2, -\sqrt{2})$.

For clarity the graphs of the asymptotes are omitted in Figure 9.24. The radius of the circle is $\sqrt{6} \approx 2.4$.

FIGURE 9.24

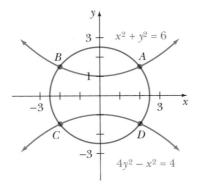

3 Solving Nonlinear Systems with Complex Solutions

We have seen that if we attempt to solve a system such as $y = 2x + 3$ and $y = 2x - 1$, then we arrive at the false equation $3 = -1$. This tells us that the system has no solution. Similarly, $x^2 + y^2 = 1$ and $x^2 + y^2 = 2$ reduces to $1 = 2$, so this system also has no solution. Geometrically, the graphs of these systems do not intersect, because the first one represents parallel lines and the second one concentric circles. However, some nonlinear systems do not intersect but have solutions that involve imaginary numbers; that is, ordered pairs of complex numbers exist that satisfy both equations, but they do not represent points in the real xy-plane. This fact is illustrated in the following example.

EXAMPLE 5

Solve the system $xy = -1$
$$y = 4x$$

SOLUTION

FIGURE 9.25

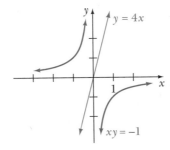

From their graphs in Figure 9.25, we can see that the line does not intersect the hyperbola. Therefore, the system has no real solutions. To determine

(continued)

whether imaginary solutions exist, substitute $y = 4x$ in $xy = -1$:

$$xy = -1$$
$$x(4x) = -1$$
$$x^2 = -\frac{1}{4}$$
$$x = \pm\sqrt{-\frac{1}{4}} = \pm\frac{1}{2}i$$

If $x = \frac{1}{2}i$, then $y = 4x = 4 \cdot \frac{1}{2}i = 2i$. If $x = -\frac{1}{2}i$, then $y = 4\left(-\frac{1}{2}i\right) = -2i$. Thus, $\left(\frac{1}{2}i,\ 2i\right)$ and $\left(-\frac{1}{2}i,\ -2i\right)$ are the solutions.

✔ CHECK   If $x = \frac{1}{2}i$ and $y = 2i$,   then

$$xy = \frac{1}{2}i(2i) = i^2 = -1 \quad \text{and} \quad y = 4x = 4\left(\frac{1}{2}i\right) = 2i.$$

The other solution is checked in a similar way.

4   Solving Word Problems

A variety of word problems can be represented by a system of nonlinear equations. In each of the following examples a system of equations is derived and the answer is given. The solutions to the systems are left as exercises.

EXAMPLE 6

The sum of two numbers is 4, and the sum of their squares is 6. Find the numbers.

SOLUTION   Let x and y represent the two numbers. Then the system of equations is

$$x + y = 4$$
$$x^2 + y^2 = 6$$

$\{2 + i,\ 2 - i\}$ is the solution.

EXAMPLE 7

Find the dimensions of a rectangle whose perimeter is 5 meters and whose area is 1 square meter.

SOLUTION   Let L = the length and W = the width.
$2L + 2W = P$ is the perimeter and $LW = A$ is the area. Thus, the system is

$$2L + 2W = 5$$
$$LW = 1$$

$L = 2$ m and $W = 1/2$ m is the solution.

EXERCISE SET 9.3

A

1 For the following systems: a. graph the equations and predict the number of real solutions; b. solve the systems with the addition-substitution method.

1. $y = x^2$
$y = x + 2$

2. $y = -x^2 + 1$
$2x + y = 1$

3. $x^2 + y^2 = 25$
$y - x = 7$

4. $xy = 1$
$x + y = 2$

5. $x^2 - y^2 = 1$
$y = 2$

6. $9x^2 + 4y^2 = 36$
$x = -1$

2

7. $y = x^2 - 1$
$y = -x^2 + 1$

8. $y = 3x^2 + 2$
$y = -4x^2 + 2$

9. $y^2 - x^2 = 1$
$2x^2 - y^2 = 4$

10. $y = 4x^2 - 2$
$4x^2 + y^2 = 4$

3

11. $y = x^2 + 1$
$y = -3$

12. $x^2 + y^2 = 4$
$x^2 + y^2 = 9$

13. $x^2 + y^2 = 1$
$x^2 + 4y^2 = 16$

14. $xy = 4$
$x + y = 2$

Solve the following systems of equations.

15. $y - x = 1$
$2y - 2x = 2$

16. $y^2 - x^2 = 1$
$2y^2 - 2x^2 = 2$

17. $y = 3x + 1$
$y = 3x - 1$

18. $y = 3x^2 + 1$
$y = 3x^2 - 1$

19. $x^2 + y^2 = 2$
$x^2 - y^2 = 6$

20. $x^2 + 2y = 4$
$x^2 + y^2 = 4$

21. $2x^2 - 4y^2 = 8$
$2y^2 - x^2 = -4$

22. $y = -x^2$
$y = -4$

23. $y = x^2 + 4x + 2$
$y = x^2 + 3x + 1$

24. $y = -x^2 + 6x - 1$
$y = -x^2 + 5x + 1$

25. $y = x^2 + x + 1$
$y = -x^2 + 4x + 3$

26. $y = -2x^2$
$y = -7x + 3$

27. $y = -x^2 + 1$
$y = 2x - 2$

28. $3x^2 - 6y^2 = 9$
$x^2 - 2y^2 = 6$

29. $xy = -2$
$y = 2x$

30. $y = x^2 - 8x + 19$
$y = -2x^2 + 16x - 29$

4 Solve the system of equations in:

31. Example 6 (p. 442) **32.** Example 7 (p. 442)

Use a system of equations to solve the following problems. Define each variable.

33. The sum of two numbers is 20, and their product is 36. Find the numbers.

34. The sum of two numbers is 20, and their product is 101. Find the numbers.

35. The sum of two numbers is 2, and the sum of their squares is 0. Find the numbers.

36. One number is 4 more than another number. The sum of their squares is 10. Find the numbers.

37. The difference of two numbers is 8, and the difference of their squares is 16. Find the numbers.

38. Find the dimensions of a rectangle whose perimeter is 8 and whose area is 1.

39. The hypotenuse of a right triangle is $\sqrt{13}$, and the sum of the legs is 5. Find the legs of the triangle.

40. One leg of a right triangle is 8. The sum of the other two sides is 16. Find the hypotenuse and the other leg.

41. The base of a triangle is 3 more than its height. The area is 14. Find the height and base.

42. The height of a rectangular solid is 2. Its surface area is 52, and the area of its base is 12. Find its length and width.

43. Ted went on a 36-mile hike. His time was 3 less than 5 times his average rate of travel. Find his rate and time for the hike.

44. On a 2000-mile cross-country trip, Amy's average rate of travel was 10 less than her time. Find her rate and time for the trip.

B

The shortest and longest distances from a point P to a circle are found using the line determined by P and the center of the circle. Graph the circle $x^2 + y^2 = 9$ and $P(4,5)$.

45. Find the minimum distance to the circle from P.

46. Find the maximum distance to the circle from P.

Solve the following systems of equations.

47. $-x^2 + 2y = 6$
$\quad\; x^2 + y^2 = 4$

48. $x^2 + y^2 = 25$
$\quad\; 3y - 4x = 25$

49. $xy = 1$
$\quad\; x^2 + y^2 = 4$

50. $xy = 2$
$\quad\; 2x^2 + y^2 = 18$

C

Answer the following questions with complete sentences.

51. What is meant by a "nonlinear system of equations"?

52. Discuss the number of complex solutions that are possible with a nonlinear system of equations.

REVIEW EXERCISES

Graph the following inequalities. (See Section 3.5.)

53. $y \le -x + 1$

54. $y > 2x + 2$

55. $y \le x$
$\quad\; x + y > 3$

56. $y > -x$
$\quad\; x - y \ge -4$

Graph the solution sets of the following systems of inequalities. (See Section 3.5.)

9.4 NONLINEAR SYSTEMS OF INEQUALITIES IN TWO VARIABLES

> **1** Graphing Quadratic Inequalities
>
> **2** Solving Systems of Nonlinear Inequalities by Graphing

1 Graphing Quadratic Inequalities

In Section 3.5 we graphed linear inequalities and solved systems of linear inequalities by graphing them. We will now repeat these procedures for quadratic inequalities and nonlinear systems of inequalities.

Recall that the boundary of a linear inequality is a line. For quadratic inequalities the boundaries are conic sections. The approach to both types of problems is the same: We graph the boundary and then use as many test points as needed. The following examples discuss the details.

EXAMPLE 1

Graph $x^2 + y^2 > 9$.

SOLUTION   The boundary is the circle $x^2 + y^2 = 9$, whose radius is $\sqrt{9} = 3$. It is graphed as a broken circle, because the inequality does not include its boundary. The circle divides the plane into two regions: the interior and the exterior of the circle. The test point $A(0, 0)$, does not satisfy the inequality because $0^2 + 0^2 \not> 9$. Therefore, the correct region is the exterior of the circle, as indicated in Figure 9.26.

FIGURE 9.26

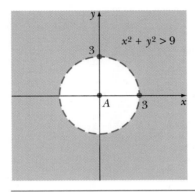

$$x^2 + y^2 > 9$$

EXAMPLE 2

Graph $y \le x^2$.

SOLUTION

The boundary is the parabola $y = x^2$, which is graphed as a solid curve, because the inequality includes its boundary. The parabola divides the plane into two regions. Because $(0, 0)$ is a point on the curve, we need another test point, say $P(2, -1)$. Because $-1 < 2^2$ is a true statement, all the points in the region containing P will also satisfy the inequality. This region is the one colored in Figure 9.27.

FIGURE 9.27

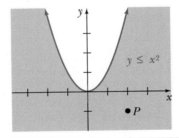

$$y \le x^2$$

$\bullet P$

EXAMPLE 3

Graph $y^2 - x^2 \le 4$.

SOLUTION

The boundary is the hyperbola $y^2 - x^2 = 4$, whose vertices are $(0, 2)$ and $(0, -2)$. When $x = 2$ or -2, then $y = \sqrt{8}$ or $-\sqrt{8}$, as indicated in Figure 9.28. For clarity the graphs of the asymptotes are omitted. The curve

(continued)

separates the plane into three regions, for which $A(0, 3)$, $B(0, 0)$, and $C(0, -3)$ are test points. Substituting them in $y^2 - x^2 < 4$, we have

A: $3^2 - 0^2 \not< 4$ B: $0^2 - 0^2 < 4$ C: $(-3)^2 - 0^2 \not< 4$

Thus, the colored region containing B is the solution set.

FIGURE 9.28

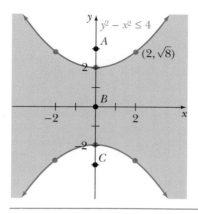

2   Solving Systems of Nonlinear Inequalities by Graphing

We now consider nonlinear systems of inequalities. The most efficient way to solve these systems is the graphical method. We graph each inequality on the same set of axes. The solution is the set of all ordered pairs that satisfies each inequality; that is, the intersection of the graphs of the individual inequalities.

EXAMPLE 4

Graph the solution set of the following system.

$$y > 2x + 2$$
$$x^2 + y^2 \leq 4$$

SOLUTION

The points $(0, 2)$ and $(-1, 0)$ determine the graph of $y = 2x + 2$ (Figure 9.29). The half-plane $y > 2x + 2$ is the one that does not contain the origin, because $0 \not> 2 \cdot 0 + 2$.

The boundary of $x^2 + y^2 \leq 4$ is the circle $x^2 + y^2 = 4$, whose radius is $\sqrt{4} = 2$. If we use $(0, 0)$ as a test point, $0^2 + 0^2 < 4$, so the interior of the circle is the correct region. The area above the line and inside the circle is the solution to the system.

FIGURE 9.29

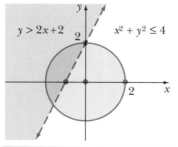

As systems of inequalities become more complicated, graphing the inequalities separately and then graphing the solution set often is the most convenient approach. This process is illustrated in the following example.

EXAMPLE 5   Graph the solution set of the following system.

$$x^2 + 9y^2 < 9$$
$$x^2 - 4y^2 \geq 1$$

SOLUTION $x^2 + 9y^2 = 9$ is an ellipse whose vertices are $(3, 0)$, $(-3, 0)$, $(0, 1)$, and $(0, -1)$. The region $x^2 + 9y^2 < 9$ contains $(0, 0)$, because $0^2 + 9 \cdot 0^2 < 9$; the inequality $x^2 + 9y^2 < 9$ is graphed in Figure 9.30.

FIGURE 9.30

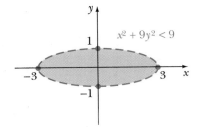

The equality $x^2 - 4y^2 = 1$ is a hyperbola whose vertices are $(1, 0)$ and $(-1, 0)$. Recall that we find the asymptotes by replacing 1 by 0 and solving for y:

$$x^2 - 4y^2 = 0$$
$$y^2 = \frac{1}{4}x^2$$
$$y = \pm\frac{1}{2}x$$

The equality $x^2 - 4y^2 = 1$ and its asymptotes are graphed in Figure 9.31. The two regions represented by $x^2 - 4y^2 > 1$ are determined by the test points $A(2, 0)$ and $B(-2, 0)$.

The intersection of the regions, which is shown in Figure 9.32, is the system's solution.

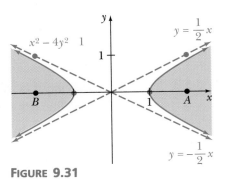

FIGURE 9.31   **FIGURE 9.32**

EXERCISE SET 9.4

A

1 Graph the following inequalities in the xy-plane.

1. $y \geq x + 1$

2. $x - 3y \leq 3$

3. $x \geq 1$

4. $y < 2$

5. $y > x + 2$

6. $x - y < 1$

7. $x^2 + y^2 < 9$

8. $y \geq x^2$

9. $y^2 - x^2 \geq 4$

10. $x^2 + 4y^2 > 4$

11. $x^2 + y^2 > 25$

12. $4x^2 + y^2 \leq 9$

13. $y^2 - x^2 < 1$

14. $x^2 - y^2 \geq 1$

15. $x^2 - 5y^2 < 5$

16. $x^2 + 4y^2 \leq 4$

17. $2x^2 + y^2 > 2$

18. $9x^2 + 4y^2 \geq 36$

19. $y > x^2 - 1$

20. $y < -x^2 + 4$

21. $y \geq x^2 - 2x + 2$

22. $xy \geq 1$

23. $xy < 2$

24. $xy \leq -3$

2 Graph the solution sets of the following systems of inequalities. If no solution exists, write "Ø."

25. $y \leq x + 2$
$y \leq -x + 2$

26. $y \geq -x + 1$
$y \leq 2x + 2$

27. $x - 2y < -2$
$x + y > 3$

28. $y \leq x + 2$
$x \geq -2$

29. $x + y > 0$
$y < 1$

30. $2x - y > -4$
$-2x + y < -1$

31. $y < 2x + 2$
$x^2 + y^2 \geq 4$

32. $y \geq -x$
$x^2 + y^2 \leq 1$

33. $y < x + 2$
$y \geq x^2$

34. $x - 3y \geq 0$
$x^2 + 9y^2 \leq 9$

35. $x + y \geq 2$
$xy \geq 1$

36. $y > x + 2$
$x^2 + y^2 \leq 2$

37. $y > x^2 - 1$
$y < -x^2 + 1$

38. $y^2 - x^2 \geq 1$
$4x^2 + y^2 \geq 4$

39. $x^2 + y^2 \leq 9$
$25x^2 + 4y^2 \geq 100$

40. $x^2 - y^2 < 1$
$x^2 + y^2 \leq 4$

41. $x^2 + y^2 \leq 25$
$xy < -1$

42. $9x^2 + y^2 \geq 9$
$x^2 + 4y^2 < 4$

43. $x^2 + y^2 < 1$
$x^2 + y^2 \geq 4$

44. $x^2 + y^2 > 1$
$x^2 + y^2 \leq 4$

45. $y \leq x^2 - 1$
$x^2 - 2y < 2$

46. $x^2 + y^2 \geq 1$
$y \geq -x^2 - 1$

47. $|x| \leq 1$
$y \geq x^2$

48. $|y| > 2$
$x^2 + y^2 \geq 9$

B

Graph the following in the xy-plane.

49. $(x - 3)^2 + (y + 4)^2 \geq 1$

50. $x^2 + y^2 - 2y \leq 0$

51. $x^2 + 4x + y^2 > 0$

52. $y \geq (x - 3)^2 - 1$

53. $y < -x^2 + 2x + 1$

54. $y \leq x^2 + 4x$

Graph the solution set of the following systems of inequalities.

55. $y \geq -x$
$y \geq x$
$y < 2$

56. $|x| < 3$
$|y| \leq 3$
$y \leq x$

57. $y \geq 2x^2 - 2$
$y < x + 1$
$y < -x + 1$

58. $x^2 + y^2 \leq 1$
$x \geq 0$
$y \geq 0$

59. $xy \geq 4$
$x + y < 6$
$y \geq 0$

60. $y \leq -x^2 + 1$
$y \geq x^2 - 1$
$y < x$

C ✏

Answer the following questions with complete sentences.

61. Describe how test points are used to graph a quadratic inequality.

62. Describe the method of solving a nonlinear system of inequalities.

Chapter Summary

KEY WORDS, DEFINITIONS, AND PROPERTIES

Definitions

Circle: $x^2 + y^2 = r^2$; the **standard form** of the equation of a circle with center $C(0, 0)$ and radius r. $(x - h)^2 + (y - k)^2 = r^2$: the standard form of the equation of a circle with center $C(h, k)$ and radius r; the general form of this equation is $x^2 + y^2 + Dx + Ey + F = 0$. (See Section 9.1.)

Ellipse: $Ax^2 + By^2 = C$; the equation of an ellipse with center $(0, 0)$, where A, B, and C have the same sign, $A \neq B$.

Hyperbola: $Ax^2 + By^2 = C$; the equation of a hyperbola with center $(0, 0)$, where A and B have different signs.

Asymptotes: the lines found by solving $Ax^2 + By^2 = 0$ for y. $xy = k$: a hyperbola; asymptotes are the x- and y-axes. (See Section 9.2.)

Inequalities in Two Variables (See Section 9.4.)

To graph an inequality in two variables:

1. Graph the **boundary** as a solid line or curve if the inequality is $\leq$ or $\geq$. Graph the boundary as a broken line or curve if the inequality is $<$ or $>$.

2. To find the correct region(s) of the plane, pick a **test point(s)** not on the boundary. If a test point makes the inequality a true statement, then the region containing the test point is a correct one. If it makes the inequality a false statement, then that region is not a correct one.

To graph a system of inequalities (a nonlinear system contains at least one inequality that is not linear):

1. Graph all the inequalities on the same xy-plane.

2. The intersection of all the regions is the solution to the system of inequalities.

CHAPTER REVIEW EXERCISES

The answers to the following exercises are in the answer section. If you have trouble, then review the material and homework problems in the sections indicated.

Find the equations of the following circles. (See Section 9.1.)

1. Center $(0, 0)$, radius $= \sqrt{3}$. Graph the circle.
2. Center $(0, 0)$ and containing the point $A(1, 3)$.
3. Center $C(3, -2)$, radius $= 5$.

Find the center and radius of the following circle. (See Section 9.1.)

4. $x^2 + y^2 + 2x - 4y + 2 = 0$

Graph the following conics and any asymptotes; give the equations of the asymptotes. Give the domain and range of each conic. (See Section 9.2.)

5. $x^2 - y^2 = 9$
6. $x^2 + y^2 = 9$
7. $4x^2 + 9y^2 = 36$
8. $xy = -1$
9. $y - x^2 = 1$
10. $y = x^2 - 4x + 3$

Solve the following systems of equations. (See Section 9.3.)

11. $y = -2x + 8$
$\quad\ \ y = x^2$

12. $x^2 + 9y^2 = 9$
$\qquad\quad x = 1$

13. $x^2 + y^2 = 6$
$\quad\ \ x^2 + y^2 = 9$

14. $x^2 - y^2 = 1$
$\quad\ \ x^2 + y^2 = 7$

15. $x^2 + y^2 = x$
$\qquad\quad y = x + 2$

16. $xy = 2$
$\quad\ \ y = x + 4$

Solve the following word problem. (See Section 9.3.)

17. Find two numbers whose sum is 6 and whose product is 11.

Graph the following inequalities. (See Section 9.4.)

18. $y > 3x - 1$

19. $x^2 + y^2 \geq 1$

20. $x^2 + 4y^2 \leq 4$

Graph the solution set of the following systems of inequalities. (See Section 9.4.)

21. $x^2 - y^2 \geq 1$
$\quad\ \ x^2 + y^2 < 4$

22. $|x| > 1$
$\quad\ \ y > x^2$

23. $9x^2 + y^2 \geq 9$
$\quad\ \ x^2 + 9y^2 \leq 9$

Find the inverses of the following conics and graph them. For the hyperbolas, find the equations of the asymptotes and graph them. (See Sections 9.1 and 9.2.)

24. $y^2 - 4x^2 = 4$

25. $x^2 + y^2 + 4x - 2y = -1$

26. $xy = 1$

27. $4x^2 + 9y^2 = 36$

Chapter Test

Treat this test as a class test and allow 50 minutes for completion. When you have finished, use the answer section for scoring. For any wrong answers, refer to the corresponding problems in the review section.

Find the equations of the following circles.

1. Center $(0, 0)$ and containing the point $A(-1, 2)$.

2. Center $C(3, -4)$ and containing the origin.

Find the center and radius of the following circle.

3. $x^2 + y^2 - 6x + 8y = 0$

Graph the following conics and any asymptotes; give the equations of the asymptotes. Give the domain and range of each conic.

4. $y^2 - x^2 = 4$

5. $4x^2 + y^2 = 4$

6. $x^2 + y = 4$

7. $xy = 4$

8. $x^2 + y^2 = 5$

9. $y = x^2 + 8x + 12$

Solve the following systems of equations.

10. $x^2 + y^2 = 1$
$\qquad\quad y = x$

11. $x + y = 2$
$\qquad\quad xy = 10$

12. $y^2 - x^2 = 1$
$\qquad\quad y = x^2 - 1$

13. $x^2 + 4y^2 = 4$
$\qquad\quad x^2 + y^2 = 4$

Graph the following inequalities.

14. $y \leq 2x + 1$

15. $x^2 + y^2 \leq 4$

16. $y^2 - x^2 > 1$

Graph the solution set of the following systems of inequalities.

17. $x^2 + y^2 \leq 4$
$\qquad\quad |y| > 1$

18. $y \geq x^2 - 1$
$\qquad\quad y < x + 1$

19. $x^2 - 4y^2 \leq 4$
$\quad\ \ x^2 + 9y^2 \leq 9$

Find the inverses of the following conics and graph them. For the hyperbolas, find the equations of the asymptotes and graph them.

20. $x^2 + 9y^2 = 9$

21. $x^2 - 9y^2 = 9$

22. $x^2 + y^2 - 6y = -8$

23. $xy = -2$

Solve the following word problems.

24. Find two numbers whose sum is 1 and whose product is 1.

25. Find the dimensions of the rectangle whose perimeter is 12 and whose area is 7.

Cumulative Review

The answers to the following exercises are given in the answer section. The section from which each question is taken is listed in brackets next to its answer. For any wrong answers, review the material in the indicated section.

Let $f(x) = 3x^2 + 4x - 3$ and $g(x) = x + 2$. Find the following.

1. $g^{-1}(x)$ **2.** f/g

Graph the following equations and systems of equations.

3. $y = x^2 - 4x + 3$ **4.** $x^2 + y^2 + 4x - 2y = 1$
5. $f(x) = -1 + \sqrt{x}$ **6.** $\begin{array}{l} y < x + 1 \\ y + 2x \geq 1 \end{array}$

Perform the indicated operations.

7. $\dfrac{\dfrac{1}{2} + \dfrac{1}{2x}}{1 - \dfrac{1}{x}}$

8. $\dfrac{m}{m + 2} + \dfrac{3}{m + 4} - \dfrac{14}{m^2 + 6m + 8}$

Solve the following for the indicated variable(s).

9. $\dfrac{m}{m + 2} + \dfrac{3}{m + 4} = \dfrac{14}{m^2 + 6m + 8}$

10. $\dfrac{5}{x + 6} = \dfrac{7}{x - 5}$

11. $2(x - 7) - 3(7x - 9) = 0$
12. $|7x - 1| = |1 - 9x|$
13. $|1 - 3x| > 8$
14. $x^2 - 3x \leq 0$
15. $x^2 - 2x + 9 = 0$
16. $4x^{-1} + 45 = x^{-2}$
17. $\sqrt{2x^2 - 1} = x$
18. $4\sqrt[3]{a} + b = b; \quad a$
19. $3x + 2y = 7x - 8y; \quad x$
20. $\dfrac{V_1}{T_1} = \dfrac{V_f}{T_f}; \quad T_1$

21. $\dfrac{1 + x}{1 - x} = w; \quad x$

22. $C = \dfrac{5}{9}(F - 32); \quad F$

23. $S = -\dfrac{1}{2}gt^2 + v_0t; \quad g$

24. $\begin{array}{l} 2x + 3y = 1 \\ 5x - 6y = -1 \end{array}$

25. $\begin{array}{l} x + y = 5 \\ x - z = 6 \\ y + 2z = -5 \end{array}$

Find the determinant of the following matrix.

26. $\begin{bmatrix} 3 & 1 \\ 4 & 3 \\ \frac{1}{7} & \frac{4}{3} \end{bmatrix}$

Solve the following for x.

27. $\begin{vmatrix} 2 & x \\ x & 8 \end{vmatrix} = 0$

Let $f(x) = \dfrac{x^2 - 7}{x^2 - 9}$.

28. Find the domain and the roots of f.

Let R_1 and R_2 denote two resistors connected in parallel. If R is the total resistance of R_1 and R_2, then

$$\dfrac{1}{R} = \dfrac{1}{R_1} + \dfrac{1}{R_2}$$

29. If $R_1 = 36$ ohms and $R = 12$ ohms, find R_2.

Express each of the following as an equation; find the constant of variation, k; and solve the equation for the indicated variable.

30. The variable a varies directly as the fourth root of b; $a = 3$ when $b = 81$. Find a when $b = 32$.

31. The variable y is directly proportional to the square of x and inversely proportional to z; $y = 12$ when $x = 2$ and $z = -3$. Find y when $x = 5$ and $z = 10$.

Express the following as an equation. Use k as the constant of variation.

32. The work, W, done by a force in moving an object varies jointly as the mass, m, of the object and distance, d, that it is moved.

Solve the following problem.

33. The weight of an object on or above the earth's surface is inversely proportional to the square of its distance from the center of the earth (use 4000 miles for the radius of the earth). If an astronaut weighs 120 pounds on the surface of the earth, what would be her weight, to the nearest pound, 400 miles above the surface of the earth?

Express the following numbers in decimal notation.

34. 1.85×10^{11} foot-pounds, the work required to put a space shuttle in a 170-mile high orbit

35. 1×10^{-16} centimeters, the diameter of an atomic nucleus

Express the following in scientific notation.

36. 30,000,000,000 centimeters per second, the speed of light

37. 0.000 000 000 001 7 centimeters, the radius of a copper atom's nucleus

Use scientific notation to solve the following problem; write your answer in scientific notation.

38. A certain computer can do one calculation in 0.000 000 3 second. How many minutes would it take the computer to do a trillion (10^{12}) calculations? How many hours?

Graph the following relation, its inverse, and $y = x$ on the same axes. Give their domains and ranges.

39. $S = \{(x, y) \mid y = |x + 1|\}$

Solve the following word problems. Use either one equation or a system of equations. Define your variable(s).

40. If the sum of a number and 1 is divided by 4, then the result is 4. Find the number.

41. The sum of two numbers is 30. Ten times the smaller number added to twice the larger number is 28. Find the numbers.

42. Find three consecutive integers such that 4 times the first plus 6 times the second minus 2 times the third is 42.

43. Find four consecutive even integers such that when the sum of the squares of the first three is added to the fourth, the result is the square of the fourth.

44. The sum of the squares of a number and 3 times the number is 90. Find the number.

45. Two numbers are in the ratio 7 : 2. Their difference is 20. Find the numbers.

46. The sum of the reciprocals of two consecutive integers is 11 divided by the product of the integers. What are the integers?

47. The numerator of a fraction is 13 less than twice the denominator. If 7 is added to the numerator and the denominator is doubled, then the new fraction is 2/5. Find the original fraction.

48. The sum of the squares of two numbers is 2. The difference of their squares is 4. Find the numbers.

49. The length of a rectangle is twice its width. The area is numerically 20 more than the perimeter. Find its length and width.

50. The two sides of an isosceles triangle are 6 meters less than the third side. The lengths of the sides are to be natural numbers, and the perimeter is to be no less than 47 meters. What are the smallest possible lengths of the sides of the triangle?

51. The combined perimeters of a square and a triangle is 26 centimeters. The shortest side of the triangle is the same as the side of the square. The longer side of the triangle is 1 less than twice the shortest side, and the longest side is 3 more than the shortest side. Find the dimensions of the two figures.

52. The height of a right circular cylinder is one-half its radius. The surface area is 108π square feet. Find its radius, height, and volume.

53. Find the volume and surface area of a rectangular room that is 6 meters long, 4 meters wide, and 3 meters high.

54. The general formula of the equation of a circle is $x^2 + y^2 + Dx + Ey + F = 0$ (see Section 9.1). Find *D, E,* and *F* so that a circle contains the points (3, 2), (3, 0), and (4, 1). *Hint*: Use the three points to write three equations in three variables and then solve the system of equations.

55. The number 37 is .5% of what other number?

56. What amounts of 70% pure silver and 85% pure silver should be melted together to yield 30 grams of 76% pure silver?

57. How much pure alcohol should be added to 15 liters of a 40% alcohol solution to obtain a 50% alcohol solution?

58. Gail inherited $8500. She invested part of it in a mutual fund at 12% and the rest in bonds at 7.5%. The annual interest earned from the mutual funds was $45 more than the income earned from the bonds. How much did she invest at each rate?

59. Roland invested a certain amount of money at 8.75% and $2000 less than this amount at 12.5%. The investment at 12.5% earned $125 more than the investment at 8.75%. How much did he invest at each rate?

60. Claudette's scores on four English exams are 86%, 91%, 97%, and 82%. What percent of the fifth test must she get correct to have an average of 90%?

61. To earn an A in her algebra class, Susan needs a final average of at least 90%. A possible 600 points based on four tests, quizzes, and homework, can be earned during the semester. The final exam is worth 200 points. Her six class scores are 88, 92, 94, 85, 91, and 86. What is the least number of points she must earn on the final exam to get an A in the class?

62. Avital has $1.65 in nickels and dimes. If she has 21 coins, how many are nickels and how many are dimes?

63. Ted has 80 pennies, nickels, and quarters. He has 6 times as many nickels as pennies and 8

more quarters than pennies. How many coins of each type does he have?

64. Marsha is four years younger than Wendy. Six years from now Wendy will be nine times as old as Marsha was six years ago. Find their current ages.

65. Two cars are traveling in the same direction; one car is 50 kilometers ahead of the other. The one in front is traveling 60 km/h, and the second car is traveling 70 km/h. How long does it take the second car to overtake the first?

66. The speed of a river is 3 mph. A boat can travel 2 miles up river in the same time that it travels 3 miles down river. Find the speed of the boat in still water.

67. Chicago is 450 miles northeast of Kansas City. A car leaves Kansas City driving due east; 6.5 hours later a small plane leaves Chicago flying due south at a speed 3 times the car's speed. The car and the plane pass each other 1.5 hours after the plane leaves Chicago. Find the speed of the car (to the nearest mile per hour) and the distance they each travel.

68. The sum of the heights of Mt. Everest and Mt. Shasta is 43,300 feet. If Mt. Everest were 860 feet higher and Mt. Shasta were 4160 feet lower, then Mt. Everest would be three times the height of Mt. Shasta. How high is each mountain?

69. A carpenter has to cut a 20-foot board into three pieces. The second piece has to be 1 foot longer than the shortest piece, and the longest piece has to be 3 feet longer than twice the shortest piece. How long is each piece?

70. An 88-inch board is cut into three pieces in the ratio 5 : 8 : 9. Find the length of each piece.

71. A medicine prescription for a 30-pound dog states that the animal is to be given 150 milliliters of the medicine per day. If this ratio is the same for all dogs, what is the correct dosage for a 75-pound dog?

72. Jorge has to write a 750-word paper on Kafka. After taking 5 days to write 2 pages, he found that they contained 323 words. At this rate, how many pages must he write to complete the paper? How long will it take him to write the paper?

73. Bill takes 4 hours longer to mow a lawn than Al takes. Working together they can mow the lawn in 4 hours and 48 minutes. How long would Al need to mow the lawn by himself?

74. An arrow is shot straight upward from 6 feet above the ground. Its height above the ground as a function of time t is given by

$$h(t) = -16t + 64t + 6$$

Find the maximum height the arrow reaches. When will it reach this height?

75. The difference of two numbers is 1. What is the smallest possible value for the sum of their squares? What are the two numbers?

TEN

Exponential and Logarithmic Functions

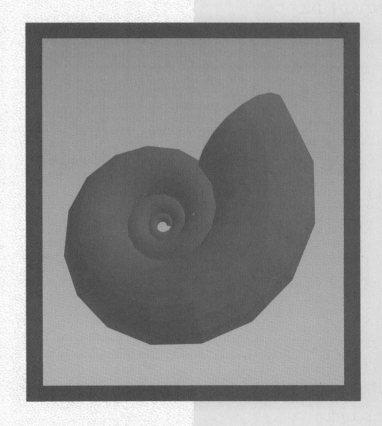

*The ammonite is an example of a logarithmic spiral; the logarithm
of the radius, r, is proportional to the angle, θ, around the center.
Exponentially $r = ae^{b\theta}$.*

Chapter 7 discussed rational exponents and their properties. We will now use this material to study two new functions: the exponential function and its inverse, the logarithmic function. An example of an exponential function is $f(x) = 2^x$. Logarithms are exponents, and their properties are actually the properties of exponents. For instance, the solution of $10^x = 2$ is $x \approx .3$, which is a logarithm.

Logarithms were developed in the early seventeenth century to simplify computations in astronomy and navigation. With the development of calculators, this use has become obsolete. However, these functions still have many important applications in mathematics and the sciences. Logarithmic functions are used to determine the pH of a solution in chemistry and to measure the magnitude of an earthquake in geology. Exponential functions are used to calculate the growth of bacteria in biology and to estimate the decay of radioactive material in nuclear medicine.

10.1 EXPONENTIAL FUNCTIONS

1	Graphing the Function $f(x) = b^x$
2	Graphing the Function $f(x) = e^x$
3	Solving Exponential Equations

1   Graphing the Function $f(x) = b^x$

This section will discuss the graph and properties of the exponential function $f(x) = b^x$. The next section will consider the inverse of f, the logarithmic function.

A function in which a variable appears in an exponent is called an **exponential function**. For example,

$$f(x) = 2^x, \qquad g(x) = (1/2)^x, \qquad \text{and} \qquad f(x) = 3^{x/2} - 1$$

are exponential functions. To graph these functions we need the properties that if $b \neq 0$, then

$$b^0 = 1 \qquad \text{and} \qquad b^{-n} = 1/b^n$$

EXAMPLE 1

Sketch the graphs of the following functions. Find their domains and ranges.

a. $f(x) = 2^x$ **b.** $h(x) = (1/2)^x$

SOLUTION   **a.** Let $x = -2, -1, 0, 1$, and 2. Then
$$f(-2) = 2^{-2} = 1/2^2 = 1/4 \quad f(-1) = 2^{-1} = 1/2$$
$$f(0) = 2^0 = 1 \qquad\qquad\qquad f(1) = 2^1 = 2$$
$$f(2) = 2^2 = 4$$
Thus, the set $\{(-2, 1/4), (-1, 1/2), (0, 1), (1, 2), (2, 4)\}$ determines the graph of $f(x) = 2^x$ (Figure 10.1). From the graph we can see that $D_f = \mathbb{R}$ and $R_f = (0, \infty)$, because $2^x > 0$ for all real numbers x. Notice that the negative x-axis is the asymptote of f (see the graph of $xy = -2$, Figure 9.12, Section 9.2).

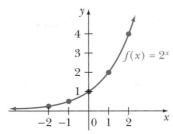

FIGURE 10.1

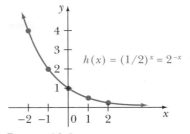

FIGURE 10.2

b. $h(x) = (1/2)^x = (2^{-1})^x = 2^{-x}$

2^{-x} is sometimes more convenient than $(1/2)^x$. Let $x = -2, -1, 0, 1,$ and 2. Then

$h(-2) = 2^{-(-2)} = 2^2 = 4$ $h(-1) = 2^{-(-1)} = 2$
   $h(0) = (1/2)^0 = 1$ $h(1) = (1/2)^1 = 1/2$
   $h(2) = (1/2)^2 = 1/4$

Thus, the set $\{(-2, 4), (-1, 2), (0, 1), (1, 1/2), (2, 1/4)\}$ determines the graph of h (Figure 10.2). $D_h = \mathbb{R}$, $R_h = (0, \infty)$, and the positive x-axis is the asymptote of h.

From our study of rational exponents, we know that $2^{1/2} = \sqrt{2}$ and that 2^x is a real number for any rational number x. A discussion of irrational powers, such as 2^π and $2^{\sqrt{3}}$, is beyond the scope of this book. However, they are real numbers, and $(\pi, 2^\pi)$ and $(\sqrt{3}, 2^{\sqrt{3}})$ are points on the graph of $f(x) = 2^x$. Thus, we will assume that b^x is a real number for all real values of x, when $b > 0$.

We now turn to the general case, $f(x) = b^x$, where b is called the **base**. Certain restrictions are placed on b. If b were negative, say -4, and $x = 1/2$, then $(-4)^{1/2} = \sqrt{-4} = 2i$, which is not a real number. If $b = 0$, then $0^x = 0$, $x \neq 0$, and if $b = 1$, then $1^x = 1$. Thus, for $b = 0$ or 1 we have a constant function.

If $b > 0$ and $b \neq 1$, then

$$f(x) = b^x$$

is the exponential function with base b.

The graph of $f(x) = 2^x$ is typical of the case when $b > 1$, and the graph of $h(x) = (1/2)^x$ is representative of the case where $0 < b < 1$. The graphs of $f(x) = b^x$ are given in Figures 10.3 and 10.4. Because $b^0 = 1$, the point $(0, 1)$ is on the graph of $f(x) = b^x$. Because $b^1 = b$, $(1, b)$ is a point on the graph. The domain of f is $\mathbb{R}$, and the range is the interval $(0, \infty)$. From the graphs we can see that if $x_1 \neq x_2$, then $b^{x_1} \neq b^{x_2}$, so f is one-to-one. Therefore, if $b^{x_1} = b^{x_2}$, then $x_1 = x_2$. Finally, the x-axis is the asymptote of $f(x) = b^x$.

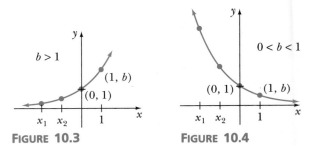

FIGURE 10.3   **FIGURE 10.4**

Properties of $f(x) = b^x$

1. $f(0) = 1$ and $f(1) = b$
2. $D_f = \mathbb{R}$ and $R_f = (0,\infty)$
3. f is one-to-one.
4. $x_1 = x_2$ if and only if $b^{x_1} = b^{x_2}$.
5. The x-axis, $y = 0$, is the asymptote of f.

Many other types of exponential functions exist besides $f(x) = b^x$. Some examples are $f(x) = 2(3^x)$, $f(x) = 5^{x+1}$, and $f(x) = 3^{x/2} - 1$. Such a function can be graphed by finding a set of ordered pairs that satisfy the equation, determining the equation of its asymptote, and knowing the basic shape of $y = b^x$.

The function $f(x) = 3^{x/2} - 1$ is graphed in Example 2. If we subtract 1 from the y-coordinate of each ordered pair that satisfies $y = 3^{x/2}$, then we lower its graph by one unit. Thus, the asymptote of $y = 3^{x/2}, y = 0$, will also be lowered one unit. Thus, $y = -1$ is the asymptote of $f(x) = 3^{x/2} - 1$. In general, $y = k$ is the asymptote of $f(x) = b^x + k$ (k a constant).

EXAMPLE 2   Graph $f(x) = 3^{x/2} - 1$ and its asymptote.

SOLUTION   To avoid radicals let $x = -2, 0$, and 2. Then
$f(-2) = 3^{-2/2} - 1 = 3^{-1} - 1 = 1/3 - 1 = -2/3$
$f(0) = 3^{0/2} - 1 = 3^0 - 1 = 1 - 1 = 0$
$f(2) = 3^{2/2} - 1 = 3 - 1 = 2$
The points $\{(-2, -2/3), (0, 0), (2, 2)\}$ are on the graph of f, and $y = -1$ is the asymptote of $f(x) = 3^{x/2} - 1$ (**see Figure 10.5**).

FIGURE 10.5

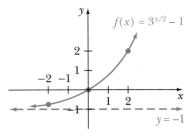

2 Graphing the Function $f(x) = e^x$

We now introduce the number e, which is suggested perhaps by the first letter of the word "exponential" and is one of the most important constants in mathematics. The number e is irrational and, to five decimal places,

$$e = 2.71828\ldots$$

We will define this number in terms of area between the x-axis and the hyperbola $y = 1/x$. Before doing this we will illustrate this concept of area with a simple example.

Consider the triangle in the first quadrant determined by the x-axis, the line $y = 2x$, and a vertical line segment at $x = 2$ (Figure 10.6). The triangle's base is 2 and its height is 4, so its area is $A = 1/2(2)(4) = 4$; that is, the area between the x-axis and the line $y = 2x$ from $x = 0$ to $x = 2$ is 4 square units.

We discussed and graphed the hyperbola $y = 1/x$ in Example 3a of Section 9.2. Examine the area in the first quadrant determined by the x-axis, the curve $y = 1/x$, and vertical line segments at $x = 1$ and $x = e$ (Figure 10.7). The number e is defined to be the number such that the area between the x-axis and the hyperbola $y = 1/x$ from $x = 1$ to $x = e$ is 1 square unit. This definition connects the hyperbolic function $f(x) = 1/x$ and the exponential function $f(x) = e^x$. This important relationship is explored in calculus.

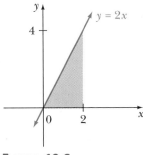

FIGURE 10.6   **FIGURE 10.7**

To graph exponential functions using e as a base, we can use 2.72 as an approximation for e and express the functional values to the nearest tenth. We can easily find these values by using a calculator.

EXAMPLE 3

Graph $f(x) = e^x$.

SOLUTION   Let $x = -2, -1, 0$, and 1, and let $e \approx 2.72$. Then

$$f(-2) = e^{-2} = \frac{1}{e^2} = \frac{1}{(2.72)^2} = \frac{1}{7.40} = .1 \quad \text{Use your } 1/x \text{ key.}$$

$$f(-1) = e^{-1} = \frac{1}{e} = \frac{1}{2.72} = .4$$

$$f(0) = e^0 = 1 \qquad\qquad\qquad b^0 = 1$$

$$f(1) = e^1 = e = 2.7$$

(continued)

The set $\{(-2, .1), (-1, .4), (0, 1), (1, 2.7)\}$ determines the graph of $f(x) = e^x$ (see Figure 10.8).

FIGURE 10.8

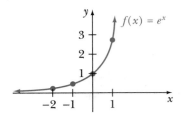

---

3   **Solving Exponential Equations**

An **exponential equation** is an equation in which the unknown is an exponent or part of an exponential expression. Two examples are

$$2^x = 16 \qquad \text{and} \qquad 7^x = 81^{2x-1}$$

We can solve $2^x = 16$ by using the following property.

$$\text{If } b^{x_1} = b^{x_2}, \quad \text{then} \quad x_1 = x_2. \text{ Thus,}$$
$$2^x = 16$$
$$2^x = 2^4, \quad \text{so}$$
$$x = 4$$

We will leave the solution of $7^x = 81^{2x-1}$ to Section 10.4 because it cannot be written as $b^{x_1} = b^{x_2}$. In general, if an exponential equation can be expressed as $b^{x_1} = b^{x_2}$, then we can let $x_1 = x_2$ and solve for x.

EXAMPLE 4

Solve the following equations.

a. $e^{2x} = \dfrac{1}{e^6}$ **b.** $25^{4y} = \dfrac{1}{125}$ **c.** $7^{3x-4} = 1$

d. $9(3^{2x}) = 27^{1-x}$

SOLUTION

a. $e^{2x} = \dfrac{1}{e^6}$

$e^{2x} = e^{-6}$

$2x = -6 \quad \text{and} \quad x = -3$

b. $25^{4y} = \dfrac{1}{125}$

$(5^2)^{4y} = \dfrac{1}{5^3}$

$5^{8y} = 5^{-3}$

$8y = -3 \quad \text{and} \quad y = -3/8$

c. Because $b^0 = 1$, for $b \neq 0$, let $1 = 7^0$

$7^{3x-4} = 1$

$7^{3x-4} = 7^0$

$3x - 4 = 0 \quad \text{and} \quad x = 4/3$

d. $9(3^{2x}) = 27^{1-x}$

$3^2(3^{2x}) = (3^3)^{1-x}$

$3^{2+2x} = 3^{3-3x}$

$2 + 2x = 3 - 3x$ and $x = 1/5$

EXERCISE SET 10.1

A

1 ⊞ Graph the following and their asymptotes.

1. $f(x) = 3^x$

2. $f(x) = 4^x$

3. $f(x) = 5^x$

4. $g(x) = \left(\dfrac{1}{3}\right)^x$

5. $g(x) = \left(\dfrac{1}{4}\right)^x$

6. $g(x) = 5^{-x}$

7. $f(x) = 6^{-x}$

8. $h(x) = 10^x$

9. $y = (.75)^x$

10. $y = \left(\dfrac{2}{3}\right)^x$

11. $y = \left(\dfrac{4}{3}\right)^x$

12. $y = (3.2)^x$

13. $f(x) = 2(3^x)$

14. $g(x) = 3(2^{-x})$

15. $y = 2^{2x}$

16. $y = 3^{-x/3}$

17. $y = 4^{x-2}$

18. $y = 2^{x+1}$

19. $y = 3^x + 1$

20. $y = 2^x - 3$

21. $y = 2^{-x} + 2$

2

22. $f(x) = e^{-x}$

23. $f(x) = -e^x$

24. $y = e^{-2x}$

25. $y = .5e^{x/2}$

26. $y = 1.2e^{-x}$

27. $y = e^x - 2$

28. $y = e^x + 1$

29. $y = e^{-x} + 3$

30. $y = e^{-x} - 1$

3 Solve the following equations. If no solutions exist, write Ø.

31. $5^x = 25$

32. $3^x = 81$

33. $2^{-x} = 32$

34. $5^{-2x} = 5^{6x-3}$

35. $6^{3x} = 36^{x+1}$

36. $8^x = 16^{4x-1}$

37. $5x = -1$

38. $e^{3x} = e^{7x-2}$

39. $1 = e^{2x+6}$

40. $6^{3x+5} = 1$

41. $\dfrac{1}{9} = 27^{2x}$

42. $\left(\dfrac{1}{5}\right)^{2x} = 125^{x+1}$

43. $e^{x+5} = \dfrac{1}{e^{6x}}$

44. $\left(\dfrac{2}{3}\right)^x = \dfrac{9}{4}$

45. $\left(\dfrac{3}{4}\right)^{2x} = \dfrac{64}{27}$

46. $4^x = 0$

47. $3^x(3^{x+1}) = 9$

48. $8(2^x) = 64$

49. $27^{-x} = 81^{3x+1}$

50. $7^{3x} = 1 - 7^0$

51. $2^x(2^{3x}) = 1$

B

52. $10^x = .01$

53. $10^x = .0001$

54. $\dfrac{1}{4^x} = 32$

55. $\dfrac{1}{9^{2x-4}} = 1$

56. $\dfrac{2^{x-1}}{2^{3-4x}} = 16^x$

57. $\dfrac{3^{1-x}}{3^x} = 9^{5x}$

Graph the following equations.

58. $y = 2^{x^2}$

59. $y = e^{x^2}$

60. $y = e^{-x^2}$

61. $y = 3^{-x^2}$

62. $y = 2^{|x|}$

63. $y = e^{|x|}$

C ✎

Answer the following questions with complete sentences.

64. Why do we not allow the base of an exponential function to be a negative number?

65. Explain why the equation $2^x = -2$ has no solution.

REVIEW EXERCISES

Given the relation S, find S^{-1} and their domains and ranges. Decide whether S is a function, and, if so, whether it is a one-to-one function. (See Section 3.6.)

66. $S = \{(1, 3), (2, 7), (6, 8)\}$

67. $S = \{(x, y) \mid y = 3\}$

68. $S = \{(x, y) \mid y = x^2\}$

69. $S = \{(x, y) \mid y = 2x\}$

Solve the following equations. (See Section 7.2.)

70. $x^{2/3} = 25$ **71.** $x^{3/2} = 27$

72. $x^{-3/4} = 8$

10.2 LOGARITHMIC FUNCTIONS

1 Graphing the Function $g(x) = \log_b x$

2 Converting Between Logarithmic and Exponential Forms

3 Solving Logarithmic Equations; Roots of a Logarithmic Function

1 **Graphing the Function $g(x) = \log_b x$**

The last section discussed several properties of the exponential function. This section will use this knowledge to establish the basic properties of the inverse of the exponential function, the **logarithmic function**.

We begin with the function $f(x) = 2^x$. The graph of f (Figure 10.1) is determined by the ordered pairs $\{(-2, 1/4), (-1, 1/2), (0, 1), (1, 2), (2, 4)\}$. Thus, $\{(1/4, -2), (1/2, -1), (1, 0), (2, 1), (4, 2)\}$ determines the graph of f^{-1}. Because the negative x-axis is the asymptote of f, the negative y-axis is the asymptote of f^{-1}. Both f and f^{-1} are graphed in Figure 10.9; note that they are symmetric with respect to the line $y = x$. Because f is a one-to-one function, f^{-1} is a one-to-one function. Also, $D_{f^{-1}} = R_f = (0, \infty)$ and $R_{f^{-1}} = D_f = \mathbb{R}$.

FIGURE 10.9

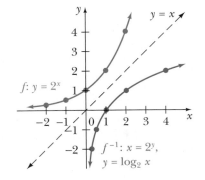

We found the equation of the inverse of a linear function, such as $k(x) = 2x + 3$, by interchanging x and y and solving for y; that is, k is the function $y = 2x + 3$, and k^{-1} is the function $x = 2y + 3$. This relationship is often written

$$k: \quad y = 2x + 3 \qquad \text{and} \qquad k^{-1}: \quad x = 2y + 3$$

So, if

$$f: \quad y = 2^x \qquad \text{then} \qquad f^{-1}: \quad x = 2^y$$

We can solve $x = 2y + 3$ for y, $y = (x - 3)/2$; but we cannot solve $x = 2^y$ for y. Instead, we give the inverse of $f(x) = 2^x$ the name *logarithm base 2 of x*, which is denoted $f^{-1}(x) = y = \log_2 x$; that is,

$$y = \log_2 x \quad \text{if and only if} \quad x = 2^y$$

We have not done something mysterious; we have only given a name to the inverse of $f(x) = 2^x$. The following examples illustrate this definition:

$$\log_2 1 = 0 \qquad \text{because} \qquad 1 = 2^0$$
$$\log_2 2 = 1 \qquad \text{because} \qquad 2 = 2^1$$

As an example of the case $0 < b < 1$, we return to $h(x) = (1/2)^x$. Its graph (Figure 10.2) is determined by $\{(-2, 4), (-1, 2), (0, 1), (1, 1/2), (2, 1/4)\}$, so $\{(4, -2), (2, -1), (1, 0), (1/2, 1), (1/4, 2)\}$ gives us the graph of f^{-1} (Figure 10.10). Note that the positive y-axis is the asymptote of h^{-1}.

FIGURE 10.10

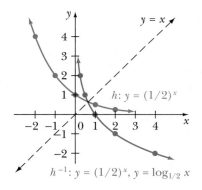

In general, we will let g be the inverse of $f(x) = b^x$; g is the **logarithmic function with base b,** and

$$y = g(x) = \log_b x \quad \text{if and only if} \quad x = b^y$$

The two most important bases are e and 10. These are denoted by

$$\ln x = \log_e x \qquad \text{and} \qquad \log x = \log_{10} x$$

We call $\ln x$ the **natural logarithm** and $\log x$ the **common logarithm.** All other logarithms have their bases indicated, such as $\log_2 x$ and $\log_3 x$. The properties of $g(x) = \log_b x$ generalize from the two examples just considered (see Figures 10.11 and 10.12). The following is a summary of these properties and the graphs of g (see Figures 10.3 and 10.4 for the graphs of f).

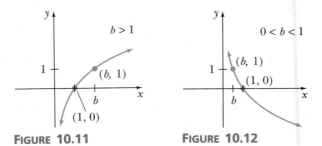

FIGURE 10.11   **FIGURE 10.12**

Properties of $g(x) = \overline{\log_b x}$

1. $y = \log_b x$ if and only if $x = b^y$.

2. $\log_b 1 = 0$ and $\log_b b = 1$

3. $D_g = (0, \infty)$ and $R_g = \mathbb{R}$

4. g is one-to-one.

5. $x_1 = x_2$ if and only if $\log_b x_1 = \log_b x_2$.

6. The y-axis, $x = 0$, is the asymptote of g.

The introduction to this chapter stated that logarithms are exponents. This statement can be justified with Property (1). If we substitute $y = \log_b x$ in $x = b^y$, we have $x = b^{\log_b x}$. This result is not important at this level and is mentioned only in passing. As another aside, logarithms of negative numbers exist, but they are imaginary numbers.* For example, $\ln(-1) = \pi i$.

EXAMPLE 1

Sketch the graphs of

a. $g(x) = \ln x$ **b.** $g(x) = \log x$

SOLUTION

a. The graph of $f(x) = e^x$ (Figure 10.8) is given by $\{(-2, .1), (-1, .4), (0, 1), (1, 2.7)\}$, so $\{(.1, -2), (.4, -1), (1, 0), (2.7, 1)\}$ determines the graph of $g(x) = \ln x$ (see Figure 10.13).

b. $y = g(x) = \log x = \log_{10} x$ iff $x = 10^y$.
   If $y = -1$,   then $x = 10^{-1} = 1/10$.
   If $y = 0$,   then $x = 10^0 = 1$.
   If $y = 1$,   then $x = 10^1 = 10$.

---

* The five most important constants in mathematics are 0, 1, π, e, and i. They are related by the equation $e^{\pi i} + 1 = 0$. Someone once said, "This is a very important equation, but nobody is quite sure what it means." Another interesting result is that i^i is a real number, and $i^i = e^{-\pi/2}$. This material is explored in advanced mathematics.

Thus, $\{(1/10, -1), (1, 0), (10, 1)\}$ and the asymptote $x = 0$ determine the graph of $g(x) = \log x$ (it is not drawn to scale in Figure 10.14).

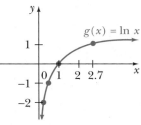

FIGURE 10.13   **FIGURE 10.14**

The domain of $y = \log_b x$ is $x > 0$, and the asymptote of this function is $x = 0$. Therefore, the domain of $y = \log_b (ax + c)$ is $ax + c > 0$ or $x > -c/a$, and $x = -c/a$ is the asymptote of this function. These concepts are used in the following example.

EXAMPLE 2   Sketch the graph of $y = \log_3 (x + 1)$ and its asymptote.

SOLUTION   The domain is $x + 1 > 0$ or $x > -1$. Thus, $x = -1$ is the equation of the asymptote. To find some points on the graph, convert the equation to its exponential form. If $y = \log_3 (x + 1)$, then

$$x + 1 = 3^y \qquad y = \log_b x \quad \text{iff} \quad x = b^y$$
$$x = 3^y - 1$$

If $y = -1$, then $x = 3^{-1} - 1 = 1/3 - 1 = -2/3$.
If $y = 0$, then $x = 3^0 - 1 = 1 - 1 = 0$.
If $y = 1$, then $x = 3^1 - 1 = 2$.
Thus, the set $\{(-2/3, -1), (0,0), (2,1)\}$ and the asymptote determine the graph of the function (Figure 10.15).

FIGURE 10.15

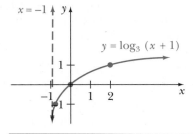

2   Converting Between Logarithmic and Exponential Forms

The last two examples used the property that $y = \log_b x$ iff $x = b^y$ to help graph logarithmic functions. Many occasions require the conversion of a logarithmic form to an exponential form or an exponential form to a logarithmic form. The next two examples illustrate this process.

EXAMPLE 3   Convert the following to exponential form.

a. $\log_3 81 = 4$ **b.** $\log_{36} 6 = 1/2$ **c.** $\log 1 = 0$
d. $\ln e = 1$

SOLUTION   If $\log_b x = y$, then $x = b^y$.
a. $\log_3 81 = 4$ so $81 = 3^4$
b. $\log_{36} 6 = 1/2$ so $6 = 36^{1/2}$
c. $\log 1 = 0$ so $1 = 10^0$
d. $\ln e = 1$ so $e = e^1$

EXAMPLE 4   Convert the following to logarithmic form.

a. $5^2 = 25$ **b.** $\sqrt[3]{8} = 2$ **c.** $\left(\dfrac{1}{4}\right)^{-2} = 16$ **d.** $7^0 = 1$
e. $7^1 = 7$

SOLUTION   If $b^y = x$, then $y = \log_b x$.
a. $5^2 = 25$ so $2 = \log_5 25$
b. $\sqrt[3]{8} = 8^{1/3} = 2$ so $1/3 = \log_8 2$

c. $\left(\dfrac{1}{4}\right)^{-2} = 16$ so $-2 = \log_{1/4} 16$

d. $7^0 = 1$ so $0 = \log_7 1$ $\log_b 1 = 0$
e. $7^1 = 7$ so $1 = \log_7 7$ $\log_b b = 1$

3   Solving Logarithmic Equations; Roots of a Logarithmic Function

We now consider logarithmic equations. The first type is $y = \log_b x$, which can be solved for one variable, given the other two. The second type uses the fact that $g(x) = \log_b x$ is one-to-one, so if $\log_b x_1 = \log_b x_2$, then $x_1 = x_2$. The next section explores this kind of equation in greater depth.

A convenient way to work with $y = \log_b x$ is to convert it to $x = b^y$ and then use the properties of exponents. In Example 5c we have to solve $x^{m/n} = k$ for x (see Section 7.2).

EXAMPLE 5   Solve the following for the unknown variables.

a. $\log x = 2$ **b.** $\log_3 \sqrt{3} = y$ **c.** $\log_b 8 = 3/2$
d. $\log_2 (x + 4) = 3$ **e.** $y = \log_5 5^{-3}$

SOLUTION $y = \log_b x$ iff $x = b^y$
a. $\log x = 2$,   so $x = 10^2 = 100$
b. $\log_3 \sqrt{3} = y$,   so $3^y = \sqrt{3} = 3^{1/2}$,   and $y = 1/2$
c. $\log_b 8 = 3/2$,   so
$$b^{3/2} = 8 \qquad \text{Raise both sides to the 2/3 power.}$$
$$(b^{3/2})^{2/3} = (2^3)^{2/3}$$
$$b^1 = 2^2$$
$$b = 4$$

d. $\log_2 (x + 4) = 3$, so
$$x + 4 = 2^3 = 8$$
$$x = 4$$
e. $y = \log_5 5^{-3}$, so $5^{-3} = 5^y$, and $y = -3$

In Example 6c and 6d we use the properties $0 = \log_b 1$ and $1 = \log_b b$. Note that we could also solve these equations by converting them to $x = b^y$.

EXAMPLE 6

Solve the following for x.

a. $\log_3 (4x - 6) = \log_3 (2x + 4)$
b. $\ln x = \ln (2x + 4)$ **c.** $\log_8 (2x - 7) = 0$
d. $\log_9 x^2 = 1$

SOLUTION

a. If $\log_3 (4x - 6) = \log_3 (2x + 4)$, then
$$4x - 6 = 2x + 4$$
$$x = 5$$
b. If $\ln x = \ln (2x + 4)$, then
$$x = 2x + 4$$
$$x = -4$$
Now if $x = -4$, then $\ln (-4)$ is not a real number. Thus, the solution is Ø, the empty set.
c. $\log_8 (2x - 7) = 0$ $0 = \log_b 1$
$\log_8 (2x - 7) = \log_8 1$, so
$$2x - 7 = 1$$
$$x = 4$$
d. $\log_9 x^2 = 1$ $1 = \log_b b$
$\log_9 x^2 = \log_9 9$
$$x^2 = 9$$
$$x = 3 \text{ or } -3$$
Note that $x = -3$ is acceptable because the domain of $\log_9 x^2$ is $x^2 > 0$, or all $x \neq 0$. Thus, the solution is $\{3, -3\}$.

From Figures 10.11 and 10.12, we can see that $\log_b 1 = 0$; that is, the root of the function $f(x) = \log_b x$ is $x = 1$. In general, if $f(x) = \log_b A$, where A is an algebraic expression, then we find the roots of f by solving the equation $A = 1$. Example 7 illustrates this method. We will only consider functions whose roots are real numbers.

EXAMPLE 7

Find the roots of the given function.

a. $f(x) = \log_2 (2x - 7)$ **b.** $f(x) = \ln (x^2 - 3)$
c. $f(x) = \log \dfrac{x - 1}{3x - 2}$

(continued)

SOLUTION   **a.** $\log_2 (2x - 7) = 0$ if $2x - 7 = 1$, because $\log_2 1 = 0.$
$$2x - 7 = 1$$
$$2x = 8$$
$$x = 4$$
The root is 4. Thus, $f(4) = \log_2 1 = 0.$

b. $x^2 - 3 = 1$
$$x^2 = 4$$
$$x = \pm\sqrt{4} = \pm 2$$
Thus, $\{2, -2\}$ are the roots.

c. $\dfrac{x - 1}{3x - 2} = 1$ Multiply by $3x - 2.$
$$x - 1 = 3x - 2$$
$$-2x - 1 = -2$$
$$-2x = -1$$
$$x = \frac{1}{2}$$
The root is 1/2.

EXERCISE SET 10.2

A

1 Graph the function f, its inverse g, and $y = x$ on the same set of axes (see Exercise Set 10.1, Exercises 1–6).

1. $f(x) = 3^x$

2. $f(x) = 4^x$

3. $f(x) = 5^x$

4. $f(x) = \left(\frac{1}{3}\right)^x$

5. $f(x) = \left(\frac{1}{4}\right)^x$

6. $f(x) = 5^{-x}$

Graph the following and their asymptotes. Give the domain and range of each function.

7. $y = \log_2 x + 2$

8. $y = \log_2 (x + 2)$

9. $y = \log_{1/3} (x - 1)$

10. $y = \log_{1/3} x - 1$

11. $y = \ln (x - 2)$

12. $y = \log x - 4$

13. $y = \log_4 (2x - 5)$

14. $y = \ln (4x + 9)$

Find the domains of the following (see Section 8.6).

15. $y = \log (x^2 - 1)$

16. $y = \ln (x^2 + 1)$

17. $y = \ln (x^3 - 9x)$

18. $y = \log_2 (x^2 + x - 2)$

19. $y = \log \dfrac{x - 1}{x + 2}$

20. $y = \ln \dfrac{x + 3}{x + 4}$

21. $y = \log_3 \dfrac{3x - 2}{x + 3}$

22. $y = \log_5 \dfrac{x^2 - 4}{x}$

2 Convert the following to exponential form.

23. $\log_2 32 = 5$

24. $\log 100 = 2$

25. $\ln 1 = 0$

26. $\log_{12} 12 = 1$

27. $\log_3 \left(\dfrac{1}{27}\right) = -3$

28. $\log_2 \left(\dfrac{1}{2}\right) = -1$

29. $\log_{25} 5 = \dfrac{1}{2}$

30. $\log_8 \left(\dfrac{1}{2}\right) = -\dfrac{1}{3}$

Convert the following to logarithmic form.

31. $2^4 = 16$

32. $3^{-2} = \dfrac{1}{9}$

33. $81^{1/4} = 3$

34. $32^{-1/5} = \dfrac{1}{2}$

35. $\left(\dfrac{1}{2}\right)^{-3} = 8$

36. $\left(\dfrac{2}{3}\right)^{-1} = \dfrac{3}{2}$

37. $5^1 = 5$

38. $5^0 = 1$

3 Solve the following for the unknown variables.

39. $y = \log_{11} 1$

40. $y = \log 1000$

41. $y = \log 1/10$

42. $y = \log_5 \sqrt{5}$

43. $\log_3 x = 0$

44. $\log_2 x = 6$

45. $\ln x = -1/3$ **46.** $\log_5 x = -2$

47. $\log_b 27 = 3$ **48.** $\log_b 1/16 = -2$

49. $\log_b 4 = -1$ **50.** $\log_b 32 = -5$

51. $\log_b 16 = 4/3$ **52.** $\log_b 27 = 3/4$

Solve the following equations.

53. $\log_6 (x - 8) = \log_6 7$

54. $\log_2 3x = \log_2 (2x + 5)$

55. $\log x = \log (3x + 4)$

56. $\log_3 (x^2 + 2) = \log_3 3x$

57. $\log_5 x^2 = \log_5 (6 - x)$

58. $\log_9 x^2 = \log_9 3x$

59. $\ln (3x - 5) = 0$

60. $\log_4 x^2 = 0$

61. $\log_4 x^2 = 1$

62. $\log (2x - 8) = 1$

Find the roots of the following functions.

63. $f(x) = \log_3 (x - 4)$

64. $f(x) = \log (3x + 5)$

65. $g(x) = \ln (x^2 - 8)$

66. $h(x) = \log_2 (x^2 - 12)$

67. $F(x) = \log (2x^2 + x - 2)$

68. $f(x) = \dfrac{x + 1}{2x - 1}$

69. $f(x) = \log \dfrac{2x - 5}{6x + 7}$

70. $G(x) = \dfrac{2x - 6}{x^2 - 3x}$

B

Solve the following equations.

71. $\log (x^2 - 7x) = 1$

72. $\log (x^2 - 2x) = \log 6$

73. $\log_b 5 = 2/3$

74. $\log_2 (x^2 - 1) = 4$

Graph the following.

75. $y = \log_2 |x|$ **76.** $y = \log_{1/2} |x|$

77. $y = \log_3 |x - 1|$ **78.** $y = \log_2 |x + 1|$

C

Answer the following questions with complete sentences.

79. How can we find the graph of $y = \log_3 x$ from the points used to graph $y = 3^x$?

80. What is the difference between the natural logarithm and the common logarithm?

REVIEW EXERCISES

Use the properties of exponents to simplify the following expressions (See Section 5.1.)

81. $(a^3)^4$ **82.** $(x^2)^{-4}$ **83.** $a^3 a^4$

84. $2^7 \cdot 2^{-4}$ **85.** a^4/a^3 **86.** y^8/y^{-4}

10.3 PROPERTIES OF LOGARITHMS

1	Using the Power Rule
2	Using the Product Rule
3	Using the Quotient Rule
4	Solving Logarithmic Equations

1   Using the Power Rule

With the definition of the exponential function and our knowledge of inverse functions the last section developed six properties of the logarithmic function. Because logarithms are exponents, they obey the laws of exponents. This section will use these laws of exponents to justify three new properties of logarithms.

From the law $(a^m)^n = a^{mn}$, we have the **power rule** of logarithms: the logarithm of a number to a power is the product of the power and the logarithm of the number; or $\log_b x^c = c\log_b x$. For example, $\log_2 3^4 = 4\log_2 3$. This seventh property is proved as follows (note that $x > 0$, $b > 0$, and $b \neq 1$):

Property (7) $\log_b x^c = c\log_b x$

Proof: Let $y = \log_b x$. Then $cy = c\log_b x$. Now $x = b^y$, because $y = \log_b x$.

$$x^c = (b^y)^c \qquad (a^m)^n = a^{mn}$$

$$x^c = b^{cy} \qquad \text{Convert to the logarithmic form.}$$

$$\log_b x^c = cy \qquad \text{and} \qquad cy = c\log_b x, \quad \text{so}$$

$$\log_b x^c = c\log_b x$$

EXAMPLE 1

Expand the following expressions.

a. $\log x^7$ **b.** $\log_5 5^{-3}$ **c.** $\log_3 16$ **d.** $\ln \sqrt{5}$

SOLUTION   **a.** $\log x^7 = 7\log x$
b. $\log_5 5^{-3} = -3 \log_5 5 = -3 \cdot 1 = -3 \quad \log_b b = 1$
c. $\log_3 16 = \log_3 2^4 = 4\log_3 2$
d. $\ln \sqrt{5} = \ln 5^{1/2} = \frac{1}{2}\ln 5$

Example 1b generalizes to

Property (8) $\log_b b^c = c$
because $\log_b b^c = c\log_b b = c \cdot 1 = c$. Property (8) also results from the property $y = \log_b x$ iff $x = b^y$. If we substitute $x = b^y$ in $y = \log_b x$, we have $y = \log_b b^y$.

2   Using the Product Rule

From the law $a^m a^n = a^{m+n}$ we have the **product rule** of logarithms: The logarithm of a product is the sum of the logarithms. For example, $\log_2 3 \cdot 5 = \log_2 3 + \log_2 5$. Symbolically,

Property (9) $\log_b x_1 x_2 = \log_b x_1 + \log_b x_2$; $x_1 > 0$ and $x_2 > 0$

Proof: Let $y_1 = \log_b x_1$ and $y_2 = \log_b x_2$. Then

$$x_1 = b^{y_1} \quad \text{and} \quad x_2 = b^{y_2}. \text{ Now}$$

$$\log_b x_1 x_2 = \log_b b^{y_1} b^{y_2} \quad a^m a^n = a^{m+n}$$

$$= \log_b b^{y_1 + y_2} \quad \log_b b^c = c$$

$$= y_1 + y_2$$

$$= \log_b x_1 + \log_b x_2$$

EXAMPLE 2

Expand the following expressions.

a. $\log_2 21$ **b.** $\log_5 10$ **c.** $\log xy^2 z$

SOLUTION

a. $\log_2 21 = \log_2 3 \cdot 7 = \log_2 3 + \log_2 7$

b. $\log_5 10 = \log_5 5 \cdot 2 = \log_5 5 + \log_5 2 = 1 + \log_5 2$

c. $\log xy^2 z = \log x + \log y^2 + \log z$

$$= \log x + 2\log y + \log z$$

---

3 Using the Quotient Rule

Our rule resulting last from the laws of exponents is a consequence of $a^m/a^n = a^{m-n}$. The **quotient rule** states that the logarithm of a quotient is the difference of the logarithms; that is,

Property (10) $\log_b \dfrac{x_1}{x_2} = \log_b x_1 - \log_b x_2$; $x_1 > 0$ and $x_2 > 0$

For example, $\log_5 \dfrac{2}{7} = \log_5 2 - \log_5 7$. The proof of Property (10) is very similar to the proof for (9) and is left as an exercise. A result of Property (10) is

Property (11) $\log_b \dfrac{1}{x} = -\log_b x$; $x > 0$

Proof: $\log_b \dfrac{1}{x} = \log_b 1 - \log_b x = 0 - \log_b x = -\log_b x$

Recall that the rules of exponents only apply to multiplication and division; no rules exist for addition or subtraction. As a result, we cannot write $\log_b (x_1 + x_2)$ as $\log_b x_1 + \log_b x_2$.

**COMMON
ERROR**

The following are common mistakes made with logarithms.

1. $\log_b (x_1 + x_2) \neq \log_b x_1 + \log_b x_2$

2. $\log_b x_1 x_2 \neq (\log_b x_1)(\log_b x_2)$

3. $\log_b \dfrac{x_1}{x_2} \neq \dfrac{\log_b x_1}{\log_b x_2}$

EXAMPLE 3

Use the properties of logarithms to expand the following.

a. $\log_3 \frac{1}{5}$ b. $\log \frac{11}{14}$ c. $\log .0001x^3$ d. $\ln \frac{\sqrt[3]{x^2}}{y^4}$

e. $\ln (x^3 + x^2)$

SOLUTION

a. $\log_3 \frac{1}{5} = -\log_3 5$

b. $\log \frac{11}{14} = \log 11 - \log 14$

$= \log 11 - \log 2 \cdot 7$
$= \log 11 - (\log 2 + \log 7)$
$= \log 11 - \log 2 - \log 7$

c. $\log .0001x^3 = \log 10^{-4}x^3 = \log 10^{-4} + \log x^3$

$= -4 + 3 \log x$ 　　　　　　　　$\log_b b^c = c$

d. $\ln \frac{\sqrt[3]{x^2}}{y^4} = \ln x^{2/3} - \ln y^4$ 　　　　$\sqrt[3]{x^2} = (x^2)^{1/3}$

$= \frac{2}{3} \ln x - 4 \ln y$ 　　　　　　$= x^{2/3}$

e. Note that $\ln (x^3 + x^2) \neq \ln x^3 + \ln x^2$.

$\ln (x^3 + x^2) = \ln x^2(x + 1)$ 　　　　　$\ln x_1 x_2 =$
$= \ln x^2 + \ln (x + 1)$ 　　　　$\ln x_1 + \ln x_2$
$= 2 \ln x + \ln (x + 1)$ 　　　　$\ln x^c = c\ln x$

EXAMPLE 4

Write each of the following as one logarithm.

a. $\ln 2 + 2 \ln 3$ b. $2 \log x - \log y$

c. $3 + \frac{1}{4} \log_2 6$ d. $5 \ln x + \frac{3}{2} \ln y - 2 \ln z$

SOLUTION

a. $\ln 2 + 2 \ln 3 = \ln 2 + \ln 3^2 = \ln 2 \cdot 3^2 = \ln 18$

b. $2 \log x - \log y = \log x^2 - \log y = \log \frac{x^2}{y}$

c. $3 = \log_2 2^3 = \log_2 8$, because $c = \log_b b^c$. Thus,

$3 + \frac{1}{4} \log_2 6 = \log_2 8 + \log_2 6^{1/4}$

$= \log_2 8(6^{1/4})$
$= \log_2 8\sqrt[4]{6}$

d. $5 \ln x + \frac{3}{2} \ln y - 2 \ln z = \ln x^5 + \ln y^{3/2} - \ln z^2$

$= \ln x^5 y^{3/2} - \ln z^2$

$= \ln \frac{x^5 y^{3/2}}{z^2}$

The next example gives the values of $\log x$ for $x = 2, 3,$ and 5 to one decimal place and performs some calculations. These values are approximations of irrational numbers, but for the sake of simplicity we will use the equal sign, $=$, rather than the approximation sign, $\approx$.

EXAMPLE 5 $\log 2 = .3$, $\log 3 = .5$, and $\log 5 = .7$. Use the properties of logarithms to evaluate the following.

a. $\log 6$ b. $\log \sqrt{2.5}$ c. $\log \dfrac{25}{81}$

SOLUTION   a. $\log 6 = \log 2 \cdot 3 = \log 2 + \log 3 = .3 + .5 = .8$

b. $\log \sqrt{2.5} = \log (2.5)^{1/2} = \dfrac{1}{2} \log \dfrac{5}{2}$

$$= \dfrac{1}{2} (\log 5 - \log 2)$$

$$= \dfrac{1}{2} (.7 - .3) = .2$$

c. $\log \dfrac{25}{81} = \log 25 - \log 81 = \log 5^2 - \log 3^4$

$$= 2 \log 5 - 4 \log 3$$
$$= 2(.7) - 4(.5) = -.6$$

4   Solving Logarithmic Equations

In the last section we solved logarithmic equations that were in the form $y = \log_b x$ or $\log_b x_1 = \log_b x_2$. We can now take equations that involve sums, differences, and products, write them in these forms, and then solve them.

EXAMPLE 6 Solve the following equations.

a. $\log_3 x - 2 \log_3 3 = 4$ b. $\log_2 x + \log_2 (x + 2) = 3$

SOLUTION   a. $\log_3 x - 2 \log_3 3 = 4$ $c \log_b x = \log_b x^c$

$\log_3 x - \log_3 3^2 = 4$ $\log_b x_1 - \log_b x_2 = \log_b \dfrac{x_1}{x_2}$

$\log_3 \dfrac{x}{9} = 4$ $\log_b x = y$ iff $x = b^y$

$\dfrac{x}{9} = 3^4$

$x = 729$

b. $\log_2 x + \log_2 (x + 2) = 3$ $\log_b x_1 + \log_b x_2 = \log_b x_1 x_2$

$\log_2 x(x + 2) = 3$

$x(x + 2) = 2^3$

$x^2 + 2x - 8 = 0$

$(x + 4)(x - 2) = 0$

$x = -4$ or $x = 2$

The domain of $\log_b x$ is $(0, \infty)$, so -4 is not a solution. Thus, $x = 2$ is the solution.

EXAMPLE 7

Solve $\log (9x - 2) = 1 + \log (x - 4)$.

SOLUTION A

$$\log (9x - 2) = 1 + \log (x - 4)$$
$$\log (9x - 2) - \log (x - 4) = 1$$
$$\log \frac{9x - 2}{x - 4} = 1$$
$$\frac{9x - 2}{x - 4} = 10^1$$
$$9x - 2 = 10(x - 4)$$
$$x = 38$$

SOLUTION B

$$\log (9x - 2) = 1 + \log (x - 4) \qquad 1 = \log_b b$$
$$\log (9x - 2) = \log 10 + \log (x - 4)$$
$$\log (9x - 2) = \log 10(x - 4)$$
$$9x - 2 = 10(x - 4)$$
$$x = 38$$

EXAMPLE 8

Solve $\ln x - \ln (x - 1) = \frac{1}{2}\ln 4$

SOLUTION

$$\ln x - \ln (x - 1) = \frac{1}{2}\ln 4$$
$$\ln \frac{x}{x - 1} = \ln 4^{1/2} \qquad 4^{1/2} = \sqrt{4} = 2$$
$$\frac{x}{x - 1} = 2$$
$$x = 2x - 2$$
$$x = 2$$

In Section 8.2 we solved equations that are quadratic in form, which are equations that can be written in the form $au^2 + bu + c = 0$. For example, $x^4 - 5x^2 + 4 = 0$ can be written as $u^2 - 5u + 4 = 0$. Many logarithmic equations are quadratic in form, as illustrated in the next example.

EXAMPLE 9

Solve $\ln^2 x = \ln x^5 - 4$

SOLUTION

First write the equation with 0 on one side. Then use the fact that $\ln^2 x = (\ln x)^2 = u^2$:

$$\ln^2 x = \ln x^5 - 4$$
$$\ln^2 x - \ln x^5 + 4 = 0 \qquad\qquad \ln x^5 = 5\ln x$$
$$(\ln x)^2 - 5\ln x + 4 = 0 \qquad\qquad \text{Let } \ln x = u.$$
$$u^2 - 5u + 4 = 0$$
$$(u - 4)(u - 1) = 0$$
$$u = 4 \quad \text{or} \quad u = 1 \qquad u = \ln x$$
$$\ln x = 4 \qquad \ln x = 1 \qquad \text{If } \log_b x = y, \text{ then } x = b^y.$$
$$x = e^4 \quad \text{or} \quad x = e^1$$

Thus, $\{e, e^4\}$ is the solution of the equation.

EXERCISE SET 10.3

A

1 Use the properties of logarithms to expand each expression as far as possible.

1. $\log_2 5^4$ **2.** $\log_6 6^8$

3. $\log 10{,}000$ **4.** $\log_2 \sqrt[3]{3}$

5. $\log_2 \sqrt[4]{9}$ **6.** $\ln \sqrt[3]{e^2}$

2

7. $\log_2 xy$ **8.** $\log_3 35m$

9. $\log_2 22n$ **10.** $\log 500$

11. $\log_2 3x^4$ **12.** $\ln 8y^3$

3

13. $\log \dfrac{3}{5}$ **14.** $\log \dfrac{5}{3}$

15. $\log \dfrac{x^2}{100}$ **16.** $\log \dfrac{1}{7}$

17. $\ln \dfrac{1}{9}$ **18.** $\ln (e^2 + e)$

19. $\log \dfrac{wx}{yz}$ **20.** $\log_2 \dfrac{8x^3}{9y^6}$

21. $\log_3 \dfrac{25x^4}{31y^7}$ **22.** $\ln (x^2 - x)$

23. $\log .01\sqrt{x}$ **24.** $\log_7 49x^4\sqrt{y}$

25. $\log_b x^{2/3}y^{3/4}$ **26.** $\log_b \dfrac{b\sqrt[3]{4}}{\sqrt{5}}$

27. $\log_b x\sqrt{\dfrac{x}{y}}$ **28.** $\log \sqrt[3]{x^2y^4}$

29. $\log \dfrac{y^3\sqrt{z}}{\sqrt[3]{x}}$ **30.** $\ln \sqrt{\dfrac{xy^3}{z^6}}$

31. $\ln \sqrt{ey^5}$ **32.** $\log (x^2 - 2x + 1)$

Write the following as single logarithms.

33. $\log_b x + \log_b y$ **34.** $\log_b x - \log_b y$

35. $3 \log x - 4 \log y$ **36.** $2 \log_3 10 + 4 \log_3 2$

37. $1 + \dfrac{1}{2} \log_2 x$ **38.** $2 - \dfrac{1}{3} \log_5 y$

39. $\log x + \log y - \log z$

40. $2 \ln x - 3 \ln y - \ln z$

41. $4 \ln x - \dfrac{2}{3} \ln y - \ln z$

42. $\dfrac{1}{3} \log 5 - 2 \log x + \dfrac{1}{3} \log 2$

43. $2 \log_3 \sqrt{x} - 3$

44. $\dfrac{3}{2} \ln x - 4$

Given that $\log 2 = .3$, $\log 3 = .5$, $\log 5 = .7$, and $\log 7 = .8$, use the properties of logarithms to evaluate the following. Give the answers correctly to one decimal place.

45. $\log 15$ **46.** $\log \sqrt{7}$

47. $\log 56$ **48.** $\log 30$

49. $\log \dfrac{1}{7}$ **50.** $\log \dfrac{49}{15}$

51. $\log \dfrac{\sqrt{5}}{8}$ **52.** $\log \dfrac{\sqrt[3]{9}}{\sqrt{14}}$

53. $\log .2$ **54.** $\log .07$

55. $\log \sqrt{3.5}$ **56.** $\log \sqrt{.21}$

4 Solve the following equations.

57. $\log_3 4 + \log_3 x = 1$

58. $\log x + \log 5 = 2$

59. $\log 30 - \log 2x = 1$

60. $2 \log_2 3 - \log_2 (x + 1) = 3$

61. $2 \log_3 5 - 4 = \log_3 x$

62. $\log x + \log (x + 3) = 1$

63. $2 \log x = \log 49$

64. $\log x + \log (x - 3) = 1$

65. $\ln (x - 1) - \ln x = \ln 2$

66. $\ln x - \ln (x - 1) = \ln 3$

67. $\ln 5 + \ln (x + 2) = \ln 7$

68. $2 \log 3 - 1 = \log x$

69. $2 - \log x = \log (x + 21)$

70. $2 + \log_3 x = \log_3 (3 - 8x)$

71. $(\ln x)^2 = \ln x^2$ **72.** $\log^2 x = \log x^3$

73. $\log_{2^2} x - \log_2 x^4 = 0$

74. $\log_{3^2} x = \log_3 3$

75. $\ln^2 x + \ln x^3 + 2 = 0$

76. $\log^2 x = 12 + \log x$

B

77. $2 \log^2 x = 2 + 3 \log x$

78. $\ln x + 3\sqrt{\ln x} - 10 = 0$

79. $\log_8 x + \log_8 (x - 3) = 2/3$

80. $\log_5 \sqrt{x} + \log_5 \sqrt{6x + 5} = 1$

81. Prove Property (10).

82. Use Property (7) to prove Property (11).

83. Prove that $\log_b (x_1 + x_2) \neq \log_b x_1 + \log_b x_2$. (*Hint:* Let $b = 2$ and $x_1 = x_2 = 1$.)

84. Prove that $\dfrac{\log_b x_1}{\log_b x_2} \neq \log_b (x_1 - x_2)$. (*Hint:* Let $b = 2$, $x_1 = 8$, and $x_2 = 4$.)

85. Prove that $\dfrac{\log_b x_1}{\log_b x_2} \neq \log_b x_1 - \log_b x_2$. (*Hint:* Let $b = 2$, $x_1 = 1$, and $x_2 = 2$.)

C

Answer the following questions with complete sentences.

86. Why does no rule exist for $\log_b (x_1 + x_2)$?

87. Why must we check the solutions for a logarithmic equation?

REVIEW EXERCISES

Write the following in scientific notation. (See Section 7.7.)

88. 97,000

89. 287,630,000,000

90. .000 514 1

91. .000 000 014 72

10.4 COMPUTATIONS WITH LOGARITHMS AND A CALCULATOR*

1   **Evaluating Common and Natural Logarithms by Calculator**

2   **Solving Exponential Equations with Logarithms**

1   **Evaluating Common and Natural Logarithms by Calculator**

As mentioned earlier, logarithms were invented to simplify computations in astronomy (see the following Math in Time section). Although this use has become obsolete with the development of computers and calculators, logarithms remain essential to mathematics and the sciences. Before we can consider applications of logarithms, we must be able to find the logarithm of a number and determine a number whose logarithm we know.

Appendix A gives tables of common and natural logarithms, and Appendix B discusses their use. In the past these tables were used to obtain the logarithm of any positive number, but a calculator can now find it faster and more accurately. We will rely on a calculator in our work with log-

---

* Use a calculator throughout Section 10.4.

Math in Time

John Napier
North Wind Picture Archives

LOGARITHMS WERE INVENTED by John Napier (1550–1617), a Scottish nobleman. He spent 20 years developing them; and when he published his results in 1614, they were met with admiration and wonder. Unlike most discoveries in mathematics, which are based on previous work, Napier's "invention of logarithms came on the world as a bolt from the blue. No previous work led up to it, foreshadowed it or heralded its arrival. It stands isolated, breaking in upon human thought abruptly without borrowing from the work of other intellects or following known lines of mathematical thought" (Lord Moulton, 1915).

Napier's original idea for logarithms probably came from a formula* used by astronomers of that time to express a product as a difference. He made up the word *logarithm*, meaning "ratio number," from the Greek words *logos* (ratio) and *arithmos* (number). Napier's approach was geometric, and his tables were constructed from powers of .9999999. Just before his death he realized that more useful tables could be constructed from powers of 10 (our common logarithms). These tables were finished in 1624 by his friend Henry Briggs (1561–1630), the leading British mathematician of the day. Tables of base *e* logarithms were first published by John Speidell in 1620.

Napier spent most of his life managing his family estates near Edinburgh. His interests were wide and diverse. He was active in the religious controversies of the period and wrote a popular book to prove that the pope was the Antichrist and that the world would end between 1688 and 1700. He believed this book would ensure his place in history, but he could not have known that logarithms would have a major impact on mathematics and the sciences.

Napier gained a reputation for dabbling in magic and "the black arts," which gave rise to an amusing story. He used his servants' superstitious fear of his "powers" to determine which one of them was stealing from him. Napier told them that his black rooster would identify the thief. Each servant was sent alone into a darkened room to pet the rooster on the back. Napier had coated the bird's back with soot, and the thief, fearing to touch the rooster, returned with clean hands.

---

* $2\sin A\sin B = \cos(A - B) - \cos(A + B)$

arithms, but you might want to use the tables to check some answers. Also, you should consult the manual for your calculator on common and natural logarithms, because calculators differ in their notation and required sequences of steps in performing operations.

A scientific calculator has keys labeled **log**, or **logx**, for common logarithms (base 10) and **lnx** for natural logarithms (base *e*). Finding the common or natural logarithm of a positive number is very easy. Just enter the number and push log or lnx. For example,

$$\log 2.34 = 0.3692159 \quad \text{and} \quad \ln 2.34 = 0.8501509$$

We normally don't need seven places of accuracy, so we round off the number to as many places as are required. Because the logarithm of a

477

negative number is not real, a calculator displays "Error" if we make this mistake (enter -2.34 in your calculator and press the log key). From the graphs of $g(x) = \ln x$ (Figure 10.13) and $g(x) = \log x$ (Figure 10.14) we can see that if $0 < x < 1$, then $\ln x < 0$ and $\log x < 0$. This result is illustrated in the first example of this section.

EXAMPLE 1

Use a calculator to find each logarithm to four decimal places.

a. log 4120   **b.** ln .000 894

SOLUTION

ENTER	PRESS	DISPLAY	ANSWER
a. 4120	log	3.6148972	3.6149
b. .000 894	lnx	-7.0198048	-7.0198

Many calculators cannot display numbers that contain more than approximately eight digits. The first step in finding the logarithm of such a number is to express it in scientific notation (see Section 7.7). To find the common logarithm of the number, we use the product rule and $\log_b b^c = c$. For example,

$$\log (2.47 \times 10^{13}) = \log 2.47 + \log 10^{13} \qquad \log_b x_1 x_2 = \log_b x_1 + \log_b x_2$$
$$= .3927 + 13 \qquad\qquad \log_b b^c = c, \quad \text{so}$$
$$= 13.3927 \qquad\qquad\quad \log_{10} 10^{13} = 13$$

We find the natural logarithm of a number in scientific notation in a similar way. In this case we need $\ln 10 = 2.3026$.

EXAMPLE 2

Use a calculator to find each logarithm to four decimal places.

a. ln 287,630,000,000   **b.** log .000 000 014 72

SOLUTION

a. $\ln 287{,}630{,}000{,}000 = \ln (2.8763 \times 10^{11})$
$$= \ln 2.8763 + \ln 10^{11} \qquad \log_b x^c = c\log_b x$$
$$= 1.0565 + 11\ln 10$$
$$= 1.0565 + 11(2.3026)$$
$$= 26.3851$$

b. $\log .000\ 000\ 014\ 72 = \log (1.472 \times 10^{-8})$
$$= \log 1.472 + \log 10^{-8}$$
$$= .1679 - 8$$
$$= -7.8321$$

We also must be able to find the number whose logarithm we know; that is, given $\log N$ or $\ln N$, we need to determine N. In this situation N is called an **antilogarithm**, abbreviated **antilog** or **antiln**. Because the antilog function is the inverse of the log function, we can use the INV and log keys on a calculator to find an antilogarithm. For example, if $\log N = 1.9518$, then enter 1.9518, press INV, press log, and obtain $N = 89.495253$. If N is too large or too small to be displayed, then the answer will be given in scientific notation.

EXAMPLE 3

Use a calculator to find each antilogarithm to four places.

a. $\log N = 12.8082$ **b.** $\log N = -1.6091$
c. $\ln N = 2.2492$

SOLUTION

a. Enter 12.8082, press INV, and press log.

| 6.4298   12 | is the display, so the answer is

$N = $ antilog 12.8082
$ = 6.4298 \times 10^{12}$

b. Enter 1.6091, press $+/-$, press INV, and press log.
0.024598 is the display, so
$N = $ antilog -1.6091
$ = .0246$

c. Enter 2.2492, press INV, and press lnx.
9.4801487 is the display, so
$N = $ antiln 2.2492
$ = 9.4801$

---

2 **Solving Exponential Equations with Common Logarithms**

In Section 10.1 we solved exponential equations that could be expressed in the form $b^{x_1} = b^{x_2}$. An example was $2^x = 16$, $2^x = 2^4$, and $x = 4$. An equation such as $3^x = 16$ cannot be solved in this way because it cannot be written as $b^{x_1} = b^{x_2}$. In this situation we use the fact that if $x_1 = x_2$, then $\log x_1 = \log x_2$:

$$3^x = 16$$
$$\log 3^x = \log 16 \qquad \log N^c = c \log N$$
$$x \log 3 = \log 16$$
$$x = \frac{\log 16}{\log 3}$$
$$x = \frac{1.20412}{.47712}$$
$$x = 2.5237$$

Note that $\dfrac{\log 16}{\log 3} \neq \log 16 - \log 3 = \log \dfrac{16}{3}$, because $\log 16 - \log 3 = 1.20412 - .47712 = .7270$.

COMMON ERROR

A common mistake is to confuse $\dfrac{\log_b x_1}{\log_b x_2}$ with $\log_b \dfrac{x_1}{x_2}$:

$$\log_b \frac{x_1}{x_2} = \log_b x_1 - \log_b x_2$$
$$\frac{\log_b x_1}{\log_b x_2} \neq \log_b x_1 - \log_b x_2$$

EXAMPLE 4

Find the exact solution and a four-decimal-place approximation for the following.

a. $10^x = 2$ **b.** $7x = 81^{2x-1}$

SOLUTION   **a.** $10^x = 2$

$\log 10^x = \log 2$

$x \log 10 = \log 2$ $\log_b b = 1$

$x = \log 2$ is the exact answer;

$x = .3010$ is an approximation.

b. $7^x = 81^{2x-1}$

$\log 7^x = \log 81^{2x-1}$

$x \log 7 = (2x - 1)\log 81$

$x \log 7 = x (2 \log 81) - \log 81$

$x \log 7 - x (2 \log 81) = -\log 81$

$x (\log 7 - 2 \log 81) = -\log 81$

$x = \dfrac{-\log 81}{\log 7 - 2 \log 81}$ is the exact answer;

$x = \dfrac{-1.90849}{.84510 - 2(1.90849)}$

$x = .6422$ is the approximation.

Many exponential equations involve e to a power. In such a case we use the property that if $x_1 = x_2$, then $\ln x_1 = \ln x_2$.

EXAMPLE 5

Solve $e^{.08t} = 3$ to the nearest hundredth and give the exact answer.

SOLUTION $e^{.08t} = 3$

$\ln e^{.08t} = \ln 3$

$.08t \ln e = \ln 3$ $\log_b b = 1$, so

$.08t = \ln 3$ $\ln e = 1$

$t = \dfrac{\ln 3}{.08}$ is the exact answer;

$t = \dfrac{1.09861}{.08}$

$t = 13.73$

EXERCISE SET 10.4

A

1   Use a calculator to find the common logarithm of each number to five decimal places.

1. 4   **2.** 6   **3.** 1.48

4. 263   **5.** .0168   **6.** .001 479

7. 8164   **8.** 92,173,000

9. .000 001 914   **10.** 1.63×10^{14}

11. 3.094×10^{-12} **12.** 4.208×10^{-8}

13. 86,140,000,000,000

14. 900,400,000,000,000,000

15. .000 000 000 000 876

16. .000 000 000 000 018 263

Use a calculator to find the natural logarithm of each number to five decimal places.

17. 2.071   **18.** 3.122

19. 2268   **20.** .0147

21. .000 26   **22.** 22,800,000

23. 92,300,000,000,000

24. 216,450,000,000,000,000

25. .000 000 000 17

26. .000 000 000 000 008

Use a calculator to find each antilogarithm to four places.

27. $\log N = .13876$ **28.** $\log N = 1.2479$

29. $\log N = -.6187$ **30.** $\log N = -3.14926$

31. $\log N = 14.13721$ **32.** $\log N = -12.3148$

33. $\ln N = 4.6123$ **34.** $\ln N = -1.41276$

35. $\ln N = -9.21684$ **36.** $\ln N = 13.106$

2   Find the exact solutions to the following. Give a four-decimal-place approximation for each irrational answer.

37. $3^x = 81$ **38.** $2^x = 81$

39. $5^x = 8$ **40.** $5^x = 25$

41. $10^x = 6$ **42.** $10^{x+4} = 27$

43. $6^{x+2} = 12$ **44.** $(2.757)^x = 10$

45. $e^x = 4$ **46.** $e^{3x} = 2$

47. $2e^{.01x} = 18$ **48.** $e^{6x} = e^{x-4}$

49. $(1/2)^x = 1000$ **50.** $3^{-x} = 81$

51. $2^{-x} = 81$ **52.** $3e^{2x-1} = 12$

53. $5e^{1-4x} = 3$ **54.** $6^{3-2x} = 12^{x-5}$

Approximate the following to four decimal places. Express large or small numbers in scientific notation.

55. $(35)^6$ **56.** $(204)^{10}$

57. $(.13)^{12}$ **58.** $\sqrt[3]{17}$

59. $-(7.32)^{2/3}$ **60.** $(4.62)^{2.08}$

61. $-\sqrt[5]{.0399}$ **62.** $-\sqrt[4]{.000\ 417\ 7}$

B

63. $\left(\dfrac{.5462}{7930}\right)^{10}$ **64.** $\dfrac{(921)(.645)}{(3.218)(.043)}$

65. $\sqrt[3]{\dfrac{(24)^4(17)^2}{56}}$ **66.** $\dfrac{\sqrt{192}\ \sqrt[3]{291}}{\sqrt[4]{675}}$

67. 2^{100} **68.** 3^{100}

69. $(473)^{10}$ **70.** $(.513)^{100}$

C ✏

Answer the following questions with complete sentences.

71. What is an antilogarithm?

72. How did Napier's invention of logarithms differ from most discoveries in mathematics?

The decimal approximations for $\ln 2$ are found by adding and subtracting the terms of Equation (1):

$$\ln 2 = 1 - \frac{1}{2} + \frac{1}{3} - \frac{1}{4} + \frac{1}{5} - \frac{1}{6} + \cdots \quad (1)$$

$$\ln 2 = .6931472 \ldots \quad (2)$$

In words, the more terms that we add and subtract in Equation (1), the better approximation that we get for $\ln 2$ in Equation (2). Combine the first n terms in Equation (1) to approximate $\ln 2$; express each answer to six decimal places; for example, the sum of the first three terms is

$$\ln 2 \approx 1 - \frac{1}{2} + \frac{1}{3} = \frac{6}{6} - \frac{3}{6} + \frac{2}{6} = \frac{5}{6} = .833333$$

73. 4 terms   **74.** 7 terms   **75.** 10 terms

REVIEW EXERCISES

Solve the following for the indicated variables. (See Sections 2.3 and 6.5.)

76. $A = B + rt$; t **77.** $A = B + t(1 + r)$; r

78. $I/I_0 = K$; I_0 **79.** $A = B - Rt/L$; t

Convert the following to exponential form. (See Section 10.2.)

80. $y = \log_2 3$ **81.** $M = \log I$

Convert the following to logarithmic form. (See Section 10.2.)

82. $10^3 = x$ **83.** $1.2 = e^{.02t}$

10.5 APPLICATIONS*

> **1** **Changing Base and Solving Formulas**
> **2** **Applying Exponential Functions**
> **3** **Applying Logarithmic Functions**

1 Changing Base and Solving Formulas

As mentioned earlier, exponential and logarithmic functions have many applications. Population growth and radioactive decay are studied with exponential equations; and the magnitude of earthquakes and the acidity of solutions are described with logarithms. Before discussing these examples, we will examine the methods of converting between logarithms with different bases and solving formulas for a given variable.

The last property of logarithms that we will consider allows us to convert from one base to another. For example, to evaluate $\log_2 3$ we need to convert it to a base-10 logarithm, because our calculators only have base 10 and base e. Let

$$y = \log_2 3$$
$$2^y = 3$$
$$\log 2^y = \log 3$$
$$y \log 2 = \log 3$$
$$y = \frac{\log 3}{\log 2} \quad \text{and} \quad y = \log_2 3, \quad \text{so}$$
$$\log_2 3 = \frac{\log 3}{\log 2} = \frac{.4771213}{.3010300} \approx 1.5850$$

$y = \log_b x \quad \text{iff} \quad b^y = x$

$x_1 = x_2 \quad \text{iff} \quad \log x_1 = \log x_2$

$\log_b x^c = c\log_b x$

This example illustrates the **change of base rule**. If a and b are positive numbers other than 1 and $x > 0$, then

Property (12) $\quad \log_b x = \dfrac{\log_a x}{\log_a b}$

Proof: Let $y = \log_b x$. Then

$$b^y = x$$
$$\log_a b^y = \log_a x$$
$$y \log_a b = \log_a x$$
$$y = \frac{\log_a x}{\log_a b} \quad \text{and} \quad y = \log_b x, \quad \text{so}$$
$$\log_b x = \frac{\log_a x}{\log_a b}$$

Take $\log_a$ of both sides.

Rather than remembering this formula, converting $\log_b x$ to the corresponding exponential equation might be easier. This process is illustrated in the following example.

---

* Use a calculator throughout Section 10.5.

EXAMPLE 1 Convert $\log_9 17$ to base-4 logarithms.

SOLUTION A

$$\begin{aligned} y &= \log_9 17 \\ 9^y &= 17 && \text{Take } \log_4 \text{ of both sides.} \\ \log_4 9^y &= \log_4 17 \\ y \log_4 9 &= \log_4 17 \\ y &= \frac{\log_4 17}{\log_4 9} = \log_9 17 \end{aligned}$$

SOLUTION B

$$\log_b x = \frac{\log_a x}{\log_a b}; \quad b = 9, \quad x = 17, \quad \text{and} \quad a = 4:$$

$$\log_9 17 = \frac{\log_4 17}{\log_4 9}$$

We return now to a familiar topic: solving a formula for a given variable. The properties that we have discussed allow us to solve certain exponential and logarithmic formulas for an indicated variable.

EXAMPLE 2 Solve the following for the indicated variables.

a. $I = C10^{-Wt}$; W — electric circuits
b. $Y = 100e^{bx} - 100$; x — geology; sedimentary rocks
c. $D = 10 \log I/I_0$; I — decibel scale

SOLUTION **a.** Take the common log of both sides of the equation:

$$\begin{aligned} I &= C10^{-Wt} \\ \log I &= \log C10^{-Wt} && \log x_1x_2 = \log x_1 + \log x_2 \\ \log I &= \log C + \log 10^{-Wt} && \log x^c = c\log x \\ \log I - \log C &= -Wt \log 10 && \log 10 = 1 \\ \log I - \log C &= -Wt && \text{Multiply by } -1. \\ \log C - \log I &= Wt && \text{Divide by } t. \\ \frac{\log C - \log I}{t} &= W \end{aligned}$$

b.

$$\begin{aligned} Y &= 100e^{bx} - 100 && \text{Add 100.} \\ Y + 100 &= 100e^{bx} && \text{Take ln of both sides.} \\ \ln (Y + 100) &= \ln 100e^{bx} && \ln (Y + 100) \neq \ln Y + \ln 100 \\ \ln (Y + 100) &= \ln 100 + \ln e^{bx} \\ \ln (Y + 100) - \ln 100 &= bx \ln e && \ln e = 1 \\ \ln (Y + 100) - \ln 100 &= bx && \text{Divide by } b. \\ \frac{\ln (Y + 100) - \ln 100}{b} &= x \end{aligned}$$

c.

$$\begin{aligned} D &= 10 \log I/I_0 && \text{Divide by 10.} \\ \frac{D}{10} &= \log \frac{I}{I_0} && y = \log x \quad \text{iff} \quad x = 10^y \\ \frac{I}{I_0} &= 10^{D/10} && \text{Multiply by } I_0. \\ I &= I_0 10^{D/10} \end{aligned}$$

2 | Applying Exponential Functions

A mathematical description of an event is called a model. The formula $f(x) = b^x$ can be used as a model of certain types of growth and decay problems. If $b > 1$, then f represents growth, and if $0 < b < 1$, then it describes decay. We begin with a topic that we can all identify with — money.

If a sum of money (the principal), P, is invested at an annual rate, r, for t years, then it grows to a future amount, A, according to $A = P + I$. I is the interest, and $I = Prt$, so $A = P + Prt$. For example, if $P = \$100$, $t = 1$ year, and $r = 12\%$, then

$$A = P + Prt = 100 + 100(.12)(1) = 100 + 12 = \$112$$

Compound interest occurs when interest is paid on interest. Let us see what happens to the \$100 over a three-year period; because $t = 1$, $I = Prt = Pr$.

First year: $t = 1$, $P = 100$, $r = .12$

$$
\begin{aligned}
A &= P + I & A &= 100 \cdot 1 + 100(.12) \\
&= P \cdot 1 + Pr & &= 100(1 + .12) \\
&= P(1 + r)^1 & &= 100(1.12)^1 = \$112
\end{aligned}
$$

Second year: $t = 2$, $P = 112$, $r = .12$

$$
\begin{aligned}
A &= P(1 + r)^1 + I & A &= 112 \cdot 1 + 112(.12) \\
&= P(1 + r) \cdot 1 + P(1 + r)r & &= 112[1 + .12] \\
&= P(1 + r)[1 + r] & &= 100(1.12)[1.12] \\
&= P(1 + r)^2 & &= 100(1.12)^2 = \$125.44
\end{aligned}
$$

Third year: $t = 3$, $P = 125.44$, $r = .12$

$$
\begin{aligned}
A &= P(1 + r)^2 + I & A &= 125.44 \cdot 1 + 125.44(.12) \\
&= P(1 + r)^2 \cdot 1 + P(1 + r)^2 r & &= 125.44[1 + .12] \\
&= P(1 + r)^2[1 + r] & &= 100(1.12)^2[1.12] \\
&= P(1 + r)^3 & &= 100(1.12)^3 = \$140.49
\end{aligned}
$$

In four years the future amount is $A = P(1 + r)^4 = 100(1.12)^4 = \$157.35$, and so on.

Compound Interest or Future Amount Formulas

If a principal of P dollars is invested for t years at an interest rate of r percent compounded annually, then the yield A is given by

$$A = P(1 + r)^t$$

If P is compounded n times per year, then

$$A = P\left(1 + \frac{r}{n}\right)^{nt}$$

EXAMPLE 3

Jane invested $10,000 at 12% interest compounded monthly. How much money will she have in 20 years?

SOLUTION $P = 10,000$, $r = .12$, $n = 12$,   and $t = 20$. Thus,

$$A = P\left(1 + \frac{r}{n}\right)^{nt}$$

$$A = 10,000\left(1 + \frac{.12}{12}\right)^{12(20)}$$

$A = 10,000(1 + .01)^{240}$

$A = 10,000(1.01)^{240}$

$A = 108,925.54$

In 20 years Jane will have $108,926 to the nearest dollar.

The number e is involved in a model of human population growth. This model is important in city planning, estimating future food requirements, and so on. Human populations grow according to

$$P = P_0 e^{rt}$$

where P_0 is the size of the initial population ($t = 0$), r is the growth rate, t is the time in years ($t > 0$), and P is the population at time t.

EXAMPLE 4

In April 1987 the world population reached 5 billion. If the annual growth rate is 2%, when will it reach 6 billion?

SOLUTION $P_0 = 5$, $P = 6$,   and $r = .02$. Thus,

$P_0 e^{rt} = P$

$5e^{.02t} = 6$ Divide by 5.

$e^{.02t} = 6/5 = 1.2$ $x_1 = x_2$ iff $\ln x_1 = \ln x_2$

$\ln e^{.02t} = \ln 1.2$

$.02t \ln e = \ln 1.2$ $\ln e = 1$

$.02t = \ln 1.2$

$t = \dfrac{\ln 1.2}{.02} = \dfrac{.18232}{.02} = 9.12 \approx 9$ years

If this rate of 2% does not change, then the world population will be 6 billion in early 1996.

Certain physical quantities decrease exponentially. An example is **radioactive decay**. Some chemical elements are radioactive, which means that they change into other elements by giving off energy and particles. The basic measure of radioactive decay is the **half-life**, or the length of time needed for one-half of a quantity to decay into other elements.

Carbon-14, written ^{14}C, is a radioactive isotope of carbon with a half-life of approximately 5700 years. Suppose we have 100 grams of ^{14}C. In 5700 years half of this amount will have decayed, leaving 50 grams of ^{14}C. After another 5700 years, half of the 50 grams will have decayed, leaving 25 grams of ^{14}C, and so on. To summarize,

After 5700 years, $100(1/2) = 100(2)^{-1} = 50$ grams remain.
After 11,400 years, $100(1/4) = 100(2)^{-2} = 25$ grams remain.
After 17,100 years, $100(1/8) = 100(2)^{-3} = 12.5$ grams remain.
After t years, $100(2)^{-t/5700}$ grams remain.

In general, if $Q_0 =$ the amount of ^{14}C present at time $t = 0$, and $Q =$ the amount present at $t > 0$, then

$$Q = Q_0(2)^{-t/5700}$$

All living organisms maintain a constant ratio of radioactive carbon-14, ^{14}C, to stable carbon-12, ^{12}C. Once an organism dies the ratio of ^{14}C to ^{12}C decreases as the carbon-14 decays. By measuring the present ratio of the two carbons in the remains of an organism, archeologists can estimate its age. With modern laboratory methods radiocarbon dating can determine the age of material as old as 70,000 years.

EXAMPLE 5

A human skull is found to contain 10% of its original amount of ^{14}C. How long ago did the person live?

SOLUTION   Let $Q =$ the amount of ^{14}C present now and $Q_0 =$ the amount of ^{14}C present when the person lived. Then $Q = 10\%$ of Q_0, or $Q = .1Q_0$. Thus,

$Q_0(2)^{-t/5700} = Q$
$Q_0(2)^{-t/5700} = .1Q_0$ Divide by Q_0.
$2^{-t/5700} = .1$
$\log 2^{-t/5700} = \log .1$ $\log .1 = \log 10^{-1}$
$\left(\dfrac{-t}{5700}\right)\log 2 = -1$ $= -1$
$\dfrac{-\log 2}{5700}t = -1$

$t = \dfrac{5700(-1)}{-\log 2} = \dfrac{5700}{.30103} = 18934.99 \approx 18,935$

To the nearest 100 years, the person lived 18,900 years ago.

The equation for radiocarbon dating generalizes to any radioactive material.

Radioactive Decay

A radioactive element with a half-life, h, decays exponentially according to the formula

$$Q = Q_0(2)^{-t/h}$$

where Q_0 is the amount present at time $t = 0$ and Q is the amount present at time $t > 0$.

3   Applying Logarithmic Functions

Logarithmic equations occur in many fields. In electrical engineering they are used to express the change in voltage in an amplifier; in business they are used to predict car depreciation. We now examine two applications in geology and chemistry.

The **Richter magnitude scale**, named for Charles Richter (1900–1985), measures the magnitude, M, of an earthquake with the formula

$$M = \log I$$

where I is the size of the earthquake compared to the minimum earthquake that can be measured on a seismograph. For example, an earthquake that is 100,000 times larger than the minimum earthquake has a magnitude.

$$M = \log 100,000 = \log 10^5 = 5$$

EXAMPLE 6

On the Richter scale the 1989 Santa Cruz, California, earthquake measured 7.1, and the 1906 San Francisco earthquake measured 8.3 (see Figure 10.16). Find I in each case and determine how much larger the 1906 earthquake was than the 1989 earthquake.

FIGURE 10.16
This 8½ foot fence displacement was caused by the 1906 San Francisco earthquake.
(U.S. Geological Survey)

SOLUTION

If $\log I = 7.1$, then $I =$ antilog $7.1 = 1.26 \times 10^7$.
If $\log I = 8.3$, then $I =$ antilog $8.3 = 1.99 \times 10^8$.

$$\frac{1.99 \times 10^8}{1.26 \times 10^7} = 15.79$$

Thus, an earthquake of 8.3 is approximately 16 times larger than an earthquake of 7.1.

Chemists use a number denoted by **pH** (power of hydrogen) to measure the acidity or basicity of a solution; pH is found by the formula

$$pH = -\log [H^+]$$

where $[H^+]$ is the hydrogen-ion concentration in moles per liter, denoted by M. For example, the hydrogen-ion concentration of pure water is 10^{-7} M, so its pH is

$$pH = -\log 10^{-7} = -(-7) = 7$$

The pH of an acidic solution is less than 7, and the pH of a basic solution is greater than 7.

EXAMPLE 7

Find $[H^+]$ for the following solutions.
a. seawater, pH $= 8.5$ **b.** acid rain, pH $= 1.8$

SOLUTION   **a.** $pH = -\log [H^+] = 8.5$
$\log [H^+] = -8.5$
$[H^+] = $ antilog $-8.5 = 3.16 \times 10^{-9}$ M
b. $pH = -\log [H^+] = 1.8$
$\log [H^+] = -1.8$
$[H^+] = 1.58 \times 10^{-2}$ M

Acid rain with this pH is more acidic than lemon juice.

PEANUTS reprinted by permission of UFS, Inc.

EXERCISE SET 10.5

A

1 Approximate the following logarithms to four decimal places.

1. $\log_5 6$ **2.** $\log_6 5$

3. $\log_3 64$ **4.** $\log_2 871$

5. $\log_8 2.46$ **6.** $\log_7 .023$

7. $\log_{12} .003$ **8.** $\log_{100} 135$

9. $2 \log_2 3$ **10.** $3 \log_5 2$

11. $\frac{1}{2} \log_2 100$ **12.** $\frac{1}{3} \log_7 27$

Convert the following to the indicated bases.

13. $\log_2 3$ to base 8

14. $\log_3 2$ to base 9

15. $\log_6 5$ to base e

16. $\log_9 2$ to base 11

17. $\log 7$ to base 5

18. $\log .12$ to base e

19. $\ln .23$ to base 10

20. $\ln 86$ to base 9

Solve the following for the indicated variables.

21. $A = A_0 e^{-kt}$; t X-ray absorption

22. $Q = Q_0 e^{-.025t}$; t nuclear reactors; stron-tium-90 decay

23. $x = Ce^{kt} + 45$; k Newton's law of cool-ing

24. $G = 25 - 10e^{-.2t}$; t business; sales growth pattern

25. $A = P10^R$; R **26.** $A = B10^{3x} - 1$; x

27. $Q = 6000 \cdot 2^{2t}$; t **28.** $P = P_0 e^{rt}$; r

29. $A = P(1 + r)^t$; t **30.** $Q = Q_0(3)^{-t/6}$; t

31. $\log E = 12.2 + 1.44M$; E geology; earth-quake formula

32. $L = 8.8 + 5.1\log D$; D astronomy; lim-iting magnitude

33. $\log K_w = \log [H^+] + \log [OH^-]$; $[H^+]$ chemistry; ionization formula

34. $-\dfrac{1}{.21}\ln\dfrac{P}{14.7} = x$; P

atmospheric pressure formula

35. $\ln y = kt$; y

36. $M = \log I$; I

37. $M = \log A/A_0$; A_0

38. $pH = -\log [H^+]$; $[H^+]$

39. $\log \dfrac{Q}{Q_0} = -\dfrac{t}{h}\log 2$; Q

40. $\dfrac{1}{k}\ln\dfrac{A}{A_0} = t$; A

2 Solve the following problems.

41. If $1000 is invested at 7% compounded an-nually, what is its yield in 25 years?

42. The Khans purchased their house in 1980 for $100,000. If the value of real estate increases at a rate of 10% per year, how much would their house be worth, to the nearest dollar, in 1995?

43. Jan purchased her house in 1982 for $35,000. If the value of real estate increases at a rate of 15% per year, when, to the nearest year, will her house be worth $300,000?

44. Steve invested $20,000 at 12% compounded annually. How long, to the nearest tenth of a year, will it take him to triple his investment? In other words, when does $A = 3P$?

45. Irit invested $20,000 at 12% compounded four times a year. How long, to the nearest tenth of a year, will it take her to triple her investment?

46. Ken invested $10,000 at 16% compounded twice a year. How long, to the nearest tenth of a year, will it take him to double his invest-ment?

47. We invest $1000 at 14% for 10 years, com-pounded monthly. Find the future amount to the nearest dollar.

48. We invest $1000 at 14% for 10 years, com-pounded daily (use 365). Find the future amount to the nearest dollar. (The difference between the answers to this exercise and the last one is approximately $17!).

49. Assume that the world population in 1996 will be 6 billion. Determine, to the nearest year, when it will be 7 billion if the growth rate is:
   a. .5%   **b.** 2%   **c.** 5%

50. The world population was 4 billion in 1976 and 5 billion in 1987. Find the growth rate as a percent correctly to one decimal place for this period of time.

51. A city grew from 130,000 in 1975 to 275,000 in 1985. Find, to one decimal place, the growth rate for that period of time.

52. A small town has a populaiton of 1200. The projected growth rate for the next four years is 3.5%. What will the population be in four years?

Let Q_0 = the number of bacteria in a culture at time $t = 0$ and Q = the number present at time $t > 0$. If we assume that each bacterium divides into two bacteria every k hours, then

$$Q = Q_0 2^{t/k}$$

53. A certain bacterium divides once every three hours on average. If we initially have 500, de-termine how many will be present in
   a. 3 hours   **b.** 15 hours   **c.** 10 days

54. A bacterium divides once every two hours on average. After six hours 96,000 are present. How many were present initially? How many will be present in 14 hours?

55. Suppose the skull in Example 5 contained 1% of its original ^{14}C. How long ago would the person have lived to the nearest 100 years?

56. A piece of charcoal is found to contain 6% of its original amount of ^{14}C. How long ago was the fire that produced the charcoal to the nearest 100 years?

57. If 100 grams of ^{14}C are present originally, how many grams will remain after 28,500 years correctly to one decimal place.

58. The half-life of plutonium-239, an extremely dangerous element produced in nuclear reactors, is 25,000 years. If 100 pounds of plutonium-239 were buried in a toxic waste site today, how many pounds would be left in 100,000 years?

59. The half-life of caffeine in the bloodstream is approximately six hours. One cup of coffee contains some 100 milligrams of caffeine. Kathy had coffee with dinner at 8 P.M.; at 8 A.M. the next morning she had 50 milligrams of caffeine in her bloodstream. How many cups of coffee did she have with dinner?

60. The half-life of radium is 1600 years. After 1800 years a certain amount of radium has decayed, leaving 4.585 milligrams of radium. How much radium, to the nearest milligram, was present initially?

3

61. On the Richter scale the 1983 Coalinga, California, earthquake measured 6.5, and the 1964 Anchorage, Alaska, earthquake measured 8.6. Find I in each case and determine how much larger the 1964 earthquake was than the 1983 earthquake.

The following are two values of M on the Richter scale. Find the corresponding values of I and determine how much larger the second earthquake is than the first.

62. 4, 6   **63.** 4.4, 6.9   **64.** 3.1, 8.5

Find the pH, to the nearest tenth, of the following solutions with the given hydrogen ion concentrations, [H^+].

65. .063 M,   stomach acid

66. 2.5×10^{-6} M,   normal rain

67. 2×10^{-8} M,   human saliva

Find [H^+] for the following solutions with the given pH.

68. 5.7,   milk   **69.** 3.8,   orange juice

70. 7.2,   blood

The **decibel scale**, named for Alexander Graham Bell (1874–1922), the inventor of the telephone, measures the magnitude of sound D with the formula

$$D = 10\log I/I_0$$

where I is the intensity of the sound wave, and I_0 is the intensity of a barely audible sound wave. Find the decibel ratings of the following sounds to the nearest decibel.

71. $I = I_0$

72. $I = (3.16 \times 10^6)I_0$,   normal conversation

73. $I = 10^7 I_0$,   a busy city street

74. $I = 10^{12}I_0$, a nearby jet engine, the threshold of pain

B

The formula for finding the monthly payment on a loan is

$$M = \frac{Pr}{1 - (1 + r)^{-n}}$$

where M = the monthly payment; P = the amount borrowed; n = the number of months; and r = the monthly interest rate as a decimal, which is the yearly rate divided by 12.

75. Find the monthly car payment on a $10,000 loan at 12% per year for four years.

76. Find the monthly house payment on a $40,000 loan at 9% per year for 25 years.

Solve the following for the indicated variables.

77. $4 = (1 + r)^{10}$; r

78. $A = (1 + r/n)^{nt}$; t

79. $t = \dfrac{1}{k}\ln\dfrac{x - B}{A}$; x

80. $\dfrac{1}{t_1 - t_2} = \ln\dfrac{A_1}{A_2}$; A_1

Approximate the following to four decimal places.

81. $\log_2 5 + \log_2 3$ **82.** $\log_3 8 - \log_3 2$

83. $2\log_5 6 - \dfrac{1}{2}\log_5 9$

84. $\dfrac{1}{3}\log_7 8 + 3\log_7 2$

Answer the following questions with complete sentences.

85. What is the purpose of the "change of base rule"?

86. What is the connection between radioactive decay and half-life?

We have seen that the base-10 logarithm is used to describe earthquakes. Another application of log-arithms in geology is in the classification of sediments, such as cobbles, sand, silt, and clay (see Figure 10.17.) These sediments are named on the basis of the sizes of the particles. The base-2 log-arithm is used to grade these sediments using a formula called the phi (ϕ) scale:

$$\phi = -\log_2 d$$

where d is the diameter of the particles in milli-meters (mm). For cobbles, $d = 64$ mm   and $\phi = -\log_2 64 = -\log_2 2^6 = -6$; for fine sand, $d = .125$ mm $= 2^{-3}$ mm   and $\phi = -\log_2 2^{-3} = -(-3) = 3$. Recall that $\log_2 2^n = n\log_2 2 = n \cdot 1 = n$.

Find the value of ϕ for the given value of d.

87. $d = 4$ mm,   pebbles

88. $d = 1$ mm,   very coarse sand

89. $d = .25$ mm

90. $d = 2^{-7}$ mm

Find the value of d for the given value of ϕ.

91. $\phi = 8$,   clay   **92.** $\phi = 1$,   coarse sand

93. $\phi = -1$ **94.** $\phi = -5$

FIGURE 10.17
Layered sedimentary rock
U.S. Geological Survey

Chapter Summary

KEY WORDS, DEFINITIONS, AND PROPERTIES

Exponential Function: $f(x) = b^x$; $b > 0$ and $b \neq 1$. (See Section 10.1.)

1. $f(0) = 1$ and $f(1) = b$
2. $D_f = \mathbb{R}$ and $R_f = (0, \infty)$
3. f is one-to-one.
4. $x_1 = x_2$ if and only if $b^{x_1} = b^{x_2}$.
5. The x-axis, $y = 0$, is the asymptote of f.

Logarithmic Function: $g(x) = \log_b x$ (See Sections 10.2 through 10.5.)

Natural Logarithm: $\ln x = \log_e x$

Common Logarithm: $\log x = \log_{10} x$

Antilogarithm: N in $y = \log_b N$

1. $y = \log_b x$ if and only if $x = b^y$.
2. $\log_b 1 = 0$ and $\log_b b = 1$
3. $D_g = (0, \infty)$ and $R_g = \mathbb{R}$
4. g is one-to-one.
5. $x_1 = x_2$ if and only if $\log_b x_1 = \log_b x_2$.
6. The y-axis, $x = 0$, is the asymptote of g.
7. $\log_b x^c = c\log_b x$
8. $\log_b b^c = c$
9. $\log_b x_1 x_2 = \log_b x_1 + \log_b x_2$
10. $\log_b \dfrac{x_1}{x_2} = \log_b x_1 - \log_b x_2$
11. $\log_b \dfrac{1}{x} = -\log_b x$
12. $\log_b x = \dfrac{\log_a x}{\log_a b}$

Applications of Exponential and Logarithmic Functions (See Section 10.5.)

1. **Compound interest:** If a principal of P dollars is invested for t years at an interest rate of r percent compounded annually, then the future amount is $A = P(1 + r)^t$. If n times per year, then $A = P\left(1 + \dfrac{r}{n}\right)^{nt}$.

2. **Population growth:** A population grows according to $P = P_0 e^{rt}$; P_0 = the population at time $t = 0$, P = the population at time $t > 0$, and r = the growth rate.

3. **Radioactive decay:** A radioactive element with a half-life, h, decays according to the formula $Q = Q_0(2)^{-t/h}$; Q_0 = the amount present at $t = 0$ and Q = the amount present at $t > 0$.

4. **Richter magnitude scale:** $M = \log I$; I = the size of the earthquake and M = its magnitude.

5. **pH scale:** $\text{pH} = -\log [H^+]$; $[H^+]$ = the hydrogen ion concentration in moles per liter, M.

6. **Bacteria growth:** $Q = Q_0 2^{t/k}$; Q_0 = the number of bacteria at $t = 0$, which divide every k hours, and Q = the number present at $t > 0$.

7. **Decibel scale:** $D = 10\log I/I_0$; D = the magnitude of the sound, I = the intensity of the sound wave, and I_0 = the intensity of a barely audible sound wave.

CHAPTER REVIEW EXERCISES

The answers to the following problems are given in the answer section. If you have trouble, then review the material and homework problems in the sections indicated.*

Sketch the graphs of the following. (See Sections 10.1 and 10.2.)

1. $y = e^{2x}$
2. $f(x) = (1/3)^x$
3. $g(x) = \log_{1/3} x$

---

* Use a calculator as needed.

Convert each exponential form to logarithmic form and each logarithmic form to exponential form. (See Section 10.2.)

4. $5^3 = 125$ **5.** $\log_7 49 = 2$

Use the properties of logarithms to expand each expression as far as possible. (See Section 10.3.)

6. $\log_3 9\sqrt{x}$ **7.** $\ln 3x/y$

8. $\log .01x^4$ **9.** $\log (10x + 20)$

Write the following as single logarithms. (See Section 10.3.)

10. $3 \log_2 x$ **11.** $1 + 4 \ln t$

12. $\frac{1}{3} x - 2 \log y$

Use a calculator to find each logarithm and antilogarithm. Approximate the answers to four decimal places. (See Section 10.4.)

13. $\log .00179$

14. $\log 1,842,000,000,000$

15. $\log N = -11.3017$

16. $\ln N = 5.231$

Solve the following equation. (See Section 10.3.)

17. $\log^2 x = \log 10,000$

Approximate the following to four decimal places. (See Section 10.5.)

18. $\log_6 11$

Convert the following to a base-*e* logarithm. (See Section 10.5.)

19. $\log 14$

Find the exact solutions to the following. Give a four-decimal-place solution for each irrational number. (See Sections 10.1 and 10.4.)

20. $8^{x-1} = 4^{3x}$ **21.** $e^{4x-2} = 1$

22. $2^x = 9$ **23.** $3^{x+1} = 5^x$

Solve the following for the indicated variables. (See Section 10.5.)

24. $A = P(1.09)^t; \quad t$

25. $\log R = \log S + 2 \log T; \quad S$

Solve the following logarithmic equations. (See Sections 10.2 and 10.3.)

26. $\log (7x - 1) = \log 5x$

27. $y = \log_2 32$

28. $\log_b 1/125 = -3$

29. $\log_3 x = 1/4$

30. $2 \log x = \log 36$

31. $\log_6 x - 3 \log_6 2 = 2$

Find the roots of the following function. (See Section 10.2.)

32. $f(x) = \log (3x - 11)$

Solve the following problems. (See Section 10.5.)

33. We invest $100 at 12% compounded four times a year. Find the future amount in five years.

34. The atmospheric pressure at sea level is 14.7 pounds per square inch; at *x* miles above sea level it is $P = 14.7e^{-.21x}$. At what height will the pressure be 10% of sea level pressure?

35. How much larger is a 7.5 earthquake than a 4.3 earthquake?

CHAPTER TEST

Treat this test as a class test and allow 50 minutes for completion.* When you have finished, use the answer section for scoring. For any wrong answers, refer to the corresponding problems in the review section.

Sketch the graphs of the following.

1. $y = e^{-2x}$ **2.** $f(x) = 3^x$

3. $g(x) = \log_3 x$

---

* Use a calculator as needed.

Convert each exponential form to logarithmic form and each logarithmic form to exponential form.

4. $(1/3)^{-2} = 9$ **5.** $\log_2 16 = 4$

Use the properties of logarithms to expand each expression as far as possible.

6. $\log_2 \sqrt{m/n}$ **7.** $\log 100x^4$

8. $\ln (e^3 - e^2)$

Write the following as a single logarithm.

9. $3 \log_2 3 - 4 \log_2 x$

Use a calculator to find each logarithm and antilogarithm. Approximate the answers to four decimal places.

10. $\ln 13.47$ **11.** $\log N = 14.1302$

Approximate the following to four decimal places.

12. $\log_2 17$

Solve the following equations and formulas for the indicated variable.

13. $5^{7x} = 1/25$ **14.** $\log_b 8 = 3$

15. $\log (2x - 8) = 0$ **16.** $3^x = 12$

17. $9^{x+4} = 27^{3x-1}$ **18.** $\ln (x + 1) = 1 + \ln x$

19. $e^{1-2x} = 1$ **20.** $Q = Q_0(2)^{t/3};\quad t$

21. $\dfrac{1}{k} \ln \dfrac{A}{A_0} = t;\quad A_0$

Find the roots of the following function.

22. $g(x) = \ln (x^2 - 15)$

Solve the following problems.

23. Craig purchased a house for $270,000. If the value of real estate increases at a rate of 8% per year, when, to the nearest year, will his house be worth $400,000?

24. Some animal bones contain .5% of their original ^{14}C. How long ago, to the nearest 100 years, did the animal live? Use $Q = Q_0(2)^{-t/5700}$.

25. The pH of sauerkraut is 3.7. Find its hydrogen-ion concentration; $pH = -\log [H^+]$.

Sequences and Series

*If a ball is dropped, it will bounce back up to some fraction of its
original height. The height of successive bounces
is a geometric series.*

This final chapter will discuss sequences and series. Sequences occur in everyday life. Both sequences and series are used extensively throughout mathematics, the sciences, and business. This chapter serves as a very brief introduction to an extremely important part of mathematics.

For example, suppose that Lisa earns $1000 in her first year in college and that she gets a 10% raise each year for the next three years. Her second year's salary is $1000 + .10(1000) = \$1100$, her third year's is $1100 + .10(1100) = \$1210$, and her fourth year's is $1210 + .10(1210) = \$1331$. The set of numbers {1000, 1100, 1210, 1331} is called a **geometric sequence**.

11.1 SEQUENCES

1	**Sequences**
2	**Arithmetic Sequences**
3	**Word Problems**

1   Sequences

We begin this section by introducing the general concepts involved with sequences and considering examples of different types of sequences. Then we will discuss a specific type, arithmetic sequences.

Intuitively, we think of a sequence as a set of numbers arranged in order; that is, a first number, a second number, a third number, and so forth. These numbers are called the **terms** of the sequence. Because each term in a sequence corresponds to a natural number, we are dealing with a function, which is defined as follows.

Sequences

An **infinite sequence** is a function whose domain is the set of natural numbers $N = \{1, 2, 3, \ldots\}$.

A **finite sequence** with m terms is a function whose domain is the subset of the natural numbers $\{1, 2, 3, \ldots, m\}$.

Instead of our usual functional notation, $f(x)$, a sequence is usually written

$$\{a_n\} = \{a_1, a_2, a_3, \ldots, a_n, \ldots\}$$

where

$$a_1 = \text{first term}, \ a_2 = \text{second term}, \ldots, \ a_n = n\text{th term}$$

We also call a_n the **general term** of the sequence. The subscript of each term represents the term number. Sometimes other letters are used for sequences, such as b_n, c_n, s_n, and so forth.

An example of an infinite sequence is

$$a_n = 2n - 1$$

Then

$$a_1 = 2 \cdot 1 - 1 = 1$$
$$a_2 = 2 \cdot 2 - 1 = 3$$
$$a_3 = 2 \cdot 3 - 1 = 5$$

and, in general,

$$\{a_n\} = \{2n - 1\} = \{1, 3, 5, \ldots, 2n - 1, \ldots\}$$

An example of a finite sequence with five terms is

$$b_n = n^2 + 1 \quad \text{for} \quad n = 1, 2, 3, 4, 5$$

Thus,

$$\{b_n\} = \{2, 5, 10, 17, 26\}$$

EXAMPLE 1

Find the first four terms of the following sequences.

a. $a_n = \dfrac{1}{2^n}$ **b.** $b_n = \dfrac{n + 1}{n + 2}$ **c.** $c_n = (-2)^n$

SOLUTION   **a.** $a_1 = \dfrac{1}{2^1} = \dfrac{1}{2}$ $a_2 = \dfrac{1}{2^2} = \dfrac{1}{4}$

$a_3 = \dfrac{1}{2^3} = \dfrac{1}{8}$ $a_4 = \dfrac{1}{2^4} = \dfrac{1}{16}$

b. $b_1 = \dfrac{1 + 1}{1 + 2} = \dfrac{2}{3}$ $b_2 = \dfrac{2 + 1}{2 + 2} = \dfrac{3}{4}$

$b_3 = \dfrac{3 + 1}{3 + 2} = \dfrac{4}{5}$ $b_4 = \dfrac{4 + 1}{4 + 2} = \dfrac{5}{6}$

c. $c_1 = (-2)^1 = -2$ $c_2 = (-2)^2 = 4$

$c_3 = (-2)^3 = -8$ $c_4 = (-2)^4 = 16$

c_n is an example of an **alternating sequence**, which is a sequence whose terms alternate positive and negative (or negative and positive).

Many sequences involve the product of a **natural number**, n, and all the natural numbers less than n. This product is called n **factorial** and is denoted $n!$; that is,

$$n! = n(n - 1)(n - 2)(n - 3) \ldots (2)(1)$$

so

$$1! = 1$$
$$3! = 3 \cdot 2 \cdot 1 = 6$$
$$4! = 4 \cdot 3 \cdot 2 \cdot 1 = 4[3!] = 4[6] = 24$$

We can generalize $4! = 4[3!]$ to $n!$; that is, $n! = n[(n - 1)!]$. If $n = 1$ in the formula $n[(n - 1)!] = n!$, then

$$1[(1 - 1)!] = 1!$$
$$1[0!] = 1,$$

so we define $0!$ as

$$0! = 1$$

EXAMPLE 2

Find the first seven terms of $a_n = \dfrac{1}{(n - 1)!}$ and find a_{11}.

SOLUTION

$$a_1 = \frac{1}{(1 - 1)!} = \frac{1}{0!} = \frac{1}{1} = 1$$

$$a_2 = \frac{1}{(2 - 1)!} = \frac{1}{1!} = \frac{1}{1} = 1$$

$$a_3 = \frac{1}{(3 - 1)!} = \frac{1}{2!} = \frac{1}{2 \cdot 1} = \frac{1}{2}$$

$$a_4 = \frac{1}{(4 - 1)!} = \frac{1}{3!} = \frac{1}{3 \cdot 2 \cdot 1} = \frac{1}{6}$$

$$a_5 = \frac{1}{(5 - 1)!} = \frac{1}{4!} = \frac{1}{24}$$

$$a_6 = \frac{1}{(6 - 1)!} = \frac{1}{5!} = \frac{1}{120}$$

$$a_7 = \frac{1}{(7 - 1)!} = \frac{1}{6!} = \frac{1}{720}$$

$$a_{11} = \frac{1}{(11 - 1)!} = \frac{1}{10!} = \frac{1}{3,628,800}$$

Use the n! key on the calculator.

If we are given the first few terms of a sequence, and no other information, then we cannot assume that the indicated pattern continues; that is, more than one general term that produces the same first few terms is possible. For example, let

$$a_1 = 1, \quad a_2 = 4, \quad \text{and} \quad a_3 = 9$$

Based on the fact that $1^2 = 1$, $2^2 = 4$, and $3^2 = 9$, we might assume that $a_n = n^2$ and that $a_4 = 4^2 = 16$. However, if

$$a_n = n^2 + (n - 1)(n - 2)(n - 3)$$

then

$$a_1 = 1^2 + (1 - 1)(1 - 2)(1 - 3) = 1 + 0 = 1$$
$$a_2 = 2^2 + (2 - 1)(2 - 2)(2 - 3) = 4 + 0 = 4$$
$$a_3 = 3^2 + (3 - 1)(3 - 2)(3 - 3) = 9 + 0 = 9$$

but

$$a_4 = 4^2 + (4 - 1)(4 - 2)(4 - 3) = 16 + 3 \cdot 2 \cdot 1 = 22$$

so

$$\{n^2\} \neq \{n^2 + (n - 1)(n - 2)(n - 3)\}$$

When three dots, . . . , are used in a sequence, it means that the indicated pattern continues. The next part of this section will discuss a type of sequence whose general term can be determined from the first few terms because other information is provided.

2 | Arithmetic Sequences

An **arithmetic sequence** (or *arithmetic progression*) is a sequence in which each term after the first is obtained by adding the same number to the preceding term. For example,

$$\{1, 6, 11, 16, 21, 26, 31, \ldots\}$$

is an arithmetic sequence because each term after 1 is found by adding 5 to the previous term ($6 = 1 + 5$, $11 = 6 + 5$, . . .). The number that is added to each term is called the **common difference**, d, because the difference between any two consecutive terms is d. In this example $d = 5$, because

$$5 = 6 - 1 = 11 - 6 = 16 - 11 = \ldots$$

EXAMPLE 3

The first term of an arithmetic sequence is $a_1 = 2$, and the common difference is $d = 3$. Find the next four terms.

SOLUTION $a_2 = a_1 + 3 = 2 + 3 = 5$ $a_3 = a_2 + 3 = 5 + 3 = 8$
$a_4 = a_3 + 3 = 8 + 3 = 11$ $a_5 = a_4 + 3 = 11 + 3 = 14$

EXAMPLE 4

Find the common difference, d, for the following arithmetic sequences.

a. $\{-1, 1, 3, 5, \ldots\}$ **b.** $\{5, 1, -3, -7, \ldots\}$

SOLUTION **a.** $d = 2$, because $1 - (-1) = 3 - 1 = 5 - 3 = 2$
b. $d = -4$, because $1 - 5 = -3 - 1 = -7 - (-3) = -4$

The general term of an arithmetic sequence, a_n, can be found from the first term, a_1, and the common difference, d. Consider the example

$$\{1, 6, 11, 16, 21, 26, 31, \ldots\}; \quad a_1 = 1, \quad \text{and} \quad d = 5$$
$$a_2 = 1 + 5 = 6$$
$$a_3 = (1 + 5) + 5 = 1 + 2 \cdot 5 = 11$$
$$a_4 = (1 + 2 \cdot 5) + 5 = 1 + 3 \cdot 5 = 16$$
$$a_5 = (1 + 3 \cdot 5) + 5 = 1 + 4 \cdot 5 = 21$$
$$a_6 = (1 + 4 \cdot 5) + 5 = 1 + 5 \cdot 5 = 26$$
$$\vdots$$
$$a_n = 1 + (n - 1)5$$

In general, if a_1 is the first term and d is the common difference of an arithmetic sequence, then

$$a_2 = a_1 + 1d$$
$$a_3 = (a_1 + d) + d = a_1 + 2d$$
$$a_4 = (a_1 + 2d) + d = a_1 + 3d$$
$$a_5 = (a_1 + 3d) + d = a_1 + 4d$$
$$\cdot$$
$$\cdot$$
$$\cdot$$
$$a_n = a_1 + (n - 1)d$$

Arithmetic Sequences

The general term, a_n, of an arithmetic sequence with the first term a_1 and common difference d is

$$a_n = a_1 + (n - 1)d$$

EXAMPLE 5

For the arithmetic sequence $\{10, 13, 16, \ldots\}$ find the following.

a. a_n **b.** a_{20} **c.** a_{100}

SOLUTION   **a.** $a_1 = 10$ and $d = 13 - 10 = 3$. Thus,
$$a_n = a_1 + (n - 1)d$$
$$a_n = 10 + (n - 1)3$$
$$a_n = 3n + 7$$
b. $a_{20} = 3 \cdot 20 + 7 = 67$
c. $a_{100} = 3 \cdot 100 + 7 = 307$

EXAMPLE 6

Find the general term of the arithmetic sequence where $a_3 = 1$ and $a_{11} = 17$.

SOLUTION   From the formula $a_n = a_1 + (n - 1)d$, $a_3 = a_1 + (3 - 1)d = a_1 + 2d = 1$,   and $a_{11} = a_1 + (11 - 1)d = a_1 + 10d = 17$
This gives us the system of equations:
$$a_1 + 2d = 1 \quad (1)$$
$$a_1 + 10d = 17 \quad (2)$$
Multiply (1) by -1 and add it to (2):
$$-a_1 - 2d = -1$$
$$\underline{a_1 + 10d = 17}$$
$$0 + 8d = 16$$
$d = 2$,   and from (1), $a_1 = 1 - 2d = 1 - 2 \cdot 2 = -3$.   Thus,
$$a_n = a_1 + (n - 1)d$$
$$a_n = -3 + (n - 1)2$$
$$a_n = 2n - 5$$

Math in Time

AFRICAN MATHEMATICS

African mathematics began more than 8000 years ago. A carved bone dating from between 9000 B.C. and 6500 B.C. was found at Ishango in Zaire. The markings indicate that these prehistoric people used a base-10 number system (as we do) and were familiar with prime numbers and the operation of multiplying by 2. A series of notches on the Ishango bone appear to approximate a lunar calendar. "Here, then, is possible evidence of one of man's earliest intellectual activities, . . . , a lunar calendar, comprising a period of almost six months" (Marshack, 1972).

By 3100 B.C. the Egyptians were using a base-10 number system and writing numbers in the millions to keep records of military campaigns. By 1850 B.C. they had developed arithmetic rules for natural numbers and fractions. They used the method of doubling to multiply two natural numbers. For example, to find $33 \cdot 26$ they wrote 26 as $2 + 8 + 16$ and then used the distributive property: $33 \cdot 26 = 33(2 + 8 + 16) = 33 \cdot 2 + 33 \cdot 8 + 33 \cdot 16 = 858$. The method of doubling is used in today's computers. Egyptian arithmetic also was used by the Greeks and Romans.

The Egyptians made many contributions to geometry. For instance, they used 3.16 for the value of π, discovered the formulas for the area of a triangle and a trapezoid, and determined a formula for the volume of the frustum of a pyramid (a cutoff pyramid). Knowledge of Egyptian geometry made its way to Greece through Thales (ca. 640–550 B.C.) and Pythagoras (ca. 580–500 B.C.), who studied mathematics in Egypt.

The African peoples living south of the Sahara developed several types of number systems. The majority of them are base-5. As economies improved some of these base-5 systems were extended to base-10, as in ancient Egypt, or base-20, as used by the Mayan Indians of Central America.

The Yoruba people of Nigeria used a base-20 system and arithmetic operations to write certain numbers. For example, they wrote 46 as $20 \cdot 3 - 10 - 4$. The Yoruba used the number 20,000 to write numbers in the millions. They also developed the concept of infinity.

Many cultures consider certain numbers to be significant. For instance, 13 is considered unlucky by many people in the United States (the Empire State building in New York City does not have a thirteenth floor). The Mesopotamians considered 7 to be auspicious, and as a result we have a seven-day week. However, many African peoples consider 7 to be unlucky, and they avoid the word "seven" by saying "six plus one."

3 Word Problems

Sequences are used in theoretical mathematics and have applications in the sciences and business. We conclude this section with an example of a word problem involving a sequence.

EXAMPLE 7   A company had sales of $20,000 during its first year of operation. If its sales increased by $4000 per year, find the sales in the fifteenth year.

(continued)

SOLUTION   The company's sales can be represented by an arithmetic sequence, where
$a_1 = 20{,}000$ and $d = 4000$.
$a_n = a_1 + (n - 1)d$,   so
$a_{15} = 20{,}000 + (15 - 1)4000$
$= 20{,}000 + 14 \cdot 4000$ Use a calculator.
$= 20{,}000 + 56{,}000$
$= 76{,}000$
The company's sales in its fifteenth year were \$76,000.

EXERCISE SET 11.1

A

1 Find the first five terms of the following sequences.

1. $a_n = 2n + 1$

2. $a_n = 6n - 2$

3. $a_n = 1 - 4n$

4. $a_n = n^2 + 1$

5. $a_n = n^3 - n$

6. $a_n = 2^{n-1}$

7. $a_n = 3^{n+1}$

8. $a_n = (n - 1)!$

9. $a_n = (2n)!$

10. $a_n = \dfrac{n}{(n - 1)!}$

11. $a_n = \dfrac{n^2}{n!}$

12. $a_n = \dfrac{1}{2^n}$

13. $a_n = \dfrac{1}{3^n}$

14. $a_n = \dfrac{n - 1}{n + 1}$

15. $a_n = \dfrac{n + 4}{n + 5}$

16. $a_n = 1 + \dfrac{1}{n}$

17. $a_n = \left(1 + \dfrac{1}{n}\right)^n$

18. $a_n = \left(1 + \dfrac{1}{n}\right)^{-n}$

19. $a_n = (-3)^n$

20. $a_n = 1 + (-1)^n$

21. $a_n = \dfrac{(-1)^{n+1}}{n}$

22. $a_n = \dfrac{(-1)^{n+1}}{2^n}$

23. $a_n = n^3$

24. $a_n = n^3 + (n - 1)(n - 2)(n - 3)(n - 4)$

Find the indicated terms for each sequence.

25. $a_n = 2n - 1$; a_{10}, a_{25}

26. $a_n = 2n^2 - 1$; a_7, a_{20}

27. $a_n = 2$; a_4, a_{100}

28. $a_n = 3n - n^2$; a_9, a_{11}

29. $a_n = \dfrac{n + 1}{n + 2}$; a_{30}, a_{75}

30. $a_n = \dfrac{(-1)^{n+1}}{2^n}$; a_9, a_{10}

31. $a_n = \dfrac{(-1)^n}{3n}$; a_6, a_{27}

32. $a_n = \dfrac{-n}{2n + 1}$; a_7, a_{35}

Find a general term, a_n, for the given terms of the following sequences.

33. $\{2, 4, 6, 8, \ldots\}$

34. $\{5, 5, 5, 5, \ldots\}$

35. $\{1, 8, 27, 64, \ldots\}$

36. $\{0, 3, 8, 15, \ldots\}$

37. $\{1, -1, 1, -1, \ldots\}$

38. $\{-3, 9, -27, 81, \ldots\}$

39. $\left\{1, \dfrac{1}{4}, \dfrac{1}{9}, \dfrac{1}{16}, \ldots\right\}$

40. $\left\{\dfrac{1}{2}, \dfrac{2}{3}, \dfrac{3}{4}, \dfrac{4}{5}, \ldots\right\}$

2 Determine whether the given sequence is arithmetic. If it is, find the common difference, d, and the next three terms.

41. $\{1, 2, 3, \ldots\}$

42. $\{0, -2, -4, -6, \ldots\}$

43. $\{1, 2, 4, 7, \ldots\}$

44. $\{1, -8, 27, -64, \ldots\}$

45. $\left\{\dfrac{1}{2}, \dfrac{1}{3}, \dfrac{1}{4}, \dfrac{1}{5}, \ldots\right\}$

46. $\left\{\dfrac{1}{2}, 1, \dfrac{3}{2}, 2, \ldots\right\}$

47. $\{10, 5, 0, -5, \ldots\}$

48. $\{1, 4, 9, 16, \ldots\}$

49. $\{1, -2, 3, -4, \ldots\}$

50. $\{3, 6, 9, 12, \ldots\}$

The following problems refer to arithmetic sequences.

51. If $a_1 = 2$ and $d = 3$, find a_n and a_{30}.

52. If $a_1 = 5$ and $d = -2$, find a_n and a_{50}.

53. If $a_1 = 6$ and $a_2 = 10$, find d, a_n, and a_{10}.

54. If $a_1 = 1$ and $a_3 = 5$, find d, a_n, and a_{100}.

55. If $a_3 = 9$ and $a_9 = 33$, find d, a_n, and a_{20}.

56. If $a_2 = 9$ and $a_{13} = 20$, find d, a_n, and a_{200}.

57. If $a_4 = -10$ and $a_9 = -20$, find d, a_n, and a_{60}.

58. If $a_5 = 0$ and $a_{11} = 18$, find d, a_n, and a_2.

59. If $a_3 = 5$ and $a_9 = 8$, find d, a_n, a_{15}, and a_{20}.

60. If $a_4 = 1$ and $a_{16} = 5$, find d, a_n, a_{19}, and a_{30}.

3 Use arithmetic sequences to solve the following problems.

61. A company had sales of $33,000 during its first year of operation. If its sales increased by $5600 per year, what would its sales be in the twelfth year?

62. A new firm loses $1800 in its first month, but its profit increases by $500 in each succeeding month for the next year. Find its profit in the twelfth month.

63. Jennifer is given a starting salary of $19,000 and is guaranteed a $2200 raise each year. How much will she be making in her ninth year on the job?

64. A man gives his grandson 10¢ on January 1, 15¢ on January 2, 20¢ on January 3, and so on. How much did he give him on January 31? If this continues, how much will he give his grandson on December 31? (Assume it is not a leap year.)

65. Brian is given a starting salary of $27,000 and a $1800 raise each year. How many years will it take for his starting salary to double?

66. Tom is given a starting salary of $18,000 and a $2250 raise each year. How many years will it take for his starting salary to triple?

67. A machine cost $10,000, and its value decreases by $650 per year. How much is it worth in its sixth year?

68. A machine costs $21,000, and its value decreases by $1100 per year. How much is it worth in its eighth year?

B

69. Kathy is offered two jobs. The first one has a starting salary of $20,000, with yearly raises of $900. The second job has a starting salary of $18,000, with yearly raises of $1200. Which job will pay her more money in her tenth year?

70. If Jeff retires at age 55, he will receive $16,000 that year with an increase of $1900 per year for each succeeding year. If he retires at age 60, he will receive $24,000 that year with an increase of $1700 per year for each succeeding year. Which plan will provide him with a greater income at age 70? (*Note*: Age 55 to 70, inclusive, is 16 years.)

The number e is the base of the natural logarithm, $\ln x$, and $e = 2.7182818284 \dots$. As n increases, the terms of the sequence $a_n = \left(1 + \dfrac{1}{n}\right)^n$ get closer and closer to e. We can use the y^x key on a calculator to approximate $e \approx a_n$. For example,

$$a_{100} = \left(1 + \frac{1}{100}\right)^{100} = (1.01)^{100} = 2.7048138$$

Use a calculator to approximate a_n to seven decimal places for n equal to:

71. 1000　　　　　**72.** 10,000

73. 100,000　　　**74.** 1,000,000

As n increases, the terms of the sequence $b_n = \left(1 + \dfrac{1}{n}\right)^{-n}$ get closer and closer to $1/e = 0.3678794412 \dots$. We can use the y^x and $+/-$ keys on a calculator to approximate $1/e \approx b_n$. Use a calculator to approximate b_n to seven decimal places for n equal to:

75. 1000　　　　　**76.** 10,000

77. 100,000　　　**78.** 1,000,000

Find two general terms, a_n and b_n, that produce the four given terms of the following sequences.

79. $\{1, 4, 9, 16, \dots\}$　　　**80.** $\{1, 8, 27, 81, \dots\}$

C

81. (*Puzzle*) The following sequence of numbers is arranged in a logical order. Determine the pattern.

$$\{8, 5, 4, 9, 1, 7, 6, 10, 3, 2, 0\}$$

82. (*Puzzle*) The letters of the alphabet are arranged in a logical order above and below the line. Determine the pattern.

$$\frac{\text{A} \qquad \text{EF HI} \quad \dots}{\text{BCD} \quad \text{G} \quad \text{J} \quad \dots}$$

✎ Answer each question with complete sentences.

83. What is the difference between an infinite and a finite sequence?

84. What is an alternating sequence?

REVIEW EXERCISES

Simplify the following. (See Section 1.4.)

85. $1 + \dfrac{1}{2} + \dfrac{1}{3} + \dfrac{1}{4}$

86. $1 + \dfrac{1}{2} + \dfrac{1}{3} + \dfrac{1}{4} + \dfrac{1}{5}$

87. $(3 \cdot 1 + 2) + (3 \cdot 2 + 2) + (3 \cdot 3 + 2) + (3 \cdot 4 + 2)$

88. $(-1)^2 2^0 + (-1)^3 2^1 + (-1)^4 2^2 + (-1)^5 2^3 + (-1)^6 2^4$

11.2 ARITHMETIC SERIES AND SIGMA NOTATION

1	Series
2	Sigma Notation
3	Arithmetic Series
4	Word Problems

1 Series

In Example 7 of the last section, we saw that if a company had sales of $20,000 in its first year and its sales increased by $4000 per year, then the sales in its fifteenth year would be $76,000. Perhaps we also want to know the total amount of sales earned in the 15 years. To determine this we must be able to find the sum of a sequence, which is the main topic of this section.

A **series** is the indicated sum of a sequence of numbers. A series is finite if the sequence is finite. For example, the series associated with the sequence $\{1, 3, 5, 7\}$ is

$$1 + 3 + 5 + 7$$

In a similar way, a series is infinite if the sequence is infinite. For instance, the series formed from the sequence $\{1, 3, 5, \dots, 2n - 1, \dots\}$ is

$$1 + 3 + 5 + \dots + 2n - 1 + \dots$$

In general, if $\{a_1, a_2, a_3, \dots, a_n, \dots\}$ is an infinite sequence, then the corresponding infinite series is

$$a_1 + a_2 + a_3 + \dots + a_n + \dots$$

where a_n is called the **general term** or the **nth term** of the series. "Infinite series" is usually shortened to "series."

The **nth partial sum, S_n,** of a series is the indicated sum of the first n terms of the series. Therefore, the partial sums of $\{a_n\}$ are

$$S_1 = a_1 \qquad\qquad \text{First partial sum}$$
$$S_2 = a_1 + a_2 \qquad \text{Second partial sum}$$
$$S_3 = a_1 + a_2 + a_3 \qquad \text{Third partial sum}$$
$$\vdots$$
$$S_n = a_1 + a_2 + \ldots + a_n \qquad \text{nth partial sum}$$
$$\vdots$$

Thus, for a given sequence $\{a_n\}$ we have the sequence of partial sums $\{S_n\}$. In calculations writing S_n in terms of S_{n-1} is often convenient:

$$S_n = a_1 + a_2 + \ldots + a_n$$
$$= (a_1 + a_2 + \ldots + a_{n-1}) + a_n$$
$$= S_{n-1} + a_n$$

EXAMPLE 1

Find the first five partial sums of the series $1 + \dfrac{1}{2} + \dfrac{1}{3} + \ldots + \dfrac{1}{n} \ldots$

SOLUTION

$$S_1 = 1$$
$$S_2 = 1 + \frac{1}{2} = \frac{3}{2}$$
$$S_3 = 1 + \frac{1}{2} + \frac{1}{3} = S_2 + \frac{1}{3} = \frac{3}{2} + \frac{1}{3} = \frac{11}{6}$$
$$S_4 = 1 + \frac{1}{2} + \frac{1}{3} + \frac{1}{4} = S_3 + \frac{1}{4} = \frac{11}{6} + \frac{1}{4} = \frac{25}{12}$$
$$S_5 = 1 + \frac{1}{2} + \frac{1}{3} + \frac{1}{4} + \frac{1}{5} = S_4 + \frac{1}{5} = \frac{25}{12} + \frac{1}{5} = \frac{137}{60}$$

2 Sigma Notation

A convenient notation for writing a series uses the general term of the corresponding sequence. **Summation notation** also is called **sigma notation**, because it is written with the Greek capital letter sigma, Σ. For example, the sum of the first four terms of the sequence whose general term is $a_n = 5n$ is written

$$\sum_{k=1}^{4} 5k$$

This expression is read, "the summation of $5k$ as k goes from 1 to 4"; that is, we replace k by 1, 2, 3, and 4 as follows:

$$\sum_{k=1}^{4} 5k = 5 \cdot 1 + 5 \cdot 2 + 5 \cdot 3 + 5 \cdot 4 = 5 + 10 + 15 + 20 = 50$$

The letter k is called the **index of summation** (i, j, and n are also used for the index of summation).

Sigma notation is used to write partial sums in a more compact form:

$$S_n = a_1 + a_2 + \ldots + a_n = \sum_{k=1}^{n} a_k$$

This notation and the infinity symbol, ∞, also are used to write an infinite series:

$$a_1 + a_2 + \ldots + a_n + \ldots = \sum_{k=1}^{\infty} a_k$$

For example, "the sum of $1/k$ as k goes from 1 to infinity" is written

$$1 + \frac{1}{2} + \frac{1}{3} + \ldots + \frac{1}{k} + \ldots = \sum_{k=1}^{\infty} \frac{1}{k}$$

EXAMPLE 2

Expand and simplify the following.

a. $\displaystyle\sum_{k=1}^{3} (k^2 - 1)$ **b.** $\displaystyle\sum_{k=1}^{5} (-1)^{k+1} 2^{k-1}$

SOLUTION

a. $\displaystyle\sum_{k=1}^{3} (k^2 - 1) = (1^2 - 1) + (2^2 - 1) + (3^2 - 1)$

$$= 0 + 3 + 8$$
$$= 11$$

b. $\displaystyle\sum_{k=1}^{5} (-1)^{k+1} 2^{k-1}$

$$= (-1)^2 2^0 + (-1)^3 2^1 + (-1)^4 2^2 + (-1)^5 2^3 + (-1)^6 2^4$$
$$= (1)1 + (-1)2 + (1)4 + (-1)8 + (1)16$$
$$= 1 - 2 + 4 - 8 + 16$$
$$= 11$$

To convert a series from its expanded form to sigma notation we have to find a general term, a_k, for the series. This search is done by inspection and trial and error. For example, each term in the series $4 + 8 + 12 + 16 + 20$ can be written as $a_k = 4k$ for $k = 1, 2, 3, 4$, and 5. Thus,

$$4 + 8 + 12 + 16 + 20 = 4 \cdot 1 + 4 \cdot 2 + 4 \cdot 3 + 4 \cdot 4 + 4 \cdot 5$$
$$= \sum_{k=1}^{5} 4k$$

EXAMPLE 3

Express the following in sigma notation.

a. $8 + 27 + 64 + 125$ **b.** $-1 + 1 - 1 + 1 - 1 + 1$

c. $\dfrac{1}{2} + \dfrac{1}{4} + \dfrac{1}{8} + \ldots + \dfrac{1}{2^n} + \ldots$

SOLUTION   **a.** $8 + 27 + 64 + 125 = 2^3 + 3^3 + 4^3 + 5^3 = \sum_{k=2}^{5} k^3$

b. $-1 + 1 - 1 + 1 - 1 + 1$
$$= (-1)^1 + (-1)^2 + (-1)^3 + (-1)^4 + (-1)^5 + (-1)^6$$
$$= \sum_{k=1}^{6} (-1)^k$$

c. $\dfrac{1}{2} + \dfrac{1}{4} + \dfrac{1}{8} + \ldots + \dfrac{1}{2^n} + \ldots$
$$= \frac{1}{2^1} + \frac{1}{2^2} + \frac{1}{2^3} + \ldots + \frac{1}{2^n} + \ldots$$
$$= \sum_{n=1}^{\infty} \frac{1}{2^n}$$

---

3   Arithmetic Series

The indicated sum of an arithmetic sequence is called an **arithmetic series**. To introduce the method of finding the nth partial sum of an arithmetic series, let us consider a problem solved by Carl Friedrich Gauss (1777–1855) when he was ten years old.

One day Carl's teacher wanted to keep the class busy for a while so he could grade papers. He told the students to find the sum of the first 100 natural numbers. Carl thought for a moment, wrote the answer on his slate, and showed it to the teacher. When the boy explained his reasoning, the teacher recognized his genius and arranged a private mathematics tutor for him. Gauss went on to become one of the greatest mathematicians who ever lived.

If we use algebra, which Gauss did not know at the age of ten, his solution would go as follows. Let

$$x = 1 + 2 + 3 + \ldots + 98 + 99 + 100 \qquad (1)$$

Now reverse the order of the numbers in Equation (1):

$$x = 100 + 99 + 98 + \ldots + 3 + 2 + 1 \qquad (2)$$

Now add Equations (1) and (2):

$$
\begin{array}{rcccccccc}
x = & 1 + & 2 + & 3 + & \ldots + & 98 + & 99 + & 100 \\
x = & 100 + & 99 + & 98 + & \ldots + & 3 + & 2 + & 1 \\
\hline
2x = & 101 + & 101 + & 101 + & \ldots + & 101 + & 101 + & 101
\end{array}
$$

We have one hundred 101's, so

$$2x = 100 \cdot 101$$
$$x = \frac{100 \cdot 101}{2} = 50 \cdot 101 = 5050$$

Thus

$$1 + 2 + 3 + \ldots + 100 = 5050$$

EXAMPLE 4

Use the method of reversing the order to find the sum

$$S_{50} = \sum_{k=1}^{50} (2k + 2)$$

SOLUTION

$$S_{50} = (2 \cdot 1 + 2) + (2 \cdot 2 + 2) + \ldots + (2 \cdot 50 + 2)$$
$$S_{50} = 4 + 6 + \ldots + 100 + 102$$
$$\underline{S_{50} = 102 + 100 + \ldots + 6 + 4}$$
$$2S_{50} = 106 + 106 + \ldots + 106 + 106$$

There are fifty 106's, so

$$2S_{50} = 50 \cdot 106$$
$$S_{50} = \frac{50 \cdot 106}{2} = 25 \cdot 106 = 2650$$

We can use the method of reversing the order to find the formula for the partial sum, S_n, of the first n terms of the arithmetic sequence $\{a_n\}$. Recall that d is the common difference between any two consecutive terms. Thus,

$$S_n = a_1 + (a_1 + d) + (a_1 + 2d) + \ldots + (a_n - 2d) + (a_n - d) + a_n$$
$$\underline{S_n = a_n + (a_n - d) + (a_n - 2d) + \ldots + (a_1 + 2d) + (a_1 + d) + a_1}$$
$$2S_n = (a_1 + a_n) + (a_1 + a_n) + (a_1 + a_n) + \ldots (a_1 + a_n)$$
$$2S_n = n(a_1 + a_n)$$
$$S_n = \frac{n}{2}(a_1 + a_n) \tag{3}$$

Recall that $a_n = a_1 + (n - 1)d$ is the general term of an arithmetic sequence. Now substitute this value in Equation (3):

$$S_n = \frac{n}{2}(a_1 + a_n) \quad \text{and} \quad a_n = a_1 + (n - 1)d$$

$$= \frac{n}{2}[a_1 + a_1 + (n - 1)d]$$

$$= \frac{n}{2}[2a_1 + (n - 1)d] \tag{4}$$

Equation (4) allows us to find S_n without having to calcualte a_n. The following box summarizes these results.

Arithmetic Series

Let $\{a_n = a_1 + (n - 1)d\}$ be an arithmetic sequence with common difference d. The nth partial sum of the corresponding arithmetic series is

$$S_n = \frac{n}{2}(a_1 + a_n) = \frac{n}{2}[2a_1 + (n - 1)d]$$

EXAMPLE 5

Find the sum of the first 20 terms of the arithmetic sequence whose first term is 5 and whose common difference is -3.

SOLUTION $a_1 = 5$, $d = -3$, and $n = 20$. Thus, the twentieth partial sum is

$$S_n = \frac{n}{2}[2a_1 + (n-1)d]$$

$$S_{20} = \frac{20}{2}[2 \cdot 5 + (20-1)(-3] = 10[10 - 57] = -470$$

4 Word Problems

In the last section we used arithmetic sequences to determine a company's or person's future income. With arithmetic series we can find the total income over this time period. To illustrate this, we return to Example 7 of Section 11.1. In this problem a company's first year sales were $a_1 = \$20,000$, and its fifteenth year sales were $\$76,000$. Its total sales for 15 years are

$$S_n = \frac{n}{2}(a_1 + a_n)$$

$$S_{15} = \frac{15}{2}(20,000 + 76,000) = 7.5(96,000) = \$720,000$$

EXAMPLE 6

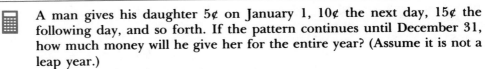

A man gives his daughter 5¢ on January 1, 10¢ the next day, 15¢ the following day, and so forth. If the pattern continues until December 31, how much money will he give her for the entire year? (Assume it is not a leap year.)

SOLUTION $a_1 = 5$, $d = 5$, and $n = 365$. Thus,

$$S_n = \frac{n}{2}[2a_1 + (n-1)d]$$

$$S_{365} = \frac{365}{2}[2 \cdot 5 + (365-1)5]$$

$$= 182.5[10 + 1820]$$

$$= 333,975$$

He will give her $\$3339.75$.

EXERCISE SET 11.2

A

1 Write but do not simplify the series associated with each sequence.

1. $\{1, 2, 3, 4, 5\}$

2. $\{1, 4, 9, 16, 25\}$

3. $\{1, -3, 5, -7, 9, -11\}$

4. $\{-2, -4, -6, -8, -10, -12\}$

5. $\{2, 4, 6, \ldots, 2n, \ldots\}$

6. $\{1, 8, 27, \ldots, n^3, \ldots\}$

7. $\left\{\frac{1}{2}, \frac{2}{3}, \frac{3}{4}, \ldots, \frac{n}{n+1}, \ldots\right\}$

8. $\left\{1, \frac{1}{3}, \frac{1}{9}, \ldots, \frac{1}{3^{n-1}}, \ldots\right\}$

Find the first five partial sums of the series associated with the given sequence.

9. $\{1, 2, 3, 4, 5\}$

10. $\{-2, -4, -6, -8, -10, -12\}$

11. $\{1, -4, 9, -16, 25, -36\}$

12. $\{1, -1, \ldots, (-1)^{n+1}, \ldots\}$

13. $\{1, 3, \ldots, 2n - 1, \ldots\}$

14. $\{1!, 2!, \ldots, n!, \ldots\}$

15. $a_n = 3n - 1$

16. $a_n = (-1)^{n-1}2n$

17. $a_n = \dfrac{1}{(n-1)!}$ **18.** $a_n = \dfrac{(-1)^{n+1}}{n}$

19. $a_n = \dfrac{(-1)^{n+1}}{2^n}$ **20.** $a_n = \dfrac{n+1}{n+3}$

2 Expand and simplify the following.

21. $\displaystyle\sum_{k=1}^{4} 3k$ **22.** $\displaystyle\sum_{k=1}^{5} (k + 3)$

23. $\displaystyle\sum_{k=1}^{3} (k^2 + 1)$ **24.** $\displaystyle\sum_{n=1}^{6} (-2)^{n-1}$

25. $\displaystyle\sum_{k=3}^{6} 4k$ **26.** $\displaystyle\sum_{k=2}^{5} 2k$

27. $\displaystyle\sum_{i=0}^{4} (3i + 1)$ **28.** $\displaystyle\sum_{j=0}^{5} \dfrac{(-1)^j}{2^j}$

29. $\displaystyle\sum_{n=0}^{5} \dfrac{1}{n!}$ **30.** $\displaystyle\sum_{n=1}^{6} \dfrac{(-1)^{n+1}}{n}$

31. $\displaystyle\sum_{k=4}^{7} \dfrac{k+1}{2}$ **32.** $\displaystyle\sum_{k=2}^{6} (-1)^k k$

Expand the following; do not simplify.

33. $\displaystyle\sum_{k=1}^{8} (2k + 1)$ **34.** $\displaystyle\sum_{n=0}^{7} (-1)^n 2^n$

35. $\displaystyle\sum_{n=1}^{\infty} (2n - 1)$ **36.** $\displaystyle\sum_{n=0}^{\infty} \dfrac{2^n}{3^n}$

37. $\displaystyle\sum_{n=1}^{\infty} \dfrac{(-1)^{n+1}}{n}$ **38.** $\displaystyle\sum_{n=0}^{\infty} \dfrac{1}{n!}$

Express the following in sigma notation.

39. $6 + 12 + 18 + 24$

40. $3 + 5 + 7 + 9 + 11$

41. $2 + 4 + 6 + \ldots + 50$

42. $1 + \sqrt{2} + \sqrt{3} + \ldots + \sqrt{15}$

43. $\dfrac{1}{4} + \dfrac{1}{5} + \dfrac{1}{6} + \ldots + \dfrac{1}{100}$

44. $\dfrac{1}{4} + \dfrac{1}{8} + \dfrac{1}{16} + \dfrac{1}{32} + \dfrac{1}{64} + \dfrac{1}{128}$

45. $-2 + 4 - 6 + 8 - 10 + 12$

46. $1 - 8 + 27 - 64 + 125$

47. $3 + 6 + \ldots + 3k + \ldots$

48. $1 + \sqrt{2} + \ldots + \sqrt[k]{k} + \ldots$

49. $\dfrac{1}{2} + \dfrac{1}{3} + \ldots + \dfrac{1}{n+1} + \ldots$

50. $\dfrac{2}{3} + \dfrac{3}{4} + \ldots + \dfrac{n+1}{n+2} + \ldots$

3 Use the method of reversing the order to find the sum of the following series.

51. $1 + 2 + 3 + \ldots + 10$

52. $1 + 2 + 3 + \ldots + 1000$

53. $S_{50} = \displaystyle\sum_{k=1}^{50} k$ **54.** $S_{10} = \displaystyle\sum_{k=1}^{10} 2k$

55. $S_{20} = \displaystyle\sum_{k=1}^{20} (2k - 1)$ **56.** $S_{100} = \displaystyle\sum_{k=1}^{100} 3k$

The following problems refer to arithmetic series.

57. If $a_1 = 2$ and $a_8 = 16$, find S_8.

58. If $a_1 = 4$ and $a_{100} = 301$, find S_{100}.

59. If $a_n = n + 5$, find S_n and S_{10}.

60. If $a_n = 1 - 4n$, find S_n and S_{100}.

61. If $a_1 = 6$ and $d = 2$, find S_n and S_{20}.

62. If $a_1 = 4$ and $d = -5$, find S_n and S_{12}.

63. If $a_2 = 8$ and $d = 4$, find S_n and S_{30}.

64. If $a_2 = -4$ and $d = -3$, find S_n and S_{60}.

4 In statistics the **arithmetic mean** of a set of n numbers (called *sample values*) is their average. If x_i are the numbers and $\bar{x}$ is the mean, then

$$\bar{x} = \frac{1}{n} \sum_{i=1}^{n} x_i = \frac{x_1 + x_2 + \ldots + x_n}{n}$$

Find the arithmetic mean of the following sets of numbers.

65. $\{5, 6, 11, 14\}$ **66.** $\{3, 5, 6, 13, 15, 24\}$

If an object is dropped from rest, then the distance in feet, a_n, that it falls in the nth second is given by

$$a_n = 16(2n - 1)$$

For example, in the 1st second it falls $a_1 = 16(2 \cdot 1 - 1) = 16$ feet, in the 2nd second it falls $a_2 = 16(2 \cdot 2 - 1) = 48$ feet, and so on. These distances form an arithmetic sequence whose nth distance (term) is a_n.

67. Find the common difference d and a formula for S_n, the sum of the distances.

68. How far does it fall in the sixth second, and how far does it fall in the first 6 seconds?

69. How far does it fall in the tenth second, and how far does it fall in the first 10 seconds?

Use arithmetic sequences and series to solve the following problems.

70. A company had sales of $40,000 during its first year, and its sales increased by $6500 per year. Find its sales in the tenth year and its total sales for the 10 years.

71. Nancy is given a starting salary of $18,500 and a raise of $1400 each year. Find her income in her twelfth year on the job and her total income for the 12 years.

72. Kathy is saving quarters. She saves 1 quarter the first day, 2 the second, 3 the third, and so on. How much money will she have saved in 60 days?

73. A child is saving pennies. He saves 1 on the first day, 3 on the second, 5 on the third, and so on. How many days will it take him to save $100?

74. A theater has 40 rows with 18 seats in the first row, 22 in the second row, 26 in the third row, and so on. How many seats are in the theater?

B

75. A stack of firewood has 27 pieces in the bottom row, 25 in the next row, and so forth, to the top row, which has 1 piece of wood. How many rows are in the stack? How many pieces of wood?

76. A stack of 256 bricks has 1 brick in the top row, 3 in the second row, 5 in the third row, and so forth.

a. How many rows are in the stack?
b. How many bricks are in the bottom row?
c. How many bricks are in the fourth row from the bottom?

As n increases, the partial sums of the series $\sum_{n=0}^{\infty} \frac{1}{n!}$ get closer and closer to $e = 2.7182818284\ldots$. Use a calculator to find S_n to seven decimal places for n equal to:

77. 5   **78.** 10

As n increases, the partial sums of the series $\sum_{n=1}^{\infty} \frac{(-1)^{n+1}}{n}$ get closer and closer to $\ln 2 = 0.6931472\ldots$. Use a calculator to find S_n to seven decimal places for n equal to:

79. 10   **80.** 15

81. Use the method of reversing the order to show that

$$\sum_{k=1}^{n} k = \frac{n(n + 1)}{2}$$

Use the formula in Exercise 81 to find the following.

82. $1 + 2 + \ldots + 10{,}000$

83. $1 + 2 + \ldots + 100{,}000$

84. $1 + 2 + \ldots + 1{,}000{,}000$

Use the formula $\sum_{k=1}^{n} k^2 = \frac{n(n + 1)(2n + 1)}{6}$ to find the following.

85. $1 + 4 + \ldots + 10^2$ **86.** $1 + 4 + \ldots + 50^2$

Use the formula $\sum_{k=1}^{n} k^3 = \left[\frac{n(n + 1)}{2}\right]^2$ to find the following.

87. $1 + 8 + \ldots + 12^3$ **88.** $1 + 8 + \ldots + 100^3$

C

Answer the following questions with complete sentences.

89. What is the difference between a sequence and a series?

90. What is meant by the "nth partial sum" of a series?

REVIEW EXERCISES

Simplify the following. (See Section 1.4.)

91. $2 + 6 + 18 + 54 + 162$

92. $1 + \dfrac{1}{2} + \dfrac{1}{4} + \dfrac{1}{8} + \dfrac{1}{16} + \dfrac{1}{32}$

Use a calculator to express the following correctly to six decimal places. (See Section 1.4.)

93. $2\left(1 - \dfrac{1}{2^{10}}\right)$ **94.** $2\left(1 - \dfrac{1}{2^{20}}\right)$

Express the following as the ratio of two integers. (See Section 2.2.)

95. $.8\overline{8}$ **96.** $.27\overline{27}$

11.3 GEOMETRIC SEQUENCES AND SERIES

1	Geometric Sequences
2	Geometric Series
3	Infinite Geometric Series and Repeating Decimals
4	Word Problems

1   Geometric Sequences

We have seen that in an arithmetic sequence each term after the first one is obtained by adding the same number to the preceding term. Now we will study a sequence (and the corresponding series) where each term after the first is found by multiplying the previous term by a fixed number.

A **geometric sequence** (or *geometric progression*) is a sequence in which each term after the first one is obtained by multiplying the preceding term by the same number. For example,

$$\{1, 2, 4, 8, 16, 32, 64, \dots\}$$

is a geometric sequence because each term after 1 is found by multiplying the previous term by 2 ($2 = 2 \cdot 1,\quad 4 = 2 \cdot 2,\quad 8 = 2 \cdot 4, \dots$). The number by which we multiply each term is called the **common ratio, r**, because the ratio of any two consecutive terms is r. In this example $r = 2$, because

$$2 = \frac{2}{1} = \frac{4}{2} = \frac{8}{4} = \frac{16}{8} = \dots$$

EXAMPLE 1   The first term of a geometric sequence is $a_1 = 4$ and the common ratio is 3. Find the next three terms.

SOLUTION $a_2 = 3 \cdot 4 = 12$ $a_3 = 3 \cdot 12 = 36$ $a_4 = 3 \cdot 36 = 108$

EXAMPLE 2

Find the common ratio, r, for the following geometric sequences.

a. $\{1000, 1100, 1210, 1331\}$ **b.** $\dfrac{1}{2}, \dfrac{1}{4}, \dfrac{1}{8}, \dfrac{1}{16}, \ldots$

SOLUTION

a. $r = 1.1$,   because $\dfrac{1100}{1000} = \dfrac{1210}{1100} = \dfrac{1331}{1210} = 1.1$

b. $r = \dfrac{1}{2}$,   because $\dfrac{1}{4} \div \dfrac{1}{2} = \dfrac{1}{8} \div \dfrac{1}{4} = \dfrac{1}{16} \div \dfrac{1}{8} = \dfrac{1}{2}.$

The general term of a geometric sequence, a_n, can be found from the first term, a_1, and the common ratio, r. For example,

$$\{1, 2, 4, 8, 16, 32, 64, \ldots\}; \quad a_1 = 1 \quad \text{and} \quad r = 2.$$
$$a_2 = 1 \cdot 2 = 1 \cdot 2^1 = 2$$
$$a_3 = (1 \cdot 2)2 = 1 \cdot 2^2 = 4$$
$$a_4 = (1 \cdot 2^2)2 = 1 \cdot 2^3 = 8$$
$$a_5 = (1 \cdot 2^3)2 = 1 \cdot 2^4 = 16$$
$$\vdots$$
$$a_n = (1 \cdot 2^{n-2})2 = 1 \cdot 2^{n-2+1} = 1 \cdot 2^{n-1}$$

In general, if a_1 is the first term and r is the common ratio of a geometric sequence, then

$$a_2 = a_1 r = a_1 r^1$$
$$a_3 = (a_1 r^1)r = a_1 r^2$$
$$a_4 = (a_1 r^2)r = a_1 r^3$$
$$a_5 = (a_1 r^3)r = a_1 r^4$$
$$\vdots$$
$$a_n = (a_1 r^{n-2})r = a_1 r^{n-2+1} = a_1 r^{n-1}$$

Geometric Sequences

The general term, a_n, of a geometric sequence with first term a_1 and common ratio r is

$$a_n = a_1 r^{n-1}$$

EXAMPLE 3

For the geometric sequence $\{2, 10, 50, 250, \ldots\}$ find the following.

a. a_n **b.** a_{30}

SOLUTION

a. $a_1 = 2$ and $r = 10/2 = 5$. Thus,
$$a_n = a_1 r^{n-1} = 2 \cdot 5^{n-1}$$
b. $a_{30} = 2 \cdot 5^{30-1} = 2 \cdot 5^{29} = 3.7253 \times 10^{20}$

EXAMPLE 4

Find the general term of the geometric sequence where $a_3 = 4$ and $a_6 = -32/27$.

SOLUTION

$a_3 = a_1 r^2 = 4$ and $a_6 = a_1 r^5 = -32/27$.
We can find r by using the ratio a_6/a_3:
$$\frac{a_6}{a_3} = \frac{a_1 r^5}{a_1 r^2} = r^3 \text{ and}$$
$$\frac{a_6}{a^3} = -\frac{32}{27} \div 4 = -\frac{32}{27} \cdot \frac{1}{4} = -\frac{8}{27} = \left(-\frac{2}{3}\right)^3$$
$$r^3 = \left(-\frac{2}{3}\right)^3 \quad \text{so}$$
$$r = -\frac{2}{3}. \quad \text{To find } a_1, \text{ let}$$
$$a_1 r^2 = a_3$$
$$a_1 = a_3 \div r^2 = 4 \div \left(-\frac{2}{3}\right)^2 = 4 \div \frac{4}{9} = 4 \cdot \frac{9}{4} = 9. \quad \text{Thus,}$$
$$a_n = a_1 r^{n-1} = 9\left(-\frac{2}{3}\right)^{n-1}$$

2   **Geometric Series**

From the geometric sequence
$$\{a_1, a_1 r, a_1 r^2, a_1 r^3, \ldots, a_1 r^{n-1}, \ldots\}$$
we have the corresponding **geometric series**
$$a_1 + a_1 r + a_1 r^2 + a_1 r^3 + \ldots + a_1 r^{n-1} + \ldots$$
whose nth partial sum is
$$S_n = a_1 + a_1 r + a_1 r^2 + a_1 r^3 + \ldots + a_1 r^{n-1}$$

As with an arithmetic series, we can calculate the nth partial sum of a geometric series with some clever arithmetic. For example, consider the sequence
$$\{2, 6, 18, 54, 162\} = \{2, 2 \cdot 3, 2 \cdot 3^2, 2 \cdot 3^3, 2 \cdot 3^4\}$$
The fifth partial sum is
$$S_5 = 2 + 2 \cdot 3 + 2 \cdot 3^2 + 2 \cdot 3^2 + 2 \cdot 3^4 \tag{1}$$

Now multiply Equation (1) by $-r = -3$:

$$-3S_5 = -3(2 + 2 \cdot 3 + 2 \cdot 3^2 + 2 \cdot 3^3 + 2 \cdot 3^4)$$
$$-3S_5 = -2 \cdot 3 - 2 \cdot 3^2 - 2 \cdot 3^3 - 2 \cdot 3^4 - 2 \cdot 3^5 \tag{2}$$

Now add Equations (1) and (2):

$$1S_5 = 2 + 2 \cdot 3 + 2 \cdot 3^2 + 2 \cdot 3^3 + 2 \cdot 3^4 \tag{1}$$
$$\underline{-3S_5 = \quad\quad - 2 \cdot 3 - 2 \cdot 3^2 - 2 \cdot 3^3 - 2 \cdot 3^4 - 2 \cdot 3^5} \tag{2}$$
$$-2S_5 = 2 - 0 \quad\quad - 0 \quad\quad - 0 \quad\quad - 0 \quad\quad - 2 \cdot 3^5$$
$$-2S_5 = 2 \cdot 1 - 2 \cdot 3^5$$
$$S_5 = \frac{2(1 - 3^5)}{-2} = -1(1 - 3^5) = 3^5 - 1 = 242$$

Now we use the method of multiplying by $-r$ to find the formula for the partial sum:

$$S_n = a_1 + a_1r + a_1r^2 + a_1r^3 + \ldots + a_1r^{n-1} \tag{3}$$
$$-rS_n = -r(a_1 + a_1r + a_1r^2 + \ldots + a_1r^{n-1})$$
$$-rS_n = -a_1r - a_1r^2 - a_1r^3 - \ldots - a_1r^{n-1} - a_1r^n \tag{4}$$

Now add Equations (3) and (4):

$$S_n = a_1 + a_1r + a_1r^2 + a_1r^3 + \ldots + a_1r^{n-1}$$
$$\underline{-rS_n = \quad\quad - a_1r - a_1r^2 - a_1r^3 - \ldots - a_1r^{n-1} - a_1r^n}$$
$$1S_n - rS_n = a_1 - 0 - \quad\quad \ldots \quad\quad - 0 \quad\quad - a_1r^n$$
$$(1 - r)S_n = a_1 \cdot 1 - a_1r^n$$
$$S_n = \frac{a_1(1 - r^n)}{1 - r} = \frac{a_1}{1 - r}(1 - r^n), \quad r \neq 1$$

Geometric Series

Let $\{a_n = a_1r^{n-1}\}$ be a geometric sequence with common ratio r. The nth partial sum of the corresponding geometric series is

$$S_n = \frac{a_1(1 - r^n)}{1 - r}, \quad r \neq 1$$

EXAMPLE 5

For the geometric series $\displaystyle\sum_{n=1}^{\infty} \frac{1}{2^{n-1}}$, find the following.

a. S_n **b.** S_{10}

(continued)

SOLUTION   **a.** $\displaystyle\sum_{n=1}^{\infty} \frac{1}{2^{n-1}} = \frac{1}{2^0} + \frac{1}{2^1} + \frac{1}{2^2} + \ldots + \frac{1}{2^{n-1}} + \ldots$

$$S_n = 1 + \frac{1}{2} + \frac{1}{2^2} + \ldots + \frac{1}{2^{n-1}} \qquad\qquad 2^0 = 1$$

$r = \dfrac{1}{2} \div 1 = \dfrac{1}{2}$ and $a_1 = 1.$ Thus,

$$S_n = \frac{a_1}{1-r}(1 - r^n)$$

$$= \frac{1}{1 - \dfrac{1}{2}}\left[1 - \left(\frac{1}{2}\right)^n\right] \qquad\qquad \frac{1}{1 - \dfrac{1}{2}} = \frac{1}{\dfrac{1}{2}} = 2$$

$$= 2\left(1 - \frac{1}{2^n}\right)$$

b. $S_{10} = 2\left(1 - \dfrac{1}{2^{10}}\right) = 2\left(1 - \dfrac{1}{1024}\right) = \dfrac{1023}{512}$

---

3   Infinite Geometric Series and Repeating Decimals

Given an infinite series, $\displaystyle\sum_{n=1}^{\infty} a_n$, what happens to the partial sums $S_n = a_1 + a_2 + \ldots + a_n$ as n increases? Under certain conditions (defined precisely in calculus), S_n can get closer and closer to a fixed number S as n gets larger and larger (see Exercises 77–80 of Section 11.2), and we say that S is the **sum** of the series, written $S = \displaystyle\sum_{n=1}^{\infty} a_n$. Under other conditions S_n can become infinite as n becomes infinite.

We begin our discussion of infinite geometric series by returning to the series in Example 5,

$$\sum_{n=1}^{\infty} \frac{1}{2^{n-1}} = 1 + \frac{1}{2} + \frac{1}{2^2} + \ldots + \frac{1}{2^{n-1}} + \ldots\,; \quad r = \frac{1}{2}\ \text{ and}$$

$$S_n = 2\left(1 - \frac{1}{2^n}\right)$$

As n becomes larger and larger, $1/2^n$ gets closer and closer to zero and S_n gets closer and closer to 2. For instance,

If $n = 10,$ then $\dfrac{1}{2^{10}} \approx .000\ 977$ and $S_{10} \approx 1.998\ 045.$

If $n = 20,$ then $\dfrac{1}{2^{20}} \approx .000\ 000\ 954$ and $S_{20} \approx 1.999\ 998.$

Thus, 2 is the sum of the series, and $2 = \displaystyle\sum_{n=1}^{\infty} \frac{1}{2^{n-1}}.$

In general, if $|r| < 1$, that is $-1 < r < 1$, then r^n approaches zero as n increases. Therefore, $1 - r^n \approx 1 - 0 = 1$ and

$$S_n = \frac{a_1(1-r^n)}{1-r} \approx \frac{a_1(1)}{1-r} = \frac{a_1}{1-r}$$

If $|r| \geq 1$ ($r \geq 1$ or $r \leq -1$), then the sum does not exist. For example, the partial sums of $\sum\limits_{n=1}^{\infty} 2^{n-1}$, where $r = 2$, are $S_n = 1 + 2 + 2^2 + \ldots + 2^{n-1} = 1(1 - 2^n)/(1 - 2) = 2^n - 1$. As n increases, S_n becomes infinite in value.

Infinite Geometric Series

If $|r| < 1$, then the sum S of the infinite geometric series with first term a_1 and common ratio r is

$$S = \frac{a_1}{1 - r}$$

If $|r| \geq 1$, then the sum does not exist.

EXAMPLE 6

Find the sum of $\sum\limits_{n=1}^{\infty} \dfrac{2}{5^{n-1}}$.

SOLUTION $\quad \sum\limits_{n=1}^{\infty} \dfrac{2}{5^{n-1}} = 2 + \dfrac{2}{5} + \dfrac{2}{5^2} + \ldots, \quad$ so

$a_1 = 2, \quad r = \dfrac{1}{5}, \quad$ and $\quad |r| < 1$. Thus,

$$S = \frac{a_1}{1 - r} = \frac{2}{1 - \dfrac{1}{5}} = 2 \div \frac{4}{5} = \frac{5}{2}$$

In Section 2.2 [3] we used linear equations to convert repeating decimals to the ratio of two integers. These decimals are infinite geometric series, and they can be expressed as fractions with the formula just discussed. For example, let

$$
\begin{aligned}
S &= .333\overline{3} \\
&= .3 + .03 + .003 + .0003 + \ldots \\
&= \frac{3}{10} + \frac{3}{10^2} + \frac{3}{10^3} + \frac{3}{10^4} + \ldots \\
&= \frac{a_1}{1 - r} \qquad\qquad\qquad a_1 = \frac{3}{10}, \quad r = \frac{1}{10} \\
&= \frac{3}{10} \div \left(1 - \frac{1}{10}\right) \\
&= \frac{3}{10} \div \frac{9}{10} \\
&= \frac{1}{3}
\end{aligned}
$$

EXAMPLE 7

Write $.\overline{45}$ as the ratio of two integers.

SOLUTION $\quad S = .4545\overline{45} = .45 + .0045 + .000045 + \ldots$

$a_1 = .45$ and $r = .01$. Because $|r| < 1$,

$$S = \frac{a_1}{1 - r} = \frac{.45}{1 - .01} = \frac{.45}{.99} = \frac{45}{99} = \frac{5}{11}$$

Thus, $.\overline{45} = \frac{5}{11}$.

---

4   Word Problems

As with arithmetic sequences and series, geometric sequences and series have many applications. This section concludes with two examples of this material.

According to an old Arabic legend from the tenth century, Sissah ibn Dahir invented chess, and his king was so pleased with the game that he told Dahir to name his own reward. Dahir's request seemed modest enough: 1 grain of wheat for the first square on a chessboard, 2 grains for the second square, 4 for the third, 8 for the fourth, and so on to the sixty-fourth square. (This amount of wheat would cover the entire state of Massachusetts with a layer 20 feet deep!) One version of the story has it that when the king realized that this was an impossible request, he solved the problem by having Dahir beheaded!

EXAMPLE 8

Let 1 grain of wheat correspond to the first square of a chessboard, 2 grains to the second, 4 to the third, and so on in a geometric sequence.

a. How many grains of wheat would correspond to the sixteenth square?
b. What would be the total amount of wheat for the entire chessboard?

SOLUTION   **a.** $\{1, 2, 2^2, 2^3, \ldots, 2^{63}\}$ is the sequence and
$a_n = a_1 r^{n-1} = 1 \cdot 2^{n-1} = 2^{n-1}$. Thus,
$a_{16} = 2^{16-1} = 2^{15} = 32{,}768$ grains of wheat.

b. $S_n = \dfrac{a_1(1 - r^n)}{1 - r} = \dfrac{1(1 - 2^n)}{1 - 2} = 2^n - 1$. So,

$S_{64} = 2^{64} - 1 = 18{,}446{,}744{,}073{,}709{,}551{,}615$ grains of wheat (from a book of tables). In scientific notation $S_{64} = 1.8447 \times 10^{19}$.

EXAMPLE 9

A new car cost $16,000, and it depreciates by 20% of its value each year. What is the value of the car at the beginning of its eighth year?

SOLUTION If the car loses 20% in a year, then its value is 80% of the previous year's value. Therefore,

$a_1 = 16000$

$a_2 = 16000(.8)$

$a_3 = [16000(.8)](.8) = 16000(.8)^2$

$a_4 = [16000(.8)^2](.8) = 16000(.8)^3$, and, in general,

$a_n = a_1 r^{n-1} = 16000(.8)^{n-1}$. So, using a calculator,

$a_8 = 16000(.8)^{8-1} = 16000(.8)^7 \approx 3355.44$

Its value will be approximately $3355.

EXERCISE SET 11.3

A

1 Determine whether the given sequence is geometric. If so, then find the common ratio, r, and the next three terms.

1. $\{2, 6, 18, 54, \ldots\}$ **2.** $\{2, 6, 10, 14, \ldots\}$

3. $\{-1, -2, -4, -8, \ldots\}$

4. $\{1, -2, 4, -8, \ldots\}$

5. $\left\{\dfrac{1}{2}, \dfrac{2}{3}, \dfrac{3}{4}, \dfrac{4}{5}, \ldots\right\}$

6. $\left\{\dfrac{1}{2}, \dfrac{1}{4}, \dfrac{1}{8}, \dfrac{1}{16}, \ldots\right\}$

7. $\left\{10, 2, \dfrac{2}{5}, \dfrac{2}{25}, \ldots\right\}$

8. $\left\{8, 4, 1, \dfrac{1}{8}, \ldots\right\}$

9. $\{27, -9, 3, -1, \ldots\}$

10. $\{5, 5, 5, 5, \ldots\}$

The following problems refer to geometric sequences.

11. If $a_1 = 3$ and $r = 2$, find a_n and a_6.

12. If $a_1 = 1$ and $r = -3$, find a_n and a_5.

13. If $a_1 = 1$ and $r = 1/3$, find a_n and a_4.

14. If $a_1 = 5$ and $a_2 = 15$, find r, a_n, and a_{20}.

15. If $a_2 = 8$ and $a_3 = 4$, find a_n, a_1, and a_{10}.

16. If $a_4 = 1/64$ and $a_5 = 1/256$, find a_n, a_1, and a_3.

17. If $a_4 = 54$ and $a_6 = 486$, find a_n and a_{10} ($r > 0$).

18. If $a_5 = 32$ and $a_7 = 128$, find a_n and a_6 ($r < 0$).

19. If $a_2 = 2$ and $a_5 = 2/27$, find a_n and a_4.

20. If $a_4 = -3$ and $a_9 = 3$, find a_n, a_{20}, and a_{77}.

2 Find the sum of each geometric series by using: a. the method of multiplying by $-r$; and b. the formula for S_n.

21. $1 + 2 + 2^2 + \ldots + 2^7$

22. $1 + 3 + 3^2 + \ldots + 3^{n-1}$

23. $1 + \dfrac{1}{5} + \dfrac{1}{25} + \ldots + \dfrac{1}{5^8}$

24. $1 + \dfrac{2}{3} + \dfrac{4}{9} + \ldots + \left(\dfrac{2}{3}\right)^{n-1}$

25. $S_{20} = \displaystyle\sum_{n=1}^{20} \dfrac{1}{2^{n-1}}$ **26.** $S_{30} = \displaystyle\sum_{n=1}^{30} \dfrac{1}{3^{n-1}}$

Find the sums of the following geometric series.

27. $\displaystyle\sum_{k=1}^{60} 3 \cdot 5^{k-1}$ **28.** $\displaystyle\sum_{k=1}^{20} 4^{k-1}$

29. $\displaystyle\sum_{k=1}^{n} 10^{k-1}$ **30.** $\displaystyle\sum_{k=1}^{n} (.2)^{k-1}$

31. $\displaystyle\sum_{k=1}^{n} 2\left(-\dfrac{3}{2}\right)^{k-1}$ **32.** $\displaystyle\sum_{k=1}^{n} -10\left(\dfrac{3}{4}\right)^{k-1}$

3 Find the sums, if they exist, for the following infinite geometric series. If a sum does not exist, so state.

33. $a_1 = 4, r = 1/2$ **34.** $a_1 = 12, r = 2$

35. $a_1 = 1, \quad r = -\dfrac{3}{2}$ **36.** $a_1 = 6, \quad r = -\dfrac{2}{3}$

37. $\dfrac{1}{2} + \dfrac{1}{4} + \dfrac{1}{8} + \dfrac{1}{16} + \ldots$

38. $\dfrac{1}{3} + \dfrac{1}{9} + \dfrac{1}{27} + \dfrac{1}{81} + \ldots$

39. $1 + \dfrac{5}{2} + \left(\dfrac{5}{2}\right)^2 + \left(\dfrac{5}{2}\right)^3 + \ldots$

40. $5 + \dfrac{5}{4} + \dfrac{5}{4^2} + \dfrac{5}{4^3} + \ldots$

41. $\displaystyle\sum_{n=1}^{\infty} \dfrac{81}{3_n}$ **42.** $\displaystyle\sum_{n=1}^{\infty} 2(.1)^{n-1}$

43. $\displaystyle\sum_{n=1}^{\infty} (-.4)^{2n}$ **44.** $\displaystyle\sum_{n=1}^{\infty} 3(-2)^n$

45. $\displaystyle\sum_{n=1}^{\infty} \dfrac{1}{(-2)^{n-1}}$ **46.** $\displaystyle\sum_{n=1}^{\infty} \dfrac{2}{(-3)^{n+1}}$

Express each decimal as the ratio of two integers by using: a. linear equations (Section 2.2) and b. geometric series.

47. $.\overline{6}$ **48.** $.\overline{21}$ **49.** $2.\overline{03}$ **50.** $.1\overline{23}$

Express each decimal as the ratio of two integers by using geometric series.

51. $.\overline{7}$ **52.** $3.\overline{4}$ **53.** $.\overline{9}$ **54.** $4.\overline{15}$

55. $.\overline{01}$ **56.** $25.\overline{36}$ **57.** $.3\overline{45}$ **58.** $9.5\overline{17}$

---

4 In Section 10.5 we used the function $A = P(1 + r)^t$ to solve compound interest problems. If P = the principal, $r = i$ = the interest rate, and $t = n$ = time, then the sequence $\{P, P(1 + i), P(1 + i)^2, \ldots, P(1 + i)^{n-1}, \ldots\}$ is geometric, and the common ratio is $1 + i$. This sequence can be used to determine a person's future income. For example, if Paul's first-year salary is $P = a_1 = \$20,000$ and he gets an 8% raise each year, then his second- and third-year salaries are

$$a_2 = 20000 + 20000(.08) =$$
$$20000(1 + .08) = 20000(1.08)$$
$$a_3 = 20000(1.08) + [20000(1.08)](.08)$$
$$= 20000(1.08)[1 + .08] = 20000(1.08)^2$$

Use this sequence to solve Exercises 59 through 61.

59. Paul's first-year salary is $20,000, and he is guaranteed an 8% raise each year for the next six years. Find his salary for the seventh year and his total income for the seven years.

60. A company's first-year sales were $40,000, and its sales increased by 10% per year. Find its sales in the tenth year and its total sales for the first 10 years.

61. A certain colony of bacteria increases in number by 12% per hour. If 10,000 are present initially, how many will be present in eight hours?

62. A certain colony of bacteria doubles in number every hour. If 10,000 are present initially, how many will be present in eight hours?

63. A new car cost $8000, and it depreciates by 25% of its value each year. What is the value of the car at the beginning of its sixth year?

64. A new machine cost $10,000, and it loses 30% of its value each year. What is its value at the beginning of its ninth year of operation?

65. For a medical test a certain radioactive dye is injected into a patient. At the end of each hour, 65% of the dye that was present at the beginning of the hour is left. If 5 cubic centimeters of the dye are injected, how many cubic centimeters will be in the patient's system at the end of eight hours (to three decimal places)?

66. Let 1¢ correspond to the first square of a chessboard, 3¢ for the second, 9¢ for the third, and so on in a geometric sequence. a. How much money would correspond to the sixteenth square? b. What would be the approximate amount of money for the entire chessboard? (Write your answer in scientific notation.)

67. When a pendulum is released, it swings through an arc of length 16 inches. Each swing after that travels 80% the length of the previous swing. a. How far will the pendulum travel on the eighth swing? b. What is the total distance traveled in the first eight swings? c. How far will the pendulum travel before it comes to rest?

68. When a pendulum is released, it swings through an arc of length 100 centimeters. Each swing after that travels 1/2 the length of the previous swing. a. How far will the pendulum travel on the tenth swing? b. What is the total distance traveled in the first 10 swings? c. How far will the pendulum travel before it comes to rest?

B

69. A ball is dropped from a height of 10 feet. Each time it hits the ground it rebounds 3/4 the previous height. Find the total distance the ball will travel if it is allowed to bounce indefinitely.

70. Repeat Exercise 69 for a height of 20 feet and a rebound of 4/5 the previous height.

If the repeating block of digits in a repeating decimal does not start repeating at the decimal point, then we can write it as two decimals to convert it to a fraction. For example,

$$.1\overline{6} = .1 + .0\overline{6} = .1 + [.06 + .006 + .0006 + \ldots] \qquad r = .1$$
$$= \frac{.06}{1 - .1} = \frac{1}{10} + \frac{1}{15} = \frac{1}{6}$$

Express each decimal as the ratio of two integers by using geometric series.

71. $1.8\overline{3}$ **72.** $.21\overline{4}$ **73.** $.5\overline{81}$

74. $.11\overline{27}$ **75.** $.2\overline{456}$ **76.** $3.89\overline{217}$

77. $.4\overline{9}$ **78.** $.24\overline{9}$

C 🖊

Answer the following questions with complete sentences.

79. Define a geometric sequence.

80. Define a geometric series.

REVIEW EXERCISES

Perform the indicated multiplications. (See Section 5.3.)

81. $(a + b)^1$ **82.** $(a + b)^2$

83. $(a + b)^3$ **84.** $(a + b)^4$

Evaluate the following expressions involving n factorial. (See Section 11.1.)

85. $\dfrac{4!}{3!}$ **86.** $\dfrac{7!}{6!}$ **87.** $\dfrac{5!}{3!2!}$ **88.** $\dfrac{6!}{0!6!}$

11.4 BINOMIAL THEOREM

| 1 | Pascal's Triangle and the Binomial Coefficient |
| 2 | Binomial Theorem |

1 Pascal's Triangle and the Binomial Coefficient

In many fields, such as probability and statistics, a binomial raised to a power must be expanded. The objective of this section is to learn how to expand $(a + b)^n$, where n is a natural number, without having to perform the indicated multiplication.

When $a + b$ is raised to a power, the result is a series. Let us expand $(a + b)^n$ for small values of n to determine the pattern of the series (Figure 11.1).

FIGURE 11.1

$$(a + b)^0 = 1$$
$$(a + b)^1 = 1a + 1b$$
$$(a + b)^2 = 1a^2 + 2ab + 1b^2$$
$$(a + b)^3 = 1a^3 + 3a^2b + 3ab^2 + 1b^3$$
$$(a + b)^4 = 1a^4 + 4a^3b + 6a^2b^2 + 4ab^3 + 1b^4$$
$$(a + b)^5 = 1a^5 + 5a^4b + 10a^3b^2 + 10a^2b^3 + 5ab^4 + 1b^5$$
$$(a + b)^6 = 1a^6 + 6a^5b + 15a^4b^2 + 20a^3b^3 + 15a^2b^4 + 6ab^5 + 1b^6$$
$$\vdots \qquad\qquad\qquad \vdots$$

We can observe several important facts about $(a + b)^n$:

1. The expansion has $n + 1$ terms; $(a + b)^3$ has four terms.

2. The first term is a^n, and the last term is b^n.

3. The exponents on a begin with n and end with zero, while the exponents on b begin with zero and end with n; $a^6 = a^6 b^0$ and $b^6 = a^0 b^6$.

4. The sum of the exponents in any term is n; for $15a^4 b^2$, $4 + 2 = 6$

The relationships between the coefficients can best be seen by writing the series without the variables (Figure 11.2). This triangle of numbers is called **Pascal's triangle** for the French mathematician Blaise Pascal (1623–1662), who studied this pattern of numbers extensively. These numbers are called the **binomial coefficients**. (An eighteenth-century Japanese

FIGURE 11.2
Pascal's triangle

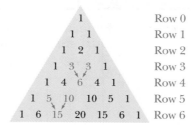

1	Row 0
1 1	Row 1
1 2 1	Row 2
1 3 3 1	Row 3
1 4 6 4 1	Row 4
1 5 10 10 5 1	Row 5
1 6 15 20 15 6 1	Row 6

version of Pascal's triangle is shown in Figure 11.3.) The nth row of this triangle gives the coefficients for $(a + b)^n$. For example, with $n = 4$ (Row 4),

$$(a + b)^4 = a^4 + 4a^3 b + 6a^2 b^2 + 4ab^3 + b^4$$

To find an entry in Pascal's triangle other than a 1 on the boundary, add the two nearest numbers in the row directly above. Thus, $3 + 3 = 6$ (Row 4) and $5 + 10 = 15$ (Row 6). Also, the binomial coefficients equidistant from the ends of a row are the same.

FIGURE 11.3
Pascal's triangle in Japan. From Murai Chūzen's *Sampō Dōshi-mon* (1781), showing also the sangi forms of the numerals.

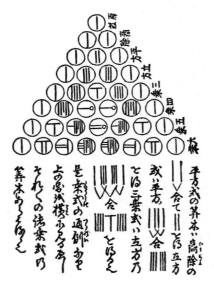

EXAMPLE 1

Use Pascal's triangle to expand the following.

a. $(a - b)^3$ **b.** $(2x + 3)^4$

SOLUTION   **a.** The coefficients are given in Row 3 of Figure 11.2, and the sum of the exponents of each term is 3. So,

$$(a - b)^3 = [a + (-b)]^3$$
$$= a^3 + 3a^2(-b)^1 + 3a^1(-b)^2 + (-b)^3$$
$$= a^3 - 3a^2b + 3ab^2 - b^3$$

b. The coefficients are given in Row 4 of Figure 11.2.
$$(2x + 3)^4 = (2x)^4 + 4(2x)^3 \cdot 3 + 6(2x)^2 \cdot 3^2 + 4(2x) \cdot 3^3 + 3^4$$
$$= 16x^4 + 96x^3 + 216x^2 + 216x + 81$$

EXAMPLE 2

Use Pascal's triangle to find 2^7.

SOLUTION   Use Row 6 to produce Row 7 for $(a + b)^7$:

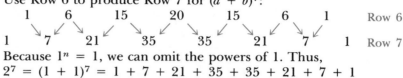

Because $1^n = 1$, we can omit the powers of 1. Thus,
$$2^7 = (1 + 1)^7 = 1 + 7 + 21 + 35 + 35 + 21 + 7 + 1$$
$$= 128$$

Recall from Section 11.1 that n factorial is defined to be $n! = n(n - 1)$ $(n - 2) \ldots (2)(1)$, for n a natural number and $0! = 1$. Also, $n! = n[(n - 1)!]$ is a useful result (see Example 5). We may conveniently use factorial notation to write the binomial coefficients in Pascal's triangle. The symbol $\binom{n}{k}$ stands for the coefficient in the nth row and the kth position from the left, where $k = 0, 1, 2, \ldots$. For example, the 6 in Row 4 corresponds to $k = 2$, and we define

$$\binom{4}{2} = \frac{4!}{2!(4 - 2)!} = \frac{4 \cdot 3 \cdot 2 \cdot 1}{2 \cdot 1 \cdot 2 \cdot 1} = 6$$

In general, the binomial coefficient is defined as follows.

Binomial Coefficient*

The binomial coefficient is defined to be

$$\binom{n}{k} = \frac{n!}{k!(n - k)!}, \quad n \geq k$$

---

* The binomial coefficient is used extensively in probability. In this field $\binom{n}{k}$ means "the number of combinations of n objects taken k at a time." For example, the number of possible five-card hands drawn from a deck of 52 playing cards is

$$\binom{52}{5} = \frac{52!}{5!(52 - 5)!} = \frac{52!}{5!47!} = 2,598,960$$

The number of possible five-card hands that are all hearts is

$$\binom{13}{5} = \frac{13!}{5!(13 - 5)!} = \frac{13!}{5!8!} = 1287$$

EXAMPLE 3

Calculate the following binomial coefficients.

a. $\begin{pmatrix} 6 \\ 3 \end{pmatrix}$ **b.** $\begin{pmatrix} 7 \\ 5 \end{pmatrix}$ **c.** $\begin{pmatrix} n \\ 0 \end{pmatrix}$ **d.** $\begin{pmatrix} n \\ n \end{pmatrix}$

SOLUTION

a. $\begin{pmatrix} 6 \\ 3 \end{pmatrix} = \dfrac{6!}{3!(6-3)!} = \dfrac{6!}{3!3!} = \dfrac{\cancel{6} \cdot 5 \cdot 4 \cdot \cancel{3} \cdot \cancel{2} \cdot \cancel{1}}{\cancel{3} \cdot \cancel{2} \cdot 1 \cdot \cancel{3} \cdot \cancel{2} \cdot \cancel{1}} = 20$

In Figure 11.2, $n = 6$ and $k = 3$.

b. $\begin{pmatrix} 7 \\ 5 \end{pmatrix} = \dfrac{7!}{5!(7-5)!} = \dfrac{7!}{5!2!} = \dfrac{7 \cdot 6 \cdot \cancel{5!}}{\cancel{5!} \cdot 2} = 7 \cdot 3 = 21$

c. $\begin{pmatrix} n \\ 0 \end{pmatrix} = \dfrac{n!}{0!(n-0)!} = \dfrac{\cancel{n!}}{1 \cdot \cancel{n!}} = 1$

d. $\begin{pmatrix} n \\ n \end{pmatrix} = \dfrac{\cancel{n!}}{\cancel{n!}(n-n)!} = \dfrac{1}{0!} = \dfrac{1}{1} = 1$

2   Binomial Theorem

We have seen that $\begin{pmatrix} n \\ k \end{pmatrix}$ is equal to the kth binomial coefficient in the nth row of Pascal's triangle. We also can use this notation in writing the series $(a + b)^n$. In the following example we use the results $\begin{pmatrix} n \\ 0 \end{pmatrix} = \begin{pmatrix} n \\ n \end{pmatrix} = 1$:

$$(a + b)^4 = \sum_{k=0}^{4} \binom{4}{k} a^{4-k} b^k$$

$$= \binom{4}{0} a^{4-0} b^0 + \binom{4}{1} a^{4-1} b^1 + \binom{4}{2} a^{4-2} b^2 + \binom{4}{3} a^{4-3} b^3$$

$$+ \binom{4}{4} a^{4-4} b^4$$

$$= a^4 + \frac{4!}{1!(4-1)!} a^3 b + \frac{4!}{2!(4-2)!} a^2 b^2 + \frac{4!}{3!(4-3)!} ab^3 + b^4$$

$$= a^4 + \frac{4 \cdot \cancel{3!}}{\cancel{3!}} a^3 b + \frac{\cancel{4} \cdot 3 \cdot 2}{\cancel{2} \cdot 2} a^2 b^2 + \frac{4 \cdot \cancel{3!}}{\cancel{3!} \cdot 1!} ab^3 + b^4$$

$$= a^4 + 4a^3 b + 6a^2 b^2 + 4ab^3 + b^4$$

In general, if a and b represent real numbers and n is a natural number, then the following formula is known as the **binomial formula** or the **binomial theorem**.

Binomial Theorem

If n is a natural number, then

$$(a + b)^n = \sum_{k=0}^{n} \binom{n}{k} a^{n-k} b^k = \sum_{k=0}^{n} \frac{n!}{k!(n-k)!} a^{n-k} b^k$$

EXAMPLE 4

Use the binomial theorem to expand $(x + 2)^5$.

SOLUTION

$$(x + 2)^5 = \sum_{k=0}^{5} \binom{5}{k} x^{5-k} 2^k$$

$$= \binom{5}{0} x^5 + \binom{5}{1} x^4 \cdot 2 + \binom{5}{2} x^3 \cdot 2^2 + \binom{5}{3} x^2 \cdot 2^3 + \binom{5}{4} x \cdot 2^4 + \binom{5}{5} 2^5$$

$$= x^5 + \frac{5!}{1!4!} 2x^4 + \frac{5!}{2!3!} 4x^3 + \frac{5!}{3!2!} 8x^2 + \frac{5!}{4!1!} 16x + 32$$

$$= x^5 + 5 \cdot 2x^4 + 10 \cdot 4x^3 + 10 \cdot 8x^2 + 5 \cdot 16x + 32$$

$$= x^5 + 10x^4 + 40x^3 + 80x^2 + 80x + 32$$

EXAMPLE 5

Write the first three terms of $(x - 5)^{10}$.

SOLUTION

$(x - 5)^{10} = [x + (-5)]^{10} = \sum_{k=0}^{10} \binom{10}{k} x^{10-k} (-5)^k$. Thus,

$$a_0 = \binom{10}{0} x^{10} (-5)^0 = x^{10}$$

$$a_1 = \binom{10}{1} x^9 (-5)^1 = \frac{10!}{1!9!} x^9 (-5) = \frac{10 \cdot 9!}{9!} (-5) x^9 = -50 x^9$$

$$a_2 = \binom{10}{2} x^8 (-5)^2 = \frac{10!}{2!8!} 25 x^8 = \frac{10 \cdot 9 \cdot 8!}{2 \cdot 8!} 25 x^8 = 5 \cdot 9 \cdot 25 x^8$$

$$= 1125 x^8$$

A single term of $(a + b)^n$ can be found without writing out the entire expansion. The following is the formula for the rth term of $(a + b)^n$.

The rth Term of $(a + b)^n$

If $n \geq r$, then the rth term of $(a + b)^n$ is

$$\binom{n}{r-1} a^{n-(r-1)} b^{r-1}$$

EXAMPLE 6

Find the ninth term of $(x^2 + y^3)^{12}$.

SOLUTION

$n = 12$ and $r = 9$, so the ninth term is

$$\binom{12}{9-1} (x^2)^{12-(9-1)} (y^3)^{9-1} = \binom{12}{8} (x^2)^4 (y^3)^8$$

$$= \frac{12!}{8!4!} x^8 y^{24} = \frac{12 \cdot 11 \cdot 10 \cdot 9 \cdot 8!}{8! \cdot 4 \cdot 3 \cdot 2} x^8 y^{24} = 11 \cdot 5 \cdot 9 x^8 y^{24}$$

$$= 495 x^8 y^{24}$$

EXERCISE SET 11.4

A

1 Use Pascal's triangle (Figure 11.2) to expand the following.

1. $(x + 3)^2$ **2.** $(a - b)^4$

3. $(x^2 - y)^5$ **4.** $(2x + 3y)^3$

5. $(x^4 + 3)^3$ **6.** $(a + 1)^6$

7. $(a^3 + b^4)^6$ **8.** $(a^4 + 2)^5$

9. Write the first 10 rows of Pascal's triangle. (See Example 2.)

10. $(a + b)^7$ **11.** $(a + b)^8$

12. $(a + b)^9$ **13.** $(a + b)^{10}$

14. $(x + 1)^8$ **15.** $(a - b)^9$

16. $(x - y^2)^{10}$ **17.** $(a + 2)^7$

18. $(x^2 + y^3)^{10}$

Use the method of Example 2 to find the following.

19. 2^9 **20.** 3^8

Calculate the following binomial coefficients.

21. $\binom{7}{0}$ **22.** $\binom{8}{8}$ **23.** $\binom{5}{3}$ **24.** $\binom{6}{2}$

25. $\binom{7}{5}$ **26.** $\binom{8}{4}$ **27.** $\binom{9}{6}$ **28.** $\binom{20}{18}$

2 Use the binomial theorem to expand the following.

29. $(a + b)^3$ **30.** $(a + b)^5$

31. $(a + 1)^6$ **32.** $(x^2 + 1)^4$

33. $(x - y)^4$ **34.** $(2x + 3)^3$

35. $(x - 1)^7$ **36.** $(a - b)^8$

37. $(x^3 + 2)^5$ **38.** $\left(\dfrac{x}{2} + 1\right)^4$

39. $\left(\dfrac{x}{3} - 2\right)^5$ **40.** $\left(\dfrac{a}{2} + \dfrac{b}{5}\right)^3$

Use the binomial theorem to write the first four terms of the following series.

41. $(a + b)^{12}$ **42.** $(a - b)^{15}$

43. $(x - 1)^{20}$ **44.** $(a^2 + b^3)^9$

Find the indicated term in each expression.

45. $(a + b)^{12}$;   sixth term

46. $(a - b)^{15}$;   eighth term

47. $(x + 1)^{16}$;   fourteenth term

48. $(x^2 + y^2)^{10}$;   fifth term

49. $(x - 2)^8$;   fourth term

50. $(x^3 + 1)^{11}$ seventh term

B

The binomial theorem can be used to approximate a decimal that is close to an integer. For example, to calculate $(1.01)^6$ correctly to four decimal places, use $1^{6-k} = 1$ and let

$$(1.01)^6 = (1 + .01)^6 = \sum_{k=0}^{6} \binom{6}{k} 1^{6-k}(.01)^k =$$

$$\sum_{k=0}^{6} \binom{6}{k}(.01)^k$$

$$= 1 + \binom{6}{1}(.01) + \binom{6}{2}(.01)^2 +$$

$$\binom{6}{3}(.01)^3 + \ldots$$

$$= 1 + 6(.01) + 15(.0001) +$$

$$20(.000001) + \ldots$$

$$= 1 + .06 + .0015 + .00002 + \ldots$$

Because the terms after the third contain four or more zeros, we only need to add the first three terms. Thus,

$$(1.01)^6 \approx 1 + .06 + .0015 = 1.0615$$

Use the binomial theorem to approximate the following decimals to the indicated number of decimal places. (*Hint*: In Exercise 54, let $.99 = 1 - .01$).

51. $(1.01)^9$;   4   **52.** $(1.02)^7$;   3

53. $(2.1)^6$;   2   **54.** $(.99)^{10}$;   2

55. $(.9)^{12}$;   3   **56.** $(1.98)^7$;   4

C

57. Find the sum of all the numbers in each row of the first six rows of Pascal's triangle (Figure 11.2). What is the pattern?

58. Find the sum of the numbers in the indicated diagonal rows of Pascal's triangle (Figure 11.4) and show that they form the Fibonacci sequence. (See Section 5.3.)

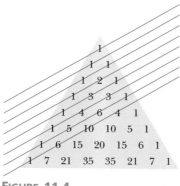

FIGURE 11.4

Answer the following questions with complete sentences.

59. How do you find an entry in Pascal's triangle?

60. What is represented by the symbol $\binom{k}{n}$?

Chapter Summary

KEY WORDS, DEFINITIONS, AND PROPERTIES

Sequence: a function whose domain is the set of natural numbers, N, or a subset of N.

Series: the indicated sum of a sequence of numbers. The *n*th partial sum of a series is

$$S_n = a_1 + a_2 + a_3 + \ldots + a_n = \sum_{k=1}^{n} a_k.$$

(See Sections 11.1 and 11.2.)

***n* factorial:** $n! = n(n - 1)(n - 2) \ldots (2)(1)$, for n a natural number; $0! = 1$. $n! = n[(n - 1)!]$. (See Section 11.1.)

Arithmetic Sequence and Series: the general term, a_n, of an arithmetic sequence with first term a_1 and common difference d is $a_n = a_1 + (n - 1)d$. The *n*th partial sum of the corresponding arithmetic series is

$$S_n = \frac{n}{2}(a_1 + a_n) = \frac{n}{2}[2a_1 + (n - 1)d].$$

(See Sections 11.1 and 11.2.)

Geometric Sequence and Series: The general term, a_n, of a geometric sequence with first term a_1 and common ratio r is $a_n = a_1 r^{n-1}$. The *n*th partial sum of the corresponding geometric series is

$$S_n = \frac{a_1(1 - r^n)}{1 - r}, \quad r \neq 1.$$

If $|r| < 1$, then the sum of the infinite geometric series is $S = \frac{a_1}{1 - r}$. If $|r| \geq 1$, then the sum does not exist. (See Section 11.3.)

Binomial Coefficient: $\binom{n}{k} = \frac{n!}{k!(n - k)!}$, n a natural number.

Binomial Theorem: $(a + b)^n = \sum_{k=0}^{n} \binom{n}{k} a^{n-k} b^k$. If $n \geq r$, then the rth term of $(a + b)^n$ is $\binom{n}{r - 1} a^{n-(r-1)} b^{r-1}$. (See Section 11.4.)

CHAPTER REVIEW EXERCISES

The answers to the following problems are given in the answer section. If you have any trouble, then review the material and homework problems in the sections indicated.

Find the first four terms of the following sequences. (See Section 11.1.)

1. $a_n = \dfrac{(-1)^{n+1}}{(n+1)!}$ **2.** $a_n = \dfrac{n}{2^{n-1}}$

Determine whether the given sequence is arithmetic. If it is, find the common difference, d, and the next three terms. (See Section 11.1.)

3. $\{1, -1, -4, -8, \ldots\}$

4. $\{1, 6, 11, 16 \ldots\}$

Determine whether the given sequence is geometric. If it is, find the common ratio, r, and the next three terms. (See Section 11.3.)

5. $\{1, 2, 4, 8, \ldots\}$ **6.** $\{1, 2, 6, 24, \ldots\}$

Exercise 7 refers to an arithmetic sequence, and Exercise 8 refers to a geometric sequence. (See Sections 11.1 and 11.3.)

7. If $a_1 = 4$ and $d = 3$, find a_n and a_6.

8. If $a_1 = 3$ and $r = -2$, find a_n and a_5.

Find the first five partial sums of the series associated with the given sequence. (See Section 11.2.)

9. $a_n = 2n - 1$ **10.** $a_n = (-1)^n n^2$

Expand and simplify the following. (See Section 11.2.)

11. $\displaystyle\sum_{k=1}^{5} (2k + 1)$ **12.** $\displaystyle\sum_{k=0}^{4} (-1)^n(n^2 + 1)$

Express the following in sigma notation. (See Section 11.2.)

13. $3 + 6 + 9 + 12 + 15$

14. $\dfrac{1}{2} + \dfrac{2}{3} + \dfrac{3}{4} + \dfrac{4}{5} + \ldots$

Find the sum of the following series by: a. the method of reversing the order; b. using the formula for S_n. (See Section 11.2.)

15. $1 + 2 + 3 + \ldots + 40$

Find the sum of the following series by: a. the method of multiplying by $-r$; b. using the formula for S_n. (See Section 11.3.)

16. $1 + 3 + 9 + 27 + 81$

Find the sums, if they exist, for the following infinite series. If one does not exist, so state. (See Section 11.3.)

17. $1 + 2 + 4 + 8 + \ldots$

18. $1 + \dfrac{1}{5} + \dfrac{1}{25} + \dfrac{1}{125} + \ldots$

Express the following decimal as the ratio of two integers by using a geometric series. (See Section 11.3.)

19. $.\overline{8}$

Use Pascal's triangle (Figure 11.2) to expand the following. (See Section 11.4.)

20. $(x + y^2)^3$ **21.** $(x - 1)^5$

Use the binomial theorem to expand the following. (See Section 11.4.)

22. $(x + y^2)^3$ **23.** $(x - 2)^7$

Calculate the following binomial coefficients. (See Section 11.4.)

24. $\dbinom{10}{3}$ **25.** $\dbinom{12}{9}$

Find the first four terms of the following expansion. (See Section 11.4.)

26. $(x^3 + y)^{12}$

Find the sixth term of the following series. (See Section 11.4.)

27. $(x^2 + y^2)^9$

Solve the following word problems. (See Sections 11.1, 11.2, and 11.3.)

28. A child is saving pennies. He saves 1 on the first day, 4 on the second day, 7 on the third day, and so on. How much money would he save on the thirteenth day? How much money would he save for the 30 days?

29. A child is saving pennies. He saves 1 on the

first day, 3 on the second day, 9 on the third day, and so on. How much money would he save on the tenth day? How much money would he save for the 10 days?

30. When a pendulum is released, it swings through an arc of length 20 inches. Each swing after that travels 75% of the length of the previous swing. How far will the pendulum travel before it comes to rest?

CHAPTER TEST

Treat this test as a class test and allow 50 minutes for completion. When you have finished, use the answer section for scoring. For any wrong answers, refer to the corresponding problems in the review section.

Find the first four terms of the following sequences.

1. $a_n = \dfrac{n + 1}{n!}$ **2.** $a_n = \dfrac{(-1)^{n+1}}{n^2}$

Each of the following sequences is either arithmetic or geometric. If it is arithmetic, find the common difference, d, and the next three terms. If it is geometric, find the common ratio, r, and the next three terms.

3. $\{1, -1, -3, -5, \ldots\}$

4. $\{2, 6, 18, 54, \ldots\}$

5. $\left\{1, \dfrac{1}{2}, \dfrac{1}{4}, \dfrac{1}{8}, \ldots\right\}$

6. $\{5, 8, 11, 14, \ldots\}$

Find the first five partial sums of the series associated with the given sequence.

7. $a_n = (-1)^n 3n$

Expand and simplify the following.

8. $\displaystyle\sum_{n=0}^{5} \dfrac{(-1)^n}{n!}$ **9.** $\displaystyle\sum_{n=1}^{4} (n^2 + 2)$

Express the following in sigma notation.

10. $1 - 3 + 5 - 7 + 9 - 11$

11. $4 + 6 + 8 + 10 + 12 + \ldots$

Find the sum of the following series by: a. the method of reversing the order; b. using the formula $S_n = \dfrac{n}{2}(a_1 + a_n)$.

12. $1 + 2 + 3 + \ldots + 30$

Find the sum of the following series by: a. the method of multiplying by $-r$; b. the formula $S_n = \dfrac{a_1(1 - r^n)}{1 - r}$.

13. $1 + \dfrac{1}{3} + \dfrac{1}{9} + \dfrac{1}{27} + \dfrac{1}{81}$

Find the sums, if they exist, for the following infinite series; $S = \dfrac{a_1}{1 - r}$. If a sum does not exist, so state.

14. $1 + \dfrac{1}{3} + \dfrac{1}{9} + \dfrac{1}{27} + \ldots$

15. $1 + \dfrac{3}{2} + \dfrac{9}{4} + \dfrac{27}{8} + \ldots$

Express the following decimal as the ratio of two integers by using a geometric series.

16. $.\overline{2}$

Use Pascal's triangle (Figure 11.2) to expand the following.

17. $(x - 3)^4$ **18.** $(x^2 + y)^6$

Use the binomial theorem to expand the following.

19. $(x - 3)^4$ **20.** $(x + 1)^8$

Calculate the following binomial coefficient.

21. $\dbinom{12}{8}$

Find the first three terms of the following expansion.

22. $(a + b)^{11}$

Find the eighth term of the following; use $\dbinom{n}{r - 1} a^{n-(r-1)} b^{r-1}$.

23. $(x^2 + 1)^{10}$

Solve the following word problems.

24. Carl is given a starting salary of $19,000 and a raise of $1600 each year. Find his income for his eighth year on the job and his total income for the eight years.

25. Pat is given a starting salary of $19,000 and an 8% raise each year. Find her income for her eighth year on the job and her total income for the eight years.

Cumulative Review

The answers to the following problems are given in the answer section. The section from which each question is taken is listed in brackets next to the answer. Therefore, for any wrong answers, you can review the material in the indicated section.

Solve the following for the indicated variable(s). For Exercises 1 and 2, write your answers in interval notation and graph them on the number line.

1. $| 1 - x | > 4$

2. $| 2x - 1 | \le 7$

3. $\dfrac{x - 4}{x + 5} \ge 0$

4. $2y + 7 = \dfrac{4}{y}$

5. $| 6x + 3 | = 15$

6. $x^{2/3} = 2x^{1/3} + 35$

7. $\sqrt{3s^2 + 3s + 1} = s$

8. $27^{2x+1} = 3^{5x}$

9. $5^{x+2} = 11$

10. $\log 3 + 2\log x = \log 27$

11. $\log_4 x = \dfrac{3}{2}$

12. $\begin{vmatrix} x & 2x - 1 \\ 0 & 3x + 2 \end{vmatrix} = 6$

13. $P = 6e^{.03t}; \quad t$

14. $8x - 3y = 4y + x; \quad y$

15. $\dfrac{1}{y} = \dfrac{3}{z} - \dfrac{2}{x}; \quad z$

16. $w = \sqrt{\dfrac{k}{3m + M}}; \quad m$

17. $2x + 3y = 3$

$y = -\dfrac{2}{3}x + 1$

18. $\begin{aligned} 2x - z &= 1 \\ 3y + 2z &= 0 \\ x - y &= -3 \end{aligned}$

Perform the indicated operations and simplify your answers.

19. $\dfrac{2}{x^2 - 9} - \dfrac{x - 1}{2x - 6}$

20. $\dfrac{1 - \dfrac{a}{b}}{\dfrac{a}{b} - \dfrac{b}{a}}$

21. $\dfrac{2i}{1 + 5i}$

22. $\dfrac{\sqrt{12x^3}}{\sqrt{5}}$

23. $(x + 5)^3$

24. $\dfrac{4x^2 + 6x + 5}{2x - 1}$

Expand $(x + 5)^3$ using

25. Pascal's triangle

26. the binomial theorem

Graph the following in the xy-plane. Give the center and radius of the circle in Exercise 28.

27. $4x^2 + 9y^2 = 36$

28. $x^2 + y^2 + 4x + 6y = 3$

29. $x - y > 1$

30. $f(x) = -x^2 + 4x - 3$

Graph $y = x, f,$ and f^{-1} on the same set of axes.

31. $f(x) = e^{x/2}$

Given the points A$(-2, 4)$ and B$(1, 3)$, find

32. the distance between A and B

33. the equation of the line $\overleftrightarrow{AB}$ (use any form)

34. the slope of any line perpendicular to $\overleftrightarrow{AB}$

Solve $x^2 + 8x + 20 = 0$:

35. by completing the square

36. with the quadratic formula

Factor the following.

37. $x^3 + 125y^3$ **38.** $ac - 2b - 2a + bc$

Find the roots of the following functions.

39. $f(x) = \sqrt{x^2 - 5} - 2$

40. $g(x) = \ln (3x - 7)$

Expand the following expression as far as possible.

41. $\ln \sqrt[3]{x^2 y}$

Approximate the following to four decimal places.

42. $\log_3 29$

Let $f(x) = 4x - 5$. Find

43. $f^{-1}(x)$

Expand and simplify the following.

44. $\displaystyle\sum_{n=1}^{4} (-1)^n 2n$

Solve the following problem.

45. The heat generated in an electric circuit is given by the formula $H = 0.24Ri^2t$, where R is the resistance in ohms, i is the current in amperes, t is the time in hours, and H is the heat in calories. If $R = 55$ and $i = 2$, how much time is needed to produce 26.4 calories of heat?

Express each of the following as an equation, find the constant of variation, k, and then solve the equation for the indicated variable.

46. y varies directly as x to the 3/2 power. $y = 18$ when $x = 9$. Find y when $x = 25$.

47. A varies jointly as B and C and inversely as D. $A = -18$ when $B = 3$, $C = -3$, and $D = 2$. Find B when $A = 10$, $C = 15$, and $D = 3$.

Solve the following problems.

48. The surface area, S, of a cube is directly proportional to the square of the length of an edge, L. A cube with an edge of 2 centimeters has a surface area of 24 square centimeters. Find the length of the edge of a cube with a surface area of 13.5 square centimeters.

49. The strength, S, of a rectangular beam varies jointly as its width, w, and the square of its height, h, and inversely as its length, L. $S = 2000$ when $w = 2$, $h = 10$, and $L = 15$. Find S when $w = 4$, $h = 8$, and $L = 12$.

Express the following in scientific notation.

50. 5,000,000,000; the world population in July 1987

51. $-0.000\ 000\ 000\ 000\ 000\ 000\ 16$ coulombs; the charge of an electron

Express the following in decimal notation.

52. 4×10^6 pounds; the weight of General Sherman, a redwood tree in northern California,

which is thought to be the heaviest living thing on earth

53. 1×10^{-6} pound; the weight of the seed that produced General Sherman

Use scientific notation to solve the following problem and write your answer in scientific notation.

54. How many times heavier is General Sherman now than the seed from which it grew? (See Exercises 52 and 53.)

Simplify the following and write your answer in scientific notation.

55. $\dfrac{(2 \times 10^8)(45 \times 10^{12})}{(6 \times 10^6)(3 \times 10^{-12})}$

Solve the following word problems by using either one equation or a system of equations. Define your variable(s).

56. The sum of 5 and 3 times a number is 7 less than the number. Find the numbers.

57. The difference of two numbers is 7/6. Twice the smaller number is 9 less than 12 times the larger number. Find the numbers.

58. The cube of a number is equal to 25 times the number. Find all such numbers.

59. The denominator of 7/2 is multiplied by a number, and the numerator is multiplied by 4 less than twice the number. The new fraction is 35/3. Find the number.

60. When 38 is divided by a number, the quotient is 7 and the remainder is 3. Find the number. (*Hint:* For $N \div D$, we have $\dfrac{N}{D} = Q + \dfrac{R}{D}$, where Q is the quotient and R is the remainder.)

61. Find three consecutive even integers such that 4 times the first plus 6 times the second is 8 times the third.

62. Find four consecutive odd integers such that the sum of the squares of the smallest and the largest is 5 more than 3 times the product of the other two integers.

The formula $m = \sqrt{ab}$ gives the **geometric mean, m**, of the two numbers a and b.

63. Find two consecutive integers whose geometric mean is $6\sqrt{2}$.

64. Find two consecutive even integers whose geometric mean is $2\sqrt{30}$.

65. Find the volume and surface area of a tin can if the radius of its base is 2 inches and its height is 7 inches. Express your answers in terms of π.

66. The sides of a box are consecutive integers, and its total surface area is 52 square feet. Find the box's dimensions.

67. A rectangular piece of land, with its length three times its width, is to be enclosed with fencing, which costs $7 per meter. A second fence, which costs $5 per meter, is built parallel to the shorter sides to divide the land in half. If the perimeter of the land is 80 meters, how much does fencing cost?

68. The sum of the perimeters of a square and a rectangle is 128 centimeters. The rectangle's length is 12 centimeters more than the side of the square, and its width is 8 centimeters less than the side of the squre. Find the dimensions of the two figures. What are their areas?

69. The numerical ratio of the perimeter to the area of a square is 1 : 2. Find the side of the square.

70. The numerical ratio of the area of a rectangle to its perimeter is 8 : 3. Find the length if it is 1 more than twice the width.

71. The longest side of a right triangle is 1 more than twice the shortest side. The third side is 15 centimeters. Find the lengths of the other sides.

72. If the diameter of a circle were increased by 6, then its area would be increased by 33π. Find the diameter of the circle.

73. Find the dimensions of a rectangle whose perimeter is 20 and area is 16.

74. The general formula of the equation of a circle is $x^2 + y^2 + Dx + Ey + F = 0$. (See Section 9.1.) Find D, E, and F so that a circle contains the points $(0, 4)$, $(-2, 6)$, and $(-4, 4)$. *Hint*: Use the three points to write three equations in three variables and then solve the system of equations.

75. Repeat Exercise 74 for $(2, 4)$, $(-3, -1)$, and $(5, 3)$.

76. The price of a book plus a 6% sales tax is $34.45. What is the price of the book?

77. How much distilled water must be added to 6 gallons of a 15% salt solution to obtain a 10% salt solution?

78. Lynne invested $6000 at 9% and $2000 at 13%. How much must she invest at 15% to earn an average of 11% on all of her investments?

79. Yola needs at least a 90% average to earn an A in her algebra class. Her scores on the four 100-point tests were 86, 92, 96, and 84. The final exam is worth 200 points. How many points must she earn on the final exam to have an average of 90%?

80. The final grade in an English class is based on three class tests of equal weight and a final exam than counts three times as much as a class test. To earn a B in this class Ed needs an average of at least 76% but less than 88%. His three class test scores were 72%, 73%, and 86%. What percent of the final must he get correct to earn a B?

81. Christine drove 345 miles. On the first part of her trip, she averaged 55 mph and on the second part, 45 mph. If she spent one hour longer driving at 45 mph than she did at 55 mph, how long did she spend on each part of the trip?

82. A truck travels from Salinas to Paso Robles in 1.5 hours with a tail wind of 20 mph. The return trip against the wind takes 4.5 hours. Find the speed of the truck in still air. How far is it from Salinas to Paso Robles?

83. On Monday afternoon a plane took 4 hours to fly with the jet stream from Honolulu to San Francisco, a distance of 2400 miles. On the return trip the next morning, the rate of the jet stream had decreased 20 mph, and after 4 hours the plane was 400 miles from Honolulu. Find the speed of the plane in still air and the speed of the jet stream on Monday.

84. Isaac can row his canoe in still water twice as fast as the speed of a stream. It takes him 2 hours less time to travel 4 miles upstream than it does to travel 15 miles downstream. Find the speed of the stream.

85. Can we possibly change a $100 bill into $1, $5, and $10 bills in such a way that we have twice as many $5 bills as $1 bills and three times as many $10 bills as $5 bills? If so, how many of each kind of bill would we need?

86. Jolynn spent $9.82 for 13¢, 20¢, and 37¢ stamps. She bought two more 20¢ stamps than 13¢ stamps and three times as many 37¢ stamps as 20¢ stamps. How many of each type of stamp did she buy?

87. A motel rents single rooms for $25 per day and double rooms for $38 per day. A total of 40 rooms were rented for one day for $1377. How many of each kind of room were rented that day?

88. Eric has 25 pennies, nickels, and dimes. The value of the pennies and nickels is 52¢. The number of pennies is 2 more than twice the number of dimes. How many pennies, nickels, and dimes does he have?

89. Maria is 24 years older than Gary. In 8 years Maria will be 5 years older than three times Gary's age 3 years ago. How old are they now?

90. The sum of Gail's and Kathy's current ages is 20 years. The product of Gail's age in 3 years and Kathy's age 3 years ago is 100. Find their current ages.

91. Pipe A can fill a pool in 8 hours, and pipe B can fill it in 10 hours. If the pool is empty and both pipes are turned on at the same time, how long does it take to fill 3/4 of the pool?

92. The amount Anastasiya spends for rent, food, and utilities is in the ratio 14 : 5 : 3. If she spends $1100 per month on these items, how much does she spend on each item per year?

93. An 1,8-foot pole casts a 12-foot shadow when a child casts a 3-foot shadow. How tall is the child, to the nearest inch?

94. If 7 milliliters of hydrochloric acid are in 72 milliliters of solution, how many milliliters of acid are in 123 milliliters of a solution of the same concentration?

95. Among all rectangles having a perimeter of 12 feet, find the length and width of the one with the maximum area. What is the maximum area?

96. Angelica wants to fence in a rectangular dog pen next to her house. She has 80 feet of fencing and will not fence the side of the pen next to her house. What are the dimensions of the largest possible pen? Find its area.

97. A manufacturer estimates that the total cost of producing x items per day is given by the function $C(x) = .02x^2 - 4x + 3000$, where C is in dollars. How many items should be produced each day so that the cost will be minimum? What will be the minimum cost?

98. A human thighbone is found to contain 8% of its original amount of ^{14}C. Determine, to the nearest 100 years, when the person died. Use $Q = Q_0(2)^{-t/5700}$.

99. The trends in 1989 indicate that the earth will have 8.2 billion people by the year 2020. The population in 1989 was 5.2 billion. Find the growth rate as a percent correctly to two decimal places. Use $P = P_0 e^{rt}$.

100. On the Richter scale the 1971 Los Angeles earthquake measured 6.7 and the 1960 earthquake in Chile measured 8.5. Find I in each case and determine how much larger the 1960 earthquake was than the 1971 earthquake. Use $M = \log I$.

Appendix A: Tables

x	0	1	2	3	4	5	6	7	8	9
1.0	.0000	.0043	.0086	.0128	.0170	.0212	.0253	.0294	.0334	.0374
1.1	.0414	.0453	.0492	.0531	.0569	.0607	.0645	.0682	.0719	.0755
1.2	.0792	.0828	.0864	.0899	.0934	.0969	.1004	.1038	.1072	.1106
1.3	.1139	.1173	.1206	.1239	.1271	.1303	.1335	.1367	.1399	.1430
1.4	.1461	.1492	.1523	.1553	.1584	.1614	.1644	.1673	.1703	.1732
1.5	.1761	.1790	.1818	.1847	.1875	.1903	.1931	.1959	.1987	.2014
1.6	.2041	.2068	.2095	.2122	.2148	.2175	.2201	.2227	.2253	.2279
1.7	.2304	.2330	.2355	.2380	.2405	.2430	.2455	.2480	.2504	.2529
1.8	.2553	.2577	.2601	.2625	.2648	.2672	.2695	.2718	.2742	.2765
1.9	.2788	.2810	.2833	.2856	.2878	.2900	.2923	.2945	.2967	.2989
2.0	.3010	.3032	.3054	.3075	.3096	.3118	.3139	.3160	.3181	.3201
2.1	.3222	.3243	.3263	.3284	.3304	.3324	.3345	.3365	.3385	.3404
2.2	.3424	.3444	.3464	.3483	.3502	.3522	.3541	.3560	.3579	.3598
2.3	.3617	.3636	.3655	.3674	.3692	.3711	.3729	.3747	.3766	.3784
2.4	.3802	.3820	.3838	.3856	.3874	.3892	.3909	.3927	.3945	.3962
2.5	.3979	.3997	.4014	.4031	.4048	.4065	.4082	.4099	.4116	.4133
2.6	.4150	.4166	.4183	.4200	.4216	.4232	.4249	.4265	.4281	.4298
2.7	.4314	.4330	.4346	.4362	.4378	.4393	.4409	.4425	.4440	.4456
2.8	.4472	.4487	.4502	.4518	.4533	.4548	.4564	.4579	.4594	.4609
2.9	.4624	.4639	.4654	.4669	.4683	.4698	.4713	.4728	.4742	.4757
3.0	.4771	.4786	.4800	.4814	.4829	.4843	.4857	.4871	.4886	.4900
3.1	.4914	.4928	.4942	.4955	.4969	.4983	.4997	.5011	.5024	.5038
3.2	.5051	.5065	.5079	.5092	.5105	.5119	.5132	.5145	.5159	.5172
3.3	.5185	.5198	.5211	.5224	.5237	.5250	.5263	.5276	.5289	.5302
3.4	.5315	.5328	.5340	.5353	.5366	.5378	.5391	.5403	.5416	.5428
3.5	.5441	.5453	.5465	.5478	.5490	.5502	.5514	.5527	.5539	.5551
3.6	.5563	.5575	.5587	.5599	.5611	.5623	.5635	.5647	.5658	.5670
3.7	.5682	.5694	.5705	.5717	.5729	.5740	.5752	.5763	.5775	.5786
3.8	.5798	.5809	.5821	.5832	.5843	.5855	.5866	.5877	.5888	.5899
3.9	.5911	.5922	.5933	.5944	.5955	.5966	.5977	.5988	.5999	.6010
4.0	.6021	.6031	.6042	.6053	.6064	.6075	.6085	.6096	.6107	.6117
4.1	.6128	.6138	.6149	.6160	.6170	.6180	.6191	.6201	.6212	.6222
4.2	.6232	.6243	.6253	.6263	.6274	.6284	.6294	.6304	.6314	.6325
4.3	.6335	.6345	.6355	.6365	.6375	.6385	.6395	.6405	.6415	.6425
4.4	.6435	.6444	.6454	.6464	.6474	.6484	.6493	.6503	.6513	.6522
4.5	.6532	.6542	.6551	.6561	.6571	.6580	.6590	.6599	.6609	.6618
4.6	.6628	.6637	.6646	.6656	.6665	.6675	.6684	.6693	.6702	.6712
4.7	.6721	.6730	.6739	.6749	.6758	.6767	.6776	.6785	.6794	.6803
4.8	.6812	.6821	.6830	.6839	.6848	.6857	.6866	.6875	.6884	.6893
4.9	.6902	.6911	.6920	.6928	.6937	.6946	.6955	.6964	.6972	.6981
5.0	.6990	.6998	.7007	.7016	.7024	.7033	.7042	.7050	.7059	.7067
5.1	.7076	.7084	.7093	.7101	.7110	.7118	.7126	.7135	.7143	.7152
5.2	.7160	.7168	.7177	.7185	.7193	.7202	.7210	.7218	.7226	.7235

TABLE 1
Common Logarithms
(*continued*)

x	0	1	2	3	4	5	6	7	8	9
5.3	.7243	.7251	.7259	.7267	.7275	.7284	.7292	.7300	.7308	.7316
5.4	.7324	.7332	.7340	.7348	.7356	.7364	.7372	.7380	.7388	.7396
5.5	.7404	.7412	.7419	.7427	.7435	.7443	.7451	.7459	.7466	.7474
5.6	.7482	.7490	.7497	.7505	.7513	.7520	.7528	.7536	.7543	.7551
5.7	.7559	.7566	.7574	.7582	.7589	.7597	.7604	.7612	.7619	.7627
5.8	.7634	.7642	.7649	.7657	.7664	.7672	.7679	.7686	.7694	.7701
5.9	.7709	.7716	.7723	.7731	.7738	.7745	.7752	.7760	.7767	.7774
6.0	.7782	.7789	.7796	.7803	.7810	.7818	.7825	.7832	.7839	.7846
6.1	.7853	.7860	.7868	.7875	.7882	.7889	.7896	.7903	.7910	.7917
6.2	.7924	.7931	.7938	.7945	.7952	.7959	.7966	.7973	.7980	.7987
6.3	.7993	.8000	.8007	.8014	.8021	.8028	.8035	.8041	.8048	.8055
6.4	.8062	.8069	.8075	.8082	.8089	.8096	.8102	.8109	.8116	.8122
6.5	.8129	.8136	.8142	.8149	.8156	.8162	.8169	.8176	.8182	.8189
6.6	.8195	.8202	.8209	.8215	.8222	.8228	.8235	.8241	.8248	.8254
6.7	.8261	.8267	.8274	.8280	.8287	.8293	.8299	.8306	.8312	.8319
6.8	.8325	.8331	.8338	.8344	.8351	.8357	.8363	.8370	.8376	.8382
6.9	.8388	.8395	.8401	.8407	.8414	.8420	.8426	.8432	.8439	.8445
7.0	.8451	.8457	.8463	.8470	.8476	.8482	.8488	.8494	.8500	.8506
7.1	.8513	.8519	.8525	.8531	.8537	.8543	.8549	.8555	.8561	.8567
7.2	.8573	.8579	.8585	.8591	.8597	.8603	.8609	.8615	.8621	.8627
7.3	.8633	.8639	.8645	.8651	.8657	.8663	.8669	.8675	.8681	.8686
7.4	.8692	.8698	.8704	.8710	.8716	.8722	.8727	.8733	.8739	.8745
7.5	.8751	.8756	.8762	.8768	.8774	.8779	.8785	.8791	.8797	.8802
7.6	.8808	.8814	.8820	.8825	.8831	.8837	.8842	.8848	.8854	.8859
7.7	.8865	.8871	.8876	.8882	.8887	.8893	.8899	.8904	.8910	.8915
7.8	.8921	.8927	.8932	.8938	.8943	.8949	.8954	.8960	.8965	.8971
7.9	.8976	.8982	.8987	.8993	.8998	.9004	.9009	.9015	.9020	.9025
8.0	.9031	.9036	.9042	.9047	.9053	.9058	.9063	.9069	.9074	.9079
8.1	.9085	.9090	.9096	.9101	.9106	.9112	.9117	.9122	.9128	.9133
8.2	.9138	.9143	.9149	.9154	.9159	.9165	.9170	.9175	.9180	.9186
8.3	.9191	.9196	.9201	.9206	.9212	.9217	.9222	.9227	.9232	.9238
8.4	.9243	.9248	.9253	.9258	.9263	.9269	.9274	.9279	.9284	.9289
8.5	.9294	.9299	.9304	.9309	.9315	.9320	.9325	.9330	.9335	.9340
8.6	.9345	.9350	.9355	.9360	.9365	.9370	.9375	.9380	.9385	.9390
8.7	.9395	.9400	.9405	.9410	.9415	.9420	.9425	.9430	.9435	.9440
8.8	.9445	.9450	.9455	.9460	.9465	.9469	.9474	.9479	.9484	.9489
8.9	.9494	.9499	.9504	.9509	.9513	.9518	.9523	.9528	.9533	.9538
9.0	.9542	.9547	.9552	.9557	.9562	.9566	.9571	.9576	.9581	.9586
9.1	.9590	.9595	.9600	.9605	.9609	.9614	.9619	.9624	.9628	.9633
9.2	.9638	.9643	.9647	.9652	.9657	.9661	.9666	.9671	.9675	.9680
9.3	.9685	.9689	.9694	.9699	.9703	.9708	.9713	.9717	.9722	.9727
9.4	.9731	.9736	.9741	.9745	.9750	.9754	.9759	.9763	.9768	.9773
9.5	.9777	.9782	.9786	.9791	.9795	.9800	.9805	.9809	.9814	.9818
9.6	.9823	.9827	.9832	.9836	.9841	.9845	.9850	.9854	.9859	.9863
9.7	.9869	.9872	.9877	.9881	.9886	.9890	.9894	.9899	.9903	.9908
9.8	.9912	.9917	.9921	.9926	.9930	.9934	.9939	.9943	.9948	.9952
9.9	.9956	.9961	.9965	.9969	.9974	.9978	.9983	.9987	.9991	.9996

TABLE 2
Natural Logarithms
In 10 = 2.3026

x	.00	.01	.02	.03	.04	.05	.06	.07	.08	.09
1.0	0.0000	0.0100	0.0198	0.0296	0.0392	0.0488	0.0583	0.0677	0.0770	0.0862
1.1	0.0953	0.1044	0.1133	0.1222	0.1310	0.1398	0.1484	0.1570	0.1655	0.1740
1.2	0.1823	0.1906	0.1989	0.2070	0.2151	0.2231	0.2311	0.2390	0.2469	0.2546
1.3	0.2624	0.2700	0.2776	0.2852	0.2927	0.3001	0.3075	0.3148	0.3221	0.3293
1.4	0.3365	0.3436	0.3507	0.3577	0.3646	0.3716	0.3784	0.3853	0.3920	0.3988
1.5	0.4055	0.4121	0.4187	0.4253	0.4318	0.4383	0.4447	0.4511	0.4574	0.4637
1.6	0.4700	0.4762	0.4824	0.4886	0.4947	0.5008	0.5068	0.5128	0.5188	0.5247
1.7	0.5306	0.5365	0.5423	0.5481	0.5539	0.5596	0.5653	0.5710	0.5766	0.5822
1.8	0.5878	0.5933	0.5988	0.6043	0.6098	0.6152	0.6206	0.6259	0.6313	0.6366
1.9	0.6419	0.6471	0.6523	0.6575	0.6627	0.6678	0.6729	0.6780	0.6831	0.6881
2.0	0.6931	0.6981	0.7031	0.7080	0.7129	0.7178	0.7227	0.7275	0.7324	0.7372
2.1	0.7419	0.7467	0.7514	0.7561	0.7608	0.7655	0.7701	0.7747	0.7793	0.7839
2.2	0.7885	0.7930	0.7975	0.8020	0.8065	0.8109	0.8154	0.8198	0.8242	0.8286
2.3	0.8329	0.8372	0.8416	0.8459	0.8502	0.8544	0.8587	0.8629	0.8671	0.8713
2.4	0.8755	0.8796	0.8838	0.8879	0.8920	0.8961	0.9002	0.9042	0.9083	0.9123
2.5	0.9163	0.9203	0.9243	0.9282	0.9322	0.9361	0.9400	0.9439	0.9478	0.9517
2.6	0.9555	0.9594	0.9632	0.9670	0.9708	0.9746	0.9783	0.9821	0.9858	0.9895
2.7	0.9933	0.9969	1.0006	1.0043	1.0080	1.0116	1.0152	1.0188	1.0225	1.0260
2.8	1.0296	1.0332	1.0367	1.0403	1.0438	1.0473	1.0508	1.0543	1.0578	1.0613
2.9	1.0647	1.0682	1.0716	1.0750	1.0784	1.0818	1.0852	1.0886	1.0919	1.0953
3.0	1.0986	1.1019	1.1053	1.1086	1.1119	1.1151	1.1184	1.1217	1.1249	1.1282
3.1	1.1314	1.1346	1.1378	1.1410	1.1442	1.1474	1.1506	1.1537	1.1569	1.1600
3.2	1.1632	1.1663	1.1694	1.1725	1.1756	1.1787	1.1817	1.1848	1.1878	1.1909
3.3	1.1939	1.1969	1.2000	1.2030	1.2060	1.2090	1.2119	1.2149	1.2179	1.2208
3.4	1.2238	1.2267	1.2296	1.2326	1.2355	1.2384	1.2413	1.2442	1.2470	1.2499
3.5	1.2528	1.2556	1.2585	1.2613	1.2641	1.2669	1.2698	1.2726	1.2754	1.2782
3.6	1.2809	1.2837	1.2865	1.2892	1.2920	1.2947	1.2975	1.3002	1.3029	1.3056
3.7	1.3083	1.3110	1.3137	1.3164	1.3191	1.3218	1.3244	1.3271	1.3297	1.3324
3.8	1.3350	1.3376	1.3403	1.3429	1.3455	1.3481	1.3507	1.3533	1.3558	1.3584
3.9	1.3610	1.3635	1.3661	1.3686	1.3712	1.3737	1.3762	1.3788	1.3813	1.3838
4.0	1.3863	1.3888	1.3913	1.3938	1.3962	1.3987	1.4012	1.4036	1.4061	1.4085
4.1	1.4110	1.4134	1.4159	1.4183	1.4207	1.4231	1.4255	1.4279	1.4303	1.4327
4.2	1.4351	1.4375	1.4398	1.4422	1.4446	1.4469	1.4493	1.4516	1.4540	1.4563
4.3	1.4586	1.4609	1.4633	1.4656	1.4679	1.4702	1.4725	1.4748	1.4770	1.4793
4.4	1.4816	1.4839	1.4861	1.4884	1.4907	1.4929	1.4951	1.4974	1.4996	1.5019
4.5	1.5041	1.5063	1.5085	1.5107	1.5129	1.5151	1.5173	1.5195	1.5217	1.5239
4.6	1.5261	1.5282	1.5304	1.5326	1.5347	1.5369	1.5390	1.5412	1.5433	1.5454
4.7	1.5476	1.5497	1.5518	1.5539	1.5560	1.5581	1.5602	1.5623	1.5644	1.5665
4.8	1.5686	1.5707	1.5728	1.5748	1.5769	1.5790	1.5810	1.5831	1.5851	1.5872
4.9	1.5892	1.5913	1.5933	1.5953	1.5974	1.5994	1.6014	1.6034	1.6054	1.6074
5.0	1.6094	1.6114	1.6134	1.6154	1.6174	1.6194	1.6214	1.6233	1.6253	1.6273
5.1	1.6292	1.6312	1.6332	1.6351	1.6371	1.6390	1.6409	1.6429	1.6448	1.6467
5.2	1.6487	1.6506	1.6525	1.6544	1.6563	1.6582	1.6601	1.6620	1.6639	1.6658
5.3	1.6677	1.6696	1.6715	1.6734	1.6752	1.6771	1.6790	1.6808	1.6827	1.6845
5.4	1.6864	1.6882	1.6901	1.6919	1.6938	1.6956	1.6974	1.6993	1.7011	1.7029
5.5	1.7047	1.7066	1.7084	1.7102	1.7120	1.7138	1.7156	1.7174	1.7192	1.7210
5.6	1.7228	1.7246	1.7263	1.7281	1.7299	1.7317	1.7334	1.7352	1.7370	1.7387
5.7	1.7405	1.7422	1.7440	1.7457	1.7475	1.7492	1.7509	1.7527	1.7544	1.7561

TABLE 2
Common Logarithms
(*continued*)

x	.00	.01	.02	.03	.04	.05	.06	.07	.08	.09
5.8	1.7579	1.7596	1.7613	1.7630	1.7647	1.7664	1.7681	1.7699	1.7716	1.7733
5.9	1.7750	1.7766	1.7783	1.7800	1.7817	1.7834	1.7851	1.7867	1.7884	1.7901
6.0	1.7918	1.7934	1.7951	1.7967	1.7984	1.8001	1.8017	1.8034	1.8050	1.8066
6.1	1.8083	1.8099	1.8116	1.8132	1.8148	1.8165	1.8181	1.8197	1.8213	1.8229
6.2	1.8245	1.8262	1.8278	1.8294	1.8310	1.8326	1.8342	1.8358	1.8374	1.8390
6.3	1.8405	1.8421	1.8437	1.8453	1.8469	1.8485	1.8500	1.8516	1.8532	1.8547
6.4	1.8563	1.8579	1.8594	1.8610	1.8625	1.8641	1.8656	1.8672	1.8687	1.8703
6.5	1.8718	1.8733	1.8749	1.8764	1.8779	1.8795	1.8810	1.8825	1.8840	1.8856
6.6	1.8871	1.8886	1.8901	1.8916	1.8931	1.8946	1.8961	1.8976	1.8991	1.9006
6.7	1.9021	1.9036	1.9051	1.9066	1.9081	1.9095	1.9110	1.9125	1.9140	1.9155
6.8	1.9169	1.9184	1.9199	1.9213	1.9228	1.9242	1.9257	1.9272	1.9286	1.9301
6.9	1.9315	1.9330	1.9344	1.9359	1.9373	1.9387	1.9402	1.9416	1.9430	1.9445
7.0	1.9459	1.9473	1.9488	1.9502	1.9516	1.9530	1.9544	1.9559	1.9573	1.9587
7.1	1.9601	1.9615	1.9629	1.9643	1.9657	1.9671	1.9685	1.9699	1.9713	1.9727
7.2	1.9741	1.9755	1.9769	1.9782	1.9796	1.9810	1.9824	1.9838	1.9851	1.9865
7.3	1.9879	1.9892	1.9906	1.9920	1.9933	1.9947	1.9961	1.9974	1.9988	2.0001
7.4	2.0015	2.0028	2.0042	2.0055	2.0069	2.0082	2.0096	2.0109	2.0122	2.0136
7.5	2.0149	2.0162	2.0176	2.0189	2.0202	2.0215	2.0229	2.0242	2.0255	2.0268
7.6	2.0281	2.0295	2.0308	2.0321	2.0334	2.0347	2.0360	2.0373	2.0386	2.0399
7.7	2.0412	2.0425	2.0438	2.0451	2.0464	2.0477	2.0490	2.0503	2.0516	2.0528
7.8	2.0541	2.0554	2.0567	2.0580	2.0592	2.0605	2.0618	2.0631	2.0643	2.0656
7.9	2.0669	2.0681	2.0694	2.0707	2.0719	2.0732	2.0744	2.0757	2.0769	2.0782
8.0	2.0794	2.0807	2.0819	2.0832	2.0844	2.0857	2.0869	2.0882	2.0894	2.0906
8.1	2.0919	2.0931	2.0943	2.0956	2.0968	2.0980	2.0992	2.1005	2.1017	2.1029
8.2	2.1041	2.1054	2.1066	2.1078	2.1090	2.1102	2.1114	2.1126	2.1138	2.1150
8.3	2.1163	2.1175	2.1187	2.1199	2.1211	2.1223	2.1235	2.1247	2.1258	2.1270
8.4	2.1282	2.1294	2.1306	2.1318	2.1330	2.1342	2.1353	2.1365	2.1377	2.1389
8.5	2.1401	2.1412	2.1424	2.1436	2.1448	2.1459	2.1471	2.1483	2.1494	2.1506
8.6	2.1518	2.1529	2.1541	2.1552	2.1564	2.1576	2.1587	2.1599	2.1610	2.1622
8.7	2.1633	2.1645	2.1656	2.1668	2.1679	2.1691	2.1702	2.1713	2.1725	2.1736
8.8	2.1748	2.1759	2.1770	2.1782	2.1793	2.1804	2.1815	2.1827	2.1838	2.1849
8.9	2.1861	2.1872	2.1883	2.1894	2.1905	2.1917	2.1928	2.1939	2.1950	2.1961
9.0	2.1972	2.1983	2.1994	2.2006	2.2017	2.2028	2.2039	2.2050	2.2061	2.2072
9.1	2.2083	2.2094	2.2105	2.2116	2.2127	2.2138	2.2148	2.2159	2.2170	2.2181
9.2	2.2192	2.2203	2.2214	2.2225	2.2235	2.2246	2.2257	2.2268	2.2279	2.2289
9.3	2.2300	2.2311	2.2322	2.2332	2.2343	2.2354	2.2364	2.2375	2.2386	2.2396
9.4	2.2407	2.2418	2.2428	2.2439	2.2450	2.2460	2.2471	2.2481	2.2492	2.2502
9.5	2.2513	2.2523	2.2534	2.2544	2.2555	2.2565	2.2576	2.2586	2.2597	2.2607
9.6	2.2618	2.2628	2.2638	2.2649	2.2659	2.2670	2.2680	2.2690	2.2701	2.2711
9.7	2.2721	2.2732	2.2742	2.2752	2.2762	2.2773	2.2783	2.2793	2.2803	2.2814
9.8	2.2824	2.2834	2.2844	2.2854	2.2865	2.2875	2.2885	2.2895	2.2905	2.2915
9.9	2.2925	2.2935	2.2946	2.2956	2.2966	2.2976	2.2986	2.2996	2.3006	2.3016

Appendix B: Linear Interpolation

1	Common Logarithms — Table Evaluation
2	Linear Interpolation

---

1   Common Logarithms — Table Evaluation

Using results from calculus, we can compute a table of common logarithms to any decimal accuracy required. Table 1 in Appendix A is a four-place table of $\log_{10} x = \log x$ for $1 \le x \le 9.99$, where x is in increments of .01. By using scientific notation (see Section 7.7) we can write any positive number in the form $a \times 10^n$, where $1 \le a < 10$ and n is an integer. Therefore, Table 1 can be used to find $\log x$ to four places for any $x > 0$.

Let's begin by discussing how to read Table 1. A portion of the table is given in Figure B.1. To find $\log 5.47$, for example, read down the left-hand column to the row labeled 5.4. Now move across this row to the column labeled 7 where the logarithm .7380 is located. Thus, $\log 5.47 = .7380$. Other examples are

$$\log 5 = \log 5.00 = .6990$$
$$\log 5.3 = \log 5.30 = .7243$$
$$\log 5.24 = .7193$$

FIGURE B.1

x	0	1	2	3	4	5	6	7	8	9
5.0	.6990	.6998	.7007	.7016	.7024	.7033	.7042	.7050	.7059	.7067
5.1	.7076	.7084	.7093	.7101	.7110	.7118	.7126	.7135	.7143	.7152
5.2	.7160	.7168	.7177	.7185	.7193	.7202	.7210	.7218	.7226	.7235
5.3	.7243	.7251	.7259	.7267	.7275	.7284	.7292	.7300	.7308	.7316
5.4	.7324	.7332	.7340	.7348	.7356	.7364	.7372	.7380	.7388	.7396

Recall that an antilogarithm is a number whose logarithm is known (see Section 10.4). If $\log N = .7126$, then from Figure B.1, $N =$ antilog $.7126 = 5.16$. Two other examples are

$$\text{antilog } .7016 = 5.03 \qquad \text{and} \qquad \text{antilog } .7308 = 5.38$$

To find $\log x$, when x is not between 1.00 and 9.99, we first write x in scientific notation. Next we use the properties of logarithms to calculate log *x*. For example,

$$\log 87{,}400 = \log 8.74 \times 10^4 \qquad \log x_1 x_2 = \log x_1 + \log x_2$$
$$= \log 8.74 + \log 10^4 \qquad \log_b b^x = x$$
$$= .9415 + 4 \qquad\qquad \text{Table 1 gives .9415.}$$
$$= 4.9415$$

As another example, consider the following:

$$\log .00147 = \log 1.47 \times 10^{-3}$$
$$= \log 1.47 + \log 10^{-3}$$
$$= .1673 - 3$$

We can add .1673 and -3 to get -2.8327, but when we are not using a calculator, $.1673 - 3$ is often a more convenient form.

EXAMPLE 1

Use Table 1 from Appendix A to find the common logarithm of the following numbers.

a. 2450 **b.** 186,000 **c.** .0447 **d.** .000 008 72

SOLUTION **a.** $\log 2450 = \log 2.45 \times 10^3 = \log 2.45 + \log 10^3$
$$= .3892 + 3 = 3.3892$$
b. $\log 186{,}000 = \log 1.86 \times 10^5 = \log 1.86 + \log 10^5$
$$= .2695 + 5 = 5.2695$$
c. $\log .0447 = \log 4.47 \times 10^{-2} = \log 4.47 + \log 10^{-2}$
$$= .6503 - 2$$
d. $\log .000 008 72 = \log 8.72 \times 10^{-6}$
$$= \log 8.72 + \log 10^{-6} = .9405 - 6$$

From Example 1 we can see that $\log x$ consists of a decimal, called the **mantissa**, and an integer, called the **characteristic**. When $1 \le x < 10$, the characteristic is 0.

To determine the antilog of an expression such as $\log N = 9.5378$, we first find the antilog of the mantissa .5378, which is 3.45. Then the antilog of the characteristic 9 is 10^9; that is, we reverse the steps in Example 1. Thus,

$$\log N = 9.5378$$
$$= .5378 + 9$$
$$N = 3.45 \times 10^9$$

EXAMPLE 2

Use Table 1 in Appendix A to find each antilogarithm.

a. $\log N = 11.6712$ **b.** $\log N = .9031 - 7$
c. $\log N = -4.6737$

SOLUTION **a.** $\log N = 11.6712 = .6712 + 11$
$$N = 4.69 \times 10^{11}$$

b. $\log N = .9031 - 7$
    $N = 8 \times 10^{-7}$

c. $\log N = -4.6737 = -4 - .6737$. To use Table 1 we must express $\log N$ as the sum of a positive decimal and an integer. We can do this by adding $0 = 5 - 5$ to -4.6737:

$$\log N = -4.6737$$
$$= -4.6737 + (5 - 5) \quad 0 = a - a$$
$$= (5 - 4.6737) - 5$$
$$= .3263 - 5$$
$$N = 2.12 \times 10^{-5}$$

---

2   Linear Interpolation

We cannot find log 2.757 or antilog .3933 directly from Table 1. However, with a method called **linear interpolation**, we can approximate these numbers indirectly from Table 1.

We begin with a geometric interpretation of linear interpolation. Figure B.2 graphs $y = \log x$ with the curvature exaggerated to help illustrate the principle involved. Suppose that $a < N < b$, where a and b are in Table 1 but N is not, such as $2.750 < 2.757 < 2.760$. The line segment $\overline{PQ}$ is used to approximate the curve from P to Q. We approximate log N on the curve with z from the line segment, hence the word *linear* in linear interpolation.

FIGURE B.2

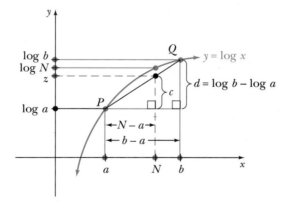

Because the two right triangles in Figure B.2 are similar, the ratios of corresponding sides are equal. Thus, the ratio of the base of the smaller triangle, $N - a$, to the base of the larger triangle, $b - a$, is the same as the ratio of the height of the smaller triangle, c, to the height of the larger triangle, $d = \log b - \log a$; that is,

$$\frac{N - a}{b - a} = \frac{c}{d} \quad \text{or} \quad \frac{N - a}{b - a} = \frac{c}{\log b - \log a} \quad (1)$$

In Proportion (1) we know all of the variables except c. Solving for c we have

$$\log N \approx z = \log a + c$$

We illustrate this procedure with $\log N = \log 2.757$; $a = 2.750$, $\log a = .4393$, $b = 2.760$, and $\log b = .4409$. Thus,

$$\frac{N - a}{b - a} = \frac{c}{d}$$

$$\frac{2.757 - 2.750}{2.760 - 2.750} = \frac{c}{.4409 - .4393}$$

$$\frac{.007}{.010} = \frac{c}{.0016}$$

 $c = .0016\left[\frac{.007}{.010}\right] = .00112 \approx .0011$

$\log N \approx \log a + c$, so

$\log 2.757 \approx .4393 + .0011 = .4404$

With a calculator, $\log 2.757 = .4404368$, so we can see that linear interpolation is quite accurate. Note that $.00112$ is rounded to $.0011$; a five-place answer is of no value when working with a four-place table.

Now we consider an abbreviated format for carrying out the calculations involved in linear interpolation. First, we will drop the decimal points in Proportion (1). This step is convenient, as long as we properly re-introduce the decimal points at the end of the calculations. We illustrate this format with $\log 2.757$.

$$10\left\{7\left\{\begin{array}{l}\log 2.750 = .4393\\\log 2.757 = z\\\log 2.760 = .4409\end{array}\right\}c\right\}16$$

$$\frac{c}{16} = \frac{7}{10}, \qquad c = \frac{7 \cdot 16}{10} = 11.2 \approx 11$$

$$z = 4393 + 11 = 4404 \qquad \text{and} \qquad \log 2.757 = .4404$$

EXAMPLE 3

Find the following logarithms.

a. $\log 5.462$ **b.** $\log .002\ 468$

SOLUTION **a.**

$$10\left\{2\left\{\begin{array}{l}\log 5.460 = .7372\\\log 5.462 = z\\\log 5.470 = .7380\end{array}\right\}c\right\}8$$

$$\frac{c}{8} = \frac{2}{10}, \qquad c = \frac{16}{10} = 1.6 \approx 2$$

$$z = 7372 + 2 = 7374, \quad \text{so}$$

$\log 5.462 = .7374$

b. $\log .002\ 468 = \log 2.468 \times 10^{-3}$

$\qquad\qquad\qquad = \log 2.468 + \log 10^{-3}$

$\qquad\qquad\qquad = \log 2.468 - 3$

$$10\left\{8\left\{\begin{array}{l}\log 2.460 = .3909\\\log 2.468 = z\\\log 2.470 = .3927\end{array}\right\}c\right\}18$$

$$\frac{c}{18} = \frac{8}{10}, \qquad c = \frac{18 \cdot 8}{10} = 14.4 \approx 14$$
$$z = 3909 + 14 = 3923, \quad \text{so}$$
$$\log 2.468 = .3923, \quad \text{and}$$
$$\log .002\ 468 = .3923 - 3$$

We can use linear interpolation to find the antilog of a number that is not in Table 1. In this case we know a, b, and the three logarithms in Proportion (1), and we have to find N. We will let $k = N - a$.

EXAMPLE 4 Find the following antilogarithms.

    a. $\log N = .3933 - 17$ **b.** $\log N = 30.103$

SOLUTION   **a.** Let $\log x = .3933$. From Table 1, .3933 is between .3927 and .3945. Thus,

$$10^k \left\{ \begin{array}{l} \log 2.470 = .3927 \\ \log x = .3933 \\ \log 2.480 = .3945 \end{array} \right\}_6 \Big\}_{18}$$

$$\frac{k}{10} = \frac{6}{18} = \frac{1}{3}, \qquad k = \frac{10}{3} = 3.3 \approx 3$$
$$2470 + 3 = 2473, \quad \text{so}$$
$$x = 2.473, \quad \text{and}$$
$$N = 2.473 \times 10^{-17}$$

    b. $\log 30.103 = .1030 + 30$. Let $\log x = .1030$. From Table 1, .1030 is between .1004 and .1038. Thus,

$$10^k \left\{ \begin{array}{l} \log 1.260 = .1004 \\ \log x = .1030 \\ \log 1.270 = .1038 \end{array} \right\}_{26} \Big\}_{34}$$

$$\frac{k}{10} = \frac{26}{34}, \qquad k = \frac{260}{34} = 7.6 \approx 8$$
$$1260 + 8 = 1268, \quad \text{so}$$
$$x = 1.268, \quad \text{and}$$
$$N = 1.268 \times 10^{30}$$

EXERCISE SET B.1

A

 Use Table 1 to find the logarithm of each number.

1. 3   **2.** 8   **3.** 7.1   **4.** 5.8

5. 2.32   **6.** 3.99   **7.** 9.08   **8.** 5.64

9. 384   **10.** 830,000,000

11. 7,880,000   **12.** 104,000,000,000

13. 900,000   **14.** .023

15. .000 507   **16.** .000 014

17. .000 000 19   **18.** .000 000 468

Use Table 1 to find each antilogarithm.

19. $\log N = .5539$ **20.** $\log N = .8882$

21. $\log N = 1.7251$ **22.** $\log N = 3.9015$

23. $\log N = 8.7875$ **24.** $\log N = 2.0128$

25. $\log N = 14.618$ **26.** $\log N = .4624 - 2$

27. $\log N = .6191 - 5$ **28.** $\log N = .9025 - 11$

29. $\log N = .8488 - 13$ **30.** $\log N = -.248$

31. $\log N = -4.4685$ **32.** $\log N = -8.9666$

33. $\log N = -1.6308$ **34.** $\log N = -9.3778$

2 Use Table 1 and linear interpolation to find the logarithm of each number.

35. 3.532 **36.** 1.713

37. 2.868 **38.** 8.267

39. 1507 **40.** 186,300

41. 506,800,000 **42.** 998,200,000,000

43. .1538 **44.** .004 003

45. .045 52 **46.** .000 004 198

Use Table 1 and linear interpolation to find each antilogarithm.

47. $\log N = .2362$ **48.** $\log N = .5838$

49. $\log N = 1.6970$ **50.** $\log N = 4.7318$

51. $\log N = 10.1685$ **52.** $\log N = 9.8301$

53. $\log N = .6908 - 2$ **54.** $\log N = .9900 - 4$

55. $\log N = .7831 - 6$ **56.** $\log N = .9213 - 8$

B

57. $\log N = -1.3126$ **58.** $\log N = -3.0947$

59. $\log N = -5.2146$ **60.** $\log N = -.6103$

Appendix C: Synthetic Division

Section 5.3 discussed the quotient of two polynomials. We now consider a shortcut method for performing this division.

When a polynomial is divided by $x - c$, the usual long-division method can be simplified to a process called **synthetic division**. We begin with an example using the long-division method and show how several shortcuts can reduce this method to synthetic division. Consider $(4x^3 - 12x^2 - 37x - 15) \div (x - 5)$:

$$
\begin{array}{r}
4x^2 + 8x + 3 \\
x - 5 \overline{)\,4x^3 - 12x^2 - 37x - 15} \\
\underline{4x^3 - 20x^2} \\
8x^2 - 37x \\
\underline{8x^2 - 40x} \\
3x - 15 \\
\underline{3x - 15} \\
0
\end{array}
$$

The positions of the coefficients determine their use, so we can perform the same division using only these numbers:

$$
\begin{array}{r}
4 \quad 8 \quad 3 \\
1 - 5 \overline{)\,4 \;\; -12 \;\; -37 \;\; -15} \\
\underline{4 \;- 20} \\
8 - 37 \\
\underline{8 - 40} \\
3 - 15 \\
\underline{3 - 15} \\
0
\end{array}
$$

The blue numbers 4, 8, and 3 are repetitions of the numbers above them so we omit them. We can also eliminate the 1:

$$
\begin{array}{r}
4 \quad 8 \quad 3 \\
-5 \overline{)\,4 \;\; -12 \;\; -37 \;\; -15} \\
\underline{-20} \\
8 \quad {}^-37 \\
\underline{-40} \\
3 \;\; -15 \\
\underline{-15} \\
0
\end{array}
$$

545

The blue numbers -37 and -15 are repetitions of the numbers above them, so we omit them and make our bottom row 4 8 3 0:

$$
\begin{array}{r}
\;\;4 \quad\;\; 8 \quad\;\; 3 \\
-5\,)\overline{4 \quad -12 \quad -37 \quad -15} \\
 -20 \quad -40 \quad -15 \\
\hline
4 \quad\;\; 8 \quad\;\; 3 \quad\;\; 0
\end{array}
$$

Instead of using -5 and subtraction, we use 5 and addition:

$$
\begin{array}{r}
\;\;4 \quad\;\; 8 \quad\;\; 3 \\
5\,)\overline{4 \quad -12 \quad -37 \quad -15} \\
 20 \quad\;\; 40 \quad\;\; 15 \\
\hline
4 \quad\;\; 8 \quad\;\; 3 \quad\;\; 0
\end{array}
$$

The blue numbers 4, 8, and 3 are repetitions of the numbers below them so we can omit them. We will use the symbols ⌐ and ⌐ to indicate the divisor, 5, and the remainder, 0:

$$
\begin{array}{r|rrrr}
5 & 4 & -12 & -37 & -15 \\
 & & 20 & 40 & 15 \\
\hline
 & 4 & 8 & 3 & \underline{|\,0}
\end{array}
$$

Let's summarize this material. To find

$$
\frac{4x^3 - 12x^2 - 37x - 15}{x - 5}
$$

write 5, 4, -12, -37, and -15 in a row with a line under it:

$$
\begin{array}{r|rrrr}
5 & 4 & -12 & -37 & -15 \\
\hline
\end{array}
$$

Now perform the following steps:

1. Bring down the 4, multiply it by 5, write the 20 under the -12, add them, and place the 8 next to the 4.
2. Multiply the 8 by 5, write the 40 under the -37, add them, and place the 3 next to the 8.
3. Multiply the 3 by 5, write the 15 under the -15, and add them; the remainder is 0.

These steps are indicated with arrows:

$$
\begin{array}{r|rrrr}
5 & 4 & -12 & -37 & -15 \\
 & & 20 & 40 & 15 \\
\hline
 & 4 & 8 & 3 & \underline{|\,0}
\end{array}
$$

The bottom row represents $4x^2 + 8x + 3$ with a remainder of 0, so

$$
\frac{4x^3 - 12x^2 - 37x - 15}{x - 5} = 4x^2 + 8x + 3
$$

EXAMPLE 1

Divide $\dfrac{x^4 - 7x^2 + 3x + 22}{x + 2}$ using

a. Long division   **b.** Synthetic division

SOLUTION

a. Use $0 = 0x^3$ as a placeholder. Then

$$
\begin{array}{r}
x^3 - 2x^2 - 3x + 9 \\
x + 2 \overline{)\, x^4 + 0x^3 - 7x^2 + 3x + 22} \\
\underline{x^4 + 2x^3} \\
-2x^3 - 7x^2 \\
\underline{-2x^3 - 4x^2} \\
-3x^2 + 3x \\
\underline{-3x^2 - 6x} \\
9x + 22 \\
\underline{9x + 18} \\
4
\end{array}
$$

b. Let $x^4 = 1x^4$ and $x + 2 = x - (-2)$ to put it in the form $x - c$. Then

$$
\begin{array}{r|rrrr}
-2 & 1 & 0 & -7 & 3 & 22 \\
   &   & -2 & 4 & 6 & -18 \\
\hline
   & 1 & -2 & -3 & 9 & \boxed{4}
\end{array}
\qquad \text{Thus,}
$$

$$
\frac{x^4 - 7x^2 + 3x + 22}{x + 2} = x^3 - 2x^2 - 3x + 9 + \frac{4}{x + 2}
$$

From this point on we will omit the arrows in the synthetic division.

EXAMPLE 2

Let $f(x) = x^3 - 2x^2 - 5x + 6$. Find $f(x) \div (x - 3)$ using synthetic division.

SOLUTION

$$
\begin{array}{r|rrrr}
3 & 1 & -2 & -5 & 6 \\
  &   & 3 & 3 & -6 \\
\hline
  & 1 & 1 & -2 & \boxed{0}
\end{array}
$$

Thus, $\dfrac{f(x)}{x - 3} = x^2 + x - 2$

EXERCISE SET C.1

A

Find the following quotients using a. long division and b. synthetic division.

1. $\dfrac{x^2 - x - 12}{x - 4}$

2. $\dfrac{2x^2 + 9x - 5}{x + 5}$

3. $\dfrac{3y^2 + 5y + 6}{y + 1}$

4. $\dfrac{a^2 - 10}{a - 3}$

5. $\dfrac{3x^3 - x^2 - 12x + 4}{x - 2}$

6. $\dfrac{y^3 + 5y^2 - 13y + 10}{y + 7}$

7. $(4x^4 + x^2 - 5) \div (x - 1)$

8. $(x^5 + 2) \div (x + 1)$

Use synthetic division to find the following quotients.

9. $\dfrac{x^2 + x - 6}{x - 2}$

10. $\dfrac{x^2 - 9}{x + 3}$

11. $\dfrac{y^2 + 3y + 7}{y + 1}$ **12.** $\dfrac{3a^2 - 2a + 5}{a - 4}$

13. $\dfrac{4y^3 - 12y^2 - y + 3}{y - 3}$

14. $\dfrac{x^3 + 4x^2 - 4x - 17}{x + 2}$

15. $(x^3 - 1) \div (x - 1)$

16. $(a^3 + 8) \div (x + 2)$

17. $(x^3 + 27) \div (x - 3)$

18. $(2y^3 - 1) \div (y + 3)$

B

19. $(x^5 - 4x^2 + 5) \div (x - 2)$

20. $(x^5 + 1) \div (x + 1)$

21. $(x^6 - 1) \div (x - 1)$

22. $(x^7 + 3) \div (x + 1)$

Appendix D:
Review of Arithmetic Fractions

1	**Definitions, Vocabulary, and Prime Factorization**
2	**Reduction of Fractions to Lowest Terms**
3	**Multiplication and Division of Fractions**
4	**Addition and Subtraction of Fractions**

---

1   Definitions, Vocabulary, and Prime Factorization

The study of arithmetic begins with the **natural numbers**: 1, 2, 3, 4, and so on. Later on fractions are considered, such as $\frac{1}{2}, \frac{2}{3}, \frac{5}{7}, \frac{32}{18}$, and so forth.

In general, a **fraction** is the indicated quotient of two quantities. In arithmetic, fractions are the indicated quotient of natural numbers. In algebra we use arithmetic fractions, but we also consider quotients of other quantities, called algebraic fractions. The rules for working with arithmetic and algebraic fractions are very similar. To be successful with algebraic fractions (Chapter 6), it is necessary to be proficient with arithmetic fractions. This appendix reviews the basic operations of arithmetic fractions in preparation for the study of algebra.

In a fraction, such as $\frac{2}{3}$, the number on top, 2, is called the **numerator** and the number on the bottom, 3, is called the **denominator**. A fraction is a **proper fraction** if its numerator is less than its denominator. Examples are

$$\frac{2}{3}, \qquad \frac{7}{11}, \qquad \text{and} \qquad \frac{8}{9}$$

An **improper fraction** is one whose numerator is greater than or equal to its denominator, such as

$$\frac{3}{2}, \qquad \frac{45}{27}, \qquad \frac{7}{7} = 1, \qquad \text{and} \qquad \frac{8}{1} = 8$$

The fraction $\frac{8}{1} = 8$ illustrates the fact that every natural number can be written as an improper fraction.

An improper fraction also can be expressed as a **mixed number**, which is a combination of a natural number and a proper fraction. For example,

$$\frac{5}{3} = 1\frac{2}{3} \qquad \text{because} \qquad 1\frac{2}{3} = 1 + \frac{2}{3} = \frac{3}{3} + \frac{2}{3} = \frac{5}{3}$$

The natural numbers greater than 1 are classified as either **prime** or **composite**. A number is prime if it is only divisible by 1 and itself. The primes are

$$2, 3, 5, 7, 11, 13, 17, 19, \text{ and so on}$$

A number is composite if it is divisible by a natural number other than 1 and itself. The composites are

$$4, 6, 8, 9, 10, 12, 14, 15, 16, 18, 20, \text{ and so on}$$

In arithmetic we commonly use $\times$ to indicate multiplication, such as $2 \times 6 = 12$. In algebra we more commonly use a raised dot, $\cdot$, so we will stay with the dot. Thus,

$$2 \times 6 = 2 \cdot 6 = 12$$

The numbers 2 and 6 are called *factors*, or *divisors*, of 12; and $2 \cdot 6$ is called a *factorization* of 12. Other factorizations of 12 are

$$3 \cdot 4 \qquad \text{and} \qquad 2 \cdot 2 \cdot 3$$

The form $2 \cdot 2 \cdot 3$ is called the **prime factorization** of 12, because each number is prime. The method of finding the prime factorization of composite numbers is illustrated in the following example.

EXAMPLE 1

Find the prime factorizations of the following.

a. 18   **b.** 36   **c.** 21   **d.** 110

SOLUTION

a. 18 is divisible by 2, so
18 = 2 · 9. Because 9 = 3 · 3,
18 = 2 · 3 · 3
b. 36 = 2 · 18
    = 2 · 2 · 3 · 3
c. 21 = 3 · 7
d. 110 = 10 · 11
     = 2 · 5 · 11

---

2   Reduction of Fractions to Lowest Terms

A fraction is said to be **reduced to lowest terms**, or **simplified**, when both the numerator and denominator cannot be divided by a natural number other than 1. Examples of simplified fractions are

$$\frac{2}{3}, \qquad \frac{8}{9}, \qquad \text{and} \qquad \frac{13}{6}$$

Prime factorization is often conveniently used to reduce a fraction to lowest terms. For example,

$$\frac{10}{15} = \frac{2 \cdot 5}{3 \cdot 5} = \frac{2}{3} \cdot \frac{5}{5} = \frac{2}{3} \cdot 1 = \frac{2}{3}, \qquad \text{or briefly,} \qquad \frac{10}{15} = \frac{2 \cdot \cancel{5}}{3 \cdot \cancel{5}} = \frac{2}{3}$$

> ### Reducing Fractions to Lowest Terms
>
> **1.** Find the prime factorization of the numerator and the denominator.
> **2.** Divide out the common primes in the numerator and the denominator.
> **3.** Multiply the remaining primes in the numerator and the denominator.

EXAMPLE 2

Simplify the following fractions.

a. $\dfrac{30}{42}$ **b.** $\dfrac{14}{70}$ **c.** $\dfrac{39}{3}$ **d.** $\dfrac{45}{27}$

SOLUTION

a. $\dfrac{30}{42} = \dfrac{2 \cdot 15}{2 \cdot 21} = \dfrac{\cancel{2} \cdot \cancel{3} \cdot 5}{\cancel{2} \cdot \cancel{3} \cdot 7} = \dfrac{5}{7}$

b. $\dfrac{14}{70} = \dfrac{2 \cdot 7}{2 \cdot 35} = \dfrac{\cancel{2} \cdot \cancel{7} \cdot 1}{\cancel{2} \cdot \cancel{7} \cdot 5} = \dfrac{1}{5}$

c. $\dfrac{39}{3} = \dfrac{\cancel{3} \cdot 13}{\cancel{3}} = 13$

d. $\dfrac{45}{27} = \dfrac{3 \cdot 15}{3 \cdot 9} = \dfrac{\cancel{3} \cdot \cancel{3} \cdot 5}{\cancel{3} \cdot \cancel{3} \cdot 3} = \dfrac{5}{3}$

We could write $\dfrac{5}{3}$ as $1\dfrac{2}{3}$, but in algebra improper fractions are usually more convenient than mixed numbers.

3   Multiplication and Division of Fractions

The product of two or more fractions is the product of their numerators divided by the product of their denominators. For example,

$$\frac{2}{3} \cdot \frac{5}{7} = \frac{2 \cdot 5}{3 \cdot 7} = \frac{10}{21}$$

To find the product of a natural number and a fraction, we can write the natural number as a fraction with a denominator of 1. For instance,

$$8 \cdot \frac{2}{11} = \frac{8}{1} \cdot \frac{2}{11} = \frac{8 \cdot 2}{1 \cdot 11} = \frac{16}{11}$$

Often the product of fractions will not be in reduced form. Rather than multiplying the numerators and denominators, a better approach is to get their prime factorizations and then reduce the fraction. This process is illustrated in the next example.

EXAMPLE 3

Find the following products and simplify the answers.

$$\textbf{a.}\ \frac{6}{11}\cdot\frac{7}{4} \qquad \textbf{b.}\ 9\cdot\frac{25}{15} \qquad \textbf{c.}\ \frac{5}{7}\cdot\frac{7}{5} \qquad \textbf{d.}\ \frac{2}{3}\cdot\frac{3}{4}\cdot\frac{4}{5}$$

SOLUTION

$$\textbf{a.}\ \frac{6}{11}\cdot\frac{7}{4}=\frac{6\cdot7}{11\cdot4}=\frac{2\cdot3\cdot7}{11\cdot2\cdot2}=\frac{3\cdot7}{11\cdot2}=\frac{21}{22}$$

$$\textbf{b.}\ 9\cdot\frac{25}{15}=\frac{9}{1}\cdot\frac{25}{15}=\frac{9\cdot25}{1\cdot15}=\frac{3\cdot3\cdot5\cdot5}{3\cdot5}=15$$

$$\textbf{c.}\ \frac{5}{7}\cdot\frac{7}{5}=\frac{5\cdot7}{7\cdot5}=1$$

$$\textbf{d.}\ \frac{2}{3}\cdot\frac{3}{4}\cdot\frac{4}{5}=\frac{2\cdot3\cdot4}{3\cdot4\cdot5}=\frac{2}{5}$$

To divide two fractions, we invert the second fraction and change the division sign to a multiplication sign. Then we proceed with the multiplication. The reason why this process works is explained in Chapter 6. For example,

$$\frac{2}{3}\div\frac{5}{7}=\frac{2}{3}\cdot\frac{7}{5}=\frac{2\cdot7}{3\cdot5}=\frac{14}{15}$$

EXAMPLE 4

Find the following quotients and simplify the answers.

$$\textbf{a.}\ \frac{2}{3}\div\frac{7}{15} \qquad \textbf{b.}\ \frac{8}{9}\div10 \qquad \textbf{c.}\ 20\div7$$

SOLUTION

$$\textbf{a.}\ \frac{2}{5}\div\frac{7}{15}=\frac{2}{5}\cdot\frac{15}{7}=\frac{2\cdot15}{5\cdot7}=\frac{2\cdot3\cdot5}{5\cdot7}=\frac{6}{7}$$

$$\textbf{b.}\ \frac{8}{9}\div10=\frac{8}{9}\div\frac{10}{1}=\frac{8}{9}\cdot\frac{1}{10}=\frac{8\cdot1}{9\cdot10}=\frac{2\cdot4}{9\cdot2\cdot5}=\frac{4}{45}$$

$$\textbf{c.}\ 20\div7=20\cdot\frac{1}{7}=\frac{20}{7}$$

4   Addition and Subtraction of Fractions

Fractions that have the same denominators are called **like fractions**, and those with different denominators are called **unlike fractions**. To add like fractions, we add their numerators and place this result over the common denominator. To subtract like fractions, we subtract their numerators and place this result over the common denominator. For example,

$$\frac{3}{7}+\frac{1}{7}=\frac{3+1}{7}=\frac{4}{7} \qquad \text{and} \qquad \frac{3}{7}-\frac{1}{7}=\frac{3-1}{7}=\frac{2}{7}$$

EXAMPLE 5

Perform the indicated operations and simplify the answers.

$$\textbf{a.}\ \frac{8}{15}-\frac{7}{15} \qquad \textbf{b.}\ \frac{9}{8}+\frac{5}{8} \qquad \textbf{c.}\ \frac{4}{9}-\frac{4}{9}$$

SOLUTION   **a.** $\dfrac{8}{15} - \dfrac{7}{15} = \dfrac{8-7}{15} = \dfrac{1}{15}$

       b. $\dfrac{9}{8} + \dfrac{5}{8} = \dfrac{9+5}{8} = \dfrac{14}{8} = \dfrac{\cancel{2}\cdot 7}{\cancel{2}\cdot 4} = \dfrac{7}{4}$

       c. $\dfrac{4}{9} - \dfrac{4}{9} = \dfrac{4-4}{9} = \dfrac{0}{9} = 0$

       Note that zero divided by any nonzero number is zero.

     To add or subtract unlike fractions, we must first convert them to fractions with the same, or common, denominator; that is, we must express them as like fractions. Often we must use the smallest common denominator, called the **least common denominator (LCD)**. Thus, the LCD is the smallest natural number divisible by each denominator. As an example, consider

$$\frac{3}{4} + \frac{1}{6}$$

First find the prime factorization of 4 and 6:

$$4 = 2 \cdot 2 \quad \text{and} \quad 6 = 2 \cdot 3$$

In the first denominator 2 appears twice, and 3 appears once in the second denominator. Thus, the LCD contains two factors of 2 and one factor of 3:

$$\text{LCD} = 2 \cdot 2 \cdot 3 = 12$$

Note that 4 is missing a factor of 3 that is in 12, and 6 is missing a factor of 2 that is in 12. Thus, multiply $\dfrac{3}{4}$ by $\dfrac{3}{3}$ and $\dfrac{1}{6}$ by $\dfrac{2}{2}$:

$$\frac{3}{4} + \frac{1}{6} = \frac{3}{4}\cdot\frac{3}{3} + \frac{1}{6}\cdot\frac{2}{2} = \frac{9}{12} + \frac{2}{12} = \frac{11}{12}$$

Note that $\dfrac{3}{3} = \dfrac{2}{2} = 1$; multiplying a fraction by 1 does not change its value.

Adding or Subtracting Unlike Fractions

1. Find the prime factorization of each denominator.

2. The LCD is the product of each factor the greatest number of times it appears in any single denominator.

3. Multiply the numerator and denominator of each fraction by the factors in the LCD that are missing in the denominator.

4. Add or subtract the like fractions.

5. Simplify your answer.

EXAMPLE 6

Perform the indicated operations and simplify the answer.

a. $\dfrac{1}{12} + \dfrac{1}{18}$ b. $\dfrac{1}{10} + \dfrac{1}{4} + \dfrac{2}{5}$ c. $\dfrac{1}{5} - \dfrac{1}{8}$

d. $\dfrac{5}{81} - \dfrac{1}{27}$ e. $3\dfrac{2}{7}$

SOLUTION

a.

$12 = 2 \cdot 2 \cdot 3$	Two factors of 2
$18 = 2 \cdot 3 \cdot 3$	Two factors of 3

$\text{LCD} = 2 \cdot 2 \cdot 3 \cdot 3 = 4 \cdot 9 = 36$

$\dfrac{1}{12} + \dfrac{1}{18} = \dfrac{1}{12} \cdot \dfrac{3}{3} + \dfrac{1}{18} \cdot \dfrac{2}{2} = \dfrac{3}{36} + \dfrac{2}{36} = \dfrac{5}{36}$

b.

$5 = 5$	One factor of 5
$10 = 2 \cdot 5$	One factor of 5
$4 = 2 \cdot 2$	Two factors of 2

The greatest number of times that 5 appears in any denominator is once; the greatest number of times that 2 appears in any denominator is twice. Thus,

$\text{LCD} = 2 \cdot 2 \cdot 5 = 20$

$\dfrac{1}{10} + \dfrac{1}{4} + \dfrac{2}{5} = \dfrac{1}{10} \cdot \dfrac{2}{2} + \dfrac{1}{4} \cdot \dfrac{5}{5} + \dfrac{2}{5} \cdot \dfrac{4}{4} = \dfrac{2}{20} + \dfrac{5}{20} + \dfrac{8}{20}$

$= \dfrac{15}{20} = \dfrac{3 \cdot \cancel{5}}{4 \cdot \cancel{5}} = \dfrac{3}{4}$

c.

$5 = 5$	One factor of 5
$8 = 2 \cdot 2 \cdot 2$	Three factors of 2

$\text{LCD} = 5 \cdot 2 \cdot 2 \cdot 2 = 5 \cdot 8 = 40$

$\dfrac{1}{5} - \dfrac{1}{8} = \dfrac{1}{5} \cdot \dfrac{8}{8} - \dfrac{1}{8} \cdot \dfrac{5}{5} = \dfrac{8}{40} - \dfrac{5}{40} = \dfrac{3}{40}$

d.

$81 = 3 \cdot 3 \cdot 3 \cdot 3$	Four factors of 3
$27 = 3 \cdot 3 \cdot 3$	Three factors of 3

The greatest number of times that 3 appears in any denominator is four times. So,

$\text{LCD} = 3 \cdot 3 \cdot 3 \cdot 3 = 81$

$\dfrac{5}{81} - \dfrac{1}{27} = \dfrac{5}{81} - \dfrac{1}{27} \cdot \dfrac{3}{3} = \dfrac{5}{81} - \dfrac{3}{81} = \dfrac{2}{81}$

e. $\text{LCD} = 7$

$3\dfrac{2}{7} = 3 + \dfrac{2}{7} = \dfrac{3}{1} \cdot \dfrac{7}{7} + \dfrac{2}{7} = \dfrac{21}{7} + \dfrac{2}{7} = \dfrac{23}{7}.$ A shortcut is

$3\dfrac{2}{7} = \dfrac{3 \cdot 7 + 2}{7} = \dfrac{21 + 2}{7} = \dfrac{23}{7}$

EXERCISE SET D.1

A

1 Give the numerator and denominator of each fraction.

1. $\dfrac{5}{6}$ **2.** $\dfrac{17}{12}$

Classify each of the following as a proper fraction, improper fraction, or a mixed number.

3. $\dfrac{9}{4}$ **4.** $\dfrac{1}{5}$ **5.** $1\dfrac{3}{4}$ **6.** $\dfrac{7}{1}$

Find the prime factorizations of the following; if one is a prime number, write "prime."

7. 12 **8.** 20 **9.** 17 **10.** 27

11. 75 **12.** 13 **13.** 54 **14.** 88

15. 96 **16.** 105 **17.** 144 **18.** 195

2 Reduce the following to lowest terms, if they are not already reduced.

19. $\dfrac{12}{22}$ **20.** $\dfrac{30}{36}$ **21.** $\dfrac{75}{27}$ **22.** $\dfrac{49}{21}$

23. $\dfrac{16}{25}$ **24.** $\dfrac{26}{39}$ **25.** $\dfrac{48}{32}$ **26.** $\dfrac{36}{12}$

27. $\dfrac{75}{25}$ **28.** $\dfrac{8}{64}$ **29.** $\dfrac{18}{144}$ **30.** $\dfrac{22}{81}$

3 Perform the indicated operations and simplify your answers.

31. $\dfrac{3}{4} \cdot \dfrac{5}{8}$ **32.** $\dfrac{6}{7} \cdot \dfrac{5}{9}$ **33.** $\dfrac{2}{3} \div \dfrac{5}{7}$

34. $\dfrac{12}{5} \cdot \dfrac{25}{18}$ **35.** $8 \cdot \dfrac{9}{20}$ **36.** $\dfrac{4}{5} \cdot \dfrac{5}{4}$

37. $\dfrac{25}{12} \div \dfrac{75}{32}$ **38.** $\dfrac{2}{7} \cdot \dfrac{5}{4} \cdot \dfrac{14}{13}$ **39.** $\dfrac{4}{6} \cdot \dfrac{3}{5} \cdot \dfrac{10}{9}$

40. $\dfrac{71}{98} \cdot \dfrac{98}{71}$ **41.** $\dfrac{1}{9} \div \dfrac{14}{18}$ **42.** $\dfrac{4}{9} \div 20$

4

43. $\dfrac{4}{7} + \dfrac{1}{7}$ **44.** $\dfrac{4}{7} - \dfrac{1}{7}$ **45.** $\dfrac{7}{8} - \dfrac{3}{8}$

46. $\dfrac{12}{17} - \dfrac{12}{17}$ **47.** $\dfrac{1}{4} + \dfrac{7}{6}$ **48.** $\dfrac{11}{12} - \dfrac{1}{18}$

49. $\dfrac{7}{15} - \dfrac{3}{20}$ **50.** $\dfrac{1}{27} + \dfrac{1}{12}$ **51.** $\dfrac{11}{6} - \dfrac{7}{5}$

52. $\dfrac{3}{8} - \dfrac{2}{9}$ **53.** $\dfrac{3}{2} + \dfrac{7}{10}$ **54.** $\dfrac{1}{16} + \dfrac{5}{8}$

55. $3 + \dfrac{1}{2}$ **56.** $2 - \dfrac{4}{3}$ **57.** $1\dfrac{5}{6} + \dfrac{1}{6}$

58. $2\dfrac{1}{3} + 3\dfrac{1}{2}$ **59.** $5\dfrac{2}{9} - 1\dfrac{1}{6}$ **60.** $\dfrac{14}{75} \div \dfrac{49}{20}$

61. $\dfrac{7}{8} \div \dfrac{14}{16}$ **62.** $1\dfrac{2}{3} \div \dfrac{10}{9}$ **63.** $12 \div 2\dfrac{3}{4}$

64. $1\dfrac{1}{6} \div 2\dfrac{1}{4}$ **65.** $\dfrac{5}{12} + \dfrac{1}{4} + \dfrac{1}{6}$ **66.** $\dfrac{4}{9} + \dfrac{5}{6} - \dfrac{1}{18}$

B

67. $\dfrac{1}{18} + \dfrac{5}{12} + \dfrac{1}{30}$ **68.** $\dfrac{1}{42} + \dfrac{1}{63} - \dfrac{1}{28}$

69. $\dfrac{3}{22} + \dfrac{2}{99} + \dfrac{5}{66}$ **70.** $\dfrac{5}{12} - \dfrac{1}{4} - \dfrac{1}{6}$

71. $\dfrac{3}{10} \cdot \dfrac{15}{49} \cdot \dfrac{14}{27}$ **72.** $\dfrac{77}{125} \cdot \dfrac{35}{22} \cdot \dfrac{10}{21}$

Solve the following word problems.

73. Pat paid $\dfrac{1}{8}$ of her Mastercard bill in May, $\dfrac{1}{6}$ in June, and $\dfrac{1}{4}$ in July. What portion of the bill was paid in these three months? What portion did she still owe?

74. The lengths of the three sides of a triangle in feet are $\dfrac{11}{12}$, $\dfrac{5}{6}$, and $\dfrac{7}{8}$. Find the total distance around the triangle.

75. Two opposite sides of a rectangle are each $\dfrac{7}{12}$ of a meter in length, and the other two sides are each $\dfrac{5}{9}$ of a meter in length. Find the total distance around the rectangle.

76. A 20-foot board is cut into four pieces. The lengths of three pieces are $2\dfrac{1}{2}$, $5\dfrac{2}{3}$, and $4\dfrac{1}{6}$ feet. Find the length of the fourth piece.

Appendix E: Geometric Formulas

RECTANGLE
Perimeter: $P = 2L + 2W$
Area: $A = LW$

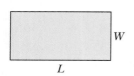

SQUARE
Perimeter: $P = 4s$
Area: $A = s^2$

TRIANGLE
Perimeter: $P = a + b + c$
Area: $A = \frac{1}{2}bh$

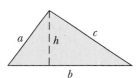

RIGHT TRIANGLE
Pythagorean Theorem: $c^2 = a^2 + b^2$

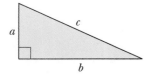

TRAPEZOID
Perimeter: $P = B + b + c + d$
Area: $A = \frac{1}{2}(B + b)h$

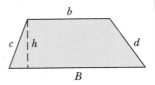

CIRCLE
Radius: r
Diameter: $d = 2r$
Circumference: $C = 2\pi r = \pi d$
Area: $A = \pi r^2$

$\pi \approx 3.14$ or $3\frac{1}{7}$

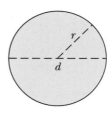

RECTANGULAR SOLID
Surface area: $S = 2LH + 2WH + 2LW$
Volume: $V = LWH$

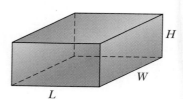

RIGHT CIRCULAR CYLINDER
Surface area: $S = 2\pi r^2 + 2\pi rh$
Volume: $V \ \pi r^2 h$

RIGHT CIRCULAR CONE
Surface Area: $S = \pi r^2 + \pi rs$
Volume: $V = \dfrac{1}{3}\pi r^2 h$

SPHERE
Surface area: $S = 4\pi r^2$
Volume: $V = \dfrac{4}{3}\pi r^3$

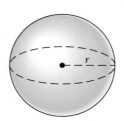

Answers to Odd-Numbered Exercises, Review Exercises, and Tests

CHAPTER 1

EXERCISE SET 1.1 (p. 7)

1. true   **3.** false   **5.** false   **7.** $4 < 6$ **9.** $5 \geq 5$
11. $14 > 0$ **13.** $>$ or $\geq$ **15.** $\leq$ or $\geq$ **17.** $10 \leq 12$
19. $30 < 40$ **21.** finite   **23.** infinite
25. $\{n \in N \mid n \leq 6\}$ **27.** $\{n \in N \mid 7 \leq n \leq 10\}$
29. $\{0, 1, 2, 3, 4\}$ **31.** $\emptyset$ **33.** $\{0, 7, 14, \ldots\}$
35. $\emptyset, \{x\}$ **37.** $\emptyset, \{7\}, \{8\}, \{7, 8\}$
39. $\emptyset, \{0\}, \{1\}, \{2\}, \{0, 1\}, \{0, 2\}, \{1, 2\}, \{0, 1, 2\}$
41. $\{2, 3, 5, 7, 8, 9\}$

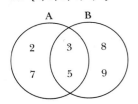

43. $\{3, 5, 8, 9, 2, 7\}$

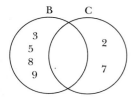

45. $C = \{2, 7\}$

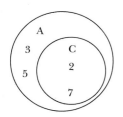

47. $\emptyset$

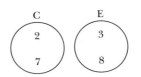

49. $\{2, 3, 5, 7, 8\}$

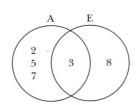

51.

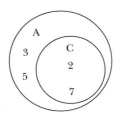

53. $\in$ **55.** $\nsubseteq$ **57.** $\subseteq$ **59.** $\notin$ **61.** $\nsubseteq$ **63.** false
65. true   **67.** true   **69.** true   **71.** true   **73.** false
75. true   **77.** true   **79.** true   **81.** true   **83.** false
85. A variable represents one or more numbers; a constant represents one number.
87. A finite set has a fixed number of elements; an infinite set has an unlimited number of elements.

EXERCISE SET 1.2 (p. 15)

1.

3.

−5   −1   1   3 4

5.

$-\frac{7}{6}$ $-\frac{1}{5}$ $\frac{1}{5}$ $\frac{4}{5}$

−1   0   1

7. <   **9.** >   **11.** <

13. True; −6 is to the left of 4 on the number line.

15. True; −3 is to the right of −7 on the number line.

17. False; −100 is to the left of −75 on the number line.

19. .35, terminating   **21.** $.17\overline{17}$ repeating

23. $-.018\overline{018}$, repeating   **25.** .7854   **27.** 2.2361

29. {8}   **31.** $\{8, -5, 0, .77, .7\overline{7}, -\frac{4}{11}, \frac{9}{2}\}$ **33.** Ø

35. $\mathbb{W}$ **37.** $\mathbb{R}$ **39.** Ø   **41.** False; $\mathbb{Q} \cap \mathbb{H} = $ Ø.

43. True; $\mathbb{N} \subseteq \mathbb{R}$.

45. True; $\mathbb{R} = \mathbb{Q} \cup \mathbb{H}$; if $x \in \mathbb{R}$ and $x \notin \mathbb{Q}$, then $x \in \mathbb{H}$.

47. False; $-8 = -\frac{8}{1}$, which is rational.

49. False; $\sqrt{2}$ is an irrational coordinate.   **51.** $\mathbb{Z}, \mathbb{Q}, \mathbb{R}$

53. $\mathbb{N}, \mathbb{W}, \mathbb{Z}, \mathbb{Q}, \mathbb{R}$ **55.** $\mathbb{H}, \mathbb{R}$ **57.** undefined

59. $\mathbb{Q}, \mathbb{R}$ **61.** true   **63.** true   **65.** true   **67.** false

69. false   **71.** false; $1 + 3 = 4 \notin \mathbb{F}$.

73. false; $7 - 8 = -1 \notin \mathbb{K}$.   **75.** true   **77.** −1; 1

79. .503; −1.988   **81.** $-\frac{7}{5}; \frac{5}{7}$ **83.** $\frac{11}{10}; -\frac{10}{11}$

85. closure   **87.** opposites   **89.** commutative

91. distributive   **93.** identity   **95.** associative

97. 1700   **99.** 0   **101.** undefined   **103.** 870

105. No; $2 + (3 \cdot 4) = 14$ and $(2 + 3) \cdot (2 + 4) = 30$.

107. No; $(a * b) * c \neq a * (b * c)$. Let $a = 2, b = 5$, and $c = 7$. Then $(2 * 5) * 7 = 11 * 7 = 40$ and $2 * (5 * 7) = 2 * 22 = 28$.

109. None exists.   **111.** None exists.

113. The natural numbers are a subset of the whole numbers, which are a subset of the integers, which are a subset of the rational numbers.

115. Terminating and repeating decimals are rational numbers, but nonterminating nonrepeating decimals are irrational numbers. All are real numbers.

117. associative   **118.** opposites   **119.** identity

120. associative   **121.** opposites   **122.** identity

EXERCISE SET 1.3 (p. 23)

1. subtraction   **3.** negative 4

5.

7.

−5   0 $|-5| = 5$

9. 30   **11.** −48   **13.** <   **15.** >   **17.** sometimes

19. sometimes   **21.** −15   **23.** 8535   **25.** −100

27. −10   **29.** −1.869   **31.** $-\frac{17}{12}$ **33.** −14

35. −1   **37.** $-\frac{43}{40}$ **39.** −1.06   **41.** 3   **43.** 9538

45. 18   **47.** −9   **49.** 0   **51.** $6x - 21$

53. $24abx - 15aby$ **55.** $6x - 14$ **57.** $5(a - b)$

59. $9x$ **61.** \$75   **63.** −15° F   **65.** 10,320

67. −\$550   **69.** 81 million years   **71.** $a = 5, b = 6$

73. $a = 1, b = 2, c = 0$

75. It must be true for all real numbers.

77. a. yes   **b.** no   **79. a.** yes   **b.** yes

81. yes, if $x > 0$. No, if $x \leq 0$.

83. multiplication property of $0, 0 \cdot C = 0$

84. opposites   **85.** distributive property

86. multiplication property of zero

87. opposites   **88.** distributive property

EXERCISE SET 1.4 (p. 32)

1. −12   **3.** −7   **5.** 0   **7.** −799,956   **9.** −5

11. 5   **13.** 0   **15.** −2   **17.** 25   **19.** 13

21. 49   **23.** −32   **25.** −1   **27.** 0   **29.** 22

31. $3\sqrt{3}$ **33.** $-6\sqrt{5}$ **35.** 8   **37.** 19   **39.** 13

41. −32   **43.** −16   **45.** 280   **47.** −28   **49.** $\frac{25}{3}$

51. undefined   **53.** 24   **55.** −5   **57.** −1   **59.** 4

61. −16   **63.** $\frac{8}{15}$ **65.** 0   **67.** −32   **69.** 4

71. −7   **73.** −2   **75.** $x + 5$ **77.** $30x$ **79.** $x > -6$

81. $x - 12$ **83.** $5x^2 - 7$ **85.** $2x + 3$ **87.** $4x + 8$

89. $5x - 3$ **91.** $x \leq -20$ **93.** $x, x + 2$

95. No, $2 \wedge 3 = 2^3 = 8$ but $3 \wedge 2 = 3^2 = 9$. No, $(2 \wedge 3) \wedge 2 = 8 \wedge 2 = 64$ but $2 \wedge (3 \wedge 2) = 2 \wedge 9 = 512$.

97. No real number has a negative square.

99. Division is defined in terms of multiplication.

CHAPTER REVIEW EXERCISES (p. 35)

1. $\{1, 2, 3, 5\}$

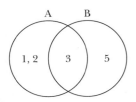

2. $\{3, 5, 4, 6\}$

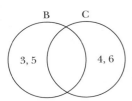

3. $\{3\}$

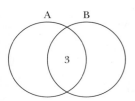

4. $\varnothing$

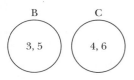

5. $\varnothing, \{w\}, \{x\}, \{y\}, \{w, x\}, \{w, y\}, \{x, y\}, \{w, x, y\}$
6. $\subseteq$ **7.** $\in$ **8.** $\notin$ **9.** $\not\subseteq$ **10.** $<$ **11.** $>$

12. $=$ **13.** $.24\overline{24}$, repeating **14.** 0.875, terminating
15. $\{0, 7\}$ **16.** $\{-8, 0, 7, \frac{3}{4}, 0.1, 0.11\}$
17. $\{\sqrt{7}, 0.1010010001\ldots\}$ **18.** $\mathbb{R}$ **19.** $\mathbb{N}$ **20.** $\mathbb{Z}$
21. $-\$15$ **22.** $13°\,C$ **23.** $x > x^2$ **24.** $4x - 8$
25. $\frac{2x}{-9}, -\frac{1}{9}(2x)$, or $(2x) \div (-9)$ **26.** $6(2x - 5)$
27. -16 **28.** -72 **29.** -72 **30.** $-\frac{2}{5}$ **31.** -14
32. -26 **33.** 1 **34.** -11 **35.** $\frac{17}{4}$ **36.** $\frac{\sqrt{26}}{2}$
37. $15\sqrt{3}$ **38.** -80 **39.** $\frac{55}{12}$ **40.** 1888

CHAPTER TEST (p. 36)

1. $\{0, 3, 5, 4\}$

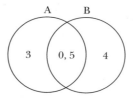

2. $\{0, 5\}$

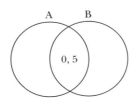

3. $\subseteq$ **4.** $\in$ **5.** $\notin$ **6.** $=$ **7.** $<$ **8.** $\{6, 0, -9\}$
9. $\{\pi, \sqrt{5}, .3738393103\ldots\}$
10. $\{6, 0, \frac{2}{3}, -9, 0.\overline{37}, 0.37\}$ **11.** $\$10,000$
12. $(n + 8)^2$ **13.** $2n + 6$ **14.** $n^2 - 4$ **15.** 40
16. 0 **17.** 20 **18.** -12 **19.** -12 **20.** 16
21. $-\sqrt{2} - 12$ **22.** undefined **23.** 11
24. $-31,768$ **25.** $\frac{11}{18}$

CHAPTER 2

EXERCISE SET 2.1 (p. 45)

1. $10x$ **3.** $-6t$ **5.** $3y^2 + y$ **7.** $2x + 19$
9. $2z + 12$ **11.** $5x^2 + 8x$ **13.** $12x + 3y$
15. $20x - 20$ **17.** -11 **19.** $\mathbb{R}$ **21.** $\varnothing$
23. $\{x \mid x \neq 0\}$ **25.** $\frac{5}{6}$ **27.** $-\frac{4}{9}$ **29.** -1

31. $\frac{2}{3}$ **33.** $-\frac{7}{3}$ **35.** $-\frac{8}{9}$ **37.** 8 **39.** $\mathbb{R}$ **41.** 16
43. $\mathbb{R}$ **45.** 0 **47.** $\varnothing$ **49.** $\frac{40}{9}$ **51.** 0 **53.** -12
55. $\frac{27}{2}$ **57.** 8 **59.** 20 **61.** -10 **63.** 15 **65.** $z = \frac{19}{3}$
67. $x = 1$
69. Like terms can be added or subtracted, but unlike terms cannot be added or subtracted.

71. Equivalent equations have the same solution.

73. 3   **74.** 6   **75.** -21

EXERCISE SET 2.2 (p. 52)

1. -2 **3.** -15 **5.** $\frac{34}{7}$ **7.** 9   **9.** $\frac{35}{12}$ **11.** $\frac{12}{5}$

13. $\frac{9}{16}$ **15.** $\frac{5}{8}$ **17.** $\frac{11}{7}$ **19.** 4000   **21.** $\frac{20}{3}$ **23.** -10

25. 2000   **27.** ± 9 **29.** $15, -1$ **31.** $-\frac{1}{2}, -\frac{1}{4}$

33. $4, \frac{2}{3}$ **35.** $5, -2$ **37.** -9 **39.** $\varnothing$ **41.** $16, -24$

43. ± 14 **45.** $\pm\frac{3}{4}$ **47.** $7, \frac{7}{3}$ **49.** $-1, \frac{1}{3}$ **51.** $-\frac{1}{2}$

53. 0   **55.** $\mathbb{R}$ **57.** $\frac{11}{25}$ **59.** $\frac{7}{33}$

61. $-\dfrac{133}{99}$ **63.** $\dfrac{3202}{999}$ **65.** $-\dfrac{1133}{900}$ **67.** $\dfrac{2678}{9999}$

69. $\frac{1}{2}(30 - L) = \frac{2}{3}L - 13$; $L = 24$

71. 17   **73.** $-12, -8$ **75.** $-30, -6$ **77.** $10, -2$

79. $13, 14, 15$ **81.** $-7, -5, -3$

83. $x + (x + 1) = 2(x + 2) - 3$, $2x + 1 = 2x + 1$, an identity

85. $x + (x + 1) = 2(x + 3)$, $2x + 1 = 2x + 6$, $1 = 6$, $\varnothing$

87. $\frac{14}{9}$ **89.** $\dfrac{2353}{1386}$ **91.** $\frac{1}{4}$ **93.** $\frac{3}{4}$

95. $.123456790123$

97. Let $x = $ the number. Multiply both sides of this equation by 10. Subtract the first equation from the second and solve for x.

98. 16   **99.** $\frac{22}{7}$ **100.** $-\frac{308}{9}$ **101.** $\frac{21}{2}$ **102.** -6

103. $-2\sqrt{3}$ **104.** $6\sqrt{2}$ **105.** 21

EXERCISE SET 2.3 (p. 62)

1. 144 miles   **3.** 10 mph   **5.** 70 miles

7. 12 centimeters   **9.** 252 square feet

11. $S = 616$ square inches, and

$V = \dfrac{4312}{3}$ cubic inches.   **13.** $y = -14$

15. $y = -9$ **17.** $p = 400$ **19.** $h = 5$ **21.** $F = 14°$

23. $x = \dfrac{y + 7}{3}$ **25.** $x = \dfrac{5y + 15}{3}$ **27.** $y = \dfrac{C - Ax}{B}$

29. $t = \dfrac{br}{a - b}$ **31.** $x = \dfrac{3a + 4b}{a - b}$ **33.** $F = \dfrac{9}{5}C + 32$

35. $y = \dfrac{ab - bx}{a}$ **37.** $a = \dfrac{K - 7 - b}{b}$ **39.** $a = \dfrac{D + bc}{d}$

41. $F = \dfrac{S - pS}{P}$ **43.** $x \pm 4$ **45.** $\pm 3\sqrt{2}$

47. $\pm\sqrt{10}$ **49.** ± 2 **51.** $c = 10$ **53.** $a = 2\sqrt{3}$

55. $b = 5$ **57.** $b = 15$ **59.** $c = 3\sqrt{2}, b = 3$

61. $a = b = 2\sqrt{2}$ **63.** $a = b = 5\sqrt{2}$

65. $b = 4\sqrt{3}, c = 8$ **67.** $a = 2\sqrt{3}, c = 4\sqrt{3}$

69. $a = 4, b = 4\sqrt{3}$ **71.** no   **73.** yes   **75.** no

77. 12 feet   **79.** $A = 400 - 100\pi$, $P = 80 - 20\pi$

81. $A = 24 + 25\pi$, $P = 12\pi$ **83.** 50 feet

85. a. $\sqrt{2}$ **b.** $\sqrt{3}$

87. A literal equation is an equation that contains more than one variable. A formula is a literal equation that describes a relationship in the physical world.

89. $16, 34$ **90.** $14, 76$ **91.** $13, 14, 15$ **92.** $6, 8, 10$

EXERCISE SET 2.4 (p. 71)

1. $W + (W - 160) = 2800$; $W = 1480$ **3.** 84

5. 6 feet   **7.** \$8.50   **9.** \$26

11. $58° + 32° = 90°$ and $32° = \frac{1}{2} \cdot 58° + 3°$

13. 5, 7, and 8 inches

15. $s = 2\sqrt{3}$ m, $p = 8\sqrt{3}$ m

17. $p = 36$ feet; 6 and 16 feet

19. 5 (square), 7 (triangle)   **21.** $35°, 70°$, and $75°$

23. $50°$ and $70°$ **25.** $38\frac{4}{7}°, 51\frac{3}{7}°$ **27.** $58\frac{1}{3}°, 121\frac{2}{3}°$

29. $40°, 50°$, and $140°$ **31.** $V = 27$ cubic centimeters, and $S = 54$ square centimeters.

33. $r = 2$ centimeters, $s = 12$ centimeters, $h = 2\sqrt{35}$ centimeters, and $V = \dfrac{8\pi\sqrt{35}}{3}$ cubic centimeters.

35. $1.5(r + 30) = 2(r - 30) + 35$; $r = 120$
$1.5(120 + 30) = 2(120 - 30) + 35 = 215$

37. 5:40   **39.** 8 hours   **41.** 10:53 A.M.   **43.** 3.5 hours

45. .1 hour; 1 mile   **47.** 225 seconds (P waves) and 400 seconds (S waves); 1800 kilometers

49. 250 mph   **51.** 3 mph   **53.** No; first integer $= 58°$.

55. $V = 72\pi$ cubic centimeters, and $S = (36 + 36\sqrt{2})\pi$.

57. Mark: 3 mph, 9 miles; Karen: 40 miles

59. When traveling with the wind (or current), the rate of travel increases. When traveling against the wind (or current), the rate of travel decreases.

60. $8500 - x$ **61.** $28 - 2n$ **62.** $4.16\overline{6}$ **63.** 6.25

64. 2.6   **65.** $3.3\overline{3}$

EXERCISE SET 2.5 (p. 80)

1. $1(28 - 2 \cdot 7) + 5 \cdot 7 + 10(7 + 2) = 14 + 35 + 90 = 139$

3. 7 dimes and 13 quarters

5. 3 packs of gum and 8 candy bars

7. 30 dimes and 18 quarters

9. 22 Haydn, 35 Beethoven, and 52 Mozart

11. Yes; 50 of each

13. 180 children, 150 adult, and 65 senior

15. $k + 13 = 18; 2(k + 9) = 18$

17. Son = 30, and Bob = 60.

19. Betty = 35; Al = 14.   **21.** 22

23. in 10 years   **25.** Tom = 12; George = 23

27. $1075 - .35(1075) = 698.75$

29. 9100%   **31.** 260%   **33.** $.16 = \frac{4}{25}$

35. $.027 = \frac{27}{1000}$ **37.** 4   **39.** 1.5%   **41.** 86%

43. 92%   **45.** $278   **47.** $64.78

49. $3700 at 9% and $6300 at 13%

51. $400 at 8% and $1200 at 15%

53. $6000 at 12% and $9000 at 5%

55. $2 \cdot 10 + 6(30) = 200$ and $5(10 + 30) = 200$

57. $.25(20 - 4) + 4 = 8$

59. 60 pounds of Delicious and 40 pounds of Jonathan

61. 20¢   **63.** 50 cc   **65.** $\frac{1}{3}$ gallon   **67.** 48 liters

69. 5 liters   **71.** 3 liters   **73.** 1.5 ounces

75. 120 men less than 30, 20 men more than 40, and 40 men between 30 and 40

77. $7000 at 8%, $14,000 at 9.25%, and $6000 at 16%

79. 30

81. (1) The amount of money invested at each rate and (2) the amount of interest earned at each rate

83. <   **84.** >   **85.** <   **86.** conditional equation

87. identity   **88.** false equation   **89.** {1, 2, 3, 5, 7, 9}

90. {3, 5, 7, 9}   **91.** {3}   **92.** Ø

EXERCISE SET 2.6 (p. 92)

1. (1, 3)

3. (−4, −1]

5. (−1, 1]

7. [−2, ∞)

9. (−∞, −4)

11. $-1 < x < 2$

13. $3 < x \leq 7$

15. $x \geq -2$

17. $x < -5$

19. >   **21.** >   **23.** >

25. $x > 4, (4, \infty)$

27. $x \geq 5, [5, \infty)$

29. $x > 3, (3, \infty)$

31. $x \geq -2, [-2, \infty)$

33. $t < -1, (-\infty, -1)$

35. $-1 < x < 2, (-1, 2)$

37. $-3 \leq x \leq 3, [-3, 3]$

39. $x < -2$ or $x > 3, (-\infty, -2) \cup (3, \infty)$

41. $x < 7, (-\infty, 7)$ **43.** $y \geq 5, [5, \infty)$

45. $\mathbb{R}, (-\infty, \infty)$ **47.** $-4 < x < 5, (-4, 5)$

49. $1 < x < 3, (1, 3)$ **51.** $-28 \leq t < 16, [-28, 16)$

53. $y \geq -1, [-1, \infty)$ **55.** $x > \frac{14}{15}, \left(\frac{14}{15}, \infty\right)$

57. $p \leq 8$ **59.** $r \geq 650$ **61.** $d \leq 20$

63. $45 \leq r \leq 50$ **65.** $77° < F < 95°$

67. $14.25 \leq MA \leq 24.75$ **69.** 16, 18, 20

71. $\mathbb{Z}$ **73.** more than 1.5 hours

75. at least 75%   **77.** 6 feet, 12 feet, and 17 feet

79. $17,500   **81.** 7 hours   **83.** 2

85. more than $12,000

87. Option B is cheaper for all mileages.

89. at least 18 years old

91.

93.

95. The solution set of a conditional linear inequality is an interval containing an infinite number of real numbers. The solution set of a conditional linear equation is *one* number.

97. The graph of an open interval does not contain its endpoints, whereas the graph of a closed interval contains its endpoints.

99. 3   **100.** 4   **101.** 4   **102.** 3   **103.** $x = 3, -3$

104. $y = 6, -6$ **105.** $\emptyset$ **106.** $x = 4, -8$

107. $x = \frac{5}{2}, -\frac{5}{2}$ **108.** $x = \frac{3}{2}, -\frac{1}{2}$

EXERCISE SET 2.7 (p. 98)

1. $-2 < x < 2$

3. $-4 \le x \le 4$

5. $-10 \le x \le 2$

7. $x > 2$ or $x < -2$

9. $t > 0$ or $t < 0$

11. $x < -4$ or $x > 6$

13. $-3 \le x \le 3, [-3, 3]$

15. $x \ge 2$ or $x \le -2, (-\infty, -2] \cup [2, \infty)$

17. $\mathbb{R}, (-\infty, \infty)$ **19.** $[-3, 4]$ **21.** $(-\infty, 2) \cup (2, \infty)$

23. $\emptyset$ **25.** ± 5 **27.** $5, -\frac{13}{3}$ **29.** $k = \frac{3}{4}$ **31.** $\emptyset$

33. $\left(-\frac{7}{3}, \frac{5}{3}\right)$ **35.** $\emptyset$ **37.** $(-7, 5)$

39. $\left(-\infty, -\frac{1}{3}\right] \cup [1, \infty)$ **41.** $(-\infty, -7] \cup [-1, \infty)$

43. $\left(-\frac{3}{2}, \frac{5}{2}\right)$ **45.** $\left(-\infty, -\frac{16}{3}\right] \cup \left[\frac{20}{3}, \infty\right)$

47. $6, 2$ **49.** $|x| < 5, -5 < x < 5$

51. $|x - 3| > 8, x < -5$ or $x > 11$

53. $|x| \le 9$ **55.** $|x| > 7$ **57.** $|x - 1| < 3$

59. $|x + 1| \ge 5$ **61.** $-3 < x < 3$

63. $|x| < 4$ is the set of all numbers whose distance from zero is less than 4—that is, all numbers between -4 and 4.

65. The solution set of $|x| < 3$ is all numbers greater than -3 and less than 3. The solution set of $|x| \le 3$ is all numbers greater than or equal to -3 and less than or equal to 3.

CHAPTER REVIEW EXERCISES (p. 100)

1. $2x + 1$ **2.** $4 - 15y$ **3.** $\frac{32}{15}$ **4.** $\frac{49}{333}$ **5.** $d = 10$

6. $x = \dfrac{3y + 18}{2}$ **7.** $a = t - 2$ **8.** $x = -3$ **9.** $x = 3$

10. $x = 8$ **11.** $k = 1$ **12.** $m = -\frac{3}{2}$ **13.** $x = \pm\sqrt{19}$

14. $y = -10$ **15.** $x = \pm 4$ **16.** $y = -3, \frac{19}{5}$

17. $x = 3, -1$ **18.** 10   **19.** 6   **20.** 36

21. $21, 16$ **22.** $-8, -7, -6$

23. $(-\infty, 4]$

24. $[-3, 2)$

25. $(-\infty, 7]$ **26.** $\left[\frac{4}{5}, \frac{21}{5}\right]$ **27.** $[-3, 6]$ **28.** $(-\infty, 5)$

29. $\left(-\infty, -\frac{15}{4}\right] \cup [2, \infty)$ **30.** $\emptyset$ **31.** $(-\infty, \infty)$

32. $38.9° \le C \le 42.2°$ **33.** $6, 6\sqrt{3}$ **34.** $27°, 63°$

35. $r = \frac{13}{8}$ square inches, and $V = \frac{2197}{512}\pi$ cubic inches.

36. square: 9 square meters; rectangle: 21 square meters

37. 65 mph   **38.** 8 mph   **39.** 87

40. 8 nickels and 14 dimes

41. Michele is 18, and Steve is 20.

42. \$179   **43.** 25 kilograms of A and 50 kilograms of B

CHAPTER TEST (p. 102)

1. $y = \dfrac{-5x + 15}{3}$ **2.** $f = \dfrac{4V + 4L}{3L}$

3. $(-3, \infty)$

4. $(1, 4]$

5. 5

6. $(-\infty, \infty)$

7. 9   **8.** $\frac{4}{3}$

9. -1 **10.** $3, -\frac{7}{3}$ **11.** $-\frac{1}{2}$

12. $\left(-\infty, -\frac{5}{3}\right] \cup [3, \infty)$

13. $\left[-\frac{6}{5}, \frac{4}{5}\right]$

14. $\frac{4}{11}$ **15.** 4 half-dollars and 20 quarters

16. 11 years old   **17.** 8 hours   **18.** 1.5 hours

19. $x = 1, \frac{1}{2}$ **20.** \$21,000   **21.** 20 liters

22. 2.25 liters   **23.** $42°, 62°,$ and $76°$ **24.** $3\sqrt{2}$

25. $60°$ and $120°$

Chapter 3

EXERCISE SET 3.1 (p. 111)

1. $(5, 0)$ **3.** $(1, 4)$ **5.** $(-5, 3)$ **7.** $(-3, 0)$
9. $(-2, -4)$ **11.** $(2, -1)$

13.

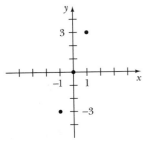

15.

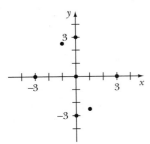

17. yes   **19.** no   **21.** yes   **23.** $\{(0, 1), (\frac{1}{3}, 0), (-2, 7)\}$
25. $\{(-2, 3), (0, 3), (4, 3)\}$ **27.** $\{(0, -2), (3, 0), (5, \frac{4}{3})\}$
29. $x = 1, y = -3$

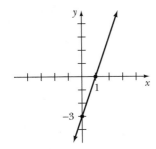

31. $x = 5, y = 4$

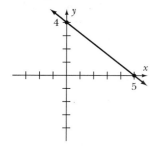

33. $x = -4$

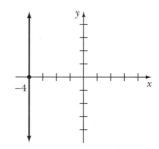

35. $x = -\dfrac{5}{3}, y = 1$

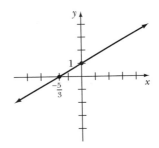

37.

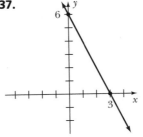

39.

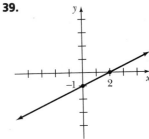

41.

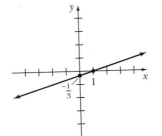

43.

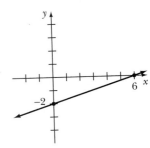

45.
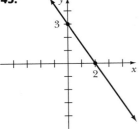

47.
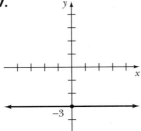

65.
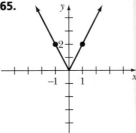

67.
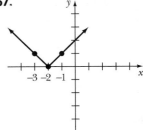

49.
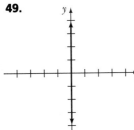

51.
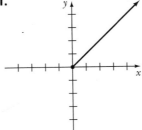

69.
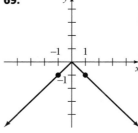

71.
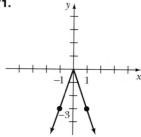

53.
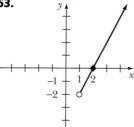

55.
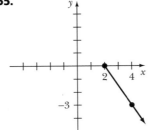

73.
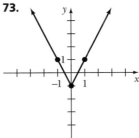

75.
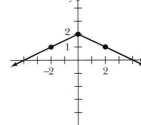

57.
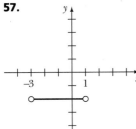

59.
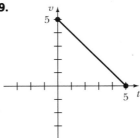

77.
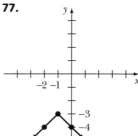

79.
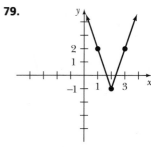

61.
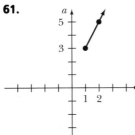

63.
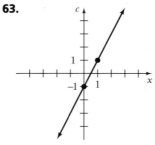

81. Descartes began with a curve and looked for its equation. Fermat started with an equation and found its graph.

EXERCISE SET 3.2 (p. 118)

1. D = {4, 8}, R = {7, 3}

3. D = {1, −2, 3}, R = {9, 0, 3}

5. D = {3, −3, 2}, R = {9}

7. D = {0, −2, −1, 1, 2}, R = {1, 5, 2}

9. D = R = (−∞, ∞)

11. D = (−∞, ∞), R = [0, ∞)

13. D = [2, ∞), R = [0, ∞)

15. {x | x ≠ 4} **17.** ℝ **19.** {t | t ≤ 4} **21.** {x | x > 3}

23. function; D = {−2, −1, 4}, R = {2, 4, −3}

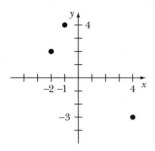

25. function; D = {−2, −1, 0, 1}, R = {2, 1, 0}

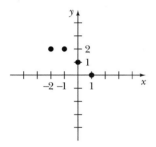

27. not a function; D = {0, 1, 4}, R = {0, 1, −1, 2, −2}

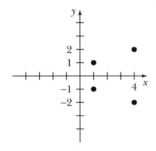

29. function; D = R = (−∞, ∞}

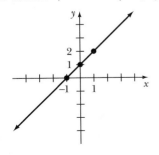

31. not a function; D = {4}, R = ℝ

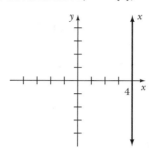

33. true; y = x + 1 **35.** false; f(x) = 3 **37.** 6

39. 16 **41.** 1 **43.** −5 **45.** −3x − 3h + 2

47. −16 **49.** −$\frac{1}{9}$ **51.** undefined **53.** −2x + 4

55. **57.**

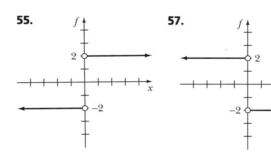

59. **61.**

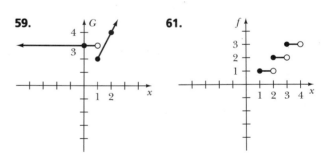

63. **65.**

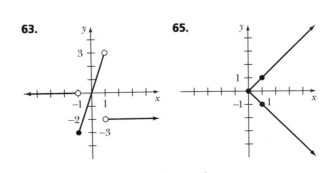

67. 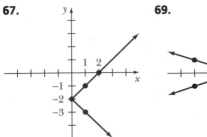 **69.**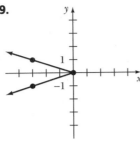

9. $3\sqrt{2}$

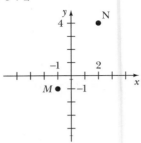

71. A relation is any set of ordered pairs. A function is a relation such that exactly one element exists in the range for a given element in the domain.

73. A piecewise function is a function that is defined by different rules over different parts of its domain.

75. The function f tells us to multiply x by 2 and then add 1 to this result.

11. 6

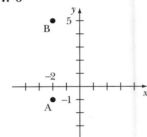

77. 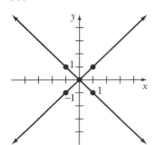 **79.**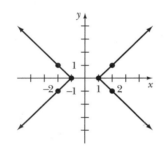

13. $\sqrt{85}$

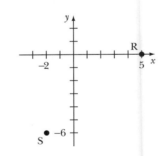

80. 40   **81.** $5\sqrt{5}$ **82.** $2\sqrt{2}$ **83.** $c = 5$
84. $c = \sqrt{125}$ **85.** $c = \sqrt{48}$

EXERCISE SET 3.3 (p. 124)

1.
$$\begin{array}{c} A \qquad\qquad B \\ \bullet \qquad\qquad \bullet \\ 0 \qquad\qquad 8 \end{array}$$
a. 8   **b.** 8

15. 3

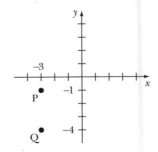

3.
$$\begin{array}{c} A \qquad\qquad B \\ \bullet \qquad\qquad \bullet \\ -1 \qquad\qquad 4 \end{array}$$
a. 5   **b.** 5

5.
$$\begin{array}{c} A \qquad\qquad B \\ \bullet \qquad\qquad \bullet \\ -6 \qquad\qquad -1 \end{array}$$
a. 5   **b.** 5

7. 5

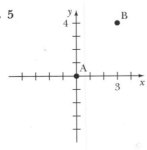

17. $\frac{4}{3}$ **19.** $-\frac{7}{6}$ **21.** 0   **23.** -1 **25.** undefined
27. $-\frac{1}{2}$ **29.** undefined   **31.** $\frac{5}{4}$ **33.** 2   **35.** 1
37. -1 **39.** undefined   **41.** $\frac{6}{5}$ **43.** 2   **45.** 3
47. -3 **49.** 2

51. Yes; $p = 8 + 8\sqrt{3}$.

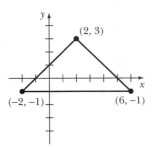

53. No; $p = 11 + \sqrt{13}$.

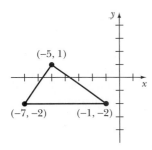

55. A(2, 6), B(3, 2), C(−1, 3); $d(A, B) = d(B, C) = \sqrt{17}$

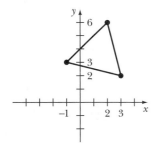

57. $D = \{(x, y) \mid x, y \in \mathbb{R}\}, R = [0, \infty)$

59. $D(A, B) = \mid x_2 - x_1 \mid + \mid y_2 - y_1 \mid$;
$D(A, B) = \mid 10 - 6 \mid + \mid 5 - 3 \mid = \mid 4 \mid + \mid 2 \mid = 6$
$D(B, A) = \mid 6 - 10 \mid + \mid 3 - 5 \mid = \mid -4 \mid + \mid -2 \mid = 6$

61. Because $(\mid x_2 - x_1 \mid)^2 = x_2 - x_1$ and $(\mid y_2 - y_1 \mid)^2 = y_2 - y_1$.

63. The change in x for two points on a vertical line is zero. Because the slope of a line is the change in y divided by the change in x, we would be dividing by zero, which is undefined.

64.

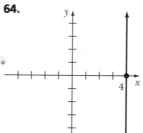

65.

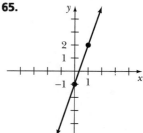

66.

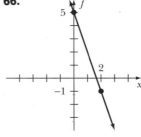

67. $2x + 5$ **68.** $2x + 2$ **69.** $2x − 1 + h$
70. $2x + 2h − 1$ **71.** $−2x + 1$ **72.** $2h$
73. $−7 − 3h$ **74.** 7 **75.** $−3h$

EXERCISE SET 3.4 (p. 132)
 1. $y − 2 = 3(x − 1)$

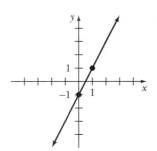

3. $y + 4 = −2(x + 6)$

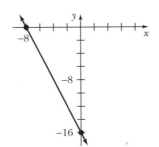

5. $y - 2 = \frac{1}{2}x$

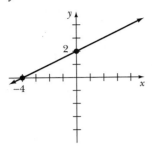

7. $y - 1 = 2(x - 2)$ **9.** $y - 4 = \frac{5}{3}(x - 1)$

11. $y + 3 = 3(x - 0)$

13. $y = 3x + 2$

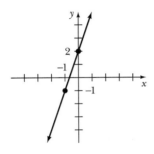

15. $y = -x - 5$

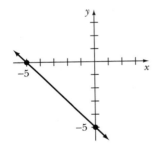

17. $y = -\frac{1}{2}x + 3$

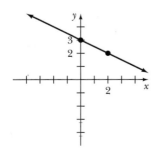

19. $y = 2x - 3$ **21.** $y = -4x - 8$

23. $y = \frac{8}{7}x - \frac{18}{7}$ **25.** $y - 1 = \frac{7}{6}(x - 1)$ **27.** $y = 4$

29. $y = -\frac{1}{2}x - 2$ **31.** $x = 2$ **33.** $x = -3$

35. $y = -8x - 3$ **37.** 3   **39.** 0   **41.** $\frac{1}{2}$ **43.** 6

45. 1   **47.** parallel   **49.** neither

51. perpendicular   **53.** parallel

55. a. $2x - y = 5$ **b.** $x + 2y = 5$

57. a. $x + y = -5$ **b.** $x - y = 3$

59. a. $x = 4$ **b.** $y = -2$

61. a. $y - 6 = 3(x + 3)$ **b.** $y - 6 = -\frac{1}{3}(x + 3)$

63. a. $y = 3$ **b.** $x = 4$

65. a. $y = -\frac{1}{5}x - 4$ **b.** $y = 5x - 4$

67. Yes; for the graph, see Section 3.3, Exercise 51.

69. No; for the graph, see Section 3.3, Exercise 53.

71. a. \$85   **b.** 13   **73.** \$35.14   **75.** 4   **77.** 6

79. The answer will vary depending on your college.

81. First find the slope, m, by dividing the change in y by the change in x. If (x_1, y_1) is one of the points, then the point–slope form of the equation is $y - y_1 = m(x - x_1)$.

83.

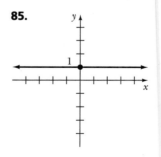

84.

85.

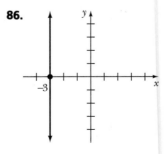

86.

EXERCISE SET 3.5 (p. 139)

1.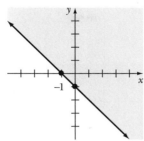

3.

17.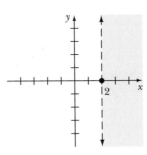

19.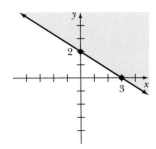

5.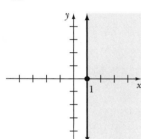

7.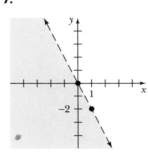

21.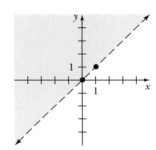

23.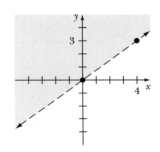

9.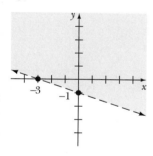

11.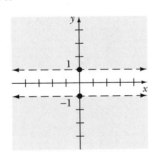

25.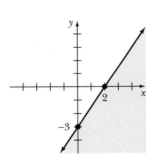

27.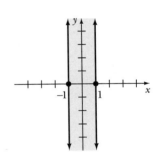

13.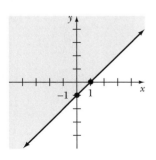

15.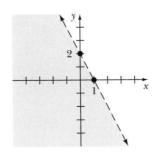

29.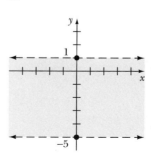

31.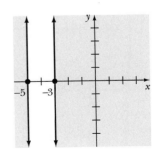

33. a.

33. b.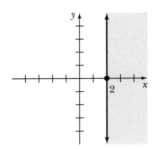

35. a.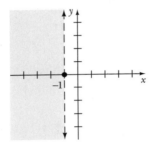

35. b.

37. a.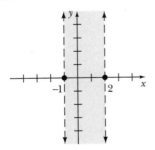

37. b.

39. a.

39. b.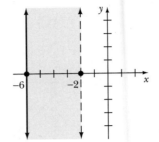

41.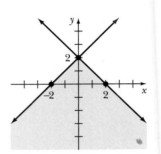

43.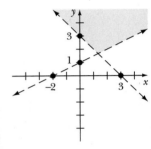

45.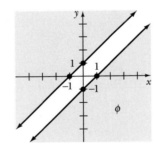

47.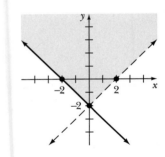

49.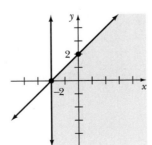

51.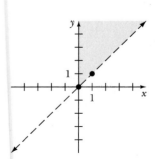

53.

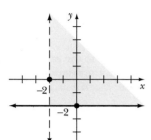

55.

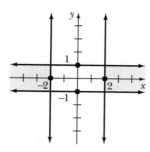

57.

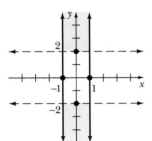

59.

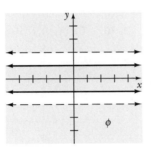

61.

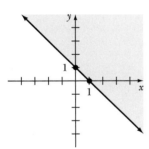

63.

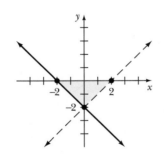

65. First graph the corresponding equation as a solid line if the inequality is $\leq$ or $\geq$. If it is $<$ or $>$, then graph the equation as a broken line. Next pick a point not on the line, the test point. If the test point makes the inequality a true statement, then shade that side of the line. If it makes the inequality a false statement, then shade the other side of the line.

67. function; D = {1, −3, 6, −4}, R = {5, 7, 8}

68. not a function; D = {6, 7, −9, 6}, R = {−8, 2, 0, 2}

69. [−2, 2)   **70.** (−∞, 4)   **71.** [−3, ∞)   **72,** $y = \dfrac{x + 4}{2}$

73. $y = \dfrac{3x - 1}{2}$ **74.** $y = \dfrac{4x + 1}{3}$

75. $y = \dfrac{12x - 9}{2}$ **76.** $y = \dfrac{1}{x - 4}$ **77.** $y = \dfrac{5x + 1}{2 - x}$

EXERCISE SET 3.6 (p. 145)

1. $S^{-1} = \{(-2, 0), (-1, 1), (1, 2)\}$

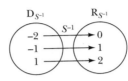

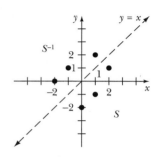

3. $U^{-1} = \{2, 4), (3, 4), (2, 1)\}$

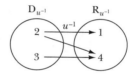

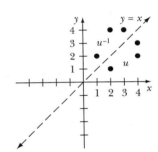

5. $f^{-1} = \{(1, -3), (3, 0), (-2, 1)\}$

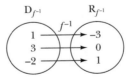

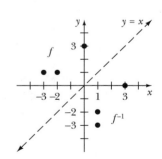

7. $D_{s^{-1}} = \{9, -6, 8\}$, $R_{s^{-1}} = \{1, 7, -4\}$

9. $D_{s^{-1}} = [2, 9]$, $R_{s^{-1}} = [-1, 5]$

11. $R_{f^{-1}} = [1, 3]$, $D_{f^{-1}} = [2, 6]$

13. $R_{f^{-1}} = (0, 2]$, $R_{f} = (-5, 0]$

15. $R_f = (-\infty, -1]$, $D_f = [-1, 0)$ **17.** true

19. False; if the temperature is less than 50° F, then it is snowing.

21. true   **23.** true   **25.** function

27. one-to-one function   **29.** one-to-one function

31. neither

33. $f^{-1}(x) = \frac{1}{2}x$

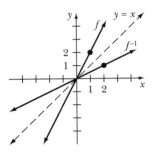

35. $h^{-1}(x) = x - 1$

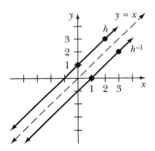

37. $2y + 3x = 6$

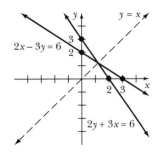

39. $f^{-1}(x) = \frac{3x - 3}{2}$

41. $f^{-1}(x) = \frac{4}{3}x + \frac{10}{9}$ **43.** $f^{-1}(x) = \frac{1}{x}$

45. $S^{-1} = \{(x, y) \mid x = 5\}$

47. $U^{-1} = \{(x, y) \mid x = 3y\}$

49. $f^{-1}(x) = \dfrac{x - b}{m}$ **51.** $f^{-1}(x) = \dfrac{x + 3}{4x + 2}$

53. $h^{-1}(x) = \dfrac{b - dx}{cx - m}$

55. The domain of the relation is equal to the range of the inverse relation. The range of the relation is equal to the domain of the inverse relation.

57. "If today is Friday, then tomorrow is Saturday," and "If tomorrow is Saturday, then today is Friday."

59. The function g^{-1} tells us to multiply x by 4 and then add 6 to this result.

CHAPTER REVIEW EXERCISES (p. 148)

1. $(0, -5), (7, 9), (4, 3)$

2. $(0, -6), (4, 0), (8, 6)$

3. $x = 2, y = -6$

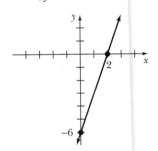

4. $x = 4, y = 3$

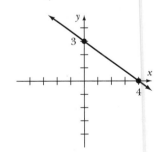

5. $y = 3$

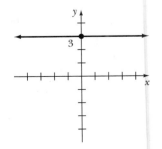

6.

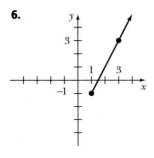

7. $D_f = (-\infty, \infty)$, $R_f = [4, \infty)$

8. $D = [3, \infty)$

9. $D = \{x \mid x \neq -3\}$

10.

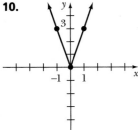

11.

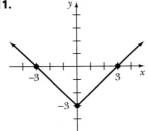

12.

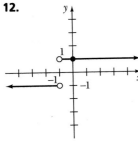

13.

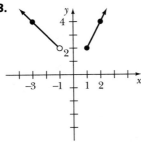

14.

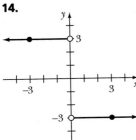

15.

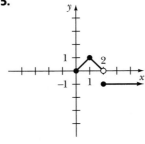

16. a. $d = 2\sqrt{5}$ **b.** $m = 2$

17. a. $d = 5$ **b.** undefined

18. a. $d = 2\sqrt{10}$ **b.** $m = -\frac{1}{3}$

19. $y - 5 = -\frac{8}{3}(x + 2)$

20. $y = 2x + 4$, $-2x + y = 4$ **21.** $y = -1$

22. $x = 1$ **23.** $y + 4 = -\frac{3}{4}(x - 5)$

24. $y + 4 = -2(x - 1)$

25. No, they are not.   **26.** -4

27.

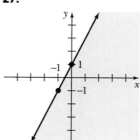

28.

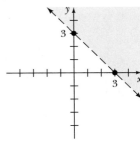

29.

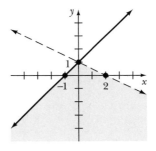

30.

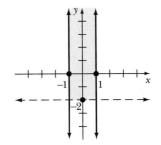

31. function; $S^{-1} = \{(16, -2), (1, 1), (16, 2)\}$;
$D_S = R_{S^{-1}} = \{-2, 1, 2\}$;
$R_S = D_{S^{-1}} = \{16, 1\}$

32. one-to-one function; $S^{-1} = \{(-8, -2), (1, 1), (8, 2), (27, 3)\}$; $D_S = R_{S^{-1}} = \{-2, 1, 2, 3\}$; $R_S = D_{S^{-1}} = \{-8, 1, 8, 27\}$

33. $f^{-1}(x) = \dfrac{x + 1}{2}$

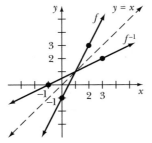

34. $g^{-1}(x) = -3x + 6$

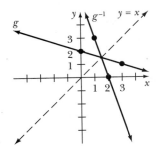

CHAPTER TEST (p. 149)

1. $f^{-1}(x) = \dfrac{x-1}{2}$

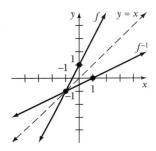

2. $g^{-1} = \{(1, -3), (2, 0), (4, 1)\}$

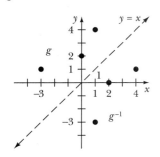

3. $D = \{x \mid x \neq 4\}$ **4.** $D = (-\infty, 2]$

5.

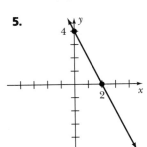

6.

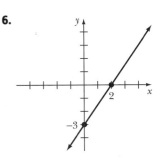

7.

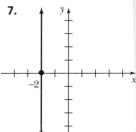

8.

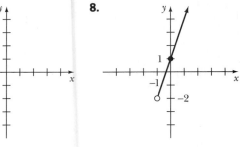

9.

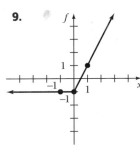

10.

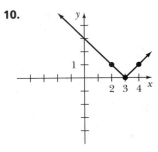

11.

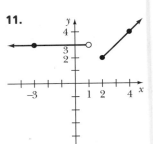

12.

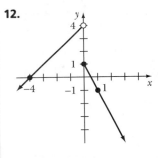

13. a. $d = 3\sqrt{5}$ **b.** $m = 2$ **14. a.** $d = 4$ **b.** $m = 0$

15. no; $d(A, C) = \sqrt{68}, d(A, B) = \sqrt{17}, d(B, C) = \sqrt{53}$;
    $68 \neq 17 + 5$

16. no; $m_{AB} = \frac{1}{4}, m_{BC} = -\frac{7}{2}, m_{AB}m_{BC} \neq -1$

17. 7   **18.** $x = -2$ **19.** $y - 1 = \frac{2}{7}(x + 1)$

20. $y - 3 = -\frac{3}{2}(x + 5)$

21. $y + 7 = \frac{5}{4}(x + 6)$

22.

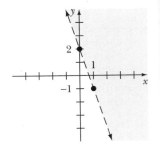

23.

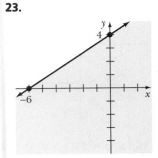

24.

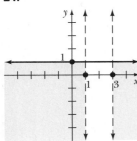

25.

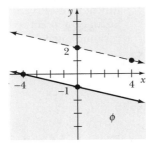

14. $\{9, 0, -5, \frac{3}{4}, .\overline{23}, .23\}$ [1.2]

15. $\{\sqrt{3}, .2324252627\ldots\}$ [1.2]   **16.** $\{9, 0, -5\}$ [1.2]

17. $\{9\}$ [1.2]   **18. a.** $\frac{4}{5}$ **b.** $-\frac{5}{4}$ [1.2]

19. 3 [2.3]   **20.** $\sqrt{65}$ [3.3]   **21.** $-\frac{7}{4}$ [3.3]

22. $y - 5 = -\frac{7}{4}(x + 1)$ [3.4]   **23.** $-\frac{3}{2}$ [3.4]

24.

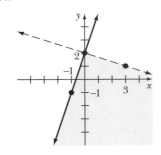

CUMULATIVE REVIEW: Chapters 1–3 (p. 150)

1. 11 [1.4]   **2.** $\frac{74}{3}$ [1.4]   **3.** 58 [1.4]   **4.** $\frac{3}{5}$ [2.1]

5. $5, -\frac{13}{3}$ [2.2]   **6.** $a = \dfrac{T - 3bc}{2b + 4c}$ [2.3]

7. $(-\infty, -1]$ [2.6]

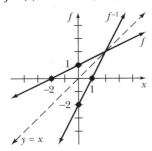

8. $y = 13$ [2.2]   **9.** 13 [3.2]   **10.** $\{x \mid x \neq \pm 2\}$ [3.2]

11. $\{1, 2, 3, 4\}$ [1.1]   **12.** $\{3\}$ [1.1]

13. $f^{-1}(x) = 2x - 2$ [3.6]

25. Ted $= 30$, Sharon $= 10$ [2.5]

26. $r = 3, h = 6$ [2.3]   **27.** between -5 and 3 [2.6]

28. The rate of car B can be any nonnegative value. [2.4]

29. 5 liters [2.5]

30. Mt. McKinley $= 20,320$ feet, Mt. Shasta $= 14,160$ feet [2.4]

CHAPTER 4

EXERCISE SET 4.1 (p. 160)

1. $(-1, 3)$

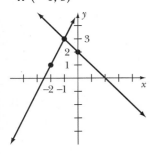

3. $y = -2x + 4$

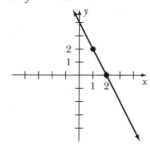

5. $\varnothing$

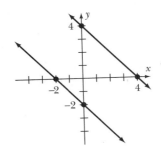

7. $(-1, 3)$ **9.** $x - 2y = 2$ **11.** Ø **13.** Ø

15. $(7, -1)$ **17.** $(3, -4)$ **19.** $2x - 4y = 8$

21. $\left(\frac{3}{38}, \frac{5}{19}\right)$ **23.** $(-2, -10)$ **25.** Ø

27. $(11, 7)$ **29.** $\left(\frac{1}{2}, \frac{3}{4}\right)$ **31.** $3x - 5y = -2$ **33.** $(1, 1)$

35. $(2, -4)$ **37.** $(-1, 2)$ **39.** $(0, 1)$ **41.** $(1, 1)$

43. $(4, 0)$ **45.** $(2000, 5000)$ **47.** $(6, 2)$ **49.** $(19, -25)$

51. In general, the answers are not integers.

53. When we solve the system we obtain a true equation, $a = a$. The graphs of the two equations produce the same line.

55. Let $L =$ the larger number; $L = (42 - L) + 6$.

56. Let $q =$ the number of quarters; $25q + 10(q + 6) = 305$.

57. Let $r =$ the speed of his plane in still air; $2(r + 32) = 314$.

EXERCISE SET 4.2 (p. 167)

1. $p = 82, s = 168$.

$\quad\quad s = 2p + 4 \quad\quad$ and $\quad\quad s + p = 250$
$\quad 168 = 2 \cdot 82 + 4 \quad\quad\quad 168 + 82 = 250$

3. $\{9, -6\}$ **5.** $\frac{5}{11}$ **7.** $\{12, 7\}$

9. Leeann has \$36, Amy has \$18.

11. He has 8 nickels and 19 dimes.

13. She has 12 pennies and 8 dimes.

15. He has 8 nickels and 12 dimes.

17. \$12,000 at $8\frac{1}{4}\%$, \$4000 at $11\frac{1}{2}\%$

19. a. \$13,780 **b.** \$19,560 **c.** $x = 100$

21. $P(x) = 37x - 3700, P(250) = \$5550$

23. Four pounds of pecans are needed; 10 pounds of nuts are in the mixture.

25. 6 liters of 5%, 14 liters of 15%

27. 14 gallons of water; 84 gallons

29. $s = 6, t = 8$; $\quad t = s + 2 \quad$ and $\quad 3t = 4s$
$\quad\quad\quad\quad\quad\quad\quad 8 = 6 + 2 \quad\quad\quad 3 \cdot 8 = 4 \cdot 6$

31. $8, 15$ **33.** $60°, 120°$ **35.** $16°, 74°$ **37.** $48°, 110°$

39. $r = 125, w = 32$.

$\quad 2(r + w) = 314 \quad$ and $\quad 3(r - w - 10) + 65 = 314$
$2(125 + 32) = 314 \quad\quad 3(125 - 32 - 10) + 65 = 314$

41. car: 210 miles; truck: 140 miles

43. speed of the river $= 3$ mph; speed of the boat $= 5$ mph

45. cutter's speed $= 30$ km/h; tide's rate $= 6$ km/h

47. Ted is 18, and Nancy is 12.

49. David's check $= \$700$, and Sarah's check $= \$500$.

51. When a company produces x items, $C(x)$ is the cost function and $R(x)$ is the revenue function. The break-even point is the value of x such that the revenue equals the cost; that is, $R(x) = C(x)$.

52. $x = y = 3$ **53.** $x = 2, y = 4$

54. $9x - 3y - 12z = -15$

55. $-x - 3y + 2z = 0$ **56.** $9x + 2y = 7$

57. $d + 4q = 17$

EXERCISE SET 4.3 (p. 175)

1. 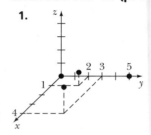 **3.**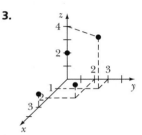

5. 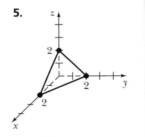 **7.**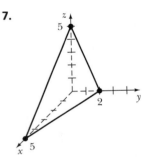

9.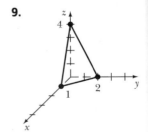

11. $(1, -1, 2)$ **13.** $(-9, -2, 5)$ **15.** Ø

17. $(0, 0, 0)$ **19.** infinitely many solutions

21. $(2, 3, -5)$ **23.** Ø **25.** $\left(\frac{1}{2}, \frac{1}{3}, \frac{1}{4}\right)$ **27.** $\left(-1, \frac{3}{2}, \frac{1}{2}\right)$

29. $(2, 3, -4)$

31. $n = 2, d = 5, q = 3$;

$\quad n + d + q = 10 \quad\quad\quad\quad 2 + 5 + 3 = 10$
$\quad\quad 0 + d - q = 2 \quad\quad\quad\quad\quad 5 - 3 = 2$
$\quad n + 2d + 5q = 27 \quad\quad 2 + 2 \cdot 5 + 5 \cdot 3 = 27$

33. First number $= -12$, second $= 15$, and third $= 20$.

35. Shortest side $= 22$ centimeters, second side $= 32$ centimeters, and third side $= 44$ centimeters.

37. $20°, 70°, 90°$

39. She has 8 pennies, 6 nickels, and 7 quarters.

41. 2000 at 7%, 5000 at 8%, and 9000 at 10%

43. He used 14 pounds of peanuts, 6 pounds of cashews, and 10 pounds of walnuts.

45. $(2, 1, 3, -1)$ **47.** $(-1, 0, 2, 1)$

49. A linear equation in three variables represents a plane in space. Thus, three such equations represent three planes.

51. $\left(-\frac{1}{38}, -\frac{8}{19}\right)$ **52.** $2x - 4y = 6$ **53.** $\emptyset$

EXERCISE SET 4.4 (p. 182)

1. $\begin{bmatrix} 3 & 1 & \vdots & 2 \\ 2 & -1 & \vdots & 0 \end{bmatrix}$

3. $\begin{array}{l} x + 3y = 5 \\ \quad\ 4y = -3 \end{array}$ **5.** $(6, 1)$ **7.** $3x - 6y = 12$

9. $\left(\frac{1}{2}, -1\right)$ **11.** $(-3, 7)$ **13.** $(4, -1)$

15. $\begin{bmatrix} 2 & 3 & -1 & \vdots & 2 \\ 1 & 4 & 7 & \vdots & 1 \\ 3 & -2 & 1 & \vdots & 0 \end{bmatrix}$

17. $\begin{array}{l} 3x + 2y + z = 5 \\ \quad\quad\ x - z = 8 \\ \quad x - 7y + 4z = 6 \end{array}$

19. $(1, 2, -1)$ **21.** $\emptyset$ **23.** $(3, 1, 2)$ **25.** $(3, -2, 1)$

27. $\left(2, \frac{1}{3}, 4\right)$

29 and 31: See the answer section for Section 4.3.

33. A 3×3 matrix has three rows and three columns.

35. -8 **36.** 10 **37.** -20 **38.** -2

EXERCISE SET 4.5 (p. 189)

1. 5 **3.** 18 **5.** 7 **7.** 0 **9.** 25 **11.** 0

13. $x^2 + 6$ **15.** $-x - y$ **17.** abc **19.** $\frac{10}{3}$

21. ± 3 **23.** 2 **25.** $(2, 3)$ **27.** $\emptyset$ **29.** $\left(\frac{1}{2}, 3\right)$

31. infinitely many solutions   **33.** $\left(\frac{7}{3}, \frac{5}{3}\right)$ **35.** $(11, 3)$

37. $(2, 0, 1)$ **39.** $\emptyset$ **41.** $\left(\frac{1}{3}, 2, 1\right)$

43. infinitely many solutions   **45.** $(2, 5, 3)$

47. $y - mx = b$,   so $y = mx + b$

49. $9\begin{vmatrix} 1 & 2 \\ -1 & 4 \end{vmatrix} = 9(4 + 2) = 54, \begin{vmatrix} 3 & 6 \\ -3 & 12 \end{vmatrix} = 36 + 18 = 54$

51. To evaluate $\begin{vmatrix} a_1 & b_1 & c_1 \\ a_2 & b_2 & c_2 \\ a_3 & b_3 & c_3 \end{vmatrix}$, multiply a_1 times

$\begin{vmatrix} b_2 & c_2 \\ b_3 & c_3 \end{vmatrix}$, then multiply $-b_1$ times $\begin{vmatrix} a_2 & c_2 \\ a_3 & c_3 \end{vmatrix}$, and

finally multiply c_1 times $\begin{vmatrix} a_2 & b_2 \\ a_3 & b_3 \end{vmatrix}$. The sum of these three numbers is the value of the determinant.

CHAPTER REVIEW EXERCISES (p. 191)

1. $(3, -2)$ **2.** $\emptyset$ **3.** $y = -3x + 1$ **4.** $(1, 2, -3)$

5. infinitely many solutions   **6.** $(3, -2)$ **7.** $\emptyset$

8. $(1, 2, -3)$ **9.** $y = -3x + 1$

10. infinitely many solutions

11. 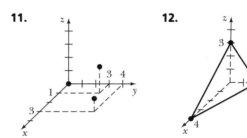   **12.**

13. 13 **14.** 4 **15.** ± 10

16. She uses 6 pounds of candy and 11 pounds of nuts.

17. length $= 17$ and width $= 10$ **18.** -17 and -6

19. He has 12 pennies, 24 nickels, and 20 quarters.

CHAPTER TEST (p. 192)

1. $\emptyset$ **2.** $(-2, 4)$ **3.** $y = 2x - 4$ **4.** $(-1, 0, 4)$

5. $\emptyset$ **6.** $y = 2x - 4$ **7.** $(-1, 0, 4)$ **8.** $(-2, 4)$

9. $\emptyset$

10. 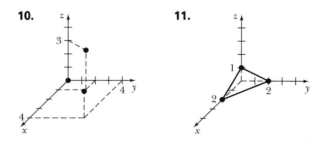   **11.**

12. 9 **13.** -28 **14.** ± 6

15. The length $= 5.5$, and the width $= 2$.

16. $12°, 120°,$ and $48°$

17. She needs 1 liter of the 6% solution and 2 liters of the 15% solution.

18. The river's speed $= 2$ mph, and the boat's speed $= 5$ mph.

CHAPTER 5

EXERCISE SET 5.1 (p. 199)

1. x^9 **3.** x^{20} **5.** a^8b^{12} **7.** $\dfrac{8}{x^3}$

9. x^8 **11.** 25   **13.** $\dfrac{y^{14}}{3}$

15. 64   **17.** 43,046,721   **19.** false, 36   **21.** true

23. false, x^9 **25.** false, 3^6 **27.** true   **29.** false, $\frac{3}{8}$

31. false, $49x^{-6}$ **33.** false, $\frac{4}{9}$ **35.** 1

37. x^{35} **39.** $\frac{13}{3}$

41. undefined   **43.** $320a^{33}$ **45.** $-\dfrac{1}{1,048,576}$

47. $\dfrac{4}{243}$ **49.** $\dfrac{10901}{24,300,000}$ **51.** x^4 **53.** $3x^{11}$ **55.** $\dfrac{1}{a^4}$

57. $\dfrac{25}{9x^4y^6}$ **59.** $\dfrac{5}{8}$ **61.** $\dfrac{11}{48}$ **63.** $\dfrac{m^{12}}{n^{12}}$ **65.** x^{2n+2}

67. a^{3n+5} **69.** $\dfrac{9}{16}$ **71.** x^{-15} **73.** $7^{-1}x^3$

75. $3^{-4}x^{-4}$ **77.** 6   **79.** $k^{-12n+18}$ **81.** $\dfrac{1}{a^{10}c^{10}}$

83. $\dfrac{2}{xy^4}$ **85.** $\dfrac{2x^n}{y^{4n+2}}$ **87.** 18^x **89.** $x^{7n}y^{7n}$

91. We want to have the same set of rules for all exponents. For this to be possible, we need to define $a^0 = 1$, for $a \neq 0$.

93. 3^2 means the product of two threes: $3^2 = 3 \cdot 3 = 9$. 3^{-2} means the reciprocal of the product of two threes: $3^{-2} = \dfrac{1}{3^2} = \dfrac{1}{3 \cdot 3} = \dfrac{1}{9}$

95. -20 **96.** 39   **97.** 19   **98.** $4x$

99. $11a^2b - ab^2$ **100.** $5y + 10$ **101.** $-2x + 3$

EXERCISE SET 5.2 (p. 205)

1. third-degree, monomial

3. first-degree, binomial

5. second-degree, or quadratic, trinomial; $y^2 - 3y + 8$

7. zero degree, monomial   **9.** linear

11. cubic   **13.** quadratic   **15.** 3   **17.** 132   **19.** 14

21. $6x^{13}$ **23.** $\dfrac{x^6}{2}$ **25.** $2x^2 + 2x$ **27.** $10x^4 + 4x^3$

29. $\frac{1}{2}x^9y^8$ **31.** $8x + 1$ **33.** a^{80} **35.** $\dfrac{1}{4x^{18}}$

37. $69x^{18}$ **39.** $7x - 1$

41. $-5x^2 + 5$ **43.** $a^3 + 4b^3 - 8b$

45. $9x^3 - 3x^2 + 7x - 4$ **47.** $-2x^2 - 6xy + 2y^2$

49. $5t^2 + 4t - 6$ **51.** $x - 6$

53. $10x - 4$ **55.** $6y^2 - 3y + 19$

57. A monomial is either a real number or the product of a real number and one or more variables raised to natural number exponents. A polynomial is the finite sum of monomials.

59. The degree of a polynomial in one variable is the largest exponent used in the polynomial.

61. $2x + 16$ **62.** $8x - 18$ **63.** $-11y - 28$

64. $x^2 + 7x + 12$ **65.** $a^2 - 10a + 24$

66. $8x^2 + 2xy - 15y^2$

EXERCISE SET 5.3 (p. 213)

1. $x^2 + 7x + 12$ **3.** $x^2 - xy - 6y^2$

5. $x^2 - 10x + 25$ **7.** $x^2 - 36$ **9.** $a^3 + 4a^2 + 4a$

11. $x^2 - 8x + 16$ **13.** $2x^2 - xy - 15y^2$ **15.** $a^3 + 8$

17. $15x^3 - 18x^2 + 12x$ **19.** $2a^{13} - 3a^{11} + a^{10}$

21. $x^5y^4z^3 - xy^{10}z^9$ **23.** $2x^2 + 5xy + 3y^2$

25. $a^2 + 3a - 10$ **27.** $16x^2 - 25y^2$

29. $6a^2 - ab - 2b^2$ **31.** $4x^2 + 12xy + 9y^2$

33. $18x^5 - 3x^3 - 6x$ **35.** $x^3 - x^2 - x + 10$

37. $x^3 + 1$ **39.** $a^3 - b^3$ **41.** $x^3 - 3x^2 + 3x - 1$

43. $3x^4 - 2x^3 - 2x^2 + 5x - 4$

45. $x^4 + 4x^3 + 6x^2 + 4x + 1$

47. $3x^2 + 4x$ **49.** $-\dfrac{9y^7}{4} - \dfrac{3y^4}{2} + 3y$

51. $\dfrac{3y^{15}}{2} - \dfrac{5y^{12}}{2} - \dfrac{1}{3y} + \dfrac{1}{6y^3}$

53. $2a^3b^4 - 6a^7b^8$ **55.** $\dfrac{6a^{10}}{b^3} - \dfrac{5b^{27}}{a} + \dfrac{1}{5ab^2}$

57. $x - 2$ **59.** $2y - 5$ **61.** $1 + \dfrac{1}{a + 2}$ **63.** $x - 7$

65. $x - 4 + \dfrac{14}{x + 4}$ **67.** $2y - 1$

69. $m - \dfrac{28}{5} - \dfrac{13}{25m + 20}$ **71.** $3n^2 + 2n - 7 + \dfrac{2}{2n - 1}$

73. $x + 1 + \dfrac{-2x + 4}{x^2 + 2x}$ **75.** $2x^2 + 3x + 2 + \dfrac{5x - 9}{3x^2 - 2x}$

77. $3x^2 + 2$ **79.** $\dfrac{1}{2} - \dfrac{23}{4x + 6}$ **81.** $3x^2 + \dfrac{5}{2}x - \dfrac{3}{4} + \dfrac{1}{8x - 4}$

83. $x^{4m} - 9$ **85.** $a^{2m} + 2a^mb^n + b^{2n}$

87. $x^2 - 7x - 8$ **89.** 377, 610, 987

91. Yes, $x^2 + (x^2 + 4)$ is quadratic.

93. No, $x^2(x^2 + 4)$ is fourth-degree.

95. Fibonacci introduced the Hindu–Arabic number system, which was superior to the Roman number system used at that time in Europe. He also developed methods of solving linear and higher degree equations. Fibonacci's sequence has applications in biology, business, and several other fields.

97. 11   **98.** 3   **99.** 7   **100.** 2   **101.** 3   **102.** -5

103. $x^2 - 25$ **104.** $a^2 - 9b^2$

105. $x^3 + 8$ **106.** $x^3 - 27$

EXERCISE SET 5.4 (p. 221)

1. $2x^2 + x - 1, D = \mathbb{R}$ **3.** $x^3 + 3x^2 - x + 1, D = \mathbb{R}$

5. $x^3 - x, D = \mathbb{R}$ **7.** $2x^3 - 2x^2, D = \mathbb{R}$

9. $4x^4, D = \mathbb{R}$ **11.** $\frac{3}{2} - \frac{1}{2x} + \frac{1}{x^2}, D = \{x \mid x \neq 0\}$

13. 14   **15.** -4 **17.** 8   **19.** $\frac{5}{17}$ **21.** 15   **23.** 6

25. 8   **27.** $3(x + 3)$ **29.** $2x(2x - 3)$ **31.** $6a^2(a - 1)$

33. $2x(2x^3 + 3x^2 - 5)$ **35.** $xy(2x^2 + 1 - 3y^2)$

37. $11(ab + cd)$ **39.** 2   **41.** $2x + h$ **43.** $4x + 2h - 1$

45. $3x^2 + 3xh + h^2$ **47.** $(y + z)(y - z)$

49. prime   **51.** $(2a + 3b)(2a - 3b)$ **53.** $9(x^2 + 4)$

55. $(x + 3 + y)(x + 3 - y)$ **57.** $3(x + 2)(x - 2)$

59. $2x(2x + 3)(2x - 3)$ **61.** $3x(x - 1)(x + 1)(x^2 + 1)$

63. $(1 - xy)(1 + xy)(1 + x^2y^2)$

65. false, $(x + 2y)(x^2 - 2xy + 4y^2)$

67. false, $(m + 10)(m^2 - 10m + 100)$

69. false, $(a + b^2)(a^2 - ab^2 + b^4)$

71. $(x + 3)(x^2 - 3x + 9)$

73. $(5x - 2y)(25x^2 + 10xy + 4y^2)$

75. $(1 - xy)(1 + xy + x^2y^2)$

77. $(a^2 + bc^2)(a^4 - a^2bc^2 + b^2c^4)$

79. $2(x - y)(x^2 + xy + y^2)$

81. $3x^2(x + 2y)(x^2 - 2xy + 4y^2)$

83. $(a - 1)(a^2 + a + 1)(a^6 + a^3 + 1)$ **85.** prime

87. $(a - b + c)(a^2 + ab - ac + b^2 - 2bc + c^2)$

89. $\left(m + \frac{1}{3}\right)\left(m^2 - \frac{1}{3}m + \frac{1}{9}\right)$

91. $-x^2(x^4 + 6x^2 + 12)$

93. $(x - y^{10})(x + y^{10})(x^4 + x^2y^{20} + y^{40})$

95. $(a - b + c - d)(a - b - c + d)$ **97.** $2b(3a^2 + b^2)$

99. Because $\left(\dfrac{f}{g}\right)(x) = \dfrac{f(x)}{g(x)}$ and their domain are often values of x for which $g(x) = 0$. Thus, $D_{f/g} = \{x \mid g(x) \neq 0\}$.

101. The polynomial cannot be factored any further over the integers.

103. $ab + 7a + bc + 7c$ **104.** $x^2z + 4x^2 + yz + 4y$

105. $x^2 + 7x + 12$ **106.** $x^2 + 3xy - 18y^2$

107. $x = \pm 3$ **108.** $x = \pm 5$

EXERCISE SET 5.5 (p. 227)

1. $(x + 5)(x - 1)$ **3.** $(r + 3)(t - 6)$

5. $5(1 + y)(a - b)$ **7.** $(x + 5)(x + 6)$

9. $(y - 3)(y + 7)$ **11.** $(3x - 2y)(x - 4y)$

13. $(x - 1)(x + 1)^2$ **15.** $(x - 3)(y + 4)$

17. prime   **19.** $ab(a - c)(b + 1)$

21. $(2 + a - b)(a + b)$ **23.** $(x + 6)(x + 5)$

25. $(x - 8)(x + 2)$ **27.** prime

29. $(x - 7)(x - 1)$ **31.** $(x + 4y)(x + 9y)$

33. $(3x + y)(4x + y)$ **35.** $3y(y^2 + y + 1)$

37. $(x - 7y)^2$ **39.** $(x - 25y)(x + 4y)$

41. $2xy^2(x - 9y)(x - 3y)$ **43.** ± 3 **45.** $-4, -6$

47. $-2, 10$ **49.** $0, 8, -2$ **51.** $2, -5$ **53.** ± 7

55. ± 2 **57.** $0, -3, 3$ **59.** $0, 1$ **61.** $0, -3, 3, -1$

63. $\pm 1, \pm 2$ **65.** $(x + 2y - 3)(x - 2y + 3)$

67. $(a + b - c)(x - 4)$ **69.** $3, -2$

71. Certain polynomials are in the form $a + b + c + d$, where no common monomial factor exists. However, by factoring the first two terms and the last two terms we often obtain a common binomial factor that can be factored out of the polynomial. This process is called "factoring by grouping."

73. $3x^2 + 11x + 10$

74. $15a^3b - 30a^2b^2 + 21a^2b - 42ab^2$

75. $4x^2 + 12xy + 9y^2$ **76.** $27y^3 - 90y^2 + 75y$

77. 0   **78.** 0; 0

EXERCISE SET 5.6 (p. 236)

1. $(x + 2)(x + 6)$ **3.** $(3x + 2)(x + 5)$

5. $(2x - 5)(3x + 2)$ **7.** $(6x + y)(2x + y)$

9. $(2x + 3)(x + 1)$ **11.** $(x - 5)(x + 3)$

13. $(9x + 4y)(2x - 3y)$ **15.** prime   **17.** prime

19. $(2x - 3y)(2x - 7y)$ **21.** $(32x - 3)(x + 1)$

23. prime   **25.** $(x + 4)^2$ **27.** $(3x - 5y)^2$ **29.** prime

31. $(x + 1 + y)(x + 1 - y)$ **33.** $(6 + x + y)(6 - x - y)$

35. $3x(x + 3)(x - 3)$ **37.** $(4n + 5)(3n - 8)$

39. $(x + 2y)(b - 3)$ **41.** $(x + 2)(x - 2)(x + 3)$

43. $(6a + 5b)(2a - 3b)$ **45.** prime

47. $ab(a - 2ab + b^2)$ **49.** $(2x - 3y + 3z)(2x - 3y - 3z)$

51. $(5 + 3x - y)(5 - 3x + y)$ **53.** $[(x + y)(x - y)]^2$

55. $2, -5$ **57.** $5, -\frac{4}{3}$ **59.** $\frac{1}{2}, -\frac{4}{3}$ **61.** $7, -2$

63. ± 5 **65.** $0, -7$ **67.** $0, 5$ **69.** 0 **71.** Q

73. $0, 1, -1, -5$ **75.** $\pm 3, \pm \frac{1}{2}$ **77.** 9

79. $-\frac{2}{3}$ **81.** ± 6 **83.** $1, -7$ **85.** $0, \pm 5$

87. $(a + b + c - d)(a + b - c + d)$

89. $(x - 3 + a - b)(x - 3 - a + b)$

91. $8(3x^2 - 5)(x^2 - 2)$ **93.** $4, -\frac{1}{2}$

95. Because Maria was fluent in Greek, Latin, and several modern languages, she was able to translate the works of English, German, and other European mathematicians into her native Italian.

97. $6, -4$ **98.** $0, 10$ **99.** $3, -4$ **100.** $12, -4$

EXERCISE SET 5.7 (p. 242)

1. $\{-6, -5\}, \{5, 6\}$ **3.** $\{-10, -8, -6\}, \{-2, 0, 2\}$

5. $x(2 - x) = 24$
If $x = 6$, then $6(2 - 6) = 6(-4) = -24$.
If $x = -4$, then $-4[2 - (-4)] = -4[6] = -24$.

7. $\{-8, 3\}$ **9.** $\{3, 10\}$ **11.** $\{0, 1\}$

13. $\{4, 10\}, \{-\frac{10}{3}, -12\}$

15. $(2R - 2)^2 + (2R)^2 = 10^2, R = 4$

17. $\{5, 12, 13\}$ **19.** 25 feet

21. 8 and 10 cubits

23. 5 and 12 mph

25. $s = 12; (s - 4)(s - 4)2 = (8)(8)2 = 128$

27. The rectangle's length = 10 feet, its width = 8 feet, and its perimeter = 36 feet.

29. $L = 10, W = 2$ **31.** $W = S = 6, L = 10$

33. height = 4, base = 16   **35.** $r = 2$

37. width = 8 feet, length = 16 feet

39. width = 16 inches, length = 18 inches

41. 1 inch by 1 inch

43. a. $V = a^3, S = 6a^2$
b. $V = 64$ cubic inches, $S = 96$ square inches
c. $a = 6$

45. $r = 2$ centimeters   **47.** 75 leaps   **49.** 7 mph

51. Andrew's age = 5, Chris's age = 7   **53.** $\sqrt{5}$

55. a. $D = 4850$ **b.** $n = 5$ **c.** $n = 10$

57. $x(x + 3) = (x + 1)(x + 2)$
$x^2 + 3x = x^2 + 3x + 2$
$0 = 2,$ so no solution exists.

59. A solution to the equation could result in the length of the side of a geometric figure being zero or negative.

CHAPTER REVIEW EXERCISES (p. 247)

1. $\dfrac{-1}{x^2}$ **2.** $9x^8$ **3.** $16x^{16}$ **4.** $\dfrac{1}{x^{20}}$ **5.** $\dfrac{x^6}{y^{10}}$ **6.** $\dfrac{69}{4}$

7. $\dfrac{3x^4}{2y^7}$ **8.** $\dfrac{8x^{18}}{y^{12}}$ **9.** 22 **10.** $6a^3 - 4a^2 + 2a - 16$

11. $-2y^4 + 6y^2 - 3y - 8$ **12.** $x^2 - 8x + 12$

13. $12x^2 + 7xy - 10y^2$ **14.** $x^3 + 15x^2 + 75x + 125$

15. $5a^2 - \dfrac{9b^7}{a} + \dfrac{2b^7}{3a^2}$ **16.** $3x - 2 + \dfrac{3}{x + 2}$ **17.** $2x + 3$

18. $2x^3 - 3x^2 + 5x - 4$ **19.** $2x + 1 + \dfrac{5}{x - 1}$

20. $4x - 1 + 2h$ **21.** $0, \pm 5$ **22.** $8, -2$ **23.** $\frac{2}{3}$

24. ± 1 **25.** $0, -\frac{3}{2}$ **26.** $3ab(2a - 1)$

27. $3x(x + 2)(x - 4)$ **28.** prime

29. $(x - 3)(x^2 + 3x + 9)$ **30.** $(2x + 7)(2x - 7)$

31. $(x + 3y)^2$ **32.** $(4a - 3b)(a + 4b)$

33. $(a - 3)(a + 3)(a^2 + 9)$ **34.** $(y + 8)(y - 4)$

35. $(x + 3)(x + 2)(x - 2)$ **36.** $(7a - 1)^2$

37. $(x + y)(3x - 5y)$ **38.** $\{3, 5\}, \{-3, -5\}$

39. $\sqrt{58}$ **40.** $L = 8, W = 6$

CHAPTER TEST (p. 247)

1. x^{14} **2.** $\dfrac{64}{x^{30}}$ **3.** y^4 **4.** $\dfrac{3x^4}{y^5}$ **5.** $\dfrac{9}{4x^8y^{10}}$

6. $9x^2 - 6xy + y^2$ **7.** $-3x^2 - 14x + 7$

8. $12x^2 + 10xy - 12y^2$ **9.** $\dfrac{2}{y^2} - \dfrac{3x^2}{2} - \dfrac{3x^8y^9}{4}$

10. $2x^2 + 3x + 9 + \dfrac{31}{x - 3}$ **11.** 20

12. $2x^3 - 10x^2 + 16x - 8$ **13.** $2x + h - 3$

14. $0, \pm 2$ **15.** $-5, 3$ **16.** $0, \frac{3}{2}$ **17.** $(x + 8)(x - 3)$

18. $(y + z)(x - 3)$ **19.** $3x(x + 2)(x^2 - 2x + 4)$

20. $(2x - 3y)(4x + y)$ **21.** $2xy(x + y)(x - y)$

22. prime   **23.** $\{-5, -4\}$ and $\{4, 5\}$

24. $\{6, 8, 10\}$ **25.** $h = 5, b = 10$

CHAPTER 6

EXERCISE SET 6.1 (p. 253)

1. $\frac{16}{13}$ **3.** $\frac{1}{5}$ **5.** $\frac{13}{8}$ **7.** $\{x \mid x \neq 5\}$ **9.** $\{x \mid x \neq -3, 2\}$

11. $\{x \mid x \neq \pm 5\}$ **13.** $\{x \mid x \neq -2, -1\}$ **15.** $\mathbb{R}$

17. true **19.** false, $x + y$ **21.** false, $\dfrac{x^2 + 3x + 1}{x + 1}$

23. true **25.** $\frac{4}{9}$ **27.** $\frac{3}{2}$ **29.** $6x^3$ **31.** $\dfrac{2a^2}{3b^5}$ **33.** $\dfrac{2a}{a}$

35. $\dfrac{2}{x - 1}$ **37.** $\frac{3}{4}$ **39.** $x + 1$ **41.** $\dfrac{x^2}{2}$ **43.** $a - b$

45. $x^2 - x + 1$ **47.** $x + 1$ **49.** $\dfrac{x - 2y}{(x + y)^7}$ **51.** $\dfrac{x + 4}{x - 5}$

53. $\dfrac{3 + x}{1 - 2x}$ **55.** $\dfrac{2a - 3b}{3a + 2b}$ **57.** $\dfrac{n - t}{nt}$ **59.** $\dfrac{3c + 1}{a - b}$

61. $\dfrac{x^2 + y^3}{y(x^2 - 2xy + 2y^2)}$ **63.** $\dfrac{ab(a - b)}{a^2 - ab + b^2}$

65. $\dfrac{-abc}{a - b + c}$ **67.** $\dfrac{2x + 3y - 2}{3xy}$ **69.** $\dfrac{2x^4 - 2x}{3x^3 + 3}$

71. A rational expression is the ratio of two polynomials, such as $\dfrac{x - 1}{y + 4}$. A rational function is the ratio of two polynomial functions, such as $f(x) = \dfrac{x^2 - 9}{x^2 - 4}$. A rational function involves one variable, but a rational expression can contain two or more variables.

73. $(fg)(x) = 2x^3 - 6x^2 - 8x + 24,\ D_{fg} = \mathbb{R}$

74. $\left(\dfrac{f}{g}\right)(x) = \dfrac{2x - 6}{x^2 - 4},\ D_{f/g} = \{x \mid x \neq \pm 2\}$

75. $\left(\dfrac{g}{f}\right)(x) = \dfrac{x^2 - 4}{2x - 6},\ D_{g/f} = \{x \mid x \neq 3\}$

EXERCISE SET 6.2 (p. 259)

1. $\frac{14}{15}$ **3.** $\frac{25}{6}$ **5.** $-\frac{42}{5}$ **7.** $\dfrac{3y^5}{2x^3}$ **9.** $-\dfrac{4c^2}{b^5}$

11. $\dfrac{-3}{x^2(x + 3)}$ **13.** $\frac{10}{21}$ **15.** $\frac{22}{9}$ **17.** $\dfrac{xy}{6}$ **19.** $\dfrac{x}{3y}$

21. $-\dfrac{32(1 - x^2)}{x^7}$ **23.** $\frac{14}{27}$ **25.** $\dfrac{10(x + 3)(x - 3)^2}{9x^2y^8}$

27. $-\dfrac{5y^8}{3x^4}$ **29.** $\dfrac{b(x - y)}{a(x + y)}$ **31.** $\dfrac{a^{28}(2a - 3)}{(a - 3)(3a + 1)}$

33. $\dfrac{3x}{x - 3}$ **35.** $\dfrac{(9x^2 - 15xy + 25y^2)(x - y)}{x + y}$

37. $\frac{30}{7}$ **39.** $\dfrac{2a^7}{3b^9}$ **41.** $a + b$

43. $\dfrac{x(x + 5)}{(x - 1)(x - 6)},\ D = \{x \mid x \neq 1, 6\}$

45. $\dfrac{x(x - 7)}{(x - 1)(x - 9)},\ D = \{x \mid x \neq 1, -9\}$

47. $\dfrac{(x + 5)(x - 7)}{(x - 6)(x + 9)},\ D = \{x \mid x \neq 6, -9\}$

49. $\dfrac{x^2}{(x - 1)^2},\ D = \{x \mid x \neq 1\}$

51. $\dfrac{x(x - 6)}{(x - 1)(x + 5)},\ D = \{x \mid x \neq 1, 6, -5\}$

53. $\dfrac{x^2}{(x - 1)(x - 8)},\ D = \{x \mid x \neq 0, 1, 8\}$

55. $\dfrac{x(x + 9)}{(x - 1)(x - 7)},\ D = \{x \mid x \neq 1, -9, 7\}$

57. $\dfrac{x(x + 5)}{(x - 6)(x - 8)},\ D = \{x \mid x \neq 6, 0, 8\}$

59. $\dfrac{(x - 8)(x + 9)}{x(x + 9)},\ D = \{x \mid x \neq 0, -9, 7\}$

61. $\dfrac{(x^2 - 1)(x^2 - 9)}{(x^2 - 4)(x^2 - 25)},\ D = \{x \mid x \neq \pm 2, \pm 5\}$

63. $\dfrac{(x^2 - 1)(2x - 1)}{(x^2 - 4)(3x + 5)},\ D\ \{x \mid x \neq \pm 2, -\frac{5}{3}\}$

65. $\dfrac{(x^2 - 9)(2x - 1)}{(x^2 - 25)(3x + 5)},\ D = \{x \mid x \neq \pm 5, -\frac{5}{3}\}$

67. $\dfrac{(x^2 - 1)(x^2 - 25)}{(x^2 - 4)(x^2 - 9)},\ D = \{x \mid x \neq \pm 2, \pm 5, \pm 3\}$

69. $\dfrac{(x^2 - 1)(x + 5)}{(x^2 - 4)(x + 3)},\ D = \{x \mid x \neq \pm 2, 4, -5, -3\}$

71. $\dfrac{(x^2 - 1)(3x + 5)}{(x^2 - 4)(2x - 1)},\ D = \{x \mid x \neq \pm 2, -\frac{5}{3}, \frac{1}{2}\}$

73. 8 **75.** $-\frac{4}{3}$ **77.** none **79.** 2, 3

81. $\dfrac{3x(x + 1)(x^2 + 1)}{(x - 1)^2}$ **83.** $\dfrac{3(x - 2)(4x - 1)}{2x + 3}$

85. First write the product of the numerators over the product of the denominators. Then factor the numerators and the denominators. Divide out the common factors so that the answer is in reduced form.

87. The domain of fg is the set of all real numbers in the domain of f and in the domain of g. Thus, exclude all real numbers that result in division by zero in either function.

89. We are dividing by zero in going from line 5 to line 6: $a = 1$, so $\dfrac{a(a - 1)}{a - 1} = \dfrac{(a + 1)(a - 1)}{a - 1}$ results in $\dfrac{a - 1}{a - 1} = \dfrac{0}{0}$.

91. $2 \cdot 3 \cdot 5 \cdot 7$ **92.** $2 \cdot 2 \cdot 3 \cdot 3 \cdot 5$ **93.** $2 \cdot 2 \cdot 5 \cdot 5$

94. 6 **95.** 1 **96.** 1 **97.** -26 **98.** 2

99. $4x^2 + 5x - 1, D = \mathbb{R}$

100. $2x^2 - 9x + 11, D = \mathbb{R}$

EXERCISE SET 6.3 (p. 270)

1. $\frac{1}{2}$ **3.** $\frac{3}{11}$ **5.** $\frac{1}{3}$ **7.** $\frac{3+x}{z}$ **9.** $\frac{11}{x}$ **11.** $\frac{1}{mn}$ **13.** 3

15. -3 **17.** $\frac{x+2}{x+3}$ **19.** 9 **21.** 110 **23.** 18

25. 210 **27.** x^2 **29.** $2x - 1$

31. $(x+1)(x-1)(x+2)$ **33.** $5x(x+3)$

35. $(x+1)(x-1)(x^2+x+1)$ **37.** $\frac{1}{7}$ **39.** $-\frac{3}{8}$

41. $\frac{x^2+y^2}{xy}$ **43.** $\frac{3x^5 - 3x^4 + 2y^3 + 2y^2}{30x^6y^4}$ **45.** $\frac{4x+1}{x^2-1}$

47. $\frac{x^3+x-3}{x^2}$ **49.** $\frac{a+b}{ab}$ **51.** $\frac{5x^2+3x+5}{(x^2+1)(x^2+x+1)}$

53. $\frac{x^2-x+4}{(x+1)(x-1)(x+3)}$ **55.** $\frac{x^3+x^2+4x+3}{(x^2-1)(x^2+x+1)}$

57. $\frac{a^4 - 3a^3 + 2a^2 - 12a - 11}{(a+2)(a-2)(a^2+4)}$

59. $\frac{x-1}{x(x+1)(x^2-x+1)}$ **61.** $\frac{9}{10}$ **63.** $\frac{3}{4}$ **65.** $\frac{x+9}{3x^2}$

67. $\frac{-6x^2+2x+1}{x^3}$ **69.** $\frac{4x-1}{9(x-1)}$

71. $\frac{-x^2+2x+2}{x^2-1}, D = \{x \mid x \neq \pm 1\}$

73. $\frac{-x^2+2x+2}{x^2-4}, D = \{x \mid x \neq \pm 2\}$

75. $\frac{-x^4+3x^3+6x^2-9x-8}{(x^2-4)(x^2-1)}, D = \{x \mid x \neq \pm 2, \pm 1\}$

77. $\frac{-x^2+x+1}{(1-x)(x+2)}, D = \{x \mid x \neq 1, \pm 2\}$

79. $\frac{x^3+5x^2-6x+8}{(x^2-x+2)(x^2+x-2)}$ **81.** $\frac{a^2-c^2}{(a+1)(a-b)(b+c)}$

83. Like fractions are fractions that have the same denominator. Unlike fractions are fractions that have different denominators. When we add two like fractions we add the numerators and place this result over the common denominator. To add two unlike fractions we determine their LCD, convert them to like fractions, and then add them.

85. The same way we find the domain of fg (see Section 6.2, Exercise 87).

87. $\frac{11}{30}$ **88.** $\frac{3}{8}$ **89.** $\frac{26}{25}$ **90.** $\frac{3}{4}$ **91.** $\frac{7}{4}$ **92.** $\frac{9y^2}{25x^2}$

EXERCISE SET 6.4 (p. 278)

1. $\frac{6}{35}$ **3.** $-\frac{5}{6}$ **5.** $\frac{8ab^2}{3}$ **7.** $\frac{x-1}{2(x+1)}$ **9.** $x+y$ **11.** $\frac{11}{30}$

13. $\frac{3xy-y}{2xy+x}$ **15.** $\frac{3b^2+4a}{24ab^2-6b}$ **17.** $\frac{y(x+2y)}{x}$

19. $\frac{3m-4}{m-6}$ **21.** $\frac{1}{2}$ **23.** $\frac{-1}{x(x+h)}$ **25.** $\frac{a^2b^2c^2}{bc+ac-ab}$

27. $\frac{7}{4}$ **29.** $\frac{x}{x+1}$ **31.** false, $1 + xy$

33. false, $\frac{a^6}{(a+1)^2}$ **35.** true **37.** true

39. $\frac{x^{-1}y}{y^{-1}x} = \frac{yy}{xx}$; the rules of exponents *only* apply to multiplication and division.

41. $\frac{x^{-1}+y}{y^{-1}+x} = \frac{\frac{1}{x}+y}{\frac{1}{y}+x} \cdot \frac{xy}{xy} = \frac{y+xy^2}{x+x^2y} = \frac{y(1+xy)}{x(1+xy)} = \frac{y}{x}$

43. $\frac{7}{12}$ **45.** 12 **47.** $-\frac{b^2}{a}$ **49.** $\frac{2ab}{a+b}$ **51.** $\frac{a^3+b^4}{a^2b^3}$

53. a. $\frac{5}{11}$ **b.** $\frac{3}{2}$ **55. a.** -2.46 **b.** -3.75

57. $\frac{-3}{x(x+h)}$ **59.** $\frac{-3}{(x-1)(x+h-1)}$

61. $\frac{5}{(x+2)(x+h+2)}$ **63.** $\frac{-2x-h}{x^2(x+h)^2}$

65. No, it is 40 mph. **67.** 36 mph **69.** 48 km/h

71. $\frac{20x}{20+x}, x = $ number purchased for \$10.

73. $\frac{40x}{40-3x}, x = $ number purchased for \$16.

75. $x(x+1)$ **77.** $\frac{a}{a^2-b^2}$ **79.** $\frac{n+1}{5n}$ **81.** -1

83. A simple fraction is one whose numerator and denominator are polynomials. A complex fraction is one whose numerator, denominator, or both contain one or more simple fractions.

85. Write a^{-2} as $\frac{1}{a^2}$ and a^{-1} as $\frac{1}{a}$. **87.** $\frac{24}{5}$ **88.** -5

89. $w = \frac{1+x}{1-x}$ **90.** $D = \frac{df}{d-f}$ **91.** $y = \frac{5x-10}{2}$

92. $\pi = \frac{3V}{r^2h}$ **93.** $-5, 3$ **94.** $-4, \frac{1}{2}$

95. $D = \{x \mid x \neq -5\}$ **96.** $D = \{x \mid x \neq \pm 2\}$

EXERCISE SET 6.5 (p. 287)

1. a. $x = 3; \frac{x^2+3x}{5x+25} - \frac{2}{x+5} = \frac{18}{40} - \frac{2}{8} = \frac{1}{5}$

b. $x = -4; 2(-4) + 7 = -1$ and $\dfrac{4}{-4} = -1$

$x = \dfrac{1}{2}; 2 \cdot \dfrac{1}{2} + 7 = 8; \dfrac{4}{\frac{1}{2}} = 8$

3. -12 **5.** 5 **7.** 3 **9.** -6 **11.** $\varnothing$ **13.** $6, -5$
15. $-\frac{21}{4}$ **17.** $\varnothing$ **19.** $\frac{1}{2}, -5$ **21.** $\varnothing$ **23.** 2 **25.** $\varnothing$
27. $-\frac{1}{2}$ **29.** $2, \frac{1}{2}$ **31.** $\dfrac{75 - 2x}{10x}$ **33.** 2 **35.** $\dfrac{x + 2}{2x(x - 3)}$
37. $\pm 2, -1$ **39.** $\frac{18}{7}$ **41.** 3 **43.** -16 **45.** $4, -3$
47. $x = \dfrac{24 - 3y}{4}$ **49.** $y = \dfrac{8x - 6}{3}$ **51.** $T_f = \dfrac{T_i P_i V_f}{P_i V_i}$
53. $S = \dfrac{n}{y - f}$ **55.** $y = mx + b$ **57.** $B = \dfrac{CA}{C - A}$
59. $a = \dfrac{bc}{d}$ **61.** $y = \dfrac{tw - 2ts}{2w}$ **63.** $f_2 = \dfrac{f_1 f}{f_1 - f}$
65. $V = \dfrac{TV_1 + V_0}{T - 1}$ **67.** $a_1 = \dfrac{Aa_2}{4 - A}$ **69.** $m = \dfrac{n}{Mn + M}$
71. $x = \dfrac{5zA + 4y}{5}$ **73.** $R_1 = \dfrac{R_2 R}{R_2 - R}$
75. Because some possible value of the variable could make the denominator equal to zero.
77. $\frac{116}{5}$ **78.** $\frac{116}{5}$ **79.** $V_2 = \dfrac{P_1 V_1}{P_2}$
80. 132 centimeters **81.** 30 inches

EXERCISE SET 6.6 (p. 292)

1. $\frac{3}{11}$ **3.** $\frac{3}{2}$ **5.** $\frac{31}{1}$ miles per gallon **7.** $\frac{3}{5}$ **9.** 6
11. 18 and 15 **13.** 6, 18, and 21 centimeters
15. width $= \frac{15}{2}$ meters, and length $= 10$ meters
17. height $= 20$ feet and base $= 25$ feet
19. $20°$ and $160°$
21. 15 nickels, 20 dimes, and 35 quarters
23. rate $= 45$ mph and time $= 6$ hours **25.** true
27. false **29.** 45 feet **31.** 9.2 inches
33. 9 pounds **35.** 40.9 kilograms **37.** 880 pounds
39. $1600 **41.** 8.0 liters **43.** 96.92 atmospheres
45. $288,000 **47.** $300,000 **49.** $35,000
51. 60 centimeters **53.** 12 ohms **55.** $R = \dfrac{1}{2}R_2$
57. $\frac{8}{3}$ ohms **59.** $w = 5$ meters
61. $5,500, $12,500 **63.** 2.4 feet
65. A ratio, $\frac{a}{b}$, is the quotient of two quantities, such as $\frac{3}{4}$. A proportion is the statement of equality between two ratios, such as $\frac{3}{4} = \frac{6}{8}$.

67. $\{18, 19\}$ **68.** $\{-8, -6, -4\}$ **69.** $r = 6$ mph
70. $r = 3$ mph **71.** 1.5 hours **72.** $r = 52$ mph

EXERCISE SET 6.7 (p. 300)

1. $\dfrac{1}{x + 2} - \dfrac{1}{x} = -\dfrac{1}{24}$;

$x = 6: \dfrac{1}{8} - \dfrac{1}{6} = -\dfrac{1}{24}$;

$x = -8: \dfrac{1}{-6} - \dfrac{1}{-8} = -\dfrac{1}{24}.$

3. -2 or $-\frac{1}{6}$ **5.** $\frac{10}{32}$ **7.** $\frac{5}{11}$
9. 13 **11.** 20 and 70
13. $\dfrac{20}{r - 3} + \dfrac{20}{r + 3} = 7; r = 7: \dfrac{20}{4} + \dfrac{20}{10} = 7$
15. 3 mph **17.** 8 mph
19. car: 175 miles, 3.5 hours; truck: 253 miles, 5.5 hours.
21. $r = 32$ mph; A's time $= 2.25$ hours, B's time $= 5.25$ hours
23. car: 4 hours, 70 km/h; truck: 6 hours, 50 km/h
25. $\frac{24}{5}$ hours **27.** $\frac{7}{4}$ hours **29.** $\frac{12}{5}$ hours **31.** 24 hours
33. 12 hours **35.** $\frac{2}{5}$ of a day **37.** 2 hours
39. $\{-10, -8\}$ **41.** 120 apples
43. Going down river the current is pushing the boat, so we add the rate of the current to the rate of the boat. Going up river the current acts as resistance to the boat, so we subtract the rate of the current from the rate of the boat.

CHAPTER REVIEW EXERCISES (p. 303)

1. $\frac{11}{7}$ **2.** $-\frac{2}{13}$ **3.** $D = \{x \mid x \neq 5\}$, roots $= \{-4\}$
4. $D = \{x \mid x \neq \pm 6\}$, roots $= \{\pm 5\}$
5. $\dfrac{-a(a + 5)}{a + 2}$ **6.** $\dfrac{4x^2 - 2xy + y^2}{xy}$ **7.** $\dfrac{18a^3}{5b^3}$ **8.** $\dfrac{2xw}{3}$
9. $\dfrac{x(x - 3)}{y}$ **10.** $\dfrac{x + 5}{3(x + 1)}$ **11.** $\dfrac{21a + 10b}{12ab}$
12. $\dfrac{11 + 5x}{60x^2}$ **13.** $\dfrac{2xy - 2y^2 - x^2y}{x(x + y)(x - y)}$ **14.** $\dfrac{x^2 + 5x + 1}{(x + 3)(x + 2)^2}$
15. 840 **16.** $(x + 1)(x - 1)(x + 2)(x - 2)$ **17.** $\frac{3}{2}$
18. $x - y$ **19.** $\dfrac{2a - 24a}{3a^2 + 12}$ **20.** $\dfrac{x^2 - y^2 - x + y}{x^2 - y^2 + x + y}$
21. $\dfrac{x + 1}{x^3}$ **22.** -6
23. $\dfrac{x^2 - x - 3}{(x - 2)(x - 3)}$, $D = \{x \mid x \neq 2, 3\}$
24. $\dfrac{x^2 + 3x - 2}{(x - 3)(x + 3)}$, $D = \{x \mid x \neq \pm 3\}$

25. $\dfrac{x^2 - 3x + 3}{(x - 2)(x - 3)}$, $D = \{x \mid x \neq 2, 3\}$

26. $\dfrac{x}{(x - 2)(x - 3)}$, $D = \{x \mid x \neq 2, 3\}$

27. $\dfrac{x - 3}{x(x - 2)}$, $D = \{x \mid x \neq 0, 2, 3\}$　　**28.** $\frac{4}{19}$　　**29.** -2

30. -5　　**31.** $y = \dfrac{10x - 15}{3}$　　**32.** $r = \dfrac{nE - IR}{In}$

33. $n = \dfrac{IR}{E - Ir}$　　**34.** 45 mph　　**35.** 14 ohms　　**36.** $\frac{13}{11}$

37. $r = 36$ mph; truck: 54 miles; car: 126 miles

38. 6 hours　　**39.** 6, 8, and 10 centimeters

40. Angle $= 25°$, complement $= 65°$, and supplement $= 155°$.

CHAPTER TEST (p. 304)

1. -5　　**2.** $D = \{x \mid x \neq \pm 3\}$, roots $= \{\pm 1\}$

3. $\dfrac{x^2 + x + 1}{2}$　　**4.** $\dfrac{-2(2x^2 + 2x + 3)}{(x - 7)(x + 3)(x + 4)}$

5. $\dfrac{3x^2 y^7}{32}$　　**6.** $\dfrac{15y + 2xy - 2x^2}{36x^2 y^2}$

7. $\dfrac{2x^2 - 5}{(x + 5)(x - 5)(x + 4)}$　　**8.** $\dfrac{xy}{x + y}$

9. $\dfrac{x}{x - y}$　　**10.** $\dfrac{5x^2 - 6x}{2x - 3}$　　**11.** $\dfrac{-5}{x(x + h)}$

12. $x(x - 1)(x + 1)(x^2 + 1)(x^2 - x + 1)$

13. $\dfrac{x^2 + 3x - 1}{x(x + 1)(x - 1)}$, $D = \{x \mid x \neq 0, \pm 1\}$

14. $\dfrac{x + 1 - x^2}{x(x + 1)}$, $D = \{x \mid x \neq 0, -1\}$

15. $\dfrac{1}{x + 1}$, $D = \{x \mid x \neq 0, -1\}$

16. $\dfrac{3}{x(x - 1)}$, $D = \{x \mid x \neq 0, \pm 1\}$

17. $y = 2$　　**18.** $x = -5$　　**19.** $P_1 = \dfrac{P_2 V_2}{V_1}$

20. $x = \dfrac{a}{y - b}$　　**21.** 6, 9, and 15 centimeters

22. $500　　**23.** 4 hours　　**24.** $\{-5, -3\}$　　**25.** 65 mph

CUMULATIVE REVIEW: Chapters 1–6 (p. 306)

1. $-58\,[1.3]$　　**2.** $-19\,[1.4]$　　**3.** $\frac{9}{8}\,[5.1]$　　**4.** $\dfrac{x^5}{3}\,[5.1]$

5. $\dfrac{4x^{10}}{25}\,[5.1]$　　**6.** $\dfrac{2(x + 3)}{3(x - 3)}\,[6.2]$

7. $\dfrac{x^3 + x^2 + 3x + 2}{(x - 1)(x + 1)(x^2 + x + 1)}\,[6.3]$　　**8.** $\dfrac{-a}{a + b}\,[6.4]$

9. $\frac{9}{5}\,[2.1]$　　**10.** $\frac{3}{2}, -\frac{1}{3}\,[5.6]$　　**11.** $-\frac{12}{5}\,[6.5]$

12. $\pm 2\,[6.5]$　　**13.** $y = \dfrac{5x - 15}{3}\,[2.3]$

14. $b = \dfrac{ac}{a - c}\,[6.5]$　　**15.** $2, -\frac{3}{2}\,[2.2]$

16. $(-\frac{11}{3}, 3)\,[2.7]$

17. $(-\infty, -4]\,[2.6]$

18. $(-\frac{7}{36}, -\frac{5}{18})\,[4.1]$　　**19.** $\varnothing\,[4.1]$

20. $(-3, 1, 6)\,[4.3]$　　**21.** $(2, 1)\,[4.4]$　　**22.** $(2, 1)\,[4.5]$

23. $[3.5]$　　**24.** $[3.1]$

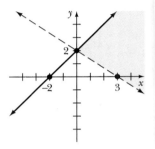　　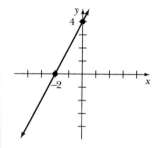

25. $[3.1]$　　　　　　　**26.** $[3.1]$

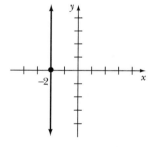　　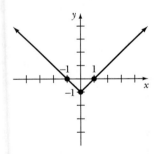

27. $2\sqrt{5}\,[3.3]$　　**28.** $y = 2x + 5\,[3.4]$　　**29.** $-\frac{3}{2}\,[3.4]$

30. $D = \{1, 3\}$, $R = \{2, 7, 8\}\,[3.2]$　　**31.** $2x + h - 3\,[5.4]$

32. $f^{-1}(x) = \dfrac{x + 1}{4}\,[3.6]$　　**33.** $8x^2 + 10x - 3\,[5.4]$

34. $2x(x + 2)(x - 2)\,[5.4]$　　**35.** $(a + b)(c - 2)\,[5.5]$

36. $D = \mathbb{R}\,[5.2]$　　**37.** Roots $= \{0, \pm 3\}\,[5.6]$

38. $\{-2, 0, 1\frac{2}{3}, .27, .\overline{27}\}\,[1.2]$

39. $\{\sqrt{5}, .272829 \ldots\}\,[1.2]$　　**40.** $\{0, 1\}\,[1.2]$

41. 1 liter of 6%, 2 liters of 15%$\,[4.2]$

42. $p = 4, n = 5$, and $d = 15\,[4.3]$

43. $\{-3, -2, -1, \ldots\}$ [2.6]   **44.** $30°$ [6.6]

45. 6, 8, and 10 [5.7]

46. radius = 5 centimeters, diameter = 10 centimeters, and circumference = 10πcm [2.4]

47. $\{6, 4\}$ [5.7]   **48.** \$300 at 8%, \$600 at 12% [2.5]

49. 2.5 hours [2.4]

50. Rachel is 12 and David is 16. [2.5]

CHAPTER 7

EXERCISE SET 7.1 (p. 314)

1. 1   **3.** x^{31} **5.** $\frac{1}{729}$ **7.** $\frac{27y^{18}}{x^6}$ **9.** $\frac{y^8}{x^{20}}$ **11.** $\frac{25}{9x^6y^8}$

13. $\frac{3}{4}$ **15.** 10   **17.** 0   **19.** 3   **21.** 1   **23.** $7x$

25. x^2 **27.** $\frac{x}{5}$ **29.** $-\frac{a^3}{2}$ **31.** $\frac{1}{x}$ **33.** $\frac{3}{a^2}$ **35.** $5x$

37. $-2x^2y^3$ **39.** x **41.** $216x^3$ **43.** x **45.** $-a$

47. $3a$ **49.** xy^2 **51.** xy^2 **53.** $|x+3|$ **55.** 3.16

57. 2.92   **59.** 1.59   **61.** -2.62 **63.** 7.42

65. 2.04   **67.** .90   **69.** .30   **71.** 3.8   **73.** 144π

75. x **77.** 8   **79.** $2x^3y$

81. The square root of a is equal to b, $b \geq 0$, if $b^2 = a$. Because $b^2 \geq 0$, if a is negative, then no real number b exists such that $b^2 = a$. Because b^3 is negative if b is negative, and $\sqrt[3]{a} = b$ if $b^3 = a$, then it follows that the cube root of a negative number is negative.

83. $\sqrt{a^2} \geq 0$ for all values at a. If $a < 0$, then $\sqrt{a^2} > 0$ and $\sqrt{a^2} \neq a$; for example, $\sqrt{(-3)^2} = \sqrt{9} = 3$ but $\sqrt{(-3)^2} \neq -3$. Thus, we need to have $\sqrt{a^2} = |a|$.

85.

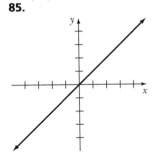

86.

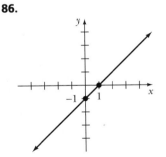

87.

88. D = $\{0, 1, 4\}$, R = $\{0, 1, 2\}$ **89.** D = R = $\mathbb{R}$

90. D = $\mathbb{R}$, R = $\{3\}$ **91.** D = $\mathbb{R}$, R = $[0, \infty)$

92. $D_f = R_{f^{-1}} = \{0, .5, 1, 4\}$, $R_f = D_{f^{-1}} = \{0, .7, 1, 2\}$, $f^{-1} = \{(0, 0), (.7, .5), (1, 1), (2, 4)\}$

93. $f^{-1}(x) = -3x$

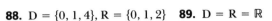

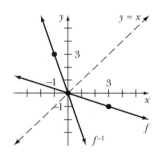

94. $g^{-1}(x) = \frac{x-1}{2}$

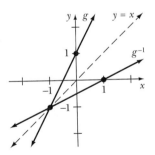

95.

96.

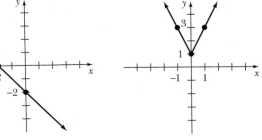

EXERCISE SET 7.2 (p. 323)

1. $\sqrt{2}$ **3.** $3\sqrt[7]{z}$ **5.** $a\sqrt{b}$ **7.** $\sqrt[4]{x^3}$ **9.** $\sqrt[5]{x^2y^3}$

11. $\sqrt{4^{-3}} = \frac{1}{8}$ **13.** $\sqrt[4]{x^2y^3}$ **15.** $\sqrt[6]{a^3b^2}$ **17.** $ba^{1/2}$

19. $a^{1/2}b^{3/2}$ **21.** $2x^2y^{1/2}$ **23.** $a^{5/4}b^{1/4}$

25. $(a + b)^{1/2}$ **27.** $(a - b)^2$ **29.** 5   **31.** -27 **33.** $\frac{1}{6}$

35. $-\frac{1}{8}$ **37.** $\frac{1}{3}$ **39.** $\frac{25}{4}$ **41.** 2   **43.** -243 **45.** 9

47. 27   **49.** 27   **51.** 15   **53.** 32   **55.** $\frac{1}{20}$ **57.** 3.162

59. 7.238   **61.** 1.817   **63.** 5.308   **65.** 1.481

67. 2.933   **69.** $6x$ **71.** $a^{5/12}$ **73.** $\dfrac{y^9}{x^2}$ **75.** x^4

77. a^4 **79.** $\dfrac{2x^2}{y}$ **81.** $a^{1/2}$ **83.** $-3x^{3/2}y^{1/5}$

85. $a^{2/3}b^2$ **87.** $\dfrac{1}{2x^2y^3}$ **89.** 4   **91.** $\frac{1}{4}$ **93.** $-\dfrac{1}{27}$

95. $f^{-1}: x = 2\sqrt{y}, \quad D_f = R_{f^{-1}} = [0, \infty), \quad R_f = D_{f^{-1}} = [0, \infty)$

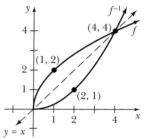

97. $f^{-1}: x = -\sqrt{y}, \quad D_f = R_{f^{-1}} = [0, \infty), \quad R_f = D_{f^{-1}} = (-\infty, 0]$

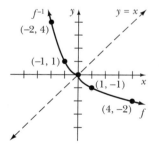

99. $f^{-1}: x = \sqrt{y} - 1, \quad D_f = R_{f^{-1}} = [0, \infty), \quad R_f = D_{f^{-1}} = [-1, \infty)$

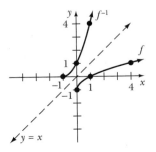

101. $f^{-1}: x = \sqrt{4 - y}, \quad D_f = R_{f^{-1}} = (-\infty, 4], \quad R_f = D_{f^{-1}} = [0, \infty)$

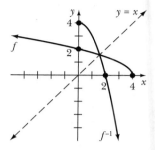

103. $f^{-1}: S = -\sqrt{22} - 2, \quad D_f = R_{f^{-1}} = [0, \infty), \quad R_f = D_{f^{-1}} = (-\infty, -2]$

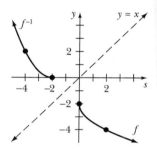

105. $T^{-1} = \{(x, y) \mid x = \mid 3y \mid\}, \quad D_T = R_{T^{-1}} = (-\infty, \infty), \quad R_T = D_{T^{-1}} = [0, \infty)$

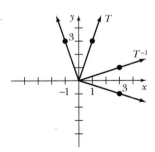

107. $V^{-1} = \{(x, y) \mid x = -\mid 2y \mid\}, \quad D_V = R_{V^{-1}} = (-\infty, \infty), \quad R_V = D_{V^{-1}} = (-\infty, 0]$

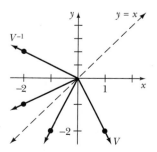

109. $T^{-1} = \{(u, v) \mid u = -3 \mid v \mid\}$, $D_T = R_{T^{-1}} = (-\infty, \infty)$, $R_T = D_{T^{-1}} = (-\infty, 0]$

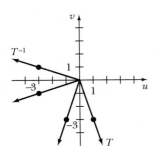

111. $D = [-3, \infty)$, $R = (-\infty, 1]$

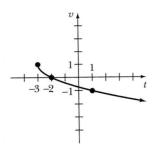

113. $D = (-\infty, 1]$, $R = [-1, \infty)$

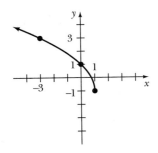

115. $D = R = (-\infty, \infty)$

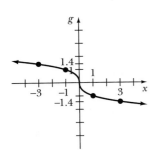

117. $D = R = [0, \infty)$

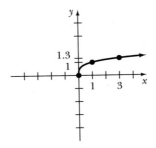

119. By defining $a^{1/n}$ to be equal to $\sqrt[n]{a}$, a to the exponent $\frac{1}{n}$ and the nth root of a have the same meaning.

121. First determine a set of ordered pairs, S, that gives us the graph of f. Then interchange the coordinates of the ordered pairs in S. This new set determines the graph of f^{-1}.

123. 6   **124.** $|x|$ **125.** x **126.** $|y|$
127. $5^{1/2}$ or $\sqrt{5}$ **128.** $5^{1/2}$ or $\sqrt{5}$
129. $3^{1/3}$ or $\sqrt[3]{3}$ **130.** $2^{1/4}$ or $\sqrt[4]{2}$

EXERCISE SET 7.3 (p. 329)

1. $3\sqrt{2}$ **3.** $-3x\sqrt{5}$ **5.** $2\sqrt[3]{3}$ **7.** $6x\sqrt[4]{2}$
9. $2x^2y^3\sqrt{5y}$ **11.** $a^3b^3\sqrt[3]{ab}$ **13.** $a\sqrt[3]{a + b^2}$
15. $2ab^3c^4\sqrt{2ab}$ **17.** xy^2 **19.** $-2x^2$ **21.** $2x\sqrt[7]{x}$
23. $10\sqrt{3}$ **25.** $\dfrac{\sqrt{5}}{3}$ **27.** $\dfrac{\sqrt[3]{3}}{2}$ **29.** $\dfrac{\sqrt{a}}{2b}$ **31.** $5x$
33. $8xy^3\sqrt{5x}$ **35.** $\dfrac{a\sqrt{15a}}{3}$ **37.** $\dfrac{\sqrt{14}}{7}$ **39.** $\dfrac{\sqrt[4]{686}}{7}$
41. $3x^2\sqrt[3]{3x^2}$ **43.** $\dfrac{\sqrt[4]{108x^2}}{6x}$ **45.** $2\sqrt[4]{72x^3}$
47. $\dfrac{3y\sqrt[3]{4x^2y}}{2x}$ **49.** $|3x|\sqrt{3}$ **51.** $|x^2y^3|$
53. $-2x\sqrt[5]{2x}$ **55.** $\dfrac{\sqrt{2}\,|a|}{2b^2}$
57. $\sqrt{3}$ **59.** $\sqrt{2}$ **61.** $\sqrt[3]{3}$
63. $\sqrt[4]{5}$ **65.** $\sqrt[6]{5}$ **67.** $\sqrt{2}$ **69.** $\sqrt[12]{a^6}$ **71.** $\sqrt[12]{c^3}$
73. $\sqrt{18}$ **75.** $\sqrt[6]{243}$ **77.** $\sqrt{\dfrac{25}{7}}$ **79.** $\sqrt[6]{7}$ **81.** $\sqrt[4]{45}$
83. $\sqrt[8]{xy^2}$ **85.** $\sqrt[6]{108}$ **87.** $\sqrt[15]{x^5y^3}$ **89.** $\sqrt[4]{12}$
91. $\sqrt[6]{\dfrac{x^2}{y^3}}$ **93.** $\sqrt[12]{a^{13}}$ **95.** $\sqrt[12]{a^{25}}$ **97.** $7^{2/3}$
99. $a = 0$, $\sqrt{a + b} = \sqrt{0 + b} = \sqrt{b}$, $\sqrt{a} + \sqrt{b} = \sqrt{0} + \sqrt{b} = 0 + \sqrt{b} = \sqrt{b}$
101. $2x^2 + 8xy$ **102.** $x^2 + 7x + 12$ **103.** $1 - x^2$
104. $1 + x^3$

EXERCISE SET 7.4 (p. 334)

1. $8\sqrt{2}$ **3.** $5\sqrt[3]{5x}$ **5.** $9\sqrt[3]{3x} + \sqrt[3]{5x}$ **7.** $9 + 5\sqrt{3}$

9. $-22\sqrt[3]{3y^2}$ **11.** $4x\sqrt[4]{2}$ **13.** $18x\sqrt[3]{x} + 24\sqrt[3]{x}$

15. $-33x^2\sqrt{x}$ **17.** $\frac{13}{12}\sqrt{2}$ **19.** $2\sqrt{3}$ **21.** $-\frac{7}{10}\sqrt[3]{2}$

23. $-\frac{17}{15}\sqrt{5}$ **25.** $7\sqrt{2}$ **27.** $7\sqrt{2}$ **29.** $2 + \sqrt{6}$

31. $10\sqrt{2} + 50\sqrt{3}$ **33.** $2ab - a^2b$

35. $\sqrt{6} + 2\sqrt{2} + 5\sqrt{3} + 10$

37. $2\sqrt{3} - 3\sqrt{2} + \sqrt{6} - 3$

39. $a + \sqrt{5a} - \sqrt{10a} - 5\sqrt{2}$

41. $28 + 10\sqrt{3}$ **43.** $x - 8\sqrt{x} + 16$ **45.** 1 **47.** 1

49. $a - b$ **51.** $x - x^2$ **53.** $a - 5a^{1/2} + 6$

55. $x + 8x^{1/2} + 16$ **57.** $\sqrt{5} + 2$

59. $-\frac{6 + \sqrt{3}}{11}$ **61.** $\sqrt{6} - \sqrt{5}$

63. $-1 + \sqrt{5}$ **65.** $\frac{\sqrt{3}\,y - 6}{y^2 - 12}$ **67.** $\sqrt{y} + 1$

69. $\frac{3\sqrt{2} + 3\sqrt{3} + \sqrt{6} + 3}{3}$ **71.** $(x + y)(\sqrt{x} - \sqrt{y})$

73. $4\sqrt{a} + 6\sqrt{b}$ **75.** $1 - \sqrt[3]{3} + \sqrt[3]{9}$

77. $-(4 + 2\sqrt[3]{9} + 3\sqrt[3]{3})$ **79.** $\sqrt[3]{2} - 1$

81. We add like monomials with the distributive property, such as $4x + 5x = (4 + 5)x = 9x$. In a similar way the distributive property is used to add like radicals. For example, $4\sqrt{2} + 5\sqrt{2} = (4 + 5)\sqrt{2} = 9\sqrt{2}$

83. ± 5 **84.** $2, 4$ **85.** $m = \frac{x - kM}{3k}$

86. $y = \frac{10x - 15}{12}$ **87.** $d = \frac{2ab}{c}$

EXERCISE SET 7.5 (p. 342)

1. 12 **3.** -32 **5.** 23 **7.** 3 **9.** $-\frac{2}{9}$ **11.** 5

13. 1 **15.** $\frac{1}{4}$ **17.** 8 **19.** 12 **21.** 13 **23.** 4 **25.** 2

27. -1 **29.** $\varnothing$ **31.** $\frac{4}{7}$ **33.** $\pm\sqrt{14}$ **35.** 4

37. $y = \frac{x^2 + 45}{9}$ **39.** $y = \frac{x^2 + 2x - 3}{4}$ **41.** $M = \frac{Rc^2}{6G}$

43. $P = \frac{A}{(r + 1)^2}$ **45.** $s = \frac{s - \pi r^2}{2\pi r}$ **47.** $H = \frac{3V^2}{4g}$

49. $x = \pm\sqrt{r^2 - y^2}$ **51.** $y = x^2 - 3x + 1$

53. $a = \frac{b^3 - 64b}{64}$ **55.** $y = \frac{81 - 2x}{3}$

57. 125 lb   **59.** $180{,}048$ mps   **61.** 4.6 in.

63. 60 mph   **65.** 27 mph   **67.** 10.6 **69.** 486 ft

71. $12 - 6\sqrt{2}$ **73.** 41 **75.** $\frac{11}{2}$ **77.** 7 **79.** 12

81. 5 **83.** 4 **85.** 14 **87.** $3, \frac{1}{9}$ **89.** $0, \frac{25}{27}$

91. a. $V = \frac{c}{L_0}\sqrt{L_0^2 - L^2}$ **b.** $c = \frac{L_0 v}{\sqrt{L_0^2 - L^2}}$

93. Let $a = b$ be the original radical equation and $a^n = b^n$ the resulting polynomial equation. A solution to $a^n = b^n$ that is not a solution to $a = b$ is called an *extraneous solution*.

95. Square both sides of the equation.

97. $k = \frac{3}{2}$ **98.** $x = 2$ **99.** $t = 4$ **100.** $k = \frac{27}{5}$

EXERCISE SET 7.6 (p. 349)

1. $y = 4x$, $y = -12$ **3.** $y = 3x^2$, $x = \frac{\sqrt{78}}{3}$

5. $r = \frac{1}{2}\sqrt{s}$, $s = 36$ **7.** $y = \frac{2}{x}$, $y = \frac{1}{6}$

9. $A = \frac{10}{B^2}, B = \frac{\sqrt{5}}{2}$ **11.** $y = \frac{6}{\sqrt[3]{x}}$, $y = -3\sqrt[3]{2}$

13. $A = LW$, $A = 35$ **15.** $a = \frac{1}{3}bcd$, $c = \frac{1}{5}$

17. $y = \frac{1}{10}\frac{xw}{t^2}$, $x = 80$ **19.** $V = kr^3$ **21.** $S = kv^6$

23. $C = \frac{kw}{L}$ **25.** $N = \frac{kP_1P_2}{d}$ **27.** 144 feet

29. $P = 40$ pounds per square inch

31. $40{,}500$ pounds   **33.** $119{,}808$ pounds

35. y changes by a factor of $\frac{1}{9}$; $y_2 = \frac{1}{9}y_1$.

37. The volume changes by a factor of 27; $V_2 = 27\,V_1$.

39. y is inversely proportional to x if a constant k exists, $k \neq 0$, such that $y = \frac{k}{x}$ or $xy = k$.

41. Joint variation means that one quantity, say y, varies directly as two or more quantities, say x and w, that is, $y = kxw$.

42. 100 **43.** $1{,}000{,}000$ **44.** $\frac{1}{1000}$ **45.** $\frac{1}{100{,}000}$

46. 410 **47.** $2{,}610{,}000$

48. 0.00264 **49.** $0.000\ 079\ 3$

EXERCISE SET 7.7 (p. 355)

1. $40{,}000$ **3.** $250{,}000{,}000$

5. $4{,}000{,}000{,}000{,}000{,}000{,}000{,}000{,}000{,}000{,}000{,}000{,}000{,}000$

7. $.000\ 000\ 6$ **9.** $.000\ 000\ 000\ 000\ 1$

11. 8.2×10^{10} **13.** 3×10^{10} **15.** 6.38×10^8

17. 1.0936×10^0 **19.** 2.2×10^{-6} **21.** 8.2×10^9

23. 1.7×10^{-11} **25.** 9×10^{12} **27.** 2.4×10^{-1}

29. 4×10^{11} **31.** 2.8×10^{-2} **33.** 2.7×10^7

35. 3.6×10^2 sec $= 6 \times 10^0$ minutes

37. 2.39×10^{11} **39.** 5×10^{12} **41.** 1.912×10^{16}

43. 1.25×10^{20} **45.** 8×10^{12} **47.** 3.84×10^7

49. 7.2×10^1 **51.** 3×10^6 **53.** 2×10^{-4}

55. 1.1259×10^{15} **57.** 5.1538×10^{47}

59. -8.4729×10^{11} **61.** 1.0486×10^{-14}

63. $D_s = \dfrac{2 \times 10^{30}}{\frac{4}{3}\pi(3.43 \times 10^{26})}$, $D_e = \dfrac{6 \times 10^{24}}{\frac{4}{3}\pi(2.62 \times 10^{20})}$,

$\dfrac{D_e}{D_s} = 3.93 \approx 4$

65. a. Move the decimal point in 2.35 six places to the right.

   b. Move the decimal point in 2.35 six places to the left.

67. ± 3 **68.** $\pm\sqrt{2}$ **69.** $\pm\dfrac{5\sqrt{3}}{3}$ **70.** $\pm 3\sqrt{3}$

71. $\{8\}$ **72.** $\{8, -3, 0\}$ **73.** $\{8, -3, .\overline{66}, -\frac{4}{5}, 0\}$
74. $\{\sqrt{2}, \sqrt[3]{-5}\}$

EXERCISE SET 7.8 (p. 364)

 1. $\{0\}$ **3.** $\{.25, .\overline{25}, \sqrt[3]{-8}, 0, -1\}$
 5. $\{\sqrt{-4}, 3 + 4i, i\}$ **7.** $\{4, -i^2\}$ **9.** B
11. $\{\sqrt{-7}, -6i, 1 - i\}$ **13.** true   **15.** true
17. false   **19.** true   **21.** false
23.

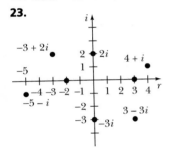

25. $3 + 9i$ **27.** $1 - 10i$ **29.** $14 - 4i$ **31.** $5 + 7i$

33. $\dfrac{11}{15} + \dfrac{1}{12}i$ **35.** 10 **37.** $6 + 12i$ **39.** $-16 - 12i$

41. $1 + 7i$ **43.** $-10 - 24i$ **45.** $2i$ **47.** -4

49. $2 - 11i$ **51.** 29 **53.** $\dfrac{2}{29} - \dfrac{5}{29}i$ **55.** i

57. $\dfrac{\sqrt{2}}{3} - \dfrac{1}{3}i$ **59.** $\dfrac{2}{13} - \dfrac{3}{13}i$ **61.** $0 - \dfrac{2}{5}i$

63. $-\dfrac{1}{2} - \dfrac{1}{2}i$ **65.** ± 4 **67.** $\pm 2i$ **69.** $\pm\sqrt{7}i$

71. $\pm 2\sqrt{5}i$ **73.** $\pm\dfrac{5\sqrt{2}}{2}i$ **75.** $0, 2$ **77.** -6

79. $-6\sqrt{2}$ **81.** $-\sqrt{6}i$ **83.** $\dfrac{\sqrt{5}}{3}i$ **85.** $\frac{2}{5}$

87. $\dfrac{\sqrt{2}}{5}i$ **89.** $3\sqrt{3}i$ **91.** $22\sqrt{5}i$ **93.** $5\sqrt{2}i$

95. $(a + 5i)(a - 5i)$ **97.** $x(x + 10i)(x - 10i)$
99. $(x + 1)(x - 1)(x + i)(x - i)$
101. No, $1 + 1 = 2 \notin A$.   **103.** yes
105. $-i$ **107.** 1 **109.** 1 **111.** -1 **113.** $-i$

115. $\left(\dfrac{\sqrt{2}}{2} + \dfrac{\sqrt{2}}{2}i\right)^2 = \left(\dfrac{\sqrt{2}}{2} + \dfrac{\sqrt{2}}{2}i\right)\left(\dfrac{\sqrt{2}}{2} + \dfrac{\sqrt{2}}{2}i\right)$

$= \dfrac{2}{4} + \dfrac{2}{4}i + \dfrac{2}{4}i + \dfrac{2}{4}i^2$

$= \dfrac{2}{4} + \dfrac{4}{4}i - \dfrac{2}{4}$

$= i$

117. $\sqrt[3]{a} = b$ if $b^3 = a$. Thus, $(-i)^3 = (-i)(-i)(-i) = -1(-i) = i$

119. $\begin{vmatrix} a & -b \\ i & 1 \end{vmatrix} = a \cdot 1 - (-b)i = a + bi$

121. Any real number, r, can be written as $r + 0i$, which is in the form $a + bi$.

123. In both cases we use the property $(a + b)^2 = a^2 + 2ab + b^2$. Thus, $(1 + 2x)^2 = 1^2 + 2(2x) + (2x)^2 = 1 + 4x + 4x^2$, and $(1 + 2i)^2 = 1 + 2(2i) + (2i)^2 = 1 + 4i + 4i^2 = -3 + 4i$.

CHAPTER REVIEW EXERCISES (p. 367)

 1. $\dfrac{x^8}{9}$ **2.** a^{23} **3.** 8 **4.** $\dfrac{x^{16}}{y^2}$ **5.** 3 **6.** $4a^{3/4}$ **7.** $\dfrac{9x}{y^2}$

 8. -4 **9.** $4i$ **10.** $2a$ **11.** $|2b|$ **12.** $2x\sqrt{2x}$
13. $2\sqrt[3]{3}$ **14.** $9\sqrt{5x}$ **15.** $5\sqrt{2} - 2\sqrt{10}$

16. $\dfrac{12 - 9i}{5}$ **17.** $\dfrac{\sqrt{15}}{5}i$ **18.** $-\dfrac{\sqrt[3]{75}}{5}$ **19.** $12 + 6i$

20. $6 - 3\sqrt{2} - 2\sqrt{3} + 3\sqrt{6}$ **21.** -6
22. 1.2533×10^{-17} **23.** $27 - 8i$ **24.** $\pm 2\sqrt{2}i$

25. 6 **26.** $\{6, 14\}$ **27.** $b = \dfrac{a^2 - 19a + 25}{9}$

28. $R \pm\sqrt{Z^2 - X^2}$ **29.** 81
30.   **31.**

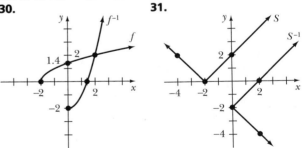

32. 2.7×10^{12} **33.** $\frac{16}{5}$ **34.** 4
35.

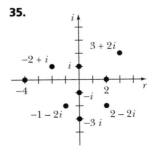

36. $x = 36$ **37.** 729 units

1. x^{-10} **2.** $\frac{1}{4}$ **3.** $x^{5/2}$ **4.** $a^{1/3}b^3$ **5.** $-2x^3\sqrt[3]{3x^2}$

6. -6.863×10^{13} **7.** $-5\sqrt{2}$ **8.** $6 + 2\sqrt{2}$

9. $\dfrac{20 + 12i}{17}$ **10.** $4\sqrt{5}$ **11.** $14 + 6\sqrt{5}$ **12.** -23

13. $-1 + 10i$ **14.** $2x\sqrt[3]{2x^2}$ **15.** 5   **16.** ± 27 **17.** 5

18. $\pm 2\sqrt{3}i$ **19.** $L = \dfrac{1}{4\pi^2 Cf^2}$ **20.** $2^{2x} + 2 + 2^{-2x}$

21. $D_f = R_{f^{-1}} = (-\infty, 1]$, $R_f = D_{f^{-1}} = [0, \infty)$

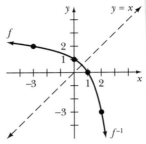

22. ± 3 **23.** 1.34 seconds   **24.** $x = \pm\frac{\sqrt{6}}{2}$

25. $W = 34.66$

CHAPTER 8

1. ± 5 **3.** $\pm 3\sqrt{2}i$ **5.** $\pm\frac{2}{3}$ **7.** $2 \pm \sqrt{5}$

9. $-1 \pm 10i$ **11.** $\dfrac{1 \pm \sqrt{7}}{3}$ **13.** $\dfrac{1 \pm \sqrt{10}}{2}$

15. $-6 \pm \sqrt{2}i$ **17.** $x^2 + 20x + 100 = (x + 10)^2$

19. $y^2 - 4y + 4 = (y - 2)^2$

21. $x^2 + 7x + \frac{49}{4} = (x + \frac{7}{2})^2$

23. $x^2 - \frac{2}{3}x + \frac{1}{9} = (x - \frac{1}{3})^2$ **25.** $-1, 3$

27. $3 \pm i$ **29.** $-6 \pm 2\sqrt{10}$ **31.** $0, -4$

33. $\dfrac{-3 \pm \sqrt{13}}{2}$ **35.** $\dfrac{1 \pm \sqrt{26}}{5}$

37. $-1 \pm \sqrt{3}$ **39.** $-1, -\frac{1}{2}$

41. $\dfrac{-5 \pm \sqrt{13}}{2}$ **43.** $-1 \pm \sqrt{3}i$ **45.** $\frac{1}{2}, -3$

47. 3   **49.** $-6 \pm \sqrt{2}$ **51.** $1 \pm \sqrt{3}i$ **53.** $\pm\frac{2}{3}$

55. $-3 \pm \sqrt{11}$ **57.** $4, -\frac{1}{2}$ **59.** 3

61. $\dfrac{\sqrt{5} \pm 5}{2}$ **63.** $\dfrac{-1 \pm \sqrt{1 + 3\sqrt{5}}}{3}$

65. $\dfrac{2i \pm \sqrt{14}i}{2}$ **67.** $-4, \frac{1}{3}$ **69.** $-1, \dfrac{1 \pm \sqrt{3}i}{2}$

71. $\dfrac{-\sqrt{2} \pm \sqrt{2 - 12\sqrt{7}}}{6}$ **73.** $1 + 2i, 1 + i$

75. $\dfrac{-5 \pm \sqrt{29}}{2}$ **77.** $\dfrac{-3 \pm \sqrt{39}i}{4}$

79. First add 2 to both sides of the equation to produce $x^2 + 6x = 2$. Then add $(\frac{1}{2} \cdot 6)^2 = 9$ to both sides to give $x^2 + 6x + 9 = 2$ or $(x + 3)^2 = 2$. Next take the square root of both sides so that $x + 3 = \pm\sqrt{2}$, and then subtract 3. The answer is $x = -3 \pm\sqrt{2}$.

81. If $x = 0$ or -1, then we would be dividing by zero in the equation $\dfrac{1}{x} + \dfrac{x}{x + 1} = \dfrac{2}{3}$.

83. $E = mc^2$ **84.** $h = \dfrac{V}{\pi r^2}$

85. $P = \dfrac{A}{(1 + r)^2}$ **86.** $h = \dfrac{S - 2\pi r^2}{2\pi r}$

1. $-3, -1$ **3.** $2, 6$ **5.** $0, -8$ **7.** $-2, 5$

9. $\pm\sqrt{7}$ **11.** $\dfrac{-7 \pm \sqrt{41}}{2}$ **13.** $\dfrac{1 \pm \sqrt{61}}{2}$

15. $1 \pm 3i$ **17.** $-4 \pm \sqrt{857}i$ **19.** $0, \sqrt{3}$

21. $\dfrac{-1 \pm \sqrt{2}i}{4}$ **23.** two equal real roots

25. two unequal real roots

27. two unequal imaginary roots

29. two unequal real roots

31. two unequal imaginary roots

33. $\pm\frac{1}{2}, \pm\dfrac{\sqrt{10}}{2}i$ **35.** $\pm\sqrt{2}, \pm i$ **37.** $\pm\sqrt{7}, \pm 2i$

39. $\pm i, \pm 5i$ **41.** $\pm 2\sqrt{2}, \pm i$ **43.** $\frac{1}{5}, -\frac{1}{4}$

45. $\pm\frac{1}{2}, \pm\frac{\sqrt{7}}{7}$ **47.** 9   **49.** $125, -1$ **51.** -1

53. $c = \sqrt{a^2 + b^2}$ **55.** $s = \frac{\sqrt{3}d}{3}$ **57.** $t = \pm\frac{\sqrt{d}}{4}$

59. $v = \pm\sqrt{\dfrac{Fr}{m}}$ **61.** $x = \pm\sqrt{y^2 + (z - 1)^2}$

63. $r = \pm\sqrt{\dfrac{3V}{\pi h}}$ **65.** $r = \dfrac{-\pi s \pm \sqrt{\pi^2 s^2 + 4\pi s}}{2\pi}$

67. $v = \pm\sqrt{\dfrac{r^2 g}{h + r}}$ **69.** $\sqrt{3}, \frac{1}{\sqrt{3}}$ **71.** $\dfrac{1 \pm \sqrt{15}i}{4}$

73. $1, -1$ **75.** $3 \pm 4i$ **77.** $\sqrt{3}, 2\sqrt{3}$

79. $h = 2\sqrt{7}, b = 8\sqrt{7}$ **81.** $W = 2, L = 5$

83. No; $b^2 - 4ac$ would have to be equal to zero, but this would mean that two equal real roots exist.

85. $L = \dfrac{W \pm \sqrt{5}\,W}{2}$ **87.** $x = \dfrac{-y \pm \sqrt{3 - 2y^2}}{3}$

89. $x_1 + x_2 = \dfrac{-b + \sqrt{b^2 - 4ac}}{2a} + \dfrac{-b - \sqrt{b^2 - 4ac}}{2a}$

$$= -\dfrac{b}{2a} + \dfrac{\sqrt{b^2 - 4ac}}{2a} - \dfrac{b}{2a} - \dfrac{\sqrt{b^2 - 4ac}}{2a}$$

$$= -\dfrac{2b}{2a}$$

$$= -\dfrac{b}{a}$$

91. yes **93.** no **95.** yes **97.** $-1, \dfrac{1 \pm \sqrt{3}i}{2}$

99. $\dfrac{3}{2}, \dfrac{-3 \pm 3\sqrt{3}i}{4}$ **101.** $\pm 1, \pm i$

103. When the equation is in the form $x^2 + bx + c = 0$ and b is divisible by 2.

105. An equation that is not quadratic but can be written in the form $au^2 + bu + c = 0$ is said to be quadratic in form.

107. $[0, \infty)$ **108.** $(-\infty, 0]$ **109.** $(-\infty, 3]$

110. $[-1, \infty)$ **111.** 6 **112.** $-\frac{1}{2}$ **113.** ± 1 **114.** $\pm\frac{1}{2}$

115. $D_f = R_f = D_{f^{-1}} = R_{f^{-1}} = \mathbb{R}$

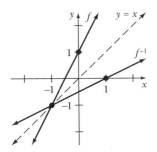

116. $D_f = R_f = D_{f^{-1}} = R_{f^{-1}} = \mathbb{R}; f(x) = f^{-1}(x)$

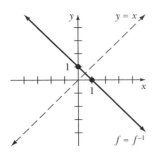

117. $D_f = R_{f^{-1}} = [0, \infty), R_f = D_{f^{-1}} = [1, \infty)$

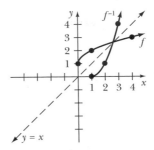

118. $D_f = R_{f^{-1}} = [2, \infty), R_f = D_{f^{-1}} = [0, \infty)$

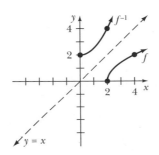

EXERCISE SET 8.3 (p. 392)

1–9. $V(0, 0), R = [0, \infty)$

1.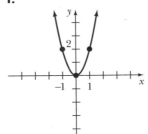

3.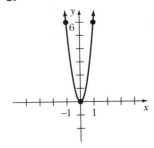

5.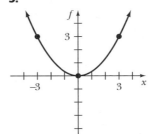

7.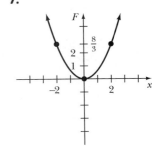

9.

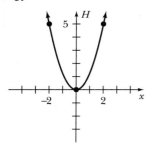

21. $V(0, 1)$, roots $= \{\pm i\}$, no x-intercepts, $R = [1, \infty)$

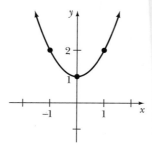

11–17. $V(0, 0)$, $R = (-\infty, 0]$

11.

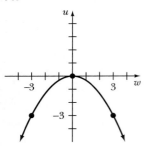

13.

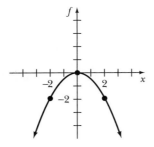

23. $V(0, 4)$, roots $= x$-intercepts $= \{\pm 2\}$, $R = (-\infty, 4]$

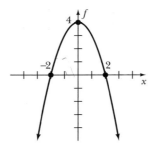

15.

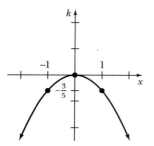

17.

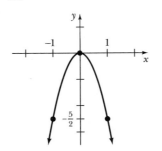

25. $V(0, -6)$, roots $= x$-intercepts $= \{\pm\sqrt{3} \approx \pm 1.7\}$, $R = [-6, \infty)$

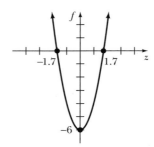

19. $V(0, -1)$, roots $= x$-intercepts $= \{\pm 1\}$, $R = [-1, \infty)$

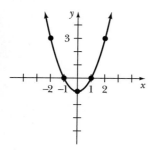

27. $V(0, 1)$, roots $= \{\pm\frac{1}{2} i\}$, no x-intercepts, $R = [1, \infty)$

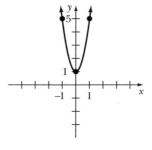

29. $V(0, -2)$, roots $= \left\{ \pm \frac{\sqrt{6}}{3}i \right\}$, no x-intercepts, $R = (-\infty, -2]$

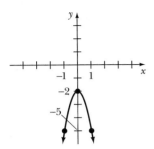

31. $V(0, 0)$, root $= x$-intercept $= \{0\}$, $R = [0, \infty)$

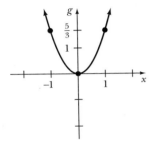

33. $V(0, 1)$, roots $= \{\pm 2i\}$, no x-intercepts, $R = [1, \infty)$

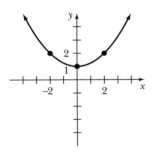

35. $V\left(0, -\frac{2}{3}\right)$, roots $= \left\{ \pm \frac{\sqrt{2}}{3}i \right\}$, no x-intercepts, $R = \left(-\infty, -\frac{2}{3}\right]$

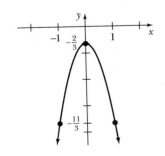

37. $V\left(0, \frac{3}{4}\right)$, roots $= \left\{ \pm \frac{\sqrt{6}}{4}i \right\}$, no x-intercepts, $R = \left[\frac{3}{4}, \infty\right)$

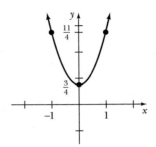

39. $V\left(0, \frac{1}{3}\right)$, roots $= \left\{ \pm \frac{\sqrt{2}}{2}i \right\}$, no x-intercepts, $R = \left[\frac{1}{3}, \infty\right)$

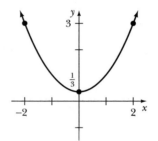

41. $V(0, -1)$, roots $= \left\{ \pm \frac{\sqrt{7}}{2}i \right\}$, no x-intercepts, $R = (-\infty, -1]$

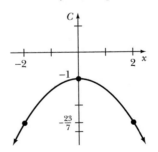

43. $V(0, 0)$, root $= \{0\}$

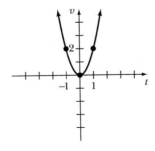

45. $V(0, 0)$, root $= \{0\}$

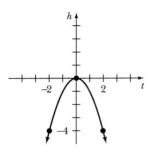

47. $S^{-1} = \{(x, y) \mid x = y^2\}, D_S = R_{S^{-1}} = \mathbb{R}, R_S = D_{S^{-1}} = [0, \infty)$

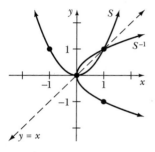

49. $S^{-1} = \{(x, y) \mid x = -4y^2\}, D_S = R_{S^{-1}} = \mathbb{R}, R_S = D_{S^{-1}} = (-\infty, 0]$

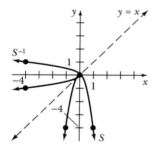

51. $S^{-1} = \{(x, y) \mid x = 4y^2 - 1\}, D_S = R_{S^{-1}} = \mathbb{R}, R_S = D_{S^{-1}} = [-1, \infty)$

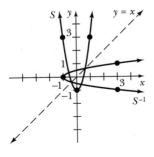

53. $S^{-1} = \{(x, y) \mid x = -y^2 + 1\}, D_S = R_{S^{-1}} = \mathbb{R}, R_S = D_{S^{-1}} = (-\infty, 1]$

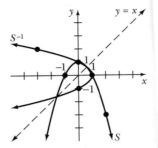

55. $S^{-1} = \{(x, y) \mid x = \frac{1}{3}y^2 + 1\}, D_S = R_{S^{-1}} = \mathbb{R}, R_S = D_{S^{-1}} = [1, \infty)$

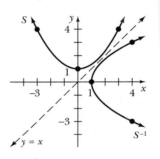

57. $S^{-1} = \{(x, y) \mid x = \frac{3}{4}y^2 + \frac{1}{2}\}, D_S = R_S = \mathbb{R}, R_S = D_{S^{-1}} = [\frac{1}{2}, \infty)$

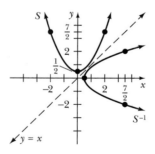

59. $S^{-1} = \{(x, y) \mid x = \frac{2}{3}y^2 - \frac{1}{4}\}, D_S = R_S = \mathbb{R}, R_S = D_{S^{-1}} = [-\frac{1}{4}, \infty)$

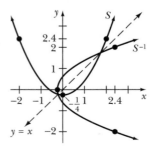

61. $S^{-1} = \{(x, y) \mid x = 1.2y^2\}, D_S = R_S = \mathbb{R},$
$R_S = D_{S^{-1}} = [0, \infty)$

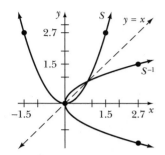

63. The parabola $y = ax^2 + c$ opens upward if a is greater than zero and downward if a is less than zero.

65. The vertex is the minimum point if $a > 0$ and the maximum point if $a < 0$.

67. $x^2 - 6x + 9 = (x - 3)^2$

68. $x^2 + 4x + 4 = (x + 2)^2$

69. $x^2 - 2x + 1 = (x - 1)^2$ **70.** $2, 4$ **71.** $1 \pm \sqrt{2}$

72. $-1 \pm i$ **73.** $2, 4$

EXERCISE SET 8.4 (p. 400)

1. a. $V(2, 0)$ **b.** $[0, \infty)$ **c.** $\{0\}$ **d.** $\{0\}$ **e.** 4
   f. $x = 2$

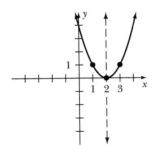

3. a. $V(-2, -1)$ **b.** $[-1, \infty)$ **c.** $\{-3, -1\}$
   d. $\{-3, -1\}$ **e.** 3 **f.** $x = -2$

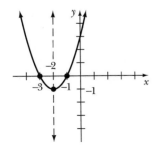

5. a. $V(-3, 0)$ **b.** $[0, \infty)$ **c.** $\{0\}$ **d.** $\{0\}$ **e.** 9
   f. $x = -3$

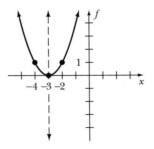

7. a. $V(-3, 1)$ **b.** $[1, \infty)$ **c.** $\{-3 \pm i\}$ **d.** none
   e. 10 **f.** $x = -3$

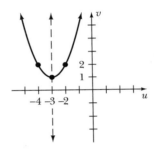

9. a. $V(2, -4)$ **b.** $[-4, \infty)$ **c.** $\{0, 4\}$ **d.** $\{0, 4\}$
   e. 0 **f.** $x = 2$

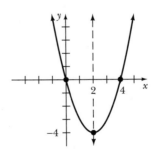

11. a. $V(1, 0)$ **b.** $(-\infty, 0]$ **c.** $\{0\}$ **d.** $\{0\}$ **e.** -1
   f. $x = 1$

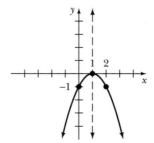

13. a. $V(4, 1)$ **b.** $(-\infty, 1]$ **c.** $\{3, 5\}$ **d.** $\{3, 5\}$
e. -15 **f.** $x = 4$

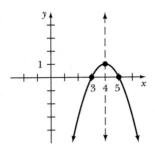

15. a. $V(\frac{1}{2}, \frac{1}{4})$ **b.** $(-\infty, \frac{1}{4}]$ **c.** $\{0, 1\}$ **d.** $\{0, 1\}$ **e.** 0
f. $x = \frac{1}{2}$

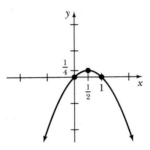

17. a. $V(-1, 3)$ **b.** $(-\infty, 3]$ **c.** $\{-1 \pm \sqrt{3}\}$
d. $\{-1 \pm \sqrt{3}\}$ **e.** 2 **f.** $x = -1$

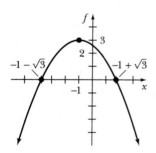

19. a. $V(2, -2)$ **b.** $(-\infty, -2]$ **c.** $\{2 \pm \sqrt{2}i\}$
d. none **e.** -6 **f.** $x = 2$

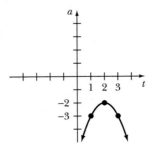

21. a. $V(1, 0)$ **b.** $[0, \infty)$ **c.** $\{1\}$ **d.** $\{1\}$ **e.** 2
f. $x = 1$

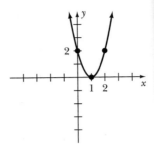

23. a. $V(-1, -3)$ **b.** $[-3, \infty)$ **c.** $\{-2, 0\}$
d. $\{-2, 0\}$ **e.** 0 **f.** $x = -1$

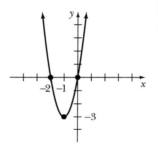

25. a. $V(-2, -4)$ **b.** $[-4, \infty)$ **c.** $\{-3, -1\}$
d. $\{-3, -1\}$ **e.** 12 **f.** $x = -2$

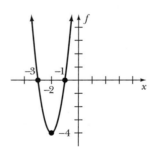

27. $V(0, -4)$ **b.** $[-4, \infty)$ **c.** $\{\pm\sqrt{2}\}$ **d.** $\{\pm\sqrt{2}\}$
e. -4 **f.** $x = 0$

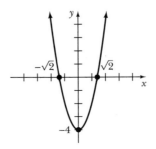

29. $V(-3, -2)$ **b.** $(-\infty, -2]$ **c.** $\{-3 \pm i\}$
d. none **e.** -20 **f.** $x = -3$

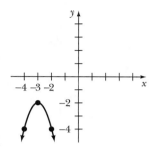

31. a. $V(\frac{1}{3}, \frac{4}{3})$ **b.** $(-\infty, \frac{4}{3}]$ **c.** $\{-\frac{1}{3}, 1\}$ **d.** $\{-\frac{1}{3}, 1\}$
e. 1 **f.** $x = \frac{1}{3}$

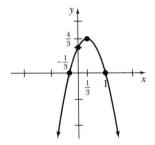

33. $V(\frac{2}{3}, -\frac{1}{3})$ **35.** $V(\frac{5}{4}, \frac{5}{8})$ **37.** $V(-\frac{3}{20}, -\frac{169}{80})$
39. $V(4, 256)$ **41.** $V(5, 25)$
43. $V(1, 1), \{1 \pm i\}$

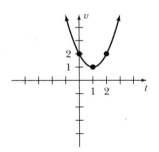

45. $V(1, 1), \{0, 2\}$

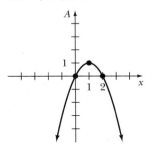

47. $S^{-1} = \{(x, y) \mid x = y^2 - 6y + 9\}, D_S = R_{S^{-1}} = \mathbb{R},$
$R_S = D_{S^{-1}} = [0, \infty)$

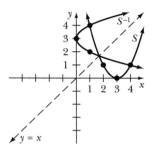

49. $S^{-1} = \{(x, y) \mid x = -y^2 - 2y - 2\}, D_S = R_{S^{-1}} = \mathbb{R},$
$R_S = D_{S^{-1}} = (-\infty, -1]$

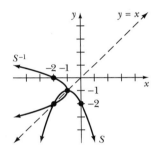

51. $S^{-1} = \{(x, y) \mid x = -y^2 + 2y\}, D_S = R_{S^{-1}} = \mathbb{R}, R_S =$
$D_{S^{-1}} = (-\infty, 1]$

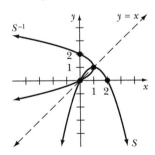

53. $S^{-1} = \{(x, y) \mid x = -2y^2 - 4y - 1\}, D_S = R_{S^{-1}} = \mathbb{R},$
$R_S = D_{S^{-1}} = (-\infty, 1]$

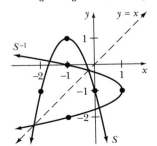

55. $a = 1, b = 0, c = -1$ **57.** $a = 2, b = -4, c = 3$

59. $a = -2, b = 0, c = 2$ **61.** $a = -1, b = 6, c = -8$

63. yes   **65.** No; it is below the x-axis.

67. No; it is above the x-axis.   **69.** yes

71. The axis of symmetry is the vertical line that intersects the x-axis at the point halfway between the x-intercepts.

73.

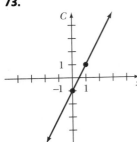

74.

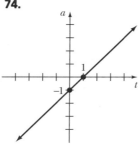

75.

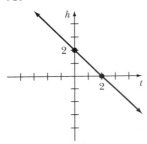

76. $f(4) = 256$ **77.** $C(200) = 1600$

EXERCISE SET 8.5 (p. 406)

1. 16 feet at 1 second; 2 seconds

3. 36 feet at $\frac{3}{2}$ seconds; 3 seconds

5. $x = 0; f(40) = 130$ **7.** 4 items; $P(4) = \$900$

9. 15 and 15; maximum value = 225

11. 6 and 14; minimum value = 204

13. -15 and 15; minimum value = -225

15. 30 yards by 60 yards; maximum area = 1800 square yards

17. $h = b = 20$ centimeters; maximum area = 200 square centimeters

19. 256 feet   **21.** 3 seconds

23. 3 by 6; maximum area = 30

25. 50 yards by 100 yards; maximum area = 5000 square yards

27. \$410,000

29. a. $A(x) = \dfrac{\pi + 4}{16\pi}x^2 - \dfrac{1}{2\pi}x + \dfrac{1}{4\pi}$

b. $x = \dfrac{4}{\pi + 4}$; minimum area $= \dfrac{1}{4(\pi + 4)}$ square meters

31. It is a parabola, $f(x) = ax^2 + bx + c$, that opens downward. This occurs when $a < 0$.

33. Two unequal real roots

34. Two unequal imaginary roots

35. $D_f = \{x \mid x \neq -5\}$ **36.** $D_g = \{x \mid x \neq \pm 3\}$

37. $D_f = \{x \mid x \geq 9\}$ **38.** $D_h = \{x \mid x \leq \frac{2}{3}\}$

39. $x > 2$

40. $x < -2$

41. $x \geq 5$

EXERCISE SET 8.6 (p. 416)

1. $x < 0$ or $x > 2$ **3.** $-1 \leq x \leq 3$

5. $x \leq -2$ or $x \geq 2$ **7.** $0 \leq x \leq 3$

9. $x \geq 1$ **11.** $\mathbb{R}$ **13.** $x < 4$ **15.** $x < 2$

17. $x < 3$ or $x > 7$ **19.** $0 < x \leq 3$

21. $x < 0$ or $x > 2$ **23.** $-1 \leq x \leq 3$

25. $x \leq -2$ or $x \geq 2$ **27.** $0 \leq x \leq 3$

29. $x < 3$ or $x > 7$ **31.** $0 < x \leq 3$

33. $(-\infty, -2) \cup (3, \infty)$ **35.** $(-\infty, \infty)$

37. $(0, 3)$ **39.** $(-\infty, -1] \cup [0, 1]$ **41.** $(-\infty, 0)$

43. $(-\infty, -\sqrt{3}] \cup [\sqrt{3}, \infty)$ **45.** $\emptyset$

47. $(-\infty, -2] \cup [1, 3]$ **49.** $(-\infty, -3] \cup \{0\}$

51. $\{4\}$ **53.** $(-2, -1]$ **55.** $(-\frac{5}{2}, 1]$ **57.** $[-12, 6)$

59. $(-\infty, 0) \cup [\frac{15}{2}, \infty)$ **61.** $(-\infty, 0) \cup (1, 4)$

63. $(-\infty, -2] \cup [0, 3)$ **65.** $(0, \infty)$

67. $(-3, -2) \cup (3, \infty)$ **69.** $(-\infty, -3) \cup (3, \infty)$

71. $(-1, 0) \cup (1, 2) \cup (2, \infty)$ **73.** $(-\infty, 1]$

75. Sonya was not allowed to attend a Russian university because they were closed to women. She was not allowed to travel abroad to study, but she got around this problem with a marriage of convenience and went to Germany. Sonya was not permitted to attend the University of Berlin, but she was able to study with Weirstrass and thus earned a Ph.D.

CHAPTER REVIEW EXERCISES (p. 418)

1. $-5, 3$ **2.** $-5, 3$ **3.** $-5, 3$ **4.** $\pm\sqrt{11}$

5. $\dfrac{1 \pm \sqrt{23}i}{4}$ **6.** $-3 \pm \sqrt{89}$

7. $0, \pm 4i$ **8.** $\pm 2i, \pm 3i$ **9.** $1, \frac{1}{8}$ **10.** $V = \pm\sqrt{\dfrac{2k}{m}}$

11. $t = \dfrac{-v \pm \sqrt{v^2 + 2gs}}{g}$ **12.** two unequal real roots

13. two unequal imaginary roots

14. two equal real roots

15. $V(0, 0), \{0\}, [0, \infty)$

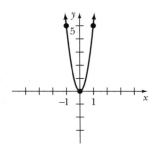

16. $V(0, 0), \{0\}, (-\infty, 0]$

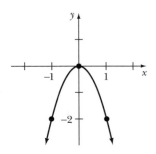

17. $V(0, -2), \left\{\pm\frac{\sqrt{6}}{3}\right\}, [-2, \infty)$

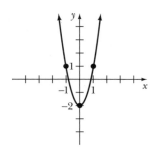

18. $V(0, 1), \{\pm 1\}, (-\infty, 1]$

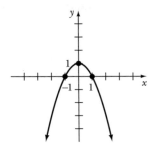

19. $V(1, -2), \{0, 2\}, [-2, \infty)$

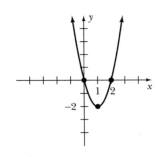

20. $V(-3, 1), \{-4, -2\}, (-\infty, 1]$

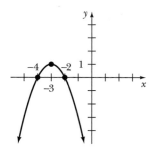

21. $x < 0$ or $x > 5$ **22.** $-3 \le x \le 3$

23. $x < -4$ or $x \ge 1$

24. $x < 0$ or $x = 1$

25. $x < -2$ or $0 < x < 3$

26. $S^{-1} = \{(x, y) \mid x = y^2 - 1\}, D_S = R_{S^{-1}} = \mathbb{R}, R_S =$
$D_{S^{-1}} = [-1, \infty)$

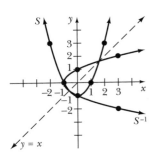

27. $2i, -\frac{i}{2}$ **28.** $W = -1 + \sqrt{2}, L = 1 + \sqrt{2}$
29. 5   **30.** -3 and 3; minimum product $= -9$

CHAPTER TEST (p. 419)

  1. $-5, 1$ **2.** $-5, 1$ **3.** $-5, 1$ **4.** $0, \pm 2$
  5. $0, \pm 5i$ **6.** $1, \frac{1}{125}$ **7.** $-5 + 2\sqrt{30}$
  8. $\dfrac{1 \pm \sqrt{14}i}{3}$ **9.** $x \leq -3$ or $x \geq 3$
  10. $d = \sqrt{\dfrac{gm_1 m_2}{F}}$ **11.** $Z = \dfrac{c}{ab}\sqrt{a^2b^2 - b^2x^2 - a^2y^2}$
  12. $-3 \leq x \leq 0$ or $x \geq 3$ **13.** $-1 < x \leq 2$
  14. two unequal real roots   **15.** two unequal real roots
  16. two unequal imaginary roots
  17. $V(0, 0), \{0\}, [0, \infty)$

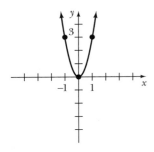

18. $V(0, 0), \{0\}, (-\infty, 0]$

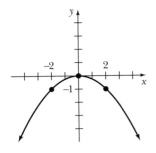

19. $V(0, -1), \{\pm 1\}, [-1, \infty)$

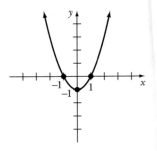

20. $V(0, 2), \left\{\pm\frac{\sqrt{6}}{3}\right\}, (-\infty, 2]$

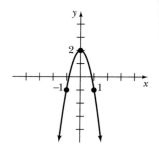

21. $V(2, 4), \{0, 4\}, (-\infty, 4]$

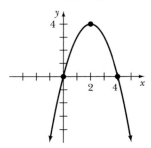

22. $S^{-1} = \{(x, y) \mid x = y^2 + 6y + 9\}, D_S = R_{S^{-1}} = \mathbb{R}, R_S$
$= D_{S^{-1}} = [1, \infty)$

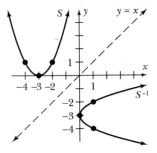

23. $2 \pm 3i$ **24.** $\sqrt{5}, 2\sqrt{5}$
25. $L = W = 3$;   maximum area $= 9$

CHAPTER 9

EXERCISE SET 9.1 (p. 426)

1. $x^2 + y^2 = 1$ **3.** $x^2 + y^2 = 49$
5. $x^2 + y^2 = 10$ **7.** $x^2 + y^2 = \frac{1}{36}$
9. $C(0, 0), r = 1$

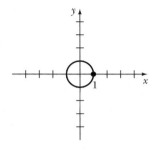

11. $C(0, 0), r = \sqrt{12}$

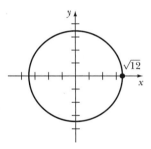

13. $C(0, 0), r = 2$

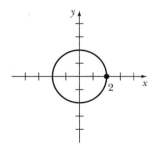

15. $x^2 + y^2 = 25$

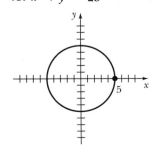

17. $x^2 + y^2 = 8$

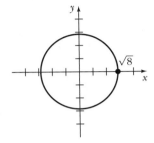

19. $x^2 + y^2 = 4$

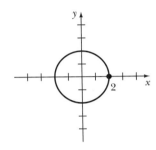

21. $x^2 + y^2 = 9$

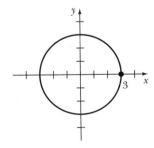

23. circle

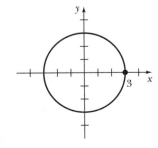

25. parabola

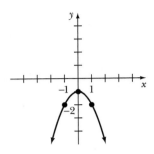

27. circle

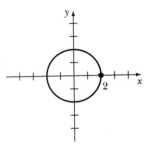

29. $(x - 2)^2 + (y - 3)^2 = 1$

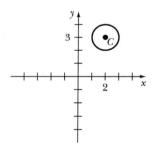

31. $(x + 3)^2 + (y + 4)^2 = 3$

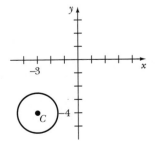

33. $(x - 4)^2 + y^2 = \frac{1}{4}$

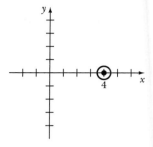

35. $(x + 2)^2 + (y - 1)^2 = 1$

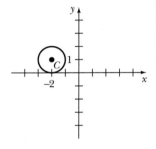

37. $C(3, 2), r = 2$

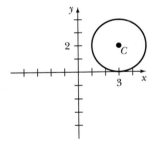

39. $C(-4, -5), r = 1$

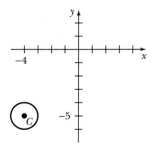

41. $(0, 3), r = 1$

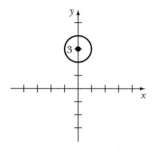

43. $C(0, 0), r = \sqrt{3}$

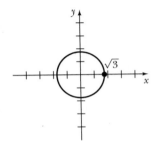

45. $x^2 + y^2 - 6x - 4y + 9 = 0$
47. $x^2 + y^2 + 2x + 4y - 2 = 0$ **49.** $C(0, 1), r = 2$
51. $C(1, 4), r = 3$ **53.** $C(-3, 1), r = \sqrt{2}$
55. $C(\frac{3}{2}, 1), r = \sqrt{2}$
57. $(x - 3)^2 + (y + 1)^2 = 10$
59. $(x + 2)^2 + y^2 = 18$
61. $(x - 3)^2 + (y - 4)^2 = 25$
63. $S^{-1} = \{(x, y) \mid y^2 + x^2 = 9\} = S, D_S = R_{S^{-1}} =$
$[-3, 3], R_S = D_{S^{-1}} = [-3, 3]$

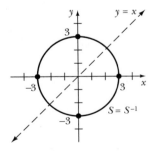

65. $S^{-1} = \{(x, y) \mid (y + 3)^2 + (x + 1)^2 = 1\}, D_S =$
$R_{S^{-1}} = [-4, -2], R_S = D_{S^{-1}} = [-2, 0]$

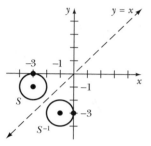

67. $S^{-1} = \{(x, y) \mid (y + 1)^2 + (x - 1)^2 = 4\}, D_S =$
$R_{S^{-1}} = [-3, 1], R_S = D_{S^{-1}} = [-1, 3)$

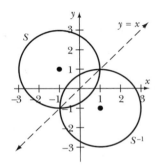

69. $S^{-1} = S = \{(x, y) \mid (x + 2)^2 + (y + 2)^2 = 1\}, D_S =$
$R_{S^{-1}} = R_S = D_{S^{-1}} = [-3, -1]$

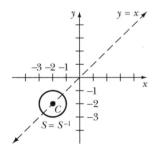

71. $(x - 1)^2 + (y - 4)^2 = 1$ **73.** $(x - 2)^2 + (y + 1)^2 = 4$
75. $S^{-1} = \{(x, y) \mid y^2 + x^2 = r^2\}$. Thus, S and S^{-1} have
the same equation, $x^2 + y^2 = r^2$. Therefore, $S =$
S^{-1}, and their graphs are the same circle.
77. $D = \{x \mid x \geq 0\}$ **78.** $D = \{x \mid x \leq -1$ or $x \geq 1\}$
79. $D = \{x \mid -5 \leq x \leq 5\}$

80.

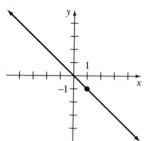

81.

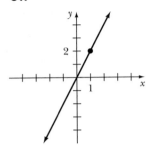

5. $D = [-1, 1], R = [-\sqrt{3}, \sqrt{3}]$

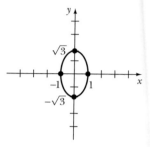

82.

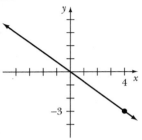

7. $D = [-2, 2], R = [-3, 3]$

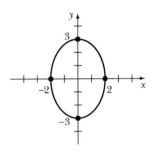

EXERCISE SET 9.2 (p. 436)

1. $D = [-4, 4], R = [-2, 2]$

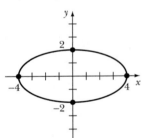

9. $D = [-3, 3], R = [-4, 4]$

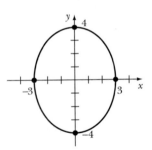

3. $D = [-2, 2], R = [-6, 6]$

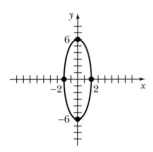

11. $D = [-\sqrt{5}, \sqrt{5}], R = [-3, 3]$

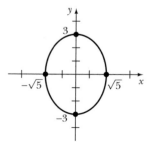

13. $D = [-3, 3], R = [-\sqrt{2}, \sqrt{2}]$

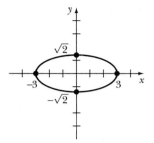

15. $D = [-\sqrt{7}, \sqrt{7}], R = [-\sqrt{5}, \sqrt{5}]$

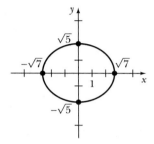

17. $D = \left[-\frac{1}{2}, \frac{1}{2}\right], R = \left[-\frac{1}{3}, \frac{1}{3}\right]$

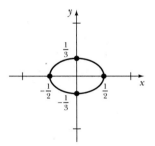

19.

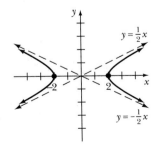

21.

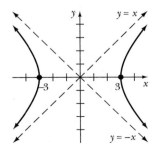

23.

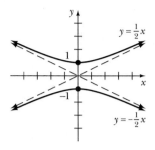

25.

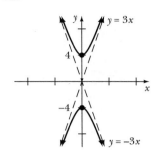

27.

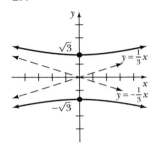

29.

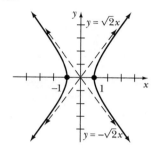

31.

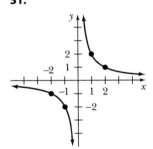

33.

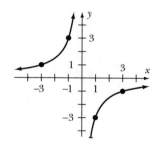

35.

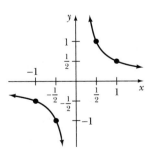

37.

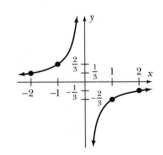

39. ellipse

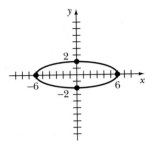

47. circle

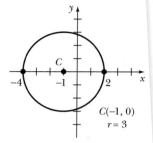

$C(-1, 0)$
$r = 3$

41. parabola

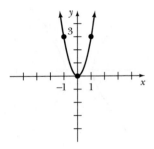

49. parabola

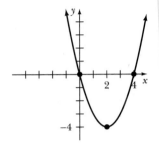

43. parabola

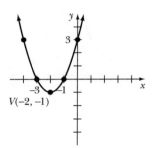

$V(-2, -1)$

51. parabola

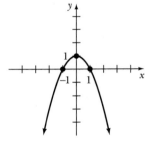

45. parabola

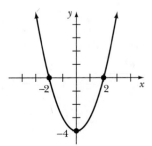

53. hyperbola

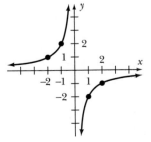

55. $4y^2 + 25x^2 = 100$

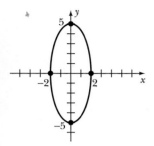

57. $y^2 - x^2 = 1$

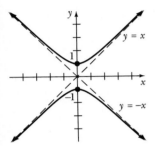

59. $9x^2 + 16y^2 = 144$

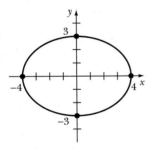

61. $yx = -2$

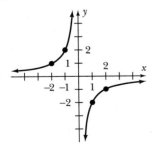

63. $x = -2y^2 - 1$

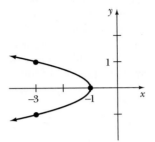

65. $25x^2 - 4y^2 = 100$

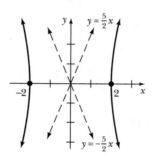

67. $y^2 + x^2 + 6y = -8$

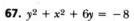

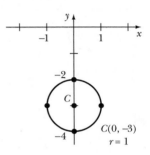

69. $9y^2 + x^2 = 9$

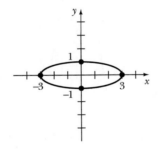

71. $y = \dfrac{1}{x^2}$

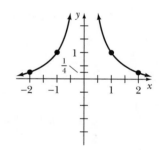

73. $y = \dfrac{-2}{x^2}$

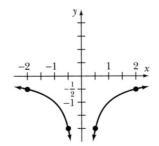

75. $y^2 = \dfrac{4}{x^2}$

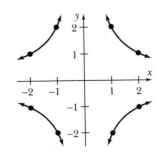

77. A parabola is used in the design of a telescope. Circles are used in the design of car engines. The orbits of the planets are ellipses. Hyperbolas are used in the construction of suspension bridges.

79. In the equation $Ax^2 + By^2 = C$, replace C with zero and solve the equation $Ax^2 + By^2 = 0$ for y. The two resulting linear equations are the equations of the asymptotes.

81. The graphs will vary.

83.

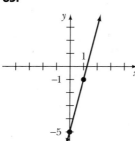

84.

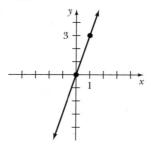

85.

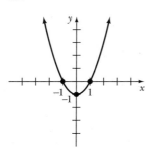

86.

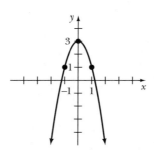

87. 4   **88.** 5   **89.** $5i$ **90.** $\frac{1}{2}i$

EXERCISE SET 9.3 (p. 443)

1. two solutions: $(2, 4), (-1, 1)$

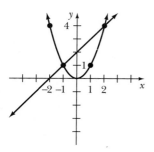

3. two solutions: $(-3, 4), (-4, 3)$

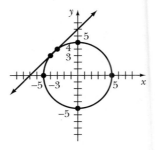

5. two solutions: $(-\sqrt{5}, 2), (\sqrt{5}, 2)$

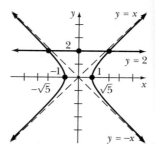

7. two solutions: $(-1, 0), (1, 0)$

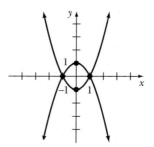

9. four solutions: $(\sqrt{5}, \sqrt{6}), (\sqrt{5}, -\sqrt{6}), (-\sqrt{5}, \sqrt{6}), (-\sqrt{5}, -\sqrt{6})$

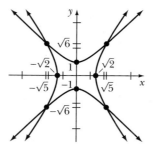

11. no real solutions: $(2i, -3), (-2i, -3)$

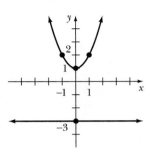

13. no real solutions: $(2i, \sqrt{5}), (-2i, \sqrt{5}), (2i, -\sqrt{5})$,
$(-2i, -\sqrt{5})$

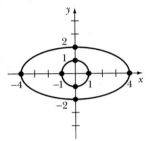

15. $y - x = 1$ **17.** $\emptyset$

19. $(2, \sqrt{2}i), (2, -\sqrt{2}i), (-2, \sqrt{2}i), (-2, -\sqrt{2}i)$

21. $2x^2 - 4y^2 = 8$ **23.** $(-1, -1)$

25. $\left(-\frac{1}{2}, \frac{3}{4}\right), (2, 7)$

27. $(1, 0), (-3, -8)$

29. $(i, 2i), (-i, -2i)$

31. $x^2 + (4 - x)^2 = 6$
$x^2 - 8x + 10 = 0$
$x = 2 + i, y = 2 - i; x = 2 - i, y = 2 + i.$
Thus, $\{2 + i, 2 - i\}$ is the solution.

33. $\{2, 18\}$ **35.** $\{1 + i, 1 - i\}$ **37.** $\{-3, 5\}$

39. $\{2, 3\}$ **41.** $h = 4, b = 7$

43. $r = 3$ mph, $t = 12$ hours

45. $\sqrt{50 - 6\sqrt{41}}$

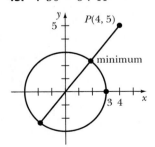

47. $\left(\sqrt{8 - 2\sqrt{11}i}, -1 + \sqrt{11}\right),$
$\left(-\sqrt{8 - 2\sqrt{11}i}, -1 + \sqrt{11}\right),$
$\left(\sqrt{8 + 2\sqrt{11}i}, -1 - \sqrt{11}\right),$
$\left(-\sqrt{8 + 2\sqrt{11}i}, -1 - \sqrt{11}\right)$

49. $\left(\sqrt{2 + \sqrt{3}}, \sqrt{2 - \sqrt{3}}\right),$
$\left(\sqrt{2 - \sqrt{3}}, \sqrt{2 + \sqrt{3}}\right),$
$\left(-\sqrt{2 - \sqrt{3}}, -\sqrt{2 + \sqrt{3}}\right),$
$\left(-\sqrt{2 + \sqrt{3}}, -\sqrt{2 - \sqrt{3}}\right)$

51. A nonlinear system of equations is one that has at least one equation that is not linear.

53.

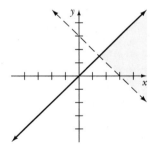

54.

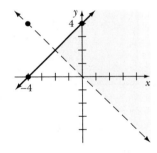

55.

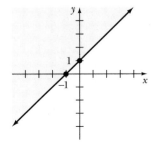

56.

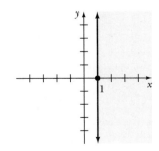

EXERCISE SET 9.4 (p. 448)

1.

3.

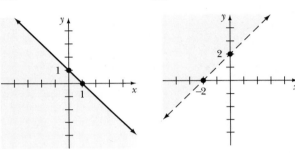

5.

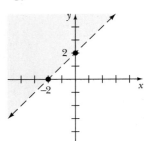

7.

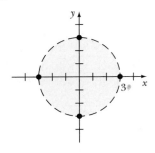

21.

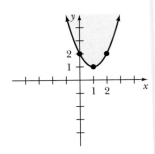

23.

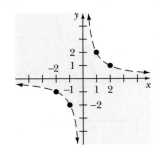

9.

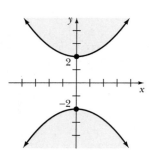

11.

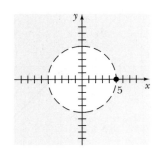

25.

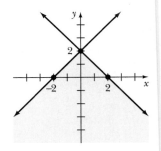

27.

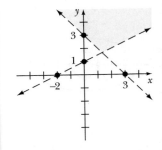

13.

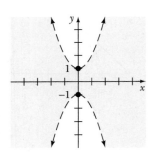

15.

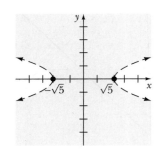

29.

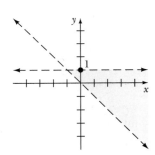

31.

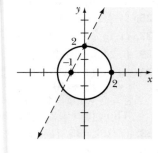

17.

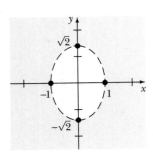

19.

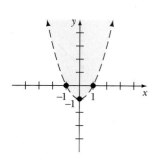

33.

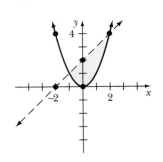

35.

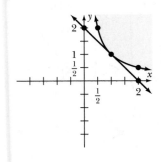

37.

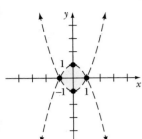

39.

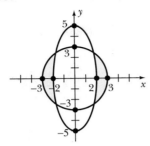

53.

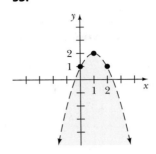

55.

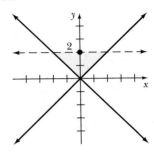

41.

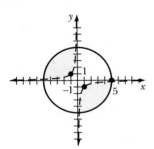

43.

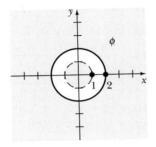

57.

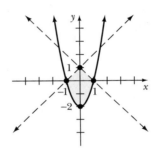

59.

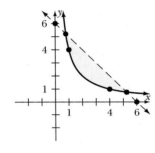

45.

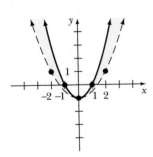

47.

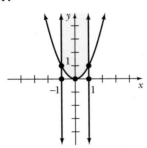

61. A quadratic equation divides the *xy*-plane into two or three regions. We pick a test point from each region and determine the test point(s) that make the quadratic inequality a true statement. Each region containing a test point that resulted in a true statement is then shaded.

CHAPTER REVIEW EXERCISES (p. 449)

1. $x^2 + y^2 = 3$ **2.** $x^2 + y^2 = 10$

3. $(x - 3)^2 + (y + 2)^2 = 25$

4. $C(-1, 2), r = \sqrt{3}$

5. $D\,(-\infty, -3] \cup [3, \infty), R = \mathbb{R}$

49.

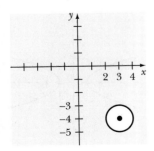

51.

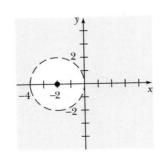

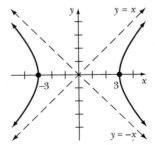

6. $D = R = [-3, 3]$

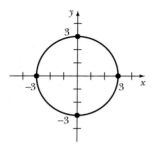

7. $D = [-3, 3], R = [-2, 2]$

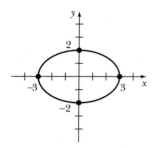

8. $D = R = (-\infty, 0) \cup (0, \infty)$

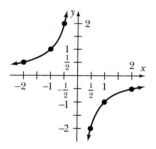

9. $D = R, R = [1, \infty)$

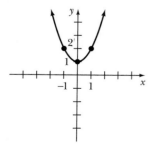

10. $D = R, R = [-1, \infty)$

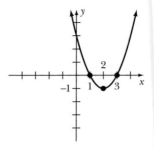

11. $(-4, 16), (2, 4)$ **12.** $\left(1, \frac{2\sqrt{2}}{3}\right), \left(1, \frac{-2\sqrt{2}}{3}\right)$

13. $\varnothing$ **14.** $(2, \sqrt{3}), (2, -\sqrt{3}), (-2, \sqrt{3}), (-2, -\sqrt{3})$

15. $\left(\dfrac{-3 + \sqrt{23}i}{4}, \dfrac{5 + \sqrt{23}i}{4}\right),$
$\left(\dfrac{-3 - \sqrt{23}i}{4}, \dfrac{5 - \sqrt{23}i}{4}\right)$

16. $(-2 + \sqrt{6}, 2 + \sqrt{6}), (-2, -\sqrt{6}, 2 - \sqrt{6})$

17. $3 + \sqrt{2}i, 3 - \sqrt{2}i$

18.

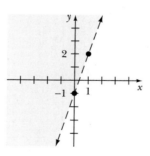

19.

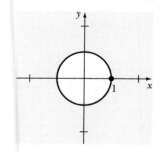

20.

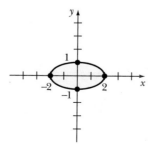

21.

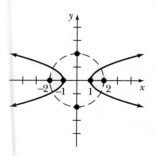

22.

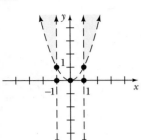

23.

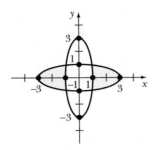

27. $4y^2 + 9x^2 = 36$

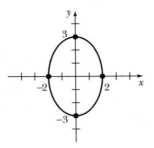

24. $x^2 - 4y^2 = 4$

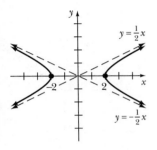

CHAPTER TEST (p. 450)

1. $x^2 + y^2 = 5$ **2.** $(x - 3)^2 + (y + 4)^2 = 25$
3. $C(3, -4), r = 5$
4. $D = \mathbb{R}, R = (-\infty, -2] \cup [2, \infty)$

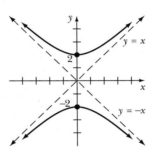

25. $y^2 + x^2 + 4y - 2x = -1$

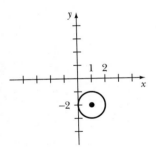

5. $D = [-1, 1], R = [-2, 2]$

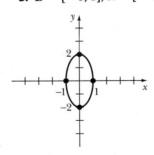

26. $yx = 1$

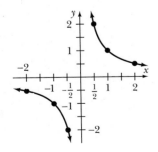

6. $D = \mathbb{R}, R = (-\infty, 4]$

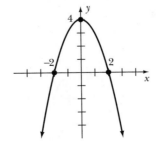

7. $D = R = (-\infty, 0) \cup (0, \infty)$

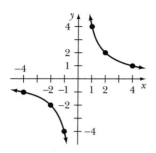

8. $D = R = [-\sqrt{5}, \sqrt{5}]$

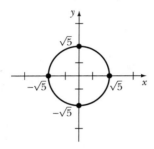

9. $D = \mathbb{R}, R = [-4, \infty)$

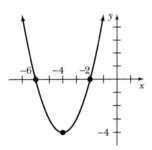

10. $\left(\frac{\sqrt{2}}{2}, \frac{\sqrt{2}}{2}\right), \left(-\frac{\sqrt{2}}{2}, -\frac{\sqrt{2}}{2}\right)$

11. $(1 + 3i, 1 - 3i), (1 - 3i, 1 + 3i)$

12. $(0, 1), (\sqrt{3}, 2), (-\sqrt{3}, 2)$ **13.** $(2, 0), (-2, 0)$

14.

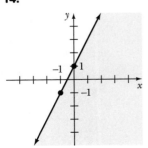

15.

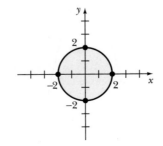

16.

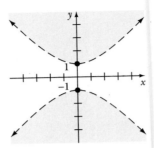

17.

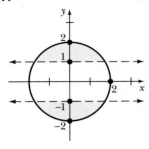

18.

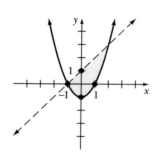

19.

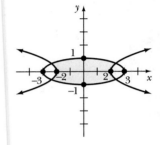

20. $y^2 + 9x^2 = 9$

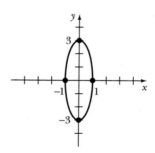

21. $y^2 - 9x^2 = 9$

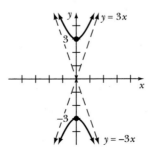

22. $y^2 + x^2 - 6x = -8$

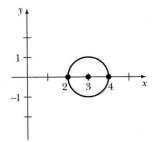

23. $yx = -2$

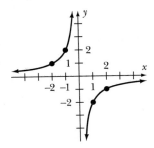

24. $\dfrac{1 + \sqrt{3}i}{2}, \dfrac{1 - \sqrt{3}i}{2}$ **25.** $W = 3 - \sqrt{2}, L = 3 + \sqrt{2}$

CUMULATIVE REVIEW: Chapters 1–9 **(p. 451)**

1. $g^{-1}(x) = x - 2$ [3.6]

2. $\left(\dfrac{f}{g}\right)(x) = 3x - 2 + \dfrac{1}{x + 2}$ [5.4]

3. [8.4]

4. [9.1]

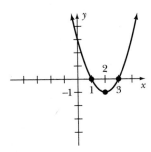

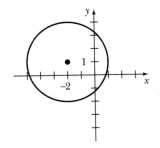

5. [7.2]   **6.** [3.5]

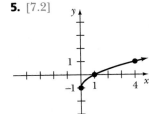

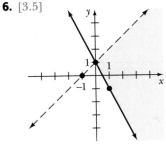

7. $\dfrac{x + 1}{2x - 2}$ [6.4]   **8.** $\dfrac{m^2 + 7m - 8}{(m + 2)(m + 4)}$ [6.3]

9. $1, -8$ [6.5]   **10.** $-\dfrac{67}{2}$ [6.5]   **11.** $\dfrac{13}{19}$ [2.1]

12. $\dfrac{1}{8}, 0$ [2.2]   **13.** $x < -\dfrac{7}{3}$ or $x > 3$ [2.7]

14. $0 \le x \le 3$ [8.6]   **15.** $1 \pm 2\sqrt{2}i$ [8.2]

16. $\dfrac{1}{9}, -\dfrac{1}{5}$ [8.2]   **17.** 1 [7.5]   **18.** $a = \dfrac{b^3 - 64b}{64}$ [7.5]

19. $x = \dfrac{5}{2}y$ [2.3]   **20.** $T_1 = \dfrac{V_1 T_f}{V_f}$ [6.6]

21. $x = \dfrac{w - 1}{w + 1}$ [6.5]   **22.** $F = \dfrac{9}{5}C + 32$ [2.3]

23. $g = \dfrac{2V_0 t - 2S}{t^2}$ [6.5]   **24.** $\left(\dfrac{1}{9}, \dfrac{7}{27}\right)$ [4.1]

25. $(2, 3, -4)$ [4.3]   **26.** $\dfrac{20}{21}$ [4.5]   **27.** $x = \pm 4$ [4.5]

28. $D = \{x \mid x \ne \pm 3\}$, roots $= \{\pm\sqrt{7}\}$ [6.1, 6.2]

29. $R_2 = 18$ ohms [6.6]   **30.** $k = 1, a = 2\sqrt[4]{2}$ [7.6]

31. $k = -9, y = -\dfrac{45}{2}$ [7.6]   **32.** $w = kmd$ [7.6]

33. 99 pounds [7.6]   **34.** 185,000,000,000 [7.7]

35. 0.000 000 000 000 000 1 [7.7]   **36.** 3×10^{10} [7.7]

37. 1.7×10^{-12} [7.7]

38. 5000 minutes; 83 hours [7.7]

39. $D_S = R_{S^{-1}} = \mathbb{R}, R_S = D_{S^{-1}} = [0, \infty)$ [7.2]

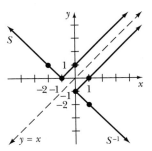

40. 15 [2.1]   **41.** $S = -4, L = 34$ [2.2]

42. $\{5, 6, 7\}$ [2.2]   **43.** $\{2, 4, 6, 8\}$ [5.7]

44. 3 [5.7]   **45.** $\{28, 8\}$ [6.6]

46. $\{5, 6\}$ [6.7]   **47.** $\dfrac{-3}{5}$ [6.7]

48. $(\sqrt{3}, i), (\sqrt{3}, -i), (-\sqrt{3}, i), (-\sqrt{3}, -i)$ [9.3]

49. $W = 5, L = 10$ [5.7]

50. 20 meters, 14 meters, and 14 meters [2.6]

51. Square: 3 centimeters; triangle: 3, 5, and
6 centimeters [2.4]

52. $r = 6$ feet, $h = 3$ feet, and $V = 108\pi$ cubic feet [2.4]

53. $V = 72$ cubic meters, $S = 108$ square meters [2.3]

54. $D = -6, E = -2$, and $F = 9$ [4.3]   **55.** 7400 [2.5]

56. 18 grams of 70% and 12 grams of 85% [4.2]

57. 3 liters [2.5]

58. fund = $3500, bonds = $5000 [4.2]

59. $10,000 at 8.75% and $8000 at 12.5% [2.5]

60. 94% [2.5]   **61.** 184 points [2.6]

62. 9 nickels and 12 dimes [4.2]

63. 9 pennies, 54 nickels, and 17 quarters [2.5]

64. Wendy is 12, and Marsha is 8 [2.5]

65. 5 hours [2.4]   **66.** 15 mph [6.7]

67. car: 49 mph, 392 miles; plane: 147 mph, 220.5 miles [2.4]

68. Everest is 29,140 feet high, and Shasta is 14,160 feet high. [4.2]

69. Shortest piece = 4 feet, second piece = 5 feet, and longest piece = 11 feet. [4.3]

70. 20, 32, and 36 inches [6.6]   **71.** 375 milliliters [6.6]

72. He must write 2.6 more pages to complete the paper; he will need 11.6 days to write the paper. [6.6]

73. 8 hours [6.7]   **74.** 70 feet after 2 seconds [8.5]

75. smallest value = $\frac{1}{2}$; numbers = $-\frac{1}{2}$ and $\frac{1}{2}$. [8.5]

CHAPTER 10

EXERCISE SET 10.1 (p. 461)

1.

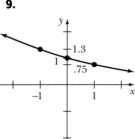

3.

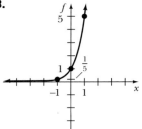

13.

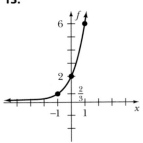

15.

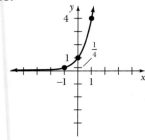

5.

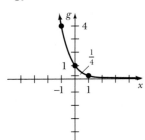

7.

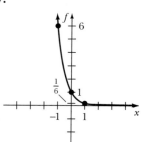

17.

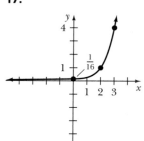

19.

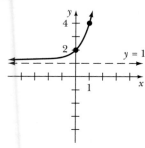

9.

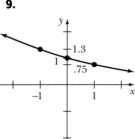

11.

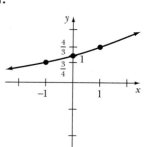

21.

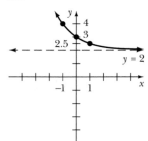

23.

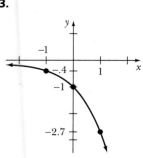

25.

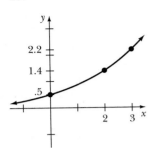

27.

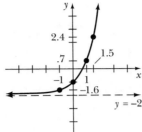

65. For any real number x, 2^x is greater than or equal to zero. Therefore, no value of x exists such that $2^x = -2$.

66. $S^{-1} = \{(3, 1), (7, 2), (8, 6)\}$, $D_S = R_{S^{-1}} = \{1, 2, 6\}$, $R_S = D_{S^{-1}} = \{3, 7, 8\}$. S is a one-to-one function.

67. $S^{-1} = \{(x, y) \mid x = 3\}$, $D_S = R_{S^{-1}} = \mathbb{R}$, $R_S = D_{S^{-1}} = \{3,\}$; S is a function but not a one-to-one function.

68. $S^{-1} = \{(x, y) \mid x = y^2\}$, $D_S = R_{S^{-1}} = \mathbb{R}$, $R_S = D_{S^{-1}} = [1, \infty)$; S is a function but not a one-to-one function.

69. $S^{-1} = \{(x, y) \mid x = 2y\}$, $D_S = R_S = D_{S^{-1}} = R_{S^{-1}} = \mathbb{R}$; S is a one-to-one function.

70. 125 **71.** 9 **72.** $\frac{1}{16}$

EXERCISE SET 10.2 (p. 468)

1.

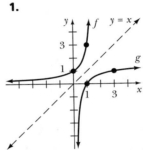

3.

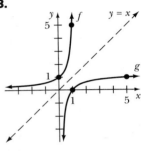

29.

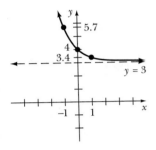

31. 2 **33.** -5 **35.** 2 **37.** $\emptyset$ **39.** -3 **41.** $-\frac{1}{3}$
43. $-\frac{5}{7}$ **45.** $-\frac{3}{2}$ **47.** $\frac{1}{2}$ **49.** $-\frac{4}{15}$ **51.** 0 **53.** -4
55. 2 **57.** $\frac{1}{12}$

59.

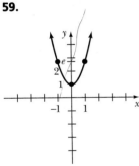

61.

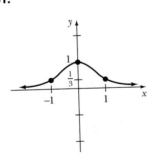

5.

7. $D = (0, \infty)$, $R = \mathbb{R}$

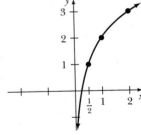

63.

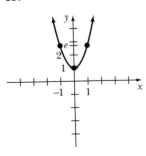

9. $D = (1, \infty)$, $R = \mathbb{R}$

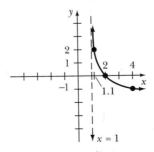

11. $D = (2, \infty), R = \mathbb{R}$

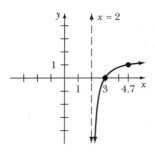

13. $D = (\frac{5}{2}, \infty), R = \mathbb{R}$

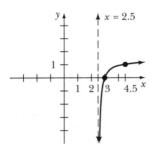

15. $D = (-\infty, -1) \cup (1, \infty)$ **17.** $D = (-3, 0) \cup (3, \infty)$
19. $D = (-\infty, -2) \cup (1, \infty)$ **21.** $(-\infty, -3) \cup (\frac{2}{3}, \infty)$
23. $32 = 2^5$ **25.** $1 = e^0$ **27.** $\frac{1}{27} = 3^{-3}$
29. $5 = 25^{1/2}$ **31.** $4 = \log_2 16$ **33.** $\frac{1}{4} = \log_{81} 3$
35. $-3 = \log_{1/2} 8$ **37.** $1 = \log_5 5$ **39.** $y = 0$
41. $y = -1$ **43.** $x = 1$ **45.** $x = e^{-1/3}$ **47.** $b = 3$
49. $b = \frac{1}{4}$ **51.** $b = 8$ **53.** 15 **55.** $\emptyset$ **57.** $-3, 2$
59. 2 **61.** ± 2 **63.** 5 **65.** ± 3 **67.** $1, -\frac{3}{2}$
69. -3 **71.** $\dfrac{7 \pm \sqrt{89}}{2}$ **73.** $b = 5^{3/2}$

75.

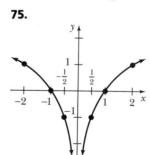

77.

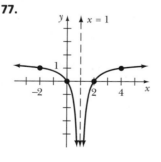

79. The points $\{(-1, \frac{1}{3}), (0, 1), (1, 3)\}$ determine the graph of $y = 3^x$. Therefore, the points $\{(\frac{1}{3}, -1), (1, 0), (3, 1)\}$ determine the graph of $y = \log_3 x$.
81. a^{12} **82.** x^{-8} **83.** a^7 **84.** 8 **85.** a **86.** y^{12}

EXERCISE SET 10.3 (p. 475)

1. $4\log_2 5$ **3.** 4 **5.** $\frac{1}{2}\log_2 3$ **7.** $\log_2 x + \log_2 y$
9. $1 + \log_2 11 + \log_2 n$ **11.** $\log_2 3 + 4\log_2 x$
13. $\log 3 - \log 5$ **15.** $2\log x - 2$
17. $-2\ln 3$ **19.** $\log w + \log x - \log y - \log z$
21. $2\log_3 5 + 4\log_3 x - 4 - 7\log_3 y$
23. $-2 + \frac{1}{2}\log x$
25. $\frac{2}{3}\log_b x + \frac{3}{4}\log_b y$
27. $\frac{3}{2}\log_b x - \frac{1}{2}\log_b y$
29. $3\log y + \frac{1}{2}\log z - \frac{1}{3}\log x$
31. $\frac{1}{2} + 5\ln y$ **33.** $\log_b xy$ **35.** $\log \dfrac{x^3}{y^4}$
37. $\log_2 2\sqrt{x}$ **39.** $\log \dfrac{xy}{z}$ **41.** $\ln \dfrac{x^4}{zy^{2/3}}$
43. $\log_3 \dfrac{x}{27}$ **45.** 1.2 **47.** 1.7 **49.** $-.8$
51. $-.6$ **53.** $-.7$ **55.** $.3$ **57.** $\frac{3}{4}$ **59.** $\frac{3}{2}$ **61.** $\frac{25}{81}$
63. 7 **65.** $\emptyset$ **67.** $-\frac{3}{5}$ **69.** 4 **71.** $1, e^2$ **73.** $1, 16$
75. e^{-1}, e^{-2} **77.** $10^{-1/2}, 100$ **79.** $4, -1$
81. Proof: Let $y_1 = \log_b x_1$ and $y_2 = \log_b x_2$. Then $x_1 = b^{y_1}$ and $x_2 = b^{y_2}$. Now

$$\begin{aligned}
\log_b \frac{x_1}{x_2} &= \log_b \frac{b^{y_1}}{b^{y_2}} && \frac{a^m}{a^n} = a^{m-n} \\
&= \log_b b^{y_1-y_2} && \log_b b^c = c \\
&= y_1 - y_2 \\
&= \log_b x_1 - \log_b x_2
\end{aligned}$$

83. $\log_b(x_1 + x_2) = \log_2(1 + 1) = \log_2 2 = 1$, $\log_b x_1 + \log_b x_2 = \log_2 1 + \log_2 1 = 0 + 0 = 0$.
85. $\dfrac{\log_b x_1}{\log_b x_2} = \dfrac{\log_2 1}{\log_2 2} = \dfrac{0}{1} = 0$, $\log_b x_1 - \log_b x_2 = \log_2 1 - \log_2 2 = 0 - 1 = -1$.
87. The domain of $\log_b x$ is $\{x \mid x > 0\}$. If we solve an equation and obtain a negative or zero value of x, then $\log_b x$ is not a real number.
88. 9.7×10^4 **89.** 2.8763×10^{11}
90. 5.141×10^{-4} **91.** 1.472×10^{-8}

EXERCISE SET 10.4 (p. 480)

1. 0.60206 **3.** 0.17026 **5.** -1.77469
7. 3.91190 **9.** -5.71806 **11.** -11.50948
13. 13.93520 **15.** -12.05750 **17.** 0.72803
19. 7.72665 **21.** -8.25483 **23.** 15.22246

25. -9.46937 **27.** 1.3764 **29.** 0.2406

31. 1.3715×10^{14} **33.** 100.7155 **35.** 0.0001 **37.** 4

39. $\dfrac{\log 8}{\log 5} = 1.2920$ **41.** $\log 6 = .7782$

43. $\dfrac{\log 12 - 2\log 6}{\log 6} = -0.6131$ **45.** $\ln 4 = 1.3863$

47. $\dfrac{\ln 9}{.01} = 219.7225$ **49.** $\dfrac{-3}{\log 2} = -9.9658$

51. $-\dfrac{\log 81}{\log 2} = -6.3398$ **53.** $\dfrac{1 - \ln .6}{4} = .3777$

55. 1.8383×10^9 **57.** 2.3298×10^{-11}

59. -3.7702 **61.** -0.5250 **63.** 2.4032×10^{-42}

65. 119.5759 **67.** 1.2677×10^{30} **69.** 5.1538×10^{47}

71. An antilogarithm is the number whose logarithm we know.

73. 0.583333 **75.** 0.645635 **76.** $t = \dfrac{A - B}{r}$

77. $r = \dfrac{A - B - t}{t}$ **78.** $I_0 = \dfrac{I}{K}$ **79.** $t = \dfrac{LB - LA}{R}$

80. $3 = 2^y$ **81.** $I = 10^M$ **82.** $3 = \log x$

83. $.02t = \ln 1.2$

EXERCISE SET 10.5 (p. 488)

1. 1.1133 **3.** 3.7856 **5.** 0.4329 **7.** -2.3377

9. 3.1699 **11.** 3.3219 **13.** $\dfrac{\log_8 3}{\log_8 2}$ **15.** $\dfrac{\ln 5}{\ln 6}$

17. $\dfrac{\log_5 7}{\log_5 10}$ **19.** $\dfrac{\log .23}{\log e}$

21. $t = \dfrac{\ln A_0 - \ln A}{k}$ **23.** $k = \dfrac{\ln (x - 45) - \ln C}{t}$

25. $R = \log A - \log P$ **27.** $t = \dfrac{\log Q - \log 6000}{2\log 2}$

29. $t = \dfrac{\log A - \log P}{\log(1 + r)}$ **31.** $E = 10^{12.2} \cdot 10^{1.44M}$

33. $[H^+] = \dfrac{K_w}{[OH^-]}$ **35.** $y = e^{kt}$ **37.** $A_0 = \dfrac{A}{10^M}$

39. $Q = Q_0 2^{-t/h}$ **41.** $\$5427$ **43.** 1997

45. 9.3 years **47.** $\$4038$

49. a. 2027 **b.** 2004 **c.** 1999 **51.** 7.5%

53. a. 1000 **b.** $16,000$ **c.** 6.045×10^{26}

55. $37,900$ years ago **57.** 3.1 grams **59.** 2 cups

61. $\log I = 6.5, I = 3.16 \times 10^6; \log I = 8.6, I = 3.98 \times 10^8; 125$ times

63. $I = 10^{4.4}, I = 10^{6.9}, 316$ times **65.** 1.2 **67.** 7.7

69. $1.6 \times 10^{-4} M$ **71.** $D = 0$ **73.** $D = 70$

75. $\$263.37$ **77.** $r = -1 + 10^{\log 4/10}$

79. $x = B + Ae^{kt}$

81. 3.9069 **83.** 1.5440

85. Calculators only have base 10 and base e. Therefore, if we need to evaluate a logarithm to a base other than 10 or e, such as $\log_2 x$, then we can do this with the change of base rule.

87. $\phi = -2$ **89.** $\phi = 2$

91. $d = 2^{-8} = .0039063$ mm

93. 2 mm

CHAPTER REVIEW EXERCISES (p. 492)

1. **2.**

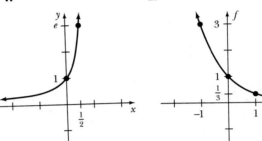

3.

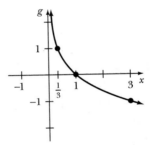

4. $3 = \log_5 125$ **5.** $49 = 7^2$ **6.** $2 + \frac{1}{2}\log_3 x$

7. $\ln 3 + \ln x - \ln y$ **8.** $-2 + 4\log x$

9. $1 + \log (x + 2)$ **10.** $\log_2 x^3$ **11.** $\ln et^4$

12. $\log \dfrac{x^{1/3}}{y^2}$ **13.** -2.7471 **14.** 12.2648

15. 4.9923×10^{-12} **16.** 186.9797 **17.** $100, .01$

18. 1.3383 **19.** $\dfrac{\ln 14}{\ln 10}$ **20.** -1 **21.** $\frac{1}{2}$

22. $\dfrac{\log 9}{\log 2} = 3.1699$ **23.** $\dfrac{\log 3}{\log 5 - \log 3} = 2.1506$

24. $t = \dfrac{\log A - \log P}{\log 1.09}$ **25.** $S = \dfrac{R}{T^2}$ **26.** $x = \frac{1}{2}$

27. $y = 5$ **28.** $b = 5$

29. $x = 3^{1/4}$ **30.** $x = 6$ **31.** 288 **32.** $x = 4$

33. $\$181$ **34.** 10.96 miles **35.** 1585 times

CHAPTER TEST (p. 493)

1.

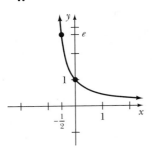

2.

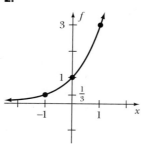

3.

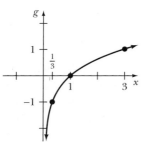

4. $-2 = \log_{1/3} 9$ **5.** $16 = 2^4$ **6.** $\frac{1}{2} \log_2 m - \log_2 n$

7. $2 + 4 \log x$ **8.** $2 + \ln (e - 1)$ **9.** $\log_2 \frac{27}{x^4}$

10. 26.0047 **11.** 1.3496×10^{14} **12.** 4.0875

13. $x = -\frac{2}{7}$ **14.** $b = 2$ **15.** $x = \frac{9}{2}$

16. $x = \frac{\log 12}{\log 3}$ **17.** $x = \frac{11}{7}$ **18.** $x = \frac{1}{e - 1}$

19. $x = \frac{1}{2}$ **20.** $t = \frac{3(\log Q - \log Q_0)}{\log 2}$

21. $A_0 = \frac{A}{e^{kt}}$ **22.** ± 4 **23.** 5 years

24. 43,800 years **25.** 1.995×10^{-4}

CHAPTER 11

EXERCISE SET 11.1 (p. 502)

1. $\{3, 5, 7, 9, 11\}$ **3.** $\{-3, -7, -11, -15, -19\}$

5. $\{0, 6, 24, 60, 120\}$ **7.** $\{9, 27, 81, 243, 729\}$

9. $\{2, 24, 720, 40, 320, 3{,}628{,}800\}$

11. $\{1, 2, \frac{3}{2}, \frac{2}{3}, \frac{5}{24}\}$ **13.** $\{\frac{1}{3}, \frac{1}{9}, \frac{1}{27}, \frac{1}{81}, \frac{1}{243}\}$

15. $\{\frac{5}{6}, \frac{6}{7}, \frac{7}{8}, \frac{8}{9}, \frac{9}{10}\}$ **17.** $\{2, \frac{9}{4}, \frac{64}{27}, \frac{625}{256}, \frac{7776}{3125}\}$

19. $\{-3, 9, -27, 81, -243\}$ **21.** $\{1, -\frac{1}{2}, \frac{1}{3}, -\frac{1}{4}, \frac{1}{5}\}$

23. $\{1, 8, 27, 64, 125\}$ **25.** $a_{10} = 19, a_{25} = 49$

27. $a_4 = a_{100} = 2$ **29.** $a_{30} = \frac{31}{32}, a_{75} = \frac{76}{77}$

31. $a_6 = \frac{1}{18}, a_{27} = \frac{-1}{81}$ **33.** $a_n = 2n$

35. $a_n = n^3$ **37.** $a_n = (-1)^{n+1}$

39. $a_n = \frac{1}{n^2}$ **41.** $d = 1, \{4, 5, 6\}$

43. no **45.** no **47.** $d = -5, \{-10, -15, -20\}$

49. no **51.** $a_n = 3n - 1, a_{30} = 89$

53. $d = 4, a_n = 4n + 2, a_{10} = 42$

55. $a_1 = 1, d = 4, a_n = 4n - 3$

57. $a_1 = -4, d = -2, a_n = -2n - 2, a_{60} = -122$

59. $a_1 = 4, d = \frac{1}{2}, a_n = \frac{n + 7}{2}, a_{15} = 11, a_{20} = \frac{27}{2}$

61. \$94,600 **63.** \$36,600 **65.** 16 years

67. \$6750 **69.** the second job **71.** 2.7169238

73. 2.7182546 **75.** .3680633 **77.** .3678831

79. $a_n = n^2, b_n = n^2 + (n - 1)(n - 2)(n - 3)(n - 4)$

81. The numbers are listed in alphabetical order.

83. A finite sequence has a fixed number of terms in the sequence. An infinite sequence has an unlimited number of terms in the sequence.

85. $\frac{25}{12}$ **86.** $\frac{137}{60}$ **87.** 38 **88.** 11

EXERCISE SET 11.2 (p. 509)

1. $1 + 2 + 3 + 4 + 5$ **3.** $1 - 3 + 5 - 7 + 9 - 11$

5. $2 + 4 + 6 + \ldots + 2n + \ldots$

7. $\frac{1}{2} + \frac{2}{3} + \frac{3}{4} + \ldots + \frac{n}{n + 1} + \ldots$

9. $\{1, 3, 6, 10, 15\}$ **11.** $\{1, -3, 6, -10, 15, -21\}$

13. $\{1, 4, 9, 16, 25\}$ **15.** $\{2, 7, 15, 26, 40\}$

17. $\{1, 2, \frac{5}{2}, \frac{8}{3}, \frac{65}{24}\}$ **19.** $\{\frac{1}{2}, \frac{1}{4}, \frac{3}{8}, \frac{5}{16}, \frac{11}{32}\}$ **21.** 18 **23.** 17

25. 72 **27.** 35 **29.** $\frac{163}{60}$ **31.** 13

33. $(2 + 1) + (4 + 1) + (6 + 1) + (8 + 1) + (10 + 1) + (12 + 1) + (14 + 1) + (16 + 1)$

35. $(2 - 1) + (4 - 1) + (6 - 1) + (8 - 1) + \ldots$

37. $1 - \dfrac{1}{2} + \dfrac{1}{3} - \dfrac{1}{4} + \ldots$

39. $\displaystyle\sum_{k=1}^{4} 6k$ **41.** $\displaystyle\sum_{k=1}^{25} 2k$ **43.** $\displaystyle\sum_{k=4}^{100} \dfrac{1}{k}$ **45.** $\displaystyle\sum_{k=1}^{6} (-1)^k 2k$

47. $\displaystyle\sum_{k=1}^{\infty} 3k$ **49.** $\displaystyle\sum_{n=1}^{\infty} \dfrac{1}{n+1}$ **51.** 55 **53.** 1275

55. 400 **57.** $S_8 = 72$ **59.** $S_n = \dfrac{n(n+11)}{2}, S_{10} = 105$

61. $S_n = n(n+5), S_{20} = 500$

63. $S_n = 2n(n+1), S_{30} = 1860$ **65.** 9

67. $32, S_n = 16n^2$ **69.** $a_{10} = 304$ feet, $S_{10} = 1600$ feet

71. $a_{12} = \$33,900, S_{12} = \$314,400$ **73.** 100 days

75. 14 rows, 169 pieces **77.** 2.7083333

79. 0.6456348 **81.** Let $x = \displaystyle\sum_{k=1}^{n} k$. Then

$x = 1 + \quad 2 \quad + \quad 3 \quad + \ldots + (n-2) + (n-1) + n$

$x = n + (n-1) + (n-2) + \ldots + \quad 3 \quad + \quad 2 \quad + 1$

$2x = (n+1) + (n+1) + \ldots + (n+1)$; we have $n (n+1)$'s:

$2x = n(n+1)$

$x = \dfrac{n(n+1)}{2}$

83. 5.001×10^9 **85.** 385 **87.** 6084

89. A sequence is a set of numbers arranged in order. A series is the indicated sum of a sequence of numbers.

91. 242 **92.** $\frac{63}{32}$ **93.** 1.998047 **94.** 1.999994

95. $\frac{8}{9}$ **96.** $\frac{27}{99} = \frac{3}{11}$

EXERCISE SET 11.3 (p. 519)

1. yes, $r = 3$ **3.** yes, $r = 2$ **5.** no **7.** yes, $r = \frac{1}{5}$

9. yes, $r = -\frac{1}{3}$ **11.** $a_n = 3 \cdot 2^{n-1}, a_6 = 96$

13. $a_n = \left(\dfrac{1}{3}\right)^{n-1}, a_4 = \dfrac{1}{27}$

15. $a_n = 16\left(\dfrac{1}{2}\right)^n, a_1 = 16, a_{10} = \dfrac{1}{32}$

17. $a_n = 2 \cdot 3^{n-1}, a_{10} = 39,366$

19. $a_n = 6\left(\dfrac{1}{3}\right)^{n-1}, a_4 = \dfrac{2}{9}$

21. $S_7 = 2^8 - 1$ **23.** $S_9 = \dfrac{5}{4}\left(1 - \dfrac{1}{5^9}\right)$

25. $S_{20} = 2\left(1 - \dfrac{1}{2^{20}}\right)$ **27.** $\dfrac{3}{4}(5^{60} - 1)$

29. $\dfrac{1}{9}(10^n - 1)$ **31.** $\dfrac{1}{5}\left[1 - \left(-\dfrac{3}{2}\right)^n\right]$ **33.** 8

35. does not exist **37.** 1 **39.** does not exist **41.** $\frac{81}{2}$

43. $\frac{4}{21}$ **45.** $\frac{2}{3}$ **47.** $\frac{2}{3}$ **49.** $\frac{67}{33}$ **51.** $\frac{7}{9}$ **53.** 1 **55.** $\frac{1}{99}$

57. $\frac{115}{333}$ **59.** $a_7 = \$31,737, S_7 = \$178,456$

61. 22,107 **63.** \$1898 **65.** .159 cubic centimeter

67. a. 3.355 inches **b.** 66.58 inches **c.** 80 inches

69. 70 feet **71.** $\frac{11}{6}$ **73.** $\frac{32}{55}$ **75.** $\frac{409}{1665}$ **77.** $\frac{1}{2}$

79. A geometric sequence is one in which each term after the first is found by multiplying the preceding term by the same number.

81. $a + b$ **82.** $a^2 + 2ab + b^2$

83. $a^3 + 3a^2b + 3ab^2 + b^3$

84. $a^4 + 4a^3b + 6a^2b^2 + 4ab^3 + b^4$

85. 4 **86.** 7 **87.** 10 **88.** 1

EXERCISE SET 11.4 (p. 526)

1. $x^2 + 6x + 9$

3. $x^{10} - 5x^8y + 10x^6y^2 - 10x^4y^3 + 5x^2y^4 - y^5$

5. $x^{12} + 9x^8 + 27x^4 + 27$

7. $a^{18} + 6a^{15}b^4 + 15a^{12}b^8 + 20a^9b^{12} + 15a^6b^{16} + 6a^3b^{20} + b^{24}$

9.

										1										Row 0
									1		1									Row 1
								1		2		1								Row 2
							1		3		3		1							Row 3
						1		4		6		4		1						Row 4
					1		5		10		10		5		1					Row 5
				1		6		15		20		15		6		1				Row 6
			1		7		21		35		35		21		7		1			Row 7
		1		8		28		56		70		56		28		8		1		Row 8
	1		9		36		84		126		126		84		36		9		1	Row 9
1		10		45		120		210		252		210		120		45		10	1	Row 10

11. $a^8 + 8a^7b + 28a^6b^2 + 56a^5b^3 + 70a^4b^4 + 56a^3b^5 + 28a^2b^6 + 8ab^7 + b^8$

13. $a^{10} + 10a^9b + 45a^8b^2 + 120a^7b^3 + 210a^6b^4 + 252a^5b^5 + 210a^4b^6 + 120a^3b^7 + 45a^2b^8 + 10ab^9 + b^{10}$

15. $a^9 - 9a^8b + 36a^7b^2 - 84a^6b^3 + 126a^5b^4 - 126a^4b^5 + 84a^3b^6 - 36a^2b^7 + 9ab^8 - b^9$

17. $a^7 + 14a^6 + 84a^5 + 280a^4 + 560a^3 + 672a^2 + 448a + 128$

19. 512 **21.** 1 **23.** 10 **25.** 21 **27.** 84

29. $a^3 + 3a^2b + 3ab^2 + b^3$

31. $a^6 + 6a^5 + 15a^4 + 20a^3 + 15a^2 + 6a + 1$

33. $x^4 - 4x^3y + 6x^2y^2 - 4xy^3 + y^4$

35. $x^7 - 7x^6 + 21x^5 - 35x^4 + 35x^3 - 21x^2 + 7x - 1$

37. $x^{15} + 10x^{12} + 40x^9 + 80x^6 + 80x^3 + 32$

39. $\dfrac{x^5}{243} - \dfrac{10x^4}{81} + \dfrac{40x^3}{27} - \dfrac{80x^2}{9} + \dfrac{80x}{3} - 32$

41. $a^{12} + 12a^{11}b + 66a^{10}b^2 + 220a^9b^3$

43. $a^{20} + 20a^{19}b + 190a^{18}b^2 + 1140a^{17}b^3$

45. $1584a^7b^5$　**47.** $560x^3$　**49.** $-448x^5$

51. 1.0937　**53.** 85.77　**55.** 0.282

57. 1, 2, 4, 8, 16, 32, 64; the sum of the numbers in the nth row is twice the sum of the numbers in the $n - 1$ row.

59. To find an entry in Pascal's triangle, add the two nearest numbers in the row directly above.

CHAPTER REVIEW EXERCISES (p. 528)

1. $\left\{\frac{1}{2}, -\frac{1}{6}, \frac{1}{24}, -\frac{1}{120}\right\}$　**2.** $\left\{1, 1, \frac{3}{4}, \frac{1}{2}\right\}$

3. no　**4.** yes, $d = 5, \{21, 26, 31\}$

5. yes, $r = 2, \{16, 32, 64\}$　**6.** no

7. $a_n = 3n + 1, a_6 = 19$

8. $a_n = 3(-2)^{n-1}, a_5 = 48$　**9.** $\{1, 4, 9, 16, 25\}$

10. $\{-1, 3, -6, 10, -15\}$　**11.** 35　**12.** 11

13. $\sum_{k=1}^{5} 3k$　**14.** $\sum_{n=1}^{\infty} \frac{n}{n+1}$

15. 820　**16.** 121　**17.** does not exist　**18.** $\frac{5}{4}$　**19.** $\frac{8}{9}$

20. $x^3 + 3x^2y^2 + 3xy^4 + y^6$

21. $x^5 - 5x^4 + 10x^3 - 10x^2 + 5x - 1$

22. $x^3 + 3x^2y^2 + 3xy^4 + y^6$

23. $x^7 - 14x^6 + 84x^5 - 280x^4 + 560x^3 - 672x^2 + 448x - 128$

24. 120　**25.** 220

26. $x^{36} + 12x^{33}y + 66x^{30}y^2 + 220x^{27}y^3$

27. $126x^8y^{10}$　**28.** $a_{30} = 88¢, S_{30} = 1335¢$

29. $a_{10} = 19,683¢, S_{10} = 29,542¢$　**30.** 80 inches

CHAPTER TEST (p. 529)

1. $\left\{2, \frac{3}{2}, \frac{2}{3}, \frac{5}{24}\right\}$　**2.** $\left\{1, -\frac{1}{4}, \frac{1}{9}, -\frac{1}{16}\right\}$

3. $d = -2, \{-7, -9, -11\}$　**4.** $r = 3, \{162, 486, 1458\}$

5. $r = \frac{1}{2}, \left\{\frac{1}{16}, \frac{1}{32}, \frac{1}{64}\right\}$　**6.** $d = 3, \{17, 20, 23\}$

7. $\{-3, 3, -6, 6, -9\}$　**8.** $\frac{11}{30}$　**9.** 38

10. $\sum_{n=1}^{6} (-1)^{n+1}(2n - 1)$　**11.** $\sum_{k=2}^{\infty} 2k$　**12.** 465

13. $\frac{121}{81}$　**14.** $\frac{3}{2}$　**15.** does not exist　**16.** $\frac{2}{9}$

17. $x^4 - 12x^3 + 54x^2 - 108x + 81$

18. $x^{12} + 6x^{10}y + 15x^8y^2 + 20x^6y^3 + 15x^4y^4 + 6x^2y^5 + y^6$

19. $x^4 - 12x^3 + 54x^2 - 108x + 81$

20. $x^8 + 8x^7 + 28x^6 + 56x^5 + 70x^4 + 56x^3 + 28x^2 + 8x + 1$

21. 495　**22.** $a^{11} + 11a^{10}b + 55a^9b^2$　**23.** $120x^6$

24. $a_8 = \$30,200, S_8 = \$196,800$

25. $a_8 = \$32,563, S_8 = \$202,096$

CUMULATIVE REVIEW: Chapters 1–11 (p. 531)

1. $(-\infty, -3) \cup (5, \infty)$ [2.7]

2. $[-3, 4]$ [2.7]

3. $x < -5$　or　$x \geq 4$ [8.6]　**4.** $-4, \frac{1}{2}$ [6.5]

5. $2, -3$ [2.2]　**6.** $343, -125$ [8.2]　**7.** $\varnothing$ [7.5]

8. -3 [10.1]　**9.** $\dfrac{\log 11 - 2\log 5}{\log 5}$ [10.4]　**10.** 3 [10.3]

11. 8 [10.2]　**12.** $\dfrac{-1 \pm \sqrt{19}}{3}$ [4.5]

13. $t = \dfrac{\ln P - \ln 6}{.03}$ [10.5]

14. $y = x$ [2.3]　**15.** $Z = \dfrac{3xy}{x + 2y}$ [6.5]

16. $m = \dfrac{k - w^2 M}{3w^2}$ [7.5]　**17.** $2x + 3y = 3$ [4.1]

18. $(-1, 2, -3)$ [4.3]　**19.** $\dfrac{-x^2 - 2x + 7}{2(x + 3)(x - 3)}$ [6.3]

20. $\dfrac{-a}{a + b}$ [6.4]　**21.** $\dfrac{5 + i}{13}$ [7.8]　**22.** $\dfrac{2x\sqrt{15x}}{5}$ [7.3]

23. $x^3 + 15x^2 + 27x + 27$ [5.3]

24. $2x + 4 + \dfrac{9}{2x - 1}$ [5.3]

25 and 26. $x^3 + 15x^2 + 27x + 27$ [11.4]

27. [9.2]

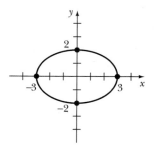

28. [9.1]

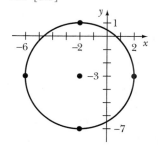

29. [3.5]

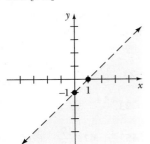

30. [8.4]

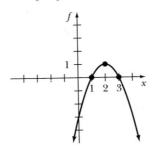

31. [10.2]

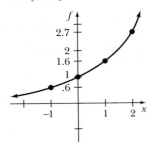

32. $\sqrt{10}$ [3.3]   **33.** $y - 4 = -\frac{1}{3}(x + 2)$ [3.4]

34. 3 [3.4]

35. $-4 \pm 2i$ [8.1]   **36.** $-4 \pm 2i$ [8.1]

37. $(x + 5y)(x^2 - 5xy + 25y^2)$ [5.4]

38. $(a + b)(c - 2)$ [5.5]   **39.** ± 3 [7.5]

40 $\frac{8}{3}$ [10.2]   **41.** $\frac{2}{3}\ln x + \frac{1}{3}\ln y$ [10.3]

42. 3.0651 [10.5]   **43.** $f^{-1}(x) = \dfrac{x + 5}{4}$ [3.6]

44. 4 [11.2]   **45.** $\frac{1}{2}$ hour [2.3]   **46.** $y = \frac{250}{3}$ [7.6]

47. $B = \frac{1}{2}$ [7.6]   **48.** 1.5 centimeters [7.6]

49. $S = 3200$ [7.6]   **50.** 5×10^9 [7.7]

51. 1.6×10^{-19} [7.7]   **52.** 4,000,000 [7.7]

53. 0.000 001 [7.7]   **54.** 4×10^{12} [7.7]

55. 5×10^{26} [7.7]   **56.** -6 [2.1]

57. $L = \frac{2}{3}, S = -\frac{1}{2}$ [2.2]   **58.** 0, ± 5 [5.7]

59. -3 [6.7]   **60.** 5 [6.7]   **61.** 10, 12, 14 [2.2]

62. $\{1, 3, 5, 7\}, \{-7, -5, -3, -1\}$ [5.7]

63. $\{8, 9\}, \{-9, -8\}$ [7.5]

64. $\{10, 12\}, \{-12, -10\}$ [7.5]

65. $S = 36\pi$ square inches, $V = 28\pi$ cubic inches [2.3]

66. 3, 4, and 5 feet [5.7]   **67.** \$610 [2.4]

68. Square: $S = 15$ centimeters, $A = 225$ square centimeters; rectangle: $L = 27$ centimeters, $W = 7$ centimeters, $A = 189$ square centimeters [2.4]

69. 8 [6.6]

70. $W = \dfrac{45 + \sqrt{2409}}{12}, L = \dfrac{51 + \sqrt{2409}}{6}$ [6.6]

71. 8, 17 [5.7]   **72.** $d = 8$ [5.7]

73. $W = 2, L = 8$ [9.3]

74. $D = 4, E = -8, F = 16$ [4.3]

75. $D = -4, E = 2, F = -20$ [4.3]

76. \$32.50 [2.5]   **77.** 3 gallons [2.5]

78. \$2000 [2.5]   **79.** 182 points [2.5]

80. at least 75% but less than 99% [2.6]

81. First part: 3 hours; second part: 4 hours [2.4]

82. 40 mph, 90 miles [2.4]

83. Plane: 540 mph; jet stream: 60 mph [4.2]

84. $\frac{1}{2}$ mph [6.7]   **85.** no [2.5]

86. 13¢: 5; 20¢: 7; 37¢: 21 [2.5]

87. double: 29; single: 11 [4.2]

88. $p = 12, n = 8, d = 5$ [4.3]

89. Gary is 18; Maria is 42. [2.5]

90. Kathy is 13; Gail is 7. [5.7]

91. $3\frac{1}{3}$ hours [6.7]

92. Rent: \$8400; food: \$3000; utilities: \$1800 [6.6]

93. 54 inches [6.6]   **94.** 12 milliliters [6.6]

95. $L = W = 3$ feet, $A = 9$ square feet [8.5]

96. $W = 20$ feet, $L = 40$ feet, $A = 800$ square feet [8.5]

97. 100 items, \$2800 [8.5]

98. 20,800 years ago [10.5]

99. 1.47% [10.5]

100. $\log I = 67, I = 5.0119 \times 10^6; \log I = 8.5, I = 3.1623 \times 10^8; 63$ times [10.5]

APPENDICES

EXERCISE SET B.1 (p. 543)

1. .4771   **3.** .8513   **5.** .3655   **7.** .9581

9. 2.5843   **11.** 6.8965   **13.** 5.9542   **15.** -3.2950

17. -6.7212 **19.** 3.58   **21.** 5.31×10^1

23. 6.13×10^8 **25.** 4.15×10^{14} **27.** 4.16×10^{-5}

29. 7.06×10^{-13} **31.** 3.40×10^{-5}

33. 2.34×10^{-2} **35.** $.5480$ **37.** $.4576$
39. 3.1781 **41.** 8.7048 **43.** $-.8130$
45. -1.3418 **47.** 1.72 **49.** 4.98×10^1
51. 1.47×10^{10} **53.** 4.91×10^{-2} **55.** 6.07×10^{-6}
57. 4.87×10^{-2} **59.** 6.10×10^{-6}

EXERCISE SET C.1 (p. 547)

1. $x + 3$ **3.** $3y + 2 + \dfrac{4}{y + 1}$ **5.** $3x^2 + 5x - 2$

7. $4x^3 + 4x^2 + 5x + 5$ **9.** $x + 3$ **11.** $y + 2 + \dfrac{5}{y + 1}$

13. $4y^2 - 1$ **15.** $x^2 + x + 1$ **17.** $x^2 + 3x + 9 + \dfrac{54}{x - 3}$

19. $x^4 + 2x^3 + 4x^2 + 4x + 8 + \dfrac{21}{x - 2}$

21. $x^5 + x^4 + x^3 + x^2 + x + 1$

EXERCISE SET D.1 (p. 554)

1. numerator = 5, denominator = 6 **3.** improper
5. mixed **7.** $2 \cdot 2 \cdot 3$ **9.** prime **11.** $3 \cdot 5 \cdot 5$
13. $2 \cdot 3 \cdot 3 \cdot 3$ **15.** $2 \cdot 2 \cdot 2 \cdot 2 \cdot 2 \cdot 3$
17. $2 \cdot 2 \cdot 2 \cdot 2 \cdot 3 \cdot 3$ **19.** $\dfrac{6}{11}$ **21.** $\dfrac{25}{9}$ **23.** $\dfrac{16}{25}$
25. $\dfrac{3}{2}$ **27.** 3 **29.** $\dfrac{1}{8}$ **31.** $\dfrac{15}{32}$ **33.** $\dfrac{14}{15}$ **35.** $\dfrac{18}{5}$
37. $\dfrac{8}{9}$ **39.** $\dfrac{4}{9}$ **41.** $\dfrac{1}{7}$ **43.** $\dfrac{5}{7}$ **45.** $\dfrac{1}{2}$ **47.** $\dfrac{17}{12}$
49. $\dfrac{19}{60}$ **51.** $\dfrac{13}{30}$ **53.** $\dfrac{11}{5}$ **55.** $\dfrac{7}{2}$ **57.** 2 **59.** $\dfrac{73}{18}$
61. 1 **63.** $\dfrac{48}{11}$ **65.** $\dfrac{5}{6}$ **67.** $\dfrac{91}{180}$ **69.** $\dfrac{23}{99}$ **71.** $\dfrac{1}{21}$
73. She paid $\frac{13}{24}$ of the bill, and she owes $\frac{11}{24}$ of the bill.
75. $\frac{41}{18}$ meters

Index

DESCARTES (1596-1650)

René Descartes, French philosopher and scientist, invented analytic geometry in 1637. His belief that knowledge comes only from scientific experimentation and mathematical reasoning was a major contribution to Western thought.

PASCAL (1623-1662)

Frenchman Blaise Pascal discovered new theorems about conic sections at the age of sixteen. With Fermat, Pascal developed the basic concepts of probability. He also invented the first computing machine and made contributions to physics and philosophy.

LEIBNIZ (1646-1716)

German mathematician and philosopher Gottfried Wilhelm Leibniz invented calculus simultaneously with and independently from Newton. At the age of fourteen, Leibniz began the reform of Aristotle's logic by using symbols to represent logical concepts.

EULER (1707-1783)

Swiss mathematician and physicist Leonhard Euler made contributions to every area of mathematics. He wrote 886 books and papers and gave us the symbols $f(x)$ for functional notation, i for $\sqrt{-1}$, e for the base of the natural logarithm, and Σ for summation.

NEWTON (1642-1727)

Sir Isaac Newton, English physicist and mathematician, invented calculus and extended Galileo's equation of a free-falling object to general laws of gravity and motion.

FERMAT (1601-1665)

French mathematician Pierre de Fermat made great contributions to the theory of numbers.

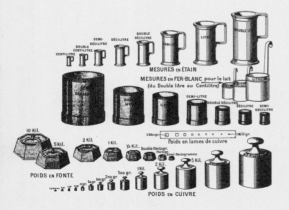

In 1795 the French adopted the metric system.

GAUSS (1777-1855)

German mathematician Carl Friedrich Gauss found an arithmetical error in his father's bookkeeping at the age of three. He made major contributions to pure and applied mathematics.

1600

1800